ENCYCLOPEDIA OF ENVIRONMENTAL SCIENCE AND ENGINEERING

Pfafflin/Ziegler

ENCYCLOPEDIA OF ENVIRONMENTAL SCIENCE AND ENGINEERING

VOLUME TWO

N—Z

GORDON AND BREACH SCIENCE PUBLISHERS
New York London Paris

Editorial office for the United Kingdom
Gordon and Breach Science Publishers Ltd.
42 William IV Street
London W.C.2.

Editorial office for France
Gordon & Breach
7–9 rue Emile Dubois
Paris 75014

Library of Congress catalog card number 72–89286. ISBN 0 677 14660 4. Printed in Great Britain.

ACKNOWLEDGMENT

THE EDITORS wish to thank their colleagues who put their knowledge on to paper and the families who endured long hours of detached work by those involved in this endeavor. One of the editors would like to acknowledge a particular debt of gratitude to the late Professor William K. Roots.

EDITORS' PREFACE

THE MAJOR purpose of the *Encyclopedia of Environmental Science and Engineering* is to bring the contributions of key environmental areas into a single readily available work. The *Encyclopedia* covers such broad subjects as Air, Water and Soil Pollution, Public Health and Ecology. Air Pollution, taken as a typical example, is then given extensive treatment by division into subjects such as Meteorology, Sources, Automotive Pollution, Effects of Atmospheric Pollutants, Energy Sources, Control of Gaseous Pollutants, Noise, Particulates, Remote Detection, Sulfur Removal, Stack Sampling, Urban Pollution Modelling and Environmental Law.

The *Encyclopedia* thus makes the information of areas related to one's own specialization readily available to the environmentalist and also provides him with a more general knowledge of his field.

The length of articles has been chosen to establish effectively the relationships among various areas within a discipline, rather than risk the segregation of concepts into overspecialized and less readable portions. In each area covered, the most significant facts and data have been sought and useful references have been provided for those wishing to pursue the field in greater depth.

Man's increased awareness of his relation to other organisms in the scheme of life has led him to examine many disciplines. Application of these disciplines to solutions of everyday problems of his surroundings has given rise to the new professions of environmental scientist and environmental engineer. It is possible that continued survival of civilization, as we know it, may depend on the energy and wisdom of the environmental worker. It is to be hoped, however, that in addition to the professional, the *Encyclopedia* will also be useful to anyone sufficiently interested in, and concerned about, the environment to seek information in the Public Library.

J. R. PFAFFLIN
Windsor, Ontario

E. N. ZIEGLER
New York, N.Y.

CONTRIBUTORS TO VOLUME 2

H. I. ALI—Department of Civil Engineering, University of Windsor. *Wastewater: Physical and Chemical Treatment*

STANLEY I. AUERBACH—Oak Ridge National Laboratory. *Radiation Ecology*

JOHN E. BARDACH—Department of Zoology, University of Michigan. *Pollution Effects on Fish*

DOMINICK P. BARTENOPE—Charles Pfizer Co. *Sulfur Removal*

J. K. BEWTRA—Department of Civil Engineering, University of Windsor. *Wastewater: Physical and Chemical Treatment*

G. P. CANEVARI—Esso Research. *Spillage into Water: Treatment*

RAUL R. CARDENAS, JR.—Department of Civil Engineering, Polytechnic Institute of New York. *Pollution Instrumentation: Wastewater*

LAWRENCE K. CECIL—Consulting Chemical Engineer, Champaign, Illinois. *Water Reuse*

S. P. CHEE—Department of Civil Engineering, University of Windsor. *Water Flow*

CHARLES C. COUTANT—Oak Ridge National Laboratory. *Thermal Effects on Fish Ecology*

DAVID W. ECKHOFF—Department of Civil Engineering, University of Utah. *Urban Runoff*

MORTON FELS—Battelle Memorial Institute. *Particulate Removal*

MARTIN FORSBERG—Harvard University. *Water Chemistry. Water: Properties, Structure and Occurrence in Nature*

R. BUCKMINSTER FULLER—Southern Illinois University. *The Terrestrial System*

SUZETTE GAUVAIN—London School of Hygiene and Tropical Medicine. *Occupational Health*

STEVEN GHERINI—Harvard University. *Water Chemistry. Water: Properties, Structure and Occurrence in Nature*

ERNST P. HALL—Environmental Protection Agency. *Pollution from Mine Drainage*

J. M. HARRINGTON—London School of Hygiene and Tropical Medicine. *Occupational Health*

JAMES P. HARTT—Department of Civil Engineering, University of Windsor. *Urban Planning*

KENNETH L. JOHNSON—Environmental Protection Agency. *Stack Sampling*

PHILIP H. JONES—Institute of Environmental Science and Engineering, University of Toronto. *Water Treatment*

ASHFAQ A. KHAN—Department of Chemical Engineering, Polytechnic Institute of New York. *Recycling of Waste Materials*

JEFFREY S. LIFE—Toxicology Center, University of Iowa. *Pollution Effects on Fish*

DAVID S. K. LIU—RAND Corp. *Urban Runoff*

GEORGE C. MALING, JR.—IBM Corp. *Noise*

CONRAD J. MASON—Department of Meteorology and Oceanography, University of Michigan. *Urban Air Pollution Modeling*

JOHN M. MATSEN—Esso Research and Engineering. *Particulate Emissions Particulate Removal*

J. A. McCORQUODALE—Department of Civil Engineering, University of Windsor. *Sediment Transport and Erosion*

ROBERT L. METCALF—Department of Zoology, University of Illinois. *Pesticides*

GEORGE MICHANOWSKY—Amazonia Foundation, Inc. *Remote Detection of Air Pollutants*

HARRY MOSES—Argonne National Laboratory. *Urban Air Pollution Modeling*

JAMES R. PFAFFLIN—Department of Electrical Engineering, University of Windsor. *Recycling of Waste Materials. Selected Properties*

SHEILA M. PFAFFLIN—Bell Telephone Laboratories. *Psychological Aspects of Man's Environment. Statistical Methods for Environmental Science*

SYED R. QASIM—Department of Civil Engineering, University of Texas at Arlington. *Wastewater: Treatment for Special Applications*

S. SOURIRAJAN—National Research Council of Canada. *Reserve Osmosis—Process Fundamentals*

WERNER STUMM—Swiss Federal Republic Institute of Technology. *Water Chemistry. Water: Properties, Structure and Occurrence in Nature*

ISRAEL WILENITZ—Quirk, Lawler and Matusky. *Systems Modeling for Water Pollution Control*

G. M. WILKENING—Bell Telephone Laboratories. *Non-Ionizing Radiations*

EDWARD N. ZIEGLER—Department of Chemical Engineering, Polytechnic Institute of New York. *Sulfur Removal. Appendix: Selected Properties. Table of Environmental Speeds*

CONTRIBUTORS TO VOLUME 1

NEAL E. ARMSTRONG—Department of Civil Engineering, University of Texas. *Estuarine Water Quality*
BRUCE A. BELL—Evirotech Corp. *Groundwater*
J. K. BEWTRA—Department of Civil Engineering, University of Windsor. *Biological Treatment of Wastewater*
RAUL R. CARDENAS, JR.—Department of Civil Engineering, Polytechnic Institute of New York. *Composting*
P. J. DITCHETT—School of Pharmacy, University of Wales. *Disinfection and Chemosterilization*
ROBERT DRESNACK—Department of Civil Engineering, Newark College of Engineering. *Eutrophication*
FRANCIS C. EVANS—Department of Zoology, University of Michigan. *Ecology of Primary Terrestrial Consumers*
W. L. FAITH—Consulting Chemical Engineer, San Marino, California. *Effects of Atmospheric Pollutants*
ERIC R. GIDLUND—Department of Civil Engineering, Polytechnic Institute of New York. *Groundwater*
CHARLES R. GOLDMAN—Division of Environmental Studies, University of California (Davis). *Aquatic Primary Production*
HELENE N. GUTTMAN—Department of Biological Sciences, University of Illinois at Chicago Circle. *Microbiology*
WALTER J. HICKEL—Anchorage, Alaska. *Conservation Planning—Alternatives*
KENNETH C. HOFFMAN—Brookhaven National Laboratory. *Energy Sources*
JOSEPH R. JONES—Windsor Metro Health Center, Windsor, Ontario. *Effects of Chemicals on Human Ecology*
PHILIP H. JONES—Institute of Environmental Science and Engineering, University of Toronto. *Environmental Studies*
PETER B. LEDERMAN—Environmental Protection Agency. *Management of Solid Waste*
CAMERON MacINNIS—Department of Civil Engineering, University of Windsor. *Municipal Wastewater*
COLIN A. MAWSON—Atomic Energy of Canada Limited. *Management of Radioactive Waste*
NELSON L. NEMEROW—Department of Civil Engineering, Syracuse University. *Liquid Wastes of Industry*
EUGENE P. ODUM—Institute of Ecology, University of Georgia. *Ecosystem Theory*
DONALD F. OTHMER—Department of Chemical Engineering, Polytechnic Institute of New York. *Desalination*
HANS A. PANOFSKY—Department of Meteorology, Pennsylvania State University. *Air Pollution Meteorology*
JAMES R. PFAFFLIN—Department of Electrical Engineering, University of Windsor. *Effects of Chemicals on Human Ecology. Municipal Wastewater*
MICHAEL C. QUICK—Department of Civil Engineering, University of British Columbia. *Hydrology*
ELROY L. RICE—Department of Botany, University of Oklahoma. *Ecology of Plants*
DONALD P. ROSEMAN—Hydronautics, Inc. *Marine Spillage—Sources and Hazards*
A. D. RUSSELL—School of Pharmacy, University of Wales. *Disinfection and Chemosterilization*
JOSEPH A. SALVATO, JR.—New York State Department of Health. *Environmental Health*
CONRAD SIMON—Environmental Protection Agency. *Air Pollution Sources*
S. SOURIRAJAN—National Research Council of Canada. *Applications of Reserve Osmosis*
MEREDITH H. THOMPSON—New York State Department of Health. *Environmental Health Administration*
STEPHEN VARRO, JR.—Ecology, Inc. *Composting*

ISRAEL WILENITZ—Quirk, Lawler and Matusky. *Modeling of River and Estuary Water Quality*
VICTOR J. YANNACONE, JR.—Yannacone and Yannacone. *Environmental Law*
EDWARD N. ZIEGLER—Department of Chemical Engineering, Polytechnic Institute of New York. *Automotive Pollution. Effects of Chemicals on Human Ecology. Gaseous Pollutant Removal*
ABEL WOLMAN—Johns Hopkins University. *Introduction*

INTRODUCTION

Only the historian will be able to diagnose the causes of the great upsurge of interest in environmental problems on the part of the man in the street. Until recently, this universal excitement was restricted primarily to the "developed" worlds of the East and West. Aroused interest is now penetrating into the less developed regions, inhabited by billions of people. The leaders of these people have observed somewhat cynically that they are concerned more about starvation than about automobile emmissions. They hasten to add, however, that, if they can, they would like to avoid the errors which industrialization, increased urbanization and excessive population growth have engendered in the more favored countries.

It was inevitable that, as public interest was aroused, a search for scapegoats for creating actual or assumed environmental ills would be pursued. This readily took the form of a retreat to a non-existent past, to a demand for reversing economic progress, to a general anti-intellectualism and, more specifically, to an attack on the "obvious" vices of science and technology. If it were not for the anti-human machinations of the scientist and the engineer, ecologic disturbance would not have occurred, nature would not have been despoiled and Utopia would have prevailed. The polemicist's argument, of course, is not new. It has been the hallmark of the ages, when each new advance was fought on the fields of religion, law, and authority. Fortunately, science and technology have much to their credit in alleviating the ills of man, in prolonging life, in providing leisure and comfort and in protecting the amenities. On the debit side, wisdom, logic and ecologic equilibrium have on occasion been distinguished by their absence. It is undoubtedly true, however, that the intellectual forces which created a better life for man, and likewise violated some of the environment, are the same forces to which one must look for correcting past and avoiding future deteriorations.

Essentially, the scientist-technologist is now challenged to recapture a role, old in practice, but apparently lost in the present drama of revolutionizing the world. Perhaps the major stress of today is to see to it that human knowledge provides a tool for facilitating human progress, as much as it is for purely scientific or technologic advancement. To the student of progress this is merely re-stating the axiom that "engineerng was an instrumentality of civilization, and not a mere physical rearrangement of physical things."*

The volumes produced here are designed to shed authoritative light upon the ingredients of a wholesome environment and how they may be assessed and developed for the benefit of the biosphere—encompassing man, plant and animal life in their multi-variate relationships. The effort to provide a source-book in so vast a field as the environment is a heroic one. Any encyclopedia poses a major challenge of coverage, of priorities and of selection, since the cumulative knowledge in the field here covered is vast, but still not great enough. Many of the contributions admit the lacunae of ignorance, as well as the depths of understanding.

These two volumes have assembled accurate information by competent and respected authorities, to which the student, the practitioner and even the interested layman might have recourse. The "television instant expert" has been avoided, not for moral or ethical reasons, but to assure the reader that the contributions are soundly based on scientific verity and not on specious propaganda.

The environment is great and coverage is likely to be deficient. The simple listing of the subjects in the table of contents serves the useful purpose of disclosing to many the tremendous spectrum of subject matter we so lightly package in the term *environment*. The assembly of topics alone should intrigue the young student threading lightly through his "earth day" exercises. In spite of the breadth and depth of the subject matter, and because of the expanding nature of the field, it may be suggested that supplements might well be on the way.

It may be emphasized, in conclusion, that the present assembly is not intended to provide a long historical record of the science and art of the control of the environment. That record is part of a "very ancient process,

---

* Nicholas Murray Butler, Introduction, *Engineers and Engineering in the Renaissance*, William Barclay Parsons. The Williams and Wilkins Company, Baltimore, Maryland, 1939.

rooted in many civilizations" and one of great accomplishment.* The present and the future are the setting for these deliberations. It is certainly to be hoped that, with appetites whetted, the reader will turn to excellent long time rehearsals of how we came to now!

Abel Wolman
The Johns Hopkins University

---

* *A History of Technology*. Edited by Charles Singer, E. J. Holmyard and A. R. Hall. Five volumes. Oxford University Press, New York and London, 1954.

N

NOISE

1. Introduction

Sound propagation is usually described in terms of small variations in the pressure above and below the ambient (atmosphere) pressure that propagate with a speed of approximately 344 m/sec under normal atmospheric conditions. Noise is usually considered to be *unwanted* sound, and therefore the presence of an observer (or *receiver*) of the noise is an important factor in any noise control problem. The overall noise problem therefore involves not only the scientific and engineering aspects of noise generation, propagation, scattering and absorption, but the psychological effects of noisiness and annoyance, physiological effects such as hearing damage, social considerations, economic considerations, and legal aspects. In this article an overall view of some of these aspects is presented so that the reader can become acquainted with some of the physical aspects of sound propagation, the terminology and quantities often used in the noise field, some of the methods that are being used to measure and rate noise, damage risk criteria, and general procedures for planning for and implementing noise control measures. In a short article, it is not possible to give a complete picture of the overall noise problem. In fact, a multi-volume report on noise has been prepared by the U.S. Environmental Protection Agency and submitted to the United States Congress. In this article some of the highlights of current practice are reviewed. It is hoped that the material presented here, together with the references cited, will enable environmental scientists and engineers to gain an understanding of the general field of noise and noise control engineering.

2. Physical Characteristics of Sound Waves

2.1 General

From a physical viewpoint, propagation of sound in a medium such as air can be regarded as a perturbation on the pressure, temperature, density and velocity that the medium would have in the absence of a sound wave. For most problems of practical interest, sound propagation can be described by *linear* differential equations, although the basic equations are inherently *non-linear*. The non-linear aspects of wave propagation are important in such problems as N-wave propagation (sonic boom), propagation in some engine mufflers, and in noise generated and propagated through jet engines. For the great majority of problems, however, the linear theory is adequate. From a noise control viewpoint, three parameters are of primary importance, the *sound pressure*, *particle velocity*, and the speed of sound. The speed of sound in air is given by

$$c = 344\sqrt{T/T_o}\ \text{m/sec}, \qquad (2.1)$$

where T is the temperature in °K, and $T_o = 293$°K (approximately 70°F). Note that it does not depend on density or pressure.

The *sound pressure* is the small variation above and below the ambient (atmospheric) pressure (approximately $1.01 \times 10^{-5}\text{N/m}^2$) that is measured by most microphones in common use in the noise control field. The sound pressure is in general a function of time, a sinusoidal function for *pure tones*, and a more-or-less random function for many noises. Methods of noise measurement, and the methods of describing the variation of sound pressure with time will be covered in the next section. In this section we will deal with some of the basic aspects of sound generation and propagation.

The *wave equation* that describes the sound pressure as a function of space and time can be derived from the three basic conservation equations, conservation of mass, momentum, and energy.[2] When these equations are linearized, and the approximation is made that the pressure variations (p)

are related to density variations (δ) in the fluid by

$$p = c^2\delta, \qquad (2.2)$$

the *wave equation*

$$\nabla^2 p - \frac{1}{c^2}\frac{\partial^2 p}{\partial t^2} = S(x, t) \qquad (2.3)$$

can be derived. Here, p is the variation in sound pressure around the ambient pressure (p_o), c is the speed of sound, and $S(x, t)$ is a *source term* that will be discussed in detail later in this section. In one dimension, and with no source terms,

$$\nabla^2 p = \frac{\partial^2 p}{\partial x^2} \qquad (2.4)$$

and $S(x, t) = 0$. The wave equation may then be written:

$$\frac{\partial^2 p}{\partial x^2} - \frac{1}{c^2}\frac{\partial^2 p}{\partial t^2} = 0 \qquad (2.5)$$

and the general solution $p = f(x\text{-}ct)$ describes the propagation of a *plane wave*. The function f is arbitrary, and depends on how the wave was generated. The pressure does not depend on y and z (hence the name plane wave), and the disturbance propagates with a speed c (surfaces of constant $x\text{-}ct$ have a constant pressure).

The *particle velocity* associated with the pressure wave is also important, and may be obtained from the linear momentum equation,

$$\rho_0 \frac{\partial u}{\partial t} = -\nabla p, \qquad (2.6)$$

the fluid equivalent of Newton's second law. u is the *particle velocity* in the medium, and ρ_0 is the ambient density (nominally 1.18 kg/m³). For a plane wave, the pressure and particle velocity are related by the *specific impedance* of the medium:

$$z_S = \frac{p}{u} = \rho c. \qquad (2.7)$$

This parameter is of importance in many practical problems, and in other types of waves such as spherical or cylindrical waves, the impedance has different values which approach the plane value when the distance from the source is large.

2.2 Sources of sound

In many practical problems, the mechanisms responsible for the generation of noise are of key practical importance, and it is only when the dependence of the generated noise on a few important parameters is known that an engineering solution to a noise problem can be found. In this section, we will discuss three of the basic sources of sound, and describe briefly the resulting pressure field. While practical sources are rarely as simple as those described here, the description will aid in an understanding of the overall propagation problem.

A *monopole* source is one that consists of a variation in mass flow into a region. This variation in mass flow (a source) produces a pressure disturbance that propagates away from the source. The source term in equation (2) is

$$S(x, t) = -\frac{\partial Q}{\partial t}, \qquad (2.8)$$

where Q is the mass added to the fluid per unit volume per unit time.

The monopole-type of source occurs in practice when a panel or other object moves essentially as a piston, and the sound is radiated from only one side of the source. The baffled loudspeaker at low frequencies is often used as an example of an "ideal" monopole, and in practice many real sources can often be thought of as a group of monopole sources. The sound field from a small monopole source is not directional, and for a source in sinusoidal motion is given by

$$p = \frac{\omega Q_o}{4\pi r}\cos(kr - \omega t). \qquad (2.9)$$

For a source strength $Q = Q_o \sin \omega t$.

The next most complex source of sound is the *dipole source* which can be thought of as two monopoles near each other and vibrating out-of-phase. Radiation from some panels and beams can also be thought of as dipole sound. An unbaffled loudspeaker is often used as an example of a dipole source. The sound radiation from the backside partially cancels the sound radiation from the front, and hence the radiation efficiency is lower than that of the monopole. The noise generated by air moving devices such as low-speed fans and centrifugal blowers is also dipole in character, and will be discussed later in this article. One of the key characteristics of a dipole is that no net mass is introduced into the medium. That is, the mass flow of the two out-of-phase monopoles results in no net mass flow and produces a net force on the medium.

The pressure field of a dipole can be written in terms of the force exerted on the medium, but when the dipole is thought of as two out-of-phase monopoles, each having a source strength Q_o, and placed a distance d apart, the resulting pressure field is

$$p = \frac{\omega Q_o}{4\pi r}(kd \cos \phi) \sin (kr - \omega t), \qquad (2.10)$$

where ϕ is the angle that the field point makes with the line joining the two monopoles, and k is the wave number, ω/c. Note that the pressure is zero at $\phi = 90°$ because the distance from each source to the field point is the same. The only reason that a dipole source produces any pressure field is because there is a difference in path length from the field point to each monopole, and hence the phase cancellation is not complete. The dipole source is said to be *directional* in contrast to the omni-directional sound pressure characteristic (no ϕ-dependence) of the monopole.

The *quadrupole* source is the next most complex source, and is characterized by the absence of a dipole moment; that is, no net force is exerted on the medium. This type of source can be important in complex panel vibration problems, and in the problem of noise generated by flow at high Mach numbers. The concept of a quadrupole is useful in the study of aerodynamic sound such as that generated by a jet engine exhaust. It can be thought of as two dipoles (which in turn each consist of two monopoles) having their dipole moments in opposite directions. A quadrupole is a less efficient source of sound than either the dipole or the monopole, and when phase cancellation can be arranged by careful choice of phasing and geometry, a net noise reduction is usually achieved.

2.3 Power output of a sound source

Another very important characteristic of a sound source is the radiated *sound power*. This power is the energy radiated per unit time by the source, and for most sources is a function of frequency, as will be described in Section 3. When the pressure and particle velocity of a source are known as a function of time, the power output may be calculated from the surface integral (over a sphere surrounding the source) of the *intensity* of the sound wave, the time average of the product of the sound pressure and the particle velocity of the wave:

$$W = \int \overline{pu}^t \, dS. \qquad (2.11)$$

In the case of a spherical wave, the output power is simply

$$W = \frac{\bar{p}^2}{\rho c} 4\pi r^2, \qquad (2.12)$$

where $\sqrt{\bar{p}^2}$ is the rms value of the sound pressure. The quantity $\bar{p}^2/\rho c$ is the *intensity* of the wave, and is particularly important in determination of the sound power from measurements in the far field. In most cases of practical interest, the sound power must be determined by measurement in specially designed test environments to be described later in this article. Normally, one measures the sound pressure produced by a source, and determines the sound power output either by computation or by comparison with the sound pressure produced by a source having a known sound power output.

3. Noise Measurement

3.1 Fundamentals

Noise measurements are usually carried out for one of three purposes:

1) To gain an understanding of the mechanisms of noise generation so that methods of engineering control of the noise can be applied;

2) to rate the sound field at various locations on a scale that is related to the physiological or psychological effects of noise on human beings.

3) To rate the sound power output of a source, usually for future engineering calculations that will result in an estimate of the sound pressure produced by the source at a given location.

We will discuss sound power in Section 3.8. In this section, methods for expressing the sound pressure in terms of a single number or set of numbers will be discussed. Noise measurements are invariably made with a *sound level meter*. A photograph of a modern meter containing a set of *octave band* filters is shown in Figure 3.1. As indicated in the block diagram, Figure 3.2, the meter consists of a microphone, amplifier, filter bank (or weighting network), a detector, and an indicating meter. The electrical signal produced by the microphone is essentially proportional to the sound pressure, p(t), at the diaphragm, and this electrical signal must then be analyzed in terms of its frequency components. As a practical matter, the frequency range between 90 and 11,200 Hz is of most importance, but some problems require measurements as low as 25 Hz and as high as about 22 kHz. The frequency spectrum is usually divided into *octaves* on portable equipment and into *one-third* octaves in laboratory equipment. The frequency range of an octave band filter extends from $(1/\sqrt{2})f_c$ to $\sqrt{2}f_c$, where f_c is the center frequency of the octave band. Standard center frequencies, upper cut-off frequencies, and lower

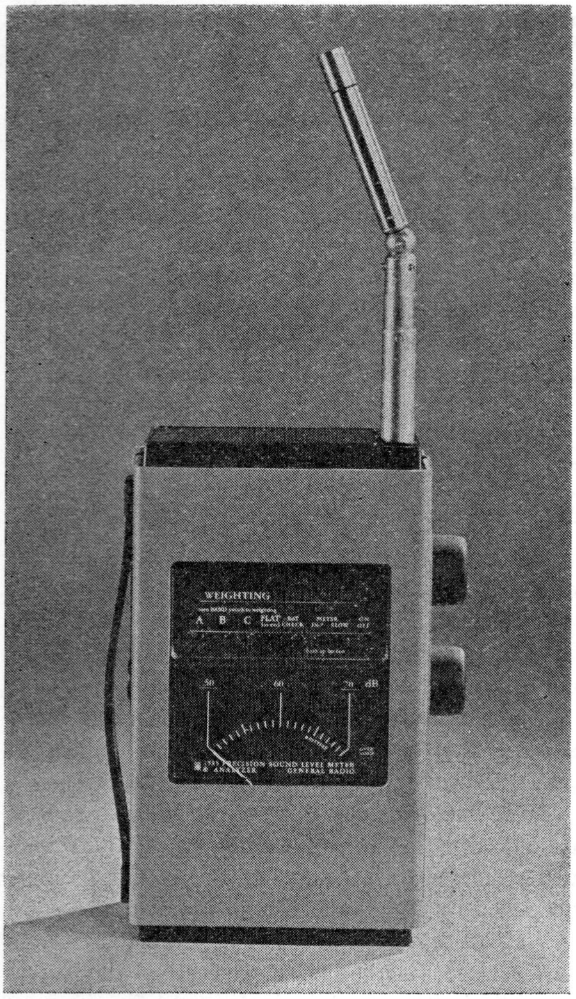

Figure 3.1 Sound level meter and octave band analyzer. (Photo Courtesy of the General Radio Company).

cut-off frequencies for octave and one-third octave band filters are given in Table 3.1.

The purpose of the detector and meter in Figure 3.2 is to obtain an estimate of the rms value of the filter outputs using either the meter characteristic "Fast" or "Slow." For many measurements, the noise is steady, and a reading using the "Slow" characteristic is usually of interest. This corresponds to the long-time rms value of the filter outputs. Other measurement techniques will be discussed in Section 3.6. Note that a reading of the meter is obtained in each octave (or one-third octave) band, and thus the octave band (or one-third octave band) spectrum of the noise is obtained. These numbers are useful for engineering purposes, or for rating the sound using methods to be described in Section 4.2. For rating of many noises in terms of human response, a simple method has evolved, measurement of a *weighted sound level.*

TABLE 3.1

Center Frequencies and Cutoff Frequencies for Octave- and One-Third Octave Bands Filter Banks

Center Frequency (Hz)		Lower Cutoff Frequency (Hz)		Upper Cutoff Frequency (Hz)	
Octave	One-third Octave	octave	One-third Octave	octave	One-third Octave
	100		90		112
125	125	90	112	180	140
	160		140		180
	200		180		224
250	250	180	224	355	280
	315		280		355
	400		355		450
500	500	355	450	710	560
	630		560		710
	800		710		900
1000	1000	710	900	1400	1120
	1250		1120		1400
	1600		1400		1800
2000	2000	1400	1800	2800	2240
	2500		2240		2800
	3150		2800		3550
4000	4000	2800	3550	5600	4500
	5000		4500		5600
	6300		5600		710
8000	8000	5600	7100	11,200	9000
	10,000		9000		11,200

Using this method, the set of octave band filters is replaced by a single "weighting network" having a transmission characteristic that weights low frequency (and high frequency) sound in a manner similar to the response of the ear. The most

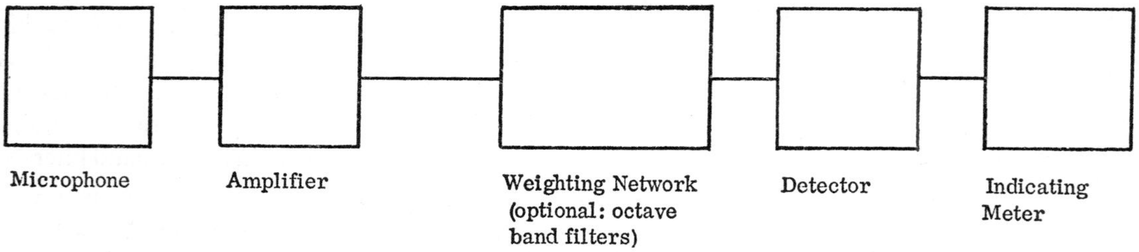

Figure 3.2 Block diagram of a typical sound level meter.

TABLE 3.2

Voltage Level Gain as a Function of Frequency for the A-Weighting Network

One-third octave band center frequency (Hz)	Voltage level gain of A-weighting network (db)
100	−19.1
125	−16.1
160	−13.4
200	−10.9
250	− 8.6
315	− 6.6
400	− 4.8
500	− 3.2
630	− 1.9
800	− 0.8
1000	0
1250	0.6
1600	1.0
2000	1.2
2500	1.3
3150	1.2
4000	1.0
5000	0.5
6300	− 0.1
8000	− 1.1
10,000	− 2.5
12,500	− 4.3

commonly used network is the A-weighting network. The transmission characteristic for this network is defined by the values given in Table 3.2. Thus, an A-weighted sound level is a single number that in many cases correlates with human response to noise. For engineering purposes, use of the octave band or one-third octve band spectrum is essential.

3.2 The decibel

Up to now, no quantitative measure (except for the sound pressure itself) has been given for noise. It has proven to be convenient to introduce a unit of level, the decibel, into many areas of acoustics, and this unit is commonly used in engineering acoustics and noise control. The level of a given rms sound pressure is given by

$$L_p = 20 \log_{10} \frac{p_{\mathrm{rms}}}{p_{\mathrm{ref}}} \, dB. \tag{3.1}$$

The quantity p_{ref} is the standard reference pressure, $2 \times 10^{-5}\,\mathrm{N/m^2}$. All sound level meters are calibrated to read in terms of the unit of level, the decibel. Note that the sound level meter of Figure 3.2 contains a set of octave band filters and weighting networks (A-weighting being the most common). In order to indicate the weighting network (or octave band filter) used, the bandwidth must be stated. For example, the sound level, A-weighted, is 80 dB. For convenience, a composite abbreviation for the decibel and A-weighting (dB A) is commonly used, and the expression "the level is 80 dB A" clearly indicates that the A-weighted level is intended. Another common composite abbreviation for the decibel and A-weighting is dB (A). When band pressure levels are intended, a common expression is "the level in the 500 Hz octave band is 65 dB."

Some "typical" A-weighted levels are shown in Table 3.3. Note that the range of levels in this table (20–120 dB) covers a range of pressures from 2×10^{-4}–$20\,\mathrm{N/m^2}$. One of the reasons for taking the logarithm of the pressure ratio in equation (3.1) is to provide a convenient scale for measurement of noise.

TABLE 3.3

"Typical" A-weighted Sound Levels for Commonly Encountered Noise Sources. The values given here are typical in the sense that they usually represent averages of various measurements that have been reported. Individual values will vary above and below the values in the Table

"Typical" Sound Level, A-weighted (dB)

"Typical" Sound Level, A-weighted (dB)	Source
120	
	Snowmobile at operator's position
110	
	Four engine turbofan aircraft-takeoff at 1000 ft
100	Air compressors (high) at operator's position
	Air compressors (low) at operator's position
90	Heavy truck at 50 ft
	Chain saw at 50 ft
80	
	Lawn mower at 50 ft
70	
	Dishwasher at 3 ft
60	
	Very noisy urban residential background
50	
	Urban residential daytime background
	Refrigerator at 3 ft
40	
	Quiet suburban daytime background
30	
20	Equivalent level at condenser microphone in an anechoic Test Room

3.3 Addition of levels

One of the consequences of using a logarithmic scale is that the resultant level produced by two sources of sound is *not* equal to the sum of the individual levels. That is, if one source produces a level of 85 dB A at a given location, and another source produces a level of 70 dB A at the same location, the level produced by the two sources operating at the same time is *not* equal to 155 dB A.

If the sound pressures (as a function of time) for the two sources are $p_1(t)$ and $p_2(t)$ respectively, the basic rule is that the resultant pressure is $p(t) = p_1(t) + p_2(t)$. Because the rms value is determined by the instrument, the resulting pressure is essentially

$$p_{\text{rms}} = \left[\frac{1}{T}\int_0^T [(p_1(t) + p_2(t)]^2\, dt\right]^{0.5}, \qquad (3.2)$$

the integral of the cross product $p_1(t)p_2(t)$ in equation (3.2) is of key importance. In most practical noise problems, this cross-product is zero, and the basic rule is to add the mean square pressures produced by the individual sources. Such sources are said to be incoherent. Thus, the level (L) resulting from several sources each having a level L_1, $L_2, \ldots, L_N$ is

$$L = 10 \log \left[\sum_{k=1}^{N} 10^{\frac{L_1}{10}} + 10^{\frac{L_2}{10}} + \cdots 10^{\frac{L_N}{10}}\right]. \qquad (3.3)$$

Thus, the level produced by two sources each having a level of 80 dB will be 83 dB.

3.4 Background noise

Usually, the sound level (or noise level) produced by a source is measured in the presence of an ambient (or background) noise, and equation 3.3 can be used to estimate the contribution of the ambient noise level to the overall (source plus ambient level). Table 3.4 shows the number of decibels to be subtracted from an overall (source plus ambient) level to determine the level produced by the source.

TABLE 3.4

Corrections to be Applied to a Source Level to Account for the Presence of a Background Level

Difference between the sound pressure level measured with sound source operating and ambient sound pressure level	Correction (in dB) to be subtracted from sound level measured with sound source operating to obtain sound pressure level due to sound source alone
(dB)	(dB)
4	2.2
5	1.7
6	1.3
7	1.0
8	0.8
9	0.6
10	0.4
11	0.3
12	0.3
13	0.2
14	0.2
15	0.1

3.5 Measurements in other bandwidths

Although octave- and one-third octave bandwidths are commonly used in the measurement of noise, narrow band measurements should be made in many practical situations. Many sources contain *discrete frequency components*, pure tones superimposed on a broad-band noise background. For example, some transformers and motors produce a discrete-frequency component at 120 Hz, and other equipment such as fans, blowers, and pumps produce a tone at a *blade passage frequency*, the frequency with which moving elements pass fixed elements in the system. One method[3] of identifying a prominent discrete-frequency component depends on how much the level of the tone (measured with a narrow band filter) projects above the broad-band spectrum. The details of the measurement technique are presented in Ref. 3, but the basic criterion is shown in Figure 3.3 for measurements in a one-tenth octave (approximately 7 percent of the center frequency) bandwidth. This curve is based on the criterion that a discrete frequency component is prominent when the level of the discrete tone is at least 10 dB above the average of the band pressure levels on each side of the tone, when the analyzer has a bandwidth equal to the "Fletcher Critical Bandwidth."[4]

3.6 Measurement of non-steady noise

It is unfortunate that many of the noises encountered in practice are not steady. That is, the

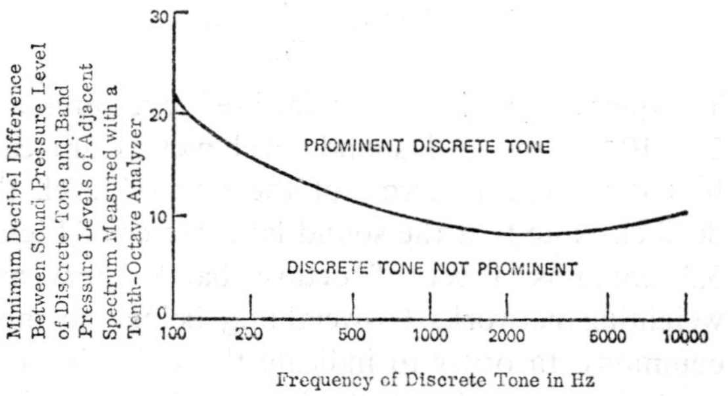

Figure 3.3 Criteria for the presence of a prominent discrete tone in the spectrum of a noise when a one-tenth octave (7% bandwidth) analyzer is used.

indicating meter on a sound level meter varies with time, and an appropriate level (or levels) must be recorded. When the fluctuations of the pointer on the indicating meter using the "slow" scale are less than ± 3 dB, the noise is *steady*, and the average value of the meter fluctuations is approximately the rms level, the quantity of greatest interest. For fluctuations of the pointer between ± 3 and ± 5 dB, the rms level is approximately 3 dB below the average of the maximum excursions of the meter. Larger variations usually require an analysis of a recording of the noise in the laboratory, except that for special situations (such as the noise produced by a passing vehicle) the maximum reading of the meter is of most interest.

Impulsive noise is a special case of non-steady noise, and two particular types of noise are of interest. *Quasi Steady Noise* is made up of impulses that occur often enough that the reading of the meter is steady, and the noise can be treated as steady. When the noise consists of isolated bursts, the measurement is more complicated. An oscilloscope capable of monitoring the variation of level with time is useful, or the peak sound pressure level may be determined, either from the oscilloscope trace or from a peak-reading circuit built into many sound level meters. In the past few years, a special level, known as the impulse sound level,[5] has been used as a measure of the level of impulsive noise, but this technique has not as yet become widely accepted in the United States.

3.7 Sound pressure measurements

Basically, the purpose of a sound pressure measurement is to determine the noise level so that engineering action can be taken, or to rate the noise in terms of human response. The former requires data in octave- or one-third octave bandwidths, and the latter may require such measurements, although the use of a simple A-weighted level is becoming common. When making measurements around a given piece of equipment, the microphone is usually placed at a height of 1.5 m and 1 m from the smallest possible imaginary parallelepiped that surrounds the source. Measurements centered on the four sides are usually adequae, but for large sources, additional microphone positions spaced 1 m apart are useful. If the equipment is operator-attended, an additional measurement should be made at the operator's position. Detailed measurement procedures from which test codes for specific pieces of equipment can be prepared are given in an ANSI Standard.[6]

3.8 Determination of sound power

Although some equipment is rated in terms of its sound power spectrum,[7] the sound power level is usually thought of as a characteristic of the source of sound. When used for rating purposes, the characteristics of the path between the source and receiver are usually taken into account. The unit of sound power level is the decibel, and is defined as

$$L_W = 10 \log \frac{W}{W_{\text{ref}}}, \tag{3.4}$$

where W is the sound power output of the source in W, and the quantity W_{ref} is the standard reference pressure, 10^{-12} W. Some sound power data are still expressed in terms of decibels referenced to 10^{-13} W, but this reference is not currently being used. As mentioned previously, sound power is usually determined from a sound pressure measurement, and hence all of the remarks concerning filter bandwidths and addition of levels in Sections 3.2 and 3.3 are applicable. For a non-directional source over a plane, the rms sound pressure at a distance r is

$$p_{\text{rms}} = \sqrt{W\left(\frac{\rho c}{2\pi r^2}\right)}. \tag{3.5}$$

In terms of levels, the sound pressure level at 1 m is 8 dB below the sound power level, and decreases at a rate of 6 dB per doubling of distance if such effects as ground attenuation, thermal and wind gradients, and the scattering of sound by turbulence are neglected.

Sound power is usually determined from a pressure measurement, either in a free field, free field over a reflecting plane, or in a diffuse field. Indoors, an anechoic (all surfaces absorb sound) room or a semi-anechoic (5 absorbing surfaces, rigid floor) room may be used, and detailed techniques for sound power determination may be found in an American National Standard.[8]

The diffuse field method of determination of sound power has been widely used because the facility used, a reverberation room, is usually less costly than an anechoic room, and because the measurement is usually less time consuming. Since a reverberation room is designed to have highly reflective surfaces and the measurement is made in that portion of the room where reflected sound energy is predominent, information concerning the directivity of the source is lost. In many cases of practical importance, information concerning directivity is not necessary, and the reverberation room technique is very useful. Detailed measurement methods may be found in an American National Standard.

4. The Effects of Noise on Man

4.1 General

The problem of human response to noise is complex, and individual judgments with respect to loudness or noisiness tend to vary over a relatively wide range. Many rating methods have been developed that allow a given noise spectrum or time-varying noise to be reduced to a single number related to human response, and these methods have proved to be useful in many practical situations.

In recent years, the A-weighted sound level has become a widely-used measure of the effects of noise on man, both psychological and physiological, and is a reasonably good indicator of noisiness or loudness provided that the frequency spectrum of the noise covers several octaves. When a single frequency or octave band dominates the spectrum, the A-weighted level often tends to overestimate the loudness or noisiness of a particular sound.

4.2 Noise rating methods

Two of the basic problems encountered in determination of a single-number rating for a given noise are:

a) The ear is not equally sensitive to all frequencies, and an adjustment must be made to the octave band levels to account for this non-uniformity. Also, a relationship must be specified that can be used to combine the adjusted levels into a single-number rating.

b) A method must be specified to account for the variation of the level with time.

The former, the rating of steady noise, has received the most attention, and the methods currently in use can be classified as *band selection*, *band summation*, and *band averaging*. For example, the ISO Noise Rating Method[10] (*N*-value) is a band selection method. A value $NR(J)$ for each octave band from 125–8000 Hz is computed from the corresponding octave band level, $L(J)$, by

$$NR(J) = [L(J) - A(J)] \div B(J), \tag{4.1}$$

where values of $A(J)$ and $B(J)$ for each octave band are given in Table 4.1. The highest value of $NR(J)$ is *selected* as the rating for the spectrum. The adjustment of each octave band level (determined by the values of A and B) is similar to the weighting provided by the A-network in a sound level meter. The Noise Rating Method requires that an octave band spectrum be determined for the noise, an advantage when the ultimate purpose of the measurement is engineering control of the noise.

TABLE 4.1

Constants for the Determination of ISO Noise Rating (N-) Values

Octave band center frequency (Hz)	Index number (J)	A(J)	B(J)
63	1	35.5	0.79
125	2	22.0	0.87
250	3	12.0	0.93
500	4	4.8	0.974
1000	5	0	1.0
2000	6	−3.5	1.015
4000	7	−6.1	1.025
8000	8	−8.0	1.030

An example of the *band summation* method is the determination of the loudness according to Steven's Mark VI procedure.[11] Here, the octave band levels are converted to a loudness index according to the graph of Figure 4.1, and the resulting indices in each octave band are summed according to

$$I_t = I_m + 0.3[(\Sigma I) - I_m], \tag{4.2}$$

where I represents the loudness indices in all of the octave bands, and I_m is the maximum index. Finally, the loudness level (L) is determined according to the relationship

$$L = 40 + 10 \log_2 I_t. \tag{4.3}$$

An example of a *band averaging* method is the preferred speech interference level (PSIL). This level is the average of the levels in the octave bands centered on 500, 1000, and 2000 Hz, and is a useful measure of the effects of noise on speech communication.[12]

Other methods have been used for the rating of steady noise, for example, the perceived noisiness (in PNdB) and the effective perceived noise level (EPNL)[13] are widely used for the rating of aircraft noise. The EPNL includes a correction for the duration of the noise. Other criteria such as the Composite Noise Rating, Noise Exposure Forecast and Community Noise Equivalent Level have also been used[14] for rating noise. The background noise level in offices and other similar areas is often rated in terms of a noise criteron (NC) number [15] or in terms of a newer preferred noise criterion (PNC)[16] number. The loudness of sound can be determined using the Steven's Mark VI method as described above, by Zwicker's Method,[17] or by a new method, Steven's Mark VII. The latter has been proposed[18]

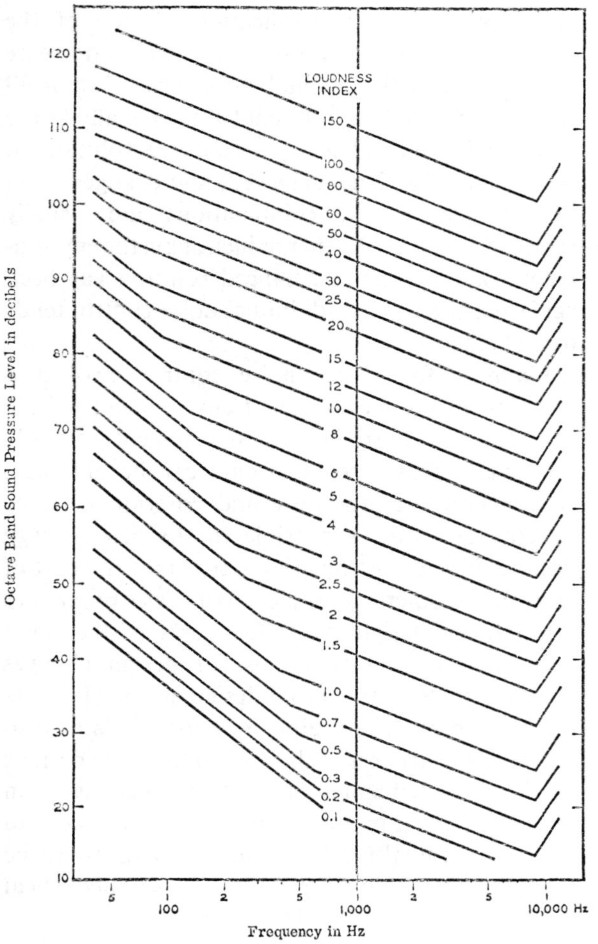

Figure 4.1 Graph for determination of loudness index using octave band sound pressure levels. The same graph may be used for one-third octave band data, in which case the constant 0.3 in equation 4.2 should be changed to 0.15.

as a compromise between many of the methods previously suggested to determine loudness or noisiness.

4.3 Damage risk criteria

One of the problems associated with exposure to noise is that the hearing acuity of an individual may be damaged by exposure to excessive noise. This often occurs as a temporary threshold shift (TTS) that eventually becomes a permanent threshold shift (PTS) as a result of repeated exposure to the noise. A wide variety of damage criteria have been suggested in the literature.[19–21] One set of criteria that has been adopted by the Federal Government and by many state governments are those specified in the Williams–Steiger Occupational Safety and Health Act (OSHA) of 1970.[22] Another set of criteria are those specified in an International Recommendation[23] on Conservation of hearing in industrial environments. One of the key differences between these two criteria is the "trading relationship" between sound level and time. The former uses a 5 dB factor (an 8-hr exposure to 90 dB A is assumed to be equivalent to a 4-hr exposure to 95 dB A), and the latter uses a 3 dB "trading relationship." Exposures allowed under the 1970 OSHA Regulations are given in Table 4.2.

5. Control of Noise

The statement is often made that technology is available to control the noise produced by nearly any source of sound. However, the definition of the problem and the application of the technology required to solve the problem is usually complicated by the many factors that must be considered in a typical noise control situation. For example, the cost of noise control is vitally important; the weight and bulk of a given treatment may be excessive, accessibility may be affected, and cooling the equipment may become more difficult. In a noise control program, all of these factors must be considered in arriving at an optimal solution to a given problem. These and other factors make it difficult to assign a "Dollars per decibel" figure to the cost of noise reduction, and this figure may vary over several orders of magnitude depending on the particular problem.

It is usually convenient to think of a noise control problem in terms of the *source* of noise, the *path*

TABLE 4.2

1970 Noise Limits — Occupational Safety and Health Administration (OSHA)

Noise level dB A (Slow)	Maximum permissible exposure (hr)
90	8
92	6
95	4
97	3
100	2
102	1.5
105	1
110	0.5
115	0.25

NOTES:

1) First time varying levels, the sum $(C_1/T_1) + (C_2/T_2) + (C_3/T_3) + \ldots$ must not exceed unity. $C_1, C_2 \ldots$ are the actual exposure times to a given level over an 8-hr interval, and $T_1, T_2 \ldots$ are the permitted exposure times given in the Table.

2) Exposure to impact or impulsive noise should not exceed a *peak* sound pressure level of 140 dB.

over which noise is transmitted, and the *receiver*. Usually, the receiver is man, and the various criteria outlined in Section 4 may be combined with the measurement methods described in Section 3 to select a goal for the particular noise control problem. If the path is *airborne* the noise is transmitted through air directly to the receiver. *Structure-borne* noise arises when waves are transmitted through solid structures which in turn vibrate and become the actual source of sound.

The *source* can be characterized in several ways, either using sound pressure or sound power. Control of noise at the source is usually the most desirable and at the same time the most difficult kind of noise control to implement. The following sections contain general guidelines concerning planning for noise control, techniques for reduction of noise along the transmission path, and source noise control.

5.1 Planning for noise control

The wide variety of situations in which noise control must be considered make it very difficult to present a straightforward description of the planning process for noise control. However, many situations have several features in common. This subject can conveniently be divided into two parts, *environmental noise control* and *source noise control*. The latter involves planning for control of the noise produced by a particular source during the product development phase, and the former usually involves consideration of multiple sources, analysis of transmission paths, and selection of an appropriate criterion for a given environment. One usually starts with an analysis of the overall problem. Estimates are made of the levels produced by one or more sources, usually on an octave band basis. These levels are then modified by the attentuation expected over each of the transmission paths to the receiver, and finally the levels are combined to make an estimate of the environmental noise level at a given location. The estimated values are then compared with the criterion that has been selected. If the noise environment is not satisfactory, plans must be made to (1) change the location of the receiver (2) increase the attentuation along the path, and (3) to modify the levels or locations of the sources (or to select different sources). One important point is that the most highest level that contributes to the environmental noise level must be selected for modification because of the way that levels are added. As an example, if one particular source/path combination produces a level 5 dB above the levels produced by a few other source/path combinations, modification of one of the latter levels will not produce a significant decrease in the total environmental noise level. When all source/path combinations contribute equally to the total environmental level, a *balanced* solution to the problem has been achieved, and changes in all of the source/path combinations are usually required to achieve further reductions in the environmental level. When a balanced solution has been achieved, the cost of additional noise control tends to be high.

Planning for source noise control involves a selection of the measurement environment for the source, and a controlled test environment is usually selected so that repeatable data can be obtained. A measurement procedure and criterion must be selected as early as possible in the design stage because it is almost invariably true that the cost of noise control increases rapidly as a device progresses through the design cycle. Estimates of the noise levels and recommendations for design changes must be made in the initial design stage. Measurements on prototype equipment must be planned so that the effectiveness of the initial recommendations can be evaluated and additional design changes can be proposed. Finally, plans must be made to evaluate the final product, and a program must be set up to insure that the product meets its acoustical specifications when it is in production.

5.2 Methods of noise control

Several approaches to the noise control problem are generally used depending on the particular problem. Engineering control of the noise at the source is always desirable, and has been designated as the preferred method with respect to control of occupational noise exposure.[24] Other approaches are through administrative measures. For example, restricting the exposure time of employees to a given noise, or allowing equipment to operate only at certain hours of the day or night. Procedural methods may be used, for example, use of prescribed take-off and landing procedures at an airport, or selected routing of vehicular traffic through a city. Legal control of noise has often been attempted,[25] and in some cases has proved to be effective. One of the major problems is that quantitative levels must usually be prescribed for effective legal control, and enforcement then requires sound measuring equipment and trained personnel to monitor the noise. While this may not prove to be a problem with respect to monitoring noise at an airport, control of a wide variety of community noise sources is difficult.

Engineering control of noise requires application of the many techniques that have been developed[26,27] for various noise control situations. One of the major considerations in source control is identification of the sources of noise. For equipment that operates sequentially, identification of the source by the time at which an event or impact occurs is most useful, and spectral information often provides relatively little guidance. On the other hand, sources of noise in rotating equipment are usually best identified by narrow band frequency analysis, and the solutions may involve isolation of equipment from large surfaces that are effective sound radiators, changes in gear or bearing design, changes in clearance between rotating parts within the equipment, addition of sound absorbing treatment, or addition of vibration damping material to particular surfaces, etc.

Control of environmental noise can only be achieved when an estimate of the levels of the various sources that contribute to the environmental level is made, the attenuation (or amplification) on the paths from source to receiver is known, and a suitable quantitative criterion for the environmental noise level has been selected. Modification of the attentuation provided by the various paths is usually the most feasible method of controlling environmental noise. For example, the location of the source (or receiver) may be changed to achieve a greater attenuation along the path. More commonly, the source is enclosed, and the two most important factors are that the transmission loss of the enclosure must be adequate and that sound absorbing material must be used inside the enclosure to absorb the sound produced by the device. If the sound absorption provided inside the enclosure is not adequate, the level inside will increase because of reflection of sound from the surfaces of the enclosure. As a result, the noise reduction provided by the overall enclosure will be reduced. Other path problems involve the selection of walls, floor, and ceiling structures having satisfactory transmission loss characteristics.[28] In a room, careful attention must be paid to the sound absorbing characteristics of room surfaces if the receiver is in that portion of the room in which the level is controlled by reflections from the various wall surfaces.[29] Many other environmental problems involve sound transmission through ducts and mufflers, and techniques have been developed[26,30] to preduct the attenuation provided by ducts, and the levels generated in a given environment as a result of transmission through ducts.

REFERENCES

1. U.S. Environmental Protection Agency. Report to the President and Congress on Noise. 31 December 1971. A listing of the title of each volume may be found in *NOISE/NEWS* 1, 31 (1972). Published by the Institute of Noise Control Engineering, Suite 707, 1730 M Street NW, Washington, DC 20036.
2. Morse, P. M. and K. U. Ingard (1968). *Theoretical Acoustics*, McGraw–Hill Book Company, New York.
3. American National Standard Methods for the Measurement of Sound Pressure Levels, S1. 13–1971. Published by the American National Standards Institute, 1430 Broadway, New York, NY 10018. See Appendix A.
4. Fletcher, H. (1953). *Speech and Hearing in Communication*, D. VanNostrand Co., Inc., New York. p. 101.
5. Draft Supplement to IEC Publication 179, *Precision Sound Level Meters*, Additional Requirements for the Measurement of Impulsive Sounds, IEC Document Number 29C (Central Office) 16, International Electrotechnical Commission, Geneva, Switzerland. November 1971.
6. See Ref. 3, particularly Chapters 6 and 7.
7. ARI Standard 270–67, Sound Rating of Outdoor Unitary Equipment, Air Conditioning and Refrigeration Institute, 1815 North Fort Meyer Drive, Arlington, VA 22209.
8. American National Standard Methods for the Physical Measurement of Sound, S1. 2–1962. American National Standards Institute, 1430 Broadway, New York, NY 10018.
9. American National Standard Methods for the Determination of Sound Power Radiated by Small Noise Sources in Reverberation Rooms. S1.21-1972. American National Standards Institute, 1430 Broadway, New York, NY 10018.
10. ISO Recommendation R1996, Assessment of Noise with Respect to Community Response, International Organization for Standardization, Geneva, Switzerland. May 1971.
11. American National Standard Procedure for the Computation of Loudness of Noise, S3. 4–1968. American National Standards Institute, 1430 Broadway, New York, NY 10018.
12. Webster, J. C. (1969). *SIL*, Past, present, and future Sound and Vibration, **3**, 22.
13. Federal Aviation Regulation–36. (1969) Published in the *Federal Register*, **34**, 221.
14. Young, R. W. (1972). Definitions of Terms, *NOISE/NEWS*, **1**, 39, 62. Institute of Noise Control Engineering, Suite 707, 1730 M Street NW, Washington, DC 20036.
15. Beranek, L. L. (1960). *Noise Reduction*, pp. 518–519. McGraw-Hill Book Company, New York.
16. Beranek, L. L. (1971). Revision of noise criteria curves, *J. Acoust. Soc. Am.*, **50**, 96(A).
17. ISO Recommendation R532, Method for Calculating Loudness Level. International Organization for Standardization, Geneva, Switzerland, 1966.
18. Stevens, S. S. (1972). Perceived level of noise by Mark VII and Decibels (E). *J. Acoust. Soc. Am.*, **51**, 575.
19. Kryter, K. D., W. D. Ward, J. D. Miller and D. H. Eldredge, (1966) Hazardous exposure to intermittent and steady state noise, *J. Acoust. Soc. Am.*, **39**, 451.
20. Botsford, J. H. (1967). Simple method for identifying acceptable noise exposures, *J. Acoust. Soc. Am.*, **42**, 810.
21. Kryter, K. D. (1970). *The Effects of Noise on Man*, Academic Press, New York.
22. 1970 Occupational Safety and Health Act, 29 U.S.C. 656. See also the noise limits published in the *Federal Register*, **34**, 7948 (1969).

23. ISO Recommendation 1999, Assessment of Noise Exposure During Work for Hearing Conservation Purposes. International Organization for Standardization, Geneva, Switzerland, 1970.
24. Bulletin 334, Guidelines to the Department of Labor's Occupational Noise Standards. U.S. Department of Labor, Washington, DC, 1971.
25. Compilation of state and local ordinances on noise control. Congressional Record, 29 October 1969, 32178–32259. Entered by Senator Mark Ha field.
26. Beranek, L. L. (1971). *Noise and Vibration Control*, McGraw-Hill Book Company, New York.
27. Crocker, M. J. Editor, *Noise and Vibration Control Engineering*, Proceedings of the Purdue Noise Control Conference, July 1971. Purdue University, Lafayette, IN 47907, 1972.
28. Berendt, R.D., G.E. Winzer and C. B. Burroughs, A Guide to Airborne, Impact, and Structureborne Noise Control in Multifamily Dwellings, FT/TS-24. U.S. Department of Housing and Urban Development, Washington, DC 20410, 1968.
29. Beranek, L. L. (1970). *op. cit.* pp. 228–229.
30. *ASHRAE Guide and Data Book*, 1972, American Society of Heating, Refrigerating and Air Conditioning Engineers, United Engineering Center, 345 E. 47th St., New York, NY 10017.

GEORGE C. MALING, JR.
I.B.M. Corporation

NON-IONIZING RADIATIONS

Lasers, microwave ovens, radar for pleasure boats, infrared inspection equipment and high intensity light sources generate so-called "non-ionizing" radiation.

Electromagnetic radiations which do not cause ionization in biological systems may be presumed to have photon energies less than 10–12 eV and may be termed "non-ionizing."

Because of the proliferation of such electronic products as well as a renewed interest in electromagnetic radiation hazards, the Congress recently enacted Public Law 90–602 the "Radiation Control for Health and Safety Act." This Act has as its declared purpose the establishment of a national electronic product radiation control program which includes the development and administration of performance standards to control the emission of electronic product radiation. The most outstanding feature of the Act is its omnibus coverage of all types of electromagnetic radiation emanating from electronic products, i.e. gamma, X-rays, ultraviolet, visible, infrared, radiofrequencies (RF) and microwaves. Performance standards have already been issued under the Act for TV sets and microwave ovens; preparations are underway for the issuance of a laser standard. In similar fashion, the recent enactment of the federal Occupational Safety and Health Act gives due attention to the potential hazards of non-ionizing radiations in industrial establishments.

For the purposes of this chapter more formal treatment is given to ultraviolet (UV) radiation, lasers, and microwave radiation than to the visible and infrared (IR) radiations. However the information on visible and IR radiation presented in the section on Laser Radiation is generally applicable to non-coherent sources.

A. Nature of electromagnetic energy

The electromagnetc spectrum extends over a broad range of wavelengths, e.g. from $< 10^{-12}$ to $> 10^{10}$ cm. The shortest wavelengths are generated by cosmic and X-rays, the longer wavelengths are associated with microwave and electrical power generation. Ultraviolet, visible and IR radiations occupy an intermediate position. Radio frequency waves may range from 10 kHz to 10^{12} Hz, IR rays from $10^{12-} \simeq 4 \times 10^{14}$ Hz (0.72 μm), the visible spectrum from approximately 0.7–0.4 μm, UV from approximately 0.4–0.1 μm and γ- and X-radiation, below 0.1 μm. The photon energies of electromagnetic radiations are proportional to the frequency of the radiation and inversely proportional to wavelength, hence the higher energies (e.g. 10^8 eV) are associated with X- and γ-radiations, the lower energies (e.g. 10^{-6} eV) with RF and microwave radiations.

Whereas the thermal energy associated with molecules at room temperature is approximately 1/30 eV, the binding energy of chemical bonds is roughly equivalent to a range of $<$ 1–15 eV. The nuclear binding energies of protons may be equivalent to 10^6 eV and greater. Since the photon energy necessary to ionize atomic oxygen and hydrogen is of the order of 10–12 eV it seems in order to adopt a value of approximately 10 eV as a lower limit in which ionization is produced in biological material.

An extremely important qualification however is that non-ionizing radiations may be absorbed by biological systems and cause changes in the vibrational and rotational energies of the tissue molecules thus leading to possible dissociation of the molecules or, more often, dissipation of energy in the form of fluorescence or heat.

In conducting research into the bioeffects of the non-ionizing radiations the investigator has had to use several units of measurement in expressing the results of his studies. For this reason Appendix A, containing definitions of many useful radiometric terms has been included. Appendix B provides a simple means for expressing radiant exposure and irradiance units in a number of equivalent terms.

Since the eye is the primary organ at risk to all of the non-ionizing radiations.

Ultraviolet Radiation

A. Physical characteristics of ultraviolet radiation

For the purpose of assessing the biological effects of UV radiation the wavelength range of interest can be restricted to 0.1–0.4 μm. This range extends from the vacuum UV (0.1 μm) to the near UV (0.4 μm). A useful breakdown of the UV region is as follows:[1]

UV region	λ-range (μm)	Photon energy (eV)
Vacuum	< 0.16	> 7.7
Far	0.16–0.28	7.7–4.4
Middle	0.28–0.32	4.4–3.9
Near	0.32–0.4	3.9–3.1

The photon energy range for wavelengths between 0.1 and 0.4 μm is 12.4–3.1 eV, respectively.

B. Representative sources of ultraviolet radiation

The major source of UV radiation is the sun, although absorption by the ozone layer permits only wavelengths greater than 0.29 μm to reach the surface of the earth. Low and high pressure mercury discharge lamps constitute significant man made sources. In low pressure mercury vapor discharge lamps over 85% of the radiation is usually emitted at 0.2537 μm, viz. at germicidal wavelengths. At the lower pressures (fractions of an atmosphere) the characteristic mercury lines predominate whereas at higher pressures (up to 100 atmos.) the lines broaden to produce a radiation continuum. In typical quartz lamps the amount of energy at wavelengths below 0.38 μm may be 50% greater than the radiated visible energy, depending upon the mercury pressure. Other man-made sources include xenon discharge lamps, lasers, and relatively new types of fluorescent tubes which emit radiation at wavelengths above 0.315 μm reportedly at an irradiance less than that measured outdoors on a sunny day.

C. Biological effects of ultraviolet radiation

The biological action spectrum for erythema (reddening) produced by UV radiation of the skin has been the subject of investigation for many years. The most recent data show that a maximum erythemal effect is produced at 0.260 μm with the secondary peak at approximately 0.290 μm.[2,3] Erythemal response to wavelengths above 0.32 μm is predictably poor. The greatly increased air absorption of wavelengths below 0.25 μm and difficulty in obtaining monocromatic radiations in this region probably account for the lack of definitive bioeffects data. This may change with the increase in the number of UV lasers.

Wavelengths between 0.28 and 0.32 μm penetrate appreciably into the corium of the epidermis; those between 0.32 and 0.38 μm are absorbed in the epidermis, while those below 0.28 μm appear to be absorbed almost completely in the stratum corneum of the epidermis.

Depending upon the total UV dose, the latent period for erythema may range from 2 to several hours; the severity may vary from simple erythema to blistering and desquamation with severe secondary effects. A migration of melanin granules from the basal cells to the malphigian cell layers of the epidermis may cause a thickening of the horny layers of the skin. The possible long-term effects of the repeated process of melanin migration is not completely understood. The available data seem to support the contention that some regions of the UV may produce or initiate carcinogenesis in the human skin. The experiments which have supported this contention indicate that the biological action spectrum for carcinogenesis is the same as that for erythema.

Cases of skin cancer have been reported in workers whose occupation requires them to be exposed to sunlight for long periods of time. The reportedly high incidence of skin cancer in outdoor workers who are simultaneously exposed to chemicals such as coal tar derivatives, benzpyrene, methyl cholanthrene, and other anthracene compounds raises the question as to the role played by UV radiation in these cases. It is a matter of common knowledge that significant numbers of workers who routinely expose themselves to coal tar products while working outdoors experience a photosensitization of the skin.

Abiotic effects from exposure to UV radiation occurs in the spectral range of 0.24–0.31 μm. In this part of the spectrum, most of the incident energy is absorbed by the corneal epithelium at the surface of the eye. Hence, although the lens is capable of absorbing 99% of the energy below 0.35 μm only a small portion of the radiation reaches the anterior lenticular surface.

Photon-energies of about 3.5 eV (0.36 μm) may excite the lens of the eye or cause the aqueous or vitreous humor to fluoresce thus producing a diffuse haziness inside the eye that can interfere with visual acuity or produce eye fatigue. The phenomenon of fluorescence in the ocular media is not of concern from a bioeffects standpoint; the condition is strictly temporary and without detrimental effect.

The development of photokeratitis usually has a latency period varying from 30 min to as long as 24 hrs depending upon the severity of the exposure. A sensation of "sand in the eyes" accompanied by varying degrees of photophobia, lacrimation and blepharospasm is the usual result. Blepharospasm is a reflex protective mechanism characterized by an involuntary tight closing of the lids, usually over a damaged cornea.

D. Exposure criteria

The biological action spectrum for keratitis peaks at 0.28 μm. At this wavelength, the threshold for injury has been determined to be approximately 0.15×10^6 ergs.[4] It has been suggested that the corneal reaction is due primarily to selective absorption of UV by specific cell constituents, for example, globulin.

Verhoeff and Bell[5] gave the first quantitative measurement of the UV energy necessary for threshold damage as 2×10^6 ergs/cm^2 for the whole UV spectrum. More recent data by Pitts,[6,7] using 10 nm bands of radiation produced a threshold of approximately 0.5×10^5 ergs/cm^2 in rabbit eyes.

The exposure criteria adopted by the American Medical Association based on erythemal thresholds at 0.2537 μm radiation are as follows: 0.5×10^{-6} W/cm^2 for exposure up to 7 hr; 0.1×10^{-6} W/cm^2 for exposure periods up to and exceeding 24 hr.[8] Although these criteria are generally thought to be very conservative, i.e. stringent, they are nevertheless in common use.

E. Measurement of ultraviolet radiation

Various devices have been used to measure UV radiation, e.g. photoelectric cells, photoconductive cells, photovoltaic cells, and photochemical detectors. It is common practice to employ the use of selective filters in front of the detecting device in order to isolate that portion of the UV spectrum of interest to the investigator.

A commonly used detector is the barrier or photovoltaic cell. Certain semiconductors such as selenium or copper oxide deposited on a selected metal develop a potential barrier between the layer and the metal. Light falling upon the surface of the cell causes the flow of electrons from the semiconductor to the metal. A sensitive meter placed in such a circuit will record the intensity of radiation falling on the cell.

Ultraviolet photocells take advantage of the fact that certain metals have quantitative photoelectric responses to specific bands in the UV spectrum. Therefore a photocell may be equipped with metal cathode surfaces which are sensitive to certain UV wavelengths of interest. One of the drawbacks of photocells is solarization or deterioration of the envelope, especially with long usage or following measurement of high intensity UV radiation. This condition requires frequent recalibration of the cell. The readings obtained with these instruments are valid only when measuring monochromatic radiation, or when the relationship between the response of the instrument and the spectral distribution of the source is known.

A desirable design characteristic of UV detectors is to have the spectral response of the instrument closely approximate that of the biological action spectrum under consideration. However, such an instrument is unavailable at this time. Since available photocells and filter combinations do not closely approximate the UV biological action spectra it is necessary to standardize (calibrate) each photocell and meter. Such calibrations are generally made at a great enough distance from a standard source that the measuring device is in the "far field" of the source. Special care must be taken to control the temperature of so-called standard mercury lamps because the spectral distribution of the radiation from the lamp is dependent upon the pressure of the vaporized mercury.

A particularly useful device for measuring UV is the thermopile. Coatings on the receiver elements of the thermopile are generally lamp black or gold black to simulate black body radiation devices. Appropriate thermopile window material should be selected to minimize the effects of air convection, the more common windows being crystal quartz, lithium fluoride, calcium fluoride, sodium chloride, and potassium bromide.

Low intensity calibration may be made by exposing the thermopile to a secondary standard (carbon filament) furnished by the National Bureau of Standards.

Other UV detection devices include (1) photodiodes, e. g. silver, gallium arsenide, silver zinc sulfide, and gold zinc sulfide. Peak sensitivity of these diodes is at wavelengths below 0.36 μm; the peak efficiency or responsivity is of the order of 50–70%; (2) thermocouples, e.g. Chromel–Alumel; (3) Golay cells; (4) superconducting bolometers, and (5) zinc sulfide Schottky barrier detectors.[10]

Care must be taken to use detection devices having the proper rise time characteristics (some devices respond much too slowly to obtain meaningful measurements). Also, when measurements are being made special attention should be given to the possibility of UV absorption by many materials in the environment, e.g. ozone or mercury vapor, thus adversely affecting the readings. The possibility of photochemical reactions between UV radiation and a variety of chemicals also exists in the industrial environment.

F. Control of exposure

Because UV radiations are so easily absorbed by a wide variety of materials appropriate attenuation is accomplished in a straightforward manner.

In the case of UV lasers no firm bioeffects criteria are available. However the data of Pitts[6,7] may be used because of the narrow band UV source used in his experiments to determine thresholds of injury to rabbit eyes.

Laser Radiation

A. Sources and uses of laser radiation

The rate of development and manufacture of devices and systems based on stimulated emission of radiation has been truly phenomenal. Lasers are now being used for a wide variety of purposes including micromachining, welding, cutting, sealing, holography, optical alignment, interferometry, spectroscropy, surgery and as communications media.

Generally speaking lasing action has been obtained in gases, crystalline materials, semiconductors and liquids. Stimulated emission in gaseous systems was first reported in a helium–neon mixture in 1961.[11] Since that time lasing action has been reported at hundreds of wavelengths from the UV to the far IR (several hundred micrometers). Helium–neon (He–Ne) lasers are typical of gas systems where stable single frequency operation is important. He–Ne systems can operate in a pulsed mode or continuous wave (CW) at wavelengths of 0.6328, 1.15, or 3.39 μm depending upon resonator design. Typical power for He-Ne systems is of the order of 1–500 mW. The carbon dioxide gas laser system operates at a wavelength of 10.6 μm in either the continuous wave, pulsed, or Q-switched modes. The power output of CO_2–N_2 systems may range from several watts to greater than 10 kW. The CO_2 laser is attractive for terrestrial and extraterrestrial communications because of the low absorption window in the atmosphere between 8 and 14 qm. Of major significance from the personal hazard standpoint is the fact that enormous power may be radiated at a wavelength which is invisible to the human eye. The argon ion gas system operates predominantly at wavelengths of 0.488 and 0.515 μm in either a continuous wave or pulsed mode. Power generation is greatest at 0.488 μm, typically at less than 10 W.

Of the many ions in which laser action has been produced in solid state crystalline materials, perhaps neodymium (Nd^{3+}) in garnet or glass and chromium (Cr^{3+}) in aluminum oxide are most noteworthy. Garnet (yttrium aluminum garnet) or YAG is an attractive host for the trivalent neodymium ion because the 1.06 μm laser transition line is sharper than in other host crystals. Frequency doubling to 0.530 μm using lithium niobate crystals may produce power approaching that available in the fundamental mode at 1.06 μm. Also through the use of electro-optic materials such as KDP, barium-sodium niobate or lithium tantalate, "tuning" or scanning of laser frequencies over wide ranges may be accomplished.[12] The ability to scan rapidly through wide frequency ranges requires special consideration in the design of protective measures.

Perhaps the best known example of a semiconductor laser is the gallium arsenide types operating at 0.840 μm, however, semiconductor materials have already operated over a range of approximately 0.4–5.1 μm. Generally speaking, the semiconductor laser is a moderately low-powered (milliwatts to several watts) CW device having relatively broad beam divergence thus tending to reduce its hazard potential. On the other hand, certain semiconductor lasers may be pumped by multi-kV electron beams thus introducing a potential ionizing radiation hazard.[34]

B. Biological effects of laser radiation

The body organ most susceptible to laser radiation appears to be the eye; the skin is also susceptible but of lesser importance. The degree of risk to the eye depends upon the type of laser beams used, notably the wavelength, output power, beam divergence, and pulse repetition frequency. The ability of the eye to refract long UV, visible, and near IR wavelengths is an additional factor to be considered in assessing the potential radiation hazard.

In the case of UV wavelengths (0.2–0.4 μm) produced by lasers the expected response is similar to that produced by non-coherent sources, e.g. photophobia accompanied by erythema, exfoliation of surface tissues and possible stromal haze. Absorption of UV takes place at or near the surface of tissues. The damage to epithelium results from the photochemical denaturization of proteins.

In the case of IR laser radiation damage results exclusively from surface heating of the cornea subsequent to absorption of the incident energy by tissue water in the cornea. Simple heat flow models appear to be sufficiently accurate to explain the surface absorption and damage to tissue.

In the case of the visible laser wavelengths (0.4–0.75 μm) the organ at risk is the retina and more particularly the pigment epithelium of the retina. The cornea and lens of the eye focus the incident radiant energy so that the radiant exposure at the retina is at least several orders of magnitude greater than that received by the cornea. Radiant exposures which are markedly above the threshold for producing minimal visions on the retina may cause physical disruption of retinal tissue by steam formation or by projectile-like motion of the pigment granules.[13,14] In the case of short transient pulses such as those produced by Q-switched systems, acoustical phenomena may also be present.[13]

There are two transition zones in the electromagnetic spectrum where bio-effects may change from one of a corneal hazard to one of a retinal hazard. These are located at the interface of the UV-visible region and the visible near IR region. It is possible that both corneal and retinal damage as well as damage to intermediate structures such as the lens and iris could be caused by devices emitting radiation in these transitional regions. Several investigators[15,16] noticed irreversible changes in electroretinograms with attendant degeneration of visual cells and pigment epithelium, when albino and pigmented rats were exposed to high illumination environments.

The chronic and long term effects of laser radiation have not been fully explored.

The biological significance of irradiating the skin with lasers is considered to be less than that caused by exposure of the eye since skin damage is usually repairable or reversible. The most common effects on the skin range from erythema to blistering and charring depending upon the wavelength, power, and time of exposure to the radiation. Depigmentation of the skin and damage to underlying organs may occur from exposure to extremely high powered laser radiation, particularly Q-switched pulses. In order that the relative eye/skin hazard potential be kept in perspective, one must not overlook possible photosensitization of the skin caused by injection of drugs or use of cosmetic materials. In such cases the maximum permissible exposure (MPE) levels for skin might be considerably below currently recommended values.

C. Exposure criteria

Permissible levels of laser radiation impinging upon the eye have been derived from short term exposure and an examination of damage to eye structures as observed through an opthalmoscope. Some investigators[18] have observed irreversible visual performance changes at exposure levels as low as 10% of the threshold determined by observation through an ophthalmoscope. McNeer and Jones[18,19] found that at 50% of the ophthalmoscopically determined threshold the ERG B wave amplitude was irreversibly reduced. Mautner[17] has reported severe changes in the visually evoked cortical potential at 25% of the ophthalmoscopically determined threshold. Since most, if not all, of the so-called laser exposure criteria have been based on ophthalmoscopically-determined lesions on the retina, the findings of irreversible functional changes at lower levels causes one to ponder the exact magnitude of an appropriate safety factor which should be applied to the ophthalmoscope data in order to derive a reasonable exposure criterion.

There is unanimous agreement that any proposed maximum permissible exposure (MPE) or threshold limit value (TLV) does not sharply divide what is hazardous from what is safe. Usually any proposed values take on firm meaning only after years of practical use. However, it has become general practice in defining laser exposure criteria to:

1) Measure the radiant exposure (J/cm^2) or irradiance (W/cm^2) in the plane of the cornea rather than making an attempt to calculate the values at the retina. This simplifies the measurements and calculations for the industrial hygienists and radiation protection officers.

2) Use a 7 mm dia. limiting aperture (pupil) in the calculations. This assumes that the largest amount of laser radiation may enter the eye.

3) Make a distinction between the viewing of collimated sources, e.g. lasers and extended sources, fluorescent tubes or incandescent lamps. The MPE for extended source viewing takes into account the solid angle subtended at the eyes in viewing the light source, therefore the unit is $W/cm^2.sr$ (Watts per square centimeter and steradian).

4) Derive permissible levels on the basis of the wavelength of the laser radiation, e.g. the MPE for neodymium wavelength (1.06 μm) should be increased, i.e. made less stringent by a factor of approximately five than the MPE for visible wavelengths.

5) Urge caution in the use of laser systems that emit multiple pulses. A conservative approach would be to limit the power or energy in any single pulse in the train to the MPE specified for direct irradiation at the cornea. Similarly the average power for a pulse train could be limited to the MPE of a single pulse of the same duration as the pulse train. More research is needed to precisely define the MPE for multiple pulses.

Typical exposure criteria for the eye proposed by several organizations are shown in 5. These data do not apply to permissible levels at UV wavelengths or to the skin. A few supplementary comments on these factors are in order: There appears to be general agreement on maximum permissible exposure levels of radiation for the skin, e.g. the MPE values are approximately as follows for exposure times greater than 1 sec, an MPE of 0.1 W/cm^2; exposure times 10^{-1}–1 sec, 1.0 W/cm^2; for 10^{-4}–10 sec, 0.1 J/cm^2, and for exposure times less than 10^{-4} sec, 0.01 J/cm^2. The MPE values apply to visible and IR wavelengths. For UV radiations the more conservative approach is to use the standards established by the American Medical Association. These exposure limits (for germicidal wavelengths viz. 0.2537 μm) should not exceed 0.1×10^{-6} W/cm^2 for continuous exposure. If an estimate is to be made of UV laser thresholds then it suggested that the more recent work of Pitts[6,7] be consulted.

D. Measurement of laser radiation

The complexity of radiometric measurement techniques, the relatively high cost of available detectors and the fact that calculations of radiant exposure levels based on manufacturers' specifications of laser performance have been found to be sufficiently accurate for protection purposes, have all combined to minimize the number of measurements needed in a protective program. In the author's experience, the output power of commonly used laser systems, as specified by the manufacturers, has never been at variance with precision calibration data by more than a factor of two.

All measurement systems are equipped with detection and readout devices. A general description of several devices and their application to laser measurements follow.

Because laser radiation is monocromatic, certain simplifications can be made in equipment design. For example, it may be possible to use narrow band filters with an appropriate type of detector thereby reducing sources of error. On the other hand, special care must be taken with high powered beams to prevent detector saturation or damage. Extremely short Q-switched pulses require the use of ultrafast detectors and short time-constant instrumentation to measure instantaneously power. Photoelectric detectors and radiation thermopiles are designed to measure instantaneous power, but they can also be used to measure total energy in a pulse by integration, provided the instrumental time-constants are much shorter than the pulse lengths of the laser radiation. High current vacuum photo-diodes are useful for measuring the output of Q-switched systems and can operate with a linear response over a wide range.

Average power measurements of cw lasers systems are usually made with a conventional thermopile or photo-voltaic cells. A typical thermopile will detect signals in the power range from 10 μW to about 100 mW. Because thermopiles are composed of many junctions the response of these instruments may be non-uniform. The correct measure of average power is therefore not obtained unless the entire surface of the thermopile is exposed to the laser beam. Measurements of the cw power output of gas lasers may also be made with semiconductor photocells.

The effective aperture or aperture stop of any measurement device used for determining the radiant exposure (J/cm^2) or irradiance (W/cm^2) should closely approximate, if not be identical to, the pupillary aperture. For purposes of safety the diameter should correspond to that of the normal dark-adapted eye, i.e. 7 mm. The response time of measurement system should be such that the accuracy of the measurement is not affected especially when measuring short pulse durations or instantaneous peak power.

Many calorimeters and virtually all photographic methods measure total energy, but they can also be used for measuring power if the time history of the radiation is known. Care should be taken to insure that photographic processes are used within the linear portion of the film density vs. log radiant exposure (gamma) curve.

Microammeters and voltmeters may be used as read out devices for cw systems; microvoltmeters or electrometers coupled to oscilloscopes may be used for pulsed laser systems. These devices may be connected in turn to panel displays or recorders, as required.[3,5]

Calibration is required for all wavelengths at which the instrument is to be used. It should be noted that Tungsten Ribbon filament lamps are available from the National Bureau of Standards as secondary standards of spectral radiance over the wavelength region from approximately 0.2–2.6 μm. The calibration procedures using these devices permit comparisons within about 1% in the near UV and about 0.5% in the visible. All radiometric standards are based on the Stefan–Boltzmann and Planck laws of blackbody radiation.

The spectral response of measurement devices should always be specified since the ultimate use of the measurements is a correlation with the spectral response of the biological tissue receiving the radiation insult.

E. Control of exposure

In defining a laser hazard control program, some attempt should be made to classify the lasers or laser system according to their potential hazard. For example, one may wish to classify the lasers in terms of their potential for exceeding the Maximum Permissible Exposure (MPE) level or Threshold Limit Values (TLV). This could mean that a classification of "low powered", "exempt" or special "protected" lasers could evolve. "Exempt" may apply to lasers and laser systems which cannot, because of inherent design parameters, emit radiation levels in excess of the MPE; "low powered" could refer to systems emitting levels greater than the MPE for direct exposure to collimated beams but less than the MPE for extended sources; "high powered" could refer to systems that emit levels greater than the MPE for direct exposure to collimated laser beams as well as the MPE for extended sources; a "protected" laser system could be one where by virtue of appropriate engineering controls the emitted levels of radiation are less than any MPE value. Other variations are possible. Once a classification scheme has been established it is possible to devise engineering measures and operating procedures to maintain all radiation at or below the desired levels, the stringency of the controls being directly related to the degree of risk to personnel in each category.

It stands to reason that certain basic control principles apply to many laser systems: the need to inform appropriate persons as to the potential hazards, the procedures and engineering control measures required to prevent injury, the electrical hazard, particularly with the discharge of capacitor banks associated with solid state Q-switched systems, the need to rely primarily on engineering controls rather than procedures, e.g. enclosures, beam stops, beam enlarging systems, shutters, interlocks and isolation of laser systems, rather than sole reliance on memory or safety goggles. The "exempt" laser system is an exception to these measures. In all cases, particular attention must be given to the safety of unsuspecting visitors or spectators in laser areas.

"High powered" systems deserve the ultimate in protective design: enclosures should be equipped with interlocks. Care should be taken to prevent accidental firing of the system and where possible, the system should be fired from a remote position. Controls on the high powered systems should go beyond the usual warning labels by installing an integral warning system such as a "power on" audible signal or flashing light which is visible through protective eye wear.

Infrared laser systems should be shielded with fireproof materials having an appropriate optical density (O.D.) to reduce the irradiance below MPE values. The main hazard of these systems is absorption of excessive amounts of IR energy by human tissue or by flammable or explosive chemicals.

Before protective eye wear is chosen, one must determine as a minimum the radiant exposure or irradiance levels produced by the laser at the distance where the beam or reflected beam is to be viewed, one must know the appropriate MPE value for the laser wavelength and finally one must determine the proper O.D. of protective eyewear in order to reduce levels below the MPE. Likewise, the visible light transmission characteristics should be known because sufficient transmission is necessary for the person using the device to be able to detect ordinary objects in the immediate field of vision.

Microwave Radiation

A. Physical characteristics of microwave radiation

Microwave wavelengths vary from about 10m to about 1mm; the respective frequencies range from 30 MHz–300 GHz. Certain reference documents,[20] however, define the microwave frequency range as 10 MHz–100GHz. The region between 10 MHz and the IR is generally referred to as the RF or radiofrequency region.

Certain bands of microwave frequencies have been assigned letter designations by industry; others, notably the ISM (Industrial, Scientific, Medical) frequencies have been assigned by the Federal Communications Commission for industrial, scientific and medical applications.

B. Sources of microwave radiation

Microwave radiation is no longer of special interest only to those in communications and navigational technology. Because of the growing number of commercial applications of microwaves, e.g. microwave ovens, diathermy, materials drying equipment, there is widespread interest in the possible new applications as well as an increased awareness of potential hazards. Typical sources of microwave energy are klystrons, magnetrons, backward wave oscillators and semiconductor transit time devices (impatt diodes). Such sources may operate continuously as in the case of some communications systems or intermittently, e.g. in microwave ovens, induction heating equipment and diathermy equipment or in the pulsed mode in radar systems. Natural sources of RF and microwave energy also exist. For example, peak field intensities of over 100 V/m are produced at ground level by the movement of cold fronts. Solar radiation intensities range from 10^{-18}–10^{-17} watts per square meter per Hz (Wm^{-2} Hz^{-1}) however, the integrated intensity at the earth's surface for the frequency range of 0.2–10 GHz is approximately 10^{-8} mW/cm^2. This value is to be compared with an average of 10^2 mW/cm^2 on the earth's surface attributable to the entire (UV, visible IR and microwave) solar spectrum.[36]

C. Biological effects of microwave radiation

The photon energy in RF and microwave radiation is considered to be too low to produce photochemical reactions in biological matter. However microwave radiation is absorbed by biological systems and ultimately dissipated in tissue as heat. Irradiation of the human body with a power density of 10 mW/cm^2 will result in the absorption of approximately 58 W[21] with a resultant body temperature elevation of 1°C, a value which is considered acceptable from a personal hazard standpoint. By way of comparison, the human basal metabolic rate is approximately 80 W for a person at rest; 290 for a person engaged in moderate work.

Microwave wavelengths less than 3 cm are absorbed in the outer skin surface, 3–10 cm wavelengths penetrate more deeply (1 mm–1 cm) into the skin and at wavelengths from 25–200 cm penetration is greatest with the potential of causing damage to internal body organs. The human body is thought to be essentially transparent to wavelengths greater than about 200 cm. Above 300 MHz the depth of penetration changes rapidly with frequency, declining to millimeter depths at frequencies above 3000 MHz. Above 10 GHz the surface absorption of energy begins to approach that of IR radiation.

Carpenter and Van Ummersen[22] investigated the effects of microwave radiation on the production of cataracts in rabbit eyes. Exposures to 2.45 GHz radiation were made at power densities ranging from 80–400 mW/cm^2 for different exposure times. They found that repeated doses of 67 J/cm^2 spaced a day, a week, or 2 weeks apart produced lens opacities even though the single threshold exposure dose at that power density (280 mW/cm^2) was 84 J/cm^2. When the single exposure dose was reduced to 50 J/cm^2 opacities were produced when the doses were administered 1 or 4 days apart, but when the interval between exposures was increased to 7 days no opacification was noted even after 5 such weekly exposures. At the low power density of 80 mW/cm^2 (dose of 29 J/cm^2) no effect developed but when administered daily for 10 or 15 days cataracts did develop. The conclusion is that microwaves may exert a cumulative effect on the lens of the eye if the exposures are repeated sufficiently often. The interval between exposures is an important factor in that a repair mechanism seems to act to limit lens damage if adequate time has elapsed between exposures.

Certain other biological effects of microwave radiation have been noted in literature. One of these is the so-called "pearl chain effect" where particles align themselves in chains when subjected to an electric field. There is considerable disagreement as to the significance of the pearl chain effect.

Investigators at the Johns Hopkins University[23] have suggested a possible relationship between mongolism (Down's Syndrome) in offspring and previous exposure of the male parent to radar. This suggested relationship was based on the finding that of 216 cases of mongolism, 8.7% of the fathers having mongol offspring vs. 3.3% of the control fathers (no mongol offspring) had contact with radar while in military service. This possible association must be regarded with extreme caution because of many unknown factors including the probability of a variety of exposures to environmental agents (including ionizing radiation) while in military service.

Soviet investigators claim that microwave radiation produces a variety of effects on the central nervous system with and without a temperature rise in the organism.[24–27] Claims are also made for biochemical changes, specifically a decrease in cholinesterase and changes in RNA at power density levels of approximately 10 mW/cm^2. The reported microwave effects on the central nervous system usually describe initial excitatory action, e.g. high blood pressure followed by inhibitory action and low blood pressure over the long term.[24] Electroencephalographic data have been interpreted as indicating the presence of epileptiform patterns in exposed subjects. Other reported effects ranged from disturbances of the menstrual cycle to changes in isolated nerve preparations.

What is often overlooked in any description of the biological effects of microwave radiation is that such radiations have produced beneficial effects. Controlled or judicious exposure of humans to diathermy or microthermy is widely practiced. The localized exposure level in diathermy may be as high as 100 mW/cm^2.

D. Exposure criteria

Schwan[28] in 1953 examined the threshold for thermal damage to tissue, notably cataractogenesis. The power density necessary for producing such changes was approximately 100 mW/cm^2 to which he applied a safety factor of 10 to obtain a maximum permissible exposure level of 10 mW/cm^2. This number has been subsequently incorporated into many official standards. The current American National Standards Institute C95 standard[20] requires a limiting power density of 10 mW/cm^2 for exposure periods of 0.1 hr or more; also an energy density of 1 milliwatt-hour per square centimeter (1 mWh/cm^2) during any 0.1 hr period is permitted. The latter criterion allows for intermittency of exposure at levels above 10 mW/cm^2, on the basis that such intermittency does not produce a temperature rise in human tissue greater than 1°C. More recently, Schwan[29] has suggested that the permissible exposure levels be expressed in terms of current density rather than power density, especially when dealing with measurements in the near or reactive field where the concept of power density loses its meaning. He suggests that a permissible current density of approximately 3 mA/cm^2 be accepted since this value is comparable to a far field value of 10 mW/cm^2. At frequencies below 100 KHz this value should be somewhat lower and for frequencies above 1 GHz it can be somewhat higher.

The new performance standard for microwave ovens specifies a level of 1 mW/cm^2 at any point 5 cm or more from the external oven surfaces at the time the oven is fabricated by the manufacturer. 5 mW is permitted throughout the useful life of the oven.

Because Soviet investigators believe that effects on the central nervous system are more appropriate measures of the possibly detrimental effects of microwave radiation than are thermally induced responses, their studies have reported "thresholds" which are lower than those reported in Western countries. Soviet permissible exposure levels are several orders of magnitude below those in Western countries.

The Soviet Standards for whole body radiation are as follows: 0.01 mW/cm^2 for 5 hr per day exposure, 0.1 mW/cm^2 for 2 hr exposure per day and 1 mW/cm^2 for a 15–20 min exposure provided protective goggles are used. These standards apply to frequencies above 300 MHz.

There appears to be no serious controversy about the power density levels necessary to produce thermal effects in biological tissue. The nonthermal CNS effects reported by the Soviets are not so much controversial as they are a reflection of the fact that Western investigators have not used the conditioned reflex as an end point in their investigations.

E. Measurement of microwave radiation

Perhaps the most important factor underlying some of the controversy over biological effects is the lack of standardization of the measurement techniques used to quantify results. To date, unfortunately, there seems to be little promise that such standardization will be realized in the near future.

The basic vector components in any electromagnetic wave are the electric field (E) and the magnetic field (H). The simplest type of microwave propagation consists of a plane wave moving in an unbounded isotropic medium, where the electric and magnetic field vectors are mutually perpendicular to each other and both are perpendicular to the direction of wave propagation. Unfortunately the simple proportionality between the E and H fields is valid only in free space, or in the so-called "far field" of the radiating device. The far field is the region which is sufficiently removed from the source to eliminate any interaction between the propagated wave and the source. The energy or power density in the far field is inversely proportional to the square of the distance from the source and in this particular case the measurement of either E or H suffices for their determination.

Plane-wave detection in the far field is well understood and easily obtained with equipment which has been calibrated for use in the frequency range of interest. Most hazard survey instruments have been calibrated in the far field to read in power density (mW/cm²) units. The simplest type of device uses a horn antenna of appropriate size coupled to a power meter.

To estimate[30] the power density levels in the near field of large aperture circular antennas one can use the following simplified relationship

$$W = \frac{16P}{\pi D^2} = \frac{4P}{A} \quad \text{(near field)},$$

where P is the average power output, D is the diameter of the antenna, A is the effective area of the antenna and W is power density. If this computation reveals a power density which is less than a specified limit, e.g. 10 mW/cm², then no further calculation is necessary because the equation gives the maximum power density on the microwave beam axis. If the computed value exceeds the exposure criterion then one assumes that the calculated power density exists throughout the near field. The far field power densities are then computed from the Friis free space transmission formula

$$W = \frac{\mathrm{GP}}{4\pi r^2} = \frac{\mathrm{AP}}{\lambda^2 r^2} \quad \text{(far field)},$$

where λ is the wavelength, r is the distance from the antenna and G is the far field antenna gain.

The distance from the antenna to the intersection of the near and far fields is given by

$$r_1 = \frac{\pi D^2}{8\lambda} = \frac{A}{2\lambda}.$$

These simplified equations do not account for reflections from ground structures or surfaces; the power density may be four times greater than the free space value under such circumstances.

Special note should be made of the fact that microwave hazard assessments are made on the basis of average, not peak power of the radiation. In the case of radar generators, however, the ratio of peak to average power may be as high as 10^5.

Most microwave measuring devices are based on bolometry, calorimetry, voltage and resistance changes in detectors and the measurement of radiation pressure on a reflecting surface. The latter three methods are self-explanatory. Bolometry measurements are based upon the absorption of power in a temperature sensitive resistive element, usually a thermistor, the change in resistance being proportional to absorbed power. This method is one of the most widely used in commercially available power meters. Low frequency radiation of less than 300 MHz may be measured with loop or short whip antennas. Because of the larger wavelengths in the low frequency region, the field strength in volts per meter (V/m) is usually determined rather than power density.

One troublesome fact in the measurement of microwave radiation is that the near field (reactive field) of many sources may produce unpredictable radiative patterns. Energy density rather than power density may be a more appropriate means of expressing hazard potential in the near field.[31,32] In the measurement of the near field of microwave ovens it is desirable that the instrument have certain characteristics, e.g. the antenna probe should be electrically small to minimize perturbation of the field, the impedance should be matched so that there is no backscatter from the probe to the source, the antenna probe should behave as an isotropic receiver, the probe should be sensitive to all polarizations, the response time should be adequate for handling the peak to average power of the radiation and the response of the instrument should be flat over a broad band of frequencies.

In terms of desirable broad band characteristics of instruments it is interesting to note that one manufacturer has set target specifications for the development of a microwave measurement and monitoring device as follows: frequency range

20 KHz–12.4 GHz and a power density range of 0.02–200 mW/cm^2 $\pm$ 1 dB. Reportedly two models of this device will be available: one a hand held version complete with meter read out, the other a lapel model equipped with audible warning signals if excessive power density levels develop.

F. Control measures

The control of excessive exposures to microwave radiation is basically an engineering matter. The engineering measures may range from the restriction of azimuth and elevation settings on radar antennas to complete enclosures of magnetrons in microwave ovens. The use of personnel protective devices have their place but are of much lower priority importance to engineering controls. Various types of microwave protective suits goggles and mesh have been used for special problems.

It has been shown recently[33] that cardiac pacemakers, particularly those of the demand type, may have their function seriously compromised by microwave radiation. Furthermore, the radiation levels which cause interference with the pacemaker may be orders of magnitude below levels which cause detrimental biological effects. The most effective method of reducing the susceptibility of these devices to microwave interference seems to be improved shielding. Manufacturers of cardiac pacemakers are engaged in a major program to minimize such interference.

The judicious use of appropriate signs and labels may prove useful in alerting people to the presence of dangerous microwave sources.

APPENDIX A

Useful Radiometric and Related Units

Term	Symbol	Description	Unit and abbreviation
Radiant Energy	*O*	Capacity of electromagnetic waves to perform work	Joule (J)
Radiant Power	*P*	Time rate at which energy is emitted	Watt (W)
Irradiance or radiant flux density (dose rate in photobiology)	*E*	Radiant flux density	Watt per square meter (W·M^{-2})
Radiant intensity	*I*	Radiant flux or power emitted per solid angle (steradian)	Watt per steradian (W·sr^{-1})
Radiant exposure (Dose in photobiology)	*H*	Total energy incident on unit area in a given time interval	Joule per square meter (J · m^{-2})
Beam divergence	φ	Unit of angular measure. One Radian $\approx$ 57.3° 2π Radians = 360°	Radian

APPENDIX B

Conversion Factors

A-radiant energy units

	erg	joule	W sec	μW sec	g-cal
erg =	1	10^{-7}	10^{-7}	0.1	2.39×10^{-8}
joule =	10	1	1	10^6	0.239
W sec =	10^7	1	1	10^4	0.239
μW sec =	10	10^{-6}	10^{-6}	1	2.39×10^{-7}
g-cal =	4.19×10^7	4.19	4.19	4.19×10^6	1

B-radiant exposure (dose) units

	erg/cm^2	joule/cm^2	W sec/cm^2	μW sec/cm^2	g-cal/cm^2
erg/cm^2 =	1	10^{-7}	10^{-7}	0.1	2.39×10^{-8}
joule/cm^2 =	10^7	1	1	10^6	0.239
W sec/cm^2 =	10^7	1	1	10^6	0.239
μW sec/cm^2 =	10	10^{-6}	10^{-6}	1	2.39×10^{-7}
g-cal/cm^2 =	4.19×10^7	4.19	4.19	4.19×10^6	1

C-irradiance (dose rate) units

	erg/cm^2 · sec	joule/cm^2 · sec	W/cm^2	μW/cm^2	g-cal/cm^2 · sec
erg/cm^2 · sec =	1	10^{-7}	10^{-7}	0.1	2.39×10^{-8}
joule/cm^2 · sec =	10^7	1	1	10^6	0.239
W/cm^2 =	10^7	1	1	10^6	0.239
μW/cm^2 =	10	10^{-6}	10^{-6}	1	2.39×10^{-7}
g-cal/cm^2 · sec =	4.19×10^7	4.19	4.19	4.19×10^6	1

PREFERRED READING

Clarke, A. M. (1970). "Ocular Hazards from Lasers and other Optical Sources," *CRC Critical Reviews in Environmental Control*, **1**, 307.

Cleary, S. F. (1970). "The Biological Effects of Microwave and Radiofrequency Radiation", *CRC Critical Reviews in Environmental Control*, **1**, 257.

REFERENCES

1. Matelsky, I., "The Non-ionizing Radiations" *Industrial Hygiene Highlights* Vol. 1, Indus, Hygiene Foundation of America Inc. Pittsburgh, Pa., 1968.
2. *Ibid.* p. 145.
3. *Ibid.* p. 149.
4. Cogan, D. G. and V. E. Kinsey (1946). "Action Spectrum of Keratitis Produced by Ultraviolet Radiation", *Arch. Ophthal.*, **35**, 670.
5. Verhoeff, F. H. and L. Bell (1916). "Pathological Effects of Radiant Energy on the Eye" *Proc. Amer. Acad. Arts and Sci.*, **51**, 630.
6. Pitts, D. G., J. E. Prince, W. I. Butcher, K. R. Kay, R. W. Bowman, H. W. Casey, D. G. Richey, L. H. Mori, J. E. Strong, and T. J. Tredici, "The Effects of Ultraviolet Radiation on the Eye," *Report SAM–TR*–69–10, U.S.A.F. School of Aerospace Medicine, Brooks AFB, Texas, Feb. 1969.
7. Pitts, D. G. and K. R. Kay (1969). "The Photophthalmic Threshold for the Rabbit", *Amer. J. Optom.*, **46**, 561.
8. "Permissible Limit for Continuous Ultraviolet Exposure", *Council on Physical Therapy*, Amer. Med. Assn., Chicago, 1948.
9. Bulletin No. 3, The Eppley Laboratory Inc., Newport, Rhode Island, 1964.
10. Richardson, J. R. and R. D. Baertsch (1969). "Zinc Sulfide Schottky Barrier Ultraviolet Detectors", *Solid State Electronics*, **12**, 393.
11. Javan, A., W. R. Bennett, and D. R. Herriott (1961). Population Inversion and Continuous Optical Maser Oscillation in a Gas Discharge Containing a He-Ne Mixture, *Phys. Rev. Lett.*, **6**, 106.
12. Miller, R. C. and W. A. Nordland (1967). Tunable Lithium Niobate Optical Oscillator with External Mirrors, *Appl. Phys. Lett.*, **10**, 53.
13. Ham, W. T., R. C. Williams, H. A. Mueller, D. Guerry, A. M. Clarke, and W. J. Geeraets (1965). Effects of Laser Radiation on the Mammalian Eye, *Trans. N.Y. Acad. Sci.*, **28**, 517.
14. Clarke, A. M., W. T. Ham, W. J. Geeraets, R. C. Williams, and H. A. Mueller (1969). Laser Effects on the Eye, *Arch. Environ. Health*, **18**, 424.
15. Noell, W. K., V. S. Walker, B. S. Kang, and S. Berman (1966). Retinal Damage by Light in Rats, *Invest. Ophthal.*, **5**, 450.
16. Kotiaho, A., I. Resnick, J. Newton, and H. Schwell (1966). Temperatures Rise and Photocoagulation of Rabbit Retinas Exposed to the CW Laser, *Amer. J. Ophthal.*, **62**, 644.
17. Davis, T. P. and W. J. Mautner (1969). Helium–Neon Laser Effects on the Eye, *Annual Report Contract No. DADA* 17–69–*C*–9013, U.S. Army Medical Research and Development Command, Wash., D.C.
18. McNeer, K. W., M. Ghosh, W. J. Geeraets, and D. Guerry (1963). Erg After Light Coagulation, *Acta. Opthal. Suppl.* **76**, 94.
19. Jones, A. E., D. D. Fairchild, and P. Spyropoulos (1968). Laser Radiation Effects on the Morphology and Function of Ocular Tissue, *Second Annual Report, Contr. No. DADA*–17–67–*C*–0019, U.S. Army Medical Research and Development Command, Wash., D.C.
20. Safety Level of Microwave Radiation with respect to Personnel, Committee C95–1 U.S.A. Stds. Inst. (Now Amer. Natl. Stds. Inst.) New York, N.Y. 1966.
21. Mumford, W. W. (1969). "Heat Stress due to R. F. Radiation", *Proceedings of IEEE*, **57**, 171.
22. Carpenter, R. L. and C. A. Van Ummersen (1968). *J. Microwave Power*, **3**, 3.
23. Sigler, A. T., A. M. Lillienfeld, B. H. Cohen, and J. E. Westlake (1965). Radiation Exposure in Parents of Children with Mongolism (Down's Syndrome), *Johns Hopkins Hosp. Bull.* 117, 374.
24. Tolgskaya, M. S. and Z. V. Gordon, (1960). *Trans. Inst. of Labor Hygiene and Occupational Diseases of the Acad. of Med. Sci.*, 99.
25. Orlova, A. A. (1959). *Proc. on Labor Hygiene and the Biol. Effects of Electromagnetic Radio Frequency Waves* 25.
26. Presman, A. S. and N. A. Levitina (1962). *Bull. Exp. Biol. Med. (Moscow)* **1**, 41.
27. Kholodov, Yu. A. (1962). *Proc. on Problems of the Biological Effects of Superhigh Frequency Fields*, 58.
28. Schwan, H. P. and K. Li (1953). *Proc. IRE*, **41**, 1735.
29. Schwan, H. P. (1970). *Biol. Effects and Health Implications of Microwave Radiation*, U.S. Govt. Printing Office.
30. U.S.A. Standards Institute (Now American National Standards Institute) C95. 3, *Specifications for Techniques and Instrumentation for Evaluating Radio Frequency Hazards to Personnel*, New York, N.Y. (1968).
31. Wacker, P. (1970). *Biol. Effects and Health Implication of Microwave Radiation*, U.S. Govt. Printing Office.
32. Bowman, R., *Ibid.*
33. G. R. King, A. C. Hamburger, F. Parsa, S. J. Heller, and R. A. Carleton]1970). Effect of Microwave Oven on Implanted Cardiac Pacemaker, *Jama*, **312**, 1213.
34. Wilkening G. M., The Potential Hazards of Laser Radiation, *Proceedings of Symposium on Ergonomics and Physical Environmental Factors*, Rome, Italy, 16–21, September 1968, International Labor Office, Geneva.
35. Sliney, D. H., F. C. Bason, and B. C. Freasier (1971). Instrumentation and Measurement of Ultraviolet, Visible and Infrared Radiation, *Amer. Indus. Hygiene Assn. J.*, **32**, No. 7, July.
36. Cleary, S. F. (1970). The Biological Effects of Microwave and Radiofrequency Radiation, *CRC Critical Review In Environmental Control* **1**, 257.

G. M. WILKENING

Bell Telephone Laboratories

NUTRIENT ENRICHMENT OF LAKES; see EUTROPHICATION

O

OCCUPATIONAL HEALTH

Introduction

This article is designed for management, engineers, chemists, physicists, laboratory workers and lawyers, and not primarily for physicians or hygienists, who may wish to know how to obtain help with occupational medicine and occupational hygiene problems in Government departments, universities, hospitals and other organisations.

Schilling (1972) believes that occupational health should aim to protect and improve the health of all classes and kinds of worker and that it has two complementary disciplines, occupational medicine and occupational hygiene. These physicians and hygienists have responsibilities for the recognition, measurement and control of health hazards in the physical and psycho/social environment. Occupational medicine is concerned primarily with man and the influence of work on his health. Occupational hygiene is concerned with man's environment.

Occupational health was defined by the joint International Labour Office/World Health Organisation (ILO/WHO) Committiee in 1953 as the promotion and maintenance of the highest degree of physical, mental and social well-being of workers in all occupations and places of employment. In 1959, in Recommendation 112, the International Labour Organisation described occupational health services in places of employment as a service established in or near a place of employment for the purposes of—

a) protecting the workers against any health hazard which may arise out of their work or the conditions in which it is carried on

b) contributing towards the workers' physical and mental adjustment, in particular the adaption of the work to the workers and their assignment to the jobs for which they are suited

c) contributing to the establishment and maintenance of the highest possible degree of physical and mental well-being of the workers.

Many countries in the world have signified their acceptance of these concepts.

The aim of this chapter is—

1) to outline the scope of occupational health and its relation to community health;

2) to describe changing attitides and legislation affecting occupational health in the United Kingdom of Great Britain and the United States of America;

3) to indicate our views on investigation, monitoring and control of environment hazards to health;

4) to describe occupational health services and their relationship with other medical services;

5) to outline the organisation, functions and staffing of occupational health services;

6) to indicate training facilities for occupational health staff;

7) to provide sources of information on occupational health problems.

In outlining our views, we have tried to consider the impact of occupational health in the United States of America (U.S.A.) and in the United Kingdom of Great Britain (U.K.). However, as both of us work in Great Britain our knowledge of conditions in the U.S.A. is more limited than in the U.K., therefore we hope that readers of this chapter will forgive us if they find the contents more biased towards the position of occupational health in our own country.

The Scope of Occupational Health and its Relation to Community Health

Historical background

Specific occupations have existed ever since man has lived in small or large communities and had to rely on others for some of the necessities of life. This division of labour has led to thousands of concomitant hazards.

Bernadino Ramazzini is recognised as the first

physician to appreciate the danger of work and his book "de Morbis Artificium" published in 1713 still remains a classic in occupational medicine for the accuracy and thoroughness of his descriptions, as well as for the commonsence preventive measures he proposed for avoiding such misfortunes. However, it was not until the Industrial Revolution in England that the dangers of work were appreciated more fully.

The move from the country to the town and from an agrarian economy to an industrial one brought in its wake indescribable misery and suffering to thousands of artisans. Michael Sadler, Charles Thackrah and Lord Shaftesbury were prominent Victorians who played major roles in improving the industrial and social environment of the workers. The efforts of such men eventually stimulated Acts of Parliament to protect the industrial population, especially women and children, from the worst vicissitudes of factory life.

The first major leglislation occured in 1833 when the Factory Inspectorate was started; subsequent Acts of Parliament amended, and supplemented this Bill. Factory leglislation as it affects the safety and health of the worker is described later in this chapter.

Factory reforms were always linked with social reform and it is wise to consider the worker in the context of his socio-economic status. Occupational health today should include a consideration of the worker's home background when assessing any health problem that arises at work.

The two World Wars and their need for increased productivity produced an added impetus to the study of occupational safety and health through the work carried out in Britain by the Industrial Health Research Board. In the last thirty years, improvements in safety and preventive measures in industry have reduced occupationally induced illness and injuries to relatively low levels (Schilling, 1963). Nevertheless there is no room for complacency. In Great Britain, with a working population of around twenty-five million, one thousand people are killed at their work, and five hundred thousand suffer injuries in varying degrees of severity every year. Time lost annually due to industrial injury and disease exceeds twenty-three million working days.

The origins of occupational health care should be firmly rooted in preventive medicine and this emphasis is no less important today. Modern and more sophisticated industrial procedures have ensured a continued discovery of new occupational hazards to replace the classic ones such as lead poisoning and coal workers' pneumoconiosis, though even today these diseases continue to claim victims.

Attitudes to Occupational Health

In order to clarify the purpose of occupational health, it is relevant to consider what this discipline means to the people most concerned, namely management, workers and doctors.

Management's attitudes

The prime concern and raison d'être of management is to control the production and distribution of their products and to make profits for their shareholders. Occupational health is often seen as a means of keeping the workers fit and at work and sometimes a first-aid service is believed to achieve this aim. This narrow view is widespread but by no means universal. Since the reforms introduced by Robert Owen into his New Lanark Mills in Scotland in the early nineteenth century, many employers have realised that caring for their employees and providing a safe, healthy and comfortable working environment is not only benevolent but good business sense (Trevelyan, 1942). The Cadbury family, who were Quakers, built a village for their employees at their chocolate factory near Birmingham, England which was regarded as a model of sound humanitarianism and business acumen.

Many major companies today provide occupational health services which border on the luxurious; this contrasts with the majority of small companies where such facilities are minimal or non-existent.

Workers' attitudes

The trade union movement in Great Britain and the United States have poured considerable sums of money, in recent years, into occupational medical research and they are aware that a safe job is infinitely preferable to a dangerous one. Nevertheless, dangerous or dirty jobs often carry a bonus wage and it is difficult sometimes to persuade workers that they should demand a healthier job rather than try to claim "danger money". In fact, a large sum of money was given towards the founding of the Institute in which we work to celebrate the centenary of the Trades Union Congress in Great Britain.

Doctors' attitudes

There is a growing interest amongst doctors in "community health" and in tailoring health services to meet the needs of the community. Occupational physicians are privileged to be in the position of caring for a communty. They can establish the causes of ill health in a group of workers, identify groups that are most vulnerable and employ the necessary resources to remedy the problem and help those afflicted (Raffle, 1970).

This view, unfortunately, is not universally held, and some doctors and others outside the field of occupational health still fail to appreciate the need for such factory-based services. Further reference is made to the need for such services in a later section.

A modern concept of occupational health

This involves the complex relationship of health in relation to work, and work in relation to health. The maintenance of the physical, mental and social well-being of the worker by controlling the working environment means that occupational health physicians have a primarily preventive role. Nevertheless treatment facilities form an important part of an occupational health service. The size of this function varies with the health services available outside the working environment and will be outlined later in this section. Direct contact with the worker affords an ideal opportunity for health education and counselling. Occupational physicians or nurses who fail to attempt this function have not grasped the overall aims of the services they are meant to provide.

Occupational health physicians, if they are Appointed Factory Doctors to their own industry, will have a statutory responsibility to care for those workers undertaking occupations whose hazards are recognised by legislation—such as lead process workers, coal miners, personnel handling radioactive substances and many others. In addition, routine pre-placement and periodic medical examinations may be required for such people as canteen workers, executives, or heavy goods vehicle drivers. The occupational physician is not only caring for the examinee but also insuring that there is no danger to third parties, such as the general public, who may be at risk from, for example, a lorry driver with poor eyesight or uncontrolled diabetes.

There is greater appreciation that the occupational physician or hygienist has a responsibility outside his factory and there is growing concern that those responsible for the factory environment should care about the effect of the factory on the surrounding community. Research in the last decade has demonstrated that children playing on asbestos dumps or families living near asbestos factories are at risk from asbestos-related diseases such as tumours of the pleura (Wagner, Sleggs and Marchand, 1960; Newhouse and Thompson, 1965). The Minamata disaster in Japan in 1953 demonstrated the dangers of dumping mercury effluent into the sea and the effect it can have on the community, both human and animal, living nearby. (McAlpine and Araki, 1958).

In Great Britain within the past year, a large smelting plant was forced to shut down temporarily when high levels of lead, zinc and cadmium were discovered on vegetation within a 2 mile radius of the plant. (Windeyer Report, 1972). "Excessive"levels of lead in blood have also been found in children living near a lead works in East London following the discovery of high lead levels in street dust near the factory. (The State of the Public Health, 1972, Annual Report of Chief Medical Officer).

The environmental pollution caused by industrail processes is so well known that the occupational physicians and hygienists employed at such plants should be concerned that the ecology of the surrounding area is disturbed as little as possible by the activities of the factory.

The advent of man-made lakes on the deltas of the Nile and Upper Volta have brought in their wake an increased incidence of the parasitic disease, schistosomiasis, especially in fishermen and this disabling affliction is rapidly approaching epidemic proportions in areas where previously it was virtually unknown (Sturrock, 1965).

In short, occupational health is concerned not only with the factory environment and its workers but also with the community at large.

As mentioned earlier in this section, the role that occupational health plays in a nation's health facilities varies depending on the services provided outside the workplace. The World Health Organisation and the International Labour Office have done a great deal to establish standards of occupational health and safety and their dicta are generally accepted throughout the world (see section on legislation).

In Great Britain, the home-based National Health Service is the prime source of health care and treatment services for the community. Occupational health services tend to be restricted to the larger industrial concerns and occupational physicians employed therein have little clinical responsibility outside the plant. Nevertheless, the Dale Committee in 1951 stated that industrial health services were "complementary" to the National Health Service, and that the former should be expanded and widened to include more workplaces. In addition they recommended that Industrial Health Services, Public Health Services and the National Health Service should be co-ordinated, preferably under one Government department. The Porritt Report ten years later expressed similar sentiments, though the latest report (Robens Committee, 1972) did not entirely agree. In essence, separate health services covering different aspects of community life should be co-ordinated. These views will be expanded later.

The United States of America has comparable occupational health services to Great Britain but as yet does not possess a nationalised health service. Recent legislation has, however, considerably clarified the safety and health requirements in that country and attempted to rationalise the services available.

In many developing countries, large industrial complexes provide health service facilities not only for their work force, but also for the family and dependants. A large rubber company in Liberia provides full medical care for over 45,000 people although they employ less than half that number. This inevitably leads to wide variations in the standard of health care amongst the surrounding population.

In totalitarian societies with their greater emphasis on the worker as the basic unit of economy, the occupational health services often form the major part of the community health facilities with polyclinics providing inpatient and outpatient treatment services which are factory orientated. Specialist advice and treatment is available at these centres and occupational health research is often better endowed than other branches of medical science.

In summary, occupational health is a discipline concerned with the safety and health of people at work, its emphasis is primarily preventive but its scope should include the community at large rather than just be confined to the hazards of the immediate workplace.

Changing Attitudes and Legislation Affecting Occupational Health in the United Kingdom of Great Britain and the United States of America

The primary purpose of an occupational health service is to create and maintain maximal standards for positive health in all grades of workers.

To attempt to succeed in this aim, it is necessary to convince management that such a service will be of benefit to the management themselves and to the workers for whom they are responsible.

The occupational physician, if appointed to an organisation, has the responsibility of influencing the attitudes of management and workers towards acceptance of these principles.

Firstly, it is necessary to be aware of the legislative requirements for the safety and health of workers in the federation, country or state in which the organisation is situated and to have knowledge of the special health problems of concern to the organisation in order that correct advice may be given.

In all countries of the world, legislation is bedevilled by its historical origins. Laws have been made as a response, often grudging, to the urgent needs of a past age and these laws may not be in any way appropriate to present conditions.

United Kingdom

In 1911, Sydney Webb in his preface to Hutchins and Harrison's "A History of Factory Legislation" stated that—

> This century of experiment in factory legislation affords a typical example of English practical empiricism. We began with no abstract theory of social justice or the rights of man. We seem always to have been incapable even of taking a general view of the subject we were legislating upon. Each successive statute aimed at remedying a single ascertained evil. It was in vain that objectors urged that other evils, no more defensible, existed in other trades or amongst other classes, or with persons of ages other than those in which the particular Bill applied. Neither logic nor consistency, neither the over-nice consideration of even-handed justice nor the quixotic appeal of general humanitarianism, was permitted to stand in the way of a practical remedy for a proved wrong.

Robens (1972) discussing this concept makes the point that the practical, empirical approach has been associated with the development of high standards of safety protection, but that it has resulted in a body of detailed law which has to be constantly extended and elaborated to deal with new problems.

The Factories Act 1961 with its supporting orders and regulations covers approximately eight and a half million employees in factories, shipyards, docks and construction sites.

The Offices Shops and Railway Premises Act 1963 covers approximately eight million employees. These two acts are administered by the *Department of Employment* and enforced by its Factory Inspectorate and partly by Local Authorities.

The Mines and Quarries Act 1954 covers provisions for the health and safety of about 345,000 employees. Enforcement and administration comes under the Department of Trade and Industry and the Inspectorates of Mines and Quarries. *The Agriculture (Poisonous Substances) Act 1952* and *The Agriculture (Safety Health and Welfare Provisions) Act 1956* are concerned with about 340,000 employees in agriculture. Administration and enforcement is the responsibility of safety and field officers in the *Ministry of Agriculture, Fisheries and Food* and the *Department of Agriculture and Fisheries for Scotland.*

There are a number of other Acts which provide for special regimes of control over certain specified industrial activities and substances such as explosives and nuclear installations.

Legislation is also in force to deal with emissions and effluents from work places. This legislation spans occupation, safety, general public health and environmental pollution. *The Alkali etc. Works Regulation Act 1906* is enforced by the *Department of the Environment* and their Alkali and Clean Air Inspectorate.

In addition to the complexity of these acts and the numerous departments responsible for their administration, the statutory system has developed in such a way that there is too much law. For example, since 1960, 107 statutory instruments were issued under the Factories Act. A change of attitude and a change of approach to legislation is obviously essential. These were the motivating factors in setting up the Committee on Safety and Health at Work under the Chairmanship of Lord Robens (1972); this report is now being considered by interested parties and the present Government have declared their intention to bring in new amending legislation in the future.

One change has already taken place which was first proposed by the Labour Government. *The Employment Medical Advisory Service Act 1972* which amends the Factories Act 1961 by introducing the new Employment Medical Advisory Service in the Department of Employment is scheduled to start operating in February 1973. Under this new Act changes will be made to increase the effectiveness of the advice given on medical problems connected with employment. The new Service of more than one hundred full and part-time doctors will study and advise on various subjects including the effects of particular jobs on health; the medical precautions to be taken in working with poisonous or hazardous substances; the medical requirement for different kinds of work and the particular problems of the disabled. The Service will have a special responsibility for the health of young people at work; it will carry out medical surveys and other investigations but will not provide medical treatment. The Department of Health and Social Security have the responsibility, under the *National Health Service Act 1946*, to provide free medical attention to all and free medical prescriptions to those who are classified as in special need because of their financial position (old age pensioners) and those whose health requires special attention such as pregnant mothers, young children and the chronically sick.

Under the *National Insurance (Industrial Injuries) Act 1965*, also administered by the Department of Health and Social Security; "a person who is under this Act insured against personal injury caused by accident arising out of, and in the course of his employment shall be insured also against any prescribed disease and against any prescribed personal injury not so caused, being a disease or injury due to the nature of that employment and developed after 4th July 1948." There are forty-seven prescribed occupational diseases, (Notes on the Diagnosis of Occupational Diseases, 1970; Pneumoconiosis and Allied Occupational Chest Diseases 1967). Injury disablement, death and other subsidiary benefits can be claimed under this Act. "The State of the Public Health (1972)" lists the Injury Benefit (Prescribed Diseases) in Great Britain and analyses annual certified incapacity (new spells). All prescribed diseases accounted for over 20,000 new spells per year over the last four years. The most important contribution to this total is made by dermatitis, about 15,000 new spells being reported each year, next in importance were traumatic inflammation of the tendons of the hand, forearm, etc., and beat knee. Lead poisioning still accounts for about one hundred new spells per year. The relative unimportance, in terms of incapacity, of prescribed diseases due to toxicological substances is noteworthy, and should be compared with claims for sickness benefit, which were, in fact, ten and a half million for new spells of certified incapacity from all causes in males and females. The major contribution is made by diseases of the chest, mental disorders and musculoskeletal ailments, including arthritis and rheumatism.

In addition to the "prescribed diseases" sixteen diseases are "notifiable" under the Factories Act 1961 for the purposes of prevention. The H.M. Chief Inspector of Factories in his Annual Report 1971 recorded 123 cases of lead poisoning and a total of all cases of notifiable industrial disease of 324. The two different types of recording lead to discrepancies in published figures.

Major occupational health problems in industry causing absence from work are therefore not generally toxicological, though these are of great importance to the individual. Ill health caused by non-occupational disease, but possibly accentuated by the affects of occupation are of far greater concern.

Special legislative problems

Ionising radiations are a relatively new hazard which have been anticipated by special and effective regulations put out as statutory instruments under The Factories Act 1961. *The Ionising Radiations (Sealed Sources) Regulations 1961* and *The Ionising Radiations (Unsealed Radioactive Substances) Regulations 1968.*

Hazards which are currently under consideration for legislation include—

Noise

Noise may be defined as unwanted sound. This "unwanted sound" is often caused by factory processes, boiler rooms, and aircraft. The noise produced may be detrimental to the health of workers within the factory or to the population living in the noisy environment. A major difficulty in defining legislation for workers within the factory is to distinguish if deafness in a worker is *wholly* attributable to occupational noise. This difficulty has led the Department of Employmeny to publish a Code of Practice for Reducing the Exposure of Employed Persons to Noise (1972). The Secretary of State for Employment states in his foreward "The general solution to this problem which is a complex one has been hampered more by ignorance than by neglect . . . I regard the publication of the Code as the first important step in the prevention of loss of hearing due to noise at work. It should be considered as a blue print for action." By means of this code of practice, advice is given on the engineering aspect of noise exposure of employed persons, however "it does not include advice to machinery manufacturers, which it is proposed to cover separately, or on the medical management of noise exposed personnel, or on the place of audiometry." Nevertheless, it is a most valuable document and should make a major contribution to the prevention of occupational deafness, which is not yet a "prescribed" disease.

Vibration syndrome

The Industrial Injuries Advisory Council in accordance with Section 62 of the National Insurance (Industrial Injuries) Act 1965 is at present considering whether disease of bones, joints, muscles, blood-vessels or nerves of the hand, arm or shoulder (including Raynaud's phenomenon) caused by vibrating machines should be prescribed under the Act. An interim report presented to Parliament in 1970 concluded "that further enquiries are necessary on all aspects of the question referred to them".

Problems arising on prescription are

a) the difficulty of distinguishing between occupational and non-occupational cases;

b) the difficulty of deciding and defining the occupational cover;

c) the problem of diagnosis and assessment;

d) the triviality of disablement in the majority of cases.

The Common Law

In 1971, John Munkman in his book "Employer's Liability at Common Law" stated—

> At the present day, therefore the law is favourable to the injured workman. He receives insurance benefits whether he was to blame for his accident or not. In addition he is entitled to damage at common law if the accident was caused by the fault of his employer, of his fellow-workmen, or of third parties and if the workmans' own negligence contributed to the accident, the effect is not to defeat his claim but to reduce the damages in proportion to his fault.

Negligence

In relation to the worker, the employer has a duty of care. Lord Wright expressed this as— "The obligation is three fold, the provision of a competent staff of men, adequate material and a proper system and effective supervision." (Wilsons and Clyde Coal vs. English, 1938, A.C.57.) Later authorities have added a further class: a safe place of work.

Generally the employee claims against the employer in tort on the basis of his negligence or breach of statutory duty although such claims can be found in contract (Matthews vs. Kuwait Bechtel Corp., 1959, 2 Q.B.57). The tort consists of the employer either acting or failing to act in accordance with such a duty and thereby causing the employee damage (generally personal injury) that is not too remote (i.e. reasonably forseeable).

Discussion

From the above description of the law as it affects the worker, sympathy must be felt with the recommendation made by the Roben's Committee (1972) paragraph 125, "That the statutory provisions dealing with safety and health at work should be revised and reorganised; that so far as possible they should be unified within the framework of a single comprehensive enactment; and that they should be administered by a new Authority for Safety and Health at Work." It is envisaged that this new authority would have responsibility, not only for all the groups of workers already mentioned, but also for those workers in universities, laboratories and hospitals not at present covered by any of the present acts.

United States of America

The Federal Government has made and is making changes in a comparable way to the British Government. The present position is, we believe, best explained by quoting directly from the NIOSH Fact Sheet put out by Health Services and Mental Health Administration, U.S. Department of Health, Education and Welfare, The National Institute for Occupational Safety and Health, 5600 Fishers Lane, Rockville, Maryland, 20852—

The National Institute for Occupational Safety and Health was established within the Department of Health, Education, and Welfare under the provisions of Public Law 91-596—the Occupational Safety and Health Act of 1970. Administratively, NIOSH is located within HEW's Health Services and Mental Health Administration.

As the Federal agency responsible for formulating new or improved occupational safety and health standards, NIOSH not only carries out HEW's responsibilities under the Occupational Safety and Health Act, but also the health program of the Federal Coal Mine Health and Safety Act of 1969 (P. L. 91-173). NIOSH is the principal Federal agency engaged in research, education and training in a national effort to eliminate on-the-job hazards to the health and safety of America's working men and women.

Under the Occupational Safety and Health Act, NIOSH has the responsibility for conducting research designed at producing recommendations for new occupational safety and health standards. These recomendations are transmitted to the Department of Labor which has the responsibility for the final setting, promulgation and enforcement of the standards.

In the case of the Federal Coal Mine Health and Safety Act, NIOSH transmits recommended health standards to the Department of the Interior which has the enforcement responsibilities under that law.

The Institute's main research laboratories are in Cincinnati, Ohio, where studies center on the effects of exposure to hazardous substances used in the workplace, as well as on the psychological, motivational, and behavioral factors involved in occupational safety and health. Much of the Institute's research focuses on specific health and safety hazards such as asbestos, beryllium, carbon monoxide, lead, mercury, noise pollution, heat stress and others.

At NIOSH's Appalachian Center for Occupational Safety and Health (ACOSH) in Morgantown, West Virginia, research is being conducted on the problem of coal workers pneumoconiosis ("black lung disease") and on other occupational respiratory diseases. Thousands of coal miners have been given X-rays and medical examinations as part of the research effort into the causes and characteristics of "black lung disease".

NIOSH's Western Area Occupational Health Laboratory, based in Salt Lake City, Utah is engaged in health and safety research relative to uranium mining, and in the provision of technical assistance to western states. This laboratory also provides analytical and instrument calibration services to Department of Labor compliance officers in the field.

Education and training are also major functions of NIOSH Under the Occupational Safety and Health Act, NIOSH is required to conduct " . . education programs to provide an adequate supply of qualified personnel to carry out the purposes of this Act . . . " There is, at present, a severe national shortage of occupational safety and health professionals. NIOSH has embarked on a training grant program to develop two-year, baccalaureate and graduate programs in colleges and universities across the nation. These programs, coupled with an expanding short course training activity conducted at the Cincinnati laboratories are helping to produce a balanced number of qualified personnel to deal with the problems of occupational safety and health.

NIOSH also maintains staff in ten Regional Offices throughout the United States. The Regional Offices are focal points for special surveys and evaluations of existing occupational safety and health problems, consultative services to the states, and other activities.

The programs that are at present the concern of the National Institute for Occupational Safety and Health for compliance with their mandate under the *Occupational Safety and Health Act (1970)* have been described by Baier and Key (1972).

Criteria documents

Two types of documents are being produced, comprehensive and partial documents. Priorities are

1) A population index of workers exposed

2) A relative toxicity index, comparing a substance which can produce mild transient effects to a substance which produces permanent disability.

3) An incidence index, which is a determination of the number of workmen showing effects from exposure to the substance or hazard.

4) A quantity index, the amount produced annually or the number of sources of physical agents and

5) A trend index, which is an estimate of usage.

Criteria for a recommended standard of occupational exposure to beryllium, carbon monoxide, asbestos, noise and hot environments have already been published. In addition to these two types of criteria documents, NIOSH is preparing a recommendation for dealing with carcinogenic compounds listed in Appendix A of the Threshold

Limit Value list and perhaps other carcinogens. There will probably be recommended methods of control which prohibit manufacture, use, and other activities which involve human exposure without express approval of the enforcement agency.

The other kind of document is one for biologic threshold limits, being prepared with the help of an external Biologic Standards Review Committee.

List of toxic substances

The Occupational Safety and Health Act (1970) requires the Secretary of Health, Education and Welfare to publish "within six months of enactment of the Act and thereafter as needed, but at least annually, a list of known toxic substances by generic family or other useful grouping, and the concentrations at which such toxicity is known to occur."

In 1971 NIOSH compiled a list of 8000 substances, Toxic Substances Annual List 1971 available from the U.S. Governmant Printing Office, Washington D.C. A second edition has been published in 1972.

National Occupational Hazard Survey and health evaluations

A research activity of NIOSH is to gather data from the National Occupational Hazard Survey and from hazard evaluations, the latter are undertaken on request from employers or employees.

Human factors research

The Occupational Safety and Health Act (1970) requires studies to be undertaken into the motivational aspects of work. A further study is considering "the impact of shift work, time rotation, fixed tasks which require very little physical activity or no thought (boredom), and high stress situations such as those experienced by air traffic control, tower operators." Behavioural studies, which will include changes resulting from exposure to chemical neurotoxic agents are in progress.

Survey of needed manpower

The Bureau of Labor Statistics and the Occupational Safety and Health Administration in the Department of Labor are assisting NIOSH "in initiating a contract to evaluate the feasibility of developing a National Survey to determine manpower requirements to implement the Act".

Occupational injury and disease reporting in the United States

A Status Report (Trasko, 1971) under the above title "brings together information on (1) the status of State Law and regulations requiring the reporting of occupational injuries and diseases to official agencies and (2) the availability of published statistics on number and costs of occupational injuries and diseases." Included also is a brief reference to the "Proposed National System for Uniform Recording and Reporting of Occupational Injuries and Illnesses" recommended by a special study group, appointed by the American National Standards Institute. The basic purpose of this report is to furnish background information that may be useful in the implementation and administration of the National system for collection and reporting statistics on injuries and illnesses provided for in the Occupational Safety and Health Act of 1970 (PL.91-596).

This comprehensive report includes in an Appendix "the list of laws and regulations providing for the reporting of occupational injuries and diseases to Workmen's Compensation agencies, State health and Labor authorities." A revealing comment in the report states (p. 20)— "Reasons for the failure of systems providing for medical reporting of occupational diseases are numerous and include: shortcomings in the reporting laws and regulations themselves; failure to enforce laws, which would be difficult to do so under any system; difficulties in diagnosing occupational diseases by physicians in general practice and the consequent failure to recognise them; the insidious nature of many diseases, especially those of slow development, the absence of standard methods of classification, and of a uniform defination of conditions that constitute an occupational disease as contrasted with an accidental injury." To combat some of these difficulties, the U.S. Department of Labor, Occupational Safety and Health Administration has published Recording Requirements under the Williams–Steiger Occupational Safety and Health Act of 1970. This states "Beginning July 1, 1971, every employee who is covered under this Act must keep occupational injury and illness records for his employees in the establishment at which his employees usually report to work." Details of the type of recording required are included in the Recording Requirements.

We stress again that the change in attitude in the United States of America with regard to

Occupational Safety and Health is parallel in many respects with changes in Great Britain.

Under Public Law 91–596, the 91st Congress S.2193 on December 29th, 1970 made history with

An act to assure safe and healthful working conditions for working men and women; by authorising enforcement of the standards developed under the Act—by assisting and encouraging the States in their efforts to assure safe and healthful working conditions by providing for research, information and education, and training in the field of occupational safety and health; and for other purposes. Be it enacted by the Senate and House of Representatives of the United States of America in Congress assembled, that this Act may be cited as the "Occupational Safety and Health Act of 1970."

The wind of change blowing through both these industrial nations must have immense effects on the future safety and health of all workers.

Investigation Monitoring and Control of Environmental Hazards

The complex relationship of work and health has been alluded to previously. Examples of this interaction include:

a) Occupationally induced illness

The hazards faced by an individual in the course of his daily work may lead to illness, injury or disease. The construction industry in Britain is one of the more dangerous occupations. In 1971, 196 persons were killed on site, that is 20 deaths per 100,000 employees. In addition over 7000 building workers were seriously injured. (Annual Report, HM Chief Inspector of Factories 1971.)

Despite legislation on lead processing which has been in existence, with modifications for over 50 years, as already mentioned, 123 cases of lead poisoning were "notified" in Britain in 1971. Workers in the coal mines, cotton mills, smelting and chemical industries are also frequently at risk from specific occupational illnesses.

b) Non-occupational illness

A worker, however, suffering from a non-occupational disease may find that his job exacerbates his illness. Chronic bronchitis is a good example. There is an increased morbidity and mortality from chronic bronchitis in certain occupational groups which have in common, hard physical work, air pollution—both at work and in the general environment—as well as adverse socio-economic factors. The available evidence suggests that occupational factors exacerbate rather than cause this disease (Gilson, 1970). Nevertheless, there can be little doubt that a chronic bronchitic should not be exposed to airborn dusts or irritant gases and fumes, nor be employed on heavy work, if his respiratory symptoms are not to be worsened.

Heart disease, particularly coronary thombosis, seems to be more prevalent in certain occupations. There is some epidemiological evidence to suggest that the stress of "high pressure" occupations increases the workers' chance of developing a heart-attack (Russek, 1967). The occupational physician must then consider what preventive measures should be taken before such a man develops symptoms or signs of coronary artery disease. If, however, an individual is so affected, an attempt should be made to reduce the stress. The physician should try to take care that such an illness does not itself render the worker more worried about his worth as an employee, especially if his personal responsibility is lessened temporarily or permanently.

Other examples of non-occupational diseases which can be adversely affected by work are deafness, varicose veins and back injuries. The differential diagnosis of disease in a worker must take into account the possibilities, therefore, that the illness is occupationally induced, occupationally exacerbated or simply non-occupational. The relative weight of these aetiological factors must be assessed by the examining doctor in the light of the man's work and home environment (Harrington and Schilling, 1973).

c) Discomfort at work

This discussion, however, should not be restricted to overt disease, injury or accidents. Discomfort at work has been shown to lead to increased sickness absence and inflated accident rates. The fact that ambient office temperatures of below 60°F or above 75°F do not cause serious disease, does not prevent them from materially affecting work output, error rates in calculations and general discomfort. Legislation on noise levels where it exists, usually fixes the minimum 40 hr week exposure to 85–90 dB (A), but levels of 70–75 dB (A) can produce considerable psychosomatic disturbance to the individuals faced with such background noise—particularly if mental work is involved.

The occupational physician or hygienist thus has a responsibility not only to prevent classic occupational disease but also to ensure that the working environment is as conducive as possible to the maintenance of efficient and comfortable work.

The epidemiological approach

Throughout this section so far, workers have been considered as individuals, but it should be emphasised that occupational health is really concerned with groups. The physician or hygienist working in the industrial milieu should think in terms of groups and to do this satisfactorily, he must possess a good grounding in epidemiological methods. Statistics are an integral part and he should, therefore, also be conversant with basic concepts of statistical technique.

Epidemiology may be defined as the study of the distribution and determinants of disease frequency in man (MacMahon and Pugh, 1970). Although this subject was initially restricted to the investigation of epidemics of infectious disease, the major advances in methodology in the past 20 yrs have been in the field of non-infective chronic illness such as coronary disease, chronic bronchitis and cancer. A few basic epidemiological concepts will be outlined here to demonstrate the need for this knowledge in anyone concerned with groups rather than individuals.

To the initiated, many of these concepts may appear self-evident. Our excuse for re-iterating them here is that, in our experience, many post-graduates do not appreciate their importance, and without this appreciation, group-orientated medical research becomes impossible.

Firstly the concepts of *rates.* Many statistics are quoted as simple numbers, for example 200 workers were killed on building sites in 1971. The risk of dying however will depend on the total number of workers exposed. If the overall population was 2000 there is greater cause for concern than if this total was two million. Quoting this statistic as 20/100,000 persons employed per year puts the number who died into perspective and affords an opportunity for comparing it with other working groups. The need to establish a "population at risk" is fundamental to all comparative epidemiological studies.

The concept of rates can be narrowed to more specific entities. For example, the overall death rate for a particular cause may hide important variations between age groups, sex, social class, occupation etc., so that the use of age or sex-specific rates is often necessary to demonstrate these latent differences. With these specific rates it is possible to compare the experience of one group with another and various standardisation techniques are available for this purpose. The interested reader is referred to the standard texts for more details of this and other statistical techniques (Bradford Hill, 1971).

In epidemiology, the timing, place and type of person affected is an essential prerequisite in assessing a potential risk to health. If the time, the place and the people suggest a causative link with a given agent then this is useful corroborative evidence. Nevertheless, the researcher needs to be aware of the pitfalls involved in making the terms "causation" and "association" synonymous. In science in general and medicine in particular it is rarely possible to prove beyond all doubt that *X* causes *Y*. The use of epidemiology and statistical significance tests may strengthen the association but proof is often hard to find.

Cigarette smoking has been associated with lung cancer and the evidence for a causative link is very strong. Nevertheless proof is difficult to establish. Association is strengthened by many factors such as a statistical link between the prevalence of lung cancer in smokers compared with non-smokers. Many researchers have demonstrated this using several different methodological approaches. The sites of the cancer seem to be specific and the time factor shows that smoking almost invariably precedes the disease. A dose/response relationship has been demonstrated, animal experiments have confirmed the cancer risk and carcinogenic substances have been isolated from cigarette smoke. In short, all the evidence points to a cause/effect relationship.

The corroborative evidence demonstrated in this example should be sought in all such association studies. Rarely, however, is the link between an agent and its effect as clear cut as in the smoking-lung cancer example.

Occupational Health Practice

1) Investigation

The type of investigation undertaken will of course depend on the nature of the problem to be studied. The preliminary assessment of an occupational health hazard may require a rough estimate of this risk by comparing the numbers affected in that work group with those of a comparable work force not exposed to the suspected danger. If this line of enquiry seems fruitful then a more formal investigation could be instituted.

With suspected mortality or morbidity problems, an accurate assessment of the rates specific to that group by age, sex, occupation and time interval must be established. Comparisons with national or local figures can than be undertaken. Such studies have limited applicability unless the offending environment is investigated simultaneously. Therefore measurements of the levels of the toxic agent such as dusts or gases must be undertaken at the workplace. For example, if lead poisoning is suspected, lead-in-air measurements will be needed and the variation in concentration linked to the work procedure undertaken at that time. It may be discovered that only certain manoeuvres provoke hazardous lead levels and steps must then be taken to consult engineers and hygienists in order to eliminate such risks in the future. The medical management of individuals affected by the toxic agent is a separate issue and the reader is referred to standard texts for the treatment of occupational diseases (Price, 1972).

Some conditions encountered in industry have long latent periods or are so rare that large samples of individuals need to be studied before an accurate assessment can be made. The large sample may consist of many workers followed for a few years or a few workers for many years. It is common practice now to assess "exposure" in terms of person/time units such as man years. It will be clear that 1000 man/years could be 1000 men followed for 1 yr or 20 followed for 50 yrs or any intermediate combination. A mortality study of haematite miners in Cumberland, England, is a good example of the "man years at risk" mortality study combined with environmental measurements in the mines (Boyd et al., 1970)

Cohort analysis, and prospective longitudinal studies are examples of the more time consuming and expensive investigations which may be required to follow on from the cheaper, quicker, retrospective studies. It is necessary however to think in terms of progressively more complicated and expensive studies depending on the findings of preliminary work. Embarking on detailed research should be avoided until after consultation with a statistician, to define clearly the aims of the research and to enable him to assess the likelihood of achieving valuable results.

2) Monitoring

Monitoring may be environmental or biological. The former implies some device for detecting the offending agent be it gas, dust, fumes or vapours in the environment, whereas the latter is a measurement of the toxic agent in the human—commonly pulmonary function, blood or urine levels. It is often argued, with some justification, that biological monitoring is like closing the stable door after the horse has bolted. If it detects measurable levels, this may be evidence of a hazardous environment and therefore such procedures use the worker in the same way as miners formerly used canaries for detecting dangerous gas. Nevertheless, although it is preferable to measure environmental contaminations, rather than biological effect, unless the sampling is done near the operative at risk, the results are meaningless. For example, there may be high levels of cotton dust near the carding engines in a cotton mill but if the operative rarely stands nearby, the conclusions drawn from high sustained cotton dust concentrations in the air may be false in terms of human exposure. In this example the use of a personal sampling device attached to the cardroom worker close to his face will give a more accurate assessment of the cotton dust to which he is exposed.

A further factor affecting risk is the size of the inhaled particle. Respirable particles of 5–7 μ in diameter are those most likely to reach the deepest levels in the lung and in many dust diseases, this is the area most vulnerable to damage. In other words, dust measurements should take particle size into consideration as well as proximity to the workers (Muir, 1972).

The hazardous environment should be regularly checked to ensure that the levels of a toxic agent are kept well below the maximum permissible levels laid down by Government or State authority. The Threshold Limit Values (TLV) and maximum allowance concentrations (MAC) of many substances have been established by the American Conference of Governmental Industrial Hygienists and are widely accepted in Western countries. In the USSR, the MAC and TLV's vary considerably from the American values. In general the levels quoted are lower than those adopted by the AGGIH (1972).

In summary, monitoring requires constant vigilance and regular checking of the work place and general environment to ensure that hazardous situations are avoided. Should excessive levels be detected then corrective measures to counteract the fault must be swift and effective.

3) Control

This is the final objective of all investigative and monitoring procedures: the control of the working environment. The worker is safe if he is prevented from coming into contact with the hazardous material; though even the best run enterprises may have the occasional accident or fault which could produce a disaster.

Control of occupationally induced illness involves prevention. Substitution of dangerous materials for less dangerous ones is the most important aspect of primary prevention. For example, asbestos can cause fibrosis and cancer of the lungs, and although its use is most valuable for many purposes, the less hazardous fibreglass can sometimes be substituted. β naphthylamine, a dyestuff, is a potent carcinogenic agent causing bladder cancer in a high proportion of workers often many years after exposure has occurred. Its manufacture and importation is now banned in many countries and substitute materials have been found to replace this valuable but highly dangerous amine.

Injury and illness can also be eliminated by guarding the man from his machine and the machine from the man. To make the machine safe is far better than to rely on the worker to protect himself and such safety measures should be fool-proof. The guards around machinery should be sufficiently sophisticated to discourage tampering by the worker.

Regular inspection of plant and persons, whether statutory or voluntary, also helps to control risks and such inspections should be combined with equally regular exhortation to the workers to maintain high standards of cleanliness and good "housekeeping". These inspections offer an opportunity to educate work people both verbally and by drawing their attention to posters, booklets and notices.

All of these measures should be repeated regularly and a constant watch kept on changes in plant and personnel. When all these factors are adequately covered, accident and illness rates should fall considerably. Such measures often lead to codes of practice for that particular procedure or industry. These may later be extended to form recommendations or regulations. If the hazard is widespread or particularly dangerous, statutory control or modification of existing legislation may be required, and such measures will need the approval of the federal or state government. Although laws may give added weight and power to safety enforcement, the implementation of safety measures still largely rests with the plant operators, and most importantly the management, and the factory inspectorate.

Examples of Occupational Health Practice

The generalisations above are best illustrated by a few examples of occupational health problems that have arisen in recent years. The three chosen demonstrate the interaction of investigation, monitoring and control. Occupational health practice is discussed in greater detail elsewhere (Schilling, 1973).

a) Nasal cancer

In 1958 it was noted that the nickel workers at a refining plant in South Wales had a 150 times increased risk of dying of cancer of the nose compared with the general population (Doll, 1958). This research was stimulated by information gleaned from accurate records of illness kept at the factory. An analysis of the deaths showed that all the men affected were working at the plant before 1924 and no-one employed after that time seemed to suffer from the same risk. The victims were not employed in processes involving metallic nickel nor the gaseous nickel carbonyl. They were, however, associated with the calcination procedures and the dust from the process probably contained the offending agent. In 1924 precautions were instituted to protect workers from this dust which contained arsenic, and certain processes involving calcination were curtailed. Two workers who underwent operations for lung cancer–this malignancy carried a five times increased risk amongst these employees –were noted to have high arsenic concentrations in their hair, lungs and urine. In this example the demonstration of the risk, the timing of the alteration in the calcination process, combined with environmental and biological monitoring, suggests that arsenic rather than nickel was the carcinogenic agent.

The discovery of this nasal cancer risk was made by the works medical officer. In another example of occupational nasal cancer, the initiator of the research was an ear, nose and throat specialist in Buckinghamshire, England. She noted several cases of an unusual type of cancer of the nose in the High Wycombe area. All those affected were men working in the furniture industry. Subsequent studies detected many more cases and it has been computed that the risk of getting this type of cancer is 1000 times greater in furniture makers than in the general population (Acheson *et al.*, 1968). Studies of the working conditions in the factories suggests that the risk is associated with dust either from the beechwoods or from resins used in the manufacture of furniture. The polishers, who by way of their craft, have to work in a dust-free atmosphere, have never experienced similar risks from this form of cancer. The hygiene in these furniture factories has improved dramatically in the last 30 yrs, and it seems unlikely from recent monitoring investigations that the cancer risk still exists. Nevertheless, follow-up studies would be required to prove this.

b) Asbestosis

Since the discovery that asbestos was a potentially dangerous substance and could cause fibrosis and cancer of the lungs, much work has been done to ascertain the degree of risk and the likely aetiological agents. Asbestos manufacturing processes such as cement, pipe and cloth making have been extensively studied in Britain, and insulation workers in the United States have been followed for some years (Selikoff *et al.*, 1965). It appears that there is a differential risk depending on the type of asbestos handled and that smoking enhances the risk of tumours in a multiplicative fashion rather than a summatory one. Mining the ore carries a lesser risk according to Canadian studies (McDonald *et al.*, 1972).

Considerable attention has been drawn to the widespread danger of asbestos and legislation imposed on its use in Britain has set threshold limits varying from 2–0.2 fibres/m^3 depending on the type of asbestos. Vast improvements in exhaust ventilation, more efficient dust control, and protective clothing for the workers has greatly diminished the risk of asbestos-related disease in todays' employees. Nevertheless, the toll of disease and death is not yet over because, with the long latent period and indefinite exposure threshold to disease, more workers already exposed have yet to develop their occupationally induced illnesses. Biological monitoring by chest X-ray and pulmonary function tests will help to detect these cases earlier, but the outlook for many who develop asbestosis is grave. The disease appears to be progressive despite removal from exposure to asbestos dust.

c) Medical laboratory workers

Of the working population in the United Kingdom of around twenty-five million, approximately seven million are self employed or work in such places as universities, laboratories or hospitals. In Britain at any rate they have yet to be included in any specific factory legislation. Medical laboratory workers are an example of an occupational group not so covered. Laboratory workers are at risk not only from research activities where unknown hazards may be present, but also from routine and diagnostic procedures. Medical laboratory workers in Britain 20 yrs ago were shown to have a 2–9 times increased risk of developing tuberculosis compared with a matched group of non-laboratory workers (Reid, 1957).

Reid's research resulted in new codes of practice for handling tuberculous material, but there is some evidence to suggest that the high risk remains. Work is at present being undertaken at our Institute to investigate the whole problem of laboratory health and safety. In dealing with a widely dispersed group of people like laboratory staff, survey methods offer the most convenient means of obtaining information and postal enquiries have the advantage of quick, cheap and wide dissemination of questionnaires. Such techniques, however, are impersonal and it is difficult to check the veracity of the data collected. Therefore a follow-up prospective analysis in a stratified sample of the laboratories is necessary. In addition a mortality study of medical laboratory personnel is envisaged to assess the risk of cancer in this group.

There is some evidence that certain cancers in animals are transmissable from host to host, such as cat leukaemia, and the possibility of this being due to a virus cannot be ruled out. No one knows whether this transmission can occur from animals to humans or indeed from humans to humans, but, if this is possible, then the people handling material from cancerous patients or working with cancer in experimental animals could be at risk. Furthermore, known oncogenic substances such as benzidine, ortho tolidine and radio isotopes have been used extensively in laboratory work.

This last example of a potentially vulnerable group is used to demonstrate that there is an increased tendency nowadays not to wait for the health risk to present itself but to look for it on the basis of extrapolation from other circumstances or experience. Frequently the watchful occupational physician or hygienist in industry can anticipate a hazard from past experience. The manufacture of xenylamine (4–amino diphenyl) was abandoned in the United States when its carcinogenic activity in dogs was demonstrated. Since the start of its manufacture approximately 11 % of the population exposed had already developed bladder tumours. Since similar or improved technical effects could be achieved with non-carcinogenic compounds, no other chemical company in any country has attempted to make this carcinogen (Walpole and Williams, 1960).

Walpole and Williams' perspicacity was valuable and life saving. Responsibility of this kind may fall on the shoulders of the occupational physician or hygienist and his decision may cost the manufacturer considerable sums of money already spent in research and development. Great expertise and ethical courage is required to make such decisions, which can undoubtedly save lives.

ADVICE ON OCCUPATIONAL HEALTH

Occupational health is therefore a discipline concerned not only with investigations, hygiene considerations, prevention and treatment but also the day to day advice needed by management or workers, either corporately or individually. The advisory role may require a major decision as in the carcinogenic amine example above but, much more frequently, advice is required on smaller items, The occupational physician or hygienist needs to fulfil these minor advisory duties promptly and satisfactorily. Only then will he be in a favourable position to influence major decisions when they arise.

No one would expect all such advice to be immediately forthcoming from the occupational practitioners' personal knowledge. Therefore he should possess the necessary reference works to aid him in these decisions. Many large companies produce codes of practice for their own industry and publish notes on the more dangerous materials handled. The National Institute of Occupational Safety and Health in Washington D.C. publish an exhaustive list of hazardous compounds with references to source data and further reading. Such sources of information are referred to later in this chapter and the occupational physician or hygienist should ensure that he possesses the source reference data relating to the particular working environment for which he has responsibillity.

Occupational Health Services and Their Relationship With Other Medical Services

The need for occupational health services has been debated hotly, often passionately, in the United Kingdom in and out of Parliament for many years.

In 1962 a committee under the Chairmanship of Sir Arthur Porritt was set up to review the Medical Services in Great Britain; their recommendations on occupational health services were put foward in Chapter 15, (paragraphs 541–559). In an article in the Lancet (1968) Tyrer and Murray developed these ideas further. In a discussion of the Porritt Report, the Working Party on National Health Service Administration of the British Medical Association in 1968 stated: "It would seem that the reorganisation of the National Health Service now foreseen and the creation of area health authorities as proposed by the Working Party would be an opportunity for the setting up of the framework of an occupational health service. I this opportunity is missed it may be many years before another such opportunity occurs."

The Report of the Royal Commission on Medical Education (Todd Committee) 1965–68 disappointed many by its very limited references to Occupational Medicine (paragraphs 23, 33, 52, 119). But, under the heading of Community Medicine (paragraphs 133–144) there is reference to doctors who wish to specialise in occupational medicine. It was, however, the comment in paragraph 52 . . . ". . . but rather in the fact that this country has given first priority to the establishment of a comprehensive system of medical services fully available to all sections of the community. The existance of such a system must limit the scope of the services demanded of British Industrial Medicine, and we do not expect any major changes in this respect in the forseeable future . . ." that caused alarm.

The publication of the Tunbridge Report on the Care of the Health of Hospital Staff in 1968 urged "the early establishment of an occupational health service for all people who work in the hospital service." The Lancet (**11**, 341, 1968) in its annotation "Health within the Hospital" states: "This poses the wider question of why a comprehensive national service should need as an appendage a separate service to deal with occupational health. The answer seems to be that if the N.H.S. worked perfectly such a service would not be required. But since the N.H.S. is, regrettably, more concerned with caring for ill-health than safeguarding good health, an occupational health service, the objectives of which are primarily preventive, has proved necessary."

These opinions are widely divergent. As already mentioned the present Government has obtained the Royal Assent to the Employment Medical Advisory Service Act 1972, which will establish an enlarged occupational medical service in the Department of Employment. Objections have been raised by many occupational physicians and others because this service has not been established within the Department of Health and Social Security; however, the Government has stated that there is no reason why this service should not be transferred to the Department of Health and Social Security later, if this appears advisable. There are, we believe, advantages in its present position, even though occupational health still remains outside the National Health Service. However, we also believe, that there remains a very great need for independent occupational health services within industry. Contrary to many opinions, it is our view that managements will be encouraged to provide their own occupational health services in future, because, it is likely that the work and research undertaken by the new Employment Medical Advisory Service, University Departments of Occupational Health and other research organisations will point to the need for more intensive occupational health care of the worker in the future.

Occupational Health Services

In large industries

The National Coal Board, The British Steel Corporation, The Air Corporation Joint Medical Services (BEA/BOAC) and The Post Office are examples of Government concerns with their own occupational health services. All the above employ large numbers of physicians—many of whom have had formal training in occupational medicine—in addition, in most cases, to occupational hygienists and occupational health nurses.

There are a number of independent industries who employ occupational physicians. Imperial Chemical Industries in Britain, for example, has twenty-four full-time occupational physicians.

In the United Kingdom the Association of Industrial Medical Officers was founded in 1935 with twenty members. In 1972 there are over nine hundred members and the name has been changed to the Society of Occupational Medicine. Members are full and part-time occupational physicians working in nationalized industries, (which have some of the best industrial medical services in this country); independent industries and physicians working in group health services for small factories. The need for these services has been recognised by those employers whose physicians are members of the Society. There are, of course, other employers, mostly those who run small factories, who do not employ their own physicians, but many of these factories have general practitioners who visit on a part-time basis and some of these physicians are also Appointed Factory Doctors (A.F.D.). These doctors are appointed by Her Majesty's Government to undertake certain duties under the Factories Act 1961. However, the present A.F.D. system will be superseded by the new Employment Medical Advisory Service in 1973.

In non-industrial organisations

Occupational medicine is an important part of preventive medical care of personnel serving in the armed forces, and is recognised as needing specialist training. Many physicians in the armed forces medical services have been sent for courses of instruction to the Institute in which we work.

The National Health Service has taken note of the recommendations in the Tunbridge Report and our Institute has been commissioned to ascertain the need for occupational health services in hospitals. A five year research project investigating this need is at present being undertaken.

Universities in the United Kingdom have since 1929 had provisions in some universities, for the care of student health. Student health services are widely accepted as essential at the present time. The need for comprehensive occupational health health services in universities is only just gaining recognition in this country. One of our physicians, who obtained the Degree of Master of Science in Occupational Medicine in 1972, has just been appointed as occupational health physician to a University Health Service—the first such appointment in Britain.

The London School of Hygiene and Tropical Medicine, in conjuction with the Central Institutions Student Health Service of London University, is developing a comprehensive occupational health service for staff, students and the environment. The School, through the Safety Committee, has the services of the Environmental and Industrial staff and laboratories in our Institute to investigate and give advice on the control of hazards to health. For some years, one of us has been appointed as honorary consultant in occupational health to the University College Student Health Association of London University; many important and interesting occupational health problems have been investigated and research into methods of monitoring and controlling potential hazards to health in processing enzymes in a laboratory is at present being undertaken. Many universities in the United States of America have recognised the need for occupational health services. In Harvard University, members of the staff of the University Health Service have written "College Health Administration" edited by Dana Farnsworth in which college health services are fully discussed and which includes a chapter on Environmental Health and Safety.

The Organisation, Functions and Staffing of Occupational Health Services

The detailed planning varies but, in most cases, in the United Kingdom a senior or chief medical officer based in London, is usually responsible for the organisation of the services in the periphery. The great variety of expertise required allows physicians to specialise in particular problems. A noteable new book just published is "Medicine in the Mining Industries edited by Dr. John Rogan, Chief Medical Officer of the Coal Board.

An example of such a service in the United States is cited because one of us visited the Boeing Company, Aero-Space Division, in Seattle in the mid-1960's. Health and safety is particularly vital for this organisation. The Health and Safety Section housed the Medical Team and the Industrial Hygiene Engineering; Safety Administration; Safety Engineering; Minuteman Weapon System Safety and Dyna Soar Grand System Safety, the last two comprised System Safety. This organisational pattern was clearly defined and provided a comprehensive system of services in medicine, hygiene and safety under the control of the Director of Health and Safety, a physician.

The Dale Committee, which presented its Report of an Enquiry on Industrial Health Services to the Prime Minister in 1951, had as its terms of reference:

To examine the relationship (including any possibility of overlapping) between the preventive and curative health services provided for the population at large and the industrail health services which make a call on medical manpower (doctors, nurses and auxillary medical personnel); to consider what measures should be taken by the Government and other parties concerned to ensure that such medical manpower is used to the best advantage; and to make recommendations.

The Committee considered—

A. The Possibility of overlapping between Employers' Voluntary Services and the National Health Service

Functions of the Industrial Medical Officer

34. In this paragraph we have tried to describe the functions which are performed by Industrial Medical Officers. In regard to these the voluntary and the statutory services can never be entirely separated. Thus an employer may voluntarily seek medical advice in connection with the discharge of his statutory responsibilities (at sub-para. (i) (h) below). Not all the functions listed below are carried out at every establishment where there is an industrial health service. Some are carried out at one establishment and some at another, though there are certain establishments where all the functions listed are in fact carried out.

i) General Advisory Services to Management on
 a) industrial hygiene, including advice, in collaboration with technical experts, on the design, construction and lay-out of buildings and machines;
 b) the conditions affecting the health of the workers;
 c) the occurence and risk of dangerous hazards;
 d) medical aspects of safety precautions, including questions as to the effects and avoidance of fatigue;
 e) medical aspects of "employee" services, including canteens and cloakrooms;
 f) study of sickness absenteeism and questions of personal and group morale;
 g) the causation and prevention of industrial disease, enlisting the help of inside and outside research and technical departments;
 h) medical aspects of legislation on health matters which places obligations on the employer.

ii) Examination of individual workers with a view to advising management as to their conditions of employment
 a) Pre-placement examinations and the examination of persons returning to work after illness or injury, with a view to determining the work on which the worker is to be employed and his fitness for it;
 b) examinations of persons exposed to occupational hazards, other than those for which a statutory examination is required;
 c) examination of persons doing work of such a nature that ill health or the development of certain disabilities might endanger the lives of themselves or others.

iii) Therapeutic Services
 a) supervision of nursing services;
 b) supervision of First-aid;
 d) follow-up treatment, where appropriate, of cases of illness and accident.

iv) Certain general health services to workers, namely
 a) diagnostic or periodic general health examinations in addition to those referred to in (ii) above;
 b) promotion of the education of workpeople collectively and individually in matters of general and personal hygiene.

35. (i) Under the heading (i) in the preceding paragraph are listed a number of matters with which managements are concerned and on which they may require the advice of doctors. No question of overlapping can arise in connection with these general advisory services to managements, which are not provided under the general health services.

ii) Similar considerations apply to the functions listed in (ii) of that paragraph. The certification of fitness for particular employment is not one of the free services provided under the National Health Service and fitness for particular employment is a matter on which the employer must be in a position to obtain medical advice.

iii) As regards the function listed in paragraph 34 (iii) it is clear that no question of overlap arises in connection with (a) and(b) supervision of nursing and first-aid services. The question does arise however, in connection with (c) and (d) which are both concerned with treatment over and above first-aid. The general burden of evidence is that where the doctor or nurse is fully occupied at the factory the overlap in these matters is justified as benefiting productivity. Furthermore, the benefit to the patient in some cases may be considerable and there will be a lessening of the load on the National Health Service.

iv) The service described in paragraph 34 (iv) present certain features on which we should like to comment. It is no part of the National Health Service to provide for periodic general health examinations, although it is a function of that Service to provide diagnostic examinations where ill-health is suspected and in respect of the latter there may, therefore, be said to be some overlapping. Within reasonable limits overlap may well be justified in the interests of the efficiency and welfare of the workers. The promotion of the education of workpeople as such, collectively and individually, in matters of general and personal hygiene is not a matter provided for in the National Health Service, though certain measures for the health education of the community are within the powers of local authorities.

To illustrate where overlap may occur, but where special services within industry may be valuable to the organisation and workers concerned, reference is made to a recent survey of the needs of the occupational physician for diagnostic radiological services (Gauvain, 1971). The findings were that diagnostic X-ray facilities, usually including access to consultant radiological opinion, were considered necessary and were greatly valued by those occupational physicians who had these radiological services provided by their own industries.

Reasons given were that radiological screening in conjunction with pre-employment and periodic medical examinations enabled the medical officer to be more effective in advice or job placement. The exclusion of fractures and bony injuries led to the saving of employee time and to the referral to hospital of only those who needed further treatment. Continued surveillance either of a statutory and voluntary nature could be easily carried out. Consultant radiological opinion on diagnostic problems and guidance in radiological techniques was sought and highly valued by many of the respondents. Joint research projects were also undertaken.

However, most occupational physicians working in industries without such facilities did not appear to have the same need for these services. Radiological examinations were less often required and were undertaken privately or through National Health Service Radiology Departments. Reasons for non-provision were often the small size of the working group and/or the expense involved.

Functions of the Industrial Nurse

36. In general, the function of industrial nurses vary, as do the functions of Industrial Medical Officers, with the size and nature of the establishment in which they are employed. The range of duties carried out is also dependent on the extent of medical supervision in the establishment. The full range of duties may be briefly summarised as follows:

i) Administration of the health department;
ii) Emergency and primary treatment;
iii) Follow-up treatment where appropriate;
iv) Assistance with medical examinations;
v) General health supervision;
vi) Health education;
vii) Factory hygiene and accident prevention;
viii) Advisory services to management and employees;
ix) Keeping of records and reports.

The considerations which arise with regard to overlapping of nursing services are similar to those which arise in connection with the work of doctors and what we have said in paragraph 35 should be taken as applying also, *mutatis mutandis*, to the employment of nurses.

They emphasise—

Need for Further Training of Medical Personnel

82. We would like to endorse the view put to us by one witness that "before any wide developments are contemplated, thought must be given to the training facilities available to meet the demands."

Without adequate training in the principles of industrial health, doctors and nurses employed in this field will not be working to their full capacity. In our view there is a real need for the provision of short intensive courses for doctors employed or contemplating employment part time in industry. This is particularly important for Appointed Factory Doctors and especially for those who have had little previous experience of industrial medicine. For those who wish to devote their whole-time to industrial medicine, full postgraduate facilities are needed. We emphasise, however, that an essential qualification for all practising industrial medicine is a good and full experience of clinical medicine, whether obtained in general practice or in specialised medical fields. Without this the mere acquisition of a number of special diplomas will not provide the high standard of medical practice required in industrial medicine.

This is an historic document. Changes in Government policy have since been made viz. The Employment Medical Advisory Service, nevertheless, the principles outlined are, in our belief, as valid now as they were then.

Training

The Joint Committee on Higher Medical Training produced its First Report in 1972; this describes the training programme proposed for occupational medicine—

General Professional Training

Either:

a) Training for three years as followed for General (Internal) Medicine; or

b) Training for three years during which a recognised examination in occupational medicine would be taken. At least two years would be devoted to a training in occupational medicine by holding appointments in industry, university, Government service or the armed forces, and taking a course of training required for the examination. The remainder of the training period would be spent in appointments in general medicine or in clinical subjects related to occupational medicine such as respiratory medicine, dermatology, psychiatry, industrial rehabilitation and rheumatology, casualty surgery.

Higher Specialist Training

This period of training should normally be for four years undertaken in approved appointments in universities, hospitals, research units, government service, armed services and occupational health services. Before admission to the register as a specialist, account would be taken of the programme followed by the trainee, reports from supervisors, publications and academic attainments. During this period of training a trainee who had not taken an M.R.C.P. would be expected to have done original work leading to an M.D. or a Ph.D.

Training Facilities Available

Occupational physicians

Postgraduate Training At present, in the United Kingdom the accepted qualification for an occupational physician is a Diploma in Industrial Health. Examinations are held by the Examining Board in England of the Royal College of Physicians of London and the Royal College of Surgeons of England and by the Society of Apothecaries of London, both biannually. The regulations demand postgraduate experience in occupational medical practice and/or a Diploma in Public Health which must be combined with a 3 months full-time course or a longer part-time course in occupational medicine before sitting for the examinations. (Examining Board in England 1970, Society of Apothecaries of London, 1965.)

Courses are held at the Universities of Manchester and Dundee and at the London School of Hygiene and Tropical Medicine of the University of London.

For the last three years an academic course leading to a M.Sc. Degree in Occupational Medicine has been run annually in this Institute (Syllabus of the M.Sc. Degree in Occupational Medicine of the London School of Hygiene and Tropical Medicine, 1972/73). A particular feature of this training is an intensive course of study in epidemiology and statistics in order that physicians may be fully equipped to undertake research and teaching as well as the practice of occupational medicine in the future.

Because the career structure in occupational medicine has been ill defined, few young able physicians have entered this specialty. The need for such recruits is urgent, particularly if one of the recommendations in the Robens Report (1972) is to be realized—"Doctors in general and hospital practice should be encouraged to show more interest in and acquire more knowledge about occupational factors in the health care of the individual. This is, of course, primarily a matter of medical education—we should very much like to see more emphasis on occupational medicine in the training of doctors" (paragraph 375). In the future it is hoped that larger numbers may be attracted, but sponsored postgraduate training opportunities must be increased, and openings must include posts in state and independent occupational medical services in the variety of organisations already referred to, with greater opportunities for academic advancement and more certain and higher financial rewards.

In the United States of America in 1955 occupational medicine was acknowledged as an affiliated specialty with aerospace medicine, public health and general preventive medicine by the American Board of Preventive Medicine. The eligibility requirements are general and special.

The *Special Requirements* include

1) Successful completion (after internship) of at least 2 academic years of graduate study in preventive and occupational medicine in a school of medicine, a university graduate school, a school of public health, or a combination of these schools, all of which must be acceptable for such graduate training by the Joint Residency Review Committee Preventive Medicine of the Council on Medical Education and Hospitals of the A.M.H. and the American Board of Preventive Medicine or training or study deemed equivalent to such graduate study.

2) Residency (after internship) of not less than 1 year, in addition to (1) above of supervised experience in occupational medical practice in an industrial or medical organisation approved by the Joint Residency Review Committee for Preventive Medicine of the American Medical Association's Council on Medical Education and Hospitals and the American Board of Preventive Medicine; or an equivalent Canadian residency approved by the Board; or a period of experience deemed by the Board to be substantially equivalent to such year of residency.

3) A period (after internship) of not less than 3 years in addition to 1 and 2 above, or special training in or teaching or practice of occupational medicine.

4) Three years of the experience outlined in 2 and 3 above, must have been obtained within the 5 year period immediately prior to application for certification.

5) Limitation of practice to full-time teaching, research, or practice of occupational medicine, Board Certification in Occupational Medicine. Report of the Education Committee of the American Academy of Occupational Medicine (1965).

For details of the training courses available the American Medical Association in Chicago should be consulted. They provide an annual directory of Approved Internships and Residencies.

Occupational Hygiene

Postgraduate training

In the United Kingdom the demand for postgraduate training is growing rapidly. The British

Occupational Hygiene Society (B.O.H.S.), who sponsor an examining board which grants certificates and diplomas of professional competance, organise short courses. In addition, the London School of Hygiene and Tropical Medicine run an academic course in occupational hygiene leading to an M.Sc. Degree (Syllabus of Courses, London School of Hygiene and Tropical Medicine, 1972/73).

The United States of America have been in advance of the rest of the world in recognising the importance of postgraduate training of scientists in order that they may be able to investigate and advise on the control of occupational hazards by engineering means. The American Industrial Hygiene Association lists thirteen institutions offering training in Industrial hygiene. Short 2 week courses are also organised by the U.S. Department of Health Education and Welfare.

Occupational Health Nursing

Postgraduate education

The United Kingdom trains nurses in the special skills required for the care of people at work. The Institute of Advanced Nursing Education in the Royal College of Nursing run full time 6 months courses and part-time 18 months courses for the Occupational Health Nursing Certificate (OHNC). Courses are also run in centres outside London, notably the University of Dundee and the Accident Hospital in Birmingham. (Syllabus for the course of Occupational Health Nursing of the Royal College of Nurses, 1972/73, and the University of Dundee, Department of Social and Occupational Medicine, 1972/73.)

So far as we know, there are no formal courses in occupational health nursing in the United States of America, but occupational health is included in Baccalaureate Nursing Education (Keller and May, 1970).

An active American Association of Industrial Health Nurses sets out the objectives of occupational nursing.

Safety Officers

Other personnel who may be part of the occupational health team are safety officers.

In the United States the new William–Steiger Occupational Safety and Health Act 1970 provides for the setting up of specific safety and health standards. Virtually all businesses will be covered.

The employer has a duty to furnish to each employee "a place of employment free from recognised hazards that are causing or are likely to cause death or serious physical harm. Employees are required to comply with standards, rules, and orders applicable to their own actions and conduct." This means that the importance of safety officers must be magnified. The Secretary of Health, Education and Welfare has the responsibility "to conduct training programmes to provide qualified personnel to implement the act and to disseminate information in the importance and use of adequate safety and health equipment. The Secretary of Labor will conduct training programmes for employers and employees on the prevention of unsafe and unhealthful working conditions." (Safety Standards, 1971.) Information on courses of training and qualifications required must be sought from Personnel Office, Room 5337, U.S. Department of Labor, 14th Street and Constitution Avenue, N.W. Washington D.C. 202110 or from the Bureau of Labor Standards regional offices.

In the United Kingdom the Institution of Industrial Safety Officers is the professional body that represents safety officers in the manufacturing and construction industries. The University of Aston in Birmingham has recently established a Chair of Safety and Hygiene. The intention is to offer both an M.Sc. and a Diploma. (Proposed Syllabus of Modular Courses in Occupational Safety and Hygiene of the University of Aston in Birmingham, 1972/73. The University of Aston in Birmingham, Gosta Green, Birmingham B4 7ET, England.)

Further information on training for occupational health personnel is described (Gauvain and Schilling, 1973).

The Occupational Health team can be welded together to form a functioning whole with the encouragement of management and with able direction in the occupational medical department of the organisations concerned.

Sources of Information

Occupational Health covers an immensely wide field and has relatively few up to date text books.

The most notable recent work is—

Encyclopaedia of Occupational Health and Safety (Vol. I, A–K, 1971; Vol. II, L–Z (1972), Industrial Labour Office, GENEVA, Switzerland.

Our own Institute is concerned with the production of two new books both of which it is hoped will be published in 1973, *Occupational Health Practice* edited by R. S. F. Schilling, to be published by Butterworths, London, which will contain far more detailed information on the topics discussed in this chapter and many others, and *Occupational Health: A Guide to Sources of Information*, edited by Suzette Gauvain, to be published by William Heinnemann Medical Books. The latter is unlikely to be published before the end of 1974.

The most up to date information can be obtained from the following journals—

The Journal of the Society of Occupational Medicine (British)

Occupational Health (A journal for Occupational Health Nurses) (British)

Occupational Health Nursing (American)

The Annals of Occupational Hygiene (British)

The Journal of Occupational Medicine (American)

The American Industrial Hygiene Association Journal

The British Journal of Industrial Medicine

The Archives of Environmental Health (American)

Ergonomics (British)

The International Journal of Industrial Medicine and Surgery (American)

The Archives of Environmental Health, Preventive and Aerospace Medicine (American)

American Journal of Epidemiology

British Journal of Social and Preventive Medicine

Further references should be sought in general medical journals such as the Lancet and British Medical Journal (United Kingdom; and the New England Journal of Medicine and the Journal of the American Medical Association (U.S.A.) A comprehensive list of specialist journals can be found at the back of Industrial Hygiene Digest (Industrial Health Foundation Incorporated, 5231 Centre Avenue, Pittsburgh, PA., 15232), which abstracts articles from the journals listed.

Other useful abstract journals are—

the *Excepta Medica Abstract Journals*,
Excepta Medica Foundation,
119–123 Herengracht,
AMSTERDAM C, Netherlands.

and

Occupational Safety and Health Abstracts,
International Occupational Safety and Health Information
Centre (CIS),
International Labour Office,
1211 GENEVA 22, Switzerland.

The Government Printing Offices in the U.S.A. and the United Kingdom provide up to date lists of publications. NIOSH publications are available from the Office of Public Information, 10114 Broadway, Cincinnati, Ohio, 45202. Government Publications, forms and other publications and the Sectional Lists from the Government Departments are obtainable from Her Majesty's Stationary Office, P.O. Box 569, London SE1 9NH.

Textbooks which the reader may wish to consult include—

The Diseases of Occupations, Donald Hunter, 4th Ed., English Universities Press (1969);

Medical Services in Transport, J. Sharp Grant, L. G. Norman, K. M. Heggie, Butterworths, London (1966);

Human Relations in Modern Industry, P. F. Tredgold, Methuen, (1965);

Chemical Carcinogenisis and Cancers by W. C. Hueper and W. D. Conway, Charles C. Thomas, Springfield, Illinois (1964);

Industrial Health Technology, B. Harvey, R. Murray, Butterworths London (1958);

Industrial Hygiene and Toxicology (3 vols.), F. A. Patty, 2nd revised Ed., Interscience Publishers, New York (1958);

Dangerous Properties of Industrial Materials, N. I. Sax, 3rd Ed., Rheinhold Book Corporation, New York (1968);

Toxicity of Industrial Metals, Ethel Browning, Butterworths (1961);

Toxicity and Metabolism of Industrial Solvents, Ethel Browning, Elsevier Publications, Amsterdam (1965);

The Effect of Abnormal Physical Conditions at Work, C. N. Davies, I. R. Davis, F. H. Tyrer, E. & S. Livingstone Ltd. (1967);

The Biology of Work, O. G. Edholm, Wevenfield and Nicholson (1967);

Inhaled Particles (2 vols.), Ed. by W. H. Walton, Unwin Brothers Ltd., Woking, England (1971).

These are in addition to the textbooks already mentioned in the references at the end of this chapter. This list has deliberately been kept short, but it is hoped that if a reader is interested in following up a particular topic, the references given in these books will lead to further sources of information.

The World Health Organisation has ten functions and the first is "to act as directing and co-ordinating authority on international health work". The Director of Occupational Health at the World Health Organisation is Professor Mustapha El Batawi. Publications are obtainable from the Distribution and Sales Unit, World Health Organisation, Avenue Appia, 1211 Geneva, Switzerland.

REFERENCES

(a) *General*

Acheson, E. D., R. H. Cowdell, E. Hadfield and R. G. Macbeth (1968). Nasal Cancer in Woodworkers in the Furniture Industry. *Brit. Med. J.*, **2**, 587.

American Conference of Government Industrial Hygienists (1972). *Threshold Limit Values of Airborne Contaminants adopted by A.C.G.I.H.*

Annual Report of H.M. Chief Inspector of Factories (1971). H.M.S.O. London.

Annual Report of the Chief Medical Officer for 1971 (1972). *The State of the Public Health*, 1972. Department of Health and Social Security. H.M.S.O. London

Approved Residences (1972) *Occupational Medicine (Academic) Annual List*. American Medical Association, 535 North Dearborn Street, CHICAGO, Ill. 60610

Baier, E. J. and M. M. Key. Programs of the National Institute of Occupational Safety and Health. *Industrial Medicine*, **41**, 7.

Boyd, J. T. R. Doll, J. S. Faulds and J.Leiper (1970). Cancer of the lung in iron ore (Haematite) miners. *Brit. J. Indust. Med.*, **27**, 97.

Criteria for a recommended standard—
- Occupational exposure to Noise 1972, H.S.M. 73-11001.
- Occupational exposure to Asbestos 1972, H.S.M. 72-10267.
- Occupational exposure to Carbon Monoxide 1972, H.S.M. 73-11000.
- Occupational exposure to Beryllium 1972, H.S.M. 72–10268.
- Occupational exposure to Hot environments 1972, H.S.M. 72–10269.
- U.S. Department of Health, Education and Welfare, Health Services and Mental Health Administration, National Institute for Occupational Safety and Health.

Doll, R. (1958). Cancer of the lung and nose in nickel workers. *Brit. J. Indust. Med*, **15**, 217.

The Dale Committee (1951) Report of a Committee of Enquiry in Industrial Health Services Cmnd. 8170, H.M.S.O. London.

Examining Board in England (1970) Regulations for obtaining Diploma in Industrial Health. Examination Hall, Queen's Square, London, W.C.1.

Farnsworth, D., Ed. (1964). *College Health Administration*, Chapter 9, Appleton–Century–Crofts. New York

Gauvain, S. (1971). The needs of the Occupational Physician for Diagnostic Radiological Services. *Trans. Soc. Occ. Med.*, **21**, 79.

Gauvain, S. and R. S. F. Schilling. Education and Training (1973). *Occupational Health Practice* Ed. by R. S. F. Schilling, Butterworths, London.

Gilson, J. C. (1970). Occupational Bronchitis. *Proc R. Soc. Med.* **63**, 857.

Goldstein, D. H., L. H. Miller, J. L. Norris, J. F. McCahan and D. L. Block. (1965) Board Certification in Occupational Medicine. Report of the Education Committee of the American Academy of Occupational Medicine. *Arch. Environ. Hlth.* **11**, 340.

Harrington, J. M. and R. S. F. Schilling (1973). Man's Work and his Health. *Occupational Health Practice*, Ed. by R. S. F. Schilling. Butterworths, London.

Health Within the Hospital—Annotation (1968), *Lancet* **ii**, 341.

Higher Medical Training—first report of the Joint Committee, Royal College of Physicians, 11 St. Andrews Place, London, NW1 4LE (1972).

Hill, A. B. (1966). *Principles of Medical Statistics* (8th Ed.) The Lancet, London.

Hunter, D. (1969). *The Diseases of Occupations* (4th revised Ed.) English Universities Press, London.

ILO/WHO Committee on Occupational Health (1953) Second Rep. Technical Report Series No. 66, WH.O., Geneva.

I.L.O. (1959) Occupational Health Services, Recommendation No. 112. International Labour Office, Geneva.

Keller, J. M. and W. T. May. (1970) *Occupational Health Content in Baccalaureate Nursing Education*. U.S. Department of Health, Education and Welfare, Cincinnati, Ohio.

Mc Alpine, D. and S. Araki (1958) Minamata disease—an unusual neurological disorder caused by contaminated fish. *Lancet* **ii**, 629.

Macdonald, J. C., M. R. Becklake, G. Fournier-Massey and C. E. Rossiter (1972). Respiratory symptoms in Chrysotile Asbestos mine and mill workers, Quebec. *Arch. Environ. Hlth.* **24**, 358.

Macmahon, B. and T. F. Pugh (1970). *Epidemiology: Principles and Methods*. Little, Brown and Co. Boston, Mass.

Matthews vs. Kuwait Bechtel Corp. **2** Queen's Bench, Report 57 (1959).

Muir, D. C. F. (1972) *Clinical Aspects of Inhaled Particles*. Heinemann Medical Books, London.

Munkman, J. (1971) *Employers Liability at Common Law*. Butterworths, London.

National Health Service Administration—Report of the Working Party. Occupational Health, p. 17. B.M.A. Tavistock Square, London, WC1H 97R (1968).

Newhouse, M. L. and H. Thomson (1965). Epidemiology of Mesothelial Tumours in the London Area, *Ann. N.Y. Acad. Sci.* **132**, 579.

N.I.O.S.H. Fact Sheet. National Institute for Occupational Safety and Health. 5600 Fishers Lane, Rockville Md. 20852.

Occupational Diseases—Notes on the diagnosis of SBN11, 7600725. H.M.S.O. London (1970).

Pneumoconiosis and Allied Chest Diseases. S.O. Code No. 76–23. Diagnosis and Procedure for claiming Industrial Injuries Benefits. H.M.S.O. London (1967).

The Porritt Committee (1962). A review of the Medical Services in Great Britain. Medical Services Review Committee, Social Assay, H.M.S.O., London.

Price's Textbook of the Practice of Medicine (1972) (11th Ed.), Ed. by Sir R. Bodley Scott. Oxford University Press. London.

Raffle, P. A. B. (1970). The Occupational Physician as Community Physician. *Proc. R. Soc. Med.* **63**, 731.

Ramazzini, B. (1940). *De Morbis Artificium Diatriba*. Geneva (1713) Trans. by W. C. Wright, Chicago University Press.

Reid, D. D. (1957). The Incidence of Tuberculosis among workers in medical laboratories. *Brit. Med. J.* **ii**, 1.

The Robens Committee (1972). Report of a Committee of Enquiry into Safety and Health at Work. Cmnd. 5034. H.M.S.O., London.

Rogan, J. M., Ed. (1972). *Medicine in the Mining Industries*. Heinemann Medical Books, London.

Russek, H. I. (1967). Emotional Stress and Coronary Artery Disease. *Dis. Chest*. **52**, 1.

Safety Standards 20, No. 2, pps. 5, 11 and 15. U.S. Department of Labor. Work Place Standards Administration, Bureau of Labor Standards. Washington D.C. 20210 (1971).

Schilling, R. S. F., Ed. (1973). *Occupational Health Practice*. Butterworths, London.

Schilling, R. S. F. (1963). Developments in Occupational Health during the last thirty years: The Cantor Lectures. *J. R. Soc. Arts.* **111**, 933.

Selikoff, I. J., J. Churg and E. C. Hammond (1965). The Occurrence of Asbestosis among Insulation Workers in the United States. *Annals N.Y. Acad. Sci.* **132**, 139.

Sturrock, R. F. (1965). Development of Irrigation and its influence on the transmission of Schistosomiasis in Tanganyika. *Bull. Wld. Hlth. Org.* **32**, 225.

The Todd Committee (1968). Report of the Royal Commission on Medical Education. Cmnd 3569. H.M.S.O., London.

Toxic Substances List. (1971, 1972). U.S. Dept. of Health, Education and Welfare. H.S.M. 72–10265 Health Services and Mental Health Administration. N.I.O.S.H. Rockville. Md. 20852.

Trasko, V. M. (1971). Occupational Injury and Disease Reporting in the U.S.A. A status report RR. 161971. Bureau of Occupational Safety and Health, U.S. Dept. of Health Education and Welfare. Public Health Service N.I.O.S.H. Cincinatti, Ohio 45202.

The Tunbridge Report (1968). The Report of the Joint Committee of Enquiry into the Care of the Health of Hospital Staff. S.B.N. 11. 320004. 8. H.M.S.O. London.

Tyrer, F. and R. Murray (1968). The place of Occupational Medicine in Community Health, *Lancet* **11**, 445.

Wagner, J. C. C. A. Sleggs and P. Marchand (1960). Diffuse pleural mesothelioma and asbestos exposure in N.W. Cape Province. *Brit J. Indust. Med.* **17**, 260.

Walpole, A. L. and M. H. C. Williams (1960). *Occupational Cancer in Modern Trends in Occupational Health*, Ed. by R. S. F. Schilling. Butterworths, London.

Webb, S. (1911). Preface to *A History of Factory Legislation* (2nd. Ed.) Hutchins B. L. and Harrison, A. Monograph No. 10. Studies in Economic and Political Sciences King and Son, London.

Wilson and Clyde Coal vs. English. Appeal Court Report 57 (1938).

The Windeyer Report (1972). Report of Committee of Enquiry into Lead Poisonings at the RTZ Smelter at Avonmouth. Cmnd. 5042. H.M.S.O. London.

(*b*) *Organisations*

1. American Association of Industrial Nurses Inc.,
79 Madison Avenue,
New York, N.Y. 10016, U.S.A.
2. American Industrial Hygiene Association,
210 Haddon Avenue, Westmont,
N.J. 08108, U.S.A.
3. University of Aston in Birmingham,
Gosta Green, Birmingham B4 7ET.
England.
4. British Occupational Hygiene Society,
Hon. Sec., Nuffield Dept. of Industrial Health,
Medical School, University of Newcastle-upon-Tyne,
Newcastle-upon-Tyne, NE1 7RU, England.
5. University of Dundee,
Department of Social and Occupational Medicine,
9 Dudhope Terrace,
Dundee, Scotland.
6. Institute of Industrial Safety Officers,
23 Queens Square,
London, W.C.1., England.
7. Industrial Medical Association,
150 North Wacker Drive,
Chicago, Ill. 60606, U.S.A.
8. London School of Hygiene and Tropical Medicine,
T.U.C. Centenary Institute of Occupational Health,
Keppel Street, London, WC1E 7HT, England.
9. Royal College of Nursing,
Henrietta Place, Cavendish Square,
London, W1M OAB, England.
10. The Society of Apothecaries,
Blackfriars Lane, Queen Victoria Street,
London, E.C.4.
11. The Society of Occupational Medicine,
at the Royal College of Physicians,
11 St. Andrews Place, Regents Park,
London, N.W.1., England.

(*c*) *Legislation*

Alkali etc., Works Regulations Act. H.M.S.O. (1960).

National Health Services Act. H.M.S.O. (1946).

Agriculture (Poisonous Substances) Act. H.M.S.O. (1952).

Mines and Quarries Act. H.M.S.O. (1954).

Agriculture (Safety, Health & Welfare Provisions) Act. H.M.S.O. (1956).

Factories Act. H.M.S.O. (1961).

Ionising Radiations (Sealed Sources) Regulations. Statutory Instruments No. 1470 H.M.S.O. (1961).

Offices, Shops and Railway Premises Act. H.M.S.O. (1963).

Vibration Syndrome, National Insurance (Industrial Injuries) Act. Cmnd. 4430 H.M.S.O. (1965).

Ionising Radiations (Unsealed Radioactive Substances) Regulations Statutory Instruments No. 780. H.M.S.O. (1968).

Occupational Safety & Health Act. Public Law 91–596. 91st Congress S 2193 (1970).

Recording Requirements under the Williams-Steiger Occupational Safety and Heath Act. U.S. Dept. of Labor, Occupational Safety and Health Administration (1970).

Employment Medical Advisory Service Act. H.M.S.O. (1972).

Code of Practice for Reducing the Exposure of Employed Persons to Noise. H.M.S.O. S.B.N. 11 360887X (1972).

J. M. Harrington
Suzette Gauvain
London School of Hygiene and Tropical Medicine

December 1, 1972

OIL SPILLAGE: see MARINE SPILLAGE—SOURCES AND HAZARDS

ORGANIC SOLID WASTE DISPOSAL: see COMPOSTING

ORGANISMS, MICRO: see MICROBIOLOGY

ORGANISMS AND THEIR ENVIRONMENT: see ECOSYSTEM THEORY

P

PARTICULATE EMISSIONS

Emission Standards

Allowable levels of particulate emissions are specified in several different ways, having somewhat different methodologies of measurement and different philosophies of important criteria for control. Permissible emission rates are in a state of great legislative flux both as to the definition of the suitable measurement and to the actual amount to be allowed. This section summarizes the various types of quantitative standards that are used in regulating particulate emissions. For a detailed survey of standards, the reader should consult works by Stern[1] and the National Air Pollution Control Administration,[2] and the Public Health Service.[3]

A. Ringlemann number

Perhaps the first attempt at quantifying particulate emissions was developed late in the 19th century by Maximilian Ringlemann. He developed the concept of characterizing a visible smoke plume according to its opacity or optical density and originated the chart shown in Figure 1 as a convenient scale for estimation of opacity. The chart consists of four grids of black lines on a white background, having fractional black areas of 20, 40, 60, and 80% which are assigned Ringlemann Numbers of 1–4. (Ringlemann 0 would be all white and Ringlemann 5 all black). For rating a smoke plume, the chart is held at eye level at a distance such that chart lines merge into shades of grey. The shade of the smoke plume is compared to the chart and rated accordingly. The history and use of the Ringlemann chart is covered by Kudlich[4] and by Weisburd.[5]

In actual practice, opacity is seldom determined by use of the chart, although the term Ringlemann Number persists. Instead, observers are trained at a "smoke school".[6] Test plumes are generated and the actual percentage of light attenuation is measured spectrophotemetrically within the stack. Observers calibrate their perception of the emerging

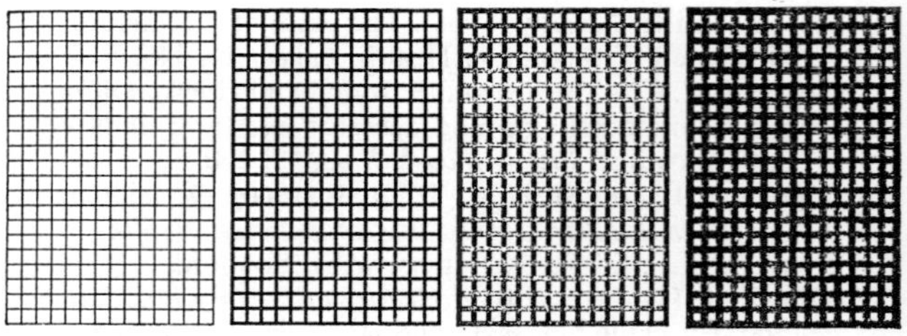

Figure 1 Ringlemann's scale for grading the density of smoke.

plume against the measured opacity. Trained observers can usually make readings correct to ± 1/2 Ringlemann number[5,7] Thus, with proper procedures, determination of a Ringlemann number is fairly objective and reproducible.

The Ringlemann concept was developed specifically for black plumes, which attenuate skylight reaching the observer's eye and appear darker than the sky. White plumes, on the other hand, reflect sunlight and appear brighter than the background sky so that comparison to a Ringlemann chart is meaningless. The smoke school approach is quite applicable, however. Observations of a white plume are calibrated against the measured light attenuation. Readings of white plumes are somewhat more subject to variation due to relative locations of observer, plume, and sun. It has been found that observations of equivalent opacity taken with the observer facing the sun are about 1 Ringlemann number higher[7] than those taken in the prescribed method with the sun at the observer's back. Nevertheless, when properly made, observations of Ringlemann numbers are reproducible among observers and agree well with actual plume opacity.

Opacity regulations specify a maximum Ringlemann number allowable on a long-term basis but often permit this to be exceeded for short prescribed periods of time. For instance, a typical requirement specifies that emissions shall not exceed Ringlemann 1, except that for up to 3 min/hr emissions up to

Ringlemann 3 are permitted. This allowance is of considerable importance to such operation as soot blowing or rapping of electrostatic precipitator plates which produce puffs of smoke despite an overall very low emission level.

Federal regulations of the Environmental Protection Agency[8] specify that opacity observations be made from a point perpendicular to the plume, at a distance of between two stack heights and one quarter of a mile, and with the sun at the observer's back. For official certification, an observer under test must assign opacity readings in 5% increments (1/4 Ringlemann number) to 25 plumes, with an error not to exceed 15% on any single reading and an average error (excluding algebraic sign of individual errors) not to exceed 7.5%. Annual testing is required for certification. In view of previous studies,[5,7] this is a very high standard of performance and probably represents the limits of visual quantification of opacity.

Perhaps the greatest advantage of the Ringlemann Number approach is that it requires no instrumentation and very little time and man-power. Readings can usually be made by control authorities or other interested parties without entering the premises of the subject source. Monitoring can be done very frequently to insure continual, if not continuous, compliance of the source. Finally, in terms of public awareness of particulate emissions, plume appearance is a logical candidate for regulation. Air pollution is, to a great extent, an aesthetic nuisance affecting the senses, and to the extent that plume appearance can be regulated and improved, the visual impact of pollution is reduced.

The Ringlemann Number concept has drawbacks reflecting its simple, unsophisticated basis. Most serious is that, at present, there is no really quantitative relationship between stack appearance and the concentration of emissions. Additional factors; such as particle size distribution, refractive index, stack diameter, color of plume and sky, and the time of day, all have a marked effect on appearance. On a constant weight concentration basis, small particles and large smoke stacks will produce a poor Ringlemann Number. Plumes that have a high color contrast against the sky have a very strong visual impact that does not correspond closely to the nature of the emissions. For example, a white plume may be highly visible against a deep blue sky, but the same emission can be practically invisible against a cloudy background. As a result, it is often difficult to predict whether or not proposed control devices for a yet unbuilt plant will produce satisfactory appearance. Certain experience factors are presented in Table 1 for emissions, measured on a weight concentration basis, which the Industrial Gas Cleaning Institute has estimated will give a Ringlemann 1 or a clear stack.

A second objective is that Ringlemann number is a purely aesthetic measurement which has no direct bearing on physiological effects, ambient dirt, atmospheric corrosion, or any of the other very real

TABLE 1

Industrial Process Emissions Expected to Produce Visually Clear (or Near Clear) Stack

Industrial classification	Process	Grains/ACF @ Stack exit temp. (°F)
Utilities and industrial power plant fuel-fired boilers	Coal—Pulverized	0.02 @ 260–320
	Coal—cyclone	0.01 @ 260–320
	Coal—stoker	0.05 @ 350–450
	Oil	0.003 @ 300–400
	Wood and bark	0.05 @ 400
	Bagasse	0.04 @ 400
	Fluid coke	0.015 @ 300–450
Pulp and paper	Kraft recovery boiler	0.02 @ 275–350
	Soda recovery boilerM	0.02 @ 275–350
	Lime kiln	0.02 @ 400
Rock products—kiln	Cement—dry	0.015 @ 450–600
	Cement—wet	0.015 @ 450–600
	Gypsum	0.02 @ 500
	Alumina	0.02 @ 400
	Lime	0.02 @ 500–600
	Bauxite	0.02 @ 400–450
	Magnesium oxide	0.01 @ 550
Steel	Basic oxygen furnace	0.01 @ 450
	Open hearth	0.01 –.015 ≈ 450–600
	Electric furnace	0.015 @ 400–600
	Sintering	0.025 @ 300
	Ore roasters	0.02 @ 400–500
	Cupola	0.015–.02 ≈ 250–400
	Pyrites roaster	0.02 @ 400–500
	Taconite roaster	0.02 @ 300
	Hot scarfing	0.025 @ 250
Mining and metallurgical	Zinc roaster	0.01 @ 450
	Zinc smelter	0.01 @ 400
	Copper roaster	0.01 @ 500
	Copper reverberatory furnace	0.015 @ 550
	Copper Converter	0.01 @ 500
	Aluminum—	
	Hall process	0.075 @ 300
	Soderberg process	0.003 @ 200
	Ilmenite dryer	0.02 @ 300
	Titanium dioxide process	0.01 @ 300
	Molybdenum roaster	0.01 @ 300
	Ore beneficiation	0.02 @ 400
Miscellaneous	Refinery catalyst regenerator	0.015 @ 475
	Incinerators	
	Municipal	0.015 @ 500
	Apartment	0.02 @ 350
	Spray drying	0.01 @ 400
	Precious metal—refining	0.01 @ 400

and costly effects of particulate air pollution. There is some concern that regulations of very low Ringlemann numbers will impose very costly control measures upon sources without producing a commensurate improvement in the quality of the environment. Thus, a high concentration of steam will produce a visually prominent plume, but produce virtually no other undesirable effects. Opacity restrictions are usually waived if opacity is due entirely to steam but not if any particles are present, even if steam may be the major offender.

B. Instrumental opacity

Many factors affecting the visual appearance of a smoke plume are external variables, independent of the nature of the emissions. In addition, visual readings cannot be taken at all at night; and manpower costs for continuous daytime monitoring would be prohibitive. For these reasons, instrumental measurements of plume opacity are sometimes desirable.

A typical stack mounted opacity meter is shown in Figure 2. It consists, basically, of a light source, an optical path traversing the smoke stack, and a phototube receiver which responds to the incident light intensity and, hence, to the light attenuation caused by the presence of smoke. Various techniques including beam splitting, chopper stabilization, and filter comparison are used to maintain stable baselines and calibrations. At present, however, there is no way to distinguish between dust particles within the gas stream and those which have been deposited on surfaces in the optical path. Optical surfaces must be clean for meaningful measurements, and cleanliness is difficult to insure for long periods of time in dusty atmosphere. The tendency, therefore, is for such meters to read high, indicating more smoke than is actually present. For this reason, and because of reluctance to have a continuous record of emissions, there has not been a very strong push by industries to supplant Ringlemann observations with opacity meters.

Stack mounted opacity meters, of course, will not detect detached plumes, which may contribute to a visual Ringlemann observation. Detached plumes are due to particles formed by condensation or chemical reaction after gas leaves the stack and are thus beyond detection of such a meter.

At present, Texas is the only state with emissions control regulations based on use of opacity meters. The Texas program was recently described by McKee.[9] The Texas regulation is written so that smoke of a greater optical density (light attenuation per unit length of light path) is permitted from low

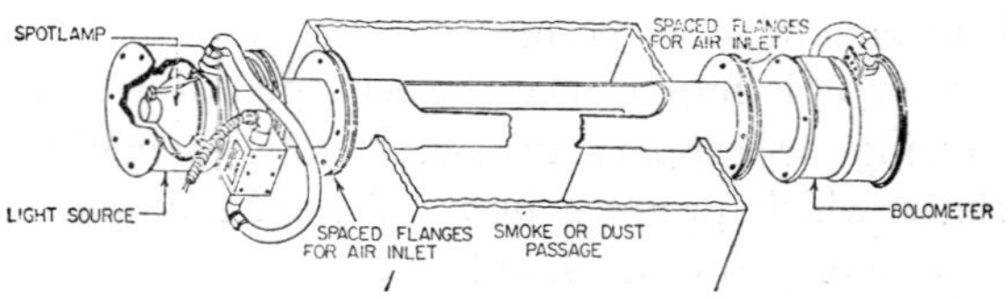

Figure 2 Stack mounted opacity meter (Bailey Meter Co.).

velocity stacks or small diameter ones. Basically, a minimum transmittance of 70% is allowed across the entire (circular) stack diameter if the stack has an exit velocity of 40 ft/sec, and adjustment equations are provided for transmittance and/or optical path length if non-standard velocity or path length is used.

Perhaps the greatest dissatisfaction with emission regulations based either on visual observation number or on instrumental opacity is due to the fact that there is presently no quantitative procedure for design of equipment to produce complying plumes. Equipment vendors will usually guarantee collection efficiency and emission concentrations by weight, but they will not give a guarantee to meet a specified opacity. This is indeed a serious problem at a time when a large precipitator installation can cost several million dollars and take twenty months to fabricate and install. Overdesign by a very conceivable factor of two can be very expensive in unneeded equipment. Underdesign can mean years of delay or operation under variance or with penalty payments.

Some progress has been made in applying classical theories of light scattering and transmission to the problem of predicting opacity. This effort has been greatly hampered by paucity of data giving simultaneous values of light attenuation, particle size distribution, and particle concentration in a stack. Perhaps the most comprehensive work to date has been that of Ensor and Pilat.[10]

C. Weight limits on particulates

Perhaps the least equivocal method of characterizing and specifying limits on particulate emissions is according to weight, either in terms of a rate (weight of emissions per unit time) or in terms of concentration (weight per unit volume). Measurement of emission weights must be done by isokinetic sampling of the gas stream, as outlined in the following section on measurement. Although the principles of such measurement are simple, they are difficult and time consuming when applied with accurate methodology to commercial installations. For this reason, such measurements have not previously been required in many jurisdictions and are almost never used as a continual monitoring technique.

Limits on weight rate of emissions are usually dependent on process size. Los Angeles, for instance, permits emissions to be proportional to process weight, up to 40 lbs/hr particulates for a plant processing 60,000 lbs/hr of material. Larger plants are limited to 40 lbs/hr. For furnaces, the determining factor is often heat input in BTU/hr rather than process weight. In cases where a particular plant location may have several independent units carrying out the same or similar processes, regulations often require that the capacities be combined for the purposes of calculating combined emissions.

Concentration limits are usually independent of process size. For instance, the EPA specifies incinerator emission of 0.01 grains particulates per standard cubic foot of flue gas (0.23 gm/NM^3). Dilution of the flue gas with excess air is usually prohibited, or else correction must be made to standard excess air or CO_2.

D. Ground level concentrations of suspended particulates

A limit on ground level concentration of particulates is an attempt to regulate emissions in accordance with their impact on population. A smoke stack acts as a dispersing device, and such regulations give incentive to build taller stacks in optimum locations.

In theory, ground level concentrations can be measured directly. Usually, however, emissions are measured in the stack, and plume dispersion equations are then used to calculate concentration profiles. Plume dispersion depends on stack height, plume buoyancy (i.e. density relative to ambient air), wind velocity, and wind patterns. In addition, plumes are never stationary but tend to meander; and correction factors are usually applied to adjust for the sampling time at a fixed location. Dispersion calculations are usually easier than direct ground level measurements; and in cases where many different sources are present, calculation offers the only practical way to assess the contributions of a specific source. A recent evaluation of plume dispersion models is given by Carpenter *et al.*[11]

In some states, a plume dispersion model is incorporated into a chart which gives an allowable weight rate of emissions as a function of effective stack height and distance from property lines. An example of this approach is shown in Figure 3. The particular regulation shown also accounts for differing toxity of certain particulates and allocates the emission factors of Table 2 accordingly.

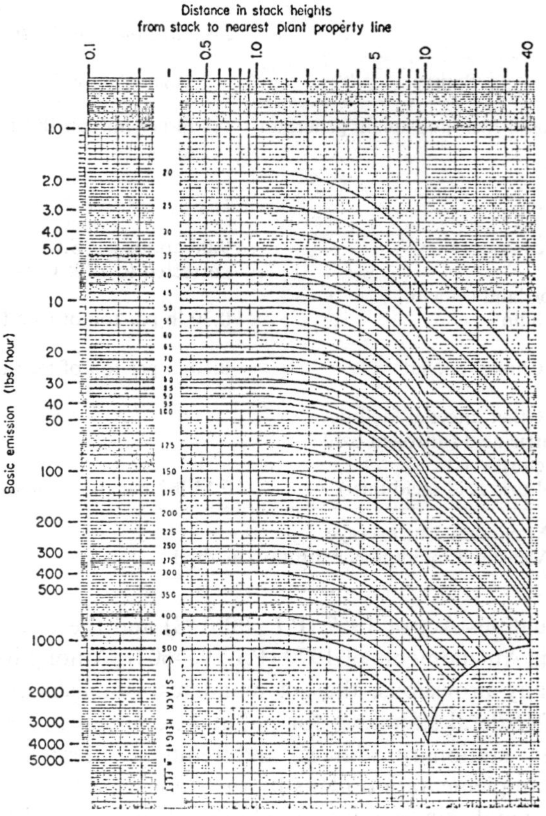

Figure 3 Emission requirements for fine particles based on plume dispersion model (New Jersey Air Pollution Code).

Very often permissible ground level concentrations are set according to other sources in the area. Thus a plant would be allowed greater emissions in a rural area than in a heavily industrialized neighborhood.

E. Dustfall

A variant on the ground level concentration limit is a dustfall limit. This basically superimposes a particle settling velocity on ground level concentration to obtain dustfall rates in weight per unit area per unit time. This is a meaningful regulation only for large particles and is not widely legislated at present.

F. Status of the Federal Clean Air Act

The present Federal Statutes concerning air pollution were codified in 1970 by the Environmental Protection Agency as "The Clean Air Act" and consisted of the Clean Air Act of 1963 (P.L. 88–206), the Motor Vehicle Air Pollution Control Act (P.L. 80–272, 1965), the Clean Air Act Amendments of 1966 (P.L. 89–675), the Air

TABLE 2

Federal Limits on Particulate Emissions from New Sources

Source	Particulate weight*	Opacity	Comments
Fossil fuel fired steam generator	0.1 lb per million Btu heat input	20% long term 40% for not more than 2 min/hr. Photoelectric or other type smoke detector must be installed	Opacity limits waived if failure to meet limits is due only to uncombined water
Incinerators	0.08 grains per S.C.F. flue, gas, corrected to 12% CO_2		
Portland cement			
Kiln	0.30 lb per ton of feed to kiln	10%	Opacity limit waived if failure to meet limits is due only to uncombined water
Clinker cooler	0.10 lb per ton of feed to kiln		
Other affected facilities		10%	
Nitric acid (nitrogen oxide emissions)		10%	
Sulfuric acid (acid mist)	0.15 lb† per ton of acid produced	10%	

* Maximum 2 hr average
† Measured by impinger titration method

Qualities Act of 1967 (P.L. 90–148) and the Clean Air Amendments of 1970 (P.L. 91–604). Among its many provisions, the act mandates establishment of Federal standards for pollutant emissions from new stationary sources, and requires submission of implementation plans by the states to attain the national air quality standards. The act makes imminent the regulation of most emissions, including particulates to the atmosphere by most stationary sources. For the great majority of industrial sources, no regulations or only weak ones were in existence in 1970. Although specific regulations are presently in a state of flux, there is no doubt that the 1970 act will be the dominant factor within a few years.

Standards for New Stationary Sources The Environmental Protection Agency promulgated a series of "Standards of Performance for New Stationary Sources" in December, 1971.[12] The regulation established definitions, applicability, and procedural details for allowable atmospheric emissions from new installations and, in addition, established specific emission limits for five classes of sources. Limits for additional classes will be added periodically.

Owners may submit plans of new sources to the EPA for technical advice. They must provide ports, platforms, access, and necessary utilities for performing required sampling tests. Notification must be given to the EPA of startup and date and results of required tests, and the EPA must be allowed to conduct tests at reasonable times. Required records and reports are available to the public except where trade secrets would be divulged. The states are in no way precluded from establishing more stringent standards or additional procedures.

In establishing limits of common, low-toxicity emission for specific types of sources, the EPA has, in general, followed the philosophy of requiring best available technology. Field tests have been run on several low emission plants in each source class, and the adopted limits have usually been close to the lowest emissions observed for a class. The EPA has made a cost analysis of measures necessary to meet the standards, and the Clean Air Act requires economic consequences to be taken into account in establishing standards.

The EPA test method specified for particulates measures only materials collectible on a dry filter at 250°F and does not include so-called condensibles. Regulations for the five types of particulate sources regulated as of Spring, 1972, are given in Table 3.

Requirements for States States were obliged to submit to the EPA by January 31, 1972[12] implementation plans for achievement of national ambient air quality standards. The EPA required no specific state regulations for source limits, but suggestions were made for "emission limitations obtainable with reasonably available technology". Some of the reasonable limits proposed for particulates were—

- Ringlemann 1 or less, except for brief periods such as soot blowing or start-up.
- Reasonable precautions to control fugitive dust, including use of water during grading or demolition, sprinkling of dusty surfaces, use of hoods and vents, covering of piles of dust, etc.

TABLE 3
Emission Effect Factors (for use with Fig. 3)
(New Jersey Air Pollution Control Code)

Material	Effect factor
Fine solid particles	
All materials not specifically hereunder	1.0
Antimony	0.9
a-naphthylthiourea	0.5
Arsenic	0.9
Barium	0.9
Beryllium	0.003
Cadmium	0.2
Chromium	0.2
Cobalt	0.9
Copper	0.2
Hafnium	0.9
Lead	0.3
Lead arsenate	0.3
Lithium hydride	0.04
Phosphorus	0.2
Selenium	0.2
Silver	0.1
Tellurium	0.2
Thallium	0.2
Uranium (soluble)	0.1
Uranium (insoluble)	0.4
Vanadium	0.2

- Incinerator emission less than 0.2 lbs/100 lbs refuse charged.
- Fuel burner emissions less than 0.3 lbs/million BTU heat input.
- For process industries, emission rates E in lbs/hr and Process weight rate P in tons/hr according to the relationships:

$$E = 3.59\ P^{0.62} \quad \text{for} \quad P \leq 30 \text{ tons/hr}$$

$$E = 17.31\ P^{0.16} \quad \text{for} \quad P \geq 30 \text{ tons/hr.}$$

"Process weight" includes all materials introduced to the process except liquid and gaseous fuels and combustion air. Limits should be set on the basis of combined process weights of all similar units at a plant.

In considering what emission limits should be established, the states are encouraged to take into account local condition, social and economic impact, and alternate control strategies and adoption of the above measures is not mandatory. It is expected, however, that such measures will become the norm in many areas.

Measurement of Particulate Emissions

As a first step in any program for control of particulate emissions, a determination must be made of the quantity and nature of particles being emitted by the subject source. The quantity of emissions determines the collection efficiency and size of required cleanup equipment. The particle size and chemical properties of the emitted dust strongly influence the type of equipment to be used. Sampling for this purpose has been mainly a matter of industrial concern. A last step in most control programs consists of measuring pollutants in the cleaned gas stream to ensure that cleanup equipment being used actually permits the pertinent emission targets to be met. With increasing public concern and legislation on air pollution, sampling for this purpose is increasingly required by statute to determine compliance with the pertinent emission regulations. To this end the local pollution control authority may issue a comprehensive sampling manual which sets forth in considerable detail the procedures to be used in obtaining raw data and the computations involved in calculating the pertinent emission levels.

Complete and comprehensive source testing procedures are beyond the scope of this paper. References 13–17 give detailed instructions for performance of such tests.

Sampling of gas streams, especially for particulates, is simple only in concept. Actual measurements require specialized equipment, trained personnel, careful experimental and computational techniques, and a considerable expenditure of time and manpower. Matters of technique and equipment are covered in source testing manuals as mentioned above and are briefly summarized later in this paper. Two additional complicating factors are usually present. First is the frequent inaccessibility of sampling points. These points are often located in duct work 50–100 ft above ground level. Scaffolding must often be installed around the points, and several hundred pounds of equipment must be lifted to that level. Probe clearances are often critical, for in order to make a sample traverse on a 12-ft dia. stack, a 14-ft probe is needed, and clearance must be available for insertion into the sampling port as well as a means for suspending the probe from above. At least one professional stack sampler is an amateur mountain climber and puts his hobby to good use on the job. A second complicating factor is the adverse physical conditions frequently encountered. A somewhat extreme but illustrative example is a refinery stream recently sampled. Gas temperature was 1200°F requiring special probes and gaskets and protective clothing for the workers. The gas stream contained 10% carbon monoxide creating potential hazards of poisoning and explosion especially since duct pressure was slightly above that of the atmosphere.

Temperature in the work area was in excess of 120°F contributing further to the difficulty of the job.

In preparation for a sampling program, work platforms or scaffolding and valved sample ports must be installed. All special fittings for adapting the sampling probes to the ports should be anticipated and fabricated. Arrangements must be made with plant operating personnel to maintain steady operating conditions during the test. The test must be carefully planned as to number and exact location of traverse sample points, and probes should be premarked for those locations. Flow nomographs for sampling nozzles should be made; and all filters, impingers, and other elements of sampling trains should be tared. With that advance preparation a 3 man sampling team would require 1–2 days to position their equipment and make gas flow measurements and 2 sample transverses at right angles in a large duct or stack.

A. Measurement of gas flow rates

A preliminary step in determination of emission rates from a stack is measurement of the gas flow rate. Detailed procedures in wide use including the necessary attention to technique have been published by the ASME,[17] ASTM,[15] the Environmental Protection Agency referred to as EPA,[8] the Los Angeles Air Pollution Control District referred to as APCD,[14] and the Western Precipitation Division referred to as WP.[17] This article will only treat the general procedures and note significant differences between popular techniques.

Velocity Traverse Points Because of flow nonuniformity which almost invariably occurs in large stacks, the stack cross section in the sampling plane must be divided into a number of smaller areas and gas velocity determined separately in each area. Circular ducts are divided by concentric circles, and 2 velocity traverses are made at right angles. Figure 4 shows a typical example. Location of the sample points can be determined from the formula

$$R_n = D\sqrt{\frac{2n-1}{2N}},$$

where R_n = distance from center of duct to the "nth" point from the center

D = duct diameter

n = sample point number, counting from center

N = total number of measurement points in the duct. The number of sample points along one diameter is $N/2$.

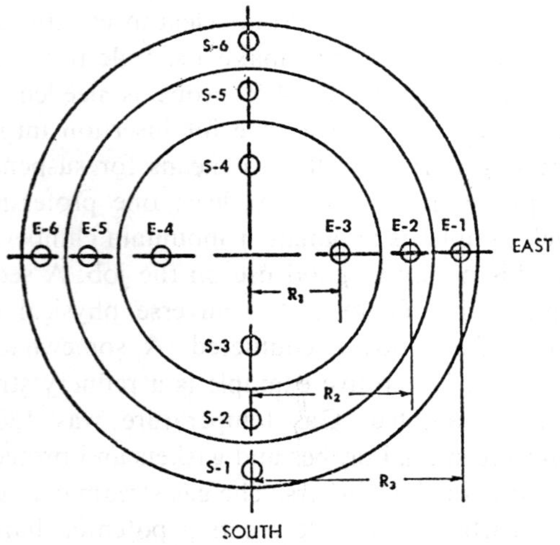

Figure 4 Velocity and sampling traverse positions in circular ducts.

For rectangular ducts the cross section is divided into N equal rectangular areas such that the ratio of length to width of the areas is between one and two. Sample points are at the center of each area.

The number of traverse points required is usually specified in the applicable test code as a function of duct area or diameter. Representative requirements are shown in Table 4. Very often more points are required if the flow is highly nonuniform or if the sampling point is near an elbow or other flow disturbance. Figure 5 shows the EPA adjustment for flow nonuniformity.

TABLE 4

Required Traverse Points

Code	Duct sizes	Number of points
EPA[8]	2 ft dia.	12 minimum
More according to Figure 2 if near flow disturbance		
WP[17]	2 ft^2	4
	2–25 ft^2	12
	25 ft^2	20 or more
APCD[14]	1–2 ft^2 (rectangular)	4
and	2–12 ft^2	6–24
ASTM[15]	12 ft^2	24
	1–2 ft dia.	12
	2–4 ft	16
	4–6 ft	20
	6	24 or more
These numbers should be doubled where only 4–6 duct diameters of straight duct are upstream.		
ASME[16]	<25 ft^2	8–12
	>25 ft^2	12–20
Double or triple these numbers for highly nonuniform flow.		

Velocity Measurement Velocity measurements in dusty gases are made with a type S (special or staubscheibe) pitot tube, shown in Figure 6, and a draft gage manometer. Gas velocity is given by

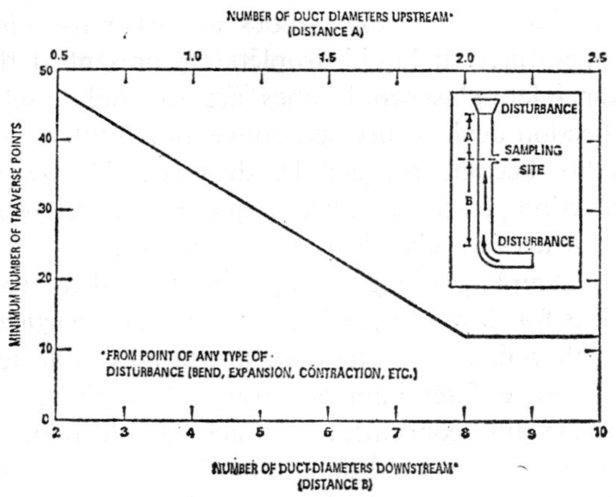

Figure 5 Sampling points required in vicinity of flow disturbance (E.P.A.).

$$V = C\sqrt{2g\, h_L\, \rho_L/\rho_g}$$

where V = gas velocity

C = pitot tube calibration coefficient. This would be 1.0 for an ideal pitot tube, but type S tubes deviate considerably

g = acceleration of gravity

h_L = liquid height differential in manometer

ρ_L = density of manometer liquid

ρ_g = gas density.

It is necessary to measure the temperature and the pressure of the gas stream and estimate or measure its molecular weight in order to calculate density.

Gas Analysis For precise work gas composition is needed for three reasons (1) so that molecular weight and gas density may be known for duct velocity calculations, (2) so that duct flow rates at duct condition can be converted to standardized conditions used for emission specifications. Standard conditions are usually 70°F, 29.92 in. mercury barometric pressure, moisture free basis with gas volume adjusted to 12% CO_2. Some codes differ from this, however. (3) For isokinetic sampling moisture content at stack conditions must be known in order to adjust for the fact that probe gas flow is measured in a wet test meter at ambient conditions.

Gas analysis for CO_2, CO, and O_2 is almost always done by Orsat analysis. Moisture may be determined gravimetically by condensation from a measured volume of gas as required by EPA.

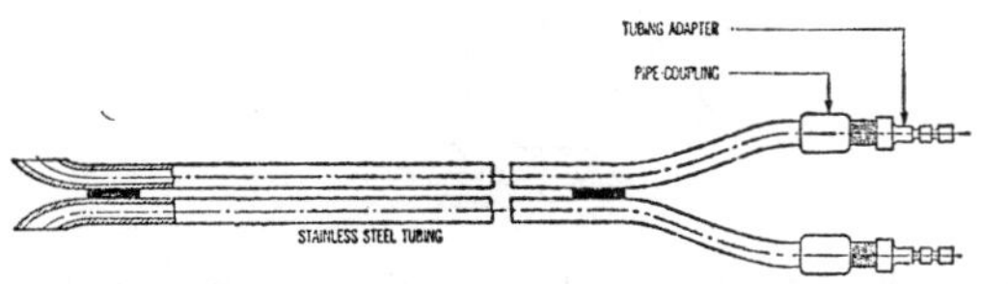

Figure 6 Type S Pitot tube for use in dusty gas stream.

Overall Flow Rate Total flow rate is calculated from duct area and average gas velocity as determined by the pitot tube measurements. Pitot tube traverse points are at the center of equal areas so no weighting is necessary to determine average velocity. This gives flow at duct conditions which is usually converted to standard conditions.

B. Measurement of particulate concentrations in stacks

Standard methods for measuring particulate concentrations in stacks depend on the principle of isokinetic sampling. Since particles do not follow gas streamlines exactly but tend to travel in straight lines, precautions must be taken that the gas being sampled experiences no change in velocity or direction in the vicinity of the sampling point. This is done by using a thin walled tubular probe carefully aligned with the gas flow and by withdrawing gas so that velocity just within the tip of the probe equals that in the main gas stream. Several recent studies[18–20] have measured effects of probe size, alignment, and velocity on accuracy of sampling. The sampled gas is drawn through a

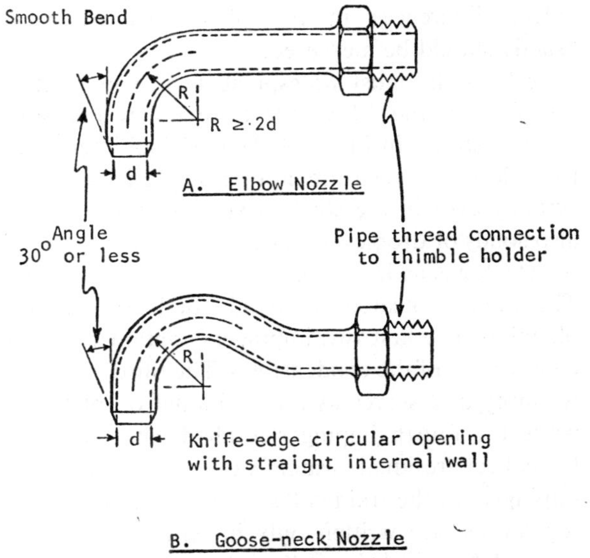

Figure 7 Nozzles for particulate sampling.

train of filters, impingers, and a gas meter by means of a pump or ejector. Typical probes are shown in Figure 7, and several types are commercially available. With these probes the necessary gas sampling velocity must be previously determined by pitot tube measurement, and the gas flow rate at the flow meter is adjusted (taking into account gas volume changes due to cooling and condensation between stack and meter) to equal that velocity. An alternate method is to use a null

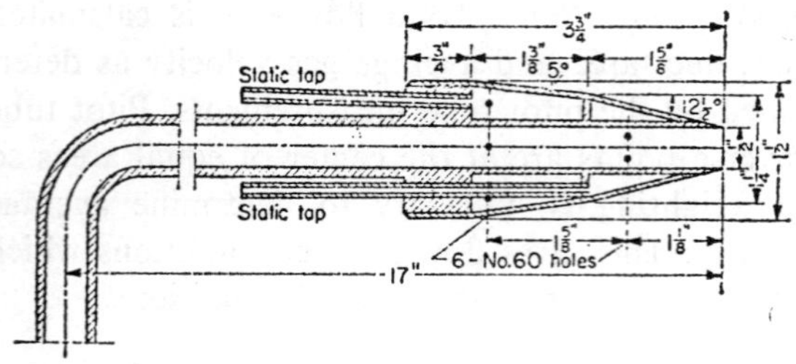

Figure 8 Null type nozzle for isokinetic sampling.

nozzle, which contains static pressure taps to the outside and inside surfaces of the sample probe as shown in Figure 8. Flow through the probe is adjusted so that the static pressures are equal at which point the velocities inside and outside the probe should be the same. The null nozzle greatly simplifies sampling, but null nozzles require careful periodic calibration and are not generally used for high precision work.

The sampling train of filters and impingers, which collects the particles, is usually carefully specified in the test method or governmental regulation in force. Differences between sampling trains to some extent reflect different technical solutions to the sampling problem but they also reflect differences in the philosophy of what exactly should be measured.

Perhaps the most widespread train will be that specified by the EPA[8] for testing new emission sources, shown in Figure 9. The original intent was to collect and measure not only particles which actually exist in the stack at stack conditions, but also solids or droplets that can be condensed out of the stack gas as it is cooled to ambient conditions. The filter is heated to avoid condensation and plugging. The first two impingers contain water to collect most of the condensibles. The third impinger is empty and serves as an additional droplet tray while the fourth impinger is filled with silica gel to collect residual water vapor. Although the impingers in the train collect condensibles, present regulations are written only in terms of the solid particulates which are collected in the filter.

The ASME power test code,[16] in contrast, is designed to measure performance of devices such as precipitators and cyclones, and thus is concerned only with substances which are particulate at conditions prevailing in the equipment. This test usually uses a filter assembly with the filter very close to the sampling probe so that the filter may be inserted into the stack avoiding condensation. No impingers are used.

To some extent filter characteristics are determined by process conditions. Alundum thimbles and glass wool packed tubes are used for high temperatures. If liquid droplets are present at the filter inlet, glass-wool tubes are the only useful collection devices, because conventional filters will readily become plugged by droplets. Glass-wool collection greatly complicates quantitative recovery of particles for chemical or size analysis.

In sampling a large duct having several traverse points for flow and particle measurement, particles for all points on a traverse are usually collected in a single filter–impinger train, thus giving an average dust concentration. Each sample point is sampled for an equal time but at its own isokinetic velocity. The probe is then immediately moved to the next point and the flow rate adjusted accordingly. Sample flow rate is adjusted by rotameter or orifice readings, but total gas flow during the entire test is taken from a dry meter.

Minimum sampling time or volume is often set by regulation. Examples are:

Bay area[13]—Sample gas volume $= 20\ L^{0.8}$, where volume is in standard cubic ft, and L is duct equivalent dia. in ft. A maximum sampling rate of 3 SCFM is specified and a minimum time of 30 min.

ASME[16]—Minimum of 2 hr with at least 10 min at each traverse point through two complete circuits.

APCD[14]—5–10 min/point for a total run of at least 1 hr.

Industrial Gas Cleaning Institute At least 2 hr or 150 ft^3 sample gas or until sample weight is greater than 30% of filter weight.

Emissions are calculated from test results of weight of particulates collected and volume of sample gas through the gas meter. Care must be taken to include particles deposited on tubing walls as well as those trapped by the filter. If condensibles are to be included, the liquid from the impinger

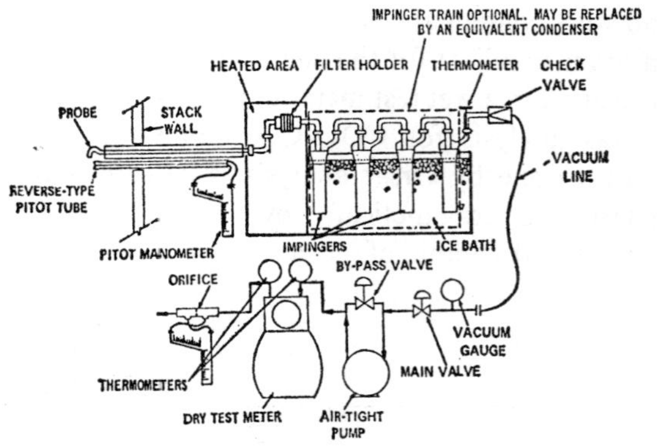

Figure 9 Environmental Protection Agency particulate sampling train.

train is evaporated to dryness, and the residue is weighed and included with the particulates. Corrections to the gas volume depend on sample train operation and on standard conditions for reporting emissions, and these are spelled out in detail in the specific test codes to be used. Results are usually expressed both as grains per cubic foot (using standard conditions defined in the code) and as lbs/hr from the whole stack.

C. Measurement and representation of particle size

A determination of the emitted particle size and size distribution is a desirable element in most control programs. Collection efficiency of any given piece of equipment is a function of particle size, being low for small particles and high for large ones, and capital and operating costs of equipment required increase steadily as the dust particle size decreases.

Perhaps the simplest method of particle size measurement, conceptually at least, is by microscope count. The minimum size that can be counted optically is about 0.5 μ which is near the wavelength of visible light. Electron microscopes may be used for sizing of smaller particles. Counting is a laborious procedure, and sample counts are often small enough to cause statistical errors at the very small and very large ends of the distribution. This method requires the smallest sample size and is capable of giving satisfactory results. Care must be taken in converting from the number distribution obtained by this method to mass distribution.

A second simple method is sieve analysis. This is commonly used for dry freely flowing materials in the size range above 44μ, a screen size designated as 325 mesh. Using special shaking equipment and very delicate micromesh sieves particles down to 10μ can be measured. Errors can be caused by "blinding" of the sieve mesh with sticky or fine particles, incomplete sieving, and particle fragmentation during sieving. A sample size of at least 5–10 g is usually required.

Another class of measurement techniques is based on the terminal falling velocity of particles in a gas (air). The quantity measured is proportional to ρd^2, where ρ is particle density and d is diameter. Hence a separate determination of density is needed. One such device is the Sharples Micromerograph (Sharples-Stokes Division, Penwalt Corporation, Warminster, Pennsylvania). The device records the time for particles to fall through a 2-m high column of air onto the pan of a continuously recording balance. Templates are available to convert fall time to ρd^2. The Micromerograph is mechanically and electrically complex but easy to use. An objection is that a significant fraction of the injected particles stick to the column walls and do not reach the balance pan. This effect can sometimes be selective, and it thus gives a biased size distribution.

A second sedimentation device is the Roller elutriator tube, Figure 10. A powder sample is placed in the tube and air is passed upwards through it for a specified time. A separation is effected with small particles being carried overhead and large ones remaining in the tube. Often a series of tubes of decreasing diameter are connected in a cascade with each successive tube having a lower air velocity and retaining finer particles. The Roller method was used quite widely in the petroleum industry for many years. However, it is slow, requires a large sample, does not give clean particle size cuts, and is sensitive to tube orientation. It is therefore being supplanted by newer methods.

A third sedimentation is centrifugal sedimentation. This is the standard test method of the Industrial Gas Cleaning Institute, and use of such devices of the Bahco type has been standardized by the ASME.[21] The Bahco analyzer consists of a rapidly spinning rotor and a superimposed radial gas flow from circumference to center. Larger particles are centrifuged to the outside diameter of the rotor, while small ones are carried to the center with a cut point determined by gas velocity and rotor speed.

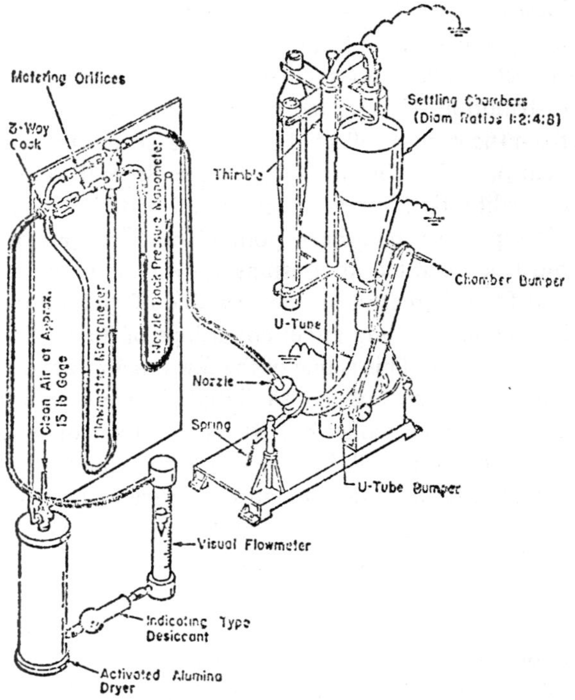

Figure 10 Air classifier for subsieve particle size analysis.

Still another method is the Coulter Counter. In this technique the test powder is dispersed in an electrolyte, which is then pumped through a small orifice. Current flow between electrodes on each side of the orifice is continuously monitored. Passage of a particle through the orifice momentarily reduces current to an extent determined by particle size. The device electronically counts the number of particles in each of several size ranges, and a size distribution can then be calculated. The method is capable of giving good results, and newer model counters are very fast.

A novel liquid phase sedimentation analyzer is the Sedigraph (Micrometrics Instrument Corporation, Norcross, Georgia). The particle sample dispersed in liquid is put into a sample cell and allowed to settle. Mass concentration is continuously monitored by attenuation of an X-ray beam, and this is mathematically related to particle size, X-ray location and time. The instrument automatically plots particle diameter as cumulative weight percent. The device can cover the size range from 0.1–100μ in a single operation, a much wider range than can be conveniently analyzed by most analyzers.

Impingement devices such as the Anderson Impactor, or the impactors developed by May or Batelle, may be used to measure particle sizes *in situ* in a combined sampling and sizing operation. As is shown in Figure 11 such a device consists of a series of orifices arranged to give gas jets of increasing velocity and decreasing diameter, which jets impinge on collection plates. Successive stages collect smaller and smaller particles, and the size distribution of aspirated particles can be obtained from the weight collected on each stage and the size "cut point" calibration of the stage. Several studies of calibrations have been published,[22–26] and discrepancies have been pointed out.[27] Impactors must be operated at constant known gas flow rate and for this reason are not capable of giving time isokinetic sampling under conditions of fluctuating duct velocity. This is one of the few types of devices which may be applied to liquid droplets, which coalesce once collected. It is capable of size determination well below 1 μ (finer than most devices). Because it eliminates recovery of particles from a filter and subsequent handling, it can be useful in measuring distributions at low concentrations.

Most particles emitted to the atmosphere are approximately spherical so that the exact meaning of "diameter" is not usually important in this context. For highly irregular particles a great many

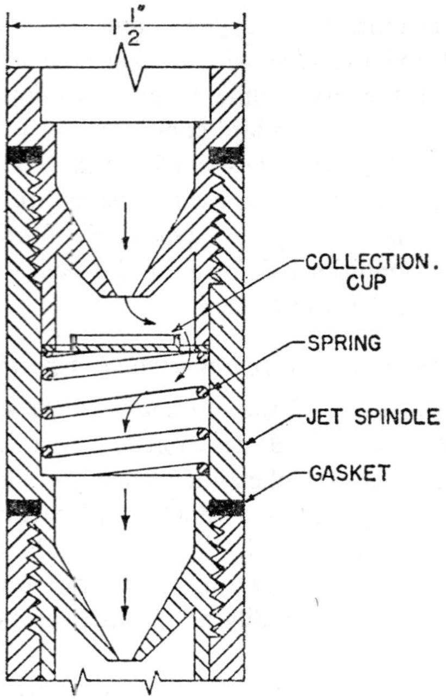

Figure 11 Stage of typical cascade impactor (Monsanto).

different diameters may be defined, each with particular applications. For purposes of particulate control equipment, persistence of airborne dusts, and physiological retention in the respiratory tract, the most meaningful diameter is usually the "aerodynamic" diameter, that of the sphere having the same free fall velocity as the particle of interest. This is the diameter measured by sedimentation, eleutriation, and inertial impaction techniques.

A large number of methods are available for expressing particle size distributions, each having properties of fitting certain characteristic distribution shapes or of simplifying certain mathematical manipulations. A comprehensive summary of various distribution functions is given by Orr.[28] The most useful function in emission applications seems to be the log–normal distribution. Commercial graph paper is available having one logarithmic scale and one cumulative normal probability scale. If particle size is plotted vs. cumulative percentage of sample at or below that size, the log-normal distribution gives a straight line. A large percentage of emissions and ambient particulate distributions have log–normal distributions, and plotting on log-probability paper usually facilitates interpolation and extrapolation even when the line is not quite straight. For a true log–normal distribution very simple relationships permit easy conversion between distributions based on number, weight, surface area, etc., which are covered in Orr.[30] Relationships between weight and number distribution are shown in Figure 12.

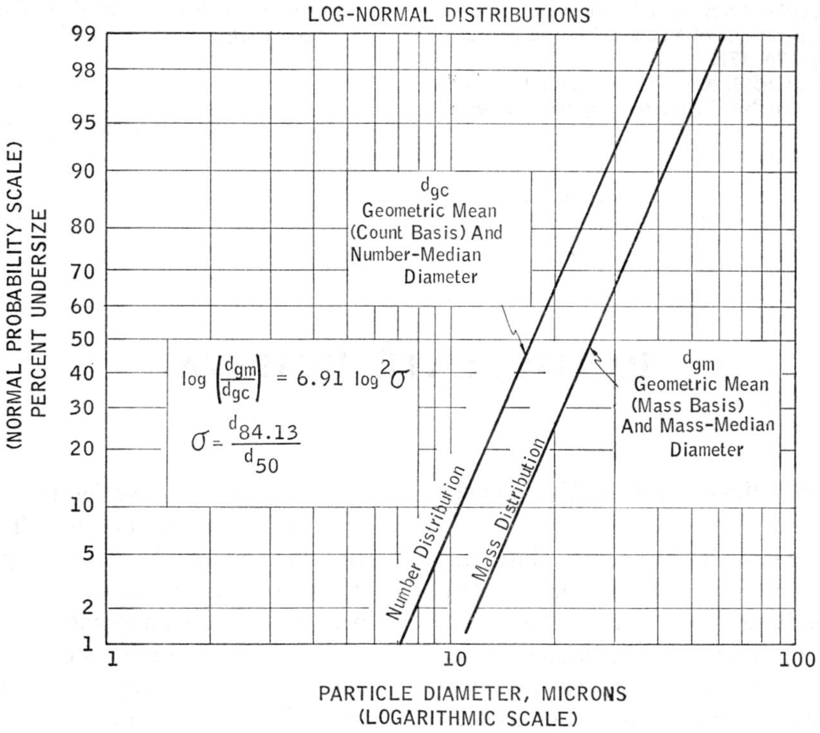

Figure 12

STANDARDS—REFERENCES

1. Stern, A. C. (1968). Air Pollution Standards, Chapter 51 in *Air Pollution*, Ed. by A. C. Stern, Academic Press, New York.
2. National Air Pollution Control Administration. *Air Quality Criteria for Particulate Matter*. NAPCA publication No AP–49. Washington. January 1961.
3. National Center for Air Pollution Control (1968). *A Compilation of Selected Air Pollution Emission Control Regulations and Ordinance*. Public Health Service Publication No. 999–AP–43. Washington.
4. Kudlich, R. Ringlemann Smoke Chart, U.S. Bureau of Mines Information Circular 7718. Revised by L. R. Burdick. August, 1955.
5. Weisburd, M. I. (1962). *Air Pollution Control Field Operations*, Chapter 10. U. S. Public Health Service, Publication 397. Washington.
6. Griswold, S. S., W. H. Parmelee, and L. H. McEwen. Training of Air Pollution Inspectors. 51st annual meeting A.P.C.A., Philadelphia, May 28, 1958.
7. Conner, W. D. and J. R. Hodkinson (1967). *Optical Properties and Visual Effects of Smoke-Stack Plumes*. P.H.S. Publication No. 999–AP–30.
8. Environmental Protection Agency. Standards of Performance for New Stationary Sources, *Federal Register*, **36**, No. 247, 24876–24895, December 23, 1971.
9. McKee, Herbert C. (1971). Instrumental Method Substitutes for Visual Estimation of Equivalent Opacity. *Jr. A.P.C.A.* **21**, 489.
10. Ensor, D. S. and M. J. Pilat (1971). Calculation of Smoke Plume Opacity from Particulate Air Pollutant Properties. *Jr. A.P.C.A.* **21**, 496.
11. Carpenter, S. B., T. L. Montgomery, J. M. Leavitt, W. C. Colbaugh, and F. W. Thomas (1931). Principal Plume Dispersion Models, *Jr. A.P.C.A.* **21**, 491.
12. Environmental Protection Agency, Requirements for Preparation, Adoption, and Submittal of Implementation Plans. *ibid* **36**, No. 158, 15486–15506, August 14, 1971.
13. Wolfe, E. A. (1966). Source Testing Methods Used by Bay Area Air Pollution Control District, BAAPCD, San Francisco.
14. Devorkin, H. (1963). Air Pollution Source Testing Manual, Air Pollution Control District, Los Angeles.
15. ASTM Standards (1971). Standard Method for Sampling Stacks for Particulate Matter, Part 23, designation D–2928–71. ASTM, Philadelphia.
16. ASME Power Test Codes (1957). Determining Dust Concentration in a Gas Stream, Test Code No. 17, ASME, New York.
17. Haaland, H. H. (1968). Methods for Determination of Velocity, Volume, Dust and Mist Content of Gases, Bulletin WP–50, Western Precipitation Division, Joy Manufacturing Company, Los Angeles.
18. Benarie, M. and S. Panof (1970). *Aerosol Sci.* **1**, 21.
19. Davies, C. N., The Entry of Aerosols into Sampling Tubes and Heads, *Staub-Reinhalt. Luft*, **28**, (June, 1968), p. 1–9.
20. Raynor, C. S. (1970). Variation in Entrance Efficiency of a Filter Sampler with Air Speed, Flow Rate, Angle, and Particle Size, *Am. Ind. Hyg. Ass. J.*, **31**, 294.
21. ASME Power Test Codes, Bacho, No. 28.
22. May, K. R. (1945). The Cascade Impactor, *J. Sci. Inst.*, **22**, 187.
23. Ranz, W. E. and J. E. Wong (1952). Impaction of Dust and Smoke Particles, *Ind. Eng. Chem.*, **44**, 1371.
24. Mitchell, R. J. and J. M. Pilcher (1959). Improved Cascade Impactor, *Ind Eng. Chem.*, **51**, 1039.
25. Brink, J. A. (1958). Cascade Impactor for Adiabatic Measurements, *Ind. Eng. Chem.*, **50**, 645.

26. Andersen, A. A. (1958). New Sampler for the Collection, Sizing, and Enumerations of Viable Airborne Particles' *J. of Bacteriology*, **76**, 471.
27. Lippmann, S. M. (1959). Review of Cascade Impactors for Particle Size Analysis, *Am. Ind. Hygiene Assoc. J.* **20**, 406.
28. Orr, C. (1966). *Particulate Technology*, Macmillan, New York.

JOHN M. MATSEN
Esso Research and Engineering

PARTICULATE REMOVAL

Types and Characteristics of Cleaning Equipment

Three principal considerations enter into the selection of particulate removal equipment. Cleaning efficiency must be sufficient to meet the desired particulate emission levels, but efficiency much beyond this lower limit is usually unwarranted. Equipment operating characteristics, such as temperature and pressure drop limitations, must be compatible with the specific process application. Economic factors such as purchase and operating cost, delivery time, and reliability must also be considered.

Cleaning performance of specific particulate removal equipment is perhaps most usefully expressed in the form of a grade efficiency curve. This is the relationship of dust particle size (or a related property such as free-fall velocity) versus corresponding collection efficiency for that size particle. Overall collection efficiency is obtained by integrating the product of weight fraction increment times collection efficiency at that particle size over the cumulative weight fraction from 0–1. Since collection efficiency is highly dependent on particle size, this approach permits calculation of overall efficiency for any particle size distribution of dust entering the device. This is a more useful way of expressing performance than is the use of adjectives such as high efficiency or low efficiency.

Representative grade efficiency curves are shown in Figure 1. The figure should not be used for design purposes, because for a given type of equipment the exact placement of a curve depends on design characteristics and operating conditions. The figure is useful for preliminary screening and evaluation of relative merit of different types of collectors.

Extensive coverage of control equipment is given by Stern.[1] Manufacturers literature and specifications have been conveniently collected[2] for many types of particulate collectors. The recent NAPCA study[3] is perhaps the most comprehensive attempt at a direct comparison of different types of equipment from the standpoint not only of operation and efficiency, but also of economics. This chapter will attempt to survey the features, performance, and selection of some of the major types of equipment in current pollution control applications.

A. Cyclones

Cyclones are one of the cheaper and simpler dust collectors available, but they have a relatively low efficiency unless used with coarse dust. A basic cyclone is shown in Figure 2. Dusty gas enters the tangential inlet, typically at velocities of 50–100 ft/sec. Gas flows in a helical path, first downward in an annulus and then upward in the center, passing out the top of the cyclone through the outlet pipe. Particles are driven to the cyclone walls by centrifugal forces on the order of 100 **g** and exit from the dust outlet at the bottom of the cyclone cone.

In many applications cyclones alone can give satisfactory particulate removal. For more stringent requirements cyclones are often used in series with other equipment with complementary characteristics. For example, cyclones can operate at almost any dust loading that a gas stream can carry and become increasingly efficient at higher loadings so that they are useful as pre-cleaners for equipment such as filters that would be choked by a high dust loading. Cyclone efficiency increases with gas throughput in direct contrast to precipitators, and thus they may serve to damp out effects of changing operating conditions.

Cyclone Performance The conceptual simplicity of cyclone operation has encouraged considerable

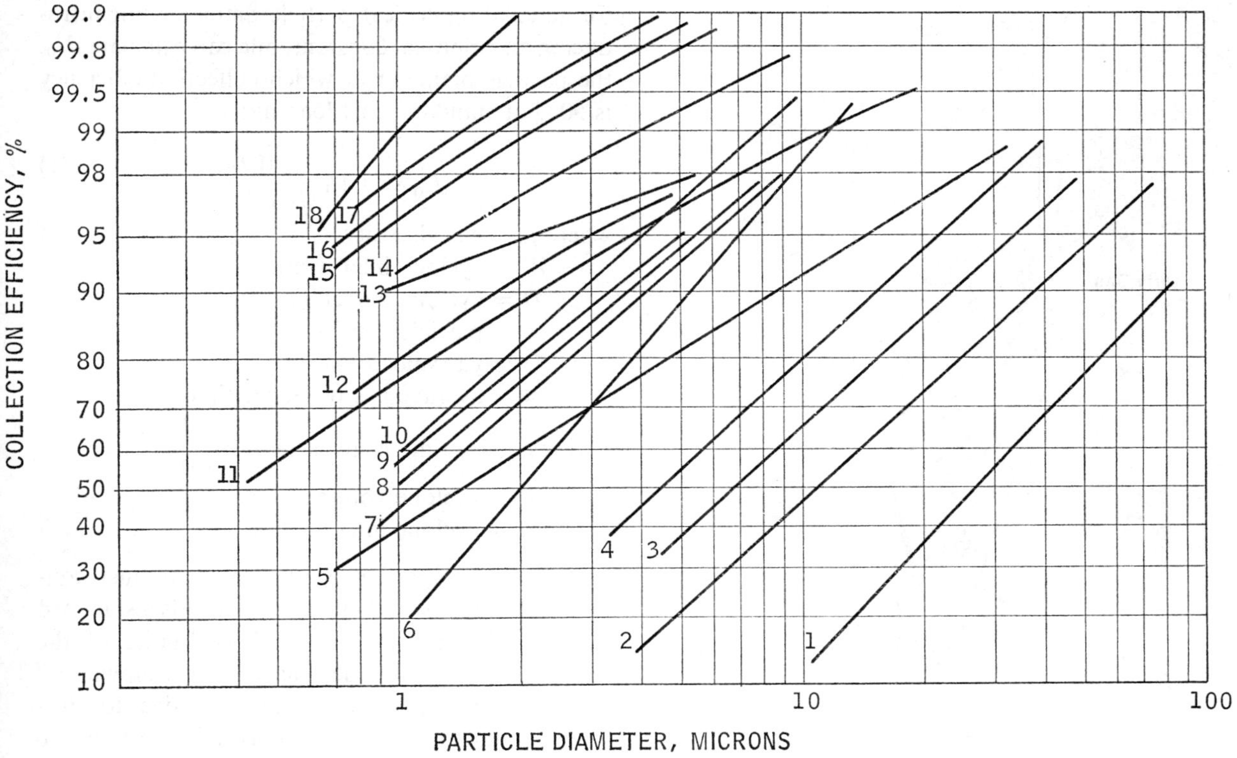

1 Settling Chamber
2 Medium Eff. Cyclone
3 Cellular Cyclone
4 High Eff. Cyclone
5 Jet Impingement Scrubber
6 Moving Impeller Cyclone
7 Self Induced Spray Cleaner
8 Wet Cyclone
9 Spray Tower
10 Fluid Bed Scrubber
11 Electrostatic Precipitator
12 Irrigated Target Scrubber
13 Disintegrator
14 Irrigated Electrostatic Precipitator
15 Low Energy Annular Throat Scrubber
16 Medium Energy Annular Throat Or Venturi Scrubber
17 High Energy Venturi Scrubber
18 Fabric Filter

Figure 1 Typical grade efficiency curves.

theoretical analysis of particle collection efficiency. The usual approach is to calculate the acceleration the particle experiences based on inlet velocity and cyclone barrel diameter, and compute a terminal velocity of particles in a radial direction based on Stokes Law. A maximum distance a particle must travel before being collected at the cyclone wall is selected (usually the width of the cyclone inlet), and a gas residence time is calculated. The result is that one can calculate a critical particle diameter, the minimum size that can, according to such over-simplified theory, be collected at 100% efficiency as well as efficiencies for smaller particles. Stern[4] has compared several such calculations.[5–11] A more recent review by Strauss[12] has included references.[13–17]

All of the above mentioned equations employ extremely simplified models of gas flow. They assume instantaneous particle acceleration and no interaction of particles as well as absence of non-idealities such as particle re-entrainment. For such reasons this purely theoretical approach has not been very successful in predicting quantitative cyclone efficiencies. It gives, however, an acceptable basis for scaling of an experimental efficiency to other operating conditions and somewhat different sizes and geometries of cyclone. A semi-empirical approach can be based on the normalized grade efficiency curve shown in Figure 3. A survey of many experiments on efficiency [15–17] indicates that most cyclone grade efficiency curves have approximately the same shape. Using the theoretical basis

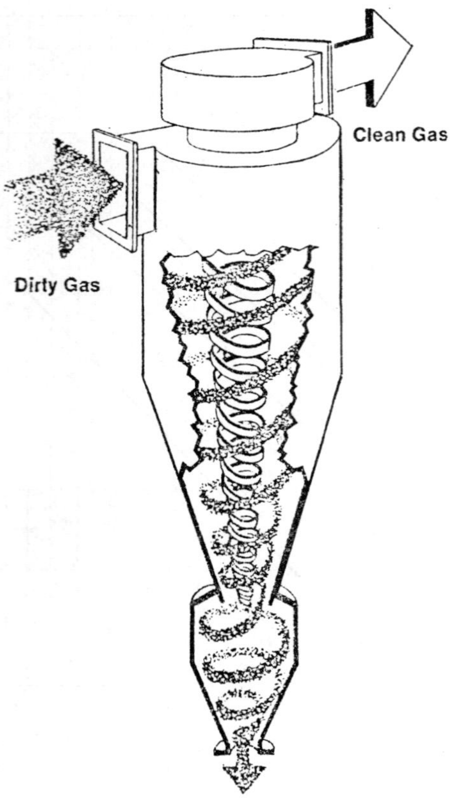

Figure 2 Conventional cyclone operation (The Ducon Co.).

for calculating critical particle diameter but introducing an empirical constant, one can calculate d_{50}°, the particle diameter at which collection efficiency is 50% at standard dust loading:

$$d_{50}^{\circ} = 1.16\sqrt{\frac{\mu WD}{\rho u^2 t}}, \tag{1}$$

where μ = gas viscosity
W = cyclone inlet width
D = cyclone barrel diameter
ρ = particle density
U = gas velocity at inlet
t = average gas residence time.

Gas residence time is given by $t = \dfrac{V}{hWU}$,

where V = cyclone volume
h = cyclone inlet height.

The above equation is applicable at dust concentrations of about 5 grains/ft³ which is a standard concentration for cyclone testing. Studies of the effect of loading on grade efficiency have shown[18,19] that cyclone efficiency is very sensitive to dust loadings, and for this reason a correction to equation is necessary for other concentrations.

$$\frac{d_{50}^{\circ}}{d_{50}} = \left(\frac{L}{L^{\circ}}\right)^{0.2}, \tag{2}$$

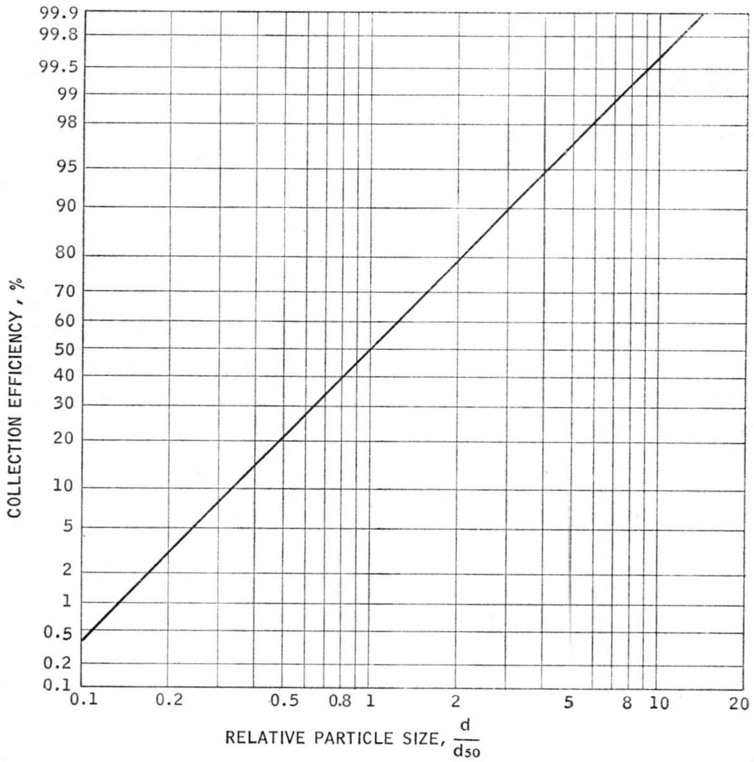

Figure 3 Generalized cyclone grade efficiency.

where the reference loading L° is 5 grains/ft^3. Using Equation 2 for d_{50}, efficiency for other particle diameters d can be found from Figure 3.

Equation 1 can give directional effects for many geometric changes in design; but if data are available on the actual geometry of interest, it is much more satisfactory to use such data to modify the numerical constant in the equation. It is especially important to note that modifications to outlet pipe diameter do not enter into Equation 1, and the numerical constant is for cyclones with normal ratios of outlet to inlet area of 1.3 : 1.5. For certain applications area ratios well below 1.0 are now being offered. Such cyclones have notably increased efficiency at the expense of much higher pressure drop. Unfortunately, suitable published data are not available on this effect to permit quantitative prediction of effect on efficiency.

Although some reviews have compiled "consensus" dimensions for cyclone design, quite a range of relative dimensions exists within the bounds of good design practice. Design is a compromise among efficiency, cyclone throughput, and pressure drop, and improvement in one factor will almost always result in debits to another. An example is shown in Figure 4 of three cyclones studied by Van Ebbenhorst Tengbergen.[18] They are drawn to the same scale and sized to have the same gas throughput and the same pressure drop. The relative costs of A : B : C are estimated as 4 : 3 : 9, but the difference in cost is reflected in the grade efficiency curves.

Pressure Drop Although pressure drop is much easier to measure than overall or grade efficiency, prediction of pressure drop from theoretical principles is not in good agreement with experiment. Stern[4] has analyzed the pressure drop predictions of several authors [20–22] and has concluded that a constant value of $X = 16$ in the equation.

$$h_n = X \frac{H_i W_i}{d_o^2}, \quad (3)$$

where h_n = pressure drop is expressed as inlet velocity heads
H_i = inlet height
W_i = inlet width
d_o = outlet pipe dia.

gives as good agreement with experimental data as does any equation for X which includes geometric factors. Measured values of X do indeed cover a wide range of values, and use of a constant value of X is merely a best guess in absence of data on the specific cyclone. Fortunately, because measurement is straightforward and simple, most vendors supply reliable information on pressure drop for their own cyclones.

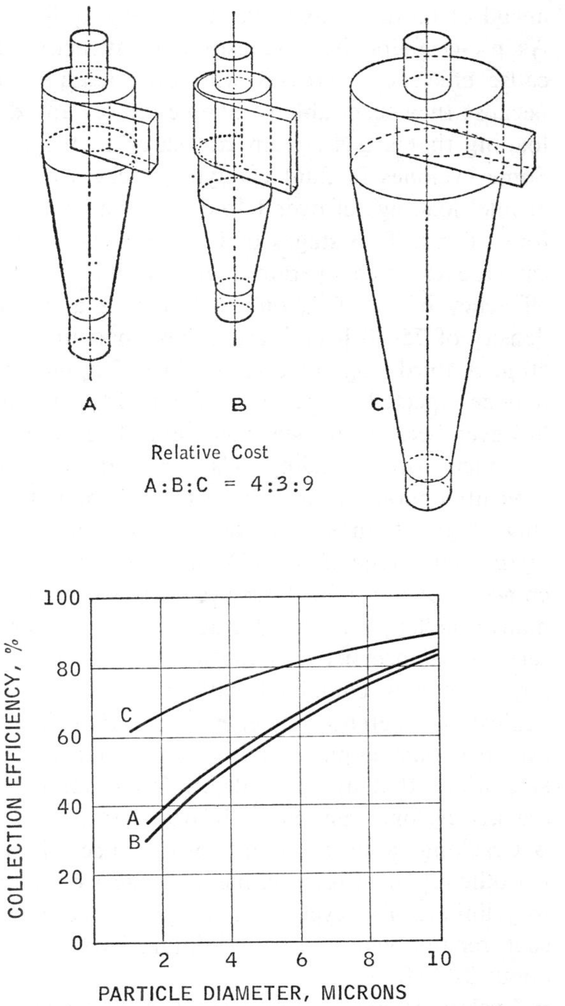

Figure 4 Relative sizes, costs and grade efficiencies of different cyclone designs having same throughput and and pressure drop.[18]

For most cyclone applications the only pressure drop of interest is that from gas inlet to gas outlet. In some applications the pressure drop from gas inlet to the dust outlet at the bottom of the cone is also important. Such is usually the case for cyclones above fluid beds where collected dust is returned directly to the bed through a fluidized standpipe or dipleg. Too great a pressure drop to the dust outlet will preclude a satisfactory pressure balance in the dipleg and prevent proper discharge of particles. As a first approximation pressure drop from inlet to dust outlet can be taken as 13.5 inlet velocity heads.

Cyclones in Series Cyclones are often installed in series either with other cyclones or as pre-cleaners ahead of more efficient dust collecting equipment. As pre-cleaners they are especially attractive because efficiency increases with dust loading and because they seem able to handle almost any dust loading that a gas stream can carry to the inlet. Some cyclones in fluid catalytic crackers operate at inlet loadings of over 1 lb dust per actual cubic foot of gas. Two stages of internal cyclones in a cat cracker often operate at an overall collection efficiency of 99.997% on catalyst with a particle density of 75–80 lbs/ft^3 and a mass median dia. of 50 μ. A third stage of cyclones in this application may be expected to operate at about 85% efficiency, however, because that stage sees much finer particles at much lower loading. Cat cracking cyclones typically operate at pressure drops of about 1 psi/stage, higher than is tolerable in many applications.

Optimum Cyclone Size and Parallel Operation The choice of one or a few large cyclones as opposed to many smaller cyclones operated in parallel represents a balance between the lower cost of a few large cyclones combined with easy manifolding against the inherently higher efficiency of the smaller cyclones. Each application is different, but the considerations that apply in determining size of cat cracker cyclones may prove instructive:

- Cracking catalyst is highly erosive necessitating periodic repair of internal metal surfaces or refractory linings. The cyclones must permit access for such repairs, which sets a minimum barrel dia. of about 3-1/2 ft.
- Cyclone length is proportional to diameter, and headroom plus dipleg pressure balance often limits diameter (a 5 ft dia. cyclone is typically 17 ft long). Reactor openings also limit diameter as does reduced efficiency.

The result is that in this application cyclone diameters usually range from about 3-1/2 to 5 ft. A large cat cracker regenerator may have 20 pairs (primary and secondary) of cyclones in parallel. The secondary cyclones discharge into a common plenum head.

Operating Conditions Upper temperature limits for cyclones are limited by materials consideration to about 1700°F in conventional designs. They can withstand pressures of several psi with normal design, but for high pressure operation enclosure or special fabrication is required. Only fairly freely flowing material can normally be discharged, and special design or operating techniques are required for sticky or coking material. Low efficiency on fine particles usually precludes use where a significant fraction of material to be collected is below 10 or 15μ in dia.

B. Multicellular cyclones

Examination of Equation 1 in the discussion of cyclones shows that d_{50}° becomes smaller and collection efficiency therefore increases as cyclone diameter decreases. Advantage is taken of this effect in multicellular cyclones, which have diameters in the range of 6–10 in. as compared to several feet for conventional cyclones. Because they are small, many cellular cyclones must be operated in parallel, and they are designed to facilitate manifolding into arrays which may number several hundred. Figure 5 shows a typical cellular cyclone. For ease of manifolding it is constructed with an axial inlet with swirl vanes to impart spin to the gas instead of having the tangential inlet of large cyclones. They are usually cast or molded in standardized designs instead of being custom fabricated as large cyclones are. An array of cellular cyclones is shown in Figure 6. This type of collector is designed to operate at low pressure drop, typically less than 4 in. of water.

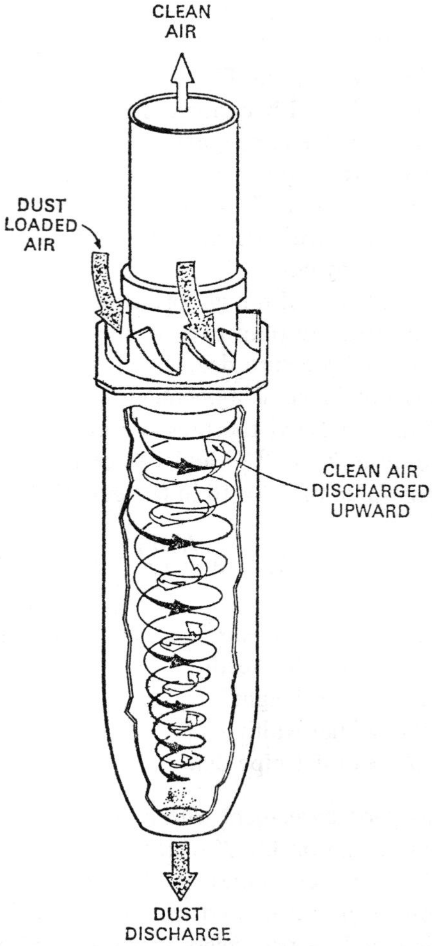

Figure 5 Multicellular cyclone with axial inlet vanes (U. O. P. Air Correction Division).

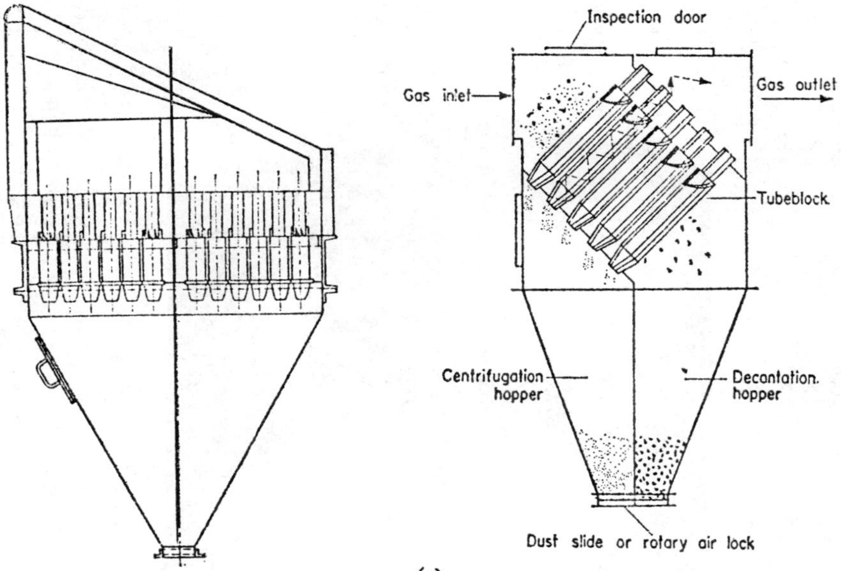

(a)

Figure 6 Typical manifolding arrangement of multicellular cyclones.

This makes it attractive for use for fly ash recovery in power plants, where only slight pressure drops can normally be accommodated.

Arrays of cellular cyclones in parallel suffer an efficiency debit compared to single cyclones of the same design. This is usually attributed to unequal distribution of gas among cyclones abetted by the low pressure drop, and to recirculation patterns of gas down through one cyclone dust outlet and up through the next. The gas upflow causes a loss of efficiency. Many vendors will cite grade efficiency curves for a single cyclone which are, however, not representative of manifolded arrays. The magnitude of the performance debit can be seen in Figure 7.

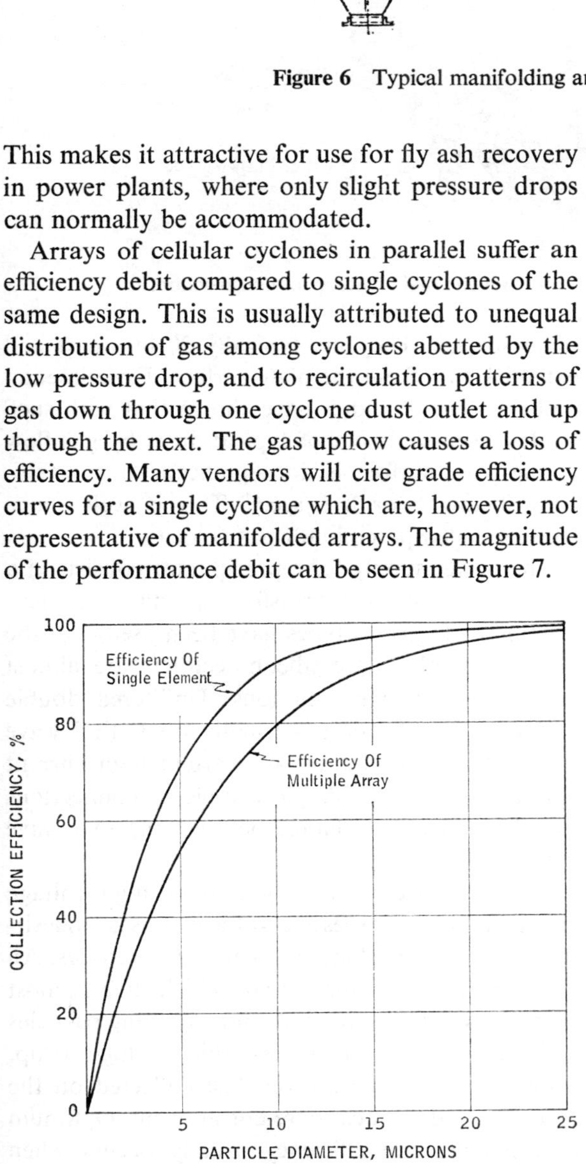

Figure 7 Performance debit for manifolding of multiclones.

C. Electrostatic precipitators

Electrostatic precipitators enjoy an image of being the ultimate in high efficiency air pollution control equipment. There is an element of reality in such a judgement, but precipitators are extremely expensive in terms of investment, operation, and space requirements, and they are often subject to obscure maladies which may cause collection efficiency to be far less than expected. Thus installation of a precipitator will be costly and may not solve a particulate emission problem.

The strong points of precipitators are (1) very low pressure drop (less than 1 in. of water, compared to about 3 in. for cloth filters, 5–30 in. for centrifugal collectors and up to 60 in. for high energy scrubber); (2) sizes to handle very high gas flow rates; (3) potential of high collection efficiency on fine dust; (4) ability to operate at high temperatures (800°F is reached in commercial practice and pilot units have operated at 1700°F), and (5) dry collection of particles avoiding a water pollution problem. These factors have been particularly suited to the requirement of coal-fired power plants, which constitute probably the most widespread users of precipitators or any other high efficiency particle collectors.

The standard text on electrostatic precipitator principles and practice is that by White.[23] A more recent work by Oglesby and Nichols[24] also includes an extensive survey of precipitator installations and performance. Other general references include the monographs by Rose[25] and Gottsclich.[26]

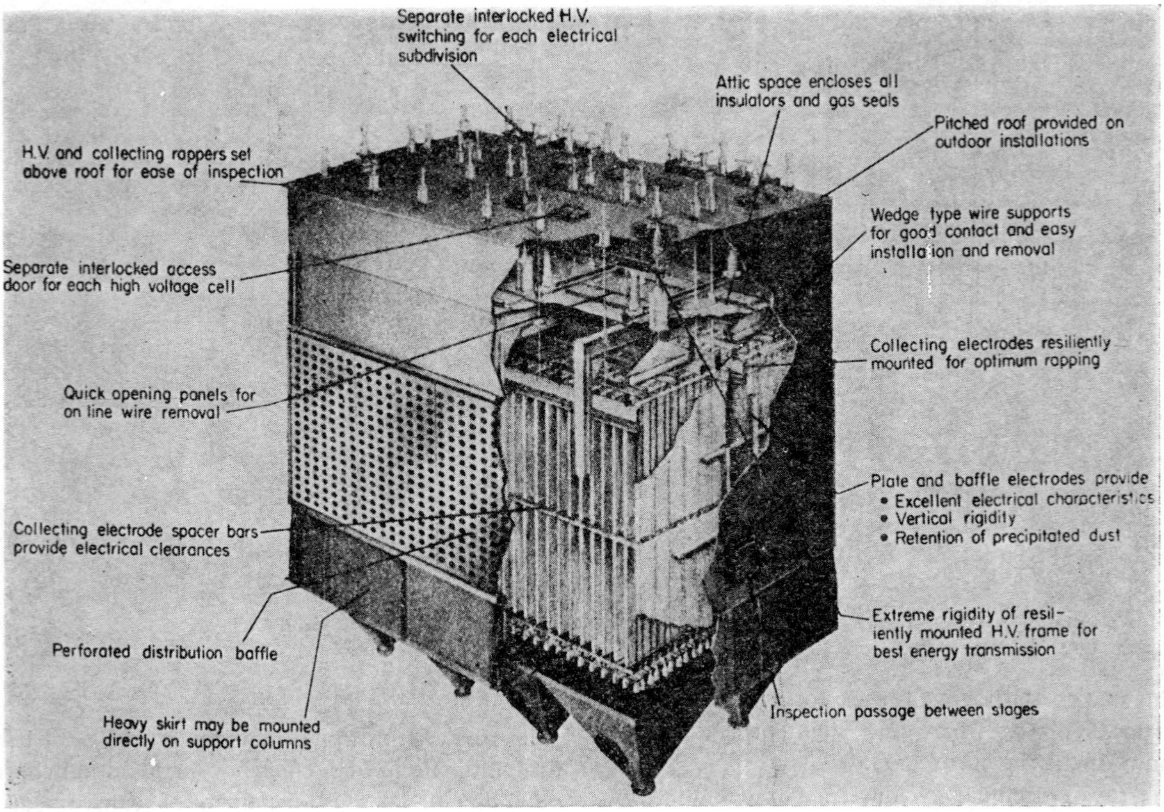

Figure 8 Large two-stage horizontal flow precipitator, showing main features of construction.

Precipitator Operation Electrostatic precipitators have been constructed in a great many configurations. Contemporary commercial practice is fairly standard, however, and only this will be considered here. A typical precipitator, shown in Figure 8, consists of an array of parallel vertical plates, spaced about 9 or 10 in. spacing. Rows of wires hang vertically between the plates. These wires, called discharge electrode, are maintained at a voltage of 30–60 kV with respect to the grounded plates. The very high electric field gradient near the wire electrode produces a corona discharge generating a high concentration of ions, which in turn charge the dust particles in the flowing gas stream. Under influence of the voltage gradient particles migrate to the plates, also called collector electrodes, where the charge is largely dissipated. A residual charge retains particles on the plates, and they are periodicaly disloged by rapping. When dislodged, the particles fall in clumps into collection hoppers beneath the electrodes.

Gas flow across a flat plate surface tends to re-entrain collected dust particles causing an appreciable debit to collection efficiency. Various types of baffles are therefore used to shield the plate surface and provide a stagnant collection zone. The usual baffles are vertical and are perpendicular to the plate surface. They are typically 20 in. apart and extend 1.5 in. from the plate surface. Experimental and theoretical studies have shown that with such baffles re-entrainment of typical dusts by gas flow at the plate surface is not significant at gas velocities below 6 or 8 ft/sec.[21] This is well above recommended percipitator gas velocity.

The power supply for a precipitator consists of a high voltage step-up transformer and a rectifier. Rectifiers of various types have been used over the years, but solid state silicon rectifiers are almost universal in new installations. Unfiltered double half wave rectification is usually used. Full wave rectification is preferable for certain high current applications, and a simple change in connections usually suffices to change between the two wave forms.

Particle collection is enhanced by high voltage and current, but excessive voltage causes undesirable arcing or sparking between the electrodes. An arc is an ionized short circuit which diverts most current away from charging and collecting particles and also causes an undesirable voltage drop. Impingement of the arc on dust collected on the plate electrode can cause re-entrainment. Optimum overall collection efficiency usually occurs when power input is adjusted to a spark rate of about

50–100 discharges/min. Modern precipitator control systems will automatically adjust voltage to maintain a pre-set sparking rate. Saturable core reactor control came into use in the late 1950's and a decade later this was being supplanted by entirely solid state (thyristor, i.e. silicon controlled rectifier or "S.C.R.") controls. SCR control has appreciably lower power losses and much faster response characteristics than the saturable core reactor and is able to operate at appreciably higher voltage and current without excessive sparking.

Large precipitators are usually sectionalized into several chambers in parallel and (within chambers) several electrical fields in series with respect to gas flow. Chambers can usually be independently isolated from gas flow so that one chamber may be shut down for maintenance while the others remain on stream. Use of several electrical fields in series permits optimum voltage control in each field. Outlet fields with low dust concentrations can tolerate higher voltage without excessive sparking than can inlet fields. Further electrical sectionalization within fields is often desirable. A spark discharge momentarily hurts the performance of an entire electrical section, and small sections obviously limit the extent of the disturbance.

Electrodes are rapped with either pneumatic or solenoid rappers. Variable frequency and intensity controls are usually provided so that rapping may be optimized. Ideally the dust layer should be disloged before becoming so thick as to interfere with electrical performance but after becoming thick enough to drop off in a coherent clump of particles. Rapping to an appreciable extent redisperses collected particles back into the gas stream, and a puff of dust is often seen in effluent gas when electrodes are rapped.

Precipitator Performance Parameters Precipitator collection efficiency is commonly expressed by the Deutsch[28] equation:

$$\eta = 1 - \exp\left(-\frac{AW}{Q}\right), \tag{4}$$

where η = collection efficiency

A = plate electrode area

Q = volumetric gas flow rate

W = effective migration velocity rate of the dust.

In practice the migration velocity is an empirical constant which depends on the application and dust and gas properties. Typical migration velocities are given in Table I. Although a considerable range of values is shown for some applications, a large part of such variation can be attributed to known causes and effects and does not represent uncertainty.

TABLE 1

Representative Precipitation Rates for Various Applications[24]

Application	Precipitation rate w ft/sec: Average	Range
Utility fly ash	0.43	0.13–0.67
Pulp and paper	0.25	0.21–0.31
Sulfuric acid	0.24	0.20–0.28
Cement (wet)	0.35	0.30–0.40
Smelter	0.06	—
Open hearth	0.16	—
Cupola	0.10	—
Blast furnace	0.36	0.20–0.46

White[23] has derived a theoretical equation for migration velocity

$$W = \frac{E_o E_p d_p}{4\pi\mu},$$

where E_o = charging field gradient, stat V/cm

E_p = collecting field gradient, stat V/cm

d_p = particle diameter, cm

μ = gas viscosity, poise.

Values of W measured on commerical installations are lower by a factor of 2–5 than the theoretical value above. Although the theoretical W is of little use for quantitative design, it does give a clue as to the influence of operating conditions on W. The term E_oE_p is roughly proportional to the power input to the precipitator, and it is clear that this should be as high as possible. From the dependence of W on d_p it is clear that precipitators have a higher collection efficiency for large particles than small ones. This is seldom taken into account in current design procedures in which an average particle size is included in the empirical W for an application.

Dust resistivity can have a very pronounced, although not quantitatively predictable, effect on precipitator preformance. If the *in situ* resistivity of a dust layer collected on the plate electrode is less than about 10^7 Ω-cm, the electrical force holding the dust particles to the electrode will be low, and significant amounts of dust may be re-entrained into the gas stream. If the resistivity is above 2×10^{10} Ω-cm, excessive sparking and back corona will occur hurting electrical performance and efficiency. Resistivity is a function not only of the dust but also of temperature and gas composition. At low temperatures surface conduction is

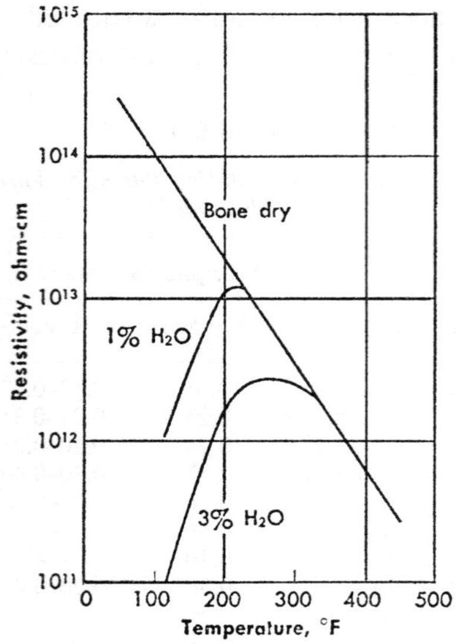

Figure 9 Effect of temperature and humidity on particle resistivity. [1]

predominant due to a thin layer of adsorbed moisture, and this decreases with increasing temperature. Volume conduction is important at high temperatures and decreases with temperature. A maximum resistivity usually occurs at about 400°F due to these opposing tendencies as is shown in Figure 9.

Gas conditioning by addition of moisture or other substances is sometimes practiced in order to improve the dust resistivity and enhance electrical performance of the electrodes. In certain instances addition of 10–20 ppm of ammonia has dramatically improved precipitator performance. Sulfur trioxide has also been used successfully, but it is expensive and creates its own pollution and safety problems. The effect of resistivity change, caused by conditioning, on precipitator efficiency is shown in Figure 10. In some gas streams conditioning agents may be naturally present which enhance precipitator operation. For instance, as

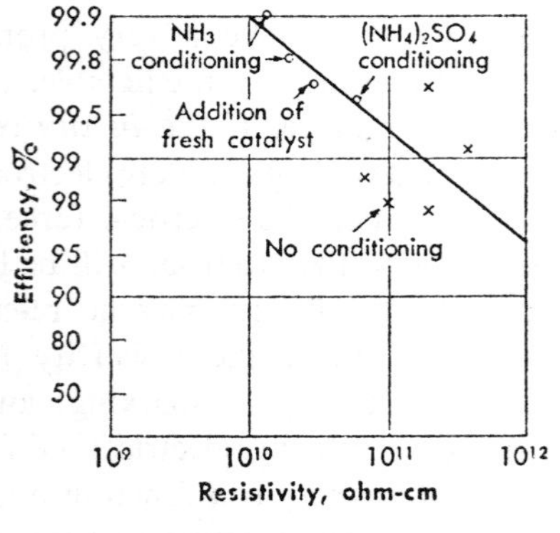

Figure 10 Effect of gas conditioning on efficiency of electrostatic precipitators. [1]

indicated in Figure 11, power plants burning high sulfur fuel have improved performance due to the conditioning properties of sulfur combustion products. The present trend towards mandating use of low sulfur fuels in many urban areas will have an adverse effect on particulate removal.

Equation 4 shows the dependence of efficiency on gas flow rate provided flow is uniform. If gas velocities are different throughout the precipitator due to maldistribution of flow, the equation will be applicable only to local efficiency and the overall precipitator efficiency will be considerably lower. For instance a precipitator which could operate at 98% effiiciency with even gas distribution would operate at only 96.5% efficiency if the same total gas flow were maldistributed so that half of the precipitator received 30% more than average and the other half received 30% less than average. Sharp turns and rapid expansion and contraction in duct work often makes it difficult to

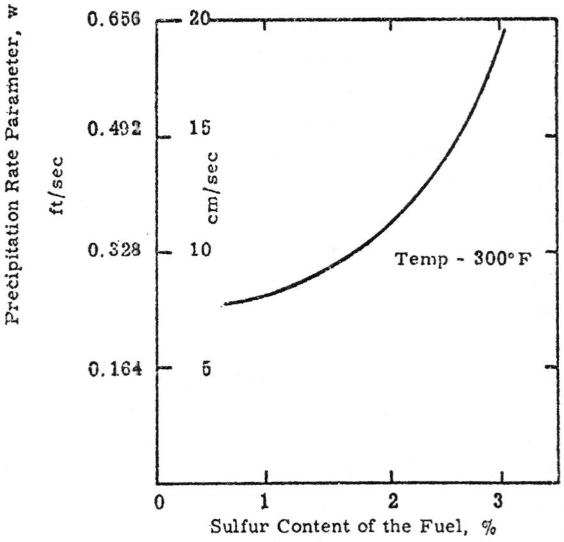

Figure 11 Effect of sulfur in fuel on precipitation velocity. [1]

achieve good gas distribution. Very often preliminary flow distribution tests are made on 1/6–1/16 scale clear plastic models using smoke as a tracer. Such model tests are helpful in calling attention to duct work designs which will cause poor gas flow patterns and allowing trials of baffle, diffusers, and turning vanes to reduce the problems.

Fabric Filtration

The process of particulate removal by filtration is one of the oldest methodologies in the gas cleaning field. Fabric filters possess several advantages, the most important one being that dust collection efficiencies of better than 99% are obtainable with sub-micron particles. Fabric filters are reliable, and relatively simple to operate, require moderate capital and operating costs and can be designed to handle a wide range of particulate loadings and gas flows. On the other hand, the choice of a fabric material limits the temperature and corrosivity characteristics of the gas, and high humidities must be avoided in order to prevent cake formation.

Removal of particulates from a gas stream by fabric filtration involves passing the gas through a filter medium made of a porous fabric. The solid is deposited on the fabric with a resultant increase in the flow resistance of the gas. A means of removing the solid matter which is built up on the filter is thus necessary to avoid excessive pressure drop of the gas through the filter cake.

Industrially, the filtration medium is contained in equipment known as a baghouse. These baghouses function to hold a large area of the filter exposed to the gas flow. The filter medium itself is generally in a tubular shape with gas flowing from the inside, through the medium, and exiting outside the tubes.

This section will deal with the mechanisms of particulate collection on fabric filters, some of the design parameters of baghouses, performance characteristics of baghouses, and some data on the cost of baghouse equipment and the cost of running a fabric filtration.

Mechanisms of particle collection

Particulate collection by fabric filters essentially involves the capture of a particle by a collecting body. The gas stream carries the particles close to the collecting body, where a variety of mechanisms are involved in the actual capture. The mechanism or mechanisms which predominate depend an the size and velocity of the particles, and on the characteristics of the filter element itself.

The three major collection mechanisms involved in fabric filtration are (1) Interception, (2) Inertial Impaction, and (3) Diffusion. In addition to these three mechanisms, gravity, electrostatic, and thermal forces may act to modify filtration performance in special cases, but in general, these effects are negligible.

The mechanism of interception can be visualized as follows. The particle is assumed to follow the streamlines of the gas flow. As the gas flows by the collector, the streamlines are bent. Interception occurs when the streamlines on which the particle travels come close enough to the collecting body such that the particle comes into contact with the body. The efficiency of interception is a function of the ratio of the diameter of the particle to the diameter of the target body and to some extent to the flow characteristics of the stream. Ranz ([29]) has developed an expression for the efficiency in the case of a cylindrical target

$$\eta = \frac{1}{2.002 - \ln \mathrm{Re}_c}\left[(1 + R)\ln(1 + R) - \frac{R(2 + R)}{2(1 + R)}\right] \qquad (1)$$

where η = collection efficiency

Re_c = Reynolds number of collector

R = ratio of the diameter of the particle to the diameter of the collector.

In the case of inertial impaction, the particle's momentum tends to carry it along the line of approach to the target rather than follow the streamlines around the filter element. The efficiency of collection by inertial impaction will increase as the particle mass and stream velocity increase. In actual practice, particle collection for particles having diameters greater than about 1μ occurs by a combination of both mechanisms.

Diffusion effects predominate for particles in the submicron size. These particles do not follow the gas streamlines, but move across them irregularily. Collection occurs by the particle diffusing from the bulk stream onto the surface of the collecting body.

Design considerations

The major design considerations of industrial filters are (1) the form of the filter bag, (2) the type of filter cloth, (3) the method employed for cleaning the cloth, and (4) the type of filter housing. This section deals with a discussion of these considerations. Additional information may be obtained from Strauss[30], Billings and Wilder[31], and Culhane[32].

Form of the Filter Bag The filter bags are of two general forms: flat or envelope shaped, and tubular. In the case of the flat bag, the solids are collected on the outside of the bag, and the bag is supported on the inside by a screen. The tubular, or cylindrical configuration of bags is the common one. The bag can be open at both ends or closed at one end and the gas can flow in either direction through the tube.

There are several variations in the design of the tubular baghouse; these are flow direction, inside or outside filtration and tube length and diameter. Traditionally, tubular baghouses were designed so that the gas flowed upward because they were slightly less expensive to construct. In the case of the down-flow design, all dust particles have some chance of not being caught by the filter and depositing in the collection hopper, whereas, if the gas is flowing upward, only those particles having settling velocities larger than the entrance velocity will deposit. On the other hand, the larger particles have a greater probability of being collected on the filter bag in the downward flow design. One consideration in the choice of design can thus be made on the particle size distribution of the dust –collection of fine, light dust may be more suited to a downflow design, whereas the heavier, larger dusts may be collected better in an upflow model. Besides particle size, other considerations dictate the eventual choice of the flow configuration. The downflow design results in a more uniform distribution of particle sizes in the cake, and a more even dust buildup along the length of the tube which leads to better filtering performance. One disadvantage of the downflow design is that because the lowest air velocity is at the hopper end, dust handling problems may occur should there be any tendency for condensation in the gas.

The choice of inside or outside filtration depends a great deal on the type of cleaning employed. In most of the downflow models, the gas enters inside the tube, and about one-half of the upward flow models are also inside filtration. Advantages of dust filtration on the inside of the bag include elimination of fabric support screens, and the ability to enter the baghouse during operation for inspection and maintenance. However, removal of the dust from the fabric involves more flexure of the bag in the case of inside filtration.

The bag diameter does not affect filtration performance, consequently, the choice of the diameter is dictated by design considerations of the enclosing structure and availability of cloth widths. Common diameters are 5 or 6 in. and 12 in. A smaller diameter bag results in a greater filtering area per unit volume of baghouse. The larger diameter bag can be made in longer lengths, and it is possible of realize a greater filtering area per unit floor area with the larger diameter bags if there is adequate head room in the plant for the higher baghouse. Of course, the smaller bags require more clamping arrangements, but are in general easier to handle.

Length to diameter ratios can vary from about 5–40; most typically they are in the range of 10–25. The longer tubes will give a higher filtering area per unit floor area, but length of the tube is limited due to considerations of (1) swaying stability, (2) cleaning methods, (3) safe tension which can be applied, and (4) difficulty of the manufacture of very long bags.

Type of Filter Cloths The proper operation of a fabric filter requires a fiber material which is compatible with the gas and particles with regard to temperature, relative humidity and corrosiveness, and a suitable fabric design. There are a large number of natural and synthetic materials available which cover a large range of properties to suit a variety of user requirements.

Traditionally, natural fibers, especially cotton and wool were used for the fabric. Cotton is still widely used because of its low cost, although it is limited in temperature to below about 180°F. Wool is no longer in wide use today.

The man-made, or synthetic fibers, have supplemented natural fibers for applications requiring greater resistance to high temperatures and chemical attack. Table 2 gives some relative physical cal properties of the various fibers in common use.

TABLE 2

Relative Properties of some Common Fabrics

Fiber	Max. temp. (dry) °F	Resistance to moist heat	Resistance to abrasion	Resistance to mineral acids	Resistance to alkalis
Cotton	180	G	G	P	G
Wool	200	F	F	F	P
Rayon	200	G	G	P	F
Nylon	200	F	E	P	G
Polypropylene	200	F	E	G	E
Acrylic	260	G	G	G	F
Polyester	275	F	E	G	F
Nomex	400	E	E	F	G
Teflon	400	E	F	E	E
Glass	550	E	P	E	P

E = excellent; G = good, F = fair, P = poor.

For applications at moderate temperatures up to about 200°F, Nylon and polypropylene are popular because of the advantage of relatively low cost, excellent abrasion resistance and high tensile strength. Polypropylene offers excellent resistance to acids and alkalis, but Nylon's resistance to acids is poor.

The acrylics (for example Orlon®, Acrilan®, Creslan®, and Crylon®) can be used at temperatures up to about 275°F, but have relatively poor resistance to alkalis. There resistance to acids and moist gases leads to application in the metallurgical industries as well as others such as carbon black, cement, fertilizers, solvents and galvanizing.

The polyesters (for example Dacron®, Fortrel®,

Vycron®, and Kodel®) can be used at temperatures of 250°F and have good resistance to alkalis at low temperatures.

Glass, Nomex and Teflon are the fibers of choice for high temperature application (400–500°F). Glass is superior to the others in terms of high chemical and thermal resistance but suffers from very poor resistance to abrasion. Abrasion resistance can be improved by coating the glass fibers with a lubricant such as silicon oil or graphite. Applications include cement, gray iron cupolas, and electric arc steelmaking. Nomex, an aromatic polyamide from duPont, can be used at temperatures up to about 400°F and has excellent abrasion and flexural resistance.

Cloth Cleaning A large amount of effort in the development of fabric filters has gone into methods of removing the deposited cake from the fabric. Several considerations are important with regard to cloth cleaning.

1) The cleaning time should be much smaller than the filtering time, otherwise effective use is not being made of the filter.

2) The cake should be moved uniformly.

3) Some residual cake is necessary after cleaning for efficient filtering.

4) The cleaning operation should not result in a large dispersion of dust because either a refiltration operation would be necessary or the efficiency of the filter would suffer.

5) The cleaning method should not result in excessive bag damage.

In general, the filter cloth is cleaned by shaking, gas flow reversal, or some combination of the two methods.

Mechanical shaking from the upper fastening is the most common method of cleaning the filter bags. Amplitudes vary from less than 1 in. to a few inches, and the frequency is usually several cycles per second. During the cleaning, the filtration is stopped, otherwise the dust will have a tendency to work through the bags and result in internal abrasion. For this purpose, the baghouse is built in several compartments to allow the isolation of one compartment at a time for cleaning. One disadvantage of this method of cleaning is the relatively large amount of fabric flexure involved especially at the top of the bags.

The second method of cleaning the bags is by flow reversal. If the dust cake is loosely adhering to the bag, then only a low–pressure reversal of fast flow will be necessary for cleaning; however, partial collapse of the bag can be done for the more adherant cakes. Although this method avoids some of the problems associated with bag flexure during shaking, it does have several disadvantages. Reverse flow without bag collapse requires that some support structures be placed within the bags (rings, screens etc.) which leads to difficulty in changing bags and chafing effects. Also, the reverse air used for cleaning has to be refiltered which results in a larger baghouse for a given filtration capacity.

A combination of the above two methods has been devised which is known as pulse cleaning. In this method, a pulse of compressed air is released from nozzles which results in a combination of flow reversal and fabric deformation. A unique feature of pulse cleaning is the short time required for cleaning. Therefore pulse cleaning is useful for equipment which must handle very high dust leadings. One of the major disadvantages of the method is its tendency to over–clean, especially for baghouses equiped with woven bags.

Other variations are available such as reverse jet cleaning which employs a jet of compressed air supplied from a ring which travels up and down on the outside of the bag. Occasionaly, sonic vibration is used to aid in the cleaning.

Baghouse Construction The type of baghouse construction depends on the moisture condensation and temperature configurations. Below a temperature of about 135°F, an open-sided design can be used (inside filtration) which is the least expensive type. A closed baghouse is used at higher temperatures, and above 160°F, the structure is usually insulated.

Materials of construction are selected with regard to corrosiveness of the glass handled. Steel, aluminum, and asbestos cement are some typical materials of construction.

Performance of Fabric Filters The two parameters which are important in determining the performance of the fabric filters are its efficiency and pressure drop. The efficiency is a measure of how effective the device is performing its job. The pressure drop is one of the major variables which determines operating cost because it affects the fan power necessary to move the gas through the filter, and also determines the frequency and duration of the cleaning cycle.

There are several factors affecting filter efficiency. The major one is particle size. In general, particles having diameters $> 1\mu$ will be filtered with a 99+ % removal efficiency. Efficiencies are about 90% for particles $<1\mu$. In a typical baghouse application, most of the particles passing through the filter are of sub-micron size.

The amount of dust buildup on the filter medium also affects the efficiency of collection, because a particle has a greater probability of being trapped by one of the filtration mechanisms discussed previously if there is a greater amount of cake. Thus, cleaning should not be too thorough.

The dust loading *per se* does not affect the efficiency significantly; however in the case of very low dust loadings (<0.5 gr/ft^3), a low efficiency will be observed for a time because of the low dust buildup on the fabric. To circumvent this problem, a precoat is often used.

The relative humidity of the gas affects the efficiency somewhat, depending on the material being filtered. For some particles, an increase in relative humidity results in increased particle adhesion force which tends to increase the rate at which the openings in the filter medium are bridged, resulting in an increase in the collection efficiency. The filtering velocity does not appear to affect efficiency significantly, except that higher velocities would tend to force more dust through defects in the cloth.

The pressure drop of the gas through the filter is a function mainly of the gas velocity, the thickness of the dust cake, and of the particle characteristics which determine the porosity of the cake which has built up. There have been a number of studies on pressure drop through fabric filters, and the reader is referred to Billings and Wilder[31] for a more complete treatment of this subject.

Economics of fabric filtration

A detailed survey of fabric filtration costs was done by Billings and Wilder.[31] There was a relatively large range of reported costs. Capital investment was found to vary from less than \$1 per cfm to greater than \$10 per cfm, operating costs varied from about \$1–\$7 per cfm per year. Values of about \$2.50/cfm capital and \$1.10/cfm annual operating can be considered typical. These costs are broken down into component parts in Table 3. It is apparent from an examination of the items contribution to the total economic picture that the costs for a specific installation will depend a great deal on many factors specific to the installation and gas being handled.

Figure 12 Before and after. The photograph on the left shows the typical dense smoke and soot being emitted from the stack of an industrial oil-fired boiler during the daily tube blowing or cleaning process. The photograph on the right shows the same stack during tube blowing with an emission control unit in operation.

TABLE 3

Breakdown of Capital and operating Costs for Fabric Filtration

I. *Capital Investment*

Item	Percentage of Total Cost
Planning and design	4.2
Baghouse, FOB	33.6
Freight	2.0
Fan and motor	10.5
Ducting	27.5
Dust disposal	4.2
Instrumentation	2.0
Installation labor	11.8
Start-up	4.2

II. *Operating Cost*

Item	Percentage of Total Cost
Electric power	11.4
Labor	28.6
Plant overhead	23.8
Cloth	9.5
Depreciation	15.2
Interest	11.5

Guarantee Specifications

Equipment vendors usually make a guarantee of overall particle collection efficiency as a part of bid proposals, but historically such guarantees have been more an indication of anticipated performance than an enforced or enforceable contract for several reasons. The isokinetic sampling always necessary for a proper efficiency test is difficult and time consumings and in some cases, e.g. for internal cyclones above fluid beds, it is a practical impossibility. Secondly, in the days of less stringent emission statutes the mere presence of control equipment often served to satisfy the spirit if not the letter of the law. Most guarantees in the past were written for a fixed set of operating conditions and were not legally enforceable at the deviant conditions that usually obtained during a test. Finally a legal recourse to poor performance is seldom spelled out in a contract. In the present climate of stringent emission limits and enforcement thereof, of substantial penalties for non-compliance, and of long equipment delivery times, purchasers are obliged to become more insistent that equipment perform according to a strict guarantee. Accordingly, the following suggestions are made for the writing of a performance specification.

A guarantee can only deal with the cleaning efficiency of a piece of equipment on the dusty gas stream actually entering it. Vendors quite understandably will refuse to guarantee an outlet loading, a Ringlemann number, or a dustfall, because these depend directly on the amount and particle size of dust entering the equipment as well as on the inherent capabilities of that equipment. In addition, optical properties of plumes are too little understood for generally acceptable prediction of Ringlemann numbers, even when the concentration and particle size of the emissions are known.

Performance guarantees are often written for a single set of design conditions without any provision for adjustment if, as usually happens, the design and actual test conditions are different. In such a situation the likelihood of proving and receiving compensation for substandard performance is small. It is therefore desirable that a range of operating conditions be specified and a procedure be defined for adjusting the guarantee performance at design conditions to a consistent performance at other conditions. The adjustment should be based on generalized efficiency relationships, e.g. equation 1 for cyclones and 4 for precipitators, or else on vendors design procedures. For instance equation 1 predicts that for a given cyclone, the response to changes in operating conditions is given by

$$d_{50} \propto \sqrt{\frac{\mu}{\rho U}}.$$

This used with the generalized grade efficiency curve, Figure 1, and the dust loading correction will give a suitable adjustment for changes in operating conditions so that starting from a guarantee performance at design conditions corresponding performance for other conditions may be calculated. In essence this establishes a guarantee envelope or curve to replace guarantee of a single point.

"Outlet stoppers," i.e. low outlet dust loadings to be accepted as *prima facie* evidence of satisfactory performance regardless of actual efficiency, are sometimes included in guarantees. The reasons are that isokinetic sampling is laborious and increasingly imprecise at low dust loadings, and that certain types of equipment are thought to have inherent limits on outlet loadings, e.g. precipitators have rapping losses which may control overall efficiency in the low loading range. It is felt, however, that outlet stoppers should be used only to exclude certain tests of the guarantee and not as evidence that the guarantee has been met. Cases are known in which the purchaser desired an outlet loading of approximately .003 grains/ft^3 in order to meet anticipated regulations, but precipitator vendors specified outlet stoppers of .01 grains/ft^3.

Generally speaking, it is desirable to the purchaser to operate equipment for a number of weeks before making a guarantee acceptance test. Deterioration from factory performance will often occur in such a time span. This time span should be used only as a shakedown period and not a life test.

Consideration should be given to the action to be taken if equipment does not satisfy the guarantee performance, and a guarantee will usually be the better for spelling out such remedies. One frequent clause specifies that the vendor remove below par equipment and refund the purchase price. This gives considerable incentive to the vendor to meet the guarantee, but removal of pollution control equipment may mean complete shutdown of production at a loss of tens of thousands of dollars per day to the user. Another arrangement is the bonus–penalty clause, under which the vendor on a sliding scale receives a bonus or pays a penalty if equipment performs above or below guarantee. At present the bonus payment aspect is unattractive to the purchaser, because he receives no benefit from producing less pollution than the law allows although this would change if a system of effluent taxation were implemented. Most often the most satisfactory approach is to require the vendor to upgrade installed equipment and make additions as needed so that the guaranteed performance level is reached.

REFERENCES

1. Stern, A. C. Ed. (1968) *Air Pollution* Chapters 42–46. 2nd Edition, Academic Press, New York 1968.
2. Pazar, C. *Air and Gas Cleaning Equipment*, Noyes Data Corp., Park Ridge, N. J., November, 1970
3. National Air Pollution Control Administration, *Control Techniques for Particulate Air Pollutants*, NAPCA Publication AP–51, Washington, January, 1969.
4. Stern, A. C., K. J. Caplan and P. D. Bush (1956) *Cyclone Dust Collectors*, American Petroleum Institute, New York.
5. Davies, C. N. (1952) Separation of Airborne Dusts and Particles, *Inst. Mech. Eng. Proc.* (B) **1B** 5, 185.
6. Gardiner, J. E., Tech. Report No. 1-CT/19, Shell Petroleum Co., Ltd., London.
7. Lapple, C. E., (1950) Gravity and Centrifugal Separation, *Indust. Hygiene Quart.* **11**, 40.
8. Lapple, C. E. and C.B. Shepherd, (1940) Calculation of Particle Trajectories, *Ind. Eng. Chem.* **32**, 605.
9. Muhlrad, S. W. (1954) *Chaleur et Ind.* **35**, 41.
10. Rosin, P., E. Rammler and W. Intlemann (1932) Theory and Limits of Cyclone Dust Removal, (In German), *Zeit. Ver. Deut. Ing.* **76**, 433.
11. Tarjan, G. (1950) Contributions to the Kinematics of the Cyclone and the Cyclone Scrubber, (In Hungarian) *Acta. Tech. Acad. Sci. Hung.* **1**, 22.
12. Strauss, W. (1966) *Industrial Gas Cleaning*, Pergamon Press, Oxford.
13. Rietema, K. (1961) *Cyclones in Industry*, Elsevier, Amsterdam.
14. Feifel, E., Cyclone Dust Collection; The Ideal Eddy Sink and Its Approximation, (in German) *Ver. Deut. Ing. Forschungshefte* **9**, 68 (1938); **10**, 212 (1939).
15. Stairmand, C. J. (1951) The Design and Performance of Cyclone Separators, *Trans. Inst. Chem. Engng.* (Lond.) **29**, 356.
16. Barth, W. (1956) Calculation and Interpretation of Cyclones on the Basis of New Studies, (In German) *Brennstoff-Warme-Kraft*, **8**, 1.
17. Ter Linden, A. J. (1953) Studies of Cyclone Separators, (In German) *Tonindustrie Zeitung* **22** (iii), 49.
18. Van Ebbenhorst Tengbergen, H. J., Dust Cyclones–Law of Similarity–Influence of the Dust Concentration, *De Ingenieur*, Irg 77 No. 2, Wl, January 8, 1965.
19. Kriegel, E. (1967) Model Studies of Cyclone Separators, *Techn.Mitt. Krupp Forsch.-Ber.* **25**, 21.
20. Alexander, R. McK. (1949) Fundamentals of Cyclone Design and Operation, *Aust. Inst. Min. Met. Proc.*, New Series **152–3**, 202.
21. First, M. W., Cyclone Dust Collector Design, Am. Soc. Mech. Eng. Paper 49–A–127 (1949).
22. Sheperd, C. B., C. E. and Lapple, Flow Pattern and Pressure Drop in Cyclone Dust Collectors, *Ind. Eng. Chem.* **31**, 972 (1939); **32**, 1246 (1940).
23. White, H. J. (1963) *Industrial Electrostatic Precipitation*, Addison Wesley, Reading, Mass.
24. Oglesby, S. and G. B. Nichols, *A Manual of Electrostatic Precipitator Technology*, Southern Research Institute, Birmingham, August, 1970. Distributed by National Technical Information Service No. PB–196–380.
25. Rose, H. E. and A. J. Wood (1966) *An Introduction to Electrostatic Precipitation in Theory and Practice*, Constable, London.
26. Gottschlich, C. F. (1961) *Electrostatic Precipitators*, American Petroleum Institute, New York.
27. Halow, J. S., Personal Communication.
28. Deutsch, W. (1922) *Ann. der Physik* **68**, 335.
29. Ranz, W. E., Technical Report No. 8, University of Illinois Engineering Experimental Station, (January 1953).
30. Strauss, W. (1966) *Industrial Gas Cleaning*, Pergamon Press, New York.
31. Billings, C. E. and J. Wilder, *Handbook of Fabric Filter Technology Volume I*, Report from GCA Corporation, Bedford, Mass. to National Air Pollution Control association (EPA), December, 1970.
32. Culhane, F. R. (1968) Production Baghouses, *Chem. Eng. Prog.*, **46** (1), 65.

JOHN M. MATSEN

Esso Research and Engineering

MORTON FELS

Batelle Memorial Institute

PESTICIDES

I. Introduction

Man employs pesticides as purposeful environmental contaminants in order to improve environmental quality for himself and his domesticated animals and plants. In agriculture, pesticides are used to increase the cost/benefit ratio in favor of the farmer and of the ultimate consumer of food and fiber products, the citizen. It has been widely estimated that the U.S. farmer receives an average net return of about \$5 for every \$1 invested in pesticides (PSAC, 1965). In our present era of managed ecology of monocultures, of farm mechanization, and of the complex system of food harvesting, processing, distribution, and storage, the use of pesticides often represents the slender margin between crop production and crop failure, and between economic profit and economic loss. In the developing countries where food supplies are marginal, pesticide use may represent the margin between survival and starvation.

In public health, pesticides often provide the only feasible means for the control of the invertebrate vectors of human and animal diseases. It is difficult to place monetary values on human health but for malaria in India, the World Health Organization has estimated that an investment of \$200 million in malaria control by DDT residual house spraying during 1952–66 saved 179.5 million man days of labor or an estimated saving of \$490 million. The cost/benefit ratio has thus been about \$2.7 return for every \$1 invested. In addition, during this period the annual number of cases of malaria has decreased from 75 million to 150,000 and deaths from about 750,000 to 1500 (World Health, 1968).

However, in June 1972 an almost total ban on DDT was proclaimed in the United States. The ban was immediately challenged by both DDT producers and conservation groups. The former declared the ban too severe while the latter felt that the ban did not go far enough.

In surveying the role of pesticides in environmental quality it must be remembered that pests themselves generally affect adversely the quality of the environment. The spectrum ranges from a mosquito in the bedroom or a cockroach in the pantry to a plague of locusts or the tsetse flies (*Glossina* spp.) which as vectors of trypanosomiasis have effectively prevented the development of 4.5 million square miles of Central Africa. The presence of vicious biting black flies (*Simulium* spp.) or widespread defoliation of forest and shade trees by the gypsy moth (*Porthetria dispar*) or other defoliators are effective deterrents to the resort industry in many northland vacation sites. Who can place a realistic value on the loss to environmental quality from the chestnut blight or the Dutch elm disease which have destroyed millions of North America's finest shade trees? Therefore it must be recognized that the purposeful environmental contamination by pesticides generally provides environmental benefits substantially greater than the risk of environmental pollution. It is also necessary to distinguish carefully between *environmental contamination* which may not pose any risk or hazard to the environment, and *environmental pollution* where the health or well being of man or other animals and plants may be severely threatened. Environmental contamination is often a matter of degree, as for example with selenium which at very low levels is essential for the normal growth and development of vertebrates yet at higher levels is an extremely poisonous pollutant. What is wanted then in an exploration of "pesticides in the environment" is a scientific appraisal of all these elements, a judicious weighing of risk/benefit ratios, and where deleterious effects on environmental quality are detected, the prompt substitution of remedial measures and/or alternative pesticides which pose no environmental hazard.

Another measure of the economic value of pesticides is the total extent to which they are used. Pesticide use in the United States for the period 1962–1970 is shown in Table I. The average annual rate of increase in total pesticide use is about 7%/yr. Herbicide usage approximately doubled between 1962 and 1965 and nearly doubled again from 1965 to 1969. The total use of insecticides and fungicides shows signs of leveling off. In terms of application to the 350 million acres of U.S. cropland, the U.S. Department of Agriculture estimated that in 1966, herbicides were applied to 27%, insecticides to 12%, and fungicides to 2.6%. In aggregate, pesticides are applied to about 5% of the total land surface of the continental United States.

TABLE I

Sales of Synthetic Organic Pesticides in the United States[a]

Year	Fungicides	Herbicides	Insecticides	Total
	Millions of pounds			
1962	97	95	442	634
1963	93	123	435	651
1964	95	152	445	692
1965	106	184	473	763
1966	118	221	502	841
1967	120	288	489	897
1968	130	318	511	959
1969	124	311	493	928
1970	129	308	444	881

[a] U.S. Tariff Commission data and estimates.

There are approximately 400 individual chemical compounds registered as pesticides in the United States including about 80 fungicides, 100 herbicides, and 200 insecticides. On a world wide basis more than 900 chemical compounds are in commercial use as pesticides and the number of different formulations is estimated to exceed 100,000 (Melnikov, 1971). The chemical properties, biological behavior, and environmental fate of these pesticides is exceedingly complex and is beyond the scope of this discussion (see Kraybill, 1969; Melnikov 1971; Menzies 1969; White-Stevens 1971). The role of these chemicals in pest control and crop production has been studied intensively and their use has become virtually indispensible to modern agriculture. Nevertheless, for the majority of the individual pesticides there is only superficial knowledge of the effects of their long term use on the quality of the environment.

As a guide to the types of chemicals which are most widely applied as pesticides, the estimates of U.S. production of individual pesticides shown in Table II will be helpful. It appears that less than 30 individual pesticidal compounds comprise about 95% of the total U.S. production. About 80% of the total is the organochlorine compounds such as DDT, toxaphene, 2,4–D, chlorinated phenols, and cyclodienes, which are the most environmentally persistent of all pesticides.

II. Pesticides as environmental contaminants

Pesticides are microchemical environmental contaminants, and their rates of utilization are such that they contaminate soil, water and food in terms of parts per trillion (0.000001 ppm) to parts per million (ppm).* Thus a pesticide applied at 1 lb/acre (1.12 kg/ha) contaminates the top 1 foot (30 cm) of soil (approximately 4 million lb. or 1800 metric tons) to 0.25 ppm. Where such contamination is deleterious to environmental quality the pesticide becomes a microchemical pollutant, exhibiting such objectionable properties as (1) high physiological and ecological specificity, (2) resistance to biochemical degradation, (3) sequential concentration in organisms of the trophic web, and (4) capacity for delayed onset of intoxication (Warner, 1967).

TABLE II

Estimated Annual Production of Pesticides in the United States

Pesticide	Production in millions of pounds[a]
Creosote	1000
Petroleum oils	500
DDT	123
Toxaphene, chlordane, aldrin, dieldrin, heptachlor	107
Triazine herbicides	100
Alachlor, amiben, propachlor, trifluralin	90
2,4–D acid, esters, salts	57
Carbaryl	50
Pentachlorophenol and salts	46
Copper sulfate	42
Methyl parathion	41
Dithiocarbamates	40
Malathion	35
Sodium chlorate	30
Methyl bromide	20
Captan	18
Parathion	15
2,4,5–T acid, esters, salts	12

[a] Data from U.S. Tariff Commission and personal communication.

A. Pesticides in Air

The widespread application of pesticides in particulate sprays and dusts insures that appreciable contamination of the air is a consequence of pesticide use. Much of the total application of pesticides is from aircraft (about 80% of pesticide application in California in 1963 was by aircraft; Mrak, 1969) where the propeller wash and wing vortices characteristically throw small particles high into the air and wind currents may drift them for miles away from the target site. When released 10 ft above the ground into a 3 mph wind, 2 μ dia. particles drifted 21 miles, 10 μ particles 1 mile, and 50 μ particles 200 ft (Akesson and Yates, 1964). It is evident that air applications produce increased air pollution, and Wasserman *et al.* (1960) found air concentra-

* Contamination of a substrate at 1 ppm represents 1 μg of contaminant per gram of substrate.

tions in forests after air application of DDT at 18.9–170.9 mg/m^3 as compared with 4.6–25.5 mg/m^3 for ground application. Comparative values for BHC were: air 4.1–53.7 mg/m^3 and ground 4.6–25.5 mg/m^3. It has been estimated that 50% of the pesticide released in aerial spraying of forest drifts away from the target site.

The use of more than 90 million individual aerosol spray dispensers annually in the United States discharges substantial amounts of such pesticides as pyrethrins-piperonyl butoxide, dichlorvos, malathion, methoxychlor, chlordane, diazinon, propoxur, etc. indoors in homes, stores, warehouses, and aircraft, in the 5–30 μ dia. range. Pesticides are applied annually in the U.S. on more than 100 million acres of land. Organic insecticides have appreciable vapor pressures, ranging from 1.5×10^{-7} mm Hg for DDT, 1.2×10^{-2} for dichlorvos and 1420 mm for methyl bromide. Thus volatilization is a major factor in dispersal of pesticides into the air, and accounts for much of the dissipation of pesticides from treated plant surfaces and buildings and from soil (Harris and Lichtenstein, 1961). Wind erosion of dust from treated soil, etc. is also a substantial factor in the dispersal of pesticides through the air.

Occupational Exposure The degree of air pollution resulting from a variety of occupational uses of pesticides is shown in Table III (Jegier, 1969). These values illustrate the maximum air-borne concentrations to which humans are likely to be exposed and demonstrate the substantially higher exposures experienced indoors as compared to outdoors. Spray operators during average spraying operations are exposed to minute fractions of the combined dermal and respiratory toxic dose: 0.29% for endrin, 0.43% for parathion, 0.72% for azinphos, and 1.43% for demeton; four highly toxic insecticides. The greatest hazards from air borne exposure to highly toxic materials are found during filling spray tanks with wettable powders.

TABLE III

Occupation Exposure to Insecticides in Air[a]

Insecticide	Use	Mean concentration $\mu g/m^3$
Azinphos	Orchard spraying	670
Carbaryl	Orchard spraying	600
Malathion	Orchard spraying	590
Parathion	Orchard spraying	150–360
Endrin	Vegetable spraying	50
Demeton	Greenhouse spraying	9150
Chlordane	Household spraying	440
Diazinon	Household spraying	2680
Methoxychlor	Barn and cattle spraying	7680
Lindane	Household vaporizer	100
Azinphos	Tank filling	2270
Parathion	Tank filling	530

[a] Data from Jegier (1969).

Residential Exposure Agricultural spraying operations, especially those from aircraft produce considerable air pollution and traces of pesticides have been identified for many miles downwind. Where highly toxic pesticides such as tetraethyl pyrophosphate have been dusted on orchards by air, typical cholinergic symptoms of poisoning have been observed in inhabitants of neighboring rural communities (Quinby and Doornick, 1965). Spraying of apple orchards from ground air blast equipment has resulted in concentrations in nearby residential areas of azinphos, carbaryl, malathion, and parathion as high as 0.5 mg/m^3 (Jegier, 1969). Studies of the effect of DDT spraying operations upon air pollution of rural and urban communities have produced values ranging from <0.1 ng/m^3 (0.000001 mg/m^3) to >8500 ng/m^3. Ranges observed in specific localities included: Fresno, California 0.3–19; Sacramento, California 0–2; Florida City, Florida 0.1–7.6; Fort Valley, Georgia 0.3–9.9; Leland, Mississippi 0.4–22; and Lake Apopka, Florida 0.3–8500 (Jegier, 1969). Pesticides are apparently present in the air everywhere as Risebrough *et al.* (1968) measured the concentrations in the air over Barbados as ranging from 13×10^{-6} to 380×10^{-6} ng/m^3 as compared to that of La Jolla, California where the average was 7.0×10^{-2} ng/m^3.

A comprehensive study by Stanley (1968) to determine the atmospheric contamination by pesticides in urban and rural sites of 9 U.S. cities showed that only DDT was present in all localities. The maximum concentrations found were DDT 1560 ng/m^3, toxaphene 2520 ng/m^3, and parathion 465 ng/m^3. The pesticides were mostly present in the atmosphere as particulates and the levels were generally correlated with spraying practices on particular crops.

In another study of pesticides in the air near 10 urban communities (Tabor, 1966), the maximum concentrations found near the center of town and at least a mile from agricultural operations were: DDT 22 ng/m^3, chlordane 6, aldrin 4, and toxaphene 15. Where communities were being fogged for control of pests DDT was found up to 8000 ng/m^3 and malathion up to 140.

Pesticides in Dust The windblown erosion of dust from agricultural lands treated by pesticides can become a substantial source of air pollution. Cohen and Pinkerton (1966) investigated the transport of pesticides to Cincinnati in a violent dust storm originating in the southern high plains of Texas in 1965. The major pesticide components of the dust and their concentrations in the dried dust particles after precipitation by rain in Cincinnati were: DDT 0.6 ppm, chlordane 0.5 ppm, ronnel 0.2 ppm, DDE 0.2 ppm, heptachlor epoxide 0.04 ppm, 2,4,5–T 0.04 ppm, and dieldrin 0.003 ppm.

Pesticides in Rainwater Many analyses of rainwater have shown substantial content of various pesticides indicating their general distribution in the atmosphere. As an example, the following mean concentrations of pesticides were found in three locations in Ohio in ppt: DDT 0.07–0.34, DDE 0.005–0.03, and BHC 0.006–0.05. Chlordane, heptachlor, aldrin, dieldrin, and 2,4,5–T isoctyl ester were also found in rainwater samples (Cohen and Pinkerton, 1966).

Study and the evaluation of pesticide pollution in air has been less intensive than comparable investigations of water and food. However, it is clear that pesticide residues are constantly being transported and redistributed from their sites of application through the atmosphere and are present in some degree in the air everywhere. The degree of human exposure is related to occupation and to geographic location and is highest for workers in pesticide plants, spray operators, and users of household aerosol sprays. Inhabitants of rural regions or those dwelling in houses where spraying operations are conducted for agricultural or public health purposes are obviously exposed to substantially higher concentrations of airborne pesticides than are typical urban dwellers.

B. Pesticides in Water

The water environment provides the ultimate sink for pesticide residues which enter it by direct contamination from rain precipitating pesticide aerosols or atmospheric codistillates, by direct application to surface waters, by runoff from treated plants and soils, by industrial and household sewage effluents, and by residues in human and animal excreta. An intrinsic property of most pesticidal molecules is high lipid solubility and low water solubility and this property strongly favors concentration from water to the lipids of living animals through partitioning through the animal cuticle and the gills. Such absorption and subsequent storage and concentration may result in aquatic animals accumulating pesticide residues hundreds and even thousands of times greater than that in the surrounding aquatic medium. This concentration process is dependent upon the initial pesticide residue in water, the length of animal exposure, i.e. lifetime, and the rate of metabolism or breakdown of the pesticide in the organism, i.e. biological half-life. Thus this subject has assumed great ecological importance.

Ground waters Pesticide residues in minute amounts eventually percolate into ground waters. There is, however, little evidence of any contamination of public well water supplies. Private wells have occasionally been contaminated with chlordane from adjacent soil applications for termite control, e.g. 3.3 μg/l or 2.4–D from weed spraying along a highway, e.g. 15.5 μg/l (Mrak, 1969) and Michigan has suggested observance of a 150-ft isolation distance between any well and storage or preparation areas for pesticides. Trace residues <1 μg/l, of such persistent pesticides as DDT, endrin, chlordane, dieldrin, and heptachlor have been reported in another preliminary survey.

Surface waters The Mrak Commission (Mrak, 1969) observes that the current U.S. annual production of pesticides, ca. 1×10^9 lb, applied to the annual U.S. runoff, ca. 1×10^6 gal/day, could result in a maximum concentration of 0.3 mg/l (0.3 ppm). Fortunately, most of the environmental contamination with pesticides is directly or indirectly to the soil where the various compounds are often tightly bound to soil colloids and/or degraded by soil microorganisms. The average runoff concentrations of 9 organochlorine insecticides, obtained from analysis of 6000 samples at 100 locations in all major U.S. river basins from 1958–65 is summarized in Table IV (Breidenback *et al.*, 1967). The maximum amounts determined, dieldrin 0.122 ppb, endrin 0.214 ppb, DDT 0.144 ppb, aldrin 0.006 ppb, heptachlor 0.002 ppb, heptachlor epoxide 0.008 ppb, and BHC 0.022 ppb; were well

TABLE IV

Organochlorine Pesticides in Major River Basins of the United States[a]

Pesticide	Positive samples of 537	Range ppb	Area of highest concentration
Dieldrin	495	0.008–0.122	lower Miss. 1964
Endrin	217	0.008–0.214	lower Miss. 1963
DDT	145	0.008–0.144	W. Gulf basin 1963
DDE	176	0.002–0.011	lower Miss. 1965
DDD	231	0.004–0.080	N. Atlantic basin 1963
Aldrin	31	<0.001–0.006	S.W. basin 1964
Heptachlor	6	0–0.002	lower Miss. 1965
Heptachlor epoxide	26	<0.001–0.008	N. Atlantic basin 1963
BHC	44	0.003–0.022	S.E. basin 1960

[a] From Breidenbach *et al.* (1967).

below the suggested Federal Drinking Water Standards (USPHS, 1968) of dieldrin 17 ppb, endrin 1 ppb, DDT 42 ppb, heptachlor 19 ppb, heptachlor epoxide 18 ppb and lindane 56 ppb; except for endrin. The yearly analyses showed dieldrin to be the dominant contaminant but declining, DDT and cogeners virtually constant, endrin reaching a peak in 1964 and declining.

In another study of 12 organochlorine pesticides in 11 streams in Western United States (Brown and Nishioka, 1967) the contaminants, positive samples, and range detected were: DDT—82, 0.01–0.12 ppb; DDE—49, 0.0–0.06; DDD—35, 0.0–0.04; 2,4–D—41, 0.01–0.35; 2,4,5–T—28, 0.01–0.07; heptachlor—27, 0.01–0.04; dieldrin—24, 0.01–0.07; silvex—14, 0.01–0.21; lindane—11, 0.01–0.04; aldrin—11, 0.01–0.07; endrin—4, 0.01–0.07; and heptachlor epoxide—2, 0.02–0.04.

A major source of pesticide pollution of ground water is from soil particles containing attached pesticide residues through erosion runoff, or flooding. Application of aldrin to rice fields at 6 oz/acre by seeding with treated rice seeds resulted in 1.6 ppb aldrin plus dieldrin in the water after 2 days and 0.07 ppb 14 weeks after seeding. Draining of the fields after 14 weeks produced 0.027 ppb in the ditches, 0.44 ppb in the stream receiving the ditches, and concentrations as high as 0.023 ppb in the river into which the stream flowed (Sparr *et al.*, 1966). In a companion study runoff from a cotton field treated 7 days before with 0.4 lb/acre of endrin, contained 0.66 ppb endrin after a 1.15 in. rain. Used irrigation water contained 0.11 ppb endrin 3 days after spraying.

Lakes and reservoirs These bodies of water often represent the sites of the most serious environmental pollution problems resulting from the applications of pesticides to both land and water. The direct application of pesticides to water for the control of mosquito or blackfly larvae, snails, or water weeds is an obvious source of contamination. Rates of application commonly range from 0.1–1 lb/acre of water surface for insecticides to as much as 100 lb/acre for 2,4–D herbicide. In water 1 ft deep these rates would range from 2 ppm at 0.1 lb/acre to 2000 ppm at 100 lb/acre.

One of the first examples of serious water pollution by pesticides resulted from the application of the larvicide DDD to Clear Lake, California for the control of Clear Lake gnat *Chaoborus astictopus* which was a severe nuisance. In 1949, 14,000 gal of emulsive concentrate of DDD was applied to the lake at a rate of 14 ppb. The gnats were nearly exterminated and it appeared that no damage to fish occurred. Reinfestation from nearby lakes resulted in retreatment with DDD at 20 ppb in 1954 and 1957. Dying Western Grebes (*Aechmophorus occidentalis*) in areas around the lake were observed in 1954, 1955, and 1957 and they had tremors characteristic of DDD poisoning. Their body tissues contained as much as 1600 ppm DDD. Subsequent study showed DDD residues of up to 10 ppm in plankton, and as much as 2375 ppm in the body fat of the white catfish, *Ictalurus catus* (Hunt and Bischoff, 1960). Thus this episode provided the first well studied example of ecological magnification of a pesticide from water through a food chain of plankton→fish→birds, which died from chronic DDD poisoning.

The application of 880 tons of 2,4–D butoxyethanol ester as a granular preparation to control water milfoil in 8000 acres of seven TVA reservoirs was studied to determine the fate of the pesticides (Smith and Isom, 1967). Persistent residues, as high as 58 ppb were found in bottom mud 10 months after treatment and there was evidence of concentration of the herbicide in fresh water mussels. Analysis of raw water samples in nine water treatment plants showed 2,4–D residues as high as 1–2 ppb.

Large fresh water lakes may have astonishingly long water retention times which magnify pesticide contamination problems. In the Great Lakes system Lake Superior with an area of 82,366 km^2 and a volume of 12,221 km^3 has an average water retention time of 189 yrs, and Lake Michigan with an area of 58,016 km^2 has an average water retention time of 30.8 yrs. Rainey (1967) has pointed out that in such bodies of water contamination is a major disaster for which there is no apparent solution. Thus the times for 90% waste removal are >500 yrs for Lake Superior and 100 yrs for Lake Michigan, as compared to 20 yrs for Lake Ontario and 6 yrs for Lake Erie. Lake Michigan is exposed to pesticide contamination from intensive agriculture and from effluents from the densely populated urban areas within its 117,845 km^2 watershed. Analyses of Lake Michigan surface waters in 1968–1969 showed DDT $2.0–2.8 \times 10^{-6}$ ppm, DDE $0.8–1.4 \times 10^{-6}$ ppm, and DDD $0.3–0.5 \times 10^{-6}$ ppm; while grab samples at the Chicago filtration plant had DDT $0.034–0.058 \times 10^{-3}$ ppm, lindane $0.01–0.02 \times 10^{-3}$ ppm, aldrin 0.019×10^{-3} ppm, and heptachlor epoxide $0.019–0.049 \times 10^{-3}$ (Mrak, 1969). The ecological significance of these trace amounts is shown by studies reporting concentrations of DDT in the Lake

Michigan ecosystem of 0.014 ppm in bottom muds, 0.410 ppm in amphipods, 3.22 ppm in yellow perch, 6.9 ppm in lake trout, 6.71 ppm in lake herring, and 99 ppm in herring gulls (Reinert, 1970; Harrison *et al.*, 1970). The overall concentration of DDT from water to fish-eating bird is $>10^7$. Dieldrin was present in lake trout and lake herring to 0.20 ppm (Reinert, 1970), for an overall concentration of about 2×10^5.

Estuaries The importance of estuarine waters to commercial and sports fishing makes these locations especially vulnerable targets to the runoff of pesticides in streams and rivers from agricultural practices and industrial operations. It has been estimated (PSQC, 1965) that more than 50% of the total harvest of sea foods from waters of the United States is composed of species whose existence or spawning grounds are in the estuarine zone and this harvest includes some of the most valued sea foods—shrimp, lobster, crabs, oysters, salmon, menhaden, and game fish. Agricultural pesticides are more toxic to the marine life than any other group of chemicals and lethal concentrations for the organochlorine insecticides aldrin, dieldrin, heptachlor, endrin, DDT, lindane, and toxaphene range from 0.0006–0.06 ppm. Molluscs in particular can concentrate extraordinary quantities of stable pesticides and oysters have been found to accumulate DDT to 70,000 times the amount in the surrounding water. Thus these organisms are especially useful as biological indicators of pesticide pollution. Woodwell *et al.* (1967) estimated that the Carmans River estuary of Long Island contained about 0.00005 ppm DDT in the water, with concentrations of 0.04 ppm in plankton, 2–3 ppm in small fish, and up to 75.5 ppm in the ring-billed gull (*Larus delawarensis*).

Oceans Little information exists about pesticide residues in the oceans. As these compounds are leached from the land or precipitated by rains, they circulate initially in the mixed layer above the thermocline and may eventually be transferred slowly into the abyss which provides a reservoir of virtually infinite capacity (Woodwell *et al.*, 1971). The organochlorine compounds such as DDT with their high lipid solubility and very low water solubility must be largely absorbed into organic matter. Woodwell *et al.* (1971) estimate concentrations of DDT in algae of the oceans ranging from 0.1–1.0 ppm and a maximum accumulation in the mixed layer of the ocean of about 15 ppt. Scattered observations suggest that DDT is present in most marine animals, with levels in whales of 0.4–6 ppm, tuna up to 2 ppm, oysters 0–5.4 ppm, and sea birds up to 10 ppm (Butler, 1966; Wolman and Wilson, 1970). Virtually nothing is known of the presence of other pesticides in marine organisms. Trapping of pesticides in petroleum slicks, which may contain up to 10,000 ppm DDT, provides another facet to marine pollution.

C. Pesticides in Soils

Pesticides are most frequently applied directly to soil or to plant surfaces above it and concern for the persistence of pesticide residues in soils has existed since the first widespread use of lead and calcium arsenate. A study by Jones and Hatch (1937) reported that 3500 lb. of lead arsenate was applied to a commercial apple orchard over a 25 yr period. Most of the lead and arsenic was confined to the upper 6–8 in. of soil and did not harm the roots of the fruit trees. However, the residual levels were highly toxic to cover crops or to young newly planted trees.

Pesticides are applied to crops and soils in most of the agricultural areas of the United States. The U.S.D.A. estimated in 1966 that of 350×10^6 acres of cultivated land in the United States, herbicides were applied to 27%, insecticides to 12%, and fungicides to 2.6%. Soils in intensively farmed areas have higher frequencies of application, e.g. Illinois in 1969, when herbicides were applied to 42% of the farmland and insecticides to 30%, most of these as direct applications to the soil (Metcalf, 1971).

Soil residues of pesticides Monitoring studies made of pesticide residues in soils of the heavily treated cotton growing areas of the Mississippi Delta (Gentry, 1966) have given a general picture of the extent to which agricultural soils may be contaminated. In an area where a cumulative total of 30 lb of DDT/acre had been applied over a 9 yr period 1955–63, the level in the top soil in 1964 was 1.3 ppm or about 1.3 lb/acre. In another area where 13 applications of endrin at 0.21 lb/acre were applied since 1956, the average level in the soil in 1964 was 0.05 ppm. Aldrin and dieldrin, although not used since about 1955, were found in the study area in 1964 at levels of up to 0.06 ppm dieldrin and 0.13 ppm aldrin, and benzene hexachloride was found at about 0.02 ppm. Toxaphene was present in the soils at 0.8–3.7 ppm, and calcium arsenate, although not used for many years, had left an arsenic level of 2.8–12.8 ppm.

The occurrence of residues of chlorinated hydrocarbon insecticides in soils from 31 farms in Southern Ontario has been explored by Harris *et al.* (1966). Orchard soils contained the highest levels of

DDT 19.9–118.9 ppm, DDE 3.4–15.7 ppm, DDD 0.2–3.5 ppm, and dicofol 2.4–6.9 ppm. A vegetable farm where radishes were grown on muck soil had the highest concentrations of dieldrin 1.6 ppm, aldrin 2.1 ppm, endrin 3.8 ppm, together with DDT 13.8 ppm, DDE 0.8 ppm, and DDD 0.4 ppm. The highest levels of other pesticides found were: heptachlor 0.2 ppm, chlordane 0.6 ppm, and endosulfan 1.4 ppm. The average levels found in soils from 16 farms in this area in 1966 were aldrin 0.47 ppm, dieldrin 0.78 ppm, endrin 0.12 ppm, and DDT 23.9 ppm (Harris, 1971).

The rate of degradation of any pesticide in the soil is a function of its chemical structure and the formulation applied whether emulsion, granular, or seed treatment. Most pesticide degradation in soil is accomplished by the wide range of soil microorganisms which can use the compound as an energy source, although hydrolysis and photochemical oxidations may also play a role. Soil factors which determine the actual rate of persistence are (1) soil type, (2) soil moisture, (3) temperature, (4) uptake by plants, (5) leaching by water, (6) wind erosion. Thus it is difficult to generalize about soil persistence of pesticides, which is, however, greater in muck soils heavy in organic matter than in light sandy soils. Some idea of the relative persistence of various pesticides in soils is given in Table V, from data by Edwards (1964), Lichtenstein (1969), and Harris (1970).

TABLE V

Persistence of Pesticides in Soils

Pesticide	Approximate time for 70–95% loss[a]
DDT	4–10 yrs
Dieldrin	3– 8 yrs
Lindane	3– 6 yrs
Chlordane, heptachlor	3– 5 yrs
Aldrin	2– 3 yrs
Picloram	1– 2 yrs
Simizine, atrazine	10–12 months
Monuron, fenuron, diuron	8–10 months
Trifluralin	6 months
Carbaryl, carbofuran	4– 6 months
2,4,5–T	3– 5 months
Parathion, azinphos, diazinon	3– 6 months
Toxaphene	2 months
Amiben, dicamba, MCPA	2– 3 months
Dalapon, propham, CDAA, CDEC, EPTC	1– 2 months
Phorate, disulfoton	2– 6 weeks
2,4–D	4– 6 weeks
Captan	3– 6 weeks
Malathion	1– 2 weeks

[a] Data from Edwards (1961), Kearney, Nash and Isensee (1969).

Uptake of pesticides by plants Plants obviously absorb pesticides from the soil and translocate them throughout the leaves and fruits or pre-emergent herbicides would have little activity in killing weeds and systemic insecticides would fail to protect plants against insect attack. The actual amounts absorbed by plant roots are dependent upon the solubility of the pesticide in the lipids of the root cuticle, and the amounts translocated are a function of the water solubility of the pesticide in the translocation stream.

The organochlorine insecticides are absorbed in trace amounts by root crops such as carrots, radishes, and potatoes, and these crops grown in soil treated with 1 lb/acre of aldrin, contained as much as 0.03–0.05 ppm of the pesticide (Lichtenstein, 1969). Residues of these pesticides also enter above ground portions of crops and Lichtenstein (1969) has calculated that alfalfa grown on soil treated with aldrin and heptachlor at 1 lb/acre would contain approximately 0.005 ppm aldrin and dieldrin and 0.015 ppm of heptachlor and heptachlor epoxide. In contrast, residue studies made of the results of soil and seed treatments with phorate and disulfoton showed residues in the leaves after 39 days ranging from 5–12 ppm in alfalfa, 32–137 ppm in cotton, and 7–46 ppm in sugar beets (Reynolds *et al.*, 1957). These residues dissipated rapidly as the plants grew older and in practical use conform to the residue tolerance levels in hay and cottonseed.

D. *Pesticides in Foods*

The most direct avenue for pesticide contamination of the human body is through ingestion of pesticide residues on food products. Perhaps 75% of all pesticide production is used for the production or protection of agricultural commodities and widespread contamination of food products is the inevitable result. However, much of the initial pesticide load is lost by "weathering", through action of rain and dew and by photochemical oxidations, by enzymatic destruction in the tissues of plants or animals and through losses in harvesting and food processing. The processes of degradation and persistence of pesticide residues usually follow first order chemical kinetics and can be plotted semilogarithmically as straight lines of log. residue in ppm vs. time elapsed since treatment. Such residue persistence curves give values for residue half-lives or RL^{50} (Gunther and Blinn, 1955) which are independent of initial concentration and thus represent a characteristic of each pesticide on or in a particular substrate such as leaf surface, fruit peel, plant wax or juice, etc. This concept then supports the empirically derived practice of observing a "safe period" after pesticide application and before harvest to permit the pesticide residue to attenuate to levels which long term animal feeding studies have shown to be innocuous to animal health. Based on these animal feeding studies and incorporating a safety factor, ideally 100-fold to allow for peculiar human metabolic idiosyncracies and sensitivities, together with the potential daily intake in foods, the U.S. Food and Drug Administration has established pesticide residue tolerances for each registered pesticide use on a food commodity. The range of tolerances for commonly used pesticides is shown in Table VI.

The actual occurrence of pesticide residues in human foods has been studied by FDA from 1964–1966, through the examination of 26,326 samples including raw agricultural products, milk, and dairy products, processed animal feeds, shell eggs, fish and shell fish, meat, canned and frozen foods, vegetable oils, and special dietary products (Duggan, 1969). Residues of 81 different pesticide chemicals were detected, with 11 chemicals accounting for 95% of the residues found. Those most commonly detected in domestic foods were, in order of importance: DDT 25%, DDE 24%, dieldrin 17%, DDD 9%, heptachlor epoxide 7%, lindane 4.5%, BHC 2.6%, endrin 2.3%, aldrin 1.8%, toxaphene 1.4% and dicofol 0.7%. Animal tissues contained in addition, methoxychlor and chlordane. Approximately 95% of the residues were below 0.5 ppm, 78% below 0.1 ppm and 58% below 0.03 ppm. Excessive residues, above tolerances, were found in 3.6% of the samples. It is apparent that the chlorinated organics provided the great majority of readily detectable residues in food products, because of their high stability and fat solubility.

The exposure of humans to pesticide residues in a well balanced diet has been studied by FDA since 1962. For 1964–1966 this has been calculated to contain an average of 0.025 ppm chlorinated organics, 0.003 ppm organophosphates, 0.003 ppm chlorophenoxy acids, and 0.05 ppm carbamates. The average daily intake of 15 pesticides in 516 diet composites sampled by FDA is shown in Table VII (Duggan, 1969).

TABLE VI

Typical Pesticide Residue Tolerances in the United States[a]

Pesticide	Crops, commodities	Tolerance ppm
Aldrin	Fruits, vegetables	0.1–0.25
Azinphos methyl	Fruits, vegetables, forage	0.3–5
Captan	Fruits, vegetables	100
Carbaryl	Fruits, vegetables, forage	5–100
Chlorbenzylate	Fruits, vegetables	0.2–5
Coumaphos	Milk, eggs, meat	0–1
Cryolite	Fruits, vegetables	7
DDT	Fruits, vegetables	1–7
2,4–D	Fruits	5
Diazinon	Fruits, vegetables, forage	0.75–40
Dieldrin	Fruits, vegetables	0.1–1
Disulfoton	Vegetables, forage	0.75–12
Diuron	Fruits, vegetables, forage	0.2–7
Dormant oils	Fruits	exempt
Endosulfan	Fruits, vegetables	2
Endrin	Fruits, vegetables	0
Ethylene dibromide	Vegetables	5–75
Ferbam	Fruits, vegetables	0.1–7
Heptachlor	Fruits, vegetables, forage	0–0.1
Lindane	Fruits, vegetables	10
Malathion	Fruits, vegetables, forage	8–135
Maneb	Fruits, vegetables	0.1–10
Methoxychlor	Fruits, vegetables, forage	1–100
Methyl bromide	Fruits, vegetables, nuts	2–240
Nicotine	Fruits vegetables	2
Paraquat		0.5
Parathion, methyl parathion	Fruits, vegetables, forage	1
o-phenylphenol	Fruits, vegetables	10–20
Pyrethrins	Fruits, vegetables	exempt
Ronnel	Meat	0
Rotenone	Fruits, vegetables	exempt
Simazine	Alfalfa, grass	15
Tetradifon	Fruits	1–5
Thiram	Fruits	1–7
Toxaphene	Fruits, vegetables	3–7
Zineb	Fruits, vegetables	7–60

[a] Environmental Protection Agency (1970–1971).

TABLE VII

Average Daily Intake and Incidence of Pesticides in U.S. Human Diet Composites[a]

Pesticide	Daily intake from total diet mg/kg	% positive samples	FAO–WHO acceptable intake mg/kg
DDT	0.0005	37.4	0.01
Dieldrin	0.00009	20.2	0.0001
Lindane	0.00006	13.6	0.0125
Heptachlor epoxide	0.00004	12.6	0.0006
Carbaryl	0.0012	4.7	0.02
Malathion	0.0001	4.5	0.02
Aldrin	0.00003	4.5	—
2,4–D	0.00005	3.5	0.017
Diazinon	0.000014	3.0	—
Dicofol	0.00011	2.5	—
Pentachlorophenol	0.00006	2.5	—
Endrin	trace	2.3	—

[a] Data from Duggan (1969).

III. Pesticides in Wildlife

The widespread use of pesticides has occasioned much concern about adverse affects on wildlife.

Significant reviews of this important subject include Hunt (1966), Dustman and Stickel (1966, 1969), and Cope (1971). Concern in this area has moved from studies of acute toxicity (Rudd and Genelly, 1956) to physiological, behavioral, and ecological implications of the toxicity to non-target organisms (Cope, 1966; Newsom, 1967; Johnson, 1968; Pimentel, 1971). Despite the implications of selective toxicity inherent in pesticide application it is evident that pesticide usage often has deleterious effects on non-target organisms. As Pimentel (1971) points out, pesticide usage in the United States is aimed at about 2000 pest species of plants and animals but many of the remaining 200,000 non-target plants and animals, the great majority of which are necessary for human survival, are affected directly or indirectly. The anthropomorphic concepts of pest and beneficial species are not valid ecologically and it is obvious that both target and non-target organisms respond to pesticide contamination in a variety of essentially similar ways (Newsom, 1967).

A. Acute toxicity of pesticides

An important first step in assessing pesticide effects on organisms is the determination of the acute toxicity as LD_{50} in terms of dose applied, eaten, or injected; or LC_{50} in terms of concentration in the water, causing 50% mortality of an animal population. Knowledge of the comparative toxicities of a variety of pesticides to representative organisms is important in selecting pesticides for various uses and in assessing risks to non-target species. Unfortunately most of the large amount of data on quantitative toxicology deals with effects of a few compounds on a wide variety of species and there is little uniform data on a wide representation of species for the important pesticides. Table VIII presents a selection of toxicity values to a variety of organisms for the widely used pesticides for which adequate data is available. From the comparative viewpoint, the table shows the impossibility of profound generalizations about pesticide toxicity. Methoxychlor and malathion, two of the very safest materials to mammals and birds are highly toxic to fish and invertebrates. Carbaryl with low toxicity to mammals, birds, and fish is highly toxic to invertebrates. Zectran and carbofuran, among the most toxic compounds to mammals and birds,

TABLE VIII

Comparative Toxicity of Pesticides to Various Organisms[a]

Pesticide	Oral LD_{50}, mg/kg Rat	Mallard	Pheasant	24-hr LC_{50} Rainbow trout	Blue gill	Fairy shrimp[b]	Stonefly[c]	Water flea[d]	Topical LD_{50}, μg/g *Musca domestica*	*Apis mellifera*
Aldrin	36–60	520	16.8	0.0061	0.010	45	0.008(2d)	0.028	2.9	4.5
Atrazine	3080	> 2000		12.6(2d)				3.6		> 100
Carbaryl	850	> 2179	> 2000	2.0	2.5	0.040	0.030	0.0064	900	2.3
Carbofuran	5	0.40	4.2		0.24(4d)				4.6	
Chlordane	335–430	1200		0.022	0.095	0.160	0.170	0.029	6.0	
Diazinon	108– 76	3.5	4.3	0.380	0.052	0.80	0.06(2d)	0.0009	2.95	
DDT	113–118	> 2240	1296	0.012	0.005(2d)	0.0047	0.041	0.0036	1.9	20.0
Dicamba	2900		673–800	35(2d)	130(2d)	10				> 100
Dieldrin	46–46	381	79	0.0031	0.015	1.4	0.006	0.240	0.95	2.2
Disulfoton	6.8–2.3	6.5			0.040(2d)	0.110	0.040			
Diuron	3400	> 2000				0.70	3.6	1.4		> 100
2,4–D acid	375	> 1000	472		8	1.4–6.8 (ester)	8.5 (ester)	0.2		> 100
Endrin	17.8–7.5	5.6	1.8	0.0028	0.0008	0.0064	0.004	0.020	3.15	20.8
Heptachlor	100–162	> 2000		0.013	0.026	0.150	0.008	0.042	2.25	
Lindane	88–91		500–600	0.018(2d)	0.10	0.120	0.012	0.460	0.85	2.0
Malathion	1375–1000	1485		0.130	0.110	0.0038	0.035	0.0018	26.5	1.1
Methoxychlor	6000	> 2000		0.074	0.083	0.0047	0.030	0.00078	9.0	
Parathion, ethyl	13–3.6	1.9–2.1	12.4	2.0	0.047	0.012	0.028	0.0004	0.9	3.5
Parathion, methyl	14–24	10.0	8.2	2.75(3d)	8.0(2d)				1.2	0.84
Phorate	2.3–1.1	0.62	7.1		0.0055(2d)	0.024				
Toxaphene	90–80	70.7	40	0.004(2d)	0.0066	0.180	0.018	0.015	11.0	274
Trifluralin	> 10,000	> 2000	> 2000	0.098	0.130	8.8	13	0.240		
Zectran	14.1–19	3.0	4.5	8	11.2	0.086	0.032	0.01	65	0.6

[a] Values from Pimentel (1971), Hayes (1963).
[b] *Gammarus lacustris*.
[c] *Pteronarcys californicus*.
[d] *Daphnia pulex*, 2 day values.

are of low toxicity to fish. Endrin, phorate, disulfoton, and parathion are general biocides, highly toxic to nearly all animals. Only the herbicides such as dalapon, dicamba, diquat, diuron, endothall, paraquat, 2,4-D, 2,4,5-T and simazine, seem relatively safe to all the animals listed.

B. Ecological magnification

This descriptive term applies to the ability of living organisms to concentrate stable, lipid soluble, water insoluble substances in their bodies either through successive accumulation in food chains or directly from water by partitioning. In this manner residues of substances such as DDT and dieldrin have been concentrated in fish $>1 \times 10^6$ and $>1 \times 10^5$ fold respectively over the concentration in the water. The first demonstration of this remarkable phenomenon resulted from the treatment of Clear Lake, California with DDD at 0.014–0.02 ppm and the observance of DDD residues in Western grebes and predaceous fish at 1600–2500 ppm. The overall magnification was about 120,000-fold (Hunt and Bishoff, 1960). Woodwell *et al.* (1967) describe a Long Island, New York estuary where a DDT concentration of 0.00005 ppm became successively magnified in plankton (0.04 ppm), invertebrates (0.16–0.42 ppm), fish (0.17–2.07 ppm), and predatory birds (3.15–75.5 ppm). The DDT level was concentrated about 10-fold in each trophic level and appeared in the upper levels of the food web largely as DDE the most stable metabolite. The overall magnification was about 120,000-fold. The magnification of aldrin through a terrestrial ecosystem where Missouri cornfields were treated over a 15 yr period with a total of about 25 lb/acre was studied by Korschgen (1970). The soil contained an average residue of 0.06 ppm aldrin, earthworms averaged 1.49 ppm; seed-eating ground beetles *Harpalus* contained 1.1 ppm; the predaceous beetle *Poecilus* 9.67 ppm; the seed-eating mice *Peromyscus*, *Mus*, and *Reithrodontomys* averaged 0.98 ppm; toads, *Bufo americanus*, feeding on insects and other invertebrates, 4.60 ppm; and garter snakes *Thamnophis sirtailis* which eat salamanders, toads, earthworms, and small birds and mammals, accumulated 10.3–14.4 ppm. Most of the aldrin was stored as the more stable metabolic oxidation product dieldrin and the overall magnification was about 200-fold.

The aquatic habit favors the concentration of trace residues of the stable organochlorine compounds in invertebrates and fish. Dustman and Stickel (1969) cite examples such as: fathead minnows concentrated endrin 10,000 ×; croakers concentrated DDT 20,000 ×; trout concentrated dieldrin 3300 ×; oysters concentrated lindane 60 ×; DDT 15,000 ×; and heptachlor 17,600 ×. In these cases, the water and the animal tissue, especially the lipids, seem to form a system of liquid–liquid partitioning between two immiscible solvents and Hamelink *et al.* (1971) suggest that in fish the pesticide passes through two partitions from water →blood, and from blood→fat. They suggest that the partition coefficients for the various organochlorine pesticides are roughly proportioned to their solubility in fat (ca 10 g/l)→solubility in water (DDT 0.0012, γ chlordane 0.009, aldrin 0.027, heptachlor 0.056, dieldrin 0.186, endrin 0.23, heptachlor epoxide 0.35, and lindane 10 ppm). Calculated partition coefficients for fat/water are: DDT ca 10^6, dieldrin 5×10^4, heptachlor epoxide 3×10^4, and lindane 10^3 which are remarkably close to the actual levels of concentration observed in nature.

C. Pesticides and fish

It will be noted from Table VIII that many of the organic insecticides are extremely toxic to fish in the ppb range, e.g. endrin, dieldrin, aldrin, heptachlor, toxaphene, chlordane and DDT. Disastrous fish kills have resulted from industrial effluents, accidental spillages and unwise disposal of spray tank residues into ponds and streams where fish and invertebrates may be killed for many miles downstream. Examples of such accidents include massive fish kills in the lower Mississippi River in 1963 attributed to effluents from the manufacture of endrin (Barthel *et al.*, 1969) and in the lower Rhine River from the sinking of a barge load of endsulfan.

DDT spraying of the Yellowstone River System in 1955 at 1 lb/acre by air for spruce budworm control was responsible for widespread mortality of mountain whitefish (*Proposium williamstoni*), brown trout (*Salmo trutta*) and longnose sucker (*Catostomus catostomus*). After subsequent spraying in 1957, dead fish were analyzed for DDT and the trout contained from 0.186–14.0 ppm DDT and 0–6.53 ppm DDE, and the whitefish 0.06–6.9 ppm DDT and 0–5.6 ppm DDE (Cope, 1961). The prolonged and deleterious effects of such spraying on important invertebrate sources of fish food are shown in Table IX (Cope, 1961). DDT aerial spraying of the Lake George region of New York for gypsy moth control was responsible for widespread contamination of the lake and total loss of lake trout fry in 1955–1958. The affected fry were observed to float upside down and then to sink and die. The symptoms always occurred after absorption of the yolk sac and subsequent study showed that DDT was present at 4.75 ppm or more in the fish eggs which displayed this syndrome and that as the yolk sac was absorbed the fish were poisoned and subsequently died (Burdick *et al.*, 1964).

Many other examples of the adverse effects of the organochlorine pesticides on fish could be cited and the entire problem is reviewed by Johnson (1968).

D. Pesticides and Birds

The effects of pesticides on bird populations have been more intensively considered than any other aspect of the impact of pesticides on the environment. As with fish in the aquatic environment, most of the concern has been directed at the use of the persistent organochlorine insecticides (Moore, 1965; Rudd and Genelly, 1956). Massive spraying of elms with DDT to control the elm bark beetle vectors (Scolytidae) of Dutch elm disease has resulted in dying robins and other birds (Barker, 1958; Hickey and Hunt, 1960). Such spraying contaminated the soil up to 18 ppm and earthworms contained 53–204 ppm DDT and DDE. Robins feeding on the contaminated earthworms suffered as much as 80% mortality and their bodies contained a median residue of 3 mg DDT, an amount which could be obtained by eating less than 100 earthworms. The widespread use of cereal seeds treated with dieldrin, DDT and other organochlorine insecticides has been an important cause of bird mortalities. Sowing of DDT-treated rice seed in California resulted in residues in pheasants averaging 740 ppm in body fat and lowered survival rates (Hunt, 1966). Spring seeding with dieldrin, aldrin, and heptachlor treated seed in Great Britain produced substantial evidence of bird mortality and the use of seeds treated with the organochlorine insecticides has been restricted in both the U.S. and Great Britain (Moore, 1965).

Many of the pesticides listed in Table VIII, especially carbofuran, diazinon, disulfoton, endrin, parathion, and phorate are acutely toxic to birds but their use patterns are such that damage to bird populations has not been appreciable.

Thin eggshell syndrome Drastic reductions in the populations of North American and European raptorial birds such as the peregrine falcon, (*Falco peregrinus*), sparrowhawk (*Accipiter niger*), kestrel (*Falco tinnunculus*), osprey (*Pandion haliaetus*), bald eagle (*Haliaetus leucocephalus*), and golden eagle (*Aquila chrysactos*) have been observed during the past 2 decades and these population declines coincided with the period of large scale use of DDT and other chlorinated organic insecticides. Although the complex reasons for these population declines are highly controversial, there is ample evidence that reproductive failure is a major factor (Pimentel, 1971). Egg shell fragility or thin egg shells is the most common cause and on Anacapa Island of California, where the complete reproductive failure of the brown pelican (*Pelecanus occidentalis*) was observed, egg shells were found to average 0.38 mm in thickness, or a decrease of 34% over normal (0.57 mm). Residues of DDT and DDE as high as 1200 ppm (85% DDE) were found and the fat of the adult birds, contained from 738–2603 ppm DDT and DDE (Pimentel 1971). A similar effect has been shown for the Scottish golden eagle where egg shell thickness has declined from an index of 3.146 over the period of 1848–1946, to 2.839 during 1951–1965, or a decrease of 9.9% (Ratcliffe, 1970). Bald eagle eggshells in Florida declined in weight from an average of 12.15 g in the pre-DDT era to 9.96 g in 1947–1962 or an 18% decrease, and this has been associated with a decline in the eagle population in Florida (Pimentel, 1971) although other factors must also be considered.

Laboratory experiments summarized by Pimentel (1971) show that feeding DDE to mallard ducks at 40 ppm induced a 14% decrease in eggshell thickness and in cracking of eggs. Eggshell thinning occurred at DDE levels as low as 10 ppm and duckling production per hen was reduced as much as 75% when these levels of DDE were fed. DDT

TABLE IX

Effects of DDT Forest Spraying on Bottom Insects of Yellowstone River[a]

	Number of organisms per 10 ft^2					
	Plecoptera	Ephemeroptera	Trichoptera	Diptera	Other	Total
Prespray	160	102	17	0	0	279
After 2 weeks	14	3	12	0	0	29
After 1 month	31	9	0	1	0	41
After 1 yr	35	91	103	39	15	283

[a] Data from Cope (1961).

was less effective in producing the thin-eggshell effect than DDE although this occurred in coturnix fed DDT at 10 ppm and 25 ppm.

Methylmercury fungicides These compounds, especially Panogen® or methylmercury dicyandiamide have been very widely used as fungicidal treatments for small grains. In Sweden, as much as 80% of the spring wheat sown from 1940–1965 was treated with such alkymercury fungicides. As a result, mercury became very widely distributed in wild birds. Borg *et al.* (1966) studied the mercury content of the livers of seed eating birds, pheasants, partridges, pigeons, finches, etc., which were found dead. Of 253 birds investigated, 48% had Hg levels above 2 ppm and 20% above 10 ppm. There was a remarkable increase in the incidence of high levels of Hg in these bird livers during May–June and October–November which related to the planting of seed dressed with alkylmercury fungicides during these months (Borg *et al.*, 1968)˙ When pheasants were fed wheat treated with 20 ppm methylmercury dicyandiamide, a normal rate of agricultural use, the eggs had reduced hatchability with Hg residues of 1.3–2.0 ppm and the birds died in 29–61 days with liver residues of Hg ranging from 30 to 130 ppm. Wild pheasants and partridge eggs in Sweden contained about 30 ppm Hg (Borg *et al.*, 1966).

Predatory birds, hawks, falcons, eagles, and owls, were also examined for Hg content of the liver. Of a total of 412 predators found dead, shot, or trapped for examination, 62% had Hg levels above 2 ppm and 19% above 10 ppm (Borg *et al.*, 1966).

The methylmercury readily entered food chains and it was found that hens in Sweden fed grain grown from wheat whose seed was treated with alkylmercury fungicides produced eggs abnormally contaminated with Hg. Swedish eggs on the open market, 1964–1966, averaged 0.029 ppm Hg as compared with 0.007 ppm Hg in eggs on the market in Continental Europe (Westöö, 1969). Thus a daily consumption of two Swedish eggs could exceed the FAO/WHO recommended safe level for Hg intake of 0.00005 mg per kg body weight. As a result of the wildlife contamination and the dietary egg problem, alkylmercury fungicides were banned in Sweden on February 1, 1966. Subsequently, the Hg contents of Swedish hens' eggs decreased to an average of 0.009 ppm by September 1967 (Westöö, 1969).

E. Pesticides and bees

The honeybee *Apis mellifera* is not only an important domesticated animal producing honey and bees wax valued at $50 million annually in the U.S., but also is the primary agent responsible for the pollination of fruit, vegetable, and field crops valued in excess of $5 billion annually. As representative insects, bees are highly susceptible to insecticides and are a prime non-target victim of pesticides applied during blossom time when the bees' foraging patterns take them to sprayed orchards and field; or from pesticides carelessly applied near apiaries. As an example of the damage that insect control programs can do to bee colonies, the repeated application of carbaryl to cotton in the Imperial Valley of California as part of an eradication program for the pink bollworm *Pectinophora gossypiella*, is estimated to have killed 30,000 colonies of bees in 1967.

Anderson and Atkins (1968) have classified the toxicity of pesticides to the honeybee *Apis mellifera* in groups as follows:

Group I *highly toxic* LD_{50} 0.001–1.99 μg per bee: includes the organophosphorus esters parathion, methyl parathion, azinphos, malathion, dimethoate, dichlorvos, diazinon, Dursban®, fenthion, mevinphos, phosphamidon, naled, and fenitrothion; the carbamates carbaryl, carbofuran, aldicarb, propoxur, and Zectran®; and the organochlorine compounds aldrin, dieldrin, heptachlor, lindane; and the arsenicals.

Group II *moderately toxic* LD_{50} 2.0–10.99 μg per bee includes DDT, endrin, endosulfan, mirex, chlordane, disulfoton, phorate, demeton, ronnel, coumaphos, Abate®, Ciodrin®, and carbophenothion.

Group III *relatively non-toxic* LD_{50} greater than 11.0 μg per bee includes all the common acaricides, pyrethroids, trichlorfon, cryolite, DDD, methoxychlor, Dilan®, rotenone, ryania, toxaphene, the fungicides, the herbicides, and the defoliants.

Simple precautions such as avoiding insecticide applications during bloom, or applying toxic insecticides only as soil and seed treatments can greatly minimize bee losses.

IV. Pesticides in Humans

Humans, in an ecological sense, are consumers at the top of the food pyramid and are exposed to pesticide residues contained nearly everywhere in cereals, fruits and vegetables, and in meat, fish, and poultry. Additionally humans are exposed directly to pesticides from occupational use of aerosol products in the home, from home and garden sprays, and from effluents from agricultural operations. Therefore it is not surprising that traces of the stable organochlorine insecticides are found in the body fats of humans everywhere.

DDT in humans

Elaborate monitoring studies of pesticide residues in humans have been reported by Hayes (1966), Durham (1969) and Mrak (1969). DDT was first found in human fat in 1948 and at least 9 general surveys of the DDT content of human fat have been made in various areas of the United States. These show that DDT is stored in the body fat of everyone in the United States, with a mean storage level in the 1960's of about 8 ppm combined DDT and its principal metabolite DDE. There has been no significant increase in the storage of DDT and DDE since this level was attained in 1950 as shown in Table X (Durham, 1969).

TABLE X

Storage of DDT and Metabolites in the Population of the United States[a]

Year	Location	ppm in body fat		
		DDT	DDE	Total
1950	California	5.3	–	5.3
1955	Florida	7.4	12.5	19.9
1954–56	Georgia, Washington	4.9	6.8	11.7
1956	Georgia	5.5	10.1	15.6
1961–62	Georgia, Kentucky, Arizona, Washington	4.0	8.7	12.7
1962–63	Illinois	2.9	8.2	11.1
1964	Northeast, Midwest, South, Far West	2.5	5.1	7.6
1964	Louisiana	2.3	8.0	10.3

[a] Data from Durham (1969).

The storage levels of DDT and DDE in people in other countries have also been investigated (Durham, 1969). The levels were lowest in countries where little DDT is used, e.g. Denmark with DDT 0.6 and DDE 2.7 ppm; and highest in countries such as India, DDT 16 and DDE 10 ppm, where large amounts of DDT are used in malaria eradication.

The storage of DDT in human fat is a direct function of level of intake and is lowest in meat abstainers, DDT 2.3 and DDE 3.6 ppm; and Eskimos, DDT 0.8 and DDE 2.2 ppm; whose diets contained the lowest amounts of DDT. Volunteers given 35 mg per day orally stored DDT 281 and DDE 40 ppm, and a formulator in a DDT factory had DDT 648 and DDE 483 ppm; yet these men remained in good health (Hayes, 1966). The half-life of DDT and DDE stored in humans is about 0.5 yr (Durham, 1969) so that in the absence of DDT intake the levels in human populations should slowly decline.

DDT and its metabolites DDE and DDD are also found in most other human tissues: blood DDT 0.0068 and DDE 0.0114 ppm, milk 0.08–0.13 ppm, adrenal glands 0.7 ppm (Durham, 1969). DDT ingested by humans is excreted slowly as 4,4–dichlorodiphenyl acetic acid (DDA) which is present in the urine of the general U.S. population at <0.02–0.18 ppm (Hayes, 1966). The levels of DDA in human blood and urine roughly parallel the rate of intake and can be used to monitor the exposure (Mrak, 1969).

The significance of levels of DDT and its metabolites DDE and DDD in the general population is complex. Food is generally believed to contribute as much as 89% of the total intake of DDT but recent studies showing substantial fat storage of DDT in Eskimos and in institutional patients where DDT intake is very low suggest that non-dietary sources such as house dust may contribute up to 50% of the total body burden (Mrak, 1969). The non-white population of the U.S. has significantly higher fat storage of DDT than the white population suggesting the influence of dietary factors and socioeconomic factors resulting in greater use of household insecticides. Fat storage of DDE increases with the age of the population, especially in non-whites where the level increased from 4.06 ppm in the 0–5 yrs category to 8.61 ppm at 41–50 yrs, and 15.50 ppm at 90+ yrs. Accumulation in States with cooler climates averaged 4.85 ppm as compared with 9.21 ppm in warmer States. There is no clear cut evidence of a sex difference in fat storage of DDT or in positive association with specific disease conditions (Mrak, 1969).

Other pesticides in humans

Other stable organochlorine insecticides or their stable metabolites are also found in human tissues. Surveys of the U.S. population have shown levels of these materials in fat and blood: BHC isomers—fat 0.20–0.60 ppm, blood 0.0031–0.0019 ppm; heptachlor epoxide—fat 0.10–0.24 ppm, blood 0.0008–0.0011 ppm (Hayes, 1966; Durham, 1969). In addition to these pesticides demonstrated in the blood of the general U.S. population, trace levels of chlordane, toxaphene, endrin, aldrin, pentachlorophenol, and 2,4–D have been found in tissues of humans with unusual occupational or accidental exposure.

Most of the other types of pesticides widely used, the organophosphorus esters, carbamates, phenoxy- and benzoic-acids, triazines, ureas are less persistent in the environment than the organochlorine compounds and are rapidly metabolized by enzymes in the human liver and converted to predominately water-soluble products eliminated in the urine. Therefore there is little evidence of fat storage of these compounds. Monitoring of the urinary content of water-soluble metabolites is a very sensitive measure of intake of such pesticides and has been studied for parathion, malathion and related organophorus esters, the carbamates carbaryl and propoxur, dinitro–*o*–cresol, lead, arsenic, and mercury (Hayes, 1966).

GLOSSARY

Abate, *0,0,0′,0′*-tetramethyl *0,0′*–thiodi–*p*–phenylene phosphorothionate
alachlor, 2–chloro–2′,6′–diethyl–*N*–(methoxymethyl) acetanilide
aldicarb, 2–methyl–2–methylthiopropionaldoxime *0–N*–methylcarbamate
aldrin, 1,2,3,4,10,10–hexachloro–1,4,4a,5,8,8a–hexachloro–1, 4–*endo*, *exo*–5,8–dimethanonaphthalene
amiben, 3–amino–2,5–dichlorobenzoic acid
atrazine, 2–chloro–4–ethylamino–6–isopropylamino–*s*–triazine
azinphos methyl,*0,0*–dimethyl *S*–[4–oxo–1,2,3–benzotriazin–3(4H)–ylmethyl] phosphorodithioate
BHC, mixture of stereoisomeric 1,2,3,4,5,6–hexachlorocyclohexane
captan, *N*–trichloromethylmercapto–4–cyclohexane 1,2–dicarboximide
carbaryl, 1–naphthyl *N*–methylcarbamate
carbofuran, 2,2–dimethyl–2,3–dihydro–7–benzofuranyl *N*–methylcarbamate
carbophenothion, *S*–[*p*–chlorophenyl) thiomethyl] *0,0′*–diethyl phosphorodithioate
CDAA, 2–chloro–*N,N*–diallyl acetamide
CDEC, 2–chloroallyl–*N,N*–diethyldithiocarbamate
chlorbenzilate, ethyl 4,4′–dichlorobenzilate
chlordane, 2,3,4,5,6,7,8,8–octachloro–2,3,3a,4,7,7a–hexahydro–4,7–methanoindene
Ciodrin, α–methylbenzyl–3–hydroxy–*cis*–crotonate dimethylphosphate
coumaphos, *0,0*–diethyl *0*–(3–chloro–4–methyl–7–coumarinyl) phosphorothionate
cryolite, sodium fluoaluminate
dalapon, 2,2–dichloropropionic acid
2,4–D, 2,4–dichlorophenoxyacetic acid
DDA, 4,4′–dichlorodiphenylacetic acid
DDD, 1,1–dichloro–2,2–bis–(*p*–chlorophenyl)–ethane
DDE, 1,1–dichloro–2,2–bis(*p*–chlorophenyl) ethylene
DDT, 1,1,1–trichloro–2,2–bis(*p*–chlorophenyl) ethane
demeton, 40:60 mixture of *0,0*–diethyl *S*–(2–ethylthio)ethyl phosphorothiolate with *0,0*–diethyl *0*–(2–ethylthio)ethyl phosphorothionate
diazinon, *0,0*–diethyl–*0*–(2–isopropyl–4–methyl–6–pyrimidinyl) phosphorothionate
dibromochloropropane, 1,2–dibromo–3–chloropropane
dicamba, 2–methoxy–3,6–dichlorobenzoic acid
dichloran, 2,6–dichloro–4–nitroaniline
dichlorvos, 2,2–dichlorovinyl dimethylphosphate
dicofol, 4,4′–dichloro–α–(trichloromethyl) benzhydrol
dieldrin, 1,2,3,4,10,10–hexachloro–*exo*–6,7–epoxy–1,4,4a,5,6, 7,8,8a–octahydro–1,4–*endo*, *exo*–5,8–dimethanonaphthalene
Dilan, mixture of one part 1,1–bis(*p*–chlorophenyl)–2–nitropropane and two parts 1,1–bis(*p*–chlorophenyl)–2–nitrobutane
dimethoate, *0,0*–dimethyl *S*–(*N*–methylcarbamoylmethyl) phosphorodithioate
dinitro–*o*–cresol (DNOC), 4,6–dinitro–*o*–cresol
diquat, 1,1′–ethylene–2,2′–dipyridylium dibromide
disulfoton, *0,0*–diethyl *S*–2–(ethylthio)ethyl phosphorodithioate
diuron (DCMU), *N*–3,4–dichlorophenyl–*N′,N′*–dimethyl urea
Dursban, *0,0*–diethyl *0*–3,5,6–trichloro–2–pyridyl phosphorothionate
endosulfan, 6,7,8,9,10,10–hexachloro–1,5,5a,6,9,9a–hexahydro–6,9–methano–2,4,3–benzodioxathiepin 3–oxide
Endothall, 7–oxabicyclo (2,2,1)heptane–2,3–dicarboxylic acid
endrin, 1,2,3,4,10,10–hexachloro–*exo*–6,7–epoxy–1,4,4a,5,6, 7,8,8a–octahydro–1,4,5,8–*endo*, *endo*–dimethanonaphthalene
EPTC, *S*–ethyl,*N,N*–dipropylthiocarbamate
fenitrothion, *0,0*–dimethyl *0*–(4–nitro–*m*–tolyl) phosphorothionate
fenthion, *0,0*–dimethyl *0*[4–(methylthio)–*m*–tolyl] phosphorothionate
ferbam, ferric dimethyl dithiocarbamate
heptachlor, 1,4,5,6,7,8,8–heptachloro–3a,4,5,5a–tetrahydro–4,7–*endo*–methanoindene
heptachlor epoxide, 1,4,5,6,7,8,8–heptachloro–3a,4,5,5a–tetrahydro–2,3–epoxy–4,7–*endo*–methanoindene
lindane, *gamma*–isomer of 1,2,3,4,5,6–hexachlorocyclohexane
malathion, *0,0*–dimethyl *S*–(1,2–dicarbethoxyethyl) phosphorodithioate
maneb, manganese ethylene bis(dithiocarbamate)
MCPA, 4–chloro–2–methylphenoxyacetic acid
methoxychlor, 1,1,1–trichloro–2,2–bis(*p*–methoxyphenyl) ethane
methyl parathion, *0,0*–dimethyl *0*–*p*–nitrophenyl phosphorothionate
mevinphos, 2–methoxycarbonyl–1–methylvinyl dimethyl–phosphate
mirex, dodecachlorooctahydro–1,2,3–metheno–2*H*–cyclobuta (cd) pentalene
monuron, 3–(*p*–chlorophenyl)–1,1–dimethylurea
naled, 1,2–dibromo–2,2–dichloroethyl dimethylphosphate
nicotine, *l*–1–methyl–2–(3′–pyridyl)–pyrrolidine
Panogen, methylmercury dicyandiamide
Paraquat, 1,1′–dimethyl–4,4′–bipyridynium ion
parathion, *0,0*–diethyl *0*–*p*–nitrophenyl phosphorothionate
o–phenylphenol
phorate, *0,0*–diethyl *S*–(ethylthio)–methyl phosphorodithioate
Phosphamidon, dimethyl diethylamido–1–chlorocrotonyl–(2) phosphate
picloram, 4–amino–3,5,6–trichloropicolinic acid
propachlor, 2–chloro–*N*–isopropyl–*N*–phenylacetamide
propham, isopropyl carbanilate
propoxur, *o*–isopropoxyphenyl *N*–methylcarbamate
pyrethrins, insecticidal compounds in pyrethrum flowers, *Chrysanthemum cineraiaefolium*
ronnel, *0,0*–dimethyl *0*–2,4,5–trichlorophenyl phosphorothionate
rotenone, extracts of *Derris* or *Lonchocarpus* plants
ryania, roots and stems of *Ryania speciosa*
silvex, 2–(2,4,5–trichlorophenoxy) propionic acid
simazine, 2–chloro–4,6–bis(ethylamino)–3–triazine
2,4,5–T, 2,4,5–trichlorophenoxyacetic acid
tetradifon, *S*–*p*–chlorophenyl 2,4,5–trichlorophenyl sulfone
tetraethyl pyrophosphate (TEPP)
thiram, tetramethylthiuram disulfide
toxaphene, mixture of isomers of octachlorocamphene (67–69% chlorine)
trichlorfon, dimethyl (2,2,2–trichloro–1–hydroxyethyl) phosphonate
trifluralin, α,α,α–trifluoro–2,6–dinitro–*N,N*–dipropyl–*p*–toluidine
warfarin, 3–(1′–phenyl–2′–acetylethyl)–4–hydroxycoumarin
Zectran, 4–dimethylamino–3,5–xylyl *N*–methylcarbamate
zineb, zinc ethylene–1,2–bisdithiocarbamate

REFERENCES

Akesson, N. B. and W. E. Yates (1964) *Ann. Rev. Entomol.* **9**, 285.

Anderson, L. D. and E. L. Atkins (1968) *Ann. Rev. Entomol.*, **13**, 213.

Barker, R. J. (1958) *J. Wildlife Manag.*, **22**, 269.

Barthel, W. F., J. C. Hawthorne, J. H. Ford, G. C. Bolton, L. L. McDowell, E. H. Cressinger and D. A. Parsons (1969) *Pesticide Monitoring J.*, **3**, 8.

Borg, K., H. Wanntorp, K. Erne and E. Hanko (1966) *J. App. Ecol.*, **3**, Suppl., 171.

Borg, K., H. Wanntorp, K. Erne and E. Hanko (1968) *Viltrevy*, **5**, (5)1.

Breidenback, A. W., C. G. Gunnerson, F. K. Kawahara, J. J. Lichtenberg and R. S. Green (1967) *Publ. Hlth Repts.*, **82**, 139.

Brown, E. and Y. A. Nishioka (1967) *Pesticide Monitoring J.*, **1**, 38.

Burdick, G. E., E. J. Harris, J. H. Dean, T. M. Walker, J. Skea and D. Colby (1964) *Trans. Am. Fish. Soc.*, **93**, 127.

Butler, P. A. (1966) *J. App. Ecol.*, **3**, Suppl., 253.

Butler, P. A. (1969) The significance of DDT residues in estuarine fauna. *Chemical Fallout*, Ed. by Miller, M. W. and G. G. Berg. C. C. Thomas, Springfield, Illinois.

Cohen, J. M. and C. Pinkerton (1966) Organic pesticides application of carbaryl rate to cotton in the environment, *Adv. Chem. Ser.*, 163.

Cope, O. B. (1961) *Trans. Am. Fish. Soc.*, **90**, 249.

Cope, O. B. (1966) *J. App. Ecol.*, **3**, Suppl., 33.

Cope, O. B. (1971) *Ann. Rev. Entomol.*, **16**, 325.

Duggan, R. E. (1969) *Ann. N.Y. Acad. Sci.*, **160**, 173.

Durham, W. F. (1969) *Ann. N.Y. Scad. Sci.*, **160**, 183.

Dustman, E. H. and L. F. Stickel (1966) Pesticide residues in the ecosystem. *Pesticides and Their Effects on Soils and Water*, Amer. Soc. Agronomy, Spec. Publ. 8.

Dustman, E. H. and L. F. Stickel (1969) *Ann. N.Y. Acad. Sci.*, **160**, 162.

Edwards, C. A. (1964) *Soils and Fertility*, **27**, 451.

Environmental Protection Agency (1970–1971) Summary of Registered Agricultural Pesticide Chemical Uses, Washington, D.C.

Gentry, J. W. (1966) Nat. Acad. Sci., Nat. Res. Coun., Publ. 1402, 303.

Gunther, F. A. and R. C. Blinn (1965) *Analysis of Insecticides and Acaricides*, Interscience Publishers, N.Y.

Hamelink, J. L., R. C. Waybrant and R. C. Ball (1971) *Trans Am. Fish. Soc.*, **100**, 207.

Harris, C. R. (1971) Pesticides in soil, Proc. Internat. Symposium, Michigan State Univ. p. 58.

Harris, C. R. and E. R. Lichtenstein (1961) *J. Econ. Entomol.* **54**, 1038.

Harris, C. R., W. W. Sans and J. R. W. Miles (1966) *J. Agr. Food Chem.*, **14**, 398.

Harrison, H. L., O. L. Loucks, J. W. Mitchell, D. F. Parkhurst, C. R. Tracy, D. G. Watts and V. J. Yannacone, Jr. (1970) *Science*, **170**, 503.

Hayes, W. J. Jr. (1963) Clinical Handbook Economic Poisons, U.S. Public Health Service, Communicable Disease Center, Atlanta, Ga.

Hayes, W. J. Jr. (1966) Monitoring food and people for pesticide content, Scientific Aspects of Pest Control, Nat. Acad. Sci., Publ. 1402.

Hickey, J. J. and L. B. Hunt (1960) *J. Wildlife Manag.*, **24**, 259.

Hunt, E. G. (1966) *J. App. Ecol.*, **3**, Suppl., 113.

Hunt, G. and A. I. Bishoff (1960) *Calif. Fish Game*, **46**, 91.

Jegier, Z. (1969) *Ann. N.Y. Acad. Sci.*, **160**, 143.

Johnson, D. W. (1968) *Trans. Am. Fish. Soc.*, **97**, 398.

Jones, J. S. and M. B. Hatch (1937) *Soil Sci.*, **44**, 37.

Kearney, P. C., R. G. Nash and A. R. Isensee (1969) Persistence of pesticide residues in soils, *Chemical Fallout*, Ed. by Miller, M. W. and G. G. Berg. C. C. Thomas, Springfield, Illinois.

Korschgen, L. J. (1970) *J. Wildlife Manag.*, **34**, 186.

Kraybill, H. F., Ed. (1969) Biological effects of pesticides in mammalian systems, *Ann. N.Y. Acad. Sci.*, **160**, Art. **1**.

Lichtenstein, E. P. (1969) Persistence and degradation of pesticides in the environment, *Scientific Aspects of Pest Control*, Nat. Acad. Sci., Publ. 1402.

Lichtenstein, E. P., G. R. Myrdal and K. R. Schultz (1965) *J. Agr. Food Chem.*, **3**, 126.

Melnikov, N. N. (1971) *Chemistry of Pesticides*, Springer-Verlag, N.Y.

Menzies, C. M. (1969) *Metabolism of pesticides*, U.S. Bureau Sport Fisheries, Special Scientific Rept. Wildlife, No. 1267, Washington, D.C.

Metcalf, R. L. (1972) *J. Environ. Qual.*, **1**, 10.

Moore, N. W. (1965) Environmental contamination by pesticides, *Ecology and the Industrial Society*, Ed. by Goodman, G. T., R. W. Edwards and J. M. Lambert. John Wiley and Sons, N.Y.

Mrak, E. M. (1969) Report of the Secretary's Commission on Pesticides and Their Relationship to Environmental Health, U.S. Dept. Health, Educ. Welfare, Washington, D.C.

Newsom, L. D. (1967) *Ann. Rev. Entomol.*, **12**, 257.

Pimentel, D. (1971) Ecological Effects of Pesticides on Non-Target Species, President's Office Science Technology, Washington, D.C.

President's Science Advisory Committee (PSAC) (1965) Restoring the Quality of our Environment, The White House, Washington, D.C.

Quinby, G. E. and G. M. Doornick (1965) *J. Amer. Med. Assoc.*, **191**, (1)95.

Rainey, R. H. (1967) *Science*, **155**, 1242.

Ratcliffe, D. A. (1970) *Nature*, **215**, 208.

Reinert, R. E. (1970) *Pesticide Monitoring J.*, **3**, 233.

Reynolds, H. T., T. R. Fukuto, R. L. Metcalf and R. B. March (1957) *J. Econ. Entomol.*, **56**, 527.

Risebrough, R. W., R. I. Huggett, E. D. Griffin and E. D. Goldberg (1968) *Science*, **159**, 1233.

Rudd, L. L. and R. E. Genelly (1956) *Calif. Fish Game Bull.*, **7**, 309.

Rudd, R. L. and R. E. Genelly (1956) *Auk*, **73**, 529.

Smith, G. E. and G. G. Isom (1967) *Pesticide Monitoring J.*, **1**, 16.

Stanley, C. W. (1968) Study to Determine Atmospheric Contamination by Pesticides, Final Rept. Midwest Research Inst.

Tabor, E. G. (1966) *Trans. N.Y. Acad. Sci.*, **28**, 569.

U.S. Dept. Interior (1968) Water Quality Criteria, Reports of National Technical Advisory Committee to Secretary of Interior, Fed. Water Pollution Control Administration, Washington, D.C.

Warner, R. E. (1967) *Bull. World Health Org.*, **36**, 181.

Wasserman, M. I. S., G. Mandric and P. Horvath (1960) Amer. Med. Assoc., *Arch. Ind. Health*, **21**, 503.

Westöö, G., Methylmercury compounds in animal food (1969) *Chemical Fallout*, Ed. by Miller, M. W. and G. G. Berg, p. 75. C. C. Thomas, Springfield, Illinois.

White-Stevens, R. Ed. (1971) *Pesticides in the Environment*, **1**, Pt. 1, Marcel Dekker, Inc., N.Y.

Wolman, A. A. and A. J. Wilson (1971) *Pesticide Monitoring J.*, **4**.

Woodwell, G. M., C. F. Wurster and P. A. Isaacson (1967) *Science*, **156**, 821.

Woodwell, G. M., P. P. Craig and H. A. Johnson (1971) *Science*, **174**, 1101.

World Health (1968) p. 10, April.

ROBERT L. METCALF
University of Illinois, Urbana

PHYSIOLOGICAL EFFECTS OF CHEMICALS: see EFFECTS OF CHEMICALS ON HUMAN ECOLOGY

PLANT ECOLOGY: see ECOLOGY OF PLANTS

POLLUTION EFFECTS: see EFFECTS OF ATMOSPHERIC POLLUTANTS; POLLUTION EFFECTS ON FISH

POLLUTION EFFECTS ON FISH

Introduction

During the past twenty five years, man has subjected the earth to an increasing variety of chemical substances never before encountered by living organisms. Many of these foreign substances, which originate from industrial, agricultural and municipal sources, are seriously threatening the natural environmental conditions established over geologic time by evolutionary processes. Organisms, including man, are finding it more and more difficult to escape the consequences of exposure to these compounds, many of which are known to interfere with life sustaining biochemical and reproductive mechanisms. Little is known, however, concerning the effects the vast majority of these pollutants will have on plants and animals that inhabit this planet.

The aquatic environment is the ultimate destination of most of these contaminants as a result of rainfall and runoff from the lands. The establishment of water quality requirements for the protection of fish life must, therefore, become an item of first priority. The task is complicated, however, by the fact that different species of fish as well as different developmental stages of the same or different species exhibit wide variations in their sensitivity or tolerance to foreign materials. In addition to the basic biochemical and physiological information needed to evaluate the harmful effects foreign substances have on organisms is severely lacking for fish and other aquatic organisms.

It is the purpose of this chapter to briefly discuss the current state of knowledge in regard to the response of fishes to environmental contaminants. Because of the serious lack of information in the area of fish toxicology,* it is not possible, nor is it within the scope of this discussion, to present even an outline of the toxic effects of the many foreign substances which fish encounter. Instead, representative compounds have been selected to illustrate the principles that are believed to play a major role in determining how fish respond to environmental contaminants. Unfortunately, these principles are based almost entirely on research performed over the last several decades dealing with the toxicologic responses of mammalian species, including man, to drugs and foreign compounds. Until equivalent research is performed on fishes, we will be forced to rely on these mammalian principles when attempting to evaluate the effects foreign compounds have on fish species.

* Toxicology is the scientific discipline that deals with the quantitation of injurious effects on living systems resulting from chemical and physical agents that bring about alterations in cell or organ structure and function.

Mechanisms of Toxicity

Foreign substances can injure organisms through a variety of mechanisms but these can generally be grouped into two categories: specific and non-specific injury. Chemicals that produce non-specific injury usually do so at the site of exposure, such as skin, respiratory membranes, oral mucosa, and intestinal mucose. Frequently, such injury is the result of the caustic or corrosive nature of the chemical with the cellular responses being directly related to the concentration of toxicant within the cell or tissue involved. Agents producing this type of injury are commonly referred to as "primary irritants" because they induce local, minor to severe inflammatory responses and occasionally extensive necrosis (death) of cells. Excellent examples of these chemicals are acids, bases and aldehydes, all of which are strong irritants to mucous and gill membranes.

Other compounds, unlike the non-specific action of the primary irritants, can have a high degree of specificity and act at low dose levels at certain receptor sites to produce pathological change in specific cells with subsequent alteration of the function of organ systems. The degree of injury is dependent on the efficiency of the repair mechanisms for the tissue involved. If a cell is not irreversibly damaged, functional and structural characteristics may return to normal. Cells that are premanently injured are usually replaced by fibrous (scar) tissue. Fibrosis can seriously impair the functional capability of the tissue or organ involved.

Examples of substances that exhibit specific toxicological actions are those that produce mutations by interfering with the genetic machinery of germ cells. Mutation of a dominant gene may express itself immediately and produce fetal abnormalities (teratogenic effects) or early fetal death. Other mutations may not express themselves for several generations and then suddenly appear creating serious abnormalities for that individual and its offspring. Chemicals may be carcinogenic (e.g. diethylnitrosamine and aflatoxin) and initiate the growth of malignant tumors in fish and mammals (Stanton, 1965; Ashley *et al.*, 1964). Many toxicants directly or indirectly affect reproductive mechanism, gonadal growth and development, spawning behavior, and fry survival by specific toxicological actions. This can frequently result in a depletion or extinction of a susceptible species.

Factors that Influence Toxicity

Several biological, physical and chemical factors play a part in determining the ultimate toxicological consequences of a foreign compound on an organism. To produce injurious effects, a toxicant must achieve an adequate concentration at its sites of action. The concentration attained at these sites in the animal obviously depends on the amount of foreign compound present in the animal's environment. Equally important, however, are the extent and rate of the toxicant's absorption, distribution, binding or localization in tissues, inactivation, and excretion. These factors are depicted in Figure 1 (Goodman and Gilman, 1970).

The following sections discuss each of these aspects that play the major role in the response of organisms to foreign compounds.

Absorption of the toxicant

Generally speaking, a compound with specific toxicological actions must first be absorbed and distributed (biological translocation) in an organism before it can reach its specific site of action and exert its toxic effect. The ease with which foreign substances are absorbed, therefore, is a significant factor in determining the toxicity of foreign compounds. Absorption of substances by fish occurs through the skin, oral mucosa, intestinal mucosa, and gills. Because it is necessary that gill surfaces be exposed to large volumes of water for the maintenance of adequate blood levels of CO_2 and O_2, this organ is an especially vulnerable site for the absorption of foreign materials. Fish are, therefore, exceptionally susceptible to toxicants that readily cross the gill epithelium. In addition, fish acquire many foreign substances from their diet by absorption across the gastrointestinal mucosa. It should be mentioned, however, that studies are severely lacking about this

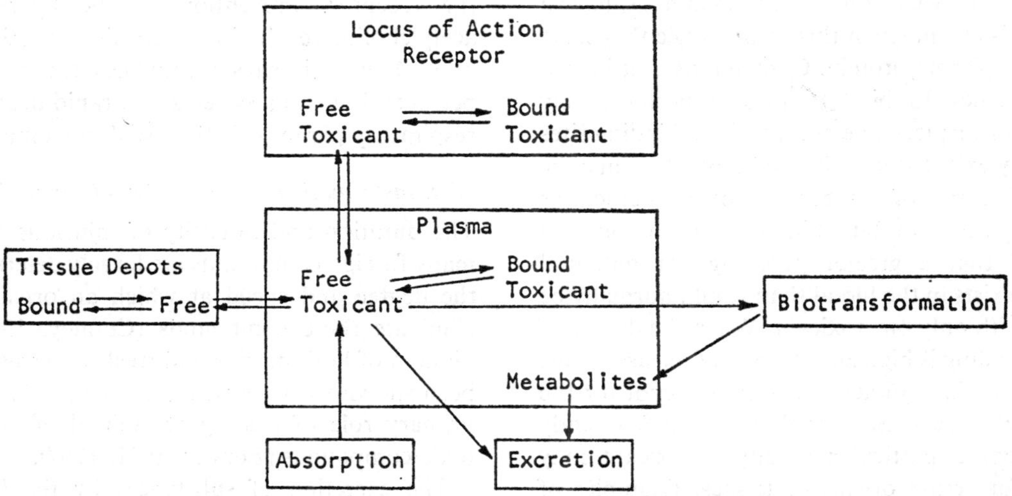

Figure 1

and other mechanisms of translocation of foreign substances in fishes.

The biochemical and physicalchemical properties of a compound determine both its ability to cross biological membranes and its distribution within an organism. In general, the non-ionized, non-polar forms of compounds are significantly soluble in fat, i.e. lipid-soluble, and are therefore readily transported across the lipoidal components which characterize animal-cell membranes (Whittaker, 1968). The chemical structure of a foreign compound also determines its ability to react with biological molecules as well as its susceptibility to biotransformation (metabolism) by organisms. The ability of an animal to metabolize foreign compounds is important to that organism because the products (metabolites) formed usually are less toxic (but occasionally greater) than the parent compound. A more detailed discussion of biotransformation mechanisms appears later in this chapter.

Distribution of the toxicant

Once the toxicant is absorbed and has entered an organism's blood or lymphatic system, it is readily transported and distributed to sites of action, centers of metabolic breakdown or detoxication, storage, and excretion.

Most toxicants are transported reversibly bound to blood proteins with only a small portion existing in the free or unbound state. Compounds must usually exist in this unbound state to react with biological molecules (receptors) and interfere with biochemical mechanisms. Therefore, the total amount of plasma protein available for the binding and transport of toxic substances plays an important role in the toxicological consequences of these compounds (Petermann, 1961). It is interesting to note that fish, when compared to mammals, have a distinct disadvantage in this regard since they have much less plasma protein. Compounds that have a high tendency to bind to plasma proteins may compete or displace one another from binding sites when they exist together in the blood. This may be the mechanism of dangerous toxic interactions because plasma protein binding sites become so saturated that a greater percenage of unbound toxicant exists in the blood than would normally be present with only one toxicant. When the degree of plasma binding is high and the rate of release is low, plasma proteins can act as a storage depot for the bound substances. Storage depots also frequently result from a particular affinity a toxicant may possess for cerain organs or tissues. Examples of this are the chlorinated hydrocarbon pesticides which are stored in body fat and heavy metals such as copper and mercury which are stored in the liver and kidney of fish (Life, 1969).

Many foreign compounds are capable of producing a specific effect, i.e. are selectively toxic, on a specific biological system or systems. These systems are said to be the site of locus of action of the chemical. The site may be confined to one anatomic location within the animal, or may be diffusely located throughout the animal. Two fundamental types of mechanisms are responsible for the selective action of chemicals on cells or cellular mechanisms.

The first type is a result of factors that increase the concentration of the toxicant at specific cell or tissue sites. This is accomplished in the organism by mechanisms of selective translocation and biotransformation. One good example is the renal tubular (kidney cell) injury produced in fish exposed to copper. Because copper is excreted by the kidney it accumulates at tubular cells. As the concentration rises injurious levels are reached and these cells are damaged or destroyed (Life, 1969).

A second mechanism in the selective toxicity of chemicals on cells involves the presence of specific targets or receptor systems in exposed cells. In this case, the concentration of the toxicant is the same for all cells, but only certain cells are affected. This is due to the specificity of action of the toxicant on receptors that are normally occupied by endogenous hormonal or neurohormonal substances. Organophosphorus compounds such as parathion and malathion are good examples of selectively toxic agents that act in this way. These cholinesterase inhibitors act to inhibit the enzyme responsible for hydrolysis of the neurotransmitter, acetylcholine. In this example cholinesterase is considered to be the receptor. Prevention of the hydrolysis of acetylcholine results in the continuous stimulation of post-synaptic sites throughout the central and peripheral nervous systems and rapid death due to respiratory paralysis is the usual outcome.

Biotransformation and excretion of the toxicant

The duration and intensity of injurious action of many foreign compounds are largely determined by the degree and speed at which an organism can eliminate these compounds (Conney, 1967). The kidneys of both marine and fresh water fishes have been shown to share with mammalian kidneys the primary role of ridding an animal of potentially toxic compounds (Forster, 1961, 1967).

The excretion of substances by the kidney is largely determined by lipid solubility characteristics of the compounds as they enter renal tubules. Molecules with a high degree of lipid solubility are readily re-absorbed from the renal tubule through lipoidal membranes back into the circulating blood and consequently are not excreted. It is only through certain specific biochemical transformations of these foreign compounds by the organism itself that lipid solubilities are altered and tubular excretion is successful (Brodie and Erdos, 1962). These reactions or transformations can be classified as oxidations, reductions, hydrolyses and syntheses (conjugation).

Most animals, including fish, transform (metabolize) foreign compounds in two successive phases, the first phase consisting of a variety of oxidations, reductions, and hydrolyses and the second phase of a limited number of syntheses or conjugations (Williams, 1967). Phase I reactions can result in:

1) The inactivation of a toxic compound;

2) The conversion of an initially inactive compound into a toxic compound; and

3) The conversion of a toxic compound into another toxic compound.

The second phase of biotransformation, consisting of synthetic reactions, most often results in the conversion of toxic compounds into inactive excretory products. This concept of the metabolism of foreign compounds can be represented as in Figure 2 (Williams, 1967).

	Phase I		Phase II	
Drug	——→	Oxidation reduction and/or Hydrolysis products	——→	Synthetic or conjugation products
	Activation or inactivation		Inactivation	

Figure 2

Biochemical reactions of both phases of metabolism are catalyzed by enzymes located in various organ systems, and it is from the study of the qualitative and quantitative variations in these enzymes that an evaluation of detoxifying capacities can be made for an organism (Williams, 1967).

Phase I reactions are carried out by enzymes of normal metabolic routes and by enzymes which occur in the smooth endoplasmic reticulum of liver cells. When these cells are ruptured in the laboratory by homogenization the endoplasmic reticulum undergoes fragmentation. High-speed centrifugation separates these fragments from the remaining cell constituents. These fragments are referred to as microsomes and it is the microsomal enzymes that are involved in the metabolism of many drugs and foreign compounds. Microsomal enzymes do not generally act on lipid-insoluble compounds but rather convert lipid-soluble materials by oxidative and reductive processes to less lipid-soluble metabolities, which are more polar substances and, therefore, readily excretable by the kidney. Without these biotransformations, the effects of some foreign substances on organisms would last for months (Brodie *et al.*, 1965). Excretion of these lipid-insoluble metabolites can be achieved by active secretion at the tubules of the kidney or by passive transport across the glomerular membrane into the renal tubule (Forster, 1961, 1967). Since the metabolite has been transformed to a less lipid-soluble derivative, it will not diffuse back into the plasma for recirculation subsequent to passing through the glomerulus into the tubule.

The microsomal enzymes were, until recently, thought to be concerned only with the metabolism of compounds which are normally regarded as foreign to the body. Conney (1967) has recently shown that steroid hormones and other normal body constituents are also substrates of the drug-metabolizing enzymes in liver microsomes and he suggests that this enzyme system may play a significant role in their regulation and physiological action. These enzyme systems are thought to operate by a mixed function oxidase mechanism whereby NADPH reduces a component in microsomes which reacts with molecular oxygen to form an "active oxygen" intermediate. The "active oxygen" is then transferred to the drug or toxicant (Gillette, 1963). Key enzymes in the overall reaction are NADP-cytochrome *c* reductase, the flavin enzyme involved in the oxidation of NADP, cytochrome P-450, and NADPH cytochrome P-450 reductase, which acts to reduce oxidized cytochrome P-450 (Gillette and Sasame, 1966).

Many foreign compounds can alter these key enzymes and enhance or impair the ability of liver microsomal enzymes to metabolize other foreign compounds and steroids (Conney, 1967). Halogenated hydrocarbon insecticides have long been known to be potent stimulators of mammalian drug-metabolizing enzymes (Hart and Fouts, 1963; Hart, Shultice and Fouts, 1963). Buhler (1966) selectively induced drug-metabolizing enzymes in rainbow trout by exposing these animals to DDT or phenylbutzaone. Organophosphate insecticides are unlike the halogenated hydrocarbons in that they inhibit, rather than stimulate, the metabolism of drugs and steroids by liver microsomes, when given chronically to rats (Rosenberg and Coon, 1958; Welch *et al.*, 1967). Some heavy metals (Fe^{++}, Cu^{++}, Zn^{++} and Co^{++}) have also been shown to be inhibitory to drug metabolism in mice and rats (Peters and Fouts, 1970). Alterations in microsomal enzyme metabolizing capacities can substantially alter an animal's response to foreign compounds as well as its ability to hydroxylate steroid hormones and other normal body constituents (Conney, 1967). Altered steroid metabolism can directly affect the animal's ability to cope with environmental stresses as well as seriously impair reproductive mechanisms.

Other than Buhler's (1966) work on rainbow trout, little is known about the effects foreign compounds have on the microsomal drug-metabolizing capacities of fishes. In addition, the current state of knowledge dealing with metabolism of foreign compounds in fishes is, at best, scanty (Adamson, 1967).

The Toxicity of Complex Effluents

Most industrial effluents contain mixtures of two or more substances. These complex effluents present special problems in evaluating their toxicities to fish and other organisms. In some cases two agents with similar pharmacologic actions can produce a response that is equal to the summation of the effects of the individual agents or greater than the summation of the independent effects of the two agents. The latter response is called "potentiation" and represents the condition whereby one compound is made more toxic in the presence of another compound which alone may produce minimal or no pharmacologic effect. Potentiation poses a special problem for the aquatic environment as well as the terrestrial environment for it is possible that a certain combination of relatively harmless substances may result in an unpredictable high level of toxicity that would seriously threaten the existance of one or many species. Usually, however, the effect of two agents is the summation of responses to each agent. Occasionally, the effect of a toxic substance is reduced on the addition of another substance, a phenomenon referrred to as antagonism. In some cases the antagonistic substance may or may not be toxic when present by itself.

Synergism (potentiation and summation) and antagonism are poorly understood phenomena and greatly confuse the understanding and prediction of the toxic effects of industrial effluents. The majority of toxicological studies conducted in this and other countries on both mammals and fish deal with the effects of single substances on organisms; only a few studies are currently investigating the responses of organisms to complex mixtures of substances. Synergism and antagonism are worthy of further investigation, for little is known about the basic mechanisms governing these processes.

Resistance of Fish to Toxicants

Resistance of animals to chemicals has been known to exist for some time now and has posed serious obstacles in the control of insects and bacteria. While the mechanisms of resistance remain thus far a mystery, we know that they are genetically based. Most susceptible populations of animals have an occasional individual which exhibits resistance and it is this member that provides the genetic material for selection pressures to act upon.

Resistance has best been demonstrated with various pesticides in several natural populations of fishes (Ferguson *et al.*, 1964, 1966), but these findings have attracted little attention. Many biologists have, in fact, believed this phenomenon to be beneficial to these animals, especially since they are useful to man.

Recently, some disturbing evidence has emerged suggesting that pesticide-resistant vertebrates pose a major hazard in natural ecosystems and that they may be creating serious toxicological problems for man (Ferguson, 1967). The reason for this is some resistant animals carry massive residues of unaltered pesticides in their tissues and aggravate the already serious problem of biological magnification. Animals whose resistance is due to enhanced abilities to metabolize toxic substances to inactive metabolites do not, however, contribute to biological magnification.

Biological magnification results when a foreign substance enters plants and small animals and is then passed rapidly along food chains to larger animals. As this happens the substance becomes more and more concentrated until it reaches dangerous levels in the large predacious fish, many of which are consumed by birds and mammals including man. Clearly, the more resistance a fish has for the particular toxicant in its tissues the greater the likelihood it will be consumed by animals living on the land. Unfortunately, these animals may not have equivalent levels of resistance and may be unable to adequately deal with these toxicants.

Current Methods of Evaluating Toxicity in Fishes

The establishment of water quality standards for concentrations of toxic pollutants that will be safe for fish has recently become a major concern of

Federal and State Governments in pollution control (Water Quality Criteria, 1968). Efforts in this regard have centered around determining lethal levels of toxicants by establishing a TLm (tolerance limit, median) for various species exposed to toxicants for periods of time up to 96 hr (Sprague, 1969).

These short term studies have been valuable in defining the upper limits of toxicity but have not considered the subtle deleterious effects of foreign compounds which may not be evident for weeks, months, or longer (Water Quality Criteria, 1963). These responses to toxicity may manifest themselves in appetite changes, metabolic alterations, disorders of the nervous system, reproductive changes, behavioral abnormalities, or alteration of vital functions which are not immediately lethal. For this reason, investigations have only recently been conducted to measure toxicity in terms of survival, growth, and reproductive alterations resulting from long-term exposure to sublethal levels of pollutants (Water Quality Criteria, 1968). The concept of a "maximum acceptable toxicant concentration (MATC)" has originated from these studies and is defined as the highest continuous concentration of a toxicant that does not significantly decrease the laboratory fish production index; an index developed by Mount and Stephen (1967) which takes into account survival, growth, reproduction, spawning behavior, viability of eggs, and growth of fry.

Because the toxicity of most pollutants varies with water characteristics and fish species, Mount and Stephen (1967) proposed the use of an "application factor", (calculated by dividing the MATC by the 96-hr TLm value), to determine safe concentrations of toxic pollutants which, when determined for one species of fish in one type of water, may be applicable to other waters and other species. Studies are currently underway to test the practicality of this approach (Mount, 1968; Mount and Stephan, 1969).

The "application factor" approach may improve upon present methods of estimating safe concentrations of toxicants. At best, however, this approach requires considerable time for collection and evaluation of data and measures only the end result of a multitude of biochemical, physiological, metabolic, pharmacological and pathological responses to toxicants. Little definitive information is gained concerning the mechanism which produces the gross changes upon which the "application factor" is based.

Because of the virtual impossibility of thoroughly assessing the individual, cumulative, synergistic and antagonistic effects of the numerous substances continually being introduced into our environment, it is imperative that we know the basic metabolic, physiologic and toxicologic responses of fish to compounds representative of broad categories of foreign substances. Only then will we be in a position to predict intelligently the biological effects of toxicants and regulate their concentrations to assure protection of this very important biological resource. If fish toxicologists continue to consider only the effect of a substance on the laboratory fish production index without understanding causitive mechanisms, they will severely limit the amount of information available for making meaningful decisions so desperately needed in water pollution control programs.

Finally, investigations of the disposition of foreign compounds in fish will shed valuable information on the evolution of enzymes that metabolize drugs, on drug metabolic pathways and excretion, and on factors affecting the biological half-life of foreign compounds in other lower species as well as higher vertebrates including man (Adamson, 1967).

REFERENCES

Adamson, R. H. (1967) *Fed. Proc.*, **26**, 1047.

Ashley, L. M., J. E. Halver and G. N. Wogan (1964) *Fed. Proc.*, **23**, 105.

Brodie, B. B., G. J. Cosmides and D. P. Rall (1965) *Science*, **148**, 1547.

Brodie, B. B. and E. G. Erdos (1962) *Proceedings of the First International Pharmacological Meeting*, Vol. 6. Macmillan, New York.

Buhler, D. R. (1966) *Fed. Proc.*, **25**, 343.

Conney, A. H. (1967) *Pharm. Rev.*, **19**, 317.

Ferguson, D. E. (1967) *Trans. Thirty-Second North Am. Wildlife and Natural Resources Conf.*

Ferguson, D. E., D. D. Culley, W. D. Cotton and R. P. Dodds (1964) *BioScience*, **14**, 43.

Ferguson, D. E., J. L. Ludke and G. G. Murphy (1966) *Trans. Am. Fish. Soc.*, **95**, 335.

Forster, R. P. (1961) Kidney cells. In *The Cell*, Ed. by J. Brachet and A. E. Mirshy, Vol. 5, pp. 89–161. Academic Press, New York.

Forster, R. P. (1967) Renal transport mechanisms. In *Proceedings of an International Symposium on Comparative Pharmacology*. Ed. by E. J. Cafruny, pp. 1008–1019. Fed. Am. Soc. Exptl. Biol., Bethesda, Maryland.

Gillette, J. R. (1963) *Prog. Drug. Res.*, **6**, 13.

Gillette, J. R. and H. A. Sasame (1966) *Fed. Proc.*, **25**, 737.

Goodman, L. S. and A. Gilman (1970) *The Pharmacological Basis of Therapeutics*, Chapter 1. Macmillan, London.

Hart, L. G. and J. R. Routs (1963) *Proc. Soc. Exp. Biol. Med.*, **114**,

Hart, L. G., R. W. Shultice and J. R. Fouts (1963) *Toxicol. App. Pharmacol.*, **5**, 371.

Life, J. S. (1969) Metabolism and Pharmacodynamics of Copper in the Goldfish (*Carassium Auratus*). Ph.D. Dissertation, The University of Michigan.

Mount, D. I. (1968) *Water Res.*, **2**, 215.

Mount, D. I. and C. E. Stephan (1967) *Trans. Am. Fish. Soc.*, **96**, 185.
Mount, D. E. and C. E. Stephan (1969) *J. Fish. Res. Bd. Canada*, **26**, 2449.
Petermann, M. L. (1961) *Med. Clin. North Am.*, **45**, 537.
Peters, M. A. and J. R. Fouts (1970) *Biochem. Pharmacol.*, **19**, 533.
Rosenberg, P. and J. M. Coon (1958) *Proc. Soc. Exp. Biol. Med.*, **98**.
Sprague, J. B. (1969) *Water Res.*, **3**, 793.
Stanton, M. F. (1965) *J. Nat. Cancer Inst.*, **34**, 117.
Water Quality Criteria (1963) Federal Water Pollution Control Administration.
Water Quality Criteria (1968) Federal Water Pollution Control Administration.
Welch, R. M., W. Levin and A. H. Conney (1967) *J. Pharmacol. Exp. Therap.*, **155**, 167.
Whittaker, V. P. (1968) *Br. Med. Bull.*, **24**, 101.
Williams, R. T. (1967) *Fed. Proc.*, **26**, 1029.

JOHN E. BARDACH
University of Michigan

JEFFRY S. LIFE
University of Iowa

POLLUTION FROM MINE DRAINAGE

Introduction

All forms of mining cause some impact on the aquatic environment, just as any other earth disturbance will impact the local hydrology. Sometimes this impact is very adverse, in which case there is usually a considerable disruption of the natural life cycles in the affected water. Other, and less noted cases may even improve the local waters. Unfortunately, the adverse impacts greatly outnumber the advantageous circumstances so that the result of mining is to severely degrade the aquatic environment.

A generalized characterization of the impact of mining on water is rather difficult, as almost any specific change in the chemical qualities of the affected waters may be found at some specific point. In almost all cases, however, there is an increase in the total dissolved solids in the mine drainage waters. Additionally, the acidity of mine drainage is increased above normal ground water levels for the area and the level of dissolved metal is increased. In some areas however, the alkalinity levels are increased by mining. Many forms of mining also increase the suspended solids content of water.

Coal mining has received the greatest amount of attention as the mining which causes water pollution. This is perhaps deserved as the mining of coal has been a major operation for many years and more coal has been mined than any other single mineral. Water pollution from coal mining was known in medieval England and the mines in Wales were known to make the creeks run red. This fact was important to the exploration of the North American continent, as early explorers deduced the presence of large deposits of coal from the natural color and character of some of the streams and creeks. Similar conditions were sometimes noted in relation to other mineral deposits in the U.S. As the outcrop materials come into contact with the atmospheric conditions, oxidation and solubilization take place and the products are transported into the streams. Hence, the natural production of some mine drainage is a natual phenomena which has existed almost from the beginning of time.

Coal mine drainage may vary from waters pure enough to drink without treatment to waters containing more than 20,000 mg/l acidity with commensurate amounts of iron and other dissolved solids. Drainage from metal mines may vary over almost equally wide ranges of acidity but often contain substantial amounts of dissolved heavy metals. In most respects the acid drainages from metal mines are similar to acid coal mine drainages. This similarity is so great that most of the treatment processes and prevention mechanisms developed and applicable to coal mine drainage can also be applied to metal mine drainage.

Origin of Acid Mine Drainage

The earth strata associated with and superjacent to coal and many other minerals almost always contain the iron sulfide mineral pyrite (FeS_2). Oxidation of the acid-forming pyritic material associated with mining is necessary for the formation of mine acids and as oxygen is a necessary part of the oxidation of these materials, there can be no significant amount of oxidation until these are exposed to air. The process of mining greatly increases the exposure of these materials to atmospheric oxidation. Oxidation of the sulfide mineral begins as soon as it is exposed to the air and continues at a rate characteristic of the geologic and atmospheric conditions. Usually this oxidation causes spalling of the mineral substance with a progressive increase in the amount of surface area available for oxidation. Time then becomes a significant factor in the amount and rate of formation of acid mine drainage.

The exact nature of the pyritic mineral which oxidizes so rapidly and causes the acid drainage from mining has been sought for many years. In appearance, the material is often grey like marcasite, and its oxidation rate is even more rapid than that of marcasite. X-ray diffraction studies of the sulfide material associated with coal, however, have confirmed by the crystal structure that the material is pyrite rather than some other crystalline form of iron sulfide.

The intricate mechanism of oxidation of this pyrite and the formation of acid drainage has been the subject of many learned discussions and research efforts extending back over fifty years or so. This reaction will occur at normal room temperature and humidity conditions with the release of SO_2 into the atmosphere. Under more humid conditions, the reaction results in all of the sulfur being converted into sulfate. Typical reactions depicting some of the several paths possible for the reaction of the iron sulfide, air, water and alkali materials are listed. This list is typical rather than all-inclusive to cover all possible reaction routes.

$$FeS_2+3O_2 \rightarrow FeSO_4+SO_2$$
$$2FeS_2+7O_2+2H_2O \rightarrow 2FeSO_4+2H_2SO_4$$
$$4FeSO_4+2H_2SO_4+O_2 \rightarrow 2Fe_2(SO_4)_3\downarrow +2H_2O$$
$$4FeSO_4+O_2+2H_2O \rightarrow 4Fe(OH)SO_4\downarrow$$
$$Fe_2(SO_4)_3+2H_2O \rightarrow 2Fe(OH)SO_4\downarrow +H_2SO_4$$
$$Ca(HCO_3)_2+FeSO_4 \rightarrow CaSO_4+Fe(HCO_3)_2$$
$$4Fe(HCO_3)_2+O_2+2H_2O \rightarrow 4Fe(OH)_3\downarrow +8CO_2\uparrow$$
$$Ca(HCO_3)_2+Fe_2(SO_4)_3+4H_2O \rightarrow CaSO_4+2Fe(OH)_3\downarrow +2CO_2\uparrow +2H_2SO_4$$
$$Ca(HCO_3)_2+H_2SO_4 \rightarrow CaSO_4+2CO_2\uparrow +2H_2O$$

There has been a continuing debate among the scientific community over the role which bacteria may play in the formation of acid mine drainage. Bacteria of the Ferrobacillus ferroxidans family are almost always found in large pools of acid mine drainage. The bacteria have been shown to have the capability of oxidizing ferrous iron to the ferric state. However, they thrive in a very limited pH range (approximately pH 3.5) and there is no evidence to indicate that they contribute directly to the primary oxidation of the pyritic substance. Ferric ion can oxidize sulfide sulfur and this could possibly provide a mechanism for the bacteria to increase the rate of oxidation of pyrite in some circumstances. Other recent studies have shown that the transfer of oxygen from the atmosphere to the pyrite surface is the rate limiting factor of the reaction, making moot arguments put forth as to whether bacterial or chemical oxidation is the principal mechanism of acid drainage formation.

Bacteria may play a significant role in the oxidation of the ferrous to ferric ion in mine drainage. This fact can be of considerable importance in the treatment of mine drainage as ferrous iron tends to retard the rate of neutralization reactions. It almost appears that this is Nature's first step in the neutralization of acid drainage. The bacterial oxidization of iron allows the alkalinity of the associated earth strata and of diluting waters to be more readily reacted with the acidity of the mine drainage waters. This concept is rather radically at variance with former concepts that considered the sterilization of a mine as a possible method of reducing or eliminating the formation of acid drainage. Bacteria has been used deliberately as a step in the treatment of mine drainage. This process allows the ferrous iron to be oxidized and accelerate the neutralization of the acid salts.

The formation of acid drainages from surface and underground mines is essentially the same process, and the two drainages are indistinguishable on the basis of the chemical qualities of the waters. In general the iron contained in drainage from surface mines and also from coal refuse piles is in the ferric state. The drainage from surface mining may contain very substantial amounts of suspended solids or sediment. Because many of the drainage problems of strip and deep mines are directly interrelated there is almost no rational way of separating the treatment or preventive measures which may be applied to the two types of mining.

Extent of Environmental Impact

The problem of environmental degradation caused by mine drainage is widespread and serious. Some form of mining occurs in each of the fifty states and many states are extensively mined. The aquatic degradation caused by coal mining in the eastern and Appalachian region is best known and has been best documented. For this reason, most statements of the damages caused by mine drainage cite only the degradation in the Appalachian area. The Appalachian Regional Commission reported that some

10,500 miles of streams in that region are affected by mine drainage and acid drainage continually pollutes nearly 5700 stream miles. Since data are not available in many mining areas, particularly in the Rocky Mountain and western areas, firm total statements of the extent of the problem cannot be made. However, enough information is available to indicate that it is very substantial.

The extent and amount of degradation which may be caused by the presence of mine drainage, and the environmental and economic impacts which may be felt, vary, of course, with the type of mine, the strata surrounding it, and other localized conditions.

For example, coal mine drainage, which is usually acidic, kills fish and other forms of aquatic biota by lowering the pH of the water and also may have an adverse economic effect upon the human population. The acidity accelerates the corrosion of bridges, culverts, boats and navigational facilities, making replacement at shorter intervals necessary. High cost water treatment may be required to make the local water supply potable or suitable for industrial use. Water contact sports may not be possible in the area, causing a loss of potential tourist industry revenues.

Although metal mining may cause the same adverse effects, it usually occurs in less densely populated regions. Additionally, metal mine drainage may render the waters toxic to humans as well as aquatic life by the presence of heavy metals.

Remedies for Mine Drainage Pollution

In the past a substantial number of investigators have simply discussed the problem and obsrved its extent so that more is known about the nature of the problem than about the mechanisms which may be applicable to correcting or mitigating it. Mine drainage may be characterized on the basis of its source and possible remedies considered by this categorization even though the chemical nature and biological impact of the drainage from the several sources is identical. For the purposes of this discussion let us consider three types of mine drainage by the source: drainage from active or operating mines, drainge from non-operating (sometimes called abandoned) mines and drainage which will be generated in the future from mines which have not yet begun operation. Separating surface and underground mines is not feasible as they frequently occur together and interact to add to the problem.

Presently operating mines have certain characteristics which differentiate them from other mines. Primarily because they are now in operation a responsible owner or operator can be located and people, equipment, machinery and power are available at the mine site. This allows consideration of procedures to treat the mine drainage as well as

TABLE I

Summary of Treatment Techniques

Pollutants removed[a]	Neutralization and aeration	Microbial iron oxidation	Reverse osmosis	Ion exchange	Flash distillation[d]	Electrodialysis	Product recovery	Silt basins
Acidity	XXX	NA	XX	X[c]	XX	X[e]	X[f]	NA
Iron	XX	XX	XXX	X[c]	XXX	?	X[f]	NA
Aluminium	XXX	NA	XXX	X[c]	XXX	X[e]	X[f]	NA
Manganese	X[b]	NA	XXX	X[c]	XXX	X[e]	X[f]	NA
Copper	XX	NA	XXX	X[c]	XXX	X[e]	X[f]	NA
Zinc	X[b]	NA	XXX	X[c]	XXX	X[e]	X[f]	NA
Hardness		NA	XXX	X[c]	XXX	X[e]	X[f]	NA
Suspended Solids	X	NA	NA	NA	NA	NA	X[f]	X
Dissolved Solids		NA	XXX	X[c]	XXX	X[e]	X[f]	NA
State of Art[g]	CU	PP	PP	R, PP, FSD[c]	FSD	R[e]	R	R, CU
Cost, $/1000[h]	0.05–4.55	UK	0.30–2.57	0.30–2.53	0.33–3.25	0.52–2.52	UK	0.02–1.0
Waste Product[j]	S	S	B	B.R	B	B	S,B,R	S

[a] NA—Not applicable, ? Questionable, X-degree to which removed, the greater number of "X"s the higher the removal.
[b] Must be raised to very high pH.
[c] Various ion exchange techniques are under evaluation. Their effectiveness and which pollutant is removed depends on the technique.
[d] 5 mgd plant is under construction in Pennsylvania. Technique has only a limited potential.
[e] Technique will not operate where iron is present in water.
[f] Various product recovery schemes are under consideration, however, all are still in research stage.
[g] R—Research, PP—Pilot Plant, FSD—Full Scale Demonstration, CU—Common Usage.
[h] Cost depend on the degree of pollution size of plant, pre- and post-treatment requirements. UK—Unknown.
[i] Each treatment process has a waste product that must be disposed of and creates additional problem. S—inert sludge, B—highly mineralized brine, R—regenerate.

procedures to reduce or minimize the amount of pollutants discharged both during the remainder of the mine's life and after mining has been terminated. Procedures presently available may be employed to minimize the amount of mine drainage pollution which issues from an operating mine but no procedures are now available which can totally eliminate it.

Non-operating, or abandoned mines, generally do not have any responsible person readily available, or any other resources such as personnel and machinery, which make abatement techniques more expensive for this type of mine than for one which is operating.

When a mine is still in the planning stage, it is easier to plan for future prevention of pollution and thereby reduce it. For instance, provisions can be pre-planned for a mine to have rapid and complete drainage during the mining operation, thereby reducing the pollutional discharges which otherwise may need to be treated. Additionally, improved mining methods can provide for minimum void spaces after mining; also water level control after mining ceases can be provided only during the mine pre-planning stages.

The methods for alleviating mine drainage may be divided into the two basic categories of treatment of mine drainage, and prevention of the formation or discharge of pollutants.

Treatment removes pollutants by physical/chemical means and generally results in only specific pollutants being removed or reduced. The

TABLE II

Cost and Effectiveness of Various At-Source Prevention and Corrective Techniques

Control techniques	Effectiveness %	Cost	Remarks
Surface mine reclamation	25–90	\$300–3000/acre	Includes backfilling, regrading, contouring and water control structures. Prevents acid formation, erosion control, runoff of dissolved soils. Cost and effectiveness controlling factors are nature of surface and overburden, slope of land, and proposed use of land.
Mine sealing (air)	0–50	\$1000–5000/seal. Additional cost of 5000–100,000/seal may be required to control entrance of air through subsidence holes, bore holes, outcrop, etc.	Sealing of an underground mine to prevent entrance of air. Prevents acid formation. Cost and effectiveness depend on the ability to locate and seal all air paths to the mine, type and condition of mine opening and type of seal. Most mines cannot be airsealed.
Mine sealing (flooding)	75–99	\$1000–20,000/seal. Additional costs of \$5000–20,000 may be required to control drainage through bore holes, outcrop, etc.	Sealing of an underground mine to completely and permanently flood the working. Prevents acid formation and sometimes all discharges. Cost and effectiveness depend on the ability to seal all discharges, size of mine, dip of seam, outcrop condition, condition of mine opening, type of seal, and amount of grouting required. Is not applicable to all mines.
Drainage diversion	25–75	\$200–20,000/acre	The prevention of water from entering the mine area. Prevention of siltation and flushing of pollutants. Cost and effectiveness depend on ability to divert as much water as possible in properly designed structures.
Impoundment	50–95	\$350–1,000/acre-ft	Flooding of surface mine pits. Prevents acid production. Cost and effectiveness depend on complete and permanent flooding of the material responsible for acid production.
Refuse pile reclamation (reject material from mining and processing)	25–75	\$1000–3000/acre	Stabilizing a refuse pile with soil, chemicals, vegetation, etc. Prevents acid production and siltation. Cost and effectiveness depend upon the availability of the land in which the refuse piles can be filled and also upon the availability of impervious materials such as clay, fly ash, or limestone for compaction over the surface of the filled area.
Reject tailing pond (reject material from mining and processing in slurry form)	25–95	\$300–2000/acre	Stabilizing of tailings by flooding, soil covering, chemicals, vegetation, etc. Prevents air pollution and discharge of suspended and dissolved solids. Cost and effectiveness depend upon the size, location.

TABLE II (*continued*)

Control techniques	Effectiveness %	Cost	Remarks
Revegetation	5–25	$70–700/acre	Establishment of vegetative cover on reclaimed surface mines, reject piles, and pond. Prevents erosion. Cost and effectiveness depend on the type of cover, soil conditioning, and thickness of cover required.
Controlled pumping and drainage	25–75	$0.1900.23/1000 gallon	Involves rapid removal of water from a mine before it gets contaminated or discharge of contaminated water at regulated rate so that dilution provides minimum contaminating effects. Cost and effectiveness depend upon the characteristics of the material in the mine, contact time between water and exposed materials, rate of pumping, pumping head, and amount of dilution water available.
Inert gas blanket	Under research and development		Filling of an underground mine with an inert gas to prevent acid production.
Sterilization	Under research		Control of the bacteria in a mining environment. Prevents acid production. Technique does not show merit at this time.
Internal sealing	Under research and development		Internal sealing of underground mine to prevent acid production and/or mine drainage discharge.
Longwall mining	Under research and development		Allows complete removal of the coal in an underground mine. Mine roof collapses behind the working face, eliminating "breathing" of the mine.
Daylighting	Under research and development		Strip mining of a previously mined underground seam. Removes pillars left before. Surface must be reclaimed.

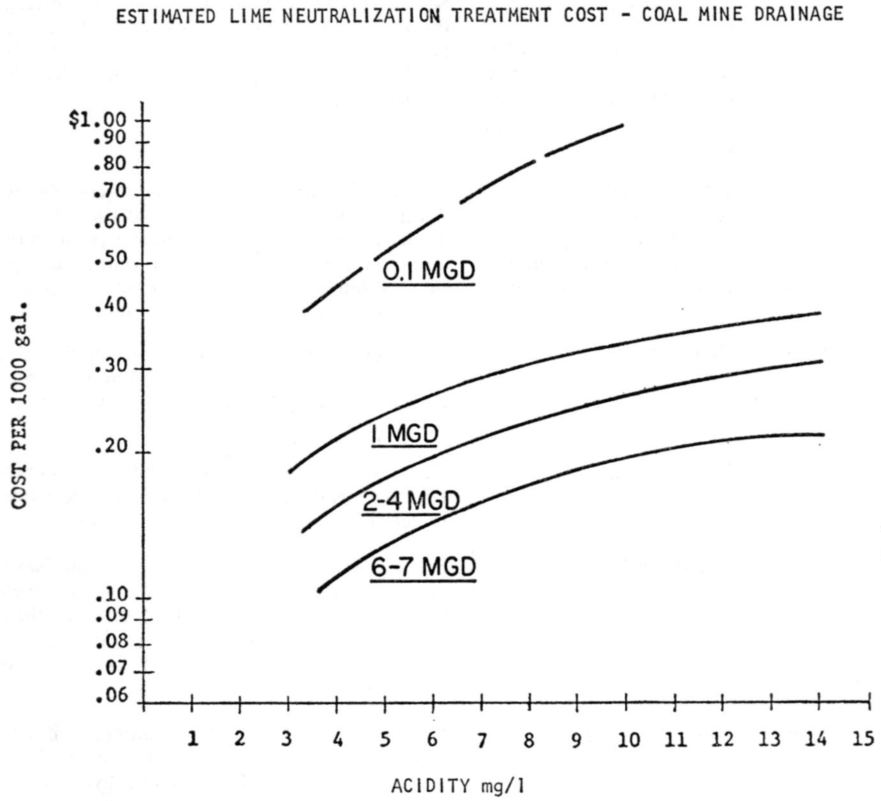

Figure 1 Estimated costs for treatment of coal mine drainage waters based upon a composite of published laboratory, pilot plant and actual plant data.

The estimate for the 0.1 MGD plant is preliminary and based upon limited information.

process must continue for as long as the source produces pollution and usually in the case of mine drainage this is tantamount to "treatment in perpetuity." Disposal of wastes and constant usage of power or chemicals make such treatment unduly consumptive of both human and physical resources. Treatment methods for coal mine drainage are summarized in Table I and many of the methods are applicable to other types of mine drainage pollution.

Prevention is the total cessation or massive reduction of the formation or discharge of pollutants during and after the operating life of the mine. Prevention of all forms of pollution, including dissolved and suspended materials, is obviously more desirable than simple treatment of pollution with its attendant problems. Provisions for prevention of the formation of pollution can be planned into a mine while it is still on the drawing board. Specific techniques for prevention and correction of pollution from mines, both operating and non-operating, are shown in Table II.

It can be seen from Table II and Fig. 1 that the cost of treating or preventing the formation of mine drainage is a wide ranging variable, dependent on the method(s) selected for use. The estimated costs for the limestone neutralization treatment of mine drainage are shown in Fig. 1 as a function of acidity and quantity to be treated.

As can be seen in the figures, the number of methods of alleviation and control of mine drainage which are highly effective are few, and most treatment processes produce undesirable by-products, as well as being expensive over the long run. It would be highly desirable to lessen the sources of mine drainage and to be able to treat it effectively with a gain in desirable by-products.

New techniques for the prevention of pollution from mining are presently in the development and demonstration stage. For example, a new technique known as "daylighting" is being demonstrated. This procedure will use strip mining techniques to remove the residual coal from shallow, non-operating deep mines and consolidate the overburden to prevent the continued discharge of acid drainage. A variety of abatement techniques related to surface mine reclamation are being demonstrated in the Appalachia region. Also there are two major efforts directed toward the development of non-pollutional mining techniques. These are the mining of coal under oxygen free conditions within the mine to prevent the oxidation of pyrite and the formation of acid drianage and the application of a new mining technique called "longwall stripping." Longwall stripping will apply longwall mining techniques to shallow cover coals, which are now strip mined, to remove the coal without inverting or dismantling the overlying earth strata.

Literature References

Most discussions of this type are buttressed by an impressive listing of reference documents citing sources of the many facts contained therein. To the casual reader, these references are useless, except for their creation of an impression of authority. The serious worker will demand to have even more references and documentation. The field of coal mine drainage is somewhat unique in that the literature of the field is regularly collected, abstracted and these abstracts published. This publication, entitled "Mine Drainage Abstracts, a Bibliography" is prepared by the Bituminous Coal Research, Inc. for the Commonwealth of Pennsylvania. Copies may be purchased from B.C.R., Monroeville, Pennsylvania. A listing of the reports of the research in this field conducted by the Environmental Protection Agency may be obtained from the Publications Branch, Office of Research and Monitoring, Environmental Protection Agency, Washington, D.C. 20460.

Ernst P. Hall
Environmental Protection Agency

POLLUTION INSTRUMENTATION — WASTEWATER

I. Introduction

Great changes have occurred in the field of water and wastewater analysis during the past five years. This is not due to any radical new technology or breakthrough in instrumentation that has come forth. Instead this can be ascribed to an enormously popular and new found public interest in the environment and a genuine desire to restore our waterways to some semblance of their former state. Much of this interest has focused upon our nation's water resources, specifically water pollution. So important is this concern that pollution abatement became an announced part of our national goals for the 1970's.

As an outgrowth of this activity there is an ever increasing demand for more and better analytical data to define the quality of our waters. Very much related is the need to evaluate the effectiveness of pollution abatement measures that have been instituted and to monitor the major waterways of our nation. There is, thus, at present, an enormous demand and need for the rapid, accurate and efficient chemical analysis of a large spectrum of parameters. Fundamentally, this is what automated analysis can do: make available quickly and efficiently a vastly increased sample analysis capacity, at a lower labor cost, thus giving more and better data. More specifically, however, automated methods refers to the use of automatic instrumentation for the continuous or semi-continuous analytical measurement of specific (or sometimes not so specific) parameters. Athough "continuous" (i.e. unattended) monitoring instrumentation capable of detecting a parameter 24 hr/day easily fits under this definition, the term automated methods is also often used to describe laboratory analytical instrumentation which is seldom totally unattended, and is probably operated on a semi-continuous, "as needed" basis.[1]

In the past, the analysis of water or wastewater parameters has been mostly by the traditional "wet" methods of chemical analysis contained in the standard reference, *Standard Methods for the Examination of Waters and Wastewaters*,[2] as well as in other commonly used references.[3,4] Until the appearance of the 1971 (13th Ed.), in fact, *Standard Methods*, did not list any automated techniques among their methods. In the past few years automated methods have become very important. The growing importance of such methods is reflected in the fact that the Federal Government has for the second time (the first being in 1969) issued a manual describing numerous automated analytical methods to define water quality.[5,6] It is to be noted that automated methods are also among the accepted methodology that may be used to quantitatively measure any discharges to navigable waters which must now be reported to the U.S. Corps of Engineers under the newly instituted permit system.[7] Recent pollution or newly unearthed abatement legislation[7,6] will increase the demand for laboratory automation as well as in monitoring.

II. Water Quality Parameters

A great many water quality parameters may be used to evaluate water quality. The federal water quality data retrieval system STORET,[10] lists several hundred such parameters. Only a few of these parameters are important in most situations.

Water quality parameters may be roughly divided into three general categories—physical, chemical and biological. Examples of some of these parameters often used in estimating water quality in wastewater discharges, or receiving waters such as streams, rivers, or lakes are shown as Table 1. Not

TABLE I

Some Typical Water Quality Parameters

Physical	Chemical	Biological
Tempeerature	Dissolved Oxygen (DO)	Bacteria
Color	Biochemical Oxygen Demand (BOD)	Coliform Bacteria
Odor	Chemical Oxygen Demand (COD)	Algae
Turbidity	pH	Viruses
Conductivity	Ammonia	
Solids	Nitrates, Nitrites	
	Phosphates	
	Alkalinity/acidity	
	Sulfates	
	Heavy metals	
	Mercury	
	Lead	
	Chromium, etc.	
	Chlorides	
	Organic pesticides, insecticides	
	Detergents	

all of these parameters are amenable to automated methods of chemical analysis.

The physical parameters listed on Table 1, while easy to define or recognize cannot always be measured so readily. For example, odor cannot be measured by automated methods and at times is even difficult to estimate even using accepted (manual) methodologies. In some instances certain parameters can only be measured within certain limits. This is true of turbidity, which can be measured using automated instrumentations under most circumstances, however, when the water being monitored exhibits wide fluctuations in turbidity or color, the usefullness of this device diminishes as will be noted in a later section.

Most parameters used to estimate water quality can be measured continuously by the use of probes or colorimetry together with wet chemical analyzers. The easiest application is, of course, the use of a probe such as the dissolved oxygen (DO) probe, a pH electrode, or a specific ion probe. In the laboratory, probably the most common approach is based on the use of wet chemical analyzers. Such analyzers generally employ conventional "wet" chemical methods found in Standard Methods[2,6] in which various chemicals are continuously added in a particular sequence and where mixing, color development and measurement are automatic, but require close attention by an operator. Besides these two general approaches there are a host of other methods which do not really fit this categorization, but which includes the use of newer instrumentation, or instrumentation not used very often (or not found in most wastewater laboratories). This includes instruments which employ as part of their detection, atomic absorption spectroscopy, emission spectroscopy, polarography, or potentiometric titration. These will not be discussed to any great extent. However, the use of probes as well as wet chemical analyzers will be considered in some detail. Many of the chemical parameters shown on Table 1, as was noted for the physical parameters, are very difficult to measure for a variety of reasons which will be noted.

While at least some physical and chemical wastewater parameters can be measured by automated methods, there are no satisfactory automated methods for measuring any of the biological parameters listed in Table 1.

III. Automated Analytical Instrumentation

Automated methods in water and wastewater analysis are fundamentally similar to automated methods used in other areas of analytical or process chemistry. Within this broad framework there are many descriptive terms which are used more or less interchangeably in the field of applied chemistry, all of which refer to analytical instrumentation. Examples of such terms include "onstream analyzers", "automatic analyzers", "process analyzers" etc.

Automated methods as employed in the water and wastewater field can be classified into two general areas of application: (1) analytical instrumentation, and (2) process instrumentation. Although there are some minor differences between laboratory analytical instrumentation and process analytical instrumentation, the basic operating principles are the same. This discussion will, in general, deal with both types of analytical instrumentation since both process and laboratory analysis rely on the same detection elements. Moreover, the discussion will be limited to those detection instruments which are most frequently employed in data collection in the water and wastewater field. Although process control instrumentation will also be discussed, the discussion will be in more general terms and will deal with this topic moreso in terms of the principles employed.

The basic principle and theory of analytical instrumentation can be found in a number of reference works such as those of Willard *et al.*,[11] Reilly and Sawyer,[12] Ewing[13] and others,[1] The application of sensors to process stream analysis can be found in the work of Fraade,[14] or the broader work of Siggia.[15]

A. Analytical instrumentation

A number of acceptable classifications for analytical instrumentation can be found in the literature. For this discussion such instrumentation will be generally categorized as either nonspecific or specific. Nonspecific instruments are used to measure such variables as temperature, conductivity, pH, oxidation–reduction potential (ORP), etc. Specific instruments are capable of detecting particular molecular or ionic species. Examples of both types of such instrumentation are shown as Table 2. While it is not possible to discuss all of the parameters measured or sensors employed in automated instrumentation, the most important should be noted.

1. Non-specific instrumentation

a. Hydrogen Ion (pH) Perhaps the most widely measured parameter in the water and wastewater field is pH. Hydrogen ion, of course, is a very basic

TABLE 2

Analytical Instrumentation Examples

Non-Specific	Specific
Chemical Oxygen Demand (COD)	Ammonia
Electrolytic Conductivity	Calcium
Oxidation–Reduction Potential	Chlorides
pH	Copper
Solids	Dissolved Oxygen (DO)
Temperature	Iron
Color	Nitrate
Turbidity	Sulfates

and important parameter which affects all chemical (and biochemical) reactions. Its measurement as well as control is very important, especially in the neutralization of process or industrial wastes. Wide variations in pH can cause fish kills as well as drastic alterations in the biota or more complex changes in the character of the water, for example, precipitations, or destruction of alkalinity reserves. Tolerable limits for pH will depend on the receiving water but will vary from pH 6.5–8.0 and may range from 6.0–8.9.

Hydrogen ion changes can be obvious—i.e. caused by the direct introduction of hydrogen or hydroxyl ion, or by the introduction of materials whose hydrolysis changes the pH (e.g. iron or aluminium)—or more subtle, as a result of further biochemical breakdown of the discharged effluent. An example of a subtle pH change which would occur at a distance remote from the discharge point would be the lowering of pH which accompanies carbohydrate (especially sugar) breakdown, or ammonia oxidation. The breakdown of salts of weak acids (e.g. citrates, etc.) or protein wastes can result in a rise of pH.

Although hydrogen ion measurements are fairly straightforward, they are not always so easy to make especially where strong acids or bases used are present in the absence of buffering substances and where wide fluctuations of pH can occur. Moreover, other factors will influence pH detection as well as control. This includes such factors as variability of flow, detection in lag, temperature, the growth of microorganisms on probes, etc.

While colorimetric methods might be used to measure pH, the most commonly used instrument to measure hydrogen ion is the pH meter. A pH meter measures the electrical potential difference between two suitable electrodes—a reference and an indicating electrode—immersed in the solution being tested. In measurement, the reference electrode assumes a constant potential irrespective of the solution components or concentration, whereas the indicator electrode will assume a potential dependent solely on the pH of the test solution. An electrolytic cell is thus formed with an output voltage directly proportional to the hydrogen ion concentration.[16] The most commonly used system for measurement of pH employs the glass electrode together with a calomel reference electrode. Electrode assemblies are available in both immersion and flow types. A potential measuring instrument (millivoltmeter of a recorder) is generally used to measure the sensor output.

The most commonly used reference electrode in water analysis is the calomel electrode. A calomel electrode consists of a mercury–calomel rod immersed in a saturated solution of potassium chloride.

The most common indicator electrode in water and wastewater analysis is the glass electrode. The glass electrode consists of a silver–silver chloride or mercury–mercurous chloride electrode immersed in a solution of known pH with the entire system completely sealed in glass. In such a system the voltage of the glass electrode is a logarithmic function of the difference in hydrogen ion activity of the solutions on either side of the glass membrane.

Although the antimony electrode is sometimes used, this electrode still has several disadvantages which make the glass electrode, despite its drawbacks of fragility and resistance, preferable. A glass electrode can be used in turbid or colloidal suspensions, and has the advantage of being impervious to oxidizing or reducing substances in solution. Glass electrodes are generally adequate for measuring pH's in the neutral ranges (pH 6–9), however, pH fluctuations at the extremes of acid or basic solutions as well as the measurement of pH in the presence of alkaline earth metals at high pH values, do not give accurate results and special electrodes must be used. Operationally, glass indicator electrodes must be periodically checked with reference solutions as well as regularly cleaned inasmuch as films of microorganisms and debris will eventually coat the surface and interfere with pH measurements. Since pH measurements are also affected by temperature fluctuations, temperature compensated instruments are often used when temperatures departing from ambient are being measured. It is worth noting that measurement of pH refers only to the concentration of hydrogen ions and not to the total acidity or alkalinity of a water or wastewater.

b. Electrolytic conductivity Electrolytic conductivity or specific conductance is one of the least complicated of the continuous measurements that may be made on waters. The electrolytic conductivity of a solution is a measure of the ability of an ionizable solution to carry a current. Since this current-carrying ability is a function of the solution concentration, it is sometimes used to detect and measure ion concentration. Thus conductivity, although not specific is directly related to all of the ions in a solution inasmuch as they all conduct current to some extent.

For most solutions specific conductance consists of the measurement of resistance. This is usually done using a Wheatstone bridge in which a variable resistance is adjusted so that it is equal to the resistance of an unknown solution between two platinized electrodes. The cells are usually a pair of metallic electrodes, i.e. platinum wires—or more often plates coated with a thin layer of amorphous platinum or platinum black to minimize polarization. Dip cells are frequently employed. The electrodes are usually built or held in an insulating chamber and designed specifically for waters of a known ionic concentration range. For any particular electrode shape and path length, a cell factor must be obtained. The electrolyte solution to be measured flows into the cell and a measurement is taken in the space between the electrodes. Since conductivity changes appreciably with temperature, the measurement must be temperature compensated. When properly constructed, the measured resistance is independent of the sample volume as well as other interfering surfaces. The measuring circuit most commonly used is an A. C. Wheatstone Bridge. Alternating current is used to reduce polarization and the effects of changes in the concentration at the electrodes. The detection device is often a galvanometer. Conductivity measuring apparatus is available for analytical as well as for automatic control and recording with and without temperature compensation as well as in dip and flow type cells. As with most sensing devices there are a number of operational as well as maintenance problems which should be noted. With the electrode type condutivity cells for example, solutions of high conductivity, or corrosive solutions as well as liquids with abrasives or fibrous materials pose certain problems in taking accurate readings.

Perhaps of broader application are the "electrodeless" type conductivity measuring devices. The "cell" is constructed externally of inert materials. Depending on the application, a large number of configurations are possible. For immersion, for example, a doughnut shaped sensor is employed. This device effectively measures the resistance of a solution passed through or contained in the closed loop of the sensor. Sensing is by the use of two toroidal coils—an output and an input. One coil is connected to a transmitter and supplies the voltage in the high audiofrequency range. The second coil is connected to a receiver and measures the output voltage. The electrical circuit consists thus of two transformers: the first having as its primary winding the input toroid, and as its secondary, the closed loop of solution. The second transformer has, as its primary winding the closed solution loop, and as its secondary, the output toroid. With constant input voltage, the output is proportional to the conductivity of the solution. The output from the amplifier is rectified in a conventional bridge-type meter rectifier. Temperature compensation as well as alarm or other control features can also be incorporated in the design.

Applications of conductivity measurements using both types of electrodes includes their use in the detection of gross changes in water or wastwater systems. For example, such instrumentation can detect a major industrial waste spill into a river or a change in an effluent stream. Conductivity measurements have also frequently been used in measuring fluoride additions in water plants.

c. Temperature Temperature is one of the simplest parameters to measure continuously. It is also one of our most important and basic environmental factors. Hot waters, or hot wastewaters are classed as pollutants (thermal pollution) since they will affect the aquatic environment in two general ways. Temperature affects the solubility of gases, especially oxygen, which is vital to a balanced, healthy aquatic environment. In addition, temperature affects all biochemical (or chemical) reaction rates as well as diffusion.

Temperature measurement devices, almost all of which can be read continuously in liquid solutions, include the use of bimetallic mechanical sensors as well as electrical thermocouples, resistance thermometers and thermistors.

A bimetallic temperature sensor is made by welding together two materials which have different coefficients of thermal expansion. As the temperature changes, the element bends and this deflection can be measured. Generally these elements have a helically wound sensing stem to amplify the motion.

Resistance thermometers take advantage of the fact that electrical resistance is a function of temperature. Resistance thermometers consist of a small length of metallic wire, coiled into a small volume. A small controlled current is passed through the wire and the resistance is measured with an electrical bridge. A thermistor type thermometer differs slightly from resistance thermometer in that the resistance wire element is made of mixtures of sintered metallic oxides. The metallic oxides have large coefficients of resistance per degree temperature changes. Variations of this principle employ germanium, carbon or silicon sensors. A thermocouple operates on the principle that when two dissimilar metallic conductors are joined as a circuit, an EMF will develop when one of the junctions is heated.

Although the instruments noted are in general rugged, and reliable sensing devices, fouling or growth or biological slime can alter response time. In the selection of such instrumentation, a number of factors should be considered, among them temperature variation in the body of water (to include seasonal as well as nocturnal variations), normal and extreme flow rates, off-shore diffusion and flow patterns and turbulance.

d. Carbon Dissolved oxygen depletion in receiving waters is one of the primary concerns of water and wastewater scientists and engineers. Since this DO depletion is caused primarily by the introduction of oxidizeable compounds, primarily waste organic matter (carbon containing), a very understandable empirical relationship between oxygen demand and oxidizeable or carbonacous compounds has evolved. Thus, in many instances, carbonaceous or oxidizeable substances may be measured indirectly in terms of oxygen demand.

Generally speaking carbon or oxidizeable substances can be measured by two general approaches: by estimating the oxygen demand noted above (and which will be further described), or by measurement of the total organic carbon. In addition there are also some newer more specialized methods that should be noted.

(1) Oxygen Demand Tests Oxygen Demand Tests can generally be considered to be tests that use the consumption of oxygen as an index of the oxygen "demand" of a substance. The demand for oxygen can be measured using either chemical or biochemical methods. While it is generally assumed that oxygen demand is caused by the presence of organic, carbonaceous materials, this is not always the case and can lead to serious error since an oxygen demand can also be caused by the presence of reduced inorganic substances. Two general approaches are used to estimate oxygen demand, Biochemical Oxygen Demand (BOD), a biological estimation, and use of the Chemical Oxygen Demand (COD) test, a chemical measurement of demand.

(a) Biochemical Oxygen Demand (BOD) The BOD test is a very old traditional tool of the sanitary engineer. Essentially what is measured is the amount of oxygen required to biologically stabilize a waste under aerobic conditions in 5 days under prescribed environmental conditions. Considering the nature of this test, its variability, and the fact that this is essentially a biological assay, the use of an automated method to obtain comparable data is a very difficult task. However, a number of devices based on respirometry have appeared which are said to give useful automated BOD data.

Most of the commercial respirometric devices on the market assume that for every molecule of carbon utilized, a molecule of carbon dioxide is formed from oxygen. Thus respirometers utilizing either carbon dioxide absorption or the measurement of pressure changes are commercially available.[17 19] Most often a closed vessel of defined volume is used and the carbon dioxide evolved is removed by use of a chemical such as KOH. This causes a pressure drop which can be read directly and continuously on a manometer and equated to oxygen. Generally by the use of such devices the BOD of a domestic wastewater can be measured in from 48–72 hrs. Still another approach consists of measuring DO concentration changes by use of a membrane electrode. A more complete description of such devices can be found in the work of Ciaccio *et al.*[1]

(b) Chemical Oxygen Demand (COD) Continuous COD analysis has been automated for some time. Although a number of strong oxidizing agents may be used, potassium dichromate is probably the most commonly used oxidant. The most popular instrument is the Technicon AutoAnalyzer. This method is based essentially on Standard Methods[2] and employs dichromate oxidation with a catalyst at elevated temperatures and colorimetric detection of either the unoxidized dichromate or reduced chromate.[22] As with all COD methods any material causing the oxidant to be consumed is measured. Thus a number of compounds other than carbon can give a COD test. This woud include such compounds as hydrogen, nitrogen, sulfite, chloride, etc.

In view of the interferences a better approach is probably the use of the Total Oxygen Demand (TOD) Analyzer or the use of the "AquaRator".[22] In the TOD analyzer the oxygen required to catalytically burn a sample in a carefully controlled gas stream of oxygen and nitrogen is measured. Essentially a change in cell current is noted and recorded as TOD. As with most of these tests, reference standards of known TOD values must be used in calibration. A similar instrument is the "AquaRator" which uses pure carbon dioxide gas as a carier gas. When the sample is contacted with the CO_2 at 900 °C, carbon monoxide is formed which is detected by use of an IR detector. Good correlation has been reported between the values obtained using both of these instruments and the standard COD test.

(2) TOTAL ORGANIC CARBON (TOC) The detection of organic carbon based on the volatilization of a sample and burning it in the presence of oxygen and a catalyst, is called the Total Organic Carbon (TOC) Test. The carbon dioxide produced is then detected either by the use of an IR detector or thermal conductivity.[23,24] Standards must also be used for reference calibration. The instrument gives an oxidation efficiency of 98–100% for most substances and very few materials cause interference.

Still another method of detecting organic carbon is by use of pyrolysis and a flame ionization detector. Essentially steam is employed as a carrier gas and the pyrolysis chamber is maintained at 800 °C. A similar system has been reported which converts a vaporized organic sample principally to methane which is then detected by use of a flame ionization detector.[25]

(3) OTHER METHODS A great deal of interest has been shown over the past few years in the detection of organic carbon. Among the methods that have come forth and which show promise as automated methods of analysis are the use of UV detection methods as well as the use of refractometers.[26]

e. Oxidation–Reduction Potential (ORP) Many chemical processes, especially in the industrial plating processes, require the monitoring of oxidation–reduction potentials as the chemical reaction sequence proceeds. The measurement of ORP can indicate the extent to which a certain ion has been oxidized or reduced, it can serve as a useful guide as to how the reaction has progressed and can also be used to control the addition of reagents. In the water and wastewater field, oxidation–reduction potentials (ORP) have been used since the 1950's. The theory and measurement of ORP may be found in the work of Ciaccio *et al.*[1]

Like the pH meter, the ORP system consists of two electrodes, a reference and a measuring electrode. The calomel reference electrode provides a constant reproducible potential against which the unknown potential of the solution can be compared. The measuring electrode is usually platinum or gold (but not silver, which forms oxides). The most common redox electrode consists of a platinum rod or plate inlaid (or fused) in glass or an inert material. The potential difference is usually measured as millivolts (positive or negative). Most pH meters—in addition to their pH measuring range, are also equipped to measure one or more millivolt ranges. A number of precautions should be taken, since ORP values are pH as well as temperature dependent. In addition, atmospheric oxygen as well as other materials in the system being sampled can influence measurements. It is also important that the inherent characteristics of the metal electrode do not affect the potential of the system to be measured, and that adequate time for equilibrium to be attained is allowed.

The most common application in the water and wastewater field is in the control of cyanide,[27] or chromate oxidation.[28] Although ORP is sometimes used for stream monitoring, its actual usefulness is questionable except in the detection of serious chemical spills. In biological waste treatment, efforts to employ ORP in aerobic (activated sludge) treatment or anaerobic digester control have met with little success, although it has been used in the laboratory for anaerobic digester control.[1]

f. Turbidity Turbidity is an expression of the optical property of a sample which causes light to be scattered and absorbed rather than transmitted in straight lines through the sample. Two general methods are used in measuring tubidity, light absorption and light scattering methods. Light absorption measures visual or photometric measurements of the light transmitted in a straight line through the water sample. Light scattering methods (also called Nephelometry) measures scattered light at an angle from 35–90°. In general, turbidity measurements are usually obtained by passing a sample stream past a window through which light is passed. A drawback, in such instrumentation is that microorganisms such as algae and bacteria will frequently grow on glass surfaces causing interference with light transfer and detection. The turbidity in the flowing sample scatters light and the amount of light striking a detector or optical cell is then measured as either direct or scattered light. There are also a number of nephelometers as well as turbidimeters, all proprietary instruments which are commercially available.[29-31] High turbidities may be measured by use of a "falling stream" turbidimeter, also a proprietary device.[32]

Surface scatter or reflection turbidimeters are also available. In general, a beam of light is directed at an angle onto a smooth flowing surface of the liquid. Part of the light enters the liquid and part is reflected striking a detector photocell located above the area of illumination. In general, fouling is not a problem although oil reflection has been reported to interfere with light transfer.

Laws affecting light scatter are complex and the amount of light scattered is highly dependent on the size and shape as well as the color and refractive index of the particles in suspension. Generally, small and large particles behave differently. Since natural waters will contain particles of a large range of sizes, it is usually hard to correlate the weight of particles with light scatter.

It should also be noted that the normal turbidimetric standard (the Tubidimetric Unit) is empirically derived and has been criticized[33] since it is dependent on suspensions of particles of the same size. Moreover, the nature of the suspended material (particle size and color) can affect turbidimetric readings. For example, dissimilar suspensions can result in equal readings on a turbidimeter, and color, reflectivity and particle shape can also affect instrument response. However, turbidity measurements are imporant and are used in measuring silt, algae, slime and other water quality factors. In addition, turbidity measurements have been used to estimate clarification in conjunction with coagulant dosage in water treatment.

As noted, a problem plaguing the operation of most instrumentation used in measuring turbidity for measuring turbidity is the accumulation of slime or algae on the surface of the detecting window. In addition, such instrumentation requires calibration as well as maintenance for satisfactory operation.

g. Solids Higher concentrations of solids can be measured by a variety of methods.[1,34,35] Such instrumentation for example, can employ automated hydrometers in a continuous flow chamber where sensing of the hydrometer buoyancy is by optical means. Other instrumentation includes the use of a fixed-weight vessel, continuously receiving a sample stream, whose weight is monitored. Both of these instrument types have the disadvantage that slimes or sediments can alter or foul the device.

More recently gamma ray meters have been used for the determination of sludge density in a waste water stream. The advantage of operation is that there is no physical contact between the device and the sample. The gamma meter operates on the principle that solid material in a waste stream will scatter or absorb a collimated radiation beam. Two methods of operation are generally used; measurement of scattered rays and measurement of transmitted rays. The sensing instrument is usually mounted around the waste water pipe. The source of radioactivity is generally cesium-135 or cobalt-60 encapsulated in a lead holder. A measuring cell converts radioactive energy directly into an electrical signal. Among the chief problem associated with this device is the handling of radioactive materials.

2. Specified Chemical Instrumentation

a. Dissolved Oxygen (*DO*) Dissolved oxygen is a very important parameter in the wastewater field. This is because for a river or receiving water to remain "healthy" and maintain a balanced biological population' dissolved oxygen must be present. The status or relative pollution of a receiving water is, in fact, determined by the DO level. Fish, for example, must have oxygen present at certain levels for their survival. At a broader level, the absence of oxygen will result in the predomination of an anaerobic microbial population whose end products are associated with severe nuisance conditions such as offensive odors, dark sludge accumulations, cloudy waters, and so forth. Such severe oxygen depletions can be caused by the biological oxidation of excessive organic compounds (or in certain cases, the oxidation of certain inorganic compounds such as ammonia), wherein the oxygen "demand" for these oxidations exceeds the ability of the body of water to replenish its oxygen stores. Less often, waste materials might have an "immediate", or non-biological oxygen demand. The monitoring of oxygen, it is obvious, is a very important operation in the wastewater field.

The most popular methods of continuously determining dissolved oxygen concentration in a water or wastewater involves the use of membrane electrodes, or more recently, the use of a potentiometric thallium electrode.

There are two general types of membrane electrode systems used for DO analysis—a voltametric membrane and a galvanic membrane electrode type.[36] The voltametric electrode relies on an external source of applied voltage to polarize the indicator electrode whereas a galvanic electrode depends upon an electrochemical reaction occurring at one of the electrode pair to generate an electrical current. Several membrane electrode systems are used for the analysis of DO in natural waters as well as wastewaters.[37-39] Reviews as well as applications can be found in the work of Mancey[37,38] and Clark,[40] Eye *et al.*[41] and Hoare *et al.*[42]

Basically the membrane electrode consists of two metal electrodes an electrolyte solution, and an oxygen permeable membrane. Normally the electrodes are imbedded in plastic with one electrode positioned centrally as a core, and surrounded by the second electrode which is mounted as a sleeve. The sensing portion of the couple, or tip, therefore consists of a disc-shaped (normally silver) electrode surrounded by a ring-shaped anode (normally lead). A thin film of electrolyte solution is spread over the tip and the oxygen permeable membrane (normally polyethylene) is stretched or positioned to cover the tip. Although the oxygen sensing cathode is normally made of silver, platinum as well as gold have also been used. The electrolyte used depends upon the anode, but is usually a KCl solution. A number of oxygen permeable membranes have been used besides polyethylene, and include teflon, mylar, polypropylene and synthetic rubber.

When a reactant, such as oxygen migrates through the semi-permeable membrane, the cathode is depolarized probably forming hydroxyl ions and consuming electrons. The resulting flow of current through the cell is in direct proportion to the amount of oxygen (or other reactant) passing through the membrane. Since the permeability of the membrane is temperature related, temperature correction is required. Membrane sensors of this design are, however, subject to certain problems such fouling by microbial growth and the action of certain chemical interferences such as H_2S. In addition, with time, the membrane tends to become distorted which in turn alters instrument calibration.

A more recently developed dissolved oxygen analyzer which operates on a different principle and does not rely on a semi-permeable membrane has been the thallium electrode marketed by Union Carbide. This electrochemical cell utilizes an exposed thallium metal electrode together with a reference electrode.[43] The dissolved oxygen reacts with an exposed thallium electrode, which in the presence of water forms thallous ions. The electrical potential of the thallium metal/thallous ion half-cell thus becomes a measure of the dissolved oxygen concentration. As with the membrane type probes, certain chemical interference is possible.

Still another method for monitoring small quantities of oxygen based on depolarization by oxygen of an inert cathode of galvanic couple is the Hersch Cell,[43] which employs a noble-metal cathode and a lead anode together with a suitable electrolyte.

Some colorimetric methods for oxygen lend themselves to automation. One application has proposed the use of chloroform extracted iodine.[44] A colorimetric method has been reported by Aleskovski[45] for low dissolved oxygen concentrations in water.

b. Chlorine The use of chlorine as a disinfectant or as an adjunct in the chemical treatment of waters and wastewaters is very important. Several methods for the continuous determination of chlorine are commonly used. These incude colorimetric methods the use of amperometric methods, and the measurement of the oxidation-reduction potential (ORP). Probably the amperometric methods are most often employed.

Colorimetric methods employ a colorimetric cell to measure the color change. The method used most often employs orthotolidine and is a modification of the procedure most commonly used by treatment plant operators, and which appears in *Standard Methods*.[2] There are a number of interferences caused by the presence of iron, manganese, nitrogen dioxide, color, and turbidity as well as certain operational problems reported.[1] This type of instrumentaion will usually measure free and combined chlorine.

The amperometric measurement of chlorine is carried out in a special cell (an amperometric cell) which employs a combination of a noble metal electrode (platinum or gold) and a non-polarizable reference electrode such as copper. The instrument operates when a strong oxidizing agent such as chlorine enters the cell. This causes a depolarization of the noble electrode and the generation of a current proportional to the chlorine which is detected. There are two requirements for detection: the pH must be maintained between 4 and 4.5, hence a buffer must be used; in addition, the electrode surfaces must be kept clean. A number of devices are employed to achieve this end, including revolving nylon balls and grit to "bombard" the electrode surface. Two general types of electrodes are used, rotating and stationary. Morrow has also reported a modification, the use of a dual polarizable electrode system (platinum) which may be used for either water or sewage.[46]

Oxidation–Reduction Potential (ORP) measurement has been employed at various times to detect chlorine. The results however have not been altogether satisfactory. This is primarily because the ORP measured is not specific for chlorine and may in fact be due to any number of other compounds. This is further complicated by the fact that an accurate measurement of chlorine is also a function of pH.

c. Hardness Hardness is caused by the presence of divalent cations such as calcium, magnesium, iron or strontium which when they are present in natural waters in high concentrations are regarded as "soap consuming" substances. Since hardness removal is usually carried out in water treatment plants, its continuous detection becomes important in both the operation and control of water treatment processes.

Instrumentation for the continuous monitoring of hardness in natural or process waters ranging down to low parts per million concentration has been commercially available for some time. Commercial potentiometric titrators, for example, in flow systems have been applied to natural as well as treated waters, using EDTA.[47] Usually these titrators use a continuous flowthrough chamber through which the sample flows at a set rate. Reagents are added at a variable rate. The quantity of reagent solution required is then measured using a tubular platinum indicator electrode.

Serfass[48] has also reported the development of a colorimetric monitori using Eriochrome black-T and magnesium EDTA for trace hardness in water. The instrument is designed to signal when a pre-set value of hardness is exceeded. The function of such a monitor would be notification that the unit removing hardness—e.g. the ion exchange resin in the water treatment process is exhausted or failing.

d. Specific Ion Electrodes The use of specific ion electrodes to measure continuously, *in situ*, the activity of such ions as chloride, cadmium, calcium, fluoride, iodide, cupric, sulfide, nitrate, sodium, potassium, total hardness (divalent ions), etc., in the water and wastewater field is not yet common. However, because of their specificity and compactness they show great potential. Specific ion electrodes give immediate readout and are extremely sensitive devices, capable of measuring specific inorganic ion activities in the low parts per billion ranges.

Specific ion electrodes are generally of three basic types—modified glass electrodes, liquid membrane electrodes, and solid-state or precipitate electrodes. A complete discussion of the theory is available in the review of Durst.[49]

The selectivity of the modified glass electrode depends on the compositon of the glass membrane. The liquid membrane device incorporates a coarse glass or plastic membrane which is in contact with the solution being measured. Its selectivity varies with the kind of liquid ion exchanger in the chamber. Three subtypes are available, a pH type, a cation-sensitive type and a sodium sensitive type. The solid-state electrode with a membrane is a single crystal membrane or a membrane consisting of particles imbedded in an inert silicone rubber matrix. The sensors selectivity changes with the composition of the crystal or of the particles imbedded.

There are a number of interferences due to changes in ionic strength, interfering ions, complexing agents and liquid junction potential which can be more or less compensated for. Applications in water and wastewater monitoring can be found in the work of Ciaccio *et al.*[1]

e. Continuous Flow Chemical Analysers A continuous flow chemical analyzer consists of a series of interconnected modules which automate, stepwise, wet chemical methodologies. The basic components of continuous chemical analyzers can be reduced to the components shown as Figure 1. In general, "wet" chemical analytical procedures are modified for continuous flow reactions. Flow is continuous and the sample as well as the reagents are sequentially and continuously introduced into the moving stream where a reaction occurs which can be detected. Readout is usually, although not always, colorimetric. Sensors, other than optical, however may also be used to evaluate the reaction (e.g. pH, ORP, flame photometer, etc.).

Automatic on-stream titration devices using step switches have also been employed,[15,47] which can automatically sample a water, wastewater or process stream, and titrate the sample. Detection of the end point in such cases is by the use of pH electrodes, flowthrough dropping electrodes, platinum electrodes, color (measured phooelectrically) or by any signal change that can be detected. Alarm systems for such instrumentation or process control for remedial action coupled to such detection systems are available. Essentially, using such a system, almost any wet chemical analytical procedure can be performed. A modification of the continuous flow system, which is really closely spaced "batch" sampling, includes the use of a programmer which controls the steps of the analysis, i.e. flushing, reagent addition, mixing, etc., giving a record of a closely spaced series of analyses.

Although a number of such systems can be found on the market, perhaps the Technicon AutoAnalyzer has been most prominently used in the

Figure 1 Continuous chemical analysis—basic components.

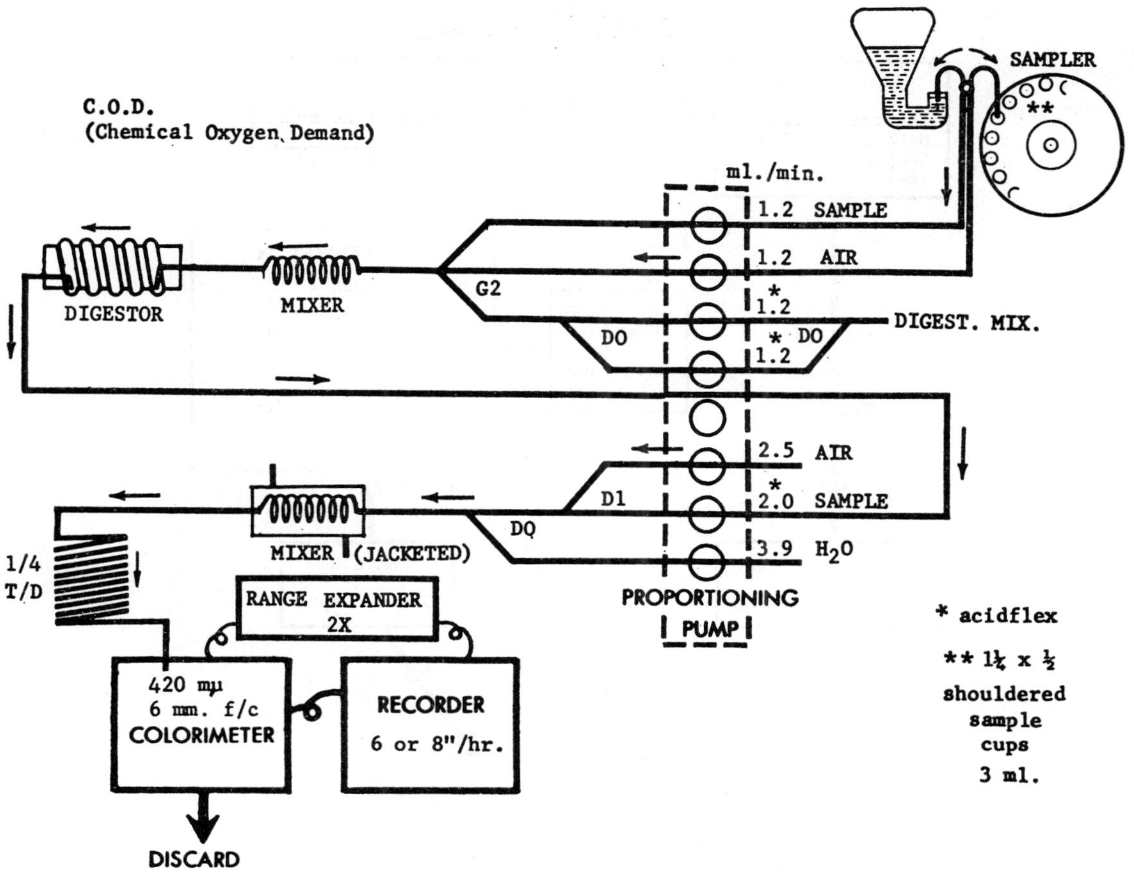

Figure 2 Automated method for Chemical Oxygen Demand (COD). AutoAnalyzer method (20).

water and wastewater field.[51] A large number of substances may be detected by use of the AutoAnalyzer. Many of these analyses are based directly on *Standard Methods* procedures.[2]

The AutoAnalyzer is a modular instrument with each component designed to perform a specific function in the analytical process. Mechanical manipulations, such as those performed in programmed, semi-continuous analyzers, are kept to a minimum through the various steps in the analysis. Figure 2 gives a typical flow diagram showing how a sample may be either withdrawn from a sampling platter from cups which are sampled sequentially, or it may be monitored directly from the sample source or stream using plastic tubing. The continuously flowing air-segmented liquid stream carries a sample past a series of stations or positions where the reagents required for the analysis are introduced and mixed into the sample stream in proper sequence. The mixture can be diluted or further processed, as required. This might include filtration to remove particulate matter, heating, dialysis, etc. The test reaction is usually colorimetric and after proper color development the mixture is passed through a colorimeter using a continuous flow cell where it is measured and recorded on a potentiometric chart recorder. Known concentrations of the specific chemical being detected are similarly treated to establish standard values which are then used for comparison. Good reproduceability and accuracy are possible. The unit may be used for the determination of a single component on a large number of samples (up to 60/hr depending on the analysis), or different analyses may be determined simultaneously by running the sample stream through different manifold and employing separate colorimetric flow cells. The most recent models are capable of as many as six simultaneous analyses. Flow-through time varies, but generally less than 10 min is required for readout.

Although continuous flow chemical analyzers make excellent laboratory tools for analytical work where many samples are involved, for monitoring the instrument cannot remain unattended for too long a period. Since reagents must be supplied and the instrument must be zeroed and standardized. Hence the particular application must always be considered.

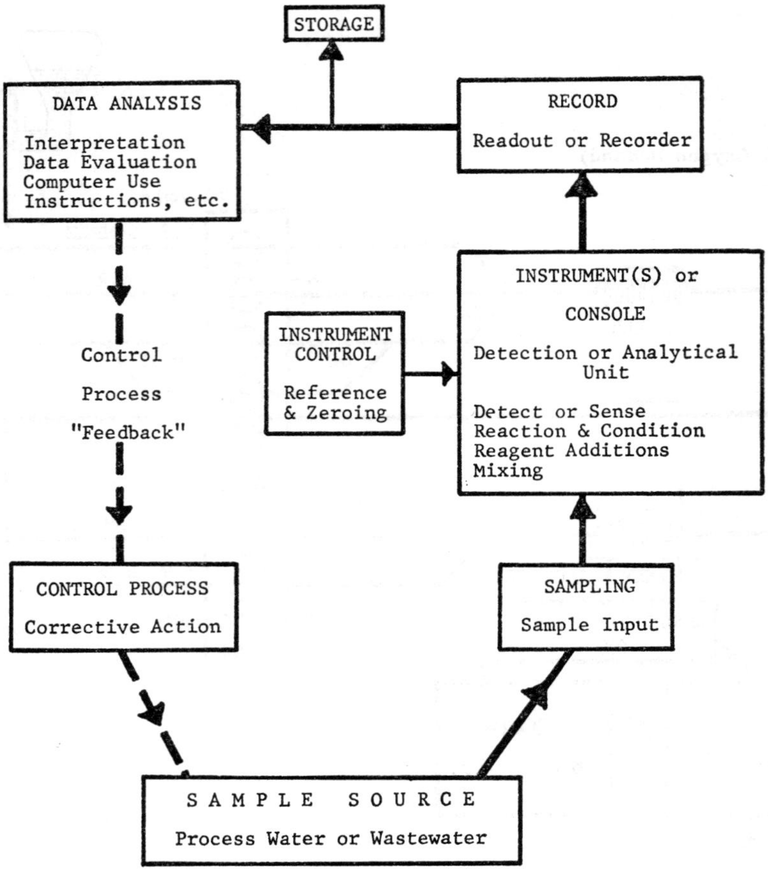

Figure 3 Automated instrument system with process control.

Recently a number of devices have been introduced in which discrete samples and individual glass or plastic reaction vessels are moved past stations a series of stations or positions where reagents are added and reactions or measurements occur.[52]

B. Process control instrumentation

Depending on the complexity of the parameter to be analyzed, an automated analytical instrumental system (or process analyzer) with process control will consist of several sub-units. A generalized, if somewhat simplified presentation of the basic components of an idealized instrumental system is shown in the flow diagram in Figure 3.

Essentially, a system representing process automation can be reduced to the five functional components indicated. The systems can be visualized as beginning with the sample removal. The sample stream is then led into the analysis or detection instrument—which may be either a relatively simple non-specific sensor or a complex specific chemical analytical detector of the type that has been described in the preceding section. In either case parametric sensing generates a signal which is subsequently recorded. Data analysis or interpretation may consist of a complex system containing programmed or predetermined instructions and employing an electronic computer, or it may simply consist of the simplest of operations—visual scanning. In a completely automated system, the data analysis circuit can, on prearranged signals, initiate remedial steps. An example would be the addition of corrective chemicals at a required dosage affecting the parameter sensed by the instrument. Thus, through a control loop, a fully automated circuit is completed. The control loop shown may or may not be a simple "feedback" control and can be a "feedforward" or a compound loop.

The complexity of such an automated system can vary widely and in some systems several of the steps indicated on the diagram may be functionally combined. For example, simple probes may be directly immersed into the sample stream (thus requiring no sampling apparatus) which directly generates a signal to the recorder with a direct readout scale for the required parameter. In practice, in the water and wastewater treatment field a complete "control loop" where a corrective action is initiated, is not often employed. More often, in continuous parametric detection, the diagram is applicable only as far as the "data analysis" box, shown in Fig. 3, which may simply consist of visually scanning a recorder strip chart. This has been indicated by a dashed line.

REFERENCES

1. Ciaccio, L., Raul R. Cardenas Jr. and J. S. Jeris (in press) Automated and Instrumental Methods in Water Analysis. Ed. by L. L. Ciaccio, *Water and Wastewater Pollution Handbook*, Vol. IV, Chap. 27, Marcel Dekker, New York.
2. Amer. Publ. Health Assoc. (1971) *Standard Methods for the Examination of Water and Wastewater*, 13th Ed., New York.
3. Amer. Soc. for Testing and Materials, 1971 *Book of, ASTM Standards*, Part 23, Water; Atmospheric Analysis Amer. Soc. for Testing and Materials, Philadelphia, Pa.
4. Strickland, J. and T. R. Parsons (1968) *A Practical Handbook of Sea Water Analysis*, Fisheries Research Board of Canada, Ottowa, Canada.
5. U.S. Dept. of Interior (1969) *FWCA Methods for Chemical Analysis of Water and Wastes*, FWQO, Cincinnati, Ohio.
6. Environmental Protection Agency, Water Quality Office, *Methods for Chemical Analysis of Water and Wastes*, 1971, Analytical Quality Control Laboratory, Cincinnati, Ohio.
7. Dept. of the Army, U.S. Corps of Engineers, *Permits for Work and Structures in and for Discharges or Deposits into Navigable Waters*, 1971.
8. Section 13, River and Harbor Act 1899, *Refuse Act*.
9. Federal Water Pollution Control Act, Sec 21(b), Amendment: Water Quality Improvement Act of 1970, P.L. 91–224, 84 Stat 108, Executive Order No. 11574 (Dec. 1970).
10. Ballinger, D. (1967) *Env. Sci. and Technol.*, **1**, 612.
11. Willard, H. H., L. Merritt and J. Dean (1965) *Instrumental Methods of Analysis*, 4th Ed., D. Van Nostrand, Princeton, N.J.
12. Reilley, C. and C. N. Sawyer (1964) *Experiments for Instrumental Methods*, McGraw-Hill, New York.
13. Ewing, G. W. (1969) *Instrumental Methods for Chemical Analysis*, 3rd Ed., McGraw-Hill, New York.
14. Fraade, D. J. (1961) *Instrum. Control Systems*, **34**, 2059.
15. Siggia, S. (1959) *Continuous Analysis of Chemical Process Streams*, John Wiley and Sons, New York.
16. Bates, R. G. (1964) *Determination of pH*. John Wiley and Sons, New York.
17. Clark, J. W. (1960) *Water and Sewage Works*, **107**, 140.
18. Liebmannm H. and K. Offhaus (1966) *Abwassertechnik*, **17**, (3), IV.
19. Arthur, R. M. (1964) *Proc. 19th Industrial Waste Conf., Purdue Univ.*, Lafayette, Ind., p. 628.
20. Molof, A. and N. Zaleiko (1964) *Proc. 19th Industrial Waste Conf., Purdue Univ.*, Lafayette, Ind., p. 84.
21. Clifford, D., *24th Annual Fall Scientific Meeting*, Midland Section, Amer. Chem. Soc., Midland, Mich. (Nov. 1967).
22. Stenger, V. and C. Van Hall (1967) *Anal. Chem.*, **39**, 206.
23. Van Hall, C. E., J. Safranko and V. A. Stenger (1963) *Anal. Chem.*, **35**, 315.
24. Von Lossberg, L. G. (1965) U.S. Patent, 3,205,045.
25. Lysyj, I., K. H. Helson and P. R. Newton (1968) *J. Water Pollution Control Federation*, **40**, R181.
26. Bramer, H. C., M. J. Walsh and S. C. Caruso (1966 *Water and Sewage Works*, **113**, 275.
27. Eckenfelder, W. W. (1966) *Industrial Water Pollution Control*, McGraw-Hill, New York, N.Y., Chap. 9.
28. Jones, R. J. (1966) *J. Instrum. Soc. of America*, **13**, 40.
29. Delta Scientific, Lindenhurst, N.Y.
30. Hach Chemical Co., Ames, Iowa.
31. Hellige, Inc., Garden City, N.Y.
32. Hach, CR Falling Steam Turbidimeter Model 1031, Hach Chemical Co, Ames, Iowa.
33. Baalsrud, K. and A. Hendriksen (1964) *J. Amer. Water Works Ass.*, **56**, 1194.
34. Eberly, G. L. (1957) in *Process Instruments and Controls Handbook*, Ed. by D. M. Considine, Section 7, p. 54. McGraw-Hill, New York.
35. Martin, P. T. (1963) *Proc. 9th National ISA Analysis Symposium*, p. 219.
36. Mancy, K. H. and T. Jaffe (1966) *Analysis of Dissolved Oxygen in Natural and Waste Waters*, USPHS Publ. No. 999-WP-37.
37. Mancy, K. H., D. A. Okun and C. N. Reilley (1962) *J. Electroanaly. Chem.*, 3.
38. Mancy, K. H., W. C. Westgart and D. A. Okun (1964) *Proc. 7th Industrial Waste Conference, Purdue Univ.*, Lafayette, Ind., p. 508.
39. Carritt, D. and J. Kanwisher (1959) *J. Anal. Chem.*, **31**, 5.
40. Clark, L. C., D. Granger and Z. Taylor (1953) *J. Appl. Physiol.*, **6**, 186.
41. Clark, L. (1956) *Trans. Am. Soc. Artificial Internal Organs*, **2**, 41.
42. Hoare, J. D. (1968) *The Electrochemistry of Oxygen*, Interscience, New York, p. 191.
43. Hersch, P. (1960) *Anal. Chem.*, **32**, 1030.
44. Elliot, J. W. (1963) *Progr. Fish Cult.*, **25**, 42.
45. Aleskovskii, V. B. (1964) *Zavodakaya Lab.*, **30**, 1, 105.
46. Morrow, J. (1966) *J. Am. Water Works Ass.*, **58**, 363.
47. Blaedel, W. J. and R. H. Laessig, *Anal. Chem.*, **36**, 1617.
48. Serfass, E. and R. Brown. In *Analysis Instrumentation*, Vol. 4, Proc. 12th Ann. Analysis Meeting (1966), p. 85.
49. Durst, R. A. Ed. (1969) *Ion Selective Electrodes*, Nat. Bur. Stand. (U.S.) Spec. Publ. 314, Washington, D.C.
50. Guilbault, G. G. (1970) *Enzymatic Methods of Analysis*, Chap. 7. Pergamon Press, Elmsford, N.Y.,
51. Technicon Instruments Co, Tarrytown, N.TY.
52. Anderson, N. G. (1949) *Science*, **166**, 317.

RAUL R. CARDENAS, JR.

Polytechnic Institute of New York

POLLUTION LAW: see ENVIRONMENTAL LAW

POLLUTION METEOROLOGY: see AIR POLLUTION METEOROLOGY

POLLUTION OF GROUNDWATER: see GROUNDWATER

PRIMARY TERRESTRIAL CONSUMERS: see ECOLOGY OF PRIMARY TERRESTRIAL CONSUMERS

PROTECTION OF THE ENVIRONMENT: see CONSERVATION PLANNING

PSYCHOLOGICAL ASPECTS OF MAN'S ENVIRONMENT

Man's interaction with his environment is an integral part of the science of psychology. Psychology has been defined as the study of human and animal behavior. Behavior does not take place in a vacuum. It is conditioned by the environment in which it occurs.

The relationship between man and his environment is interactive. Man is not only influenced by his environment; his behavior may also profoundly affect his environment. Where psychology can predict behavior for various environments, it will permit calculation of the impact of behavior on the environment. To the extent that it has developed procedures for controlling such behavior, it can alter the impact of human and animal behavior on the environment by changing that behavior.

Viewed from this perspective, psychology might be expected to have far reaching impact on any area of environmental concern; indeed, for any area of human concern.

It is not surprising, then, to find that much work in psychology is relevant to problems of concern to environmental scientists and engineers. Problems in almost any area of environmental study may have roots in psychology. Many substances whose physiological effects are of concern to environmentalists first make their effects on organisms apparent through behavioral indices and tasks studied by psychologists. Many standards problems have psychological aspects. Potable water must be acceptable to the palate, as well as meeting biological and chemical standards based on health considerations. It has been shown that existing ventilation standards for inhabited buildings originated in part from considerations of odor control. The impact of a field depends upon its achievements, as well as its domain of concern, however. One of the aims of this paper will be to consider the extent to which psychology can accomplish its aims in areas of environmental interest·

This paper will concern itself first with psychological studies relevant to man's physical environment. It will then go on to consider his psychological and social environment. These categories are to some extent artificial. The relevant environment for an organism consists of those aspects of the physical environment to which it is sensitive. This environment is not necessarily the same as the physical environment as measured by physicists or engineers. A colorblind organism will not respond to variations in the wavelength of light in the same way as one with color vision, though the physical stimulus is the same in both cases. Psychophysics is the branch of psychology concerned with the relationship between man's sensory processes and his physical environment and over one hundred years of psychophysical research has shown that the relationship is both subtle and complex. Nevertheless, such division conforms to some natural boundaries within the fields of psychology, and of environmental studies, and so it will be adopted here.

The Physical Environment

The earliest studies in psychology were concerned with the relationship between measurements of the physical environment and perceptual processes. Since one cannot determine the nature of a percept directly, what was actually measured were certain observable responses, which were taken to be indices of these percepts. Although the concept of behaviorism was not originally enunciated in connection with psychophysics, but came later in connection with studies of learning, it is well to note that problems in all areas of psychology can be formulated in behavioral terms. In the author's opinion, this should always be done. It avoids innumerable arguments over concepts and processes if one recognizes that only the behavior is measurable, and that other concepts, such as motives, feelings, images, etc., are, from this point of view, theories developed to facilitate description of the relationships between the environment and be havior, however, real these constructs may seem in other contexts.

Psychological methods for environmental study

Psychological procedures relevant to environmental questions can be conveniently divided into the following categories: studies of sensory thresholds and simple perceptual and psychomotor tasks; behavior in simple learning situations; more complex-learning and decision tasks; methods for studying opinion; and evaluation of such complex processes as emotion and personality changes in response to environmental factors.

1. *Psychophysical Procedures* The study of sensory thresholds is one of the oldest areas of psychology, going back to the work of Weber and Fechner towards the end of the nineteenth century. Classically, two types of thresholds have been determined; absolute thresholds and difference thresholds. The absolute limen, or threshold (AL), is the minimum amount of stimulus energy required to elicit a response; the difference limen (DL) or threshold, is the minimum energy change required to perceive a change in the stimulus. Because the amount of energy related to that required for a perceived change is often related to the absolute value of the stimulus, the difference limen is often given as a fraction of the absolute value.

Since the range of intensity for most of the senses is very large, it is customary to use a logarithmic scale in expression of the stimulus values. In audition, the decibel is a common unit. Intensity (I) is given in decibels (dB) by

$$I = 10 \log P_1/P_r \text{ dB},$$

where P_1 is the stimulus power, and P_r the reference level. Measurement in decibel units is less common for the other senses, but some type of logarithmic scale is frequently used.

The measurement of thresholds presents certain technical problems, due to variability in the response, and the possibility of response bias. Two major methods were devised to deal with the problem: the method of limits and the method of average error. In the method of limits, series of stimuli of varying intensity are presented and the subject is asked to make a response, according to whether subject does or does not perceive the stimulus, or stimulus change. Since threshold values obtained typically depend on whether the approach to the threshold is up (from unperceived to perceived) or down (from perceived to unperceived), several series of trials in both directions may be averaged. The method of average error is an adjustment method. The subject is asked to adjust a variable to match a standard, and the variability of the response is used as a measure of the limen. It is most suitable to difference limen measurements.

Recently, the concept of a sensory threshold has been questioned, and the most popular view at present is to view the internal process as continuous, with a criterion applied to produce a dichotomous response. This view derives from the signal detection theory of sensory processes. The extent to which this model of the threshold differs from older ones is arguable; the arbitrary nature of the threshold concept has always been recognized. However, it has led to a more systematic treatment of the problems of noise and bias in threshold measurements. Procedurally it stresses the measurement of thresholds by yes/no judgments in which the probability of a false alarm is explicitly estimated, and by forced choice techniques. Receiver operating characteristic (ROC) curves are used to analyze the data. The resulting measure of sensitivity, is usually referred to as d'. From the point of view of reliability, either the classic methods or new signal detection procedures will usually lead to satisfactory results.

The sensory dimensions have been divided into two types: intensive dimensions and qualitative dimensions. Examples of intensive dimensions are the intensity of light and sound. Examples of qualitative dimensions are color and pitch, which often have recurrences in them, such as the scale relation in pitch, which complicate analysis. Sensory intensity normally increases logarithmically with increases in the physical stimulus. Qualitative dimensions may have more complex relationships with their physical correlates. The measurement of sensory thresholds may be extended to animals by means of conditioning procedures to be described in the next section.

Several thresholds other than the absolute and differential limens are important for environmental studies. Often, concern will lie in thresholds for discomfort, and for tolerance. It may also be desired to obtain information on the degree of discomfort produced by different environmental conditions. Direct judgments of discomfort or tolerance tend to be highly variable; individual tolerances, or at least statements about these tolerances, differ from individual to individual. One technique which is sometimes used is to obtain comparison judgments about the relative discomfort caused by different stimuli. One method of measuring pain thresholds is based on this principle; the discomfort caused by various stimuli is compared with the pain caused by a known exposure to infrared light on the forehead.

A fixed standard need not be used; cross comparison of the set of stimuli of interest is possible. Techniques have been developed for taking such paired judgments, and using them to scale the stimuli along the dimension of judgment. Variations of this technique can be applied to ranked data: ranking is less time consuming than a full set of paired comparison judgments, but it requires more assumptions to generate a scale. Multidimensional scaling techniques are usefully applied to preference or similarity judgments, however obtained. They are especially useful where the relevant dimensions of the stimulus set are not clear, since they can be analyzed to obtain dimensions of judgment. It is also possible to analyze such judgments for clusterings among the subjects.

2. Classical and Operant Conditioning Classical conditioning is a type of learning pioneered by I. Pavlov, and still extensively studied by psychologists. In its simplest form, the procedure consists of presenting some stimulus which consistently elicits a response, known as the unconditioned stimulus (UCS), in combination with some other stimulus which does not normally evoke the response, known as the conditioned stimulus (CS). After a number of trials, the CS will be found to elicit the response in the absence of the UCS. Such a response is known as a conditioned response (CR).

Various complexities can be introduced into this paradigm and it has been the subject of extensive study and theoretical discussion. Its primary importance for the environmental field lies in the fact that the technique can be used to determine sensitivity to various stimuli. This can occur in two ways.

(1) The effect of various phsyiologically active stimuli on the course of acquisition and extinction of a known CR can be studied. Changes in the course of learning and extinction are evidence of the effect of the stimulus.

(2) The procedure can be used to determine threshold sensitivity to a stimulus. If a CR can be established to a given concentration or intensity of a stimulus, it is evidence that the organism is sensitive to the stimulus, though the reverse is not necessarily true. Thus, classical conditioning techniques can be used to measure sensory thresholds in animals.

A second major type of conditioning is known as operant conditioning. In operant conditioning, there is nothing equivalent to the UCS; a response which occurs is followed by some subsequent event, such as the occurence of food, which will modify the frequency of the response. The desired response may have a low probability of occurence and procedures such as shaping and the creation of special environments may be necessary. Shaping consists of reinforcing successively closer approximations to the desired response. A common example of a special environment is the Skinner box, a small enclosure whose most prominent feature is the response mechanism, usually a bar or button. The rat or pigeon in a Skinner box, pushing a bar or pecking at a lever to obtain food or avoid electric shock are examples of operant conditioning situations.

Operant conditioning procedures can be used for the same purposes as classical conditioning methods, but they have some advantages. Classical conditioning is relatively difficult to establish, is easily disturbed by any change in the environment and the CR ceases to occur (undergoes extinction) rapidly once the UCS is removed. Operant conditioning, on the contrary, is relatively easy to establish. One reinforcement often makes a marked difference in response rates. It is less sensitive to extraneous environmental interference and it can be maintained for long periods of time with a very low reinforcement rate. Records of cumulative responses to various reinforcement schedules show definite regularities. Changes in these patterns provide a sensitive measure of the effect of various chemicals on behavior and have been extensively used for this purpose in drug research. Threshold measurements in operant conditioning require a slightly more complex situation than in classical conditioning if the substance to be studied does not act as a reinforcer of behavior. However, by using it as a cue to indicate when some positive reinforcement is to be given, the thresholds of such substances can be studied by operant techniques. Both operant and classical conditioning techniques are applicable to humans as well as other organisms.

3. Other Simple Learning Situations Other types of learning situations which have been studied sufficiently to provide a basis for the study of behavioral effects of environmental factors are maze learning, discrimination learning, and a variety of simple verbal learning tasks. The former tasks may be used with either humans or animals. The verbal tasks are limited to humans. The complexity of the stimulus situation is generally greater in these tasks. Specifying the relevant dimensions of even simple mazes for learning situations is complicated, and an enormous and continuing effort has been devoted to the study of the features of verbal stimuli which affect simple learning tasks such as paired associate learning, (where people are presented with pairs of words and then asked to recall one of the words when shown the other) and serial learning, (where subjects are asked to learn lists of words). They are therefore less easy to quantify and compare across experiments than are conditioning responses and thus introduce additional problems for the study of environmental effects. However, with sufficient care, reliable measurements can be obtained.

These tasks come closer than simpler tasks to

being of a complexity relevant to behavior in real life situations. It is quite possible that some stimulus will have no measurable effect on a simple process, but will affect more complex behaviors; the reverse is sometimes also the case; environmental conditions which will affect simple and monotonous tasks may not affect more intrinsically interesting tasks. For this reason, learning tasks other than simple conditioning are often studied when the effects of various environments are under investigation.

4. More Complex Tasks The number of human performances which have been studied by psychologists is very large; no satisfactory classification has been worked out for procedures going beyond the simplest. Various bases for categorization have been proposed; for example, sensory-motor to verbal, depending on the type of response; or in terms of complexity, from simple conditioning to complex problem solving. Probably the best ultimate solution will consist of a task analysis for more complex behaviors in terms of their dependence on more simple processes, but this has not been achieved in any general way at present. The particular type of task employed and the dimensions along which it is to be analyzed can be best considered at present in terms of the particular experimental situation. If an investigator is concerned with the effects of certain pollutants on complex judgments required by some task, he will do well to construct a task as much like the criterion task as possible and test the effects by means of a suitable design. If his concern is with performance in a vigilance situation, than a vigilance type task should be selected. Generalizations from effects on simple behaviors to more complex behaviors are hazardous at present.

5. Standardized Tests of Behavior Standardized tests have been developed for a wide variety of human abilities. IQ tests are the most famous, but many others exist. Such tests have as their primary purpose either selection in connection with personnel work, or evaluation for counseling for guidance, but they may be used in the same way as other tests for the evaluation of the effect of environments on performance.

Tests of this sort may be divided into tests of general ability, tests of specific ability, and tests of personality. Both of the former have been used in connection with environmental work. Occasionally, the latter have been also, though their suitability for the purpose of evaluating temporary shifts in emotional state is often dubious. Most standardized tests are designed to measure some relatively permanent characteristic. However, some of these characteristics, such as various types of manual dexterity, are sensitive to various environmental forces in a fairly straightforward way. The effects of depressant drugs on personality tests are considerably less clear. There is also a serious problem of validity with regard to some tests, especially personality tests. The objective tests, such as the Guilford–Zimmerman or the Minnesota Multiphasic Personality Index (MMPI), have been extensively validated against certain criteria, such as psychiatric diagnosis. However, the criteria themselves are open to argument in many cases. Also the criteria used for validation are seldom those of interest if a test is to measure temporary changes in emotional state due to changed environment. The tests often appear likely to be insensitive to the types of mood changes which may be of interest to environmentalists. Projective personality tests appear, on the surface, to be more sensitive for this purpose, for they permit much freer response than objective tests, and they have been used, for example, in studies of aggression. However, they are exceedingly difficult to validate, even against the type of criteria used for objective personality tests, and their predictive value for other types of behavior is almost entirely unknown.

6. Comments on Psychological Methods In evaluating these procedures for use in the environmental field, there are some general considerations to keep in mind. First, the psychophysical procedures are generally reliable, if carefully done, and generalization to other individuals from a small sample is good. This work is often done with two or three observers, and the results are repeatable. The extreme sensitivity of the sensory systems means that very precise control over the stimulus is needed, which is often expensive. Certain stimuli, especially odors, are difficult to handle; special equipment, such as odorometers, are necessary. Timing down into the millisecond range is typically needed in visual and auditory experiments.

Other types of behaviors tend to be more variable. Only in simple conditioning situations are such small numbers of experimental subjects likely to be found, and even here, for most purposes, more than three or four subjects are necessary. The requirements for stimulus control are somewhat less rigid, in most cases. In verbal learning studies, timing to .01 sec is usually adequate; less precision is often tolerable. However, the substantial variability of organisms presented with even relatively simple learning tasks, such as mazes or simple discrimination learning, makes a larger sample desirable.

Individual experimental conditions may be tested on 10–20 subjects, or more; it is not uncommon to find verbal learning experiments which use several hundred subjects. Generalization to other populations is sometimes more of a problem and the equivalence of stimuli in different experiments is more difficult to establish. However, within these limitations, reliable results can be obtained in simple conditioning situations, and most other simple learning tasks, including simple verbal learning tasks.

Both classical and operant conditioning procedures are very sensitve to the action of certain agents. Effects of levels of ionizing radiation have been reported as low as 5.0 r in conditioning experiments. Behavioral effects of several drugs of environmental importance, such as alcohol, and amphetamines, can be found for relatively low dosages. While the information on the sensitivity of conditioning procedures to agents of interest such as SO_2 and NO_2 is sparse, there is no reason for believing that behavioral measures will not be equally applicable to many of these substances Behavioral studies done in Russia emphasize the use of classical conditioning techniques in studying various environmental factors. In such research behavioral effects for low levels are frequent, though it is difficult to evaluate due to the obscurity of much of this literature by American standards of reporting.

Problems arise when it is desired to interpret behavioral measures in a more refined fashion than simply as indicators of some physiological activity of the substances. Temporary threshold shifts from noise exposure have been extensively investigated, but their implications for permanent damage is still being debated (see Noise). Similar problems exist for other measures. The problems which have faced psychopharmacologists in interpreting effects of drugs on animal behavior in terms of drug effects on humans have their counterpart in the environmental field; granted that a certain level of ionizing radiation can serve as an aversive stimulus in operant conditioning experiments on saccharin preference, for example, how are the results to be interpreted in terms of public health standards? How long lasting must such effect be in order to be indicators of possible physical damage? If no physical damage is to be expected, there is still the question of the costs of possible functional impairment. Does impairment of operant conditioning imply that the agent will also impair more complex functions in humans, with a possible increase in errors or accidents as the result? At present, answers are not available to these questions.

More complex tasks raise more serious problems of reliability. It is not uncommon in educational research for several experiments to yield contradictory results, for reasons which are often obscure. The complexity of the materials and other variations in subjects and procedures which are difficult to control or characterize are probably responsible. Thus, a single study done on the environmental effect of a substance on complex learning should be viewed with caution. Only when a series of experiments done under varying conditions converge on a result should the result be accepted.

Certain special problems which often arise are the effects of novelty (the so-called "Hawthorne" effect) and habituation effects. Individuals may perform well under a certain test procedure, which, when put into practice proves no better than the alternative. The problem is that subjects on whom new procedures are tried may make a special effort which is not sustained under routine conditions. A similar effect arises in regard to habituation. Individuals may respond badly to a new environment, but adjust to it over time without final decrement in performance. Since adaptation for some tasks can take months, adaptation effects are often inadequately tested.

Most research involving the possibility of exposure to physically hazardous conditions is done on animals. However, a good deal of research which involves physical discomfort or emotional stress is done on humans. Also, in some research, personal information of a private nature may be obtained. Concern over possible abuses of subjects has arisen in recent years, and several profesional societies have or are developing codes of ethics to deal with these problems. There are also legal aspects to the use of human and animal subjects of which any potential research worker in these fields should make himself aware.

The Physical Environment and Behavior

1. Sensory processes

Judged purely in terms of their adequacy as detectors, sensory systems are very efficient for many, types of stimuli. The auditory system, for example is capable of detecting sound near the level of Brownian motion under suitable test conditions. The number of photons required to obtain a visual response has been estimated as low as 5–14 photons under optimal conditions. The olfactory system is also exceedingly sensitive. As has been noted, the intensity of a sensation goes up approximately as a logarithmic function of increases in intensity of the physical stimulus (the Weber–Fechner law). It applies to such sensory domains as vision, audition, etc. In specific applications, of course, this information is inadequate for most purposes and more precise information is needed. The apparent loudness of a noise will depend on its frequency as well as its intensity, for example.

When qualitative factors are under consideration, it is more difficult to make any statements. The annoying properties of a noise are a complex function of specific combinations of frequency and intensity and it is still not well understood. See the article on noise in this volume for a more complete discussion of this problem.

There are, however, a few general statements about sensory systems which may be of use to environmentalists. First, of course, the primary channels of information to human beings are the visual and the auditory systems. Senses such as touch, taste, smell, etc. are of far less importance than in the case of many animals. Of the major channels, vision has the larger channel capacity, in the information theoretic use of that term. However, this is not equivalent to an expression of their social importance. The auditory channel is the primary means of face-to-face communication between human beings, and studies indicate that loss of hearing may produce more profound personality changes than loss of vision. Early loss of hearing can produce a disastrous effect on language learning. For many purposes in adults, they may be equivalent for information transmission. When one is dealing with tasks which are purely informational, the visual channel may be more efficient, since in tasks like reading, humans can process more words than they can listen to in a given period of time.

Knowledge of visual and auditory parameters is important in the proper design of a number of environments. Consider the hazards associated with sources of glaring light along highways at night, for example. The visual system adapts relatively rapidly (usually within a minute) to large increases in light. The process of dark adaptation is much slower, however; it may take as long as half an hour to fully dark adapt the visual system. Rapid changes in the external light levels at night can therefore constitute a hazard, since they may keep the eyes of drivers in a state of adaptation to relatively high illumination levels even though the average level is relatively low.

2. Effects of various pollutants on behavior

a) Ionizing Radiation Perhaps the pollutant whose behavioral effects have been studied most extensively is ionizing radiation. Studies on both lethal and sublethal doses of both particulate and nonparticulate radiation have been done. The conclusion has been that there is relatively little effect of either on the learning behaviors for most organisms. Insofar as tests are available, this seems to be true of man also. However, the activity levels of young rats have been reported to be affected when the mothers had been irradiated with one dose of 200 r. during pregnancy.

This does not mean, however, that organisms are not sensitive to radiation. Radiation has been used to condition avoidance to a saccharin solution (normally preferred by rats). It was found to produce an 80% decrease in response rate under some conditions. The amount of the decrement has been shown to be dose dependent. Russian research, using classical conditioning techniques, has reported a variety of behavioral effects, occasionally for doses as low as 5 r.

b) Air Pollutants The effects of carbon monoxide (CO) on behavior have received a good deal of study. Among other effects, 90 min of exposure to 50 ppm CO has been shown to impair ability to discriminate among relative lengths of short time intervals. The effect of CO on the electroencephalogram (EEG) pattern in rats has been investigated. The results suggest a possible depressive effect of CO on central nervous system function. Significant reductions in tests of manual dexterity have been observed with blood carboxyhaemoglobin (COHb) levels in excess of 25%; such levels may be reached in garages and other enclosed areas containing motor vehicles. CO is known to elevate the visual threshold.

Since CO and some other pollutants have as one of their effects the reduction of the oxygen level in the blood supply, studies on the effects of hypoxia (oxygen deficiency) are relevant to the behavioral effects of gaseous pollutants. The visual threshold is very sensitive to hypoxia; significant impairment can occur at altitudes as low as 5000 ft, and at 15,000 ft twice as much light is required for minimum visibility as is required at sea level. Auditory and speech perception thresholds may also be affected slightly, especially for long exposures. Tasks requiring complex coordination, such as handwriting, deteriorate above 10,000 ft, and higher altitudes can affect simpler tasks and reaction times. Various cognitive tasks, such as card sorting, are affected, usually more than simple psychomotor tasks.

The physiological effects of a number of other pollutants such as NO_2 and SO_2 have been studied and information about their olfactory effects is also available. The olfactory system is very sensitive, and may give adequate warning for some pollutants. Sulfur dioxide, though extremely toxic is difficult to inhale at lethal concentrations without warning because of its intensely irritating properties. Habituation effects do occur with repeated exposure, however, and severe poisonings have occasionally been reported among workers who have adapted to high levels of this pollutant. It is important to note that the olfactory sense adapts very rapidly to most odors. This consideration is important when using odor tests, for chlorine in water, for example.

A number of other substances are not readily detectable by smell, however. Carbon monoxide is odorless, and nitrogen dioxide can cause fatal poisoning at concentrations which are not physically annoying.

c) Other Chemical Pollutants The behavioral effect of a number of other chemical substances which may be of environmental significance have been studied. These include alcohols, various psychoactive drugs, and various industrial chemicals. Ethyl alcohol has been found to increase reaction time by about 10% when the level of alcohol in the blood reaches 0.35%. Blood alcohol levels of 100 mg/100 ml have been reported to affect monitoring and tracking tasks, and lower levels have been reported to affect various complex tasks.

It has been possible to study the effects of a number of such chemicals in conditioning experiments. Several drugs have been shown to increase eating or drinking behavior in animals; these are usually drugs which act to reduce anxiety. Meprobamate and similar drugs usually increase eating; the barbituates chiefly affect drinking. A number of such drugs have been shown to produce decrements in escape or avoidance conditioning, an effect usually attributed to their fear or anxiety reducing properties. Morphine addiction can be induced in animals, and the drug can serve as a positive reinforcer for behavior, permitting the study of various aspects of addiction, such as withdrawal, in animals, using conditioning concepts and procedures.

Depressant drugs, such as the barbituates, have generally been found to impair memory in humans. Retrograde amnesia (failure to recall events just before administration of a drug or some traumatic incident, such as a blow to the head) has been reported for ether and for CO_2, administered post-trial. However, conflicting evidence exists. Post-trial administration of ether can also facilitate retention, and 30% nitrous oxide has also been reported to facilitate retention in humans when given after learning, though other studies have found impairment with nitrous oxide.

Facilitation effects on memory have been reported for a number of other drugs. Strychnine has been shown to improve maze learning for food rewards, discrimination learning, and other tasks. Various other substances have also been studied. However, the results are conflicting at present.

The various effects of chemicals on retention have been interpreted in various ways. It has been hypothesized that a certain period of time is necessary following learning for consolidation of the memory trace. Drugs or other events, such as a blow on the head, or the administration of electroconvulsive shock, may interfere with this process and prevent the retention of learned responses over time. Other possible explanations lie in facilitation or interference with nerve transmission or with protein synthesis. The inhibiting effects of puromycin and other antibiotics on some learned responses has been attributed to their interference with protein synthesis, though other explanations are possible. Explanations in terms of the drug effects on the animals' perception of the cues in the learning situation have also been suggested.

3. Environmental stressors

Unusual conditions of temperature, noise, lighting, vibration, etc. may be encountered in some environments. Extreme values of such stimuli are often regarded as environmental stressors, and their physiological effects have been extensively studied. Concern has also been felt about their behavioural effects, and a number of studies have been done on this question.

a) Noise Excessive noise levels are known to be capable of damaging the auditory system. Noise can also be annoying, and its annoying properties are a complex function of its spectral composition (see Noise). It can also seriously interfere with tasks which depend on auditory communication. However, studies of effects on non-verbal tasks have reported mixed results, often negative. While interference through distraction may occur with sudden unpredictable sounds, in general, noise seems to have a minimal effect on most non-verbal tasks. It should be kept in mind, however, that adapting to noisy environments may impose additional stress on the organism. Noise can induce audiogenic seizures in susceptible strains of rats, and there have been reports of sound-induced seizures in epileptics.

b) Temperature A number of studies have shown decremental effects of elevated temperatures on a variety of tasks. Telegraph operators who had been acclimatized to a hot environment (Singapore) were studied at several temperatures above that of their usual environment. Errors were found that were related logarithmically to the temperature increase in the receipt of coded messages made up of assorted letter and number strings. Similar results have been reported by artificially acclimatized subjects in England. Subjects' judgments of comfort are not necessarily reliable guides to the temperature which gave best task performance. In general, the relationship between behavior decrement and heat stress is more straightforward for tasks involving physical effort than for other tasks, but effects on both have been reported.

Cold has also been studied, chiefly in relation to its effects on manual dexterity, which it decreases. Adaptation effects are also reported to cold.

Studies have been reported which show decrements in learning and retention with elevated temperatures, and improvements with colder environments. The latter have mostly been reported with invertebrates, and it unclear whether the effect is directly temperature related, or due to restriction of activity with cold.

c) Vibration Excessive vibration has been shown to be physically damaging, especially to the circulatory system, in addition to causing symptoms such as seasickness in susceptible individuals. In terms of effects on other behaviors, the chief effect has been shown on visual acuity; most other studies have reported other behaviors to be unaffected. However, vibration has been reported to be unpleasant, if prolonged, even though the levels are below those believed to cause physiological damage, and secondary effects might be expected on monotonous tasks. The vibrations studied have varied from 0–60 Hz, these being the range of practical interest for most environmental purposes. Interactions with frequency are known to exist. Frequencies in the range of 10–24 Hz most severely impair visual acuity, while manual tracking is most seriously affected at frequencies of about 5 Hz. This frequency also produces the greatest subjective discomfort.

d) Inadequate Lighting Lighting may be inadequate either because it is too low, or because it causes glare. Excessive light intensities, such as those generated by lasers, can cause physical damage to the eye. While the eyes can adapt to a wide range of light conditions, the thresholds of the photopic receptors in the fovea of the eye are higher than in the periphery (scotopic vision). The density of receptors in the fovea is also higher, and the functioning of these receptors is important for tasks requiring good visual acuity. Threfore, if the light levels fall below the photopic threshold, such tasks will suffer. Visual acuity may be tested by means of Landolt rigns (circles with small breaks whose orientation the subject must detect) or by means of grids of varying fineness and orientation. Effects of light composition have also been shown on some tasks, even well above the photopic threshold. For most visual tasks, light levels well above the photopic threshold should be maintained.

Glare causes discomfort, and may interfere with various tasks. Two kinds of glare are distinguished; direct glare from a light source in the visual field; and specular glare due to light reflected from surfaces within the visual field. Both types of glare can be controlled by suitable adjustment of the environment. Direct lighting offers maximum light at the working surface when the source is directed downward, but it is likely to produce shadows, glare and undesirable brightness contrasts. Indirect lighting avoids these problems, and while it may lessen visual efficiency in reading over very prolonged periods, it has been shown superior to direct lighting in tests of 3 hr in length.

It should also be realized that color vision depends on the receptors in the fovea. Therefore, tasks requiring the use of colors must be performed with adequate lighting. The color of surfaces depends on the spectrum of the light which falls on them, so illuminants must be chosen to provide the proper colors for tasks involving color coding.

4. Special environments

a) Changes in Sensory Input Early reports on the effect of isolated environments from polar expeditions and the like are in agreement with later experimental findings on the undesirable effects of restricted sensory inputs. Studies on extreme sensory restriction as carried out at McGill University, where subjects wore translucent goggles and stayed in low variability environments, have shown that such effects as loss of ability to concentrate and hallucinations may result. Polar expeditions have reported compensatory behavior in the form of the development of unusually structured groups, and special interests and hobbies on the part of individual members. Similar patterns sometimes develop in such isolation situations as solitary confinement.

Studies on early sensory restriction in animals have suggested that deficits of varying degrees of permanence may develop in subsequent behavior as a result. Extreme deprivation of sensory input and social contact is known to result in a variety of deficits in human infants, even though the physical needs of the infants have been met. The monotonous effects of long periods at tasks such as monitoring sonar screens for infrequent signals, and other vigilance tasks have shown deleterious effects in terms of missed targets.

The effects of excessive sensory input are less clear. Any situation which overloads the information processing capacities of an individual will be likely to result in decremental performance. However, apart from such short-term effects, it is not clear that there are long-term effects from an overly complex environment.

The reticular activiting system in the brain stem, which has been shown to have an alerting effect, has been suggested as a possible locus for some of the effects of sensory isolation.

b) Other Special Environments Some other special environments that have received a good deal of study are submarines and simulated space capsules. The outstanding feature of the submarine environment is its limited space. Most studies have focused on physical problems associated with this environment, but a few have been concerned with the psychological effects. In general, adaptation to crowded conditions seems to be good, though there are some losses of personnel attributed to the confined conditions. One study reported a loss of 7% of 187 men over 6 months due to this factor. Complaints about lack of privacy have been reported also.

The problem of diurnal cycles arises in connection with such environments. The usual night–day shifts are lacking, of course, in extended undersea cruises, and time confusion has been reported: for example, inability to remember if it is 8.00 a.m. or p.m. It has been found desirable to introduce features, such as news reports and evening entertainments, into the daily routine which will avoid the sensation of being cut off from the rest of the world and which serve to mark diurnal cycles. It also appears that, although such cycles can be influenced by the environment to some extent, there are limits to the process. Alluisi reports evidence of diurnal cycling in performance under a variety of work–rest schedules, including some as extreme as 4 hr of work followed by four of rest.

Simulated space capsule environments have many of the features associated with sensory deprivation conditions, plus the added factor of fatigue. Prolonged exposure to such environments has been shown to produce decrements in a number of tasks, from vigilance tasks to complex decision making functions. Diurnal rhythms in efficiency have also been reported. However, it has also been found that trained pilots, who were familiar with the concept of diurnal rhythms, did not show such effects. Both motivational and adaptation processes may be at work here. It has been shown repeatedly that measures of "can" and "will" are often very different for special environments.

Diurnal cycles may be important in less exotic environments. Efficiency is a number of tasks has been shown to vary with the diurnal cycle. These variations appear to be related to the body temperature, which reaches its lowest point after several hours of sleep, and does not reach its maximum until the evening of the next day. These variations create problems for jobs with several shifts, since operator efficiency is constantly varying. While individual cycles show adaptation to changes in times spent awake and asleep, this adaptation takes time, so that several days may be required to adapt fully to a change in shift.

The Design of Environments

This section will be concerned with the design of physical environments for maximum human comfort. A later section will be concerned with psychology's role in the design of environments in a broader sense, as in urban planning.

A great many human engineering studies have been done on special environmental problems. Anthropometric measurements have been gathered to facilitate the design of objects used by humans, and a great deal of information is available on the integration of this information with special problems, such as designing handles for use with gloves. Information about the size and movement of various parts of the body are important to proper design of a wide variety of furnishings and equipment, from chairs to work areas.

The proper display of information is another important aspect of proper environmental design. Studies have shown that certain types of dials are read more easily than others. Airplane roll indicators which used a fixed artificial horizon with the position of the plane varying have been shown to be more easily interpreted than indicators which keep the plane steady and move the horizon, though the latter design had been commonly used. A good deal of information about desirable features of scales has been obtained, and some useful principles obtained. For example, operators should not have to transform information before using it. Jet aircraft tachometers, for example, may be calibrated in percentage rpm rather than actual rpm so that the pilot need not remember the maximum rpm for different engines in order to interpret the information.

Many other factors go into the proper display of information. For example, if color coding is used, it must be remembered that, while the visual system is able to discriminate a very large number of colors, in the sense of being able to say they are different if both are presented simultaneously, the number that can be correctly distinguished when only one is presented and memory must be used is far more limited. The exact number will depend on the colors, viewing conditions, and other factors such as training, but is unlikely to reliably exceed ten in many situations and may be much lower. Knowledge of these and many other aspects of visual and auditory perception are necessary for the safe and efficient design of many facets of our environment.

Another important problem is the proper integration of human operators into complex man–machine systems. Here again, knowledge of man's information processing capacities is important. Such questions as the speed with which an operator can respond, the probability of his detecting warning signals under various conditions of display and frequency, his tracking abilities with various displays and types of targets, are merely samples of the types of questions which arise and which have been extensively studied.

It should not be assumed, however, that such considerations are important only in military or industrial situations. Proper design considerations are important for the safety and comfort of the consumer as well. One study showed, for example, that different burner-control linkages on stoves resulted in different error rates even after a number of trials. Agreement among auto manufacturers on the arrangement of controls in cars with automatic transmissions is an example of the importance of establishing conventions for the design of widely used products. The list of consumer products with features whose design will affect either comfort or safety is very long indeed.

The information processing capacities of humans are important considerations in the design of any environment. The information processing capacities of any organism, including man, are limited. In such areas of environmental concern as urban planning, traffic control, etc., such considerations can be very important. Man is capable of remembering enormous amounts of information, and performing feats of processing which defy the most complex machines, but his capacity for short term information processing is distinctly limited. A large number of studies have been done on the problem of human attention and the effect of information overloads on various performances. The results are quite consistent in showing very great limitations to man's short term information processing capacities. Exceeding these capacities will result in more or less serious performance decrements. For example, DAF (delayed auditory feedback) studies have shown that mismatches in input information can greatly degrade performance. Individuals have only a very limited capacity for responding to different information input simultaneously to the two ears.

Consideration of man's information processing capacities should be made in planning facilities for human beings. In particular, if new environments are being proposed, a very careful study should be made of their information processing demands. However, concern should not be limited to unusual environments. Badly planned highway signs, which require a driver to attend simultaneously to too much information and make too many decisions too rapidly are an obvious, and unfortunately all too common, example of failure to consider man's information processing capacities in designing the environment. The adequacy of instructions and cautions in connection with the use of equipment or potentially hazardous substances may also require consideration of certain of man's information processing capacities. Court cases have hinged on the adequacy of cautions regarding the use of equipment to inform potential users of hazards.

There are psychological aspects to the design of larger aspects of the environment. A classic study done on a student housing project at MIT showed that social groupings were significantly influenced by the physical arrangement of the apartments. Other aspects of modern building design may be important. For example, most large modern buildings are air-conditioned today. Air conditioning may affect the ionic balance of the air and some concern has been felt that it may produce symptoms such as depression, though the evidence to date is inconclusive.

The possible effects of overcrowding have also been of concern. Overcrowding in animal populations has been shown to have a number of undesirable effects, even though the food supply was adequate. Territorial requirements have been shown in a number of animal species. An increase in aggressiveness seems to be one result of inadequate territory. While the implications of these findings for human populations are unclear, they suggest the need for study of this question.

Man's Social Environment

Decisions made regarding the physical environment have implications for social aspects of behavior, as we have seen in the previous section. In addition, some areas of environmental concern, such as urban planning, must consider man's psychological and social environment more or less explicitly. Population growth, for example, is greatly affected by social attitudes, as the dramatic change in the birth rate in Japan after World War II shows.

The social sciences, including psychology, have roles as information sources and in providing techniques for implementing decisions about the social environment, especially where these involve inducing changes in human behavior patterns. A vast amount of research has gone into the study of social factors which influence human behavior, and much of this information may be relevant in certain areas of environmental planning. Psychological techniques can be used to gain information about people's needs and preferences. It is not easy to design questionnaires which will provide reliable answers and many problems arise in obtaining representative samples of the target population. Psychologists and sociologists have studied these problems extensively. A great deal is known today about proper sampling techniques for such studies. General answers to designing questionnaires are more difficult to come by, but extensive experience has provided some useful practical advice. It appears likely that many difficulties which have arisen in the past in connection with such matters as public housing in urban areas, have been due in part to a failure to accurately assess the feelings and concerns of those affected by such projects. More extensive use of survey techniques might eliminate some of these problems.

Certain reservations about research on man's social environment should be mentioned, however. Large scale experimentation is obviously very difficult to do, and so reliance must often be placed on field studies. Direct measurement of behavior may be difficult, so recourse may be made to rating scales and other indirect measures whose relation to actual behavior is often uncertain. Smaller scale experiments often introduce varying degrees of unreality into a situation which may make generalization to the real world situation difficult. While all of these comments apply in some degree to all psychological research, they are especially apt to apply in areas relevant to man's social environment.

Any discussion of man's social environment must also consider areas in which psychological techniques can be employed to alter behavior. Consider, for example, the impact of problems such as crime, drug addiction, etc. on urban planning. Informational aspects of these problems certainly exist. For example, what is the evidence for a relationship between juvenile delinquency and housing conditions? Such questions have been extensively studied, and while the answers are still being debated, a great deal of information is available on observed correlations.

However, in addition to such informational aspects, the question of the role of psychologists in dealing with such questions must be considered. Plans must be made for dealing with such problems, and this means that resources must be allocated to them. Obviously, the proper allocations must depend in part on available options and their effectiveness. It is therefore reasonable to ask what techniques psychologists have available for modifying behavior and to inquire into their effectiveness.

A number of techniques, generally classified as psychotherapies, have been developed to deal with neurotic behaviors. It is difficult to characterize these procedures in any simple way, since they have diverse theoretical roots and practical implementation, but in general they depend on verbal interactions between therapist and patient to effect change.

A number of variations on the classic one-to-one patient–therapist relationship have developed in recent years. Various forms of group therapy have developed. In addition, sensitivity training procedures have been developed. These are usually aimed at changing the behavior of those not considered to be suffering from any personality disturbance, and they are likely to involve varying degrees of role playing and direct confrontation.

The effectiveness of psychotherapies has long been a matter of debate and the question has not yet been resolved. Difficulties in evaluating them in regard to neurotic behaviors stem from the high spontaneous remission rates, the difficulties of diagnosis, and the problems of defining what is meant by a cure and determining when one has occurred. The record with regard to disorders such as psychopathic personality, drug addiction, etc., is even less optimistic. Very little evidence of effectiveness is available, and many reports are discouraging.

The situation is similar for sensitivity training procedures and group therapy. While enthusiastic reports can be found, so can negative reports. Especially disturbing are reports of undesirable reactions to some kinds of sensitivity training, which can be rather aversive.

To those familiar with other health areas, these problems of evaluation may seem surprising. Clinical research has a long history in medicine, after all, and while problems such as placebo effects exist, methods have been developed to overcome them. However, in addition to the usual problems associated with any clinical research, much of the research on psychotherapies suffer from severe underlying problems associated with the entire concept of mental illness. Szasz has gone so far as to deny the utility of the concept, and has developed some interesting analogies between the concept of mental illness and the concept of witchcraft during the Middle Ages. While his views are hardly universally accepted, it is clear that the problems go beyond the merely procedural.

Behavior therapies, derived from conditioning techniques fare somewhat better. Classical conditioning techniques have had some success with alcoholics, though problems exist. Operant condition techniques have been applied extensively in the treatment of retardates, and have been used as the basis of token economies in mental institutions and homes for delinquents. It is usually somewhat easier to evaluate the behavior therapies, in part because the specification of the procedures in terms of reinforcement contingencies provides information about details of the process often lacking for other methods, and also because they focus on changing behavior. Such changes in behavior can usually be measured directly, whereas changes in personality or emotional state must be measured indirectly, and the appropriate tests are often uncertain. Behavior therapies are not invariably successful, of course, and a current weakness of the procedures is that it is difficult to establish systematic criteria for use. Another problem which has been reported are unpredicted effects on behaviors which were not under explicit control by reinforcement. These changes are not necessarily negative, but since they were not under intentional stimulus control, they may create problems. Finally, these procedures are relatively new, and the history of psychology is replete with procedures whose early promise has not been fulfilled.

Although the major use of explicit control of behavior by reinforcement contingencies has been in dealing with abnormal behaviors, the principles are not limited to such applications. An interesting example of an application in a different context is the use of reinforcement techniques to reduce littering behavior in theatres and campgrounds.

In addition to the techniques described above, psychologists and sociologists have been concerned with the effectiveness of communication in changing behavior. Much research has gone into such questions as the effect of the status of a speaker on his persuasiveness, and the role of various social pressures in changing opinion. In a sense, much educational research can be looked upon as the study of a special kind of behavior control where the concern is with inducing behaviors which result in learning in an educational setting. Rothkopf has done some interesting expreiments on methods of inducing students to adopt appropriate behaviors to facilitate learning, which he refers to as mathemagenic behaviors.

In evaluating the usefulness of such techniques in the design of the social environment, it is important to take cost-effectiveness criteria into consideration. Judged by such criteria, the more traditional psychotherapies do not come off well. They require highly trained manpower, in a relatively large supply, and effectiveness is questionable, especially in situations where the cooperation of the target population is in doubtl Modifications such as group therapy may dilute the manpower requirements somewhat, but the other problems remain. The behavior therapies show up somewhat better in such an analysis. At least, it is possible to monitor behavior change to determine whether they are effective, and once a program has been established, it can often be carried out by personnel with little formal training.

In evaluating psychology as an information source for social planning, the need for sound information from the behavioral sciences cannot be overstressed, and every effort should be made to obtain more of such information. At the same time, the many obvious limitations of our present data suggest that they be used with due caution. In particular, with the increasing use of psychological consultants in various aspects of environmental planning, the bases for various expert opinions should be scrutinized with great care. The judgment of experts in the social sciences, when it is not based on carefully controlled research, can be very misleading. The nature of the subject matter and the conditions of observation are such that it is very easy to find apparent support for a wide variety of hypotheses, many of which may be proved incorrect with more careful observation. It is always desirable to ascertain the factual basis for any recommendation, and to obtain the views of as many professionals from different backgrounds as possible.

Future Developments

The future cannot, of course, be predicted, but certain trends seem likely to continue. First, techniques for controlling behavior derived from operant conditioning procedures appear likely to come into increasing use. Environmental design will be likely to take into account more explicitly such facts in its design procedures. Human engineering procedures will also have an increasing impact on aspects of design for the environment. Certain fundamental questions about human behavior in complex situations will become better understood, and will provide the informational basis for superior design of learning environments and other special purpose environments. However, the 1984 or Brave New World fears seem unjustified at present. The more extensive attempts to control human behavior are more notable for their weaknesses than their power. Even predictive power is inversely associated with the behavioral complexity of the response. Skinnerian techniques seem to offer the best road at present to more powerful approaches. However even here caution should be noted. Most of the basic research on current contributions has been done on animals in very restricted environments. It has also been done on animals in more or less severe states of need; pigeon experiments using a food reinforcement typically maintain the birds at some percentage of *ad lib* body weight, such as .85%. Such animals are very well motivated, and the powerful effects of positive reinforcements found in these studies should be interpreted in this light. It is possible that most humans remain in a similar state of need with regard to the kinds of social reinforcers most likely to be manipulated in planning of larger environments, but the point has yet to be established. The limited environment is another factor which may lead to extensive modification of conditioning principles in larger situations, where a much wider choice of response alternatives exist. However, the positive value for effective use of environmental resources which can result from a better understanding of human needs and response to various environments is very great, and it is in this area that the greatest impact of psychology should be anticipated.

REFERENCES

Alloway, Thomas M. (1969) Effects of low temperature upon acquisition and retention in the grain beetle (*Tenebrio molitor*). *J. Comparative and Physiological Psychology*, **69**, 1.

Alluisi, E. A. and W. D. Chiles (1967) Sustained Performance, Work–Rest Scheduling, and Diurnal Rhythms in Man. *Acta Psychologica*, **27**, 436.

American Public Health Association (1971) *Standard Methods for the Examination of Water and Waste Water*, 13th Ed.

Baker, Rodney R. (1968) The Effects of Psychotropic Drugs on Psychological Testing. *Psychological Bull.*, **69**, 377.

Bare, Carole E. and R. R. Mitchell (1972) Experimental Evaluation of Sensitivity Training. *J. Appl. Behavioral Science*, **8**, 263.

Bennett, Corwin A. (1971) Toward Empirical, Practicable, Comprehensive Task Taxonomy. *Human Factors*, **13**, 229.

Bierman, Ralph, R. R. Carkhuff and M. Santilli (1972) Efficacy of Empathic Communication Training Groups for Inner City Preschool Teachers and Family Workers. *J. Appl. Behavioral Science*, **8**, 188.

Biersner, Robert J. (1972) Selective Performance Effects of Nitrous Oxide. *Human Factors*, **14**, 187.

Blake, Robert R. and Jane Srygley Mouton (1971) A Behavioral Design for the Development of Society. *J. Appl. Behavioral Science*, **7**, 146.

Breisacher, Peter (1970) Neuropsychological Effects of Air Pollution. *Am. Behavioral Scientist*, **14**, 837.

Brozek, J. (1964) Recent Developments in Soviet Psychology, in *Annual Review of Psychology*, Ed. by P. R. Farnsworth, O. McNemar and Q. McNemar, Vol. 15, pp. 493–594.

Burgess, Robert L., R. N. Clark and J. C. Hendee (1971) An Experimental Analysis of Anti-Litter Procedures. *J. Appl. Behavior Anal.*, **4**, 71.

Burns, Neal M. and D. Kimura (1963) Isolation and Sensory Deprivation, in *Unusual Environments and Human Behavior*, Ed. by Neal M. Burns, R. M. Chambers and E. Hendler. The Free Press of Glencoe, Division of The MacMillan Co., New York, pp. 167–192.

Buros, Oscar K. (Ed.) (1965) *The Sixth Mental Measurements Yearbook*. Gryphon Press, Highland Park, N.J.

Byrd, J. F. and A. H. Phelps (1968) Odor and Its Measurement, in *Air Pollution*, Ed. by A. C. Stern, (2nd Ed.), Vol. I. Academic Press, New York, pp. 305–327.

Cahoon, R. L. (1972) Simple Decision Making at High Altitude. *Ergonomics*, **15**, 157.

Calhoun, J. B. (1962) Population density and Social Pathology. *Scientific American*, **206**, 139.

Cannell, Charles F. (1968) Interviewing, in *The Handbook of Social Psychology*, Ed. by G. Lindzey and E. Aronson, (2nd Ed.), Vol. II. Addison-Wesley, Reading, Mass., pp. 526–595.

Cartwright, Dorwin and Alvin Zander (Eds.) (1960) *Group Dynamics; Research and Theory*, (2nd Ed.). Row, Peterson and Co., Illinois.

Chapanis, A. (1959) *Research Techniques in Human Engineering*. The Johns Hopkins Univ. Press, Baltimore, Md.

Chiles, W. D. and A. E. Jennings (1970) Effects of Alcohol on Complex Performance. *Human Factors*, **12**, 605.

Chiles, W. D., P. F. Iampietro and E. A. Higgins (1972) Combined Effects of Altitude and High Temperature on Complex Performance. *Human Factors*, **14**, 161.

Clark, Roger N., R. L. Burgess and J. C. Hendee (1972) The Development of Anti-Litter Behavior in a Forest Campground. *J. Appl. Behavior Analysis*, **445**, 1.

Cole, Sherwood O. (1967) Experimental Effects of Amphetamine: A Review. *Psychological Bull.*, **68**, 81.

Colquhoun, W. P., M. J. F. Blake and R. S. Edwards (1969) Experimental Studies of Shift-Work III: Stabilized 12-Hour Shift Systems. *Ergonomics*, **12**, 865.

Colquhoun, W. P. (1970) Circadian Rythms, Mental Efficiency and Shift Work. *Ergonomics*, **13** 558.

Cullen, Joseph W. (1969) Modification of salt-seeking behavior in the adrenalectomized rat via gamma-ray irradiation. *J. Comparative and Psysiological Psychology*, **68** 524.

Deese, J. and S. H. Hulse (1967) *The Psychology of Learning*. McGraw-Hill, New York.

Deutsch, J. A. (1969) The Physiological Basis of Memory, in *Annual Review of Psychology*, Ed. by P. H. Mussen and M. R. Rosensweig, Vol. 20 pp. 85–104.

Dill, D. B., E. F. Adolph and C. G. Wilber (Eds.) (1964) *Handbook of Physiology, Section 4: Adaptation to the Environment*. American Physiological Society, Washington, D.C.

Faith, W. L. (1976) Effects of Atmospheric Pollutants *The Encyclopedia of Environmental Science and Engineering*, Vol. 1. Gordon and Breach, New York.

Fiske, D. W., H. F. Hunt, L. Luborsky, M. Orne, M. B. Parloff, M. F. Reiser and A. H. Tuma (1970) Planning of Research on Effectiveness of Psychotherapy. *Am. Psychologist*, **25**, 727.

Fleishman, E. A. and C. J. Bartlett (1969) Human Abilities, in *Annual Review of Psychology*, Ed. by P. H. Mussen and M. R. Rosenzweig, Vol. 20, pp. 349–380.

Fowler, Frank D. (1972) A Consumer Ombudsman: The Human Factors Engineer. *Human Factors*, **14**, 7.

Freeman, H. E. and J. M. Giovannoni (1969) Social Psychology of Mental Health, in *The Handbook of Social Psychology*, Ed. by G. Lindzey and E. Aronson, (2nd Ed.) Vol. V. Addison-Wesley, Reading, Mass., pp. 660–719.

Furchtgott, Ernest, J. Reid Jones, R. Stephen Tacker, and John Deagle (1970) Aversive conditioning in prenatally X-irradiated rats. *Physiology and Behavior*, **5**, 571.

Goldsmith, J. R. (1968) Effects of Air Pollution on Human Health, in *Air Pollution*, Ed. by A. C. Stern, (2nd Ed.), Vol. I. Academic Press, New York, pp. 305–327.

Goodstein, Leonard D. and Ronald K. Boyer (1972) Crisis Intervention in a Municipal Agency: A Conceptual Case History. *J. Appl. Behavioral Science*, **8**, 318.

Goranson, R. E. (1970) Media Violence and aggressive behavior: a review of experimental research, in *Advances in Experimental Social Psychology*, Ed. by L. Berkowitz, Vol. 5. Academic Press, New York.

Gordon, Robert A. (1967) Issues in the Ecological Study of Delinquency. *Am. Sociological Rev.*, **32**, 927.

Graham, C. H. (Ed.) (1965) *Vision and Visual Perception*. John Wiley, New York.

Grether, Walter F. (1971) Vibration and Human Performance. *Human Factors*, **13**, 203.

Hall, R. Vance, Saul Axelrod, Lucille Tyler, Ellen Grief, Fowler C. Jones and Roberta Robertson (1972) Modification of Behavior Problems in the Home with a Parent as Observer and Experimenter. *J. Appl. Behavior Analysis*, **5**, 53.

Hendler, Edwin (1963) Temperature effects on operator performance, in *Unusual Environments and Human Behavior*, Ed. by Neal M. Burns, R. M. Chambers and E. Hendler. The Free Press of Glencoe, Division of The MacMillan Co., New York, pp. 321–352.

Herbert, E. W. and D. M. Baer (1972) Training Parents as Behavior Modifiers: Self-recording of Contingent Attention. *J. Appl. Behavior Analysis*, **5**, 139.

Hopkins, E. S., W. M. Bingley and G. W. Schucker (1970) *The Practice of Sanitation*, (4th Ed.). Williams and Wilkins, Baltimore, Md.

Jones, J. R., E. N. Ziegler and J. R. Pfafflin (1973) Effects of Chemical Pollutants on Human Ecology. *The Encyclopedia of Environmental Science and Engineering*, Vol. 1. Gordon and Breach, New York.

Kling, J. W. and L. A. Riggs (Eds.) (1971) Woodworth and Schlosberg's *Experimental Psychology*, (3rd Ed.). Holt, Rinehart and Winston, New York.

Kish, Leslie (1965) *Survey Sampling*. John Wiley and Sons, New York.

Klauss, A. K., R. H. Tull, L. M. Roots and J. R. Pfafflin (1970) History of the Changing Concepts in Ventilation Requirements. *ASHRAE J.*, 51.

Kobrick, J. L. (1972) Effects of Hypoxia on Voluntary Response Time to Peripheral Stimuli during Central Target Monitoring. *Ergonomics*, **15**, 147.

Korbel, Susan F., Kenneth D. Johnson and Paul S. Rowland (1971) Aftereffects of low intensity UHF radiation. *Psychonomic Science*, **23**, 50.

Kristt, Donald A. and Jeri A. Sechzer (1969) Behavioral thermoregulation at high environmental temperatures: The intra-session pattern of cooling and resting. *Psychonomic Science*, **16**, 151.

Kumar, R., I. P. Stolerman and Hannah Steinberg (1970) Psychopharmacology. *Ann. Rev. Psychology*, **21**, 595.

Leibowitz, Herschel W., Charles N. Abernethy, E. R. Buskirk, Oded Bar-Or, and Robert T. Hennessy (1972) The Effect of Heat Stress on Reaction Time to Centrally and Peripherally Presented Stimuli. *Human Factors*, **14**, 155.

Lieberman, Morton A., Irvin D. Yalom and Matthew B. Miles (1972) The Impact of Encounter Groups on Participants: Some Preliminary Findings. *J. Appl. Behavioral Science*, **8**, 29.

Lion, Judith S., E. Richardson and R. C. Browne (1968) A Study of the Performance of Industrial Inspectors under Two Kinds of Lighting. *Ergonomics*, **11**, 23.

Loeber, Rolf (1971) Engineering the Behavioral Engineer. *J. Appl. Behavior Analysis*, **4** 321.

Loftus, J. P. Jr. and Lois Hammer (1963) Weightlessness, in *Unusual Environments and Human Behavior*, Ed. by Neal M. Burns, R. M. Chambers and E. Hendler. The Free Press of Glencoe, Division of The MacMillan Co, New York, pp. 353–377.

Lorenz, K. (1966) *On Aggression*. Harcourt, Brace and World, New York.

Luborsky, L., M. Chandler, A. H. Auerbach, J. Cohen and H. M. Bachrach (1971) Factors Influencing the Outcome of Psychotherapy: a Review of Quantitative Research. *Psychological Bull.*, **75**, 145.

Magill, P. L., F. R. Holden, C. Ackley and F. G. Sawyer (Eds.) (1956) *Air Pollution Handbook*. McGraw-Hill, New York.

Maling, G. (1976) Noise. *The Encyclopedia of Environmental Science and Engineering*, Vol. 2. Gordon and Breach, New York.

Martin, J. C. (1968) Sex Differences in the activity wheel as a function of fetal age at irradiation. *Psychonomic Science*, **13**, 249.

Mason, W. A. and A. J. Riopelle (1964) Comparative Psychology, in *Annual Review of Psychology*, Ed. by P. R. Farnsworth, O. McNemar and Q. McNemar, Vol. 15, pp. 143–180l.

Matarazzo, J. D. (1965) Psychotherapeutic Processes, in *Annual Review of Psychology*, Ed. by P. R. Farnsworth, O. McNemar and Q. McNemar, Vol. 16, pp. 181–204.

Maxcy, K. F. (Ed.) (1956) Rosenau's *Preventive Medicine, and Public Health*, (8th Ed.). Appleton-Century-Crofts, New York.

Miller, James M. & Thomas H. Rockwell (1972) The Use of Human Subjects in Human Factors Research. *Human Factors*, **14**, 35.

Moore, W. E. (1969) Social Structure and Behavior, in *The Handbook of Social Psychology*, Ed. by G. Lindzey and E. Aronson, (2nd Ed.), Vol. IV. Addison-Wesley, Reading, Mass., pp. 283–319.

Morgan, Clifford T., Jesse S. Cook, A. Chapanis and Max W. Lund (Eds.) (1963) *Human Engineering Guide to Equipment Design*. McGraw-Hill, New York.

Nadel, Aaron B. (1963) Vibration, in *Unusual Environments and Human Behavior*, Ed. by Neal M. Burns, R. M. Chambers and E. Hendler. The Free Press of Glencoe, Division of The MacMillan Co., New York, pp. 379–394.

Peters, George A. (1972) The Role of the Human Factors Engineer in Product Liability Litigation. *Human Factors*, **14**, 13.

Phillips, E. L., E. A. Phillips, D. L. Fixsen and M. M. Wolf (1971) Achievement Place: Modification of the Behaviors of Pre-delinquent Boys within a Token Economy. *J. Appl. Behavior Analysis*, **4**, 45.

Roe, A. (1970) Community Resource Centres. *Am. Psychologist*, **25**, 1033.

Rothkopf, E. Z. (1971) Experiments on Mathemagenic Behavior and the Technology of Written Instruction, in *Verbal Learning Research and the Technology of Written Instruction*, Ed. by E. Z. Rothkopf and P. E. Johnson. Teachers College Press, New York.

Ruff, George E. (1963) Psychological and psychophysiological indices of stress, in *Unusual Environments and Human Behavior*, Ed. by Neal M. Burns, R. M. Chambers and E. Hendler. The Free Press of Glencoe, Division of The MacMillan Co., London, pp. 87–125.

Schoenfeldt, L. F. (1970) Data Archives as Resources for Research, Instruction, and Policy Planning. *Am. Psychologist*, **25**, 609.

Scott, J. P. (1969) The Social Psychology of Infrahuman Animals, in *The Handbook of Social Psychology*, Ed. by G. Lindzey and E. Aronson, (2nd Ed.), Vol. IV. Addison-Wesley, Reading, Mass., pp. 611–642.

Scott, Wm. A. (1968) Attitude Measurement, in *The Handbook of Social Psychology*, Ed. by G. Lindzey and E. Aronson, (2nd Ed.), Vol. II. Addison-Wesley, Reading, Mass., pp. 204–273.

Shontz, William D., Gerald A. Trumm and Leon G. Williams (1971) Color Coding for Information Location. *Human Factors*, **13**, 237.

Simons, David G., D. E. Flinn and B. Hartman (1963) Psychophysiology of high-altitude experience, in *Unusual Environments and Human Behavior*, Ed. by Neal M. Burns, R. M. Chambers and E. Hendler. The Free Press of Glencoe, Division of The MacMillan Co., New York, pp. 127–164.

Sommer, R. (1969) *Personal Space: the Behavioral Basis of Design*. Prentice-Hall, Englewood Cliffs, N.J.

Stokinger, H. E. and D. L. Coffin (1968) Biologic Effects of Air Pollutants, in *Air Pollution*, Ed. by A. C. Stern, (2nd Ed.), Vol. I. Academic Press, New York, pp. 445–546.

Swets, John A. (1964) *Signal Detection and Recognition by Human Observers: Contemporary Readings*. John Wiley, New York.

Szasz, Thomas (1970). *Manufacture of Madness: a Comparative Study of the Inquisition and the Mental Health Movement*. Harper and Row, New York.

Tobias, Paul R. (1963) The effect of radiation on integrated behavior, in *Unusual Environments and Human Behavior*, Ed. by Neal M. Burns, R. M. Chambers and E. Hendler. The Free Press of Glencoe, Division of The MacMillan Co., New York, pp. 395–417.

Trumbull, Richard (1966) Diurnal Cycles and Work-Rest Scheduling in Unusual Environments. *Human Factors*, **8**, 385.

Twardosz, S. and T. Sajwaj (1972) Multiple Effects of a Procedure to Increase Sitting in a Hyperactive, Retarded Boy. *J. Appl. Behavior Analysis*, **5**, 73.

Van Cleave, C. D. (1963) *Irradiation and the Nervous System*. Rowman and Littlefield, New York.

Warner, Harold D. and Norman W. Heimstra (1972) Effects of Noise Intensity on Visual Target-Detection Performance. *Human Factors*, **14**, 181.

Welch, B. L. and A. S. Welch (Eds.) (1970) *Physiological Effects of Noise*. Plenum Press, New York–London.

Weybrew, Benjamin B. (1963) Psychological problems of prolonged marine submergence, in *Unusual Environments and Human Behavior*, Ed. by Neal M. Burns, R. M. Chambers and E. Hendler. The Free Press of Glencoe, Division of The MacMillan Co., New York, pp. 87–125.

Wohlwill, Joachim (1970) The Emerging Discipline of Environmental Psychology. *Am. Psychologist*, **25**, 303.

Woodworth, R. S. and H. Schlosberg (1954) *Experimental Psychology*, (Rev. Ed.) Henry Holt and Co., New York.

Wooller, J. (1972) The Measurement of Driver Performance. *Ergonomics*, **15**, 81.

Young, R. D. (1967) Developmental Psychopharmacology: a Beginning. *Psychological Bulletin*, **67**, 73.

SHEILA M. PFAFFLIN

Bell Telephone Laboratories

PUBLIC HEALTH: see ENVIRONMENTAL HEALTH

PUBLIC HEALTH ADMINISTRATION: see ENVIRONMENTAL HEALTH ADMINISTRATION

R

RADIATION ECOLOGY

Radiation Ecology or Radioecology is a term that came into common usage in 1956 to denote that area of the broad field of ecology concerned with the assessment of radioactivity in the environment. More specifically, radiation ecology has come to be recognized as that area of ecology concerned with radioactive substances, radiation and the environment. The development and subsequent expansion of nuclear energy for military and peaceful purposes has been accompanied by environmental problems, some of which are typical of other facets of industrialization and some unique to atomic energy. The unique problems primarily concern the fate and ecological effects of radionuclides released into the environment.

The major environmental problems introduced by the Atomic Age may be grouped into several areas of scientific and public concern. Underlying each of these is the worry about the effects of ionizing radiation—on man, his domesticated plants and animals, and on the environment and its living components, Fallout from weapons testing, reactor radioactive waste effluents, radioactive waste disposal, nuclear war, and use of nuclear explosives for major engineering and related technological projects of large scale comprise the activities which have concerned society and which, because of potential impact on the environment and man, have stimulated the development of radiation ecology. Understanding the manner in which our ecological systems (eocsystems) distribute, assimilate, and affect the environmental behavior of radioactive substances, and the effects of radiations emitted from those substances, are the concern of the radioecologist.

Radionuclides of Ecological Importance

Radionuclides which are of interest to the ecologist are listed in Table 1. These radioactive elements represent the major naturally-occurring and man-made sources of radiation in the environment. Principal sources of exposure from background (natural) radiation are represented by the uranium, thorium and actinium decay series. Internal exposure to man results primarily from ^{40}K, ^{14}C, ^{226}Ra, and ^{228}Ra and their daughter products that are deposited in the body. Radionuclides such as

TABLE 1

Radionuclides of Ecological Importance

Category	Major radionuclides	Ecological importance
Naturally occurring radionuclides	Uranium Thorium Actinium series elements Potassium–40 Carbon–14	Major contributors to to background radiation (long half-lives)
Fission products	Strontium–89, 90, 91 Yttrium–90, 91 Zirconium–95 Niobium–95 Ruthenium–103, 106 Rhodium–106 Iodine–131 Cesium–137 Barium–137, 140 Lanthanum–140 Cerium–141, 144 Praeseodymium–143, 144 Neodymium–147 Promethium–147	Enter ecological systems through fallout or waste disposal (half-lives ranging from a few hours to 30 yrs)
Radioisotopes of elements essential to organisms	Hydrogen–3 Cobalt–60 Carbon–14 Sodium–22, 24 Phosphorus–32 Sulfur–35 Potassium–42 Calcium–45 Manganese–54 Iron–59 Copper–64 Zinc–65	Used as tracers in both radionuclide cycling and radiation effects studies on organisms and ecological systems

^{222}Rn and ^{220}Rn and their daughter products represent sources of internal radiation exposure to man from inhalation.

Radionuclides produced by the fissioning of uranium (fission products) are of the greatest current concern. These man-made isotopes are not essential to organisms, but they constitute the major sources of radiation in the environment whether it be from fallout or waste disposal from reactor operations. All of these radionuclides may enter ecosystems where they become part of the flux of elements that are being circulated within and between systems.

Some of the fission products which are chemically similar to biologically essential elements are of special interest. They vary greatly in their physical half-life and in the extent to which they participate in metabolic processes of living organisms. The most important radionuclides affecting plants and animals on land are strontium-90, cesium-137, and iodine-131.

Strontium-90 remains in the environment for a long time. Its half-life is 28 yrs. Strontium is chemically similar to calcium, and it can enter living organisms as a replacement for calcium. In weapons fallout strontium-90 is usually deposited in the root systems of plants. The amount of ^{90}Sr that a plant absorbs from soils depends on several factors, particularly on the quantity of calcium in the soil, the relative quantities of calcium and strontium at the depth where the roots are located, and the ability of the plant to discriminate between the two elements. The plant is the base for ^{90}Sr to enter the human food chain. This chain is a short and simple one consisting of plants, cows, and man, with cow's milk being the chief source of entry into man. There is considerable discrimination against the transfer of strontium at each step in this food chain, but the small amount that is transported to man tends to concentrate in bone tissue. It remains there, undergoing radioactive decay and emitting its radiation. Its danger is related to the fact that bone contains blood forming (erythropoetic) tissue. In sufficient quantities the radiation can cause leukaemia and bone cancer.

Strontium-90 accumulation normally is greater in children than in adults, because growing children are building bone at a greater rate and use a larger amount of calcium. A study of species in the deer family (cervidae) graphically demonstrated the effects of ^{90}Sr fallout. The levels of ^{90}Sr in the antlers of deer rose continually from 1947 through 1955, then remained constant for 2 yrs, and rose again in 1958. The concentration of ^{90}Sr was more than $8\times$ as high in 1958 as it was in 1947. With the cessation of major weapons tests in the 1960's, the levels began to drop off.

Cesium-137 is another major fission product that is found in fallout and untreated radioactive waste effluents. Cesium behaves chemically very much like potassium and follows the same metabolic route in plants and animals as potassium does. It enters plants directly through the leaves after being deposited by rain, and so it appears in plant tissues more quickly than does ^{90}Sr. From there on the route of ^{137}Cs is much the same as ^{90}Sr; it appears in the milk and muscles of cattle that eat contaminated plants, and it enters the human body in food. Once in the human body, it becomes part of muscle tissue and so has an almost uniform distribution throughout the body. It stays there for only about 4 months. Since its half-life, like that of ^{90}Sr, is about 28yrs, little of the ^{137}Cs undergoes radioactive decay while in the body.

The transfer of ^{137}Cs and ^{90}Sr from plants to animals also has been observed in species that are not important as food sources for man. The coconut crab, a land animal that lives on a diet of fruits and nuts on islands in the Pacific, was found to have accumulated radioactive materials as a result of the Pacific test explosions. Strontium-90 was found in the skeleton, and ^{137}Cs was found in the soft body parts—direct results of eating contaminated vegetation.

The third radionuclide or fission product of importance in fallout is radio-iodine (^{131}I). The chemistry of radioactive ^{131}I is exactly like that of natural ^{127}I, which is not radioactive. Therefore, its concentration in the body depends only on the concentration in the source material. Iodine becomes concentrated in the thyroid glands of veretebrate animals, where it can cause cancer of the thyroid and damage to other tissues. Like ^{90}Sr and ^{137}Cs, it enters plants as a result of radioactive fallout and then enters humans either by way of the plants themselves, or by way of contaminated milk from cows that eat the plants. The radioactivity of thyroid glands removed from certain animals can serve as a sensitive indicator of ^{131}I in the environment, because the concentration of ^{131}I in the thyroid can be as much as $10{,}000\times$ higher than the concentration in nature. The black-tailed jackrabbit is a useful animal for such measurements. It has a large thyroid gland that is easy to remove and weigh. The level of radioativity in each gram of its thyroid tissue varies directly with the fallout on vegetation.

Finally there are man-made radionuclides (activation products) which are important because they are the isotopes of elements which may be essential to plants and animals. Some of these also may enter the environment as activation products resulting from reactor operations or nuclear explosives. Examples of activation radionuclides are cobalt-60 and zinc-65. In aquatic or marine environments these radionuclides have been found to accumulate in food organisms especially shellfish and molluscs. Generally ^{60}Co can be anticipated to be accumulated by organisms or to be retained in organically enriched materials such as forest floor humus and organic sediments. Zinc-65 is of particular concern in marine environments where it is likely to be accumulated in clams and oysters. However, being an activation rather than a fission product its presence depends more on appropriate stable elements present which in turn are exposed to fast neutrons than on fissionable material.

Radiosensitivity of Ecological Systems

Although there is much current concern about the possible effect of low level, chronic radiation on ecological systems, there is relatively little comprehensive scientific data on this problem. Much more is known about the radiosensitivity of organisms exposed to radiation doses which are much higher than we expect to contend with in the normal environment. In general, higher animals are far more sensitive to radiation than are lower animals, and the very young and the aged are more sensitive than mature, healthy animals. For example Table 2 gives estimated acute doses of gamma or X-radiation necessary to kill 50% or more of the adult members of several groups of organisms. These data should be considered only as an indication of relative radiosensitivity as they represent generalized ranges. Half the humans exposed to a single dose of 500 R will die. For other mammals the lethal dose ranges from less than 300–1200 R. Frogs and newts can survive higher radiation levels, depending on their body temperatures at the time of exposure. Insects can survive doses of up to 100,000 R in a few instances; most have lethal doses in the 10,000–20,000 R range. These kinds of data do not reflect the more complex responses of organisms subjected to ionizing radiation under natural conditions. For example, most organisms go through several stages of development from egg to adult. These stages may take place in different parts of the ecosystem. Likewise, the radiosensitivity of these organisms may differ in different stages of the life cycle. In radioresistant groups such as insects, 10% or less of the lethal dose to adults may be effective at juvenile or egg stages. For example, in the bagworm a dose of 450 R is sufficient to kill 50% of 1-day old eggs, whereas a dose of approximately 10,000 R was required to produce the same effect in the larvae.

TABLE 2

Comparative Radiosensitivity of Groups of Organisms

Group	Lethal dose range[a] (rads)
Bacteria	100,000–1,000,000
Insects	5000– 100,000
Fish	1000– 300
Mammals	300– 1200
Herbaceous plants	5000– 70,000
Coniferous trees	800– 3000
Deciduous trees	4000– 10,000

[a] Estimated acute whole body gamma radiation doses required to kill 50% or more of the adult organisms.

Effects other than lethality also may be produced by radiation, especially in ecosystems where all organisms are linked through various interactive processes. Aside from genetic or reproductive effects, changes in number, growth, disease resistance, life span or response to physical environmental factors are of interest to the ecologist. Radiation-induced changes can affect the role or organisms or populations within the ecosystem. Predator–prey relationships, food chain transfers, and other ecological processes which depend on the continuing interaction between different organisms may be altered by the impact of ionizing radiation.

The effect of ionizing radiation on plants has been studied both outdoors and in greenhouses. One outdoor test field consists of 10 acres of land with a ^{60}Co source located at the center. It is installed in a vertical tube, which can be raised to different heights for irradiation and then lowered by remote control into a lead case when not in use. Various species of plants grow in the soil in concentric circles around the source. Each species is arranged in a wedge-shaped area so that the plants are located at various distances from the source and receive various intensities of radiation. Plants are exposed to radiation for 20 hr a day.

Radiation effects on plants are complex and depend on a number of factors, incuding the plant species, the maturity of the plant, its physical condition, the part of the plant exposed to radiation, the kind and amount of radiation, and the rate at which the radiation dose is applied. Woody plants generally are more sensitive to radiation than are herbaceous plants (Table 2). Gymnosperms are more sensitive to radiation than angiosperms. A pine tree shows severe growth inhibition at a level of about 10 R/day, while the same degree of inhibition in a gladiolus plant requires about 5000 R/day. Some ecollogists have speculated that radiation from a nuclear attack would destroy all pine trees and other gymnosperms in irradiated areas, leaving other plants relatively unharmed.

It is possible to predict some radiation effects in plants. The meristematic or growth regions in plants are the most radiosensitive tissues. It is the absorption of radiation energy in these regions that alters plant growth and development. Ecologists and botanists have shown that the response of plants to ionizing radiation is directly proportional to the interphase chromosome volumes in meristematic tissues. That is, plant species with large chromosomes are more sensitive; those with small chromosomes are more resistant to radiation. In general, this is an extremely useful concept, and it has been applied to predict and assess probable radiation effects on vegetation (natural and agricultural) from military uses of nuclear devices.

Seeds are far less sensitive to radiation than are growing plants. A stand of pine trees exposed to a total of 12,000 R of gamma radiation was 90% destroyed, yet 95% of the seeds taken from cones on the same trees were viable. The high resistance of seeds to radiation damage is probably associated with their low water and oxygen content. The sensitivity of dry seeds varies widely among species, however. Lily seeds show practically no ability to sprout after receiving a dose of 2000 R. Yet the seeds of other plants seem to be stimulated to sprout more vigorously than normal under the same amount of radiation or more. Such differences favor the growth of certain species over others in areas where radiation is a factor in the environment.

Effects of Radiation on Ecosystems

The effects that large scale ionizing radiation such as from a nuclear attack would have on plants and animals living together in an ecosystem have concerned radioecologists ever since the first use of atomic bombs. Several studies have been conducted involving small ecosystems in an attempt to determine what would happen on a large scale. In one study, 10,000 acres of land surrounding a nuclear reactor were exposed to radiation ranging from lethal levels to levels no higher than the natural background radiation. The ecosystem on this land consisted mainly of an oak–hickory–pine climax forest. The forest was exposed to a mixture of gamma radiation and neutrons, with an intensity similar to that expected from fallout after a nuclear attack. The radiation reached about 37,000 trees, plus many more herbaceous species and many more shrubs. Ecologists examined thousands of plants in order to differentiate between the effects of ionizing radiation and the effects of frost, disease, insect damage, drought, and other natural factors. In still another study, a community of spring and summer annuals was exposed to gamma radiation for nearly 4 months during one growing season and then was observed over the next 3 yrs. In still another study, gamma radiation was applied daily throughout one winter and spring to a forest and to an open field with a well-established cover of annual plants.

On the basis of these and other studies, radioecologists have formulated a scenario depicting how ionizing radiation would affect the plants and animals of our forests and fields if a nuclear attack occurred during the summer growing season. People emerging from shelters several weeks after the attack would find little change in their surroundings, except in areas of extremely high radiation. All plants and animals, both large and small, would have been killed in these high-radiation areas, and as the plants died they would subject the surrounding areas to further danger from fire. However, most fields and woodlands would appear unchanged by radiation when viewed from a distance. Closer inspection would reveal more clearly the extent of the damage. The ground would be littered with the bodies of birds and animals killed by the radiation. Inspection of lakes, streams, ponds and marshes would show that the lower animals had fared better. Fish, frogs, toads and salamanders would be alive and healthy. The sound of insects would be heard as before. Among the plants the damage would be least serious to those that appear early in a natural succession pattern. Mosses and lichens would be undamaged, annuals would be somewhat affected, shrubs more so, and trees most of all. The damage to pine trees would be most apparent. Pines nearest the radiation zone would have turned a brilliant red brown within a few days after the attack. Other plants in the forest and fields would undergo little change during the remainder of the summer.

In the autumn the oaks, hickories, and other hardwood trees would lose their leaves earlier than usual—perhaps as much as 7 weeks earlier in areas nearest the high-radiation zone. The following spring these areas would remain in their state of winter dormancy 7 or 8 weeks longer than usual. Examination of the hardwoods (oaks, hickories,etc.) at this time would reveal severe damage to the buds, resulting in the development of fewer leaves and of abnormal leaves. Near the high-radiation zones, the trees might be leafless. The distribution of annuals in the open fields and on the forest floor would also be changed from previous years. Certain species would grow in greater numbers, partly as a result of the stimulation of their seeds by radiation and partly as a result of the radiation in seed germination among other competing species. The delay in development of leaves on the trees would give these annuals an extra long growing season. In the abundance of sunshine, weeds would grow on the forest to heights of 8 ft or more. The absence of a leafy canopy would also cause changes in the forest soil. With greater wind flow through the bare trees and higher temperatures from direct sunlight, the soil would become drier and harder during sunny weather. In rain storms the harder impact of rain drops would wash away topsoil in areas not covered by weeds or shrubs. Throughout the first summer following the attack, birds and animals from outside the irradiated areas would move in to replace those that were killed.

Radioactive Tracers

With the threat of nuclear war receding, and nuclear reactors being equipped with ever more elaborate safeguards to reduce radioactive releases to the environment, the thrust of radioecology is changing. Activation products in controlled quantities are now being used as radioactive tracers to follow the pathways of chemical elements in the bodies of organisms and in the complex interactions of ecosystems. The radioactive materials have the advantage of being easily detected and quantitatively measured in biological materials without elaborate chemical separation of the elements otherwise necessary.

For example, the radioisotope ^{137}Cs was added to the upward flow of water in trunks of yellow poplar trees in Tennessee about 10 yrs ago. In the ensuing years radioecologists have followed the movement of this relatively inert tracer into leaves of the trees, into leaf-eating insects, into the insect eating birds, into the forest litter as the dead leaves fell, into soil insects, and so forth. Periodic sampling has confirmed the recycling of natural materials in this forest ecosystem. The radioceologists, in concert with systems analysts, are currently developing computer simulation models to mimic the ecological cycles revealed by this cesium tagging experiment. Comparable information on the exchange of materials from one component of the ecosystem to another could never have been obtained without the knowledgeable use of radioactive materials by these trained radioecologists.

Other activation products such as calcium-45 or phosphorus-32 find use in studies of metabolic processes in organisms, populations or communities Such studies lead to an understanding of regulatory processes and structural characteristics of living systems. Other examples of experimental use of radioactive tracers may range ecologically, from studying the uptake of ^{45}Ca tagged fertilizer by corn, to following the pathways of ^{32}P in a stream, including its distribution in the non-living as well as the living components.

Radiation ecology is now an area of ecological research and teaching that encompasses far more of the impacts of man on his environment than the atom bomb and nuclear reactors. Understanding of nearly all pollutant chemicals in the environment is being enhanced by use of techniques and principles of ecological cycling developed by radioecologists.

REFERENCES

1. Lansdell, Norman (1958) *The Atom and the Energy Revolution*. Philosophical Library. New York.
2. Curtis, Richard and Elizabeth Hogan (1970) *Perils of the Peaceful Atom*. Doubleday and Co., New York.
3. Bryerton, Gene (1970) *Nuclear Dilema*. Ballantine, New York.
4. Ravelle, Roger *et al.* (1969) The Ocean. *Scientific American*, September.
5. Russell, R. Scott *et al.* (1966) *Radioactivity and Human Diet*. Pergamon Press, London.

STANLEY I. AUERBACH
Oak Ridge National Laboratory

RADIOACTIVE WASTE MANAGEMENT: see MANAGEMENT OF RADIOACTIVE WASTE

RECYCLING OF WASTE MATERIALS

Recycling is the term applied to reclamation of used material for the purpose of reuse. Almost all substances can be considered to undergo recycling if sufficient time passes. However, economics of modern technology dictate time constraints.

The question of recycling, or reuse, is based almost entirely on economic considerations. If it is more profitable to utilize a raw material than a recycled material, the prudent businessman will do so. He has a responsibility to his shareholders as well as a social responsibility. To adopt uneconomical practices is to give an unfair advantage to his competitors. The question is thus resolved into how to promote economically attractive recycling incentives. Kupchick points out that a too quick reliance on recycling can be an error and cites past endeavors for this practice that were not successful. At the turn of the century, reduction plants processed food wastes, dead animals and fish for the production of glycerine, oils, fertilizer and animal hides. All were eventually abandoned for economic reasons and because of the uncontrollable nuisance they created. Anyone who has ever found himself in the vicinity of an active rendering plant can appreciate the problems associated. In the 1930s contracts were awarded to private bidders for salvage and reclamation privileges. These, also, were later discarded. A 1965 survey of more than 20 composting plants in Europe and Israel showed the economic difficulties associated with turning garbage into compost.

However, a new variable has been introduced into the total picture. Increased public awareness of environmental pollution problems, coupled with increasing difficulty in finding suitable disposal sites near large metropolitan areas, makes reuse of discarded materials more practical. National and local governments are putting more money into the search for uses for waste material and techniques for reclamation. Private industry is following the same path. More stringent regulations against former disposal practices have increased disposal costs and the search is underway for means to realize a profit, rather than a loss, from waste materials.

It should be noted that, while current emphasis is largely on new ways to deal with solid municipal and industrial wastes, the largest volume of waste generated is municipal and industrial wastewater. Airborne wastes become, for the most part, a solid waste when ready for recycling.

In past times, resources were regarded as virtually limitless and industry thought, when any thought was given to the subject, that the water, air and land could absorb any amount of pollution. However, in affluent societies particularly, increased production and consumption brings increased amounts of waste for which disposal solutions must be found. The most common solution to waste disposal has been dumping into the air or water or on land. Everyone wishes to be rid of their waste and, at the same time, wishes to be upstream of the dumping site. Unfortunately, the more developed countries of the world are no longer able to do both simultaneously. Landfill, a form of dumping, has been the most economical form of solid waste disposal. Open dumping is unacceptable from both health and aesthetic standpoints. Some experts feel that waste recycling under controlled conditions is the ultimate best answer. One must heed the thoughts of those who suggest a close look at realities of the situation, lest disappointment at results less than those predicted act as a deterrent to continued orderly progress. This point cannot be stressed too strongly. The concerned public is the strongest base for reasonable and balanced resource use. Professionals in the environmental field must exercise great care in predicting good results and bad effects. Not all segments of modern society are in favor of environmental pollution control and much money is spent in endeavors to discredit opposing views.

It is estimated that the consumption of metals, non-metallics and fossil fuels in the United States in 1980 will be double that of 1970. The same trend is seen in most of the more developed countries. Without the use of recycled materials, many of these non-renewable resources will soon be badly depleted. From a strictly utilitarian point, the use of recycled materials can reduce dependence on imported materials. Many war materials fall into this category, an important consideration in the present world state. Economics will probably not be a major consideration in this case.

There is considerable recycling of scrap metal.

Forty five per cent of the copper used in the United States is recycled and the amount of lead recycled exceeds that extracted from natural resources. The aluminium industry, a comparatively new industry, has initiated a program to buy back aluminium scrap and this program appears to be meeting with success. The National Association of Secondary Material Industries has been set up to promote and coordinate growth of the secondary materials industry. At this writing (1972) laws and taxes appear to favor virgin material processors over industries dealing with secondary materials. The improvement of the marketing position of secondary industry products, therefore, appears to require some restructuring of state and federal regulations. It has been suggested that a reduction could be granted on freight rates for recycled goods. A second suggestion put forth would require a tax on goods which must ultimately be disposed of as waste. A third approach would require that the paper industry include a specified percentage of recycled paper in all products. This, if practical, would aid greatly in promoting the recycling industry since paper occupies a major portion in the waste stream. The Environmental Protection Agency is supporting a major effort in improvement of markets for secondary materials.

Industrial wastes are more amenable to processing for reclamation than are municipal wastes, due to their relatively constant and predictable composition. Further, in many cases, the industry involved pays the transportation costs and it has already been mentioned that transportation costs are a major factor in the economics of recycling.

A look at some representative examples of present (1972) utilizations of industrial wastes is of interest. Furnace slag from the iron and steel industry has been used as aggregate in concrete pipe and construction bricks. Slag serves in dusting powder, abrasives, ceramic ware, plaster, mortar and insulating concrete. Blast furnace slag is a model picture of a waste product finding wide utilization. In order to accomplish this extensive reuse, it was necessary to create a demand. To this end, the National Slag Foundation was created. This organization explored the physical and chemical properties of slag and endeavoured to find markets for further uses. It was necessary to convince many groups of the utility of this material.

A familiar example, and a huge secondary material resource, is the iron and steel scrap from junked autos and discarded stoves and refrigerators. The U.S. Bureau of Mines is seeking ways to obtain useful metallic values from scrap at low cost. The major problem, at this time, is the cost of transporting the scrap from the collection points to processing plants. Much of the scrap is not suitable for direct charging into open hearth furnaces because of metallic impurities. The impurities are principally copper, nickel, zinc and chromium. Steel is recovered from scrap autos in the following manner. First, the radiator, battery, seats and engine are removed. The auto is then passed through a hammermill which shreds the body into fist-sized chunks. These are then passed through a magnetic separator which separates magnetic and non-magnetic components. Research is currently underway seeking a smokeless incinerator by which organics may be burned off from autos. Metallic separation from non-magnetic materials is accomplished by air elutriation. Heavy media sink–float processes are used for further separation of component metals. Feasibility of burning municipal refuse or sewage with scrap automobiles and refrigerators is being investigated. The products of the foregoing would be suitable for feed to electric furnaces.

There is an increasingly greater demand for energy, particularly in large cities. Much of this energy is supplied by electric power utilities which burn pulverized coal. Fly ash is one of the products of the combustion. At this time, fly ash is the ninth most abundant mineral produced in the U.S. Electric companies have, naturally, sought markets for fly ash. These efforts have met with considerable success but new uses must be found if anticipated increases in fly ash production prove accurate. Coal ash is used as a construction aggregate, in cement, concrete and concrete products. It finds application as a construction fill, as a road base, as a soil stabilizer and in airport runway construction. Development of a fly ash based and gas concrete has supplied the construction industry with a much needed low cost item. The fly ash based brick consists of three parts fly ash, one part slag and a small amount of sodium silicate as a binder. Gas concrete is light and strong and has good thermal and acoustical properies. Fly ash has improved strength and insulating properties over comparable products of silica sand. Fly ash is used as an inert cover for sanitary landfills. It has also been applied advantageously to land laid waste by mining. The fly ash appears to neutralize, to some degree, acid produced from the mines. Some plants are reported to have become established on the cover after application of fly ash.

Use of this material is increasing but in 1969 it was found that only 16% of the total produced was utilized as a secondary material. The Bureau of Mines is funding a number of research projects which have as their aim the development of further fly ash uses.

The mining industry, in response to increased demands for minerals, has been forced to mine lower grade ores which have a greater fraction of extraneous material. The immediate consequence is generation of greater amounts of waste, and this poses a serious disposal problem for this industry.

Mining wastes appear as rejected material after ores are crushed, sized and cleaned. While the market value of these wastes is low, there is no attractive alternative to utilizing these wastes. Any other solution requires expenditures of money for waste disposal. Mine tailings have been used in construction of highway embankments and the possibility of use in small earth fill dams is under investigation. There appears to be a promising future for mine wastes in the construction field. An interesting approach is that sponsored by the Florida Phosphate Council. Here, overburden sand, tailing and phosphate clays of the Central Florida Phosphate Field have been applied to reclamation of previously mined land.

Urban wastes are of less constant composition than most industrial wastes but, over a period of time, it will be found that the majority of the constituents will be reasonably constant. Less affluent communities will dispose of more "personal" items, such as cheaper furniture. Less variation of the character of the waste will be found as the size of the municipality increases.

It is estimated that 75% of all trash in the U.S. ends up in open dumps. Here much potentially valuable material rots and, unfortunately, burns. It has been mentioned already that open dumipng is unacceptable. It is still done, however, and refuse volumes increase and land available for this undesirable means of waste disposal is becoming more scarce. It is very possible that simple necessity will override major economic considerations of recycling.

The major problem facing recycling of municipal waste is handling and transportation costs. Collection of refuse from the source involves manual handling and is subject to cost fluctuations, usually upward. Research is continuing on possible alternative means, such as adoption of conveyors as a means of refuse transportation, or pneumatic conveyance of refuse to a central collection point large enough to warrant salvage operations. Considerable research on the collection aspects has been carried out but little practical change has been accomplished. It is obvious that a radical change in organization and thinking will be required for meaningful progress in this segment of the problem.

A factor that limits the reuse of waste material today is the high cost of separating mixed wastes due to the requirement that recycled materials be clean and free of contaminants. This aspect seriously limits utilization of municipal waste. Some communities have gone almost entirely to the use of kitchen garbage grinders. Food wastes then become water-carried and much putrescible material is kept from solid waste disposal routes.

Refuse can be segregated into main components at the source or separated by mechanical means after collection. Separation can be carried out after passage through an incinerator or pyrolysis unit.

Separation at the source usually involves cooperation of the entire community. Placing refuse in separate containers reserved for paper, glass, tin cans, aluminium cans, putrescibles and other categories is a bother and not everyone will go to the trouble. Some communities have officially discouraged this practice. A recent survey indicates that partial segregation may be practical. In Madison, Wisconsin, residents were asked to put newspapers in separate containers before refuse collection. A 40% recovery of newspaper was realized and the resulting savings more than offset the extra collection cost.

The scheme by which aluminium cans and bottles are collected at reclamation centers has been widely publicized and has proved rather successful. Price incentives are an important consideration here and it is important to note that transportation to the collection centers is provided by those turning in the waste material.

It appears that the only practical way to separate mixed refuse is by mechanical means. At the present time some separation is done at collection sites where newspapers are hand picked and magnets remove ferrous portions. Manual separation is not very satisfactory, because of cost and inefficiency. It is, further, not too reliable.

Before mechanical separations can be carried out, the refuse must be reduced in size for easier handling. In size reduction operations, enclosed materials are released and it is possible to remove organic portions. Organics can be cleaned from metals by pyrolysis or incineration. Salvage can be accomplished either before or after heating.

Shear, tension and compression are applied to large items until they fracture. Equipment to accomplish this includes crushers, cage disintegrators, shears, shredders, cutters, chippers, rasp mills, drum pulverizers, disk mills, wet pulpers (hydro pulpers) and hammermills. Hammermills are the most widely used due to their versatility. After size reduction, the waste is segregated as well as possible into component parts. This step is extremely important because marketability is strongly dependent on separation efficiency. The various techniques by which separation is carried out are based on differences in physical properties. A combination of physical property differences gives best separation. Steel and cast iron parts are removed in a two stage operation. Gross pieces are first magnetically removed and small particles are removed in the following magnetic operation. Non-magnetic metallic materials are removed by eddy current separation. Further operations, such as air classification, separate materials of different densities. Stanford Research Institute has under examination a zig-zag vertical air classifier. Results appear promising but the principal drawback is that the machine requires a feed that is dry and of closely constant size. A water classifier does away with the need for a dry feed. A vortex classifier under development at M.I.T. shows promise of application as a continuous, rather than batch, process. Techniques which use an external detector for separation of waste into different streams show promise. Detectors can be used with colored glass, for example. Computer application to waste separation is still very much in the development stage. An excellent review is presented by Wilson and Smith.

After suitable separation, materials can be directly reused or further processed into useful byproducts.

Examination of the present market situation for savage such as paper, tin cans, glass, rags, plastics and incinerator residue shows an unfavorable cost picture for the salvage dealer. Until changes are made, the cost of obtaining raw materials is till lower than the cost of using recycled materials for the same material.

Economics is the whole basis on which the future of recycling rests. Any new technology or improvements in existing technology must confer economic advantage to the recycling industry in order to be successful.

REFERENCES

1. Kupchick, G. J. Address before the American Medical Association Environmental Congress, New York, May, 1972. Reported in *Engineering Digest*, Vol. 18, No. 7.
2. Lederman, P. B. (in press) Solid Waste Management, *Encyclopedia of Env. Sci. and Eng.*, Vol. 1, Gordon and Breach, New York.
3. Cecil, L. K. (1976) Water Reuse, *Encyclopedia of Env. Env. Sci. and Eng.*, Vol. 2, Gordon and Breach, New York.
4. Nemerow, Nelson L. (1976) Liquid Wastes of Industry, *Encyclopedia of Env. Sci. and Eng.*, Vol. 1, Gordon and Breach, New York.
5. Cardenas, R. R. (in press) Composting, *Encyclopedia of Env. Sci. and Eng.*, Vol. 1, Gordon and Beach, New York.
6. Pfafflin, J. R. (1970) Water: Reuse, *Encyclopedia of Chemical Tech.* (Kirk-Othmer), 2nd Ed., Vol. 22. Interscience, New York.
7. Dole, H. M., Solid Wastes: A Natural Resource, *Proc. of the 2nd Mineral Waste Utilization Symp.*, co-sponsored by the U.S. Bureau of Mines and Ill. Inst. of Tech. Res. Inst., Chicago, Ill., March 1970.
8. Ness, H., New Technology and Economic Factors in the Secondary Materials Industry, *ibid.*
9. Eggleston, H. K., The Successful Utilization of Iron and Steel Slags, *ibid.*
10. Dean, K. C., C. J. Chiudgren and J. W. Sterner, *Research* on Processing Systems for Automotive Materials, *ibid.*
11. Sullivan, G. D., Utilization of Mining and Milling Wastes, *ibid.*
12. Melisch, W. R., Use of Waste Glass for Urban Paving, *ibid.*
13. Dean, K. C. and C. J. Chiudgren, Advances in Technology Recycled Obsolete Cars, *ibid.*
14. Timberlake, R. C., Panel Discussion on Disposal of Mining Wastes in the Central Florida Phosphate Field, *ibid.*
15. Kenehan, C. P. and E. P. Flint (1971) Bureau of Mines *ibid.*
Research Programs on Recycling and disposal of Mineral Metal and Energy Based Solid Wastes, U.S. Dept. of the Interior.
16. Lesher, B., The National Center for Resource Recovery, Inc.
17. Droby, N. L., H. E. Hull and R. F. Testin (1971) Recovery and Utilization of Municipal Solid Waste, U.S. Environmental Protection Agency.
18. Wilson, D. G. and O. E. Smith, How to Reclaim Goods from Wastes, *Technology Review*, Mass. Inst. of Tech., May 1972.

ASHFAQ A. KHAN
Polytechnic Institute of New York

JAMES R. PFAFFLIN
University of Windsor

REMOTE DETECTION OF AIR POLLUTANTS

The state of the art of the remote detection of atmospheric pollutants, not to be confused with direct sensing such as sampling and chemical analysis, is still in its infancy. With the exception of visual observation of concentrations of certain particulates and other contaminants that noticeably affect the appearance of the air, most scientific methods of identifying and quantifying aerial pollutants at a distance are still in the research and development stage, or have not even progressed beyond the phase of theoretical studies. Only very few techniques, as of today, can be considered fully operational.

The objectives of the various remote sensing methods are to detect, at distances dictated by practical circumstances, atmospherical pollutants emitted by stationary and mobile sources, and those occurring in ambient air. Plans are also under way to develop techniques or adapt existing ones to large-scale monitoring of atmospheric conditions affecting air quality from the overview vantage point of space platforms.

Among the principal stationary sources of air pollution are smoke stacks and incinerators; among mobile sources are automobile and aircraft exhausts.

The pollutants themselves, apart from natural contaminants such as ragweed pollen and similar substances, are either particulates in the form of fly ash, soot and other solids, or noxious gases, such as carbon monoxide (CO), hydrocarbons, sulphur compounds and oxides of nitrogen (NOx). The latter occur mostly as nitric oxide (NO) or nitrogen dioxide (NO_2). Under the impact of sunlight, oxides of nitrogen eventually combine with certain exhaust hydrocarbons to form so-called photochemical smog, a particularly unhealthy and irritating form of air pollution.

Among several remote detection techniques on which research has been conducted, only the following can currently be cited as fully operational within the context of their specific objectives:

Correlation Spectrometry

Use is made of special equipment consisting of a telescope to collect light from the source, a two-grating spectrometer to disperse this light, a disk-shaped multiple slit mask and an electronic recorder. The spectrum of the source is compared to replicas of absorption or emission spectra of specific pollutants to determine the quantities of these materials in the source. Fixed or mobile instruments have been used to determine total quantities of sulphur dioxide and nitrogen dioxide in large atmospheric masses [1–3]. The method may also be adapted to analysis of emissions from specific sources.

Lidar

This technique uses laser energy in radar fashion for the remote detection of atmospheric constituents. Back-scattered energy is collected by a lens or reflector and detected by a photomultiplier. The output may be displayed on an oscilloscope, recorded on magnetic tape, or used as input for a computer program to produce graphic results.[4] This technique has successfully measured concentration of many pollutants, especially large molecules and particulates at distances of up to several kilometers.[5] It is very useful in estimating average concentrations in large air masses, and variations in concentration from one segment of the atmosphere to another.[6]

The following techniques can be described as in the research and development stage:

Tunable Diode Lasers

Lasers composed of certain metal alloys emit radiation in narrow spectral ranges. They may be tuned to the radiative frequencies of certain molecular pollutants. The laser frequency excites a heterodyne resonance radiation from the pollutant that is collected by a receiving mirror and analyzed spectrometrically. The lasers employed for this technique operate at very low temperatures. They are highly sensitive indicators of trace pollutants in ambient air and can also be used to record pollutant concentrations emitted by remote sources, at distances of up to about 1 km. [7–11]

Infrared Spectroscopy

Spectra in the 3–14μ range are measured by grating spectrophotometer, interferometer and radiometer. Emission spectra from incinerators and stacks, and absorbtion spectra through ambient air to distances of about 3 km. have identified several atmospheric pollutants.[12]

Raman Scattering

This method measures back-scattered radiation from photon interaction produced by laser excitation of gas molecules. Much basic information in support of this technique is still needed and, for the time being, most applications are still laboratory-oriented [13–15].

Ultraviolet Photo-Reconnaissance

A special near-UV photographic technique, originally developed for archaeological reconnaissance, has recently shown promising results in photographing normally invisible particulates, and in remotely detecting apparent spectral signatures of nitric oxide (NO) in the engine exhaust emissions of heavy jet transports. On the basis of initial experiments, the operational range of this technique stretches from a few meters to at least 1 km. for nitric oxide, and well beyond that distance for invisible particulates.[17, 18]

Fourier Interference Spectrography

This is one of the techniques proposed for various extremely remote sensing projects utilizing instruments borne by high-altitude aircraft, artificial satellites or manned space stations. The Fourier technique envisions the production of a digital record transmitted and decoded by computer. Major masses of polluted air and their movements will thus be studied.[19, 20]

Theoretical Studies and Fundamental Research

Several reports on research projects have recently become available that are basically general or theoretical,[9,15,21–23] or present some fundamental information that eventually may be applicable to techniques for the remote detection of certain pollutants [24–26]

As the importance of being able to remotely identify and quantify atmospheric pollutants is increasingly recognized, the development and operational testing of the more promising techniques and concepts will expand as part of overall efforts toward a better air environment.

REFERENCES

1. Langan, L. (1971). Remote Sensing Measurements of Regional Gaseous Pollution, *AIAA* 71–1060.
2. Barringer, A. R. and A. J. Moffat (1969). *Proceedings of Sixth Symposium on Remote Sensing of the Environment*, Univ. of Michigan, Ann Arbor, Mich.
3. Moffat, A. J., J. R. Robbins and A. R. Barringer (1971). *Atmos. Environ.* **5**, 511.
4. Collis, R. T. H. (1970). *Appl. Optics* **9**, 1782.
5. Uthe, E. E. (1971). Lidar Observations of Particulate Distribution over Extended Areas, *AIAA* 71–1055.
6. McCormick, M. P. and W. H. Fuller, Jr. (1971). Lidar Applications to Pollution Studies, *AIAA* 71–1056.
7. Hinkley, E. D. and R. H. Kingston (1971) Remote Heterodyne Detection of Gaseous Pollutants with Tunable Lasers, *AIAA* 71–1079.
8. Dimmock, J. O. (1972). Lincoln Lab. MIT, Personal Communication.
9. Melngailis, I. (1972). The Use of Lasers in Pollutions Monitoring, *IEEE Trans. for Geoscience Electronics*, GE–10, I.
10. Hinkley, E. D. and P. L. Kelley (1971). Detection of Air Pollutants with Tunable Lasers, Science, **171**, 635.
11. Menzies, R. T. and M. S. Shumate (1971). Usefulness of the Infrared Heterodyne Radiometer in Remote Sensing of Atmospheric Pollutants, *AIAA* 71–1083.
12. Herget, W. F., H. M. Barnes Jr., C. B. Ludwig and G. W. Ashley (1971). Infrared Spectra of Pollutant Emissions from Various Stationary Sources, *AIAA* 71–1082 (Abstract).
13. Lapp, M., L. M. Goldman and G. M. Penney (1971) Fundamental Data for Raman Scattering Measurements of Species Concentrations and Temperature, *AIAA* 71–1084.
14. Lapp, M., L. M. Goldman and G. M. Penney (1971). Raman Scattering from Water Vapour, *AIAA* 71-1085.
15. Schwiesow, R. L. (1971). Raman Scattering Studies of Pollutant Systems, *AIAA* 71–1086.
16. Herget, W. F. (1972). Environmental Protection Agency, Personal Communication.
17. Michanowsky, G. (1971). The Potential of Ultraviolet Reconnaissance as a Remote Detector of Invisible Nitric Oxide, Report of Amazonia Foundation, Inc. to Federal Aviation Administration.
18. Technique Detects Nitric Oxide Emissions, *Aviation Week and Space Technology*, January 3, 1972, pp. 44/45.
19. Schindler, R. A. (1971). An Interim Report on Remote Sensing of Environmental Pollutants with a Fourier Interference Spectrometer, *AIAA* 71-1108.
20. Toth, R. A. and C. B. Farmer (1971) Global Studies of Atmospheric Pollutants and Trace Constituents, *AIAA* 71–1109.
21. McCreight, C. R. and C. L. Tien (1971). Interpretation Problems in the Correlation-Mask Sensing Technique, *AIAA* 71–1061.
22. Thomas, R. W. L. (1971). The Relationship between Aerosol Content and Errors in Telephotometry Experiments, *AIAA* 71–1062.
23. Millan, M. M., S. J. Townsend and J. H. Davies (1970). Study of the Barringer Refractor-Plate Correlations Sepctrometer as a Remote Sensing Instrument, Univ. Toronto Inst. for Aerospace Studies, *Rpt.* **146**.
24. Nill, K. W., F. A. Blum, A. R. Calawa and T. C. Harman (1971) Observation of Lambda Doubling and Zeeman Splitting in the Fundamental Infrared Band of Nitric Oxide, Report Lincoln Lab. MIT.
25. Blum, F. A., K. W. Nill, A. R. Calawa and T. C. Harman (1972). Observation of Nuclear Hyperfine Splitting in the Infrared Vibration-Rotation Absorption Spectrum of the NO molecule, Report Lincoln Lab. MIT.
26. Lavoie, G. A. (1970). Spectroscopic Measurements of Nitric Oxide in Spark Ignition Engines, *Combustion and Flame*, **15**, 97.

George Michanowsky
Amazonia Foundation, Inc.

REMOVAL OF POLLUTANTS: see GASEOUS POLLUTANT REMOVAL; PARTICULATE REMOVAL

REVERSE OSMOSIS: see APPLICATIONS OF REVERSE OSMOSIS

REVERSE OSMOSIS—PROCESS FUNDAMENTALS

Introduction

Reverse osmosis is a general separation technique. It consists in letting a solution, or fluid mixture, flow under pressure through an appropriate porous membrane and withdrawing the membrane permeated product generally at atmospheric pressure and surrounding temperature; the product is enriched in one or more constituents of the mixture leaving a concentrated solution of other constituents on the upstream side of the membrane. No heating of the membrance and no phase change in product recovery are involved in this separation process.

Reverse osmosis is applicable for the separation, concentration and fractionation of inorganic or organic substances in aqueous or nonaqueous solutions in the liquid or the gaseous phase; hence, it opens a new and versatile field of separation technology in chemical process engineering. This article is concerned only with reverse osmosis for water treatment applications including saline water conversion, water pollution control, water renovation and waste recovery.

The development of asymmetric porous cellulose acetate membranes by Loeb and Sourirajan[1] in 1960 was the starting point of the advances which have been made in recent years in the science and engineering of reverse osmosis. There are at least three major monographs[2–4] on reverse osmosis, each representing a different approach to the subject.

Osmosis and Reverse Osmosis

Neither the term "osmosis" nor "reverse osmosis" is an explanation of the mechanism of the process. Under isothermal conditions, in both osmosis and reverse osmosis, the transport of material through the membrane is always in the direction of lower chemical potential; this is a thermodynamic requirement and says nothing about the mechanism of this separation process. In the literature, the osmosis process is always associated with the existence of a membrane which is permeable only to the solvent; the cause of such semipermeability is really the fundamental question in both osmosis and reverse osmosis. Hence, it must be understood that the mechanism of both osmosis and reverse osmosis is still an open question, the distinction between the two terms is entirely one of arbitrary convention and popular usage, and the reverse osmosis process itself covers the entire possible range of solute separation obtainable by the technique.

The Preferential Sorption-Capillary Flow Mechanism

The origin of the reverse osmosis process as it is practiced today is the result of the recognition of a fundamental concept, namely that an appropriate chemical nature of the membrane surface in contact with the solution, as well as the existence of pores of appropriate size on the area of the membrane at the interface, together constitute the indispensable twin-requirement for the industrial success of this separation process. This concept, called the preferential sorption-capillary flow mechanism, is schematically represented in Figure 1, where the solution is in contact with a solid material in the form of a porous membrane. If the surface of the porous membrane in contact with the solution is of chemical nature such that it has a preferential sorption for water or preferential repulsion for solute (which is the same as a negative adsorption for the solute), then a steep concentration gradient and consequently a layer of preferentially sorbed pure water comes into existence at the membrane–solution interface. A continuous removal of this interfacial water can then be effected by letting it

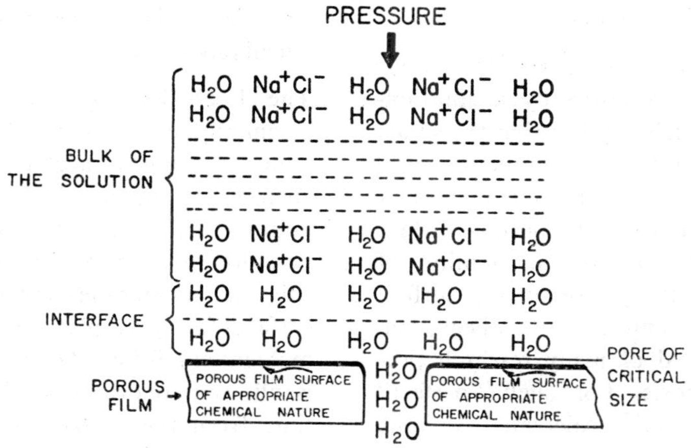

Figure 1 Schematic representation of preferential sorption-capillary flow mechanism.

flow under pressure through the membrane capillaries.

The above mechanism gives rise to the following consequences of practical interest. Reverse osmosis is a general separation technique, and it is governed, in part, by a surface (interfacial) phenomenon. The surface layer of a successful reverse osmosis membrane is microporous at all levels of solute separation. With an appropriate membrane material practically any degree of solute separation can be obtained by simply changing the pore size on the membrane suffacе, and other operating conditions of the reverse osmosis experiment. For each such membrane material–solution system, there exists a critical pore diameter for maximum solute separation and fluid permeability. This diameter is obviously twice the thickness of the interfacial pure water layer (Figure 2). Therefore, from a practical point of view, in order to obtain the highest

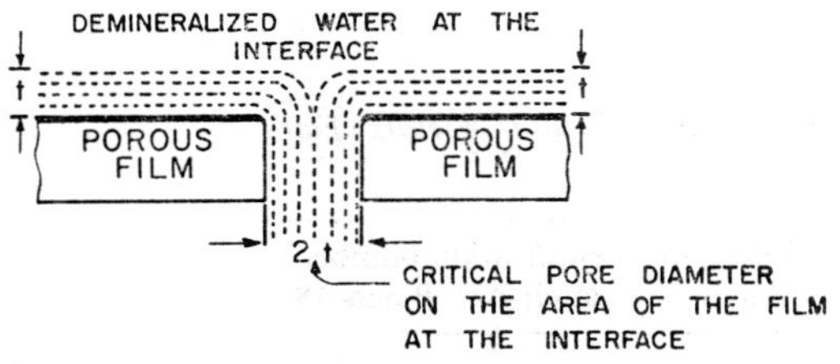

Figure 2 Critical pore diameter for maximum separation and permeability.

membrane productivity (i.e. fluid permeation rate at any given level of solute separation), the chemical nature of membrane surface must be such that it has a preferential sorption for water or preferential repulsion for solute, and the membrane surface must have the largest possible number of pores of appropriate size, interconnected with comparatively large pores in the bulk of the membrane material underneath the surface layer. The latter requirement means that the porous structure of the membrane must be appropriately asymmetric so that resistance to fluid flow is reduced to the minimum under reverse osmosis operating conditions.

Using a trial and error technique to search for suitable "semipermeable" membranes for water desalination, Reid and Breton, at the University of Florida, discovered that cellulose acetate membrane was capable of rejecting electrolytes from aqueous solutions in reverse osmosis experiments, but the water permeation rates obtained by them were too low to be of any practical interest.[5]

Following the preferential sorption-capillary flow mechanism for reverse osmosis, and completely unaware of the work of Reid and Breton, Sourirajan at the University of California, Los Angeles, (UCLA), discovered that cellulose esters—in particular, cellulose acetate and cellulose acetate butyrate—were appropriate membrane materials for the reverse osmosis separation of sodium chloride from aqueous solutions;[6] following the latter discovery, Loeb and Sourirajan at UCLA then developed a technique for making asymmetric porous cellulose acetate membranes capable of giving both high levels of solute separation and water flux in the reverse osmosis treatment of aqueous sodium chloride solutions.[1,7,8] The above discovery and development at UCLA, in turn, led to numerous other subsequent developments, all of which together have contributed to the emergence of reverse osmosis as an industrially significant process for a variety of water treatment applications.

The Solution-Diffusion Mechanism

According to Lonsdale and coworkers,[9–11] reverse osmosis separation is governed by a solution-diffusion mechanism which requires that the solute and solvent dissolve in the membrane material and permeate through the membrane by homogeneous diffusion through the nonporous surface layer. Guided by this mechanism, creation of membranes with completely nonporous surface layer (called "perfect" membranes) has been, and continues to be, the goal of many research programs in reverse osmosis. For such "perfect" membranes, Riley *et al.*[10] calculated definite theoretical levels of solute separations in reverse osmosis from solubility measurements. For example the theoretical levels of solute separations are 99.37, 99.72, and 99.82% at operating pressures of 500, 1000, and 1500 psig respectively, in reverse osmosis using membranes made of cellulose acetate (acetyl content = 39.8%) and aqueous feed solutions containging 1% NaCl. Membranes giving less than the above theoretical levels of solute separations are obviously "imperfect" according to the above mechanism.

In the author's judgment, the solution-diffusion mechanism is neither a useful nor an applicable model for reverse osmosis because the latter is not limited to the levels of solute separations calculated on the basis of solubility measurements, and because the surface layer of a practically useful reverse osmosis membrane is microporous at all levels of solute separation. The solution-diffusion model, even if applicable, can only represent a limiting case in reverse osmosis. Consequently the concept of "perfect" and "imperfect" membranes is irrelevant to the field of reverse osmosis.

Loeb-Sourirajan Type Porous Cellulose Acetate Membranes

The Loeb–Sourirajan film-making technique is essentially as follows. The film-casting solution contains cellulose acetate dissolved in a solvent, such as acetone, to which is added a water soluble additive such as an aqueous solution of magnesium perchlorate or pure formamide. With the above solution, membranes are cast on flat or tubular surfaces (e.g. glass plates or metal tubes) at specified ambient conditions. On casting, part of the solvent is allowed to evaporate for a definite period of time from the surface of the membrane at the temperature of the casting atmosphere (evaporation step). This step is followed by immersion of the membrane in ice-cold water for at least an hour; during this time, the film sets to a gel from which the solvent and the additive are leached out (gelation step) leaving a tough solid porous film on the flat or tubular surface from which it can be easily removed. Every detail relating to the casting solution composition, evaporation step, and the gelation step affects the porous structure of the resulting membrane and its subsequent performance in reverse osmosis. Some typical details for casting flat, porous, cellulose acetate membranes are given in Table I. These membranes are generally stored at the laboratory temperature either under water or dilute alcohol solution, or simply in a humid atmosphere to preserve their porous structure. On drying in air, the porous structure of the membrane often changes irreversibly. However the above membranes could be held "dry" after an initial soaking, for a few minutes, in an aqueous solution of a surface active agent such as a mixture of Tergitol 15S7 (polyoxyethylene, 9 molecules of

TABLE I

Casting Conditions for Loeb–Sourirajan–type Porous Cellulose Acetate Flat Membranes

Film casting details	Film type identification number		
	Batch–25	Batch–47	Batch–18
Casting solution composition (wt.%)			
Cellulose acetate]acetyl content, 39.8%)	22.2	25	17
Acetone	66.7	45	68
Magnesium perchlorate	1.1	—	1.5
Water	10.0	—	13.5
Formamide	—	30	—
Casting solution terperature, °C	–10	23–24	–10
Temperature of casting atmosphere, °C	–10	23–24	–10
Casting atmosphere	ambient air in all cases		
Evaporation time, min.	4	1/2	4
Gelation medium	ice cold water in all cases		
Gelation time	at least 1 hr in all cases		
Nominal film thickness	0.003–0.005 in. in all cases		

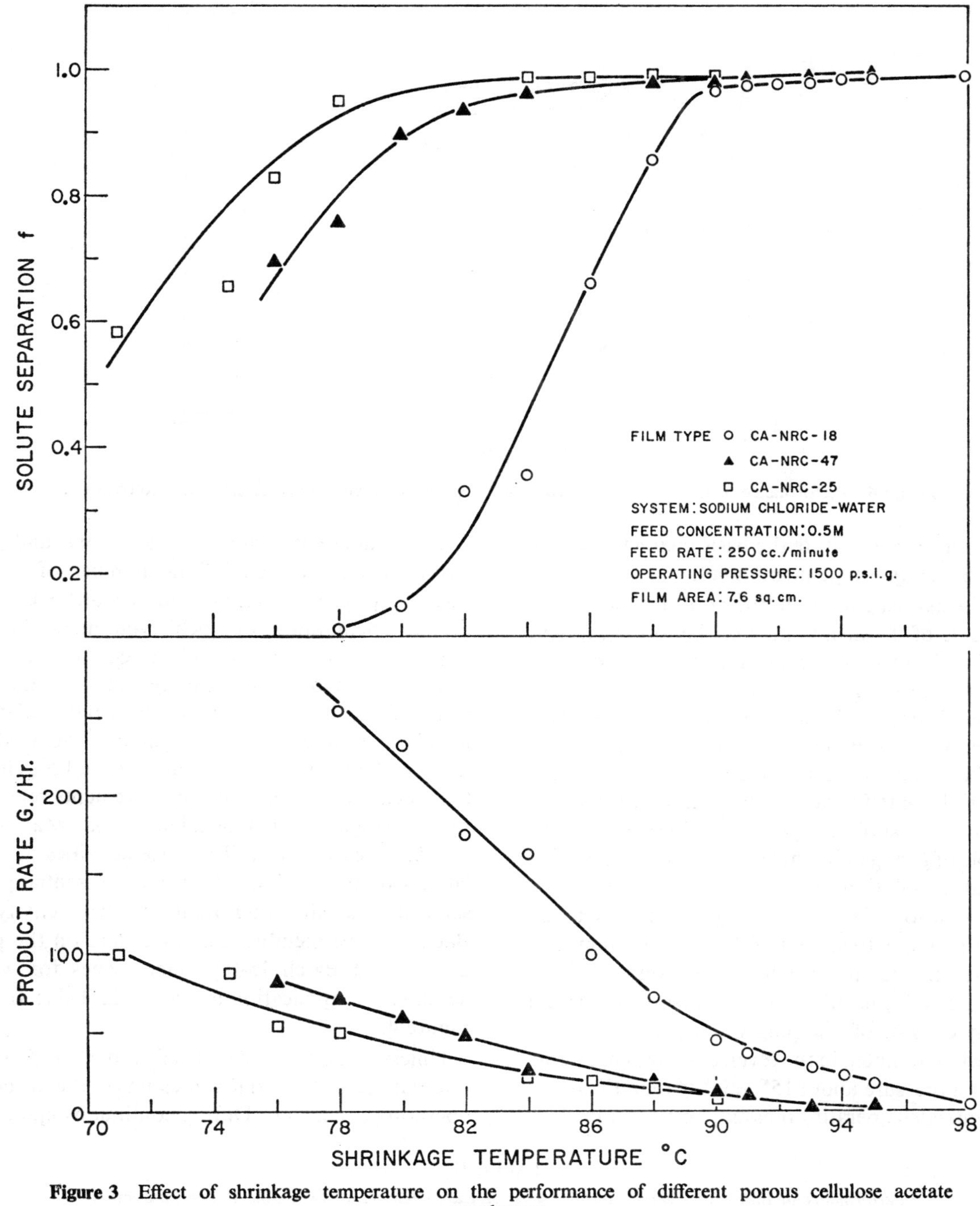

Figure 3 Effect of shrinkage temperature on the performance of different porous cellulose acetate membranes.

ethylene oxide substituted on C_{11} to C_{15} linear alkyl) and glycerol.[12]

Membranes made in the above manner have a relatively dense microporous structure (pore size probably <50 Å) on an extremely thin layer (<0.25 μ) on the film surface which was exposed to the atmosphere during casting. This side of the film is called the "surface layer side", and the other side the "back side". The bulk of the film material underneath the thin surface layer is a spongy, porous mass containing comparatively very big (~4000–10,000 Å) interconnecting pores.[13,14] Consequently the porous structure of the film is asymmetric. It is the microporous structure of the dense surface layer which governs the level of solute separation in reverse osmosis, and hence the surface layer side is held facing the feed solution during reverse osmosis operation.

Thus, asymmetric porous structure and capability for solute separation under reverse osmosis operat-

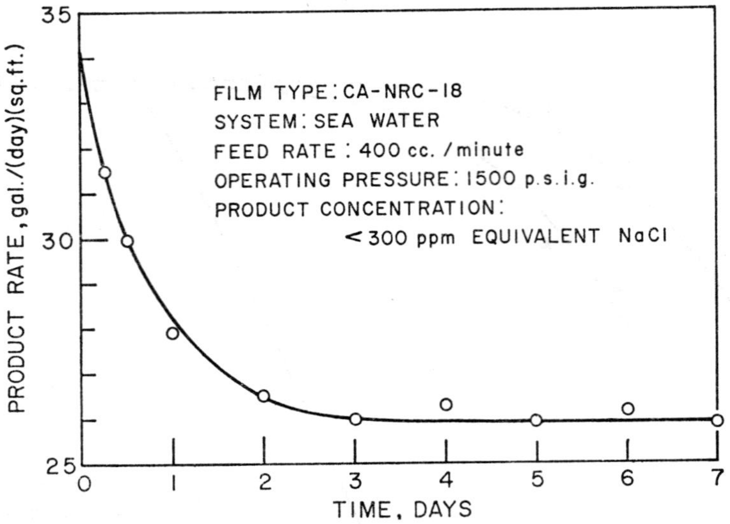

Figure 4 Performance of Batch 18–type porous cellulose acetate membranes for sea water conversion.

ing conditions constitute the basic characteristics of Loeb–Sourirajan type membranes.

In the as-cast condition, the pores on the surface layer side of the membrane may be too big to give any significant solute separation in reverse osmosis for a given feed solution. In that case, the membrane can be shrunk and pore size reduced by simply keeping the film immersed in hot water for about 10 min (temperature treatment).[7,15] By adjusting the shrinkage temperature, different (average) pore sizes on the surface layer side of the membrane capable of giving different levels of solute separation for a given solution system can be obtained (Figure 3). It is also necessary to subject the film to an initial pressure treatment, following the temperature treatment, to stabilize the overall porous structure of the film. The pressure treatment usually consists of pumping water past the surface of the film mounted in the reverse osmosis operating unit at a pressure about 15% higher than the maximum intended operating pressure for at least an hour.

Using different film-casting solutions and film casting conditions, an infinite number of Loeb–Sourirajan type membranes can be made. Cellulose acetate membranes of such type made in the author's laboratory are identified by different CA-NRC-numbers, or simply batch numbers, some of which are given in Table I. Batch 25-type membranes were the ones originally developed by Loeb and Sourirajan;[1,7,8] Batch 18- and Batch 47-type membranes were later improvements reported by Sourirajan and Govindan[16] and Manjikian *et al.*,[17] respectively. The productivities of the latter two types of membranes are essentially the same and much better than the productivity of Batch 25-type membranes. Some data on the productivity of Batch 18-type membranes for water desalination application are given in Table II and Figure 4.

Unless otherwise stated all reported product rate data refer to initial values under the specified operating conditions. During continuous operation

TABLE II

Performance of Batch–18–Type Porous Cellulose Acetate Membranes for Saline Water Conversion
(Data of Sourirajan and Govindan[16])

Film pretreatment: Shrinkage temp. °C	Film pretreatment: Pressure psig	Solute	Feed rate cm³/min	Operating pressure psig	Solute concn. in feed wt. %	Solute concn. in product ppm	Product rate gal (day) (ft²)
87	700	NaCl	300	600	0.25	400	52.4
88	700	NaCl	300	600	0.50	300	34.0
87	700	Na_2SO_4	300	600	0.25	150	53.3
87	700	Na_2SO_4	300	600	0.50	300	50.7
90	1700	NaCl	250	1500	1.44	< 100	38.5
90	1700	NaCl	250	1500	2.84	280	31.3
90	1700	NaCl	250	1500	4.20	420	24.1
90	1700	NaCl	250	1500	5.53	550	18.2

TABLE III

Some Data on Reverse Osmosis Membranes and Their Performance

Membrane material	Composition of film–casting solution	wt. ratio	Solute	Solute concn. in feed wt.%	Operating pressure psig	Solute separation %	Water flux gal/day ft²	Reference
			Typical data on membrane performance in reverse osmosis					
Cellulose acetate (CA)	CA	25	NaCl	0.5	600	94.0	28.0	18
	Acetone	30						
	Formamide	25						
	Pyridine	20						
Cellulose acetate (CA)	CA	21.4	NaCl	0.5	600	97.9	20.0	19
	Acetone	50.0						
	Glycerol	7.1						
	n–Propanol	21.5						
Cellulose acetate (CA)	CA	22.1	NaCl	0.5	600	95.0	29.4	19
	Acetone	51.4						
	Glycerol	6.6						
	n–Propanol	19.9						
Cellulose acetate (CA)	CA	10	NaCl	1.104	800	97.7	25.5	20
	Acetone	20						
	Water	3						
	Propinonamide	6						
Cellulose acetate (CA)	CA	10	NaCl	3.5	1500	98.6	10.8	21
	Acetone	30		0.5	750	92.7	35.5	
	Water	5						
	Tartaric acid	2.5						
Cellulose acetate (CA)	—		NaCl	1.0	800	33	81.0	22
						67	54.0	
						89	54.0	
						97	24.6	
						98	12.3	
Cellulose acetate (ultrathin)	—		NaCl	0.9	1560	99.81	9.7	23
					840	99.47	4.5	
Cellulose acetate (ultrathin)	—		NaCl	1.0	800	96.0	18	24
Cellulose acetate (CA) homopolar ds = 2.61	CA	10	NaCl	3.5	1500	99.56	13.3	25
	Acetone	22						
	Formamide	8						
	Maleic acid	2						
Cellulose acetate (CA) homopolar ds = 2.61	—		NaCl	3.5	1500	99.5	11.0	22
Cellulose acetate (CA) blend ds = 2.64	—		NaCl	3.5	1500	99.7	10.7	22
Cellulose acetate (CA) blend	CA (ds = 2.86)	8	NaCl	1.0	800	99.0	14.3	25
	CA (ds = 2.41)	12	Sea water		1500	99.46	10.4	
	Dioxane	55						
	Acetone	35						
	Methanol	9						
	Maleic acid	3						
Cellulose acetate (CA) Cellulose triacetate (CTA)	CA	10	NaCl	3.5	1500	99.2	12.0	21
	CTA	10						
	Dioxane	60						
	Acetone	35						
	Methanol	9						
	Maleic acid	4						

TABLE III—continued

Some Data on Reverse Osmosis Membranes and Their Performance

Membrane material	Composition of film-casting solution wt. ratio		Typical data on membrane performance in reverse osmosis: Solute	Solute concn. in feed wt.%	Operating pressure psig	Solute separation %	Water flux gal/day ft²	Reference
Cellulose acetate (CA) Cellulose triacetate (CTA) blend	—							
ds = 2.45			NaCl	3.5	1500	98.9	12.0	22
2.55						99.0	12.0	
2.63						99.0	11.9	
2.67						99.5	11.1	
2.71						99.5	11.7	
2.74						99.6	9.1	
2.79						98.7	6.8	
2.86						98.7	4.5	
Cellulose acetate (CA) —composite membrane	—		Sea water		1500	99.54	13.3	26
Cellulose acetate (CA) —hollow fiber	CA in 1:1 triethylene glycol and methyl carbitol		NaCl	0.5	600	96.8	2.3	27
				3.5	600	96.1	0.45	
Cellulose acetate (CA) —hollow fiber	CA	30	NaCl	0.3	250	76.0	6.4	28
	Acetone	28				86.0	5.3	
	Formamide	42				88.0	2.0	
						98.0	1.6	
			NaCl	1.0	500	99.0	0.6	
Cellulose triacetate (CTA)	CTA	10	NaCl	0.5	600	97.4	12.5	29
	Acetic acid	12						
	Dioxane	75.5						
	Triacetin	2.5						
Cellulose acetate propionate (CAP)	CAP	10	NaCl	3.5	1500	99.1	13.4	21
	Acetone	20						
	Formamide	9						
	Maleic acid	2						
Cellulose acetate propionate ds = 2.5	—		NaCl	3.5	1500	99.5	11.8	22
Cellulose acetate butyrate (CAB)	CAB	10	NaCl	3.5	1500	99.3	10.6	21
	Acetone	20						
	Formamide	7						
	Maleic acid	4						
Cellulose acetate butyrate ds = 2.52	—		NaCl	3.5	1500	99.8	8.7	22
Cellulose acetate butyrate (CAB)	CAB	22	NaCl	0.5	600	99.6	8.1	30
	Glycerol	2		1.0	800	99.86	8.3	
	n–Propanol	6		3.5	1000	99.8	4.7	
	Triethyl phosphate	25	Sea water		1000	99.75	4.6	
	Acetone	45						
Cellulose acetate butyrate (CAB) hollow fiber	CAB	32	NaCl	0.3	250	98.0	0.18 to 0.31	28
	Acetone	39.17						
	Triethyl phosphate	21.83						
	n–Propanol	5.23						
	Glycerol	1.77						

TABLE III—continued

Some Data on Reverse Osmosis Membranes and Their Performance

Membrane material	Composition of film–casting solution wt. ratio		Typical data on membrane performance in reverse osmosis: Solute	Solute concn. in feed wt.%	Operating pressure psig	Solute separation %	Water flux gal/day ft^2	Reference
Cellulose acetate butyrate (CAB)	CAB	22	$NaNO_3$	0.1408	600	93.48	7.2	29
	Glycerol	2						
	n–Propanol	6	HNO_3	0.1672	600	93.00	6.9	
	Triethyl phosphate	25						
	Acetone	45	$Mg(NO_3)_2$	0.1210	600	94.05	7.8	
			Na_2SO_4	0.1000	600	99.73	9.8	
			$NH_4H_2PO_4$	0.08	600	99.83	8.6	
			NH_4OH	0.088	600	41.24	8.0	
			NaOH	0.1180	600	99.9	8.0	
			$ZnCl_2$	0.1070	600	99.77	7.6	
			$BaCl_2$	0.0825	600	99.09	7.9	
			$MgSO_4$	0.09	600	99.80	7.0	
			$CuSO_4$	0.1080	600	99.9	7.1	
			LiCl	0.1400	600	99.9	7.5	
			Urea	0.1696	600	99.0	7.3	
			Urea	1.08	600	75.5	7.3	
			Boric acid	0.17	600	53.0	8.0	
			Hexachloro-phene	0.0076	600	89.5	6.2	
			Hexachloro-phene	0.1900	600	98.7	5.3	
			Phenol	0.0061	600	–16.0	10.4	
			Glycene	0.10	600	99.9	8.9	
Cellulose acetate butyrate (CAB)	CAB	22	Sea water		1500	99.4	11.8	31
	Glycerol	2						
	n–Propanol	6						
	Triethyl phosphate	25						
	Acetone	50						
	Glyoxal	5						
Cellulose acetate methacrylate (CAM)	CAM	10	NaCl	3.5	1500	99.21	10.3	21
	Acetone	20						
	Formamide	9						
	Maleic acid	3						
Cellulose acetate methacrylate ds = 2.62	—		NaCl	3.5	1500	99.7	7.6	22
				1.0	800	90.0	34.4	
				1.0	800	81.0	81.0	
Cellulose acetate methacrylate (CAM)	CAM	10	NaCl	3.5	1500	99.6	9.2	25
	Acetone	16.7						
	Formamide	9						
	Maleic acid	3						
Cellulose acetate benzoate (CA Ben)	CA Ben	10	NaCl	3.5	1500	97.5	8.1	21
	Acetone	30						
	Formamide	10						
	Maleic acid	5						
Ethyl cellulose (EC)	EC	10	NaCl	3.5	1500	94.5	4.25	32
	Methyl acetate	48						
	Methanol	12						
	Formamide	15						
	70% perchloric acid	3						
Ethyl cellulose (EC)	EC	22	NaCl	1.0	800	96.7	4.2	33
	Pyridine	35.1						
	Dioxane	23.4						
	Formamide	19.5						
Aromatic polyamide, Monsanto type	—		NaCl	3.5	1500	98.0	8.3	28

TABLE III—continued

Some Data on Reverse Osmosis Membranes and Their Performance

Membrane material	Composition of film-casting solution wt. ratio		Typical data on membrane performance in reverse osmosis: Solute	Solute concn. in feed wt.%	Operating pressure psig	Solute separation %	Water flux gal/day ft²	Reference
Aromatic polyamide, DuPont type Hollow fiber	—		NaCl	0.15	400	93.0	1.8	34
Polyelectrolyte complexes, Amicon type:								
Diaflo UM-10	—		Dextran	—	100	100	175	35
Diaflo UM-2	—		Raffinose	—	100	90	70	35
Diaflo UM-05	—		Sucrose	—	100	90	35	35
Substituted olefin, Amicon type:								
Diaflo XM50	—		Bovine serum	—	100	100	350	35
Diaflo XM100	—		Gamma Globulin	—	100	100	1050	35
Aromatic polymer, Amicon type:								
Diaflo PM-10	—		Pepsin	—	100	100	1050	35
Diaflo PM-30	—		Human Serum	—	100	100	2800	35
Cellulosic, Millipore type:								
Pellicon	—		Congo red dye	—	100	100	17.5	35
Cellulosic, Abcor type:								
HFA-100	—		Dextran 10	—	100	100	25	35
HFA-300	—		Dextran 110	—	100	5	600	35
Cellulose acetate (CA)	CA, grams	25	Proteins	1.0	50	100	23	36
	Formamide, cm³	50						
	Acetone, cm³	75						

under pressure for extended periods of time, the product rate usually drops from 10–50% depending on the operating pressure and the porous structure of the membrane. Figure 4 represents a typical product rate vs. time graph for the type of film used; similar experimental data for more extended periods of reverse osmosis operation are needed for realistic process design. The drop in product rate is usually attributed to the densification of the porous structure (compaction) of the membrane and the consequent increase in its effective thickness.

Further Data on Reverse Osmosis Membranes and their Performance

Following the development of Loeb-Sourirajan type porous cellulose acetate membranes, a very large number of similar membranes have been successfully made and tested for reverse osmosis applications. Representative data on some of the important ones are given in Table III along with pertinent references[18–36] for further details. These membranes are usually in flat, tubular, or hollow fiber form, and they are made of either cellulosic or noncellulosic polymeric materials. Among the cellulosic membranes, the cellulose ester membranes (including cellulose acetate with different degrees of substitution) are the most successful ones for reverse osmosis applications. The ultrathin membranes have usually a nominal thickness of 400–2000 Å, and they are usually cast on the surface of glass plates, floated off onto the surface of water and subsequently supported on a finely porous membrane. Since it is difficult to transfer large areas of ultrathin membranes from the water trough to the porous supporting membrane, an integral method has been developed, in which the thin membrane is formed directly on the porous supporting membrane; such membranes are called "composite membranes". Among the noncellulosic membranes, the DuPont aromatic polyamide hollow fiber membranes are gaining commercial prominence. The polyelectrolyte membranes are primarily used for the separation of high molecular weight solutes. All membranes listed in Table III are believed to have asymmetric porous structure, and exhibit separation capability for solutes in aqueous solutions under reverse osmosis operating conditions.

Solute-rejecting membranes (called "dynamically formed membranes") for reverse osmosis applications can also be formed by passing a pressurized dilute dispersion of a suitable additive over a porous support having pore diameters in the micron range.[37] A wide variety of additives has been found suitable for such dynamically formed membranes. Some typical data on such membranes are given in Tables IV, V, and VI.

While all the types of membranes mentioned above, and many new ones which will undoubtedly be developed in the future, may be expected to be used in the industrial applications of reverse osmosis, the Loeb–Sourirajan type porous cellulose acetate membranes are the ones which are being used extensively in commercial reverse osmosis equipments with the exception of those of DuPont. Very little published information is available on DuPont aromatic polyamide membranes. On the other hand, the literature is extensive on the Loeb–Sourirajan type porous cellulose acetate membranes. For these reasons, the following discussions relate specifically to the latter type of membranes. The basic principles involved may be expected to be applicable to all reverse osmosis membranes.

TABLE IV

Typical Additives for Dynamically-Formed Membranes
(Data of Kraus *et al.*[37])

Hydrous oxides (Al(III), Fe(III), Si(IV), Zr(IV), Th(IV), U(VI))
Finely ground low cross-linked ion-exchange resins
Clays (Bentonite)
Humic acid
Poly (styrene sulfonic acid)
Poly(vinylbenzyltrimethylammonium chloride)
Cellulose acetate hydrogen phthalate
Cellulose acetate N,N-Diethylamminoacetate
Poly(Methyl vinyl ether/Maleic anhydride)
Poly(4-vinyl pyridine)
Poly(4-vinyl pyridinium butyl chloride)
Poly(vinyl pyrrolidone)

TABLE V

Typical Porous Supports for Dynamically-Formed Membranes
(Data of Kraus *et al.*[73])

Material	Nominal pore diam. μ	Trade name or supplier
Silver	0.2–5	Selas Corp.
Porcelain	0.5	—
Sintered glass	ultrafine	—
Carbon	0.2–0.5	Union Carbide Corp.
Polyvinyl chloride	0.45	Metricel VM–6 (Gelman)
Polyvinyl chloride on nylon	0.45	Vinyl Acropor VNM–450 (Gelman]
Vinylidine fluoride	0.45	Metricel VF–6 (Gelman)
Cellulose acetate	5	Metricel GA–1 (Gelman)
	0.1–0.5	Millipore
Porous fiberglass tubes	—	American Standard, Havens Industries
Nuclepore	0.5	General Electric

TABLE VI

Performance of Dynamically-Formed Hydrous Zirconium Oxide Membranes
(Data of Kraus *et al.*[37])

Solute	Concentration	pH	Operating pressure	Solute separation %	Water Flux, gal/day ft^2
	(Molality)				
NaCl	0.05	3–4	400 to 600 psig	70	17 to 142
$MgCl_2$	0.027	3–4		91	
$BaCl_2$	0.025	3–4		95	
$LaCl_3$	0.029	3–4		96	
NaCl	0.05	~11.5		40	
Na_2SO_4	0.025	~11.5		60	
$BaCl_2$	0.025	~11.5		30	
	(g/l)		(atm)		
Phenol	50	—	105	10	230
n–Butanol	50	—	105	47	150
Ethylene glycol	15	—	35	23	60
Diethylene glycol	25	—	35	26	60

Basic Questions

There are three basic questions relating to the full scientific and engineering development of the reverse osmosis process: (i) what are the precise physicochemical criteria for reverse osmosis separation of solutes? (ii) what are the controlling parameters in the process of making reverse osmosis membranes? and, (iii) what are the factors governing transport through reverse osmosis membranes? The first question is concerned with the mechanism of the process, which may be expected to guide all future developments on the subject; the second question is concerned with the development of new and more productive reverse osmosis membranes, and the third question is concerned primarily with reverse osmosis process design and engineering.

No comprehensive answer to any of these questions can be given at this time; however, at least some partial and yet useful answers have unfolded themselves as a result of extensive experimental work using the Loeb–Sourirajan type porous cellulose acetate membranes. These are summarized below.

Physico-chemical Criteria for Reverse Osmosis Separation

Following the basic mechanism of reverse osmosis represented by Figure 1, Glueckauf[38] developed equations to express the repulsion which ions experience in the close vicinity of materials of low dielectric constant under reverse osmosis operating conditions. He pointed out that at the interior of a pore, the above repulsive forces were much larger than at a plane surface. Glueckauf's analysis leads to the following expression for solute separation:

$$\ln \frac{\bar{m}}{m_x} = \frac{\epsilon^2}{2DkT} \cdot \frac{Z^2(1-\alpha)Q}{(R+\alpha bQ)}, \quad (1)$$

where

$\bar{m}$ = concentration of effective feed solution on the membrane surface

m_x = concentration of membrane permeated product solution

ϵ = electronic charge

Z = valency of the ion

D = dielectric constant of solution in the pore

D' = dielectric constant of membrane material

$Q = (D - D')/D'$

k = Boltzmann constant

T = absolute temperature

R = pore radius on membrane surface

$\alpha = 1 - (1 + \kappa^2R^2)^{-\nu}$

$1/\kappa$ = mean distance of the ionic cloud according to the Debye–Huckel model, and

$\kappa = [4\pi\epsilon^2\Sigma n_i Z_i^2/DkT]\nu$

n_i = number of ions per cm^3

b = ionic radius

The above equation predicts that the ratio $\bar{m}/m_x$, and hence solute separation,

decreases with increasing pore radius R,
decreases with increasing ionic radius b,
decreases with increasing solution concentration $\bar{m}$

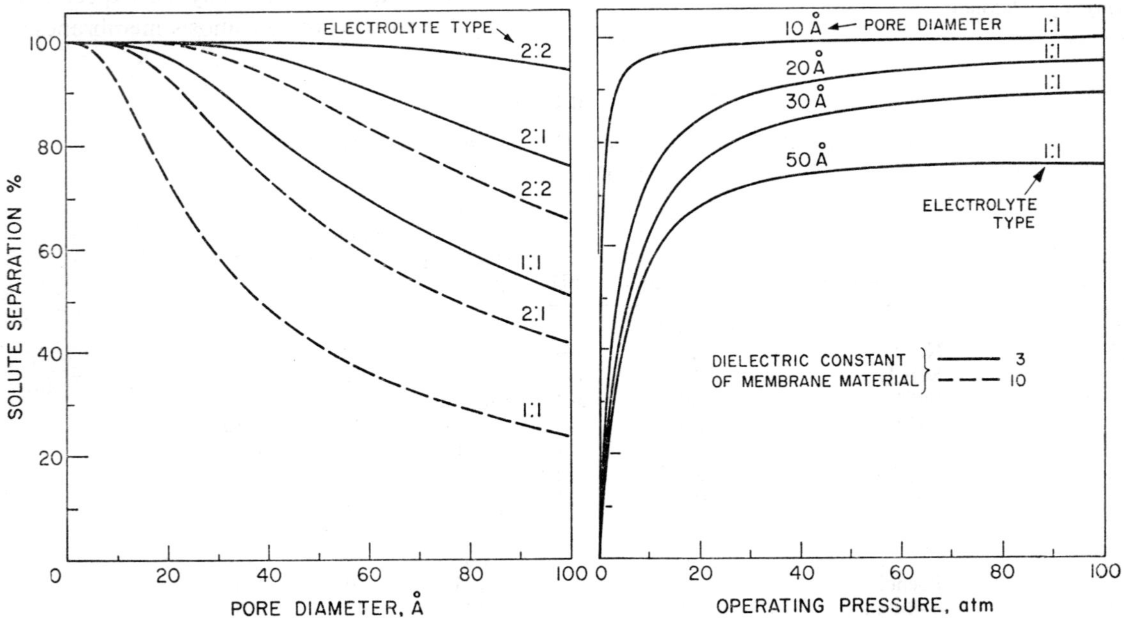

Figure 5 Effect of some physicochemical parameters on the reserve osmosis separation of electrolytic solutes in aqueous solution—Data of Bean.[41]

increases with increasing value of D/D', and
increases with increasing ionic charge Z.

All reverse osmosis experimental results involving inorganic electrolytes in aqueous solutions and porous cellulose acetate membranes are qualitatively consistent with the predictions of the Glueckauf equation.[38–40]

Bean[41] made an extensive analysis of diffusion through pores, and the electrostatic force which causes ions to avoid a region of low dielectric constant. He presented specimen results given in Figure 5 which illustrate the effects of dielectric constant of membrane material, pore diameter on membrane surface, ionic charge, and operating pressure on solute separation from dilute aqueous of electrolytes under reverse osmosis operating conditions. These results confirm explicitly the predictions of Glueckauf analysis. Bean's final equations are as follows:

$$S(P) = \frac{(1 - e^{-\Delta E/kT})(1 - e^{-P/P^*})}{1 + (e^{-\Delta E/kT} - 1)e^{-P/P^*}} \qquad (2)$$

$$\Delta E = (q^2/\epsilon_2 R) \cdot P(\epsilon_2/\epsilon_1) \qquad (3)$$

$$P^* = 8\eta D/R^2 \qquad (4)$$

where

$S(P)$ = fraction solute separation as a function of operating pressure
k = Boltzmann constant
T = absolute temperature
P = operating pressure
q = ionic charge
ϵ_2 = dielectric constant of membrane material
ϵ_1 = dielectric constant of solution in the pore
R = pore radius
η = viscosity of solution in the pore
D = diffusivity of solute in water.

It is significant to note that the above system of equations expresses solute separation in terms of dielectric constants, pore size and pressure; the length of the pore and pore density are not involved in the calculations.

Bean showed that for a membrane material of dielectric constant 3, and a dilute solution of 1–1 electrolyte, solute separations of 90, 99, and 99.9% can be obtained from 27, 13.5, and 9 Å pore respectively; assuming fraction of total membrane area occupied by pores = 0.1, dia. of pore = 9 Å, effective film thickness = 1000 Å, and operating pressure = 100 atm, water flux was calculated to be about 500 gal/day · ft^2 for the above dilute feed solution under reverse osmosis operating conditions. These data are enlightening; they illustrate the potentiality of the process, the importance of a low dielectric constant for the choice of membrane material, and the governing significance of the electrostatic repulsion of ions for the preferential sorption of water, and hence the separation of solutes, from dilute electrolyte solutions under reverse osmosis operating conditions.

Equations 1 to 4 are applicable to neutral membrane surfaces; if the latter have some fixed charges, additional effects should be expected. When a charged microporous body (for example, a porous ion exchange membrane) is in equilibrium with an external electrolyte solution, the co-ions (i.e. ions whose charge has the same sign as that of the fixed charge) are repelled from, and the counterions attracted to, the membrane surface, setting up an electrical double layer at the surface. In this double layer the ionic concentrations and the electric potential are highly nonuniform; in particular, the average co-ion concentration in the microporous solid is less than that of the effective feed solution. Methods of calculating such concentration differences are discussed extensively by Dresner.[42–45]

Reverse osmosis membranes may have neutral or charged surfaces. The surface of a cellophane membrane (cellulose material) carries a negative electric charge according to Heymann and Rabinov,[46] and van Oss.[36,47] Even though cellulose ester membranes are not generally considered to have fixed charges, they probably carry some residual negative charge; this seems evident at least with respect to cellulose acetate membranes whose separation characteristics in reverse osmosis are far more sensitive to anion than the cation for the same change in ionic charge. In any case, it must be recognized that the neutral or the charged character of the membrane surface is only a part of the essential twin-requirement specified earlier for the practical success of the reverse osmosis process.

The ability of a given cellulose acetate membrane for the reverse osmosis separation of inorganic ions in dilute solution is in the order citrate > tartrate = sulfate > acetate > chloride > bromide > nitrate > iodide > thiocyanate, and Mg,Ba,Sr,Ca > Li,Na,K—the same as the lyotropic series. This correlation simply emphasizes the basic physicochemical nature of the mechanism of reverse osmosis.[4]

The equations of Glueckauf and Bean refer specifically to the separation of completely ionized molecules. With respect to molecules which are either nonionized or only partially ionized, the work of Matsuura and Sourirajan[48] on the separation of alcohols, phenols, and monocarboxylic acids using porous cellulose acetate membranes is relevant.

With respect to alcohols, phenols, and monocarboxylic acids, solute separation in reverse osmosis is governed by the polar effect of the organic molecule, and both the functional group (—OH, —COOH etc) and the substituent group in the organic molecule affect the preferential sorption of water and hence solute separation. The polar effect of such solutes is expressed by the acidity (or the proton donating characteristic) of the molecule.

For the essentially nonionized alcohols and phenols, a measure of acidity is given by the relative hydrogen bonding ability of the molecule expressed quantitatively by the shift in the OH band maximum ($\Delta\nu_s$) in the IR spectra of the solute substances in carbon tetrachloride and ether solutions. According to Barrow,[49] $\Delta\nu_s$ is a measure of the stretching of the OH bond corresponding to the incipient ionization of the alcohol or phenol molecule in ether solution, with the hydrogen atom becoming more positively charged. Consequently an increase in the value of $\Delta\nu_s$ means that the hydrogen bonding ability of the molecule is higher. The results of reverse osmosis experiments show (Figure 6) that solute separation decreases with increase in $\Delta\nu_s$.

With respect to monocarboxylic acids which are dissociated to different extents in solution, the acidity of the molecule is quantitatively expressed by its degree of dissociation which is a function of the dissociation constant (K_a) for the molecule and its concentration in solution. A decrease in the value of pK_a ($= -\log K_a$) represents an increase in the acidity of the molecule. From Figure 6, it is clear that an increase in the acidity of the solute molecule tends to increase its hydrogen bonding ability which, in turn, tends to decrease the preferential sorption of water, and hence solute separation, in reverse osmosis. On the other hand, when the acidity of the molecule is high enough to stretch the OH bond to the point of rupture, then the molecule dissociates giving rise to ions which are subject to electrostatic repulsion in the vicinity of

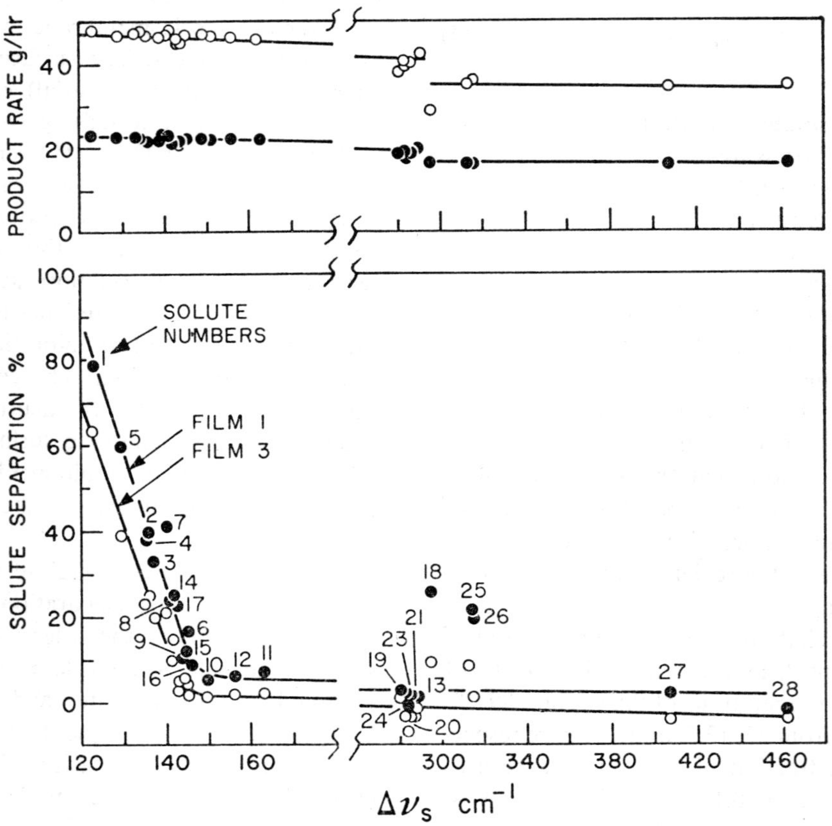

Figure 6 Effect of $\Delta\nu_s$ of solute on reverse osmosis separation of alcohols and phenols in aqueous solution using porous cellulose acetate membranes. Film type, Batch 316 (0/24); ● Film 1, O Film 3; operating pressure, 250 psig; feed concentration, 0.001–0.006 g mole/l.; membrane area, 7.6 cm^2; solute numbers are same as those given in Table VII. Data of Matsuura and Sourirajan.[48]

the membrane surface under the reverse osmosis operating conditions as expressed by the equations of Glueckauf[38] and Bean.[41] The consequence of the above electrostatic repulsion of ions is greater preferential sorption for water and hence higher solute separation in reverse osmosis, the extent of which depends on the chemical nature of the solute and the degree of dissociation. Therefore one should conclude that, up to a certain level, an increase in acidity of the molecule decreases solute separation, and beyond that level, an increase in acidity increases solute separation. Thus one would expect a point, or region, of minimum separation in the pK_a vs. solute separation correlation. This is confined experimentally by the results illustrated in Figure 7.

The degree of dissociation is higher when the dissociation constant, K_a, is higher and/or feed concentration is lower. The degree of dissociation can also be increased by increasing the pH of the solution. A higher degree of dissociation of solute molecule should result in higher separation in reverse osmosis. This is confirmed experimentally by the results illustrated in Figures 8, 9, and 10.

The acidity parameters Δv_s and K_a are naturally related to Hammet (σ) and Taft (σ^*) numbers which give a quantitative measure of the effect of the substituent group on the total polar effect of the respective molecules.[50] Figures 11 and 12 correlate reverse osmosis experimental data for aqueous feed solutions of alcohols, phenols, and monocarboxylic acids with Taft and Hammett numbers for the corresponding substituent groups. Such correlations may lead to practical methods of establishing inter-relationships of the various functional groups for a given substituent group for the reverse osmosis separation of organic solutes in aqueous solution.

The acidity parameters discussed above with respect to a number of alcohols, phenols, and monocarboxylic acids are listed in Tables VII and VIII;[48,50,51] the specifications of the porous cellulose acetate membranes used in the experiments described above (Figures 6–12) are given in Table IX for a reference solution system NaCl–H_2O, and the solute numbers indicated in Figures 6–12 refer to those listed in Tables VII and VIII.

The above results show that, with respect to alcohols, phenols, and monocarboxylic acids in aqueous solution, preferential sorption of water

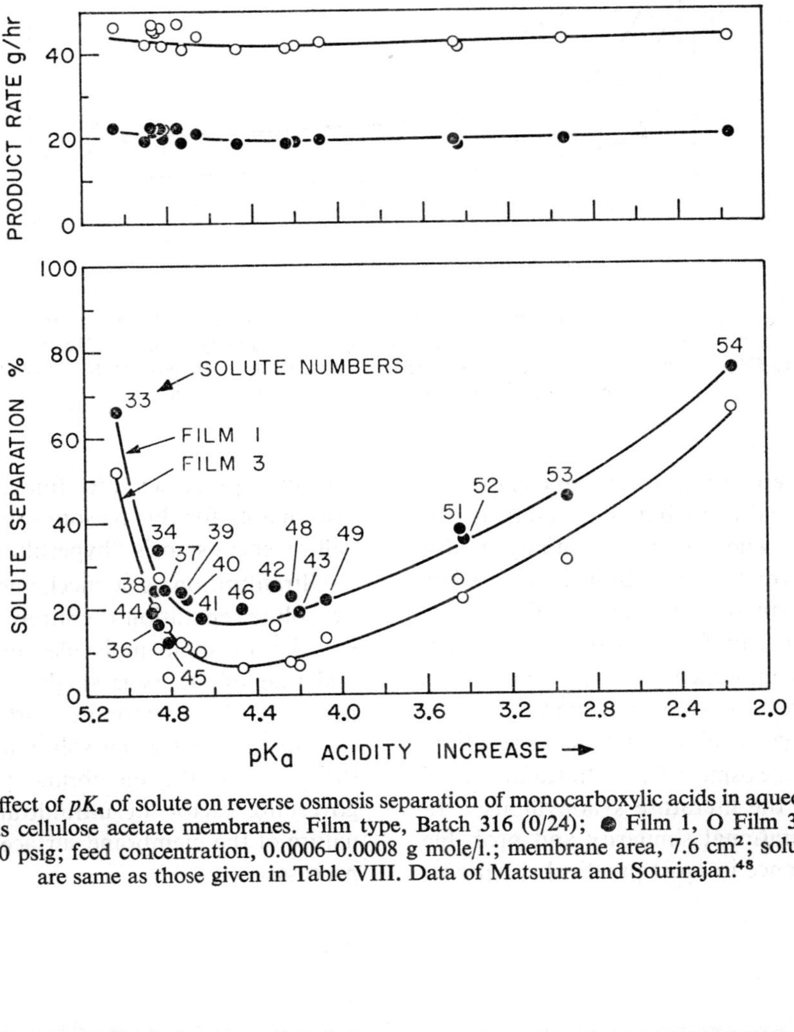

Figure 7 Effect of pK_a of solute on reverse osmosis separation of monocarboxylic acids in aqueous solution using porous cellulose acetate membranes. Film type, Batch 316 (0/24); ● Film 1, O Film 3; operating pressure, 250 psig; feed concentration, 0.0006–0.0008 g mole/l.; membrane area, 7.6 cm^2; solute numbers are same as those given in Table VIII. Data of Matsuura and Sourirajan.[48]

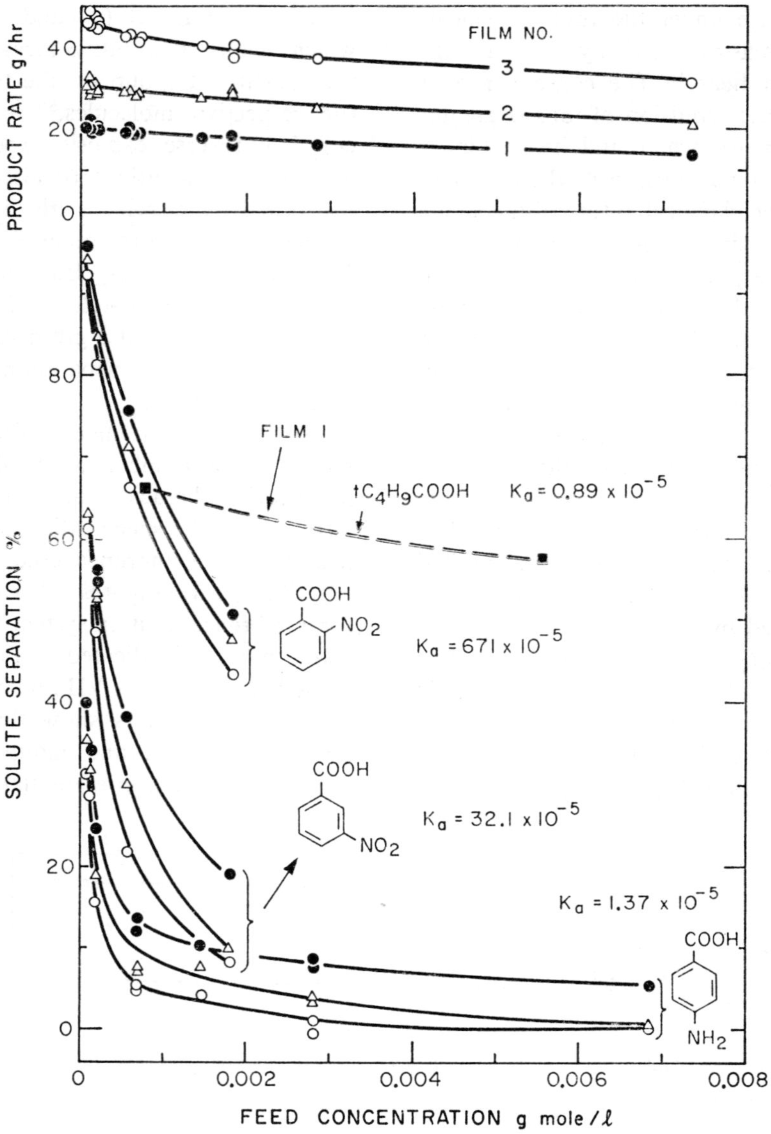

Figure 8 Effect of K_a and feed concentration on reverse osmosis separation of some monocarboxylic acids in aqueous solution using porous cellulose acetate membranes. Film type, Batch 316 (0/24); ● Film 1, △ Film 2, O Film 3: operating pressure, 250 psig; feed concentration, 0.0001–0.007 g mole/l.; membrane area, 7.6 cm^2. Data of Matsuura and Sourirajan.[48]

and hence solute separation in reverse osmosis are governed by the hydrogen bonding ability of the organic molecule when it is essentially undissociated, and electrostatic repulsion of ions when the molecule is partially or completely dissociated. These results offer a useful basis for the development of more comprehensive physico-chemical criteria for the reverse osmosis separation of a wide variety of organic solutes in aqueous solution.

The terms "reverse osmosis" and "ultrafiltration" are often used in the literature synonymously. In spite of their operational similarity and probable concurrent occurrence in most practical situations, the two processes are fundamentally different; presumably for this reason, some authors prefer to call reverse osmosis "hyperfiltration".[2]

Ultrafiltration is a mechanical sieving process, i.e. solute separation is entirely due to the fact that the size of some molecules in solution is bigger and that of others is smaller than the size of the pore on the membrane surface. Consequently, with respect to a given solution system, the size of the pore on the membrane surface is the only governing factor in ultrafiltration; the chemical nature of the membrane surface is irrelevant to the process.

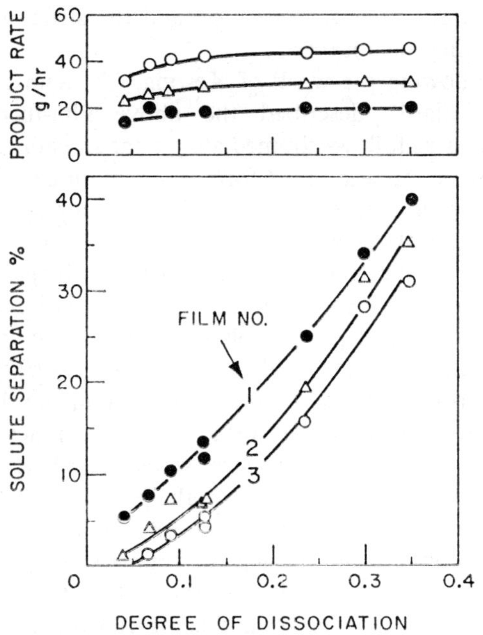

Figure 9 Effect of degree of dissociation of solute on reverse osmosis separation of *p*-aminobenzoic acid in aqueous solution using porous cellulose acetate membranes. Film type, Batch 316 (0/24); ● Film 1, △ Film 2, O Film 3; operating pressure, 250 psig; feed concentration, 0.0001–0.007 g mole/l.; membrane area = 7.6 cms. Data of Matsuura and Sourirajan.[48]

On the other hand, both the size of the pore on the membrane surface and the chemical nature of the membrane surface together govern reverse osmosis. It is this physicochemical twin-requirement criterion for reverse osmosis separation which makes reverse osmosis a new field of science, engineering, and technology whose potential industrial applications are of tremendous economic and social significance.

Reverse Osmosis Membrane Science

The overriding objective of reverse osmosis membrane science is to establish precise criteria for the creation of new and more productive membranes. Therefore the subject is concerned primarily with the physicochemical factors governing the choice of membrane material and film casting conditions including their correlation with data on membrane performance under specified reverse osmosis operating conditions. In spite of the extensive literature on membranes, a comprehensive reverse osmosis membrane science, in terms of the overriding objective stated above, has not yet emerged.

The analyses of Glueckauf,[38] Bean,[41] and Dresner[45] discussed already are important contributions with respect to the choice of the chemical nature of the membrane material, especially for the separation of electrolytic solutes in aqueous solution. With respect to film-casting conditions, and their corelation with data on membrane performance, some useful results have emerged leading to the development of more productive porous cellulose acetate membranes; a summary of these results is given below.

An understanding of the mechanism of pore formation and development in the film-making process is the key to the creation of more productive reverse osmosis membranes. The film-casting solution is usually a mixture of the polymer (e.g. cellulose acetate), a solvent (e.g. acetone), and an essentially nonsolvent swelling agent (e.g. formamide or an aqueous solution of magnesium perchloride). The film-making procedure involves

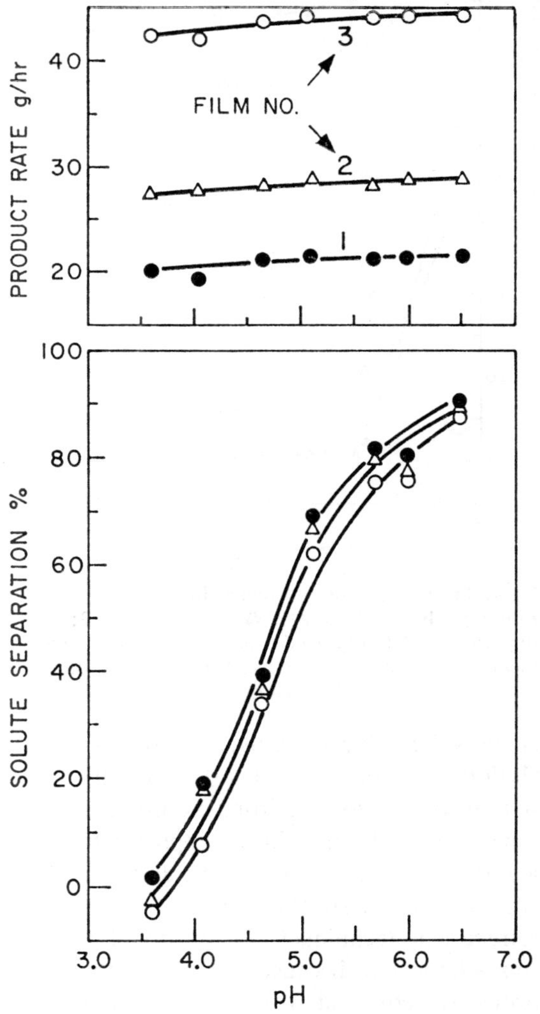

Figure 10 Effect of pH on reverse osmosis separation of benzoic acid in aqueous solution using porous cellulose acetate membranes. Film type, Batch 316 (0/24); ● Film 1, △ Film 2, O Film 3; operating pressure, 250 psig; feed concentration, 0.001 g mole/l.; membrane area, 7.6 cms. Data of Matsuura and Sourirajan.[48]

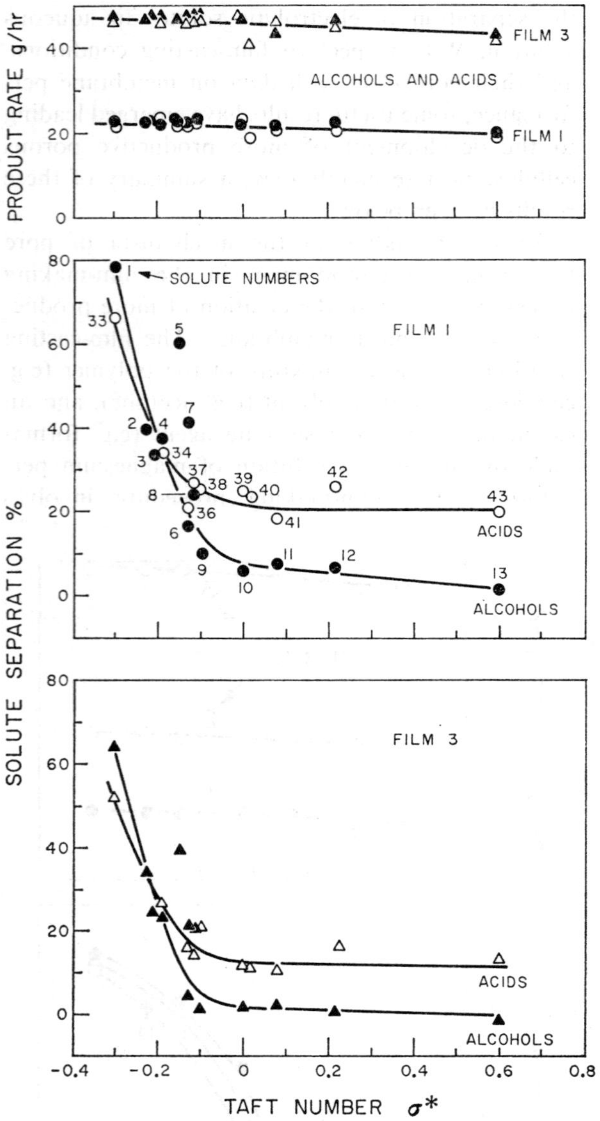

Figure 11 Reverse osmosis separation and Taft numbers-. Film type, Batch 316 (0/24); ● Film 1, O Film 3; operat ing pressure, 250 psig; feed concentration 0.001 g mole/l.; membrane area = 7.6 cms. Data of Matsuura and Sourirajan.[48]

generally the following steps: (i) casting the polymer solution as a thin film on a surface, (ii) evaporation (or removal) of solvent from the film surface, (iii) immersion of the film in an appropriate gelation medium such as cold water, and finally, (iv) shrinking, pressurization and other membrane pretreatment techniques. Each one of the above steps is important because each affects the ultimate porous structure of the entire membrane and hence its subsequent performance in reverse osmosis.

The disolvation of the polymer solution (sol) into a membrane (gel) is a phase inversion process. Kesting[52–55] has done the most extensive analysis of the sol–gel transformation and the structure of resulting membranes.

Following the work of Kesting,[52,53] Kunst and Sourirajan[56] described the above film-forming process as follows. Immediately after spreading the polymer solution in the form of a film on a surface, evaporation of solvent starts at the air–solution interface. As a result of solvent loss, a cloud point in the surface region is reached when droplets of the swelling agent separate from the solution as a second interdispersed phase with the polymer molecules concentrated at the exterior surface of the droplets. On continued desolvation, the droplets (micelles) in the surface region contact one another forming polyhedra whose number, size, and wall thickness depend on the polymer structure in the casting solution and on the desolvation conditions. The subsequent immersion of the spreaded polymer film in the gelation medium (cold water) accelerates and completes the desolvation process both in the surface layer and in the bulk region underneath. During the desolvation process, the walls of the polyhedra rupture, and closed cells give way to more numerous open cells which, together with the voids between cells, give rise to a microporous surface structure; on the other hand, in the interior bulk region of the film, the polymer molecules aggregate and precipitate rapidly giving rise to a spongy, porous mass underneath the surface layer. The final result is the formation of a completely open celled asymmetric porous structure for the entire membrane.

The above picture of phase separation and pore formation, even though still incomplete, has led to a useful physicochemical basis for the choice of film-casting conditions, and hence to a new approach to the general problem of creating more productive reverse osmosis membranes.[56–61] In this approach the state or the structure of the casting solution and the rate of solvent evaporation during film formation together constitute an important interconnected variable governing the ultimate porous structure and hence the performance of the resulting membranes in reverse osmosis.

The distinguishing feature of the solution structure–evaporation rate concept to reverse osmosis membrane development lies in the analysis of the usual film casting variables in terms of correlating membrane performance data with the casting solution structure, solvent evaporation rate during film formation and the shrinkage temperature profile. The membrane performance data are interpreted on the basis of surface pores, their number, size and size distribution. It is recognized that flux

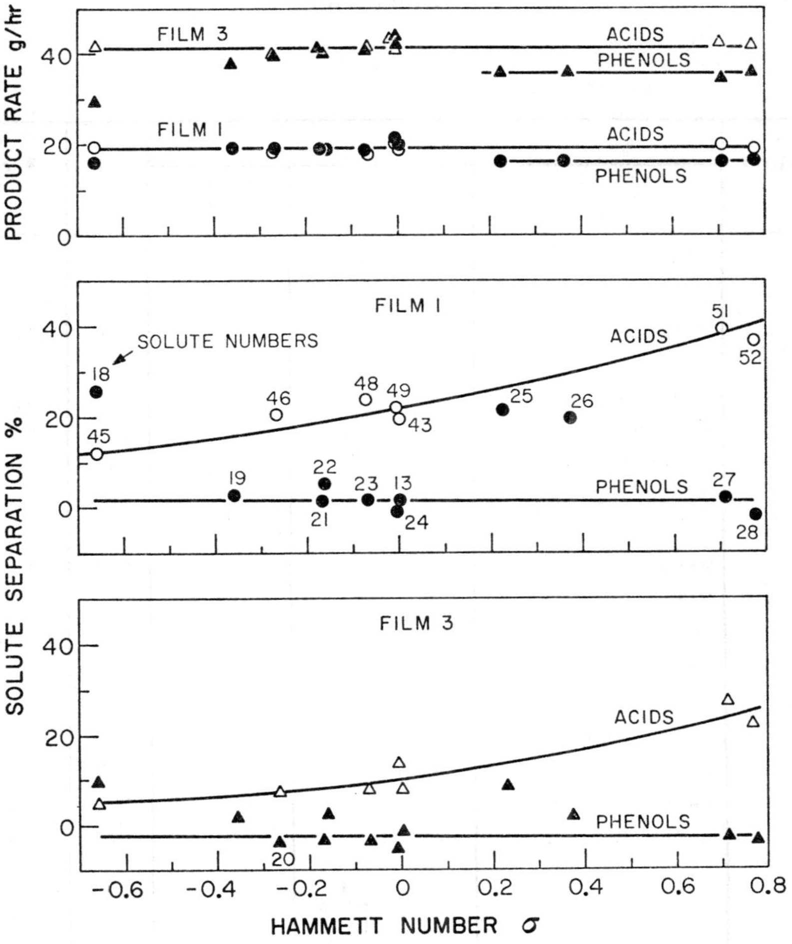

Figure 12 Reverse osmosis separation and Hammett number. Film type, Batch 316 (0/24); ● Film 1, O Film 3; operating pressure, 250 psig; feed concentration 0.001 g mole/l.; membrane area = 7.6 cm^2. Data of Matsuura and Sourirajan.[48]

changes could be caused by changes in the thickness of the surface layer also. But there is no simple way by which the thickness of the surface layer can be precisely fixed. The microporous structure of the asymmetric membrane is considered to be a continuum made up of three mutually distinct regions—namely, a comparatively very thin dense surface layer, a thicker transition layer, and a very much thicker spongy support layer—each region being successively more porous. There is however no precise boundary between adjacent regions. During film formation, any decrease in the thickness of the surface layer may also simultaneously result in the integration of a part of the transition layer into the surface region, thus affecting the size and number of pores on the membrane surface. Consequently, in a surface layer which is only a few molecular layers thick one cannot isolate the effects of changes in the thickness of the surface layer from those due to changes in the number and size of pores in that layer. For practical purposes of membrane development it has proved useful to discuss membrane performance on the basis of an effective number and size of pores on the membrane surface.

The structure of the casting solution is a function of its composition and temperature; solvent evaporation rate during film formation is a function of solution structure, temperature of casting atmosphere, and the ambient nature of casting atmosphere. Consequently the temperature of the casting solution and that of the casting atmosphere are two separate variables in the specification of film casting conditions; by appropriate choice of these two variables alone, the productivity of resulting films can be improved as illustrated by data in Figure 13.

The term solution structure essentially refers to the state of supermolecular polymer aggregation in the casting solution. No effective means of

TABLE VII

Solute No.	Solute			$\Delta\nu_s$	σ^* or σ
	Name	Formula	Molecular Weight	cm^{-1}	Ref. 50
		R in ROH			σ^*
1	t-Butyl alcohol	$t\text{-}C_4H_9$	74.1	123	-0.300
2	3-Pentanol	$3\text{-}C_5H_{11}$	88.2	136	-0.225
3	s-Butyl alcohol	$s\text{-}C_4H_9$	74.1	137	-0.210
4	i-Propyl alcohol	$i\text{-}C_3H_7$	60.1	135	-0.190
5	Cyclohexanol	$cyclo\text{-}C_6H_{11}$	102.2	129	-0.150
6	n-Butyl alcohol	$n\text{-}C_4H_9$	74.1	145	-0.130
7	i-Butyl alcohol	$i\text{-}C_4H_9$	74.1	140	-0.129
8	n-Propyl alcohol	$n\text{-}C_3H_7$	60.1	141	-0.115
9	Ethyl alcohol	C_2H_5	46.1	143	-0.100
10	Methyl alcohol	CH_3	32.0	149	0
11	Phenethyl alcohol	$C_6H_5(CH_2)_2$	122.2	163	+0.08
12	Benzyl alcohol	$C_6H_5(CH_2)$	108.1	156	+0.215
13	Phenol	C_6H_5	94.1	288	+0.600
14	n-Amyl alcohol	$n\text{-}C_5H_{11}$	88.2	142	-
15	n-Hexyl alcohol	$n\text{-}C_6H_{13}$	102.2	144	-
16	n-Heptyl alcohol	$n\text{-}C_7H_{15}$	116.2	145	-
17	n-Octyl alcohol	$n\text{-}C_8H_{17}$	130.2	142	-
		X in 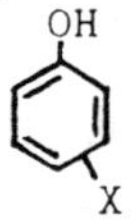			σ
18	p-Aminophenol	$p\text{-}NH_2$	109.1	-	-0.660
19	Hydroquinone	p-OH	110.1	-	-0.357
20	p-Methoxyphenol	$p\text{-}OCH_3$	124.1	283	-0.268
21	p-Cresol	$p\text{-}CH_3$	108.1	286	-0.170
22	m-Aminophenol	$m\text{-}NH_2$	109.1	-	-0.161
23	m-Cresol	$m\text{-}CH_3$	108.1	283	-0.069
24	Resorcinol	m-OH	110.1	284	-0.002
13	Phenol	-	94.1	288	0.000
25	p-Chlorophenol	p-Cl	128.6	313	+0.227
26	m-Chlorophenol	m-Cl	128.6	315	+0.373
27	m-Nitrophenol	$m\text{-}NO_2$	139.1	407	+0.710
28	p-Nitrophenol	$p\text{-}NO_2$	139.1	-	+0.778
		X in 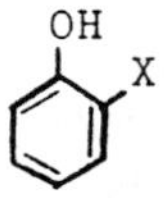			σ^*
29	o-Cresol	CH_3	108.1	282	-0.17
13	Phenol	H	94.1	288	0
30	o-Chlorophenol	Cl	128.6	-	+0.20
31	o-Nitrophenol	NO_2	139.1	-	+0.80
32	Pyrocatechol	OH	110.1	291	-

TABLE VIII

Solute No.	Solute: Name	Solute: Formula	Solute: Molecular Weight	pK_a (Ref.51)	σ* or σ (Ref.50)
		R in RCOOH			σ*
33	Pivalic acid	$t\text{-}C_4H_9$	102.1	5.05	-0.300
34	i-Butyric acid	$i\text{-}C_3H_7$	88.1	4.86	-0.190
35	Cyclohexanecarboxylic acid	$cyclo\text{-}C_6H_{11}$	128.2	4.91	-0.150
36	Valeric acid	$n\text{-}C_4H_9$	102.1	4.86	-0.130
37	n-Butyric acid	$n\text{-}C_3H_7$	88.1	4.83	-0.115
38	Propionic acid	$n\text{-}C_2H_5$	74.1	4.87	-0.100
39	Acetic acid	CH_3	60.1	4.75	0
40	4-Phenylbutyric acid	$C_6H_5(CH_2)_3$	164.2	4.73	+0.020
41	β-Phenylpropionic acid	$C_6H_5(CH_2)_2$	150.2	4.66	+0.080
42	Phenylacetic acid	$C_6H_5(CH_2)$	136.1	4.31	+0.215
43	Benzoic acid	C_6H_5	122.1	4.20	+0.600
44	Caprylic acid	$n\text{-}C_7H_{15}$	144.2	4.90	-
		X in 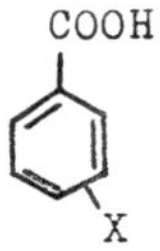			σ
45	p-Aminobenzoic acid	$p\text{-}NH_2$	137.1	4.82	-0.660
46	Anicic acid	$p\text{-}OCH_3$	152.1	4.47	-0.268
47	m-Aminobenzoic acid	$m\text{-}NH_2$	137.1	4.60	-0.161
48	m-Toluic acid	$m\text{-}CH_3$	136.1	4.24	-0.069
49	m-Hydroxybenzoic acid	m-OH	138.1	4.08	-0.002
43	Benzoic acid	-	122.1	4.20	0
50	p-Chlorobenzoic acid	p-Cl	156.6	3.99	+0.227
51	m-Nitrobenzoic acid	$m\text{-}NO_2$	167.1	3.45	+0.710
52	p-Nitrobenzoic acid	$p\text{-}NO_2$	167.1	3.44	+0.778
		X in 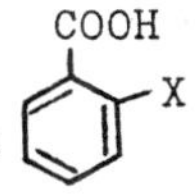			σ*
43	Benzoic acid	H	122.1	4.20	0
53	o-Chlorobenzoic acid	Cl	156.6	2.94	+0.20
54	o-Nitrobenzoic acid	NO_2	167.1	2.17	+0.80

expressing solution structure has yet emerged. However, useful conclusions seem possible from an analysis of the polymer–solvent–nonsolvent ternary phase equilibrium diagrams; for example, the remoteness of the phase boundary curves from any point representing the composition of the casting solution is a useful measure of solution structure at the temperature corresponding to the boundary curve. Therefore phase equilibrium diagrams for different casting solution systems may offer useful directions in the choice of film casting conditions.[58–60]

Supermolecular aggregation in the polymer solution is decreased by increase in the solution temperature and/or decrease in the concentration of the polymer. Small changes in the composition and/or temperature of the casting solution affect the supermolecular aggregation very significantly. Lesser supermolecular aggregation in the casting solution tends to result in smaller size pores in the surface region of the resulting membrane, as indicated by the shrinkage temperature profiles given in Figure 14.

A decrease in the temperature of the ambient

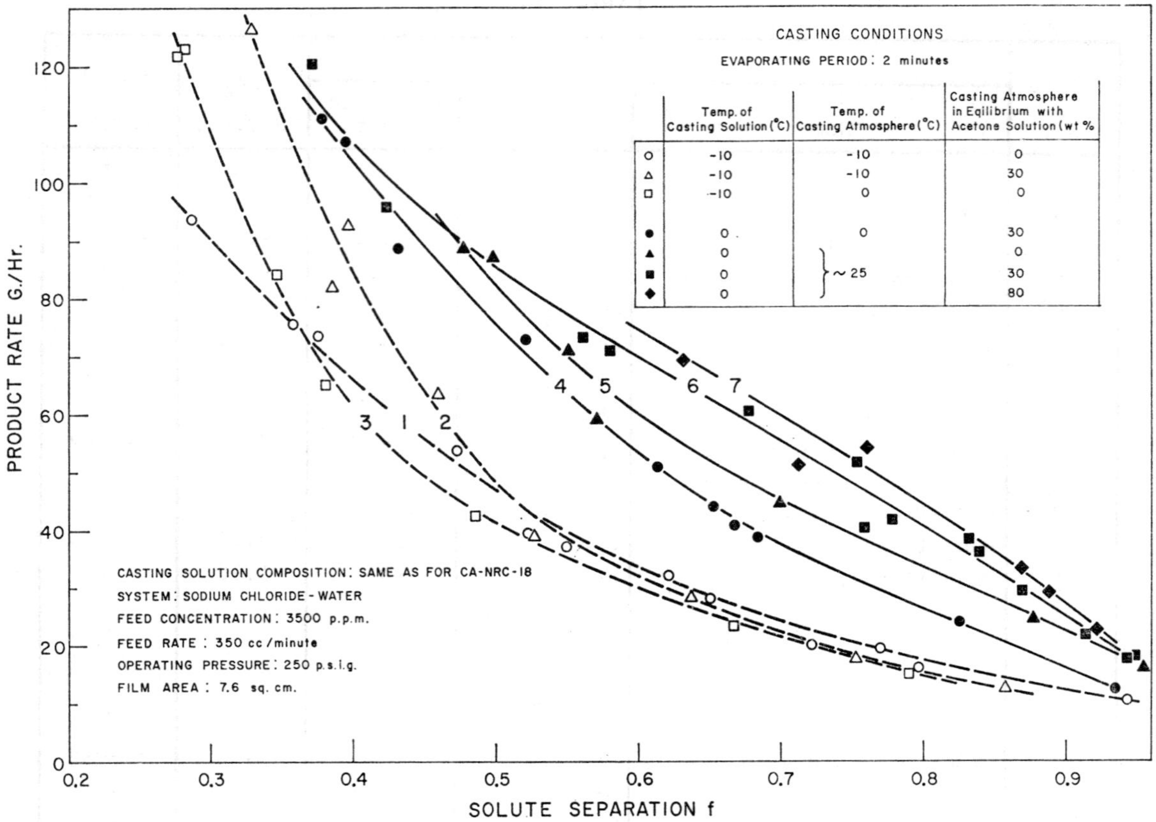

Figure 13 Effect of casting solution temperature and solvent evaporation rate on membrane performance. Data of Kunst and Sourirajan.[56]

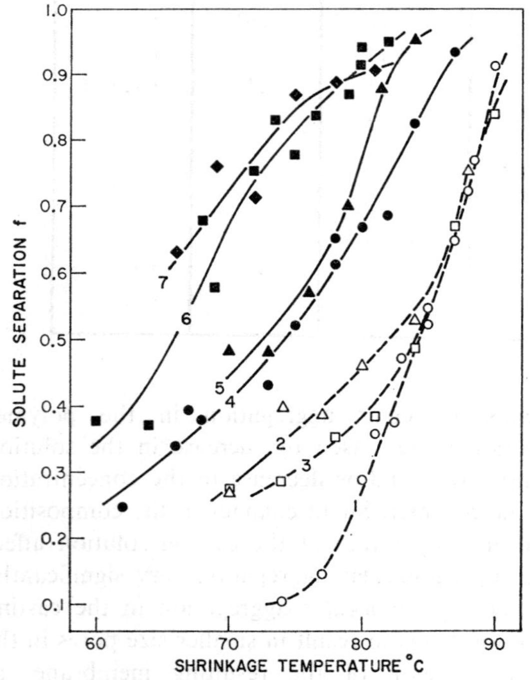

Figure 14 Effect of casting solution temperature and solvent evaporation rate on film shrinkage temperature profile. Evaporation period 2 min. Symbols same as those used in Figure 13. Data of Kunst and Sourirajan.[56]

TABLE IX

Specifications of Membranes and Some Performance Data

Film type: Batch 316 (0/24)
Operating pressure: 250 psig
Solution system: sodium chloride–water

Film No.	1	2	3
Film shrinkage temperature, °C	81	78	75
Pure water permeability constant, $A \times 10^6$ $\frac{\text{g mole}}{\text{cm}^2\text{ sec atm}}$	2.48	3.53	5.35
Solute transport parameter, $(D_{AM}/K\mu)_{NaCl} \times 10^5$ cm/sec	3.22	9.50	16.89
Performance Data:			
Feed concentration, ppm NaCl	1500	1500	1500
Mass transfer coefficient, $k \times 10^4$ cm/sec	57	57	57
Solute separation,	94.7	90.4	87.0
Product rate, gal/day ft²	14.83	21.31	32.02

casting atmosphere and/or the presence of solvent vapor in the atmosphere decrease solvent evaporation rate. With particular reference to cellulose acetate–acetone–aqueous magnesium perchlorate or formamide systems, an increase in the amount of acetone in the casting solution increases solvent evaporation rate, and the presence of acetone in the casting atmosphere decreases the solvent evaporation rate during film formation. Both these factors, for different reasons, lead to the generation of relatively smaller size pores on the membrane surface. A decrease in pore size on the membrane surface can be accomplished either by increasing the acetone content in the casting solution or by decreasing the evaporation rate or by a combination of both.

From the point of view of membrane productivity, the formation of the required size of pores on the membrane surface must also be simultaneously accompanied by the generation of the largest number of such pores. Hence the solvent evaporation rate should be appropriately adjusted to the state of the casting solution for best practical results. Too slow an evaporation rate could result in too slow a rate of droplet formation and development, which rate determines the ultimate size and number of surface pores. The solvent evaporation rate should be high enough to generate the largest number of dispersed droplets and low enough to prevent excessive rupture of the polyhedra walls prior to gelation. Thus an optimum evaporation rate would be expected for each casting solution structure for highest membrane productivity; this also means that different solution structure–evaporation rate combinations can lead to membranes at the same level of productivity.

Solvent evaporation rate during film formation can be determined experimentally by following the change in weight of the polymer film cast on a small plate, as a function of time. A typical evaporation rate curve (solvent loss vs. time) plotted on a semilog scale consists of an initial linear part (Figure 15) which can be represented by the relation:

$$(W_t - W_\infty) = (W_o - W_\infty)\,e^{-bt}, \qquad (5)$$

where W_t = weight of (casting plate + film) at any time t, and W_o = (extrapolated) value of W_t at time = 0, and W_∞ = value of W_t at the time when solvent loss has practically ceased. From the slope of the above linear part, the value of the evaporation rate constant b (time^{-1}) can be deter mined. The numerical value of b has proved to be a useful quantitative parameter to express the

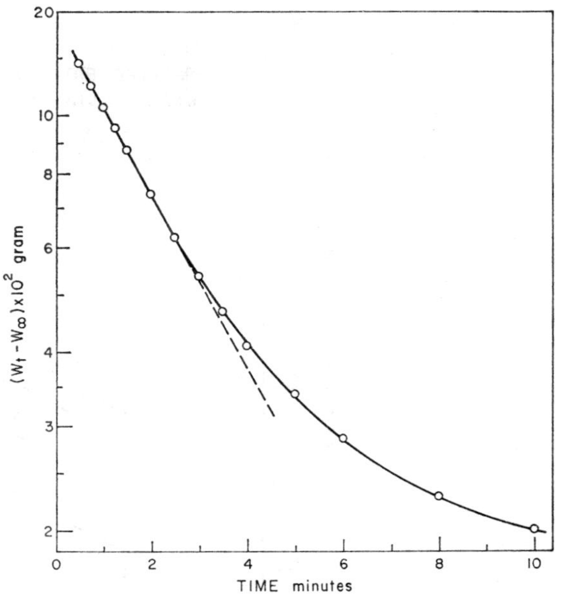

Figure 15 A typical evaporation rate curve. Film type, 316 (0/24), area of evaporation surface, ~6 cms. Data of Kunst and Sourirajan.[58]

evaporation rate condition during film formation.

The film-shrinkage temperature vs. solute separation correlation (shrinkage temperature profile) gives a relative measure of the initial size of pores on the membrane surface in the as-cast condition and of the distribution of pore size resulting from shrinkage. On the basis of the preferential sorption-capillary flow mechanism and the concept of critical pore diameters, it is only to be expected that pore size distribution will affect membrane performance significantly. While the structure of the casting solution (i.e. its composition and temperature) and the value of b are independent of evaporation period, the latter affects the initial size of surface pores and hence, the shrinkage temperature profile. In general, the longer the evaporation period, the bigger is the average size of initial pores on the membrane surface (Figure 16). By changing the evaporation period, the shrinkage temperature profile can be shifted appreciably for each solution structure–b combination. It has been shown[58] that for a given solution structure (constant composition and temperature) identical values of b (by whatever means they are achieved) give rise to same performance (productivity) in resulting membranes, provided their shrinkage temperature profiles are also identical. Thus shrinkage temperature profile has emerged as an important quality control parameter in membrane development.

The humidity of the casting atmosphere has a second order effect on the performance of the

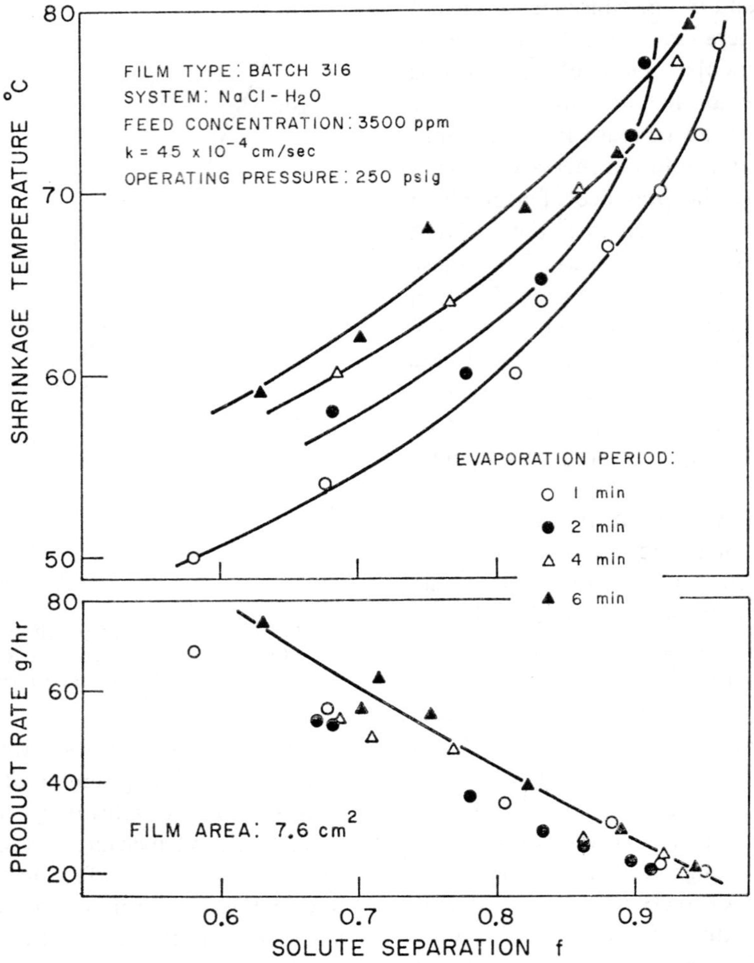

Figure 16 Effect of evaporation period on membrane performance. Film type, Batch 316 (0/24). Data of Kunst and Sourirajan.[59]

resulting membranes. A change in humidity affects slightly the value of b and hence the shrinkage temperature profile. In general an increase in humidity has the same effect as a decrease in the partial pressure of acetone (solvent) in the casting atmosphere. It is hence important to include data on the humidity of the casting atmosphere in the specification of the film-casting conditions.

As a result of investigations based on the solution structure–evaporation rate concept, more productive reverse osmosis (flat) membranes have been produced as represented by the data on Batch 301-, 316-, and 400-type membranes, details of which are given in Tables X, XI, and XII.

All data on membrane flux in Tables XI and XII refer to initial values. In long time experiments, the effect of compaction on membrane performance is no more serious with the Batch 301-, 316- and 400-type membranes than with the Batch 18-and 47-type membranes.

The fundamental cause of membrane compaction is still an open and important question. The proven significance of the solution structure–evaporation rate concept to membrane development, indicates that the morphology of the transition layer probably governs the kinetics of membrane compaction and its consequences on membrane performance. This aspect of the subject needs detailed study; in this study, the technique of Ohya and Sourirajan[62] on the determination of concentration changes on membrane surface as function of time during evaporation of film casting solutions may be useful.

Once the membrane is made, its productivity can also be increased by changing the pore size distribution on the membrane surface using the general back pressure treatment technique demonstrated by Kopecek and Sourirajan.[63] This technique consists in pumping pure water past the back side of the membrane under just enough pressure for a sufficiently prolonged period of time. After such pretreatment the membrane is used in reverse osmosis experiments in the normal manner with

TABLE X

Casting Conditions for Some Improved Porous Cellulose Acetate Membranes

Film casting details	Film type identification batch number 301	316(0/24)	400	316
Casting solution composition (wt. %)				
Cellulose acetate (acetyl content 39.8%)	17	17	17	17
Acetone	68	69.2	56	69.2
Magnesium perchlorate	1.5	1.45	—	1.45
Water	13.5	12.35	—	12.35
Formamide	—	—	27	—
Temperature of casting solution, °C	0	0	24	10
Temperature of casting atmosphere, °C	24	24	24	30
Casting atmosphere	ambient air in contact with aqueous solution of 30 wt. % acetone			ambient air
Humidity of casting atmosphere, %	*	55	*	50–65 as indicated
Evaporation time, minute	2	1	1/2	1
Gelation medium	ice-cold water in all cases			
Gelation time	> 1 hr in all cases			
Nominal film thickness	0.003 – 0.005 in. in all cases			

*not specified

TABLE XI

Performance of Batch 301–*type Porous Cellulose Acetate Membranes*
(Data of Kunst and Sourirajan[57])

Solution system: Sodium chloride–water
Feed concentration: 1500 ppm NaCl
Feed flow rate corresponds to a mass transfer coeficient (k) of 50×10^{-4} cm/sec on the high pressure side of membrane

	Film type					
	Batch 18		Batch 47		Batch 301	
Operating pressure psig	Solute Sepn. %	Product rate gal/day ft²	Solute Sepn. %	Product rate gal/day ft²	Solute Sepn. %	Product rate gal/day ft²
40	83	0.77	84.5	0.86	83.4	1.87
70	71.3	3.8	89.5	1.9	74.6	7.6
	89.0	1.8	94.8	1.5	84.4	4.9
	92.0	1.6			90.0	3.6
100	77.3	5.4	72.4	4.7	73.5	14.0
	92.3	2.9	90.5	4.5	81.6	10.9
	94.0	2.3	92.5	2.7	89.0	7.3
					93.0	5.2
150	76.4	9.3	75.0	9.0	79.6	20.5
	83.3	8.2	77.6	7.5	86.6	16.4
	95.0	4.7	95.6	4.7	92.2	9.6
					95.6	8.0
200	81.5	12.2	78.4	12.0	70.0	46.1
	88.0	10.8	81.2	10.8	84.0	26.9
	96.3	6.2	97.5	6.2	88.6	22.0
					93.8	14.9
					97.3	10.6
250	85.4	15.1	81.2	15.3	74.8	56.7
	91.7	13.7	86.2	13.1	87.2	33.6
					90.6	27.6
					94.6	18.9

TABLE XII

Typical Performance of Improved Porous Cellulose Acetate Membranes

(Data of Pageau and Sourirajan[61])

Solution system: Sodium chloride-water
Feed flow rate corresponds to a mass transfer coefficient (k) of 45×10^{-4} cm/sec on the high pressure side of membrane
Operating temperature = 2sC

Film type, Batch No.	Solute separation, % 70	80	90	95
	Membrane flux, gal/day ft²			
	Operating pressure, 250 psig; feed concn., 3500 ppm NaCl			
18	17.9	13.2	10.1	8.6
47	17.5	13.3	10.1	8.7
301	44.3	31.9	18.7	12.4
316 (0/24)	48.2	35.0	21.4	15.0
400	47.8	33.4	22.1	15.0
316[a]	44.7	32.6	21.0	15.2
316[b]	46.6	35.0	22.9	17.1
	Operating pressure, 600 psig; feed concn., 5000 ppm NaCl			
18	61.4	49.0	36.9	31.1
47	60.0	48.2	36.8	31.0
301	80.8	65.3	47.4	35.8
316 (0/24)	89.4	72.3	53.6	42.0
400	88.0	71.2	52.6	41.2
316[a]	107.2	85.5	61.4	43.5
316[b]	108.8	87.8	61.4	45.1
	Operating pressure, 1500 psig; feed concn., 28400 ppm NaCl			
18	82.4	67.6	52.1	44.7
47	82.4	67.6	52.1	44.7
301	82.4	67.6	52.1	44.7
316 (0/24)	82.4	67.6	52.1	44.7
400	82.4	67.6	52.1	44.7
316[a]	101.0	82.4	61.4	48.2
316[b]	101.0	82.4	64.5	54.4

[a]Relative humidity during film casting = 52%.
[b]Relative humidity during film casting = 65%.

the surface layer side of the membrane facing the feed solution.

There are many more aspects of membrane development which need extensive study even with respect to porous cellulose acetate membranes. The assiduous development of the reverse osmosis membrane science is the key to the development of the reverse osmosis process in all its applications. No one membrane can be ideal for all reverse osmosis applications; the development of the reverse osmosis membrane science can be expected to lead to the ideal membrane for each specific application. In this development of membrane science, the statistical techniques of investigations illustrated by Fahey and Grethlein[64] can be extremely useful.

Transport Through Reverse Osmosis Membranes

The following discussion is applicable to the isothermal reverse osmosis separation process involving binary aqueous solution systems and Loeb–Sourirajan type porous cellulose acetate or other similar membranes, having a preferential sorption for water from the aqueous solution under consideration. Figure 17 gives a diagramatic representation of the reverse osmosis process under steady state operating conditions. The existence and the continuous withdrawal of the preferentially sorbed interfacial layer through the porous membrane give rise to a membrane-permeated product solution which is less concentrated than the feed solution, and to a more concentrated boundary solution

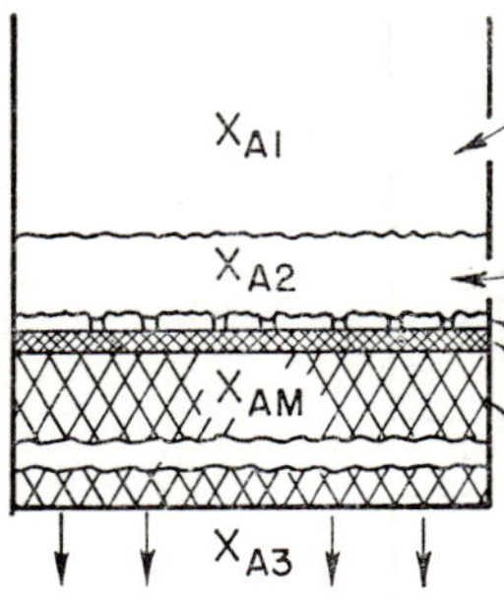

Figure 17 Reverse osmosis process under steady state conditions.

between the interfacial region and the bulk feed solution. Consequently, under steady state operating conditions, solvent and solute transport through the membrane pores, and a concentration gradient between the boundary solution and the bulk feed solution on the upstream side of the membrane (usually called "concentration polarization") occur simultaneously. The most useful analysis of reverse osmosis experimental data is that given by Kimura and Sourirajan.[65] This analysis has led to practical methods of membrane specification, expressing membrane selectivity and predicting membrane performance from a minimum of experimental data, and it offers a rational basis for reverse osmosis process design. For these reasons, the results of the above analysis are summarized below.

The Kimura–Sourirajan analysis

This is discussed in detail in Reference 4. This analysis is based on a generalized capillary flow model involving viscous flow for water transport, pore diffusion for solute transport, and "film" theory for calculating an effective mass transfer coefficient applicable to the concentration polarization situation on the upstream side of the membrane. This analysis is applicable to all levels of solute separation, and gives rise to the following basic equations relating to the pure water permeability constant A, the transport of solvent water N_B, the solute transport parameter $(D_{AM}/K\delta)$, and the mass transfer coefficient k on the high pressure of the membrane at any point (position or time) in the system under operating conditions of constant temperature and pressure.

$$A = \frac{[\text{PWP}]}{M_B \times S \times 3600 \times P} \qquad (6)$$

$$N_B = A[P - \pi(X_{A2}) + \pi(X_{A3})] \qquad (7)$$

$$= \left(\frac{D_{AM}}{K\delta}\right)\left(\frac{1 - X_{A3}}{X_{A3}}\right)(c_2X_{A2} - c_3X_{A3}) \qquad (8)$$

$$= kc_1(1 - X_{A3}) \ln\left(\frac{X_{A2} - X_{A3}}{X_{A1} - X_{A3}}\right). \qquad (9)$$

The symbols used in Equations 6–51 are defined at the end of this article.

Equation 6 defines the pure water permeability constant, A (in g mole H_2O/cm^2 sec atm), which is a fundamental quantity with respect to the membrane. The quantity A is a measure of the overall porosity of the membrane; it represents pure water transport in the absence of any concentration polarization (datum condition) on the upstream side of the membrane. The magnitude of A is independent of any solute under consideration.

Equation 7 enables one to calculate the concentration X_{A2} of the boundary solution on the high pressure side of the membrane under the reverse osmosis operating conditions. When the concentration X_{A3} of the membrane permeated product solution on the low pressure side of the membrane is less than the concentration X_{A1} of the bulk feed solution on the high pressure side of the membrane, X_{A2} is greater than X_{A1}.

Equation 8 defines the quantity $(D_{AM}/K\delta)$ for the transport of any given solute through the membrane. This quantity $(D_{AM}/K\delta)$, called the solute transport parameter, is a fundamental one for any given membrane–solution system. The parameter $(D_{AM}/K\delta)$ is not a mere proportionality constant; it is a combination of at least three distinct quantities all of which have important physical significance, but none of which can be precisely measured. [The above three quantities are the solute diffusivity through the membrane (D_{AM}), effective film thickness (δ), and the factor K which relates solute concentration in the membrane phase to that in the solution phase in equilibrium with the membrane phase.] From the point of view of reverse osmosis process design, it is sufficient to know the overall value of the parameter $(D_{AM}/K\delta)$ which plays the role of a mass transfer coefficient with respect to solute transport through the membrane; hence the parameter is treated as a single quantity for purposes of anlysis.

Equation 9 enables one to calculate the mass transfer coefficient k on the high pressure side of the membrane. The magnitude of k is a function of the nature of solute, concentration of feed solution and feed flow rate. For any reverse osmosis apparatus and operating system, the relationship

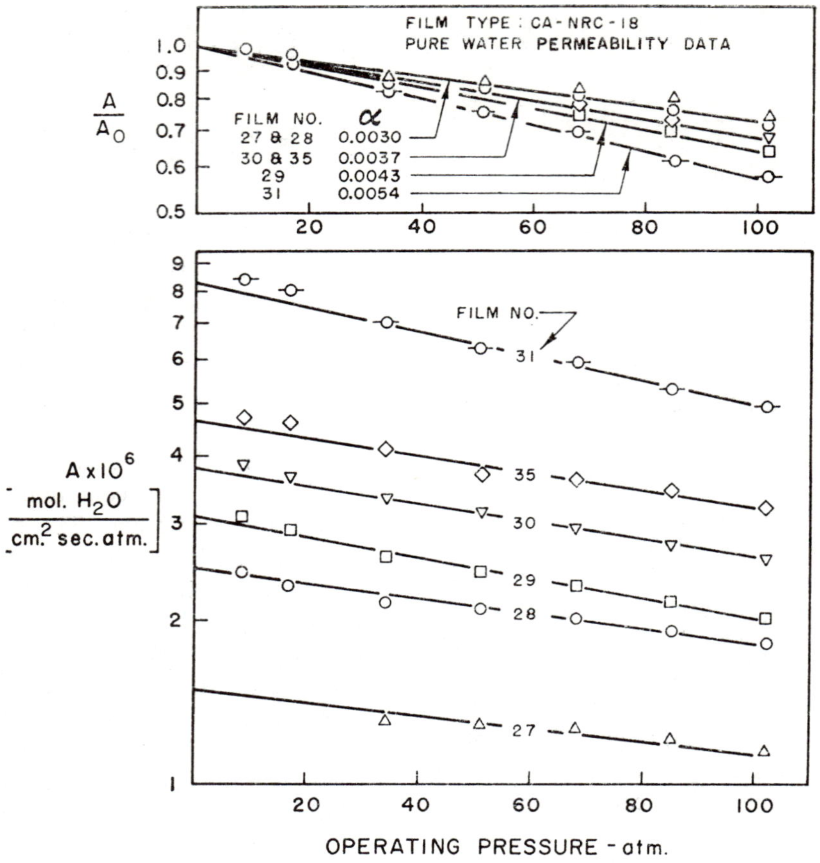

Figure 18 Effect of operating pressure on pure water permeability constant.[4]

between feed flow rate and k is needed for process design; this information may be obtained either experimentally or analytically. In any case, the feed flow condition on the high pressure side of the membrane is best described in terms of the obtainable value of k under the desired operating conditions.

In steady state operation under given experimental conditions, a single set of experimental data on pure water permeation rate [PWP], membrane permeated product rate [PR], and solute separation (f), enables one to calculate A, X_{A2} $(D_{AM}/K\delta)$, and k at any point (position or time) in the system using Equations 6–9.

None of the Equations 6–9, or any part of them, is adequate representation of reverse osmosis transport; the latter is governed simultaneously by the entire set of Equations 6–9.

In most water treatment applications of practical interest, the following approximations are valid:

(i) the molar density of the solution is constant, i.e.

$$c_1 = c_2 = c_3 = c, \tag{10}$$

(ii) the osmotic pressure of the solution is proportional to the mole fraction of solute in the concentration range involved, i.e.

$$\pi(X_A) = BX_A, \tag{11}$$

(iii) solute flux through the membrane is small compared to solvent flux, i.e.

$$N_A \ll N_B \quad \text{or} \quad X_{A3} \ll 1, \tag{12}$$

(iv) the solute transport parameter, as defined by Equation 8, is independent of feed concentration and feed flow rate, i.e.

$$(D_{AM}/K\delta) \text{ is independent of } X_{A1} \text{ and } k, \text{ and hence, } X_{A2}, \tag{13}$$

(v) longitudinal diffusion of solute is negligible, i.e.

$$P\,e\,B = (\bar{u}°L/E) = \infty. \tag{14}$$

The above approximations are assumed valid in the following discussion. Using Equations 10 and 12, the basic transport equations can be rewritten as follows:

$$A = \frac{[PWP]}{M_B \times S \times 3600 \times P} \quad (6)$$

$$N_B = A[P - \pi(X_{A2}) + \pi(X_{A3})] \quad (7)$$

$$= c\left(\frac{D_{AM}}{K\delta}\right)\left(\frac{X_{A2} - X_{A3}}{X_{A3}}\right) \quad (15)$$

$$= ck \ln\left(\frac{X_{A2} - X_{A3}}{X_{A1} - X_{A3}}\right). \quad (16)$$

Correlations of experimental reverse osmosis data

The correlations of A, $(D_{AM}/K\delta)$, and k with operating pressure, temperature, feed concentration, feed flow rate, nature of solute, and membrane compaction during continuous operation are of practical interest from the point of view of specifying membranes, and predicting membrane performance under different operating conditions. Such correlations have to be established experimentally for every specific membrane–solution–operating system. The basic transport equations themselves are independent of such correlations. Figures 18–21 illustrate a set of correlations of experimental data for the solution system sodium chloride–water which can be used as a reference system for purposes of process design. More extensive graphical and analytical correlations of experimental data are given in Reference 4.

The fact that the solute transport parameter $(D_{AM}/K\delta)$ is independent of feed concentration and feed flow rate at a given operating pressure and temperature for different solution systems is of practical importance. It offers a means of expressing membrane selectivity in terms of relative values of $(D_{AM}/K\delta)$ for different solutes as illustrated in Figure 22; it also offers a simple means of specifying

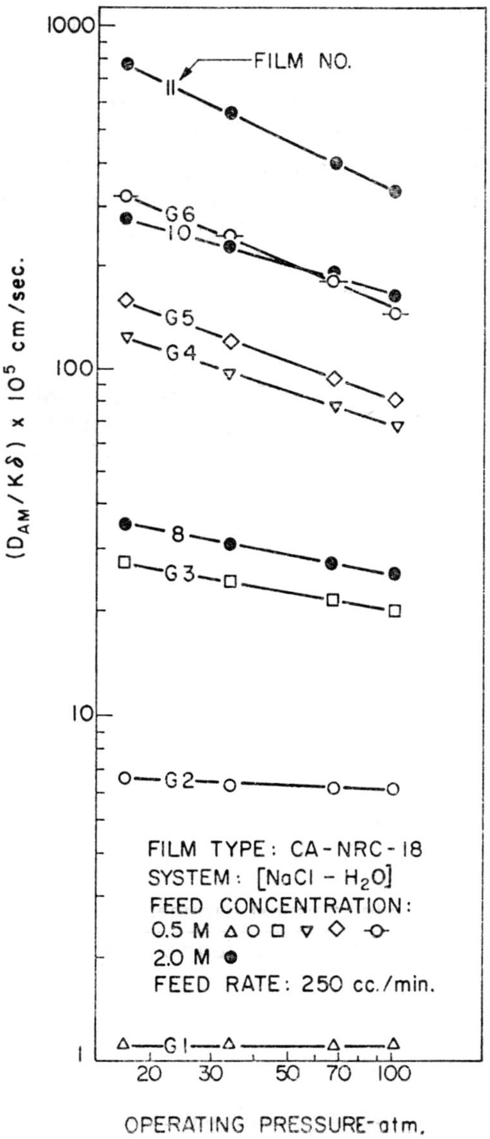

Figure 19 Effect of operating pressure on solute transport parameter for the system sodium chloride–water.[4]

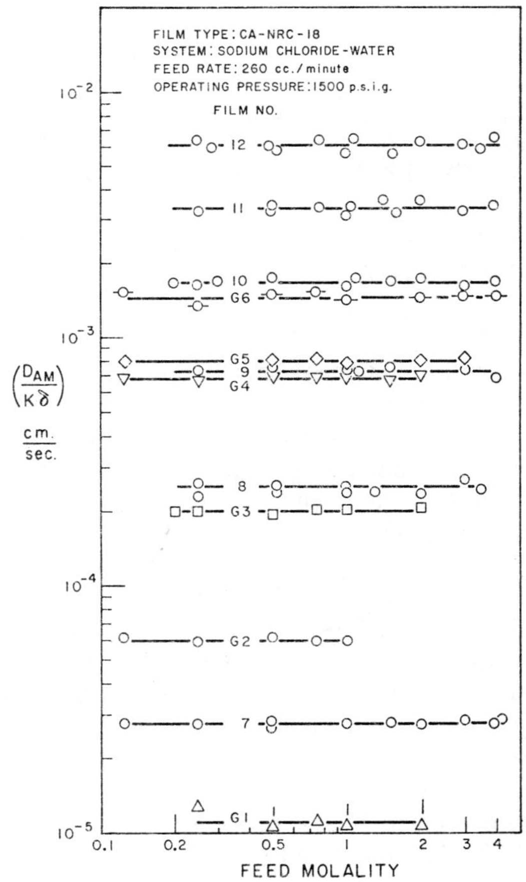

Figure 20 Effect of feed concentration on solute transport parameter for the system sodium chloride–water.[4] Film type, 18; operating pressure, 1500 psig.

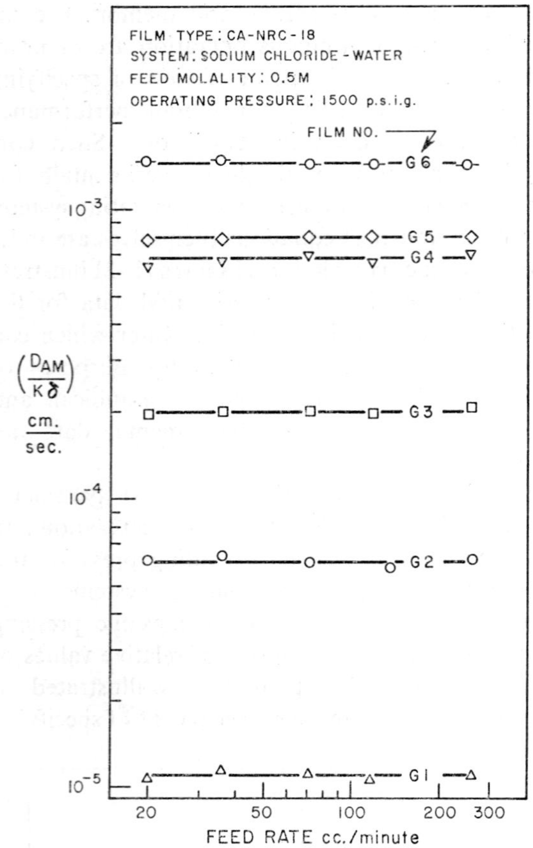

Figure 21 Effect of feed flow rate on solute transport parameter for the system sodium chloride–water.[4] Film type, Batch 18; operating pressure, 1500 psig.

reverse osmosis membranes and systems and predicting their performance as indicated below.

Membrane specifications

For a given solution system and operating pressure and temperature, a membrane is completely specified in terms of its pure water permeability constant A, and the solute transport parameter $(D_{AM}/K\delta)$ at that pressure and temperature. A single set of experimental data on pure water permeation rate [PWP], and membrane permeated product rate [PR], and solute separation f for *any* feed concentration and feed flow rate at the specified operating pressure and temperature, is sufficient to obtain data on A and $(D_{AM}/K\delta)$ for that membrane–solution system; the above experimental data also enables one to calculate the value of k corresponding to the feed concentration and feed flow rate used in the particular experiment.

While data on A and $(D_{AM}/K\delta)$ are enough to specify the membrane, they are *not* enough to predict its performance (i.e. to predict solute separation and membrane flux) at the specified operating pressure and temperature for *any* feed concentration and feed flow rate for the solution system under consideration; for such prediction, data on applicable values of k are needed in addition to those on membrane specification.

Prediction of membrane performance

Combining Equations 15 and 16, and Equations 7 and 15, the following relationships are obtained:

$$\left[\frac{X_{A2} - X_{A3}}{X_{A3}}\right] = \frac{k}{(D_{AM}/K\delta)} \ln\left[\frac{X_{A2} - X_{A3}}{X_{A1} - X_{A3}}\right] \tag{17}$$

$$A[P - \pi(X_{A2}) + \pi(X_{A3})] = c\left(\frac{D_{AM}}{K\delta}\right)\left[\frac{X_{A2} - X_{A3}}{X_{A3}}\right]. \tag{18}$$

When a membrane is specified in terms of A and $(D_{AM}/K\delta)$ for a given solution system, and operating pressure and temperature, Equations 17 and 18 can be used to calculate X_{A2} and X_{A3} for any desired values of X_{A1} and k; the above values of X_{A2} and X_{A3} can then be used to calculate membrane flux (N_B) and solute separation (f).

System specification

Any reverse osmosis membrane–solution–operating system may be specified by three fundamental nondimensional parameters—γ, θ, and λ—defined as follows:

$$\gamma = \frac{\pi(X_{A1})}{P} = \frac{\text{osmotic pressure of initial feed solution}}{\text{operating pressure}} = \frac{BX^{\circ}_{A1}}{P} \tag{19}$$

$$\theta = \frac{(D^{\circ}_{AM}/K\delta)}{v^*_w} = \frac{\text{solute transport parameter}}{\text{pure water permeation velocity}} \tag{20}$$

$$\lambda = \frac{k}{(D_{AM}/K\delta)} = \frac{\text{mass transfer coefficient on the high pressure side of membrane}}{\text{solute transport parameter}}. \tag{21}$$

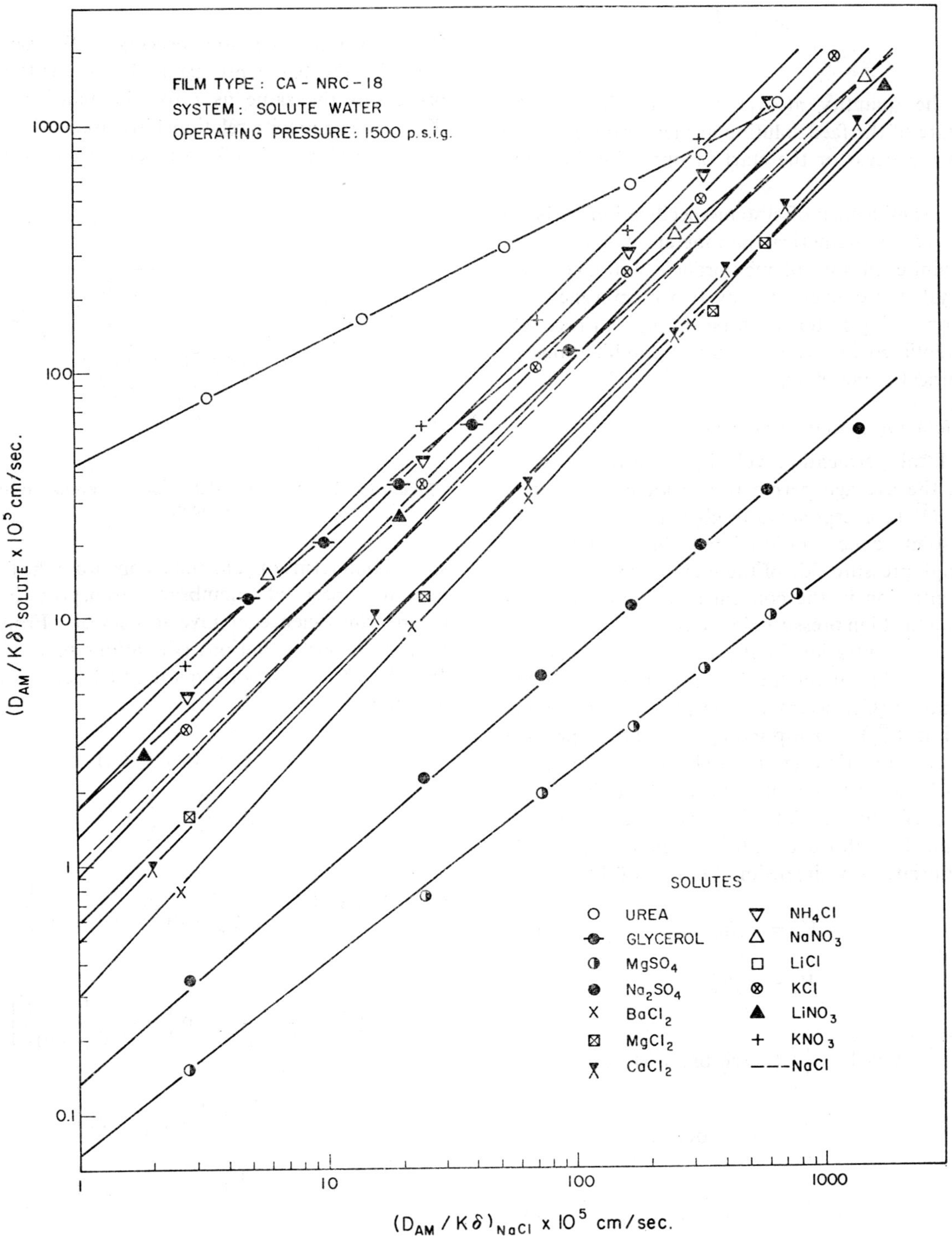

Figure 22 A relative scale of membrane selectivity for different solutes for the Batch 18–type porous cellulose acetate membranes at 1500 psig.[4]

The quantity v_w^* is the pure water permeation velocity obtained from the relation

$$v_w^* = \frac{AP}{c}, \tag{22}$$

and the quantity $\pi(X_{A1}^\circ)$ refers to the osmotic pressure of the feed solution at membrane entrance in flow process or the start of operation in batch process.

The significance of system specification is that a single set of numerical parameters can represent an infinite number of membrane–solution–operating systems; conversely, any two membrane solution operating systems can be simply and precisely differentiated in terms of unique combinations of numerical parameters.

Prediction of system performance

The local permeation velocity of product water (V_w), the average permeation velocity of product water ($\bar{V}_w$) corresponding to given product recovery (Δ), solute concentration in the bulk solution on the high pressure side of the membrane (C_1), solute concentration in the concentrated boundary solution on the high pressure side of the membrane (C_2), solute concentration in the membrane permeated product solution on the low pressure side of the membrane (C_3), average concentration of product solution ($\bar{C}_3$) corresponding to above product recovery, and time (τ in batch process) or longitudinal distance (X in flow process) are the important performance data in any reverse osmosis system. The above quantities may be defined in appropriate non-dimensional units as follows:

$$V_w = v_w/v_w^* \tag{23}$$

$$\bar{V}_w = \bar{v}_w/v_w^* \tag{24}$$

$$\Delta = 1 - \frac{V_1}{V_1^\circ} \text{ (batch process) or } 1 = \frac{\bar{u}}{\bar{u}^\circ} \text{ (flow process)} \tag{25}$$

$$C_1 = c_{A1}/c_{A1}^\circ \quad \text{or} \quad X_{A1}/X_{A1}^\circ \tag{26}$$

$$C_2 = c_{A2}/c_{A1}^\circ \quad \text{or} \quad X_{A2}/X_{A1}^\circ \tag{27}$$

$$C_3 = c_{A3}/c_{A1}^\circ \quad \text{or} \quad X_{A3}/X_{A1}^\circ \tag{28}$$

$$\bar{C}_3 = \bar{c}_{A3}/c_{A1}^\circ \quad \text{or} \quad \bar{X}_{A3}/X_{A1}^\circ \tag{29}$$

$$\tau = Sv_w^*t/V_1^\circ \quad \text{(batch process)} \tag{30}$$

$$X = v_w^*x/\bar{u}^\circ h \quad \text{(flow process).} \tag{31}$$

(When $1/h$ for the flow process is the same as S/V_1° for the batch process and $x/\bar{u}^\circ$ for the flow process is the same as t for the batch process, $X \equiv \tau$.) The precise relationships among the above quantities (Figure 23) for a reverse osmosis system

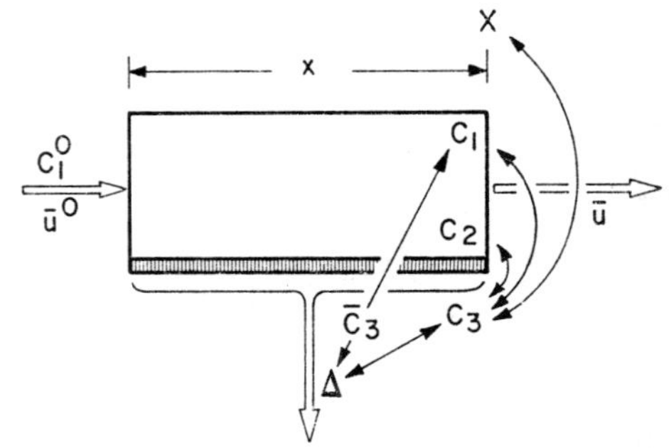

Figure 23 Performance data for a reverse osmosis system.

specified in terms of γ, θ, and λ constitute the fundamental aspect of membrane transport in the engineering science of reverse osmosis. From the basic transport equations (Equations 6, 7, 15 and 16), the above relationships may be derived to be as follows[66]

$$V_w = 1 - \gamma(C_2 - C_3) \tag{32}$$

$$\bar{V}_w = \frac{\Delta}{\tau} = \frac{\Delta}{X} \tag{33}$$

$$C_1^\circ = 1 = C_3^\circ\left[1 + \frac{1}{(\gamma C_3^\circ + \theta)}\exp\left\{-\frac{1}{\lambda(\gamma C_3^\circ + \theta)}\right\}\right] \tag{34}$$

$$C_1 = C_3\left[1 + \frac{1}{(\gamma C_3 + \theta)}\exp\left\{-\frac{1}{\lambda(\gamma C_3 + \theta)}\right\}\right] \tag{35}$$

$$C_2^\circ = C_3^\circ\left[1 + \frac{1}{(\gamma C_3^\circ + \theta)}\right] \tag{36}$$

$$C_2 = C_3\left[1 + \frac{1}{(\gamma C_3 + \theta)}\right] \tag{37}$$

$$Z = \int_{C_2}^{C_2}\left[\frac{\gamma}{\lambda(\gamma C_3 + \theta)^2} - \frac{\gamma}{(\gamma C_3 + \theta)} + \right. \\ \left. + \left\{\frac{(\gamma C_3 + \theta)}{C_3}\exp\frac{1}{\lambda(\gamma C_3 + \theta)}\right\} + \frac{1}{C_3}\right]dC_3 \tag{38}$$

$$\begin{bmatrix} \tau \\ \text{or} \\ X \end{bmatrix} = \int_{C_2}^{C_2} \left[\frac{\gamma}{\lambda(\gamma C_3 + \theta)} - \gamma + \frac{(\gamma C_3 + \theta)}{C_3} \right.$$

$$\left. \times \left\{ 1 + (C_3 + \theta) \exp \frac{1}{\lambda(\gamma C_3 + \theta)} \right\} \right] \frac{\exp(-Z)}{\theta} dC_3 \qquad (39)$$

$$\Delta = 1 - \exp(-Z) \qquad (40)$$

$$1 = C_1(1 - \Delta) + \bar{C}_3\Delta. \qquad (41)$$

Equations 34–41 show that for a specified reverse osmosis system, any one of the six quantities C_1, C_2, C_3, $\bar{C}_3$, τ or X, and Δ uniquely fix all the other five quantities. Consequently, the performance of a reverse osmosis system specified in terms of γ, θ, and λ can be predicted to express any five of the quantities C_1, C_2, C_3, $\bar{C}_3$, τ or X, and Δ as a function of the sixth. The quantities V_w and $\bar{V}_w$ can be obtained from Equations 32 and 33. The local or average values for membrane flux (N_B or $\bar{N}_B$) and solute separation (f or $\bar{f}$) can then be obtained from the relations:

$$v_w = \frac{N_B}{c} \qquad (42)$$

$$\bar{v}_w = \frac{\bar{N}_B}{c} \qquad (43)$$

$$f = 1 - C_3 \qquad (44)$$

$$\bar{f} = 1 - \bar{C}_3. \qquad (45)$$

An illustration

The following results were obtained in a reverse osmosis experiment using a Loeb–Sourirajan type porous cellulose acetate membrane whose effective area is 7.6 cm^2:

Solution system: sodium chloride–water
Feed molality: 0.51 M
Operating pressure: 1500 psig
Operating temperature: 25°C
Feed flow rate: 400 cm^3/min
Pure water permeation rate [PWP] = 134.14 g/hr
Product rate [PR] = 91.50 g/hr
Solute separation = 78.4%.

The osmotic pressure 1 molal NaCl–H_2O solution is 673 psi. Osmotic pressure is assumed proportional to mole fraction of solute in the concentration range of interest. The molar density of solution is assumed valid. Using the above set of experimental data, a number of calculations can be made, some of which are the following.

Using Equations 6, 7, 15 and 16, the specifications of the membrane used are: $A = 2.667 \times 10^{-6}$ g mole H_2O/cm^2 sec atm, and $(D_{AM}/K\delta) = 51.7 \times 10^{-5}$ cm/sec. Under the conditions of the experiment, $k = 57 \times 10^{-4}$ cm/sec. Using Equations 17 and 18, the effects of feed concentration and feed flow rate may then be predicted as illustrated in Table XIII. Under conditions of continuous

TABLE XIII

Effects of Feed Concentration and Feed Flow Rate on Membrane Performance

Solution system: Sodium chloride–water
Operating pressure: 1500 psig
Membrane specifications: $A = 2.667 \times 10^{-6}$ g mole H_2O/cm^2 sec atm
$(D_{AM}/K\delta) = 51.7 \times 10^{-5}$ cm/sec

Feed concn.		Feed flow rate corresponding to $k \times 10^4$, cm/sec									
Molality	Wt.% NaCl	10	20	30	40	50	57	75	100	150	200
		Solute separation, %									
0.1	0.5811	—	50.2	66.2	73.8	78.0	80.0	83.0	85.2	87.2	88.1
0.2	1.1555	—	54.0	67.4	74.1	77.9	79.7	82.6	84.8	86.7	87.7
0.51	2.8947	35.0	58.2	68.3	73.6	76.8	78.4	81.0	83.1	85.1	86.0
1.0	5.5222	41.3	58.9	66.7	71.2	74.0	75.4	77.8	79.8	81.8	82.8
1.5	8.0608	42.2	56.5	63.1	66.9	69.4	70.7	73.0	74.9	76.9	77.9
2.0	10.4665	40.9	52.6	58.0	61.2	63.3	64.4	66.4	68.1	69.9	70.8
		Product rate, g/hr/7.6 cm^2 of film area									
0.1	0.5811	—	113.6	120.9	125.0	127.2	128.0	129.6	130.9	132.2	132.6
0.2	1.1555	—	96.9	106.9	112.5	116.0	117.8	120.5	122.6	124.6	125.9
0.51	2.8947	54.0	69.5	79.2	85.2	89.3	91.4	95.4	99.1	102.9	104.6
1.0	5.5222	35.8	46.7	53.8	58.9	62.4	64.5	68.1	71.4	75.1	76.9
1.5	8.0608	25.7	32.9	37.5	40.8	43.1	44.5	47.1	49.6	52.4	53.9
2.0	10.4665	19.2	23.7	26.4	28.3	29.7	30.5	32.0	33.4	35.0	35.9

operation under pressure, A decreases but $(D_{AM}/K\delta)$ remains constant[67] provided the surface pore structure remains the same. A-factor is defined as the ratio of the value of A at any time to the initial value of A. Table XIV illustrates the effect of A-factor on the performance of the membrane for different feed concentrations and feed flow rates. The experimental conditions used to obtain the values of A and $(D_{AM}/K\delta)$ correspond to system specifications of $\gamma = 0.225$, $\theta = 0.105$ and $\lambda = 11.03$ or $\lambda\theta = 1.16$. Table XV illustrates the performance of the reverse osmosis system specified by the above values of γ, θ, and six different values of $\gamma\theta$. The data presented in Tables XIII–XV illustrate not only the typical performance of reverse osmosis membranes and systems but also the purpose and utility of the basic transport equations given above.

Conclusion

The foregoing is an attempt to present the basic science of reverse osmosis from the point of view of the general applicability of the technique. Even at the present stage of development, reverse osmosis is ready for large scale industrial practice. When the general applicability of the technique is more fully appreciated, the work on reverse osmosis may be expected to grow many fold leading to a more extensive understanding of the physicochemical criteria of reverse osmosis separation, the material science of reverse osmosis membranes, and the engineering science of reverse osmosis transport. Such understanding can contribute immensely to natural growth of reverse osmosis in all its applications, including those relating to water treatment

TABLE XIV

Effect of A–Factor on Membrane Performance

Solution system: Sodium chloride–water
Operating pressure: 1500 psig
Membrane specifications: $A = 2.667 \times 10^{-6}$ g mole H_2O/cm^2 sec atm
$(D_{AM}/K\delta) = 51.7 \times 10^{-5}$ cm/sec

	$k = 30 \times 10^{-4}$ cm/sec		$k = 57 \times 10^{-4}$ cm/sec		$k = 100 \times 10^{-4}$ cm/sec	
A-factor	Solute sepn., %	Product rate[a]	Solute sepn., %	Product rate[a]	Solute sepn., %	Product rate[a]
Feed concentration: 0.2 M (>1.1555 wt.% NaCl)						
1.0	67.4	106.9	79.7	117.9	84.8	122.6
0.9	67.8	98.9	79.3	107.2	84.0	111.0
0.8	68.1	89.9	78.7	96.3	83.1	99.1
0.7	68.2	80.5	77.8	85.1	81.8	87.3
0.6	68.0	70.5	76.5	73.8	80.2	75.2
0.5	67.2	59.9	74.7	62.0	78.0	63.0
0.4	65.7	48.9	72.1	50.1	74.9	50.6
0.3	62.7	37.3	67.9	38.0	70.2	38.2
Feed concentration: 0.2 M (>1.1555 wt.% NaCl)						
1.0	68.3	79.2	78.4	91.4	83.1	99.1
0.9	68.2	74.3	77.8	84.4	82.2	90.4
0.8	68.0	69.0	77.0	77.0	81.1	81.3
0.7	67.6	63.0	76.0	69.0	79.8	72.1
0.6	66.9	56.5	74.6	60.7	78.1	62.9
0.5	65.8	49.2	72.6	52.1	75.8	53.5
0.4	64.0	41.2	69.9	42.9	72.6	43.7
0.3	60.8	32.4	65.6	33.3	67.9	33.6
Feed concentration: 1.0 M (>5.5222 wt.% NaCl)						
1.0	66.7	53.8	75.4	64.5	79.8	71.4
0.9	66.4	51.4	74.6	60.5	78.9	66.2
0.8	65.8	48.5	73.7	56.0	77.7	60.7
0.7	65.2	45.2	72.6	51.2	76.3	54.7
0.6	64.2	41.5	71.0	46.0	74.5	48.6
0.5	62.9	37.1	69.0	40.4	72.1	42.1
0.4	60.9	32.1	66.2	34.1	68.8	35.2
0.3	57.6	26.2	62.0	27.2	64.2	27.8

[a]Product rate in g/hr/7.6 cm^2 of film area.

TABLE XV

Reverse Osmosis System Specification and Performance Data
System specification: $\gamma = 0.225$, $\theta = 0.105$, $\lambda\theta = 0.5$ to ∞ as indicated.

	$\lambda\theta = 0.5$					$\lambda\theta = 1.16$					$\lambda\theta = 2.0$				
Δ	C_1	C_2	C_3	$\bar{C}_3$	τ or X	C_1	C_2	C_3	$\bar{C}_3$	τ or X	C_1	C_2	C_3	$\bar{C}_3$	τ or X
0	1.000	2.316	0.3650	0.3650	0	1.000	1.627	0.2170	0.2170	0	1.000	1.366	0.1715	0.1715	0
0.1	1.069	2.411	0.3895	0.3770	0.1808	1.086	1.739	0.2379	0.2272	0.1487	1.091	1.476	0.1899	0.1804	0.1387
0.2	1.152	2.522	0.4191	0.3904	0.3673	1.190	1.870	0.2641	0.2388	0.3023	1.202	1.607	0.2133	0.1908	0.2817
0.25	1.201	2.584	0.4365	0.3979	0.4631	1.252	1.946	0.2798	0.2454	0.3815	1.268	1.684	0.2274	0.1967	0.3553
0.3	1.255	2.652	0.4559	0.4059	0.5609	1.320	2.029	0.2977	0.2526	0.4624	1.342	1.768	0.2437	0.2031	0.4306
0.4	1.384	2.809	0.5032	0.4241	0.7634	1.487	2.224	0.3426	0.2692	0.6307	1.521	1.971	0.2852	0.2182	0.5870
0.5	1.554	3.004	0.5666	0.4459	0.9777	1.710	2.474	0.4060	0.2898	0.8105	1.763	2.235	0.3452	0.2372	0.7541
0.6	1.790	3.257	0.6574	0.4731	1.208	2.025	2.808	0.5028	0.3166	1.007	2.106	2.596	0.4397	0.2624	0.9373
0.7	2.146	3.610	0.8011	0.5088	1.463	2.507	3.288	0.6695	0.3539	1.231	2.637	3.127	0.6098	0.2985	1.148
0.75	2.405	3.851	0.9115	0.5317	1.605	2.862	3.625	0.8078	0.3793	1.360	3.029	3.506	0.7568	0.3238	1.270
	$\lambda\theta = 3.0$					$\lambda\theta = 5.0$					$\lambda\theta = \infty$				
0	1.000	1.243	0.1518	0.1518	0	1.000	1.144	0.1368	0.1368	0	1.000	1.000	0.1159	0.1159	0
0.2	1.093	1.350	0.1689	0.1601	0.1343	1.095	1.248	0.1527	0.1445	0.1310	1.097	1.097	0.1299	0.1227	0.1263
0.1	1.208	1.479	0.1906	0.1697	0.2727	1.212	1.375	0.1730	0.1535	0.2657	1.217	1.217	0.1479	0.1306	0.2559
0.25	1.275	1.555	0.2038	0.1751	0.3438	1.280	1.449	0.1854	0.1586	0.3349	1.288	1.288	0.1590	0.1351	0.3224
0.3	1.351	1.639	0.2191	0.1812	0.4164	1.358	1.532	0.1998	0.1642	0.4055	1.369	1.369	0.1719	0.1402	0.3901
0.4	1.536	1.842	0.2584	0.1953	0.5674	1.548	1.734	0.2371	0.1775	0.5521	1.565	1.565	0.2057	0.1521	0.5303
0.5	1.787	2.110	0.3159	0.2133	0.7285	1.805	2.004	0.2922	0.1945	0.7084	1.833	1.833	0.2564	0.1675	0.6794
0.6	2.144	2.482	0.4081	0.2374	0.9052	2.174	2.382	0.3818	0.2176	0.8798	2.217	2.217	0.3409	0.1887	0.8426
0.7	2.697	3.038	0.5782	0.2725	1.109	2.746	2.957	0.5509	0.2517	1.078	2.818	2.818	0.5061	0.2207	1.031
0.75	3.107	3.438	0.7287	0.2975	1.228	3.171	3.376	0.7036	0.2763	1.194	3.267	3.267	0.6611	0.2445	1.143

in general and water pollution control in particular. Such applications may be expected to contribute significantly to the material prosperity and physical well-being of all mankind.

Symbols used in equations 6–51

Note The terms "high pressure side" and "low pressure side" of the membrane refer to the pressure differential across the membrane perpendicular to the direction of feed flow; this pressure difference is referred to as the "operating pressure, *P*". When the membrane permeated product is withdrawn at the atmospheric pressure, *P* is simply the operating gauge pressure, and the "low pressure side" is the atmospheric pressure side of the membrane.

A = pure water permeability constant, g mole pure water/cm³ sec atm

A_o = extrapolated value of A at $P = 0$

B = osmotic pressure proportionality constant, atm

cc = molar density of solution, g mole/cm³

c_A = solute concentration, g mole/cm³, or mole fraction

$\bar{c}_{A3}$ = average solute concentration in membrane permeated product solution corresponding to a given fraction (Δ) of product recovery, g mole/cm³, or mole fraction

C = c_A/c°_{A1} or X_A/X°_{A1}

$(D_{AM}/K\delta)$ = solute transport parameter (treated as a single quantity), cm/sec

E = longitudinal diffusion coefficient, cm²/sec

f = solute separation = $\left[1 - \dfrac{m_3}{m_1}\right] \approx 1 - C_3$

$\bar{f}$ = average solute separation corresponding to given fraction (Δ) of product recovery = $1 - \bar{C}_3$

h^{-1} = membrane area per unit volume of fluid space in the reverse osmosis unit, cm^{-1}

k = mass transfer coefficient on the high pressure side of membrane, cm/sec

L = longitudinal length over which mixing is considered, cm

m_1, m_3 = molality of bulk solution on the high pressure side of membrane, and that of membrane permeated product solution on the low pressure side of membrane

M_B = molecular weight of water

N_A = solute flux through membrane, g mole/cm² sec

N_B = solvent water flux through membrane, g mole/cm² sec

P = operating pressure, atm

PeB = $\bar{u}^\circ L/E$

[PR] = permeation rate of product solution through the membrane per specified area of membrane surface, g/hr

[PWP] = pure water permeation rate through the membrane per specified area of membrane surface, g/hr

S = area of membrane surface, cm^2

t = time, sec

$\bar{u}$ = average fluid velocity parallel to membrane surface on the high pressure side of the membrane at any position in flow process, cm/sec

$\bar{u}°$ = value of $\bar{u}$ at membrane entrance in flow process, cm/sec

v_w = solvent water permeation velocity through the membrane at any point (position or time) in the system, cm/sec

$\bar{v}_w$ = average permeation velocity of solvent water through the membrane corresponding to given fraction (Δ) of product recovery, cm/sec

v_w^* = pure water permeation velocity through the membrane, cm/sec

V_1 = quantity of solution on the high pressure side of the membrane at any time in batch process, cm^3

$V_w, \bar{V}_w$ = quantities defined by Equations 29 and 30 respectively

x = longitudinal distance along the length of the membrane from channel entrance, cm

X = quantity defined by Equation 37 for flow process

X_A = mole fraction of solute

$\bar{X}_{A3}$ = average value for the mole fraction of solute in the membrane permeated product solution corresponding to given fraction (Δ) of product recovery

Z $= \int_1^{C_1} \frac{dC_1}{C_1 - C_3}$

Greek Letters

γ = quantity defined by Equation 25

Δ = quantity defined by Equation 31

θ = quantity defined by Equation 26

λ = quantity defined by Equation 27

$\pi(X_A)$ = osmotic pressure of solution corresponding to mole fraction of solute = X_A, atm

τ = quantity defined by Equation 36 for batch process

Superscript

° = represents condition at start of operation in batch process or at membrane entrance in flow process

Subscripts

1, 2, 3 = refer to bulk solution and concentrated boundary solution on the high pressure side of membrane, and membrane permeated product solution on the low pressure side of membrane, respectively, at any point (position or time) in the system.

REFERENCES

1. University of California, Office of Public Information Press Release, 'New Water Desalting Process Developed at UCLA', August 23, 1960.
2. Johnson, J. S., Jr., L. Dresner and K. A. Kraus, in *Principles of Desalination*, K. S. Spiegler (Editor), Chapter 8, Academic Press, New York (1966).
3. Merten, U., (Editor), *Desalination by Reverse Osmosis*, M.I.T. Press, Cambridge, Mass. (1966).
4. Sourirajan, S., *Reverse Osmosis*, Logos Press, London, and Academic Press, New York (1970).
5. Breton, E. J., Jr., "Water and Ion Flow Through Imperfect Osmotic Membranes", U.S. Dept. Interior, Office of Saline Water, Research and Development Progress Report No. 16 (1957).
6. Yuster, S. T., S. Sourirajan and K. Bernstein, "Sea Water Demineralization by the Surface-Skimming Process", Department of Engineering, University of California, Los Angeles, Report No. 58–26 (1958).
7. Loeb, S. and S. Sourirajan, "Sea Water Demineralization by Means of a Semipermeable Membrane", Department of Engineering, University of California, Los Angeles, Report No. 60–60 (1961).
8. Loeb, S. and S. Sourirajan, *Advan. Chem. Ser.* No. 38, 117 (1963).
9. Lonsdale, H. K., U. Merten and R. L. Riley, *J. Appl. Polym. Sci.* **9**, 1341 (1965).
10. Riley, R. L., H. K. Lonsdale, C. R. Lyons and U. Merten, *J. Appl. Polym. Sci.* **11**, 2143 (1967).
11. Lonsdale, H. K., in *Progress in Separation and Purification*, Vol. 3, E. S. Perry and C. J. Van Oss (Editors), p. 191, Wiley–Interscience, New York (1970).
12. Merten, U., H. K. Lonsdale, R. L. Riley and K. D. Vos, "Reverse Osmosis Membrane Research", U.S. Dept. Interior, Office of Saline Water, Research and Development Progress Report No. 265 (1967).
13. Riley, R. L., J. O. Gardner and U. Merten, *Science* **143**, 801 (1964).
14. Riley, R. L., U. Merten and J. O. Gardner, *Desalination* **1**, 30 (1966).
15. Wasilewski, S., "Microwave Investigation of Temperature Induced, Transient Changes in Cellulose Acetate Osmotic Membranes", Department of Engineering, University of California, Los Angeles, Report No. 65–10 (1965).
16. Sourirajan, S. and T. S. Govindan, *Proc. First International Symp. on Water Desalination*, Washington, D.C. (1965) (Pub. U.S. Dept. Interior, Office of Saline Water, Washington, D.C.), Vol. 1, pp. 251–274.
17. Manjikian, S., S. Loeb and J. W. McCutchan, *Proc, First International Symp. on Water Desalination*, Washington, D.C. (1965) (Pub. U.S. Dept. Interior.

Office of Saline Water, Washington, D.C.), Vol. 2, pp. 159–173.
18. Manjikian, S., "Optimization of a Reverse Osmosis Sea-Water Desalination System", Report No. CR 67.027 for U.S. Naval Civil Engineering Laboratory, Port Huenema, Calif., 1966.
19. Manjikian, S. and C. Allen, "Development of Reverse Osmosis Membranes", U.S. Dept. Interior, Office of Saline Water, Research and Development Progress Report No. 378 (1968).
20. Fluke, G. A., "Process and Configuration Development for Tubular Reverse Osmosis Units", U.S. Dept. Interior, Office of Saline Water, Research and Development Progress Report No. 426 (1969).
21. Saltonstall, C. W., "Development of New and Improved Cellulose Ester Reverse Osmosis Membranes", U.S. Dept. Interior, Office of Saline Water, Research and Development Progress Report No. 434 (1969).
22. Saltonstall, C. W., *Proc. 3rd International Symp. on Fresh Water From the Sea*, Dubrovnik, Vol. 2, 579 (1970).
23. Riley, R. L., H. K. Lonsdale, C. R. Lyons and U. Merten, *J. Appl. Polym. Sci.* **11**, 2143 (1967).
24. Rozelle, L. T., J. E. Cadotte and D. J. McClure, *J. Appl. Polym. Symposia*, **13**, 61 (1970).
25. Hoernschemeyer, D. L., C. W. Saltonstall, Jr., O. S. Schaeffler, L. W. Schoellenback, A. J. Secchi and A. L. Vincent, "Research and Development of New and Improved Cellulose Ester Membranes", U.S. Dept. Interior, Office of Saline Water, Research and Development Progress Report No. 556 (1970).
26. Riley, R. L., H. K. Lonsdale and C. R. Lyons, *J. Appl. Polym. Sci.* **15**, 1267 (1971).
27. Cohen, M. E., M. A. Grable and B. M. Riggleman, "Second Report on Development of Improved Cellulose Acetate Membranes for Reverse Osmosis", U.S. Dept. Interior, Office of Saline Water, Research and Development Progress Report No. 518 (1970).
28. Orofino, T. A., "Development of Hollow Filament Technology for Reverse Osmosis Desalination Systems", U.S. Dept. Interior, Office of Saline Water, Research and Development Progress Report No. 549 (1970).
29. Manjikian, S. and M. I. Foley, "Characterization of Cellulose Acetate Butyrate Membranes", U.S. Dept. Interior, Office of Saline Water, Research and Development Progress Report No. 612 (1970).
30. Manjikian, S., S. Liu, M. Foley, C. Allen and B. Fabrick, "Development of Reverse Osmosis Membranes", U.S. Dept. Interior, Office of Saline Water, Research and Development Progress Report No. 534 (1970).
31. Manjikian, S. and M. I. Foley, "Characterization of Cellulose Acetate Butyrate Membranes", U.S. Dept. Interior Office of Saline Water, Research and Development Progress Report No. 654 (1971).
32. Saltonstall, C. W. and W. S. Higley, "Research and Development of New Polymer Systems for Reverse Osmosis Membranes", U.S. Dept. Interior, Office of Saline Water, Research and Development Progress Report No. 360 (1968).
33. Smith, J. K., E. Klein, F. Morton and T. Casebonne, "Investigation of Cellulose Ether Esters for Reverse Osmosis Membranes", U.S. Dept. Interior, Office of Saline Water, Research and Development Progress Report No. 630 (1970).
34. Caracciolo, V. P. and W. G. Smith, "The B–9 Permeator —A Major Advance in Commercial RO", Paper presentated at the OSW Conference at Roswell, N.M., Nov. 4–5, 1970.
35. Michaels, A. S., *Chem. Eng. Progress* **64** (12), 31 (1968).
36. Van Oss, C. J., in *Progress in Separation and Purification*, Vol. 3, E. S. Perry and C. J. Van Oss (Editors), p. 97, Wiley–Interscience, New York (1970).
37. Kraus, K. A., A. J. Shor, J. S. Johnson, *Desalination* **2**, 243 (1967).
38. Glueckauf, E., *Proc. First International Symp. on Water Desalination*, Washington, D.C. (1965), (Pub. U.S. Dept. Interior, Office of Saline Water, Washington, D.C.) Vol. 1, pp. 143–156.
39. Sourirajan, S., *J. Appl. Chem.* **14**, 506 (1964).
40. Govindan, T. S. and S. Sourirajan, *Ind. Eng. Chem. Process Design Develop.* **5**, 422 (1966).
41. Bean, C. P., "Characterization of Cellulose Acetate Membranes and Ultrathin Films for Reverse Osmosis", U.S. Dept. Interior, Office of Saline Water, Research and Development Progress Report No. 465 (1969).
42. Dresner, L. and K. A. Kraus, *J. Phys. Chem.* **67**, 990 (1963)
43. Dresner, L., *J. Phys. Chem.* **67**, 1635 (1963).
44. Dresner, L., *J. Phys. Chem.* **67**, 2333 (1963).
45. Dresner, L., *J. Phys. Chem.* **69**, 2230 (1965).
46. Heymann, E. and G. Rabinov, *J. Phys. Chem.* **45**, 1152, 1167 (1941).
47. Van Oss, C. J., *Science* **139**, 1123 (1963).
48. Matsuura, T. and S. Sourirajan, *J. Appl. Polym. Sci.* (in press).
49. Barrow, G. M., *J. Am. Chem. Soc.* **59**, 1129 (1955).
50. Taft, R. W., Jr., in *Steric Effects in Organic Chemistry*, M. S. Newman (Editor), pp. 556–675, John Wiley, New York, (1956).
51. *Handbook of Organic Structural Analysis*, Edited by Y. Yukawa, pp. 507, 614 and 637, W. A. Benjamin, Inc., New York, (1965).
52. Kesting, R. E., M. K. Barsh and A. L. Vincent, *J. Appl. Polym. Sci.* **9**, 1873 (1965).
53. Kesting, R. E. and A. Menefee, *Kolloid-Z. Z. Polym.* **230**, 341 (1969).
54. Kesting, R. E., "Membranes" in *Cellulose and Cellulose Derivatives*, Vol. 5, Part 5, N. Bikales and L. Segal (Editors), pp. 1233–1260, Wiley, New York (1971).
55. Kesting, R. E., *Synthetic Polymeric Membranes*, McGraw–Hill, New York (1971).
56. Kunst, B. and S. Sourirajan, *J. Appl. Polym. Sci.* **14**, 723 (1970)
57. Kunst, B. and S. Sourirajan, *Desalination* 8, 139 (1970).
58. Kunst, B. and S. Sourirajan, *J. Appl. Polym. Sci.* **14**, 1983 (1970).
59. Kunst, B. and S. Sourirajan, *J. Appl. Polym. Sci.* **14**, 2559 (1970).
60. Pilon, R., B. Kunst and S. Sourirajan, *J. Appl. Polym. Sci.* **15**, 1317 (1971).
61. Pageau, L. and S. Sourirajan, (unpublished).
62. Ohya, S. and S. Sourirajan, *J. Appl. Polym. Sci.* **15**, 705 (1971).
63. Kopecek, J. and S. Sourirajan, *J. Appl. Polym. Sci.* **13**, 637 (1969).
64. Fahey, P. M. and H. E. Grethlein, *Desalination* (in press).
65. Kimura, S. and S. Sourirajan, *A.1. Ch. E.J.* **13**, 497 (1967).
66. Ohya, H. and S. Sourirajan, *A.1. Ch. E.J.* **15**, 829 (1969).
67. Kimura, S. and S. Sourirajan, *Ind. Eng. Chem. Process Design Develop.* **7**, 197 (1968).

S. Sourirajan
National Research Council of Canada

S

SEDIMENT TRANSPORT AND EROSION

1. Introduction

The literature on the subject of erosion and sediment transport is vast and is treated in the publications of such disciplines as civil engineering, soil science, agriculture, geography and geology. This article provides a brief introduction to the subjects of soil erosion, transport of detritus by streams and the response of a stream channel to changes in its sediment characteristics.

The agriculturalist is concerned with the loss of fertile land through erosion. Sheet, gully and other erosion mechanisms result in the annual movement of about five billion tons of sediment in the United States.[1] By this process, plant nutrients and humus are washed away and conveyed to the streams, reservoir and lakes.

The sediment characteristics of a stream also affect its aquatic life. Changes in the character of the sediment load will normally tend to change the balance of aquatic life. Fine sediment, derived from sheet erosion causes turbidity in the waterways. This turbidity may interfere with photosynthesis and with the feeding habits of certain fish thus favouring the less susceptible (often less desirable) varieties of fish. The resulting mud deposits may have similar selective results on spawning. The plant nutrients (phosphates and nitrates) that accompany erosion from farmlands may contribute to the eutrophocation of the receiving waters.

Turbidity also makes waters less desirable for municipal and industrial use. Mud deposits may ruin sand beaches for recreational use.

From the engineer's point of view an understanding of sediment transport processes is essential for proper design of most hydraulic works. For example, the construction of a dam on a stream is almost always accompanied by, a reservoir siltation or aggradation problem and a degradation problem. A reasonable prediction of the rate of reservoir siltation is necessary in order to establish the probable useful life and thus the economics of a proposed reservoir. The degradation or erosion of the downstream channel and the consequent lowering of the river level may, unless properly accounted for, endanger the dam and other downstream structures (due to under-cutting). After construction of the Hoover Dam the bed of the Colorado River downstream from the dam started to degrade. In 12 years the bed level dropped about 14 feet [Brown[1]].

In addition the downstream channel may change its regime (i.e. its dominant stable geometry). For example, a wide braided channel or delta area may become a much narrower and deeper meandering channel thus affecting the prior uses of the stream. This appears to have happened as a result of the Bennett Dam on the Peace River in British Columbia.[2]

2. Classification of Stream Borne Sediments

2.1 Terminology

The materials transported by a stream may be grouped under the following type of load:

a) dissolved load,
b) bed load,
c) suspended load.

The dissolved load, although a significant portion of total stream load, is generally not considered in sediment transport processes. According to Leopold Wolman and Miller,[3] the dissolved load in U.S· streams increases with increasing annual runoff, reaching a maximum of about 125 tons/sq. mile/year for runoffs of 10 inches/year or more.

Bed load consists of granular particles, derived from the stream bed, which are transported by rolling, skipping or sliding near the stream bed. Einstein[4,5] defines the bed load as the sediment discharge within the bed layer which he assumes to have an extent of two sediment grain diameters from the bed.

Suspended sediment load is that part of the sediment load which is transported within the main body flow, i.e. above the bed layer in Einstein's terminology. Turbulent diffusion is the primary mechanisms of maintaining the sediment particles in suspension. The suspended load may be subdivided into:

a) Wash load which consists of fine sediments mainly derived from overland erosion and not found in significant quantities in alluvial beds; often wash load is arbitrarily taken to be sediments finer than .062 mm, i.e. silts and clays.

b) Suspended bed material load which is the portion of the suspended load derived primarily from the channel bed; generally the bed material is assumed to be the sediment coarser than .062 mm, i.e. sands and gravels.

Table I indicates the terminology used by the American Geophysical Union in describing various size classes of sediment.

TABLE I

Sediment Grade Scale

Group	Particle size range, mm
Boulders	4096–256
Cobbles	256– 64
Gravel	64– 2
Sand	2–.062
Silt	.062–.004
Clay	.004–.00024

2.2 Properties of sediments

An excellent review of the properties of sediments is presented by Brown.[1] He discusses the determination and significance of the following:

a) properties of the individual particle,
b) particle size distribution and
c) bulk properties of sediments.

2.2.1 Properties of the Particle Neglecting interaction effects, the behaviour of an individual particle in a stream depends on its size, specific weight, shape and the hydraulics of the stream.

Two commonly used methods of determining particle size are: (a) mechanical sieve analysis and (b) the fall velocity method. The sieve analysis method differentiates particle size on the basis of whether or not the particle will pass through a certain standard square opening in a sieve or mesh. This method is applicable for sands or coarser particles. Except in the case of spheres "sieve size" will only be an approximation to the true equivalent diameter of the particle since the results depend to some extent on the particle shape.

The fall velocity method of determining the effective sediment size is gaining in popularity in sediment transport research. On the basis of the particle's terminal velocity, in a specified fluid (water) at a specified temperature, the particle is assigned a fall or sedimentation diameter equal to the diameter of the quartz sphere which has the same terminal velocity in the same fluid at the same

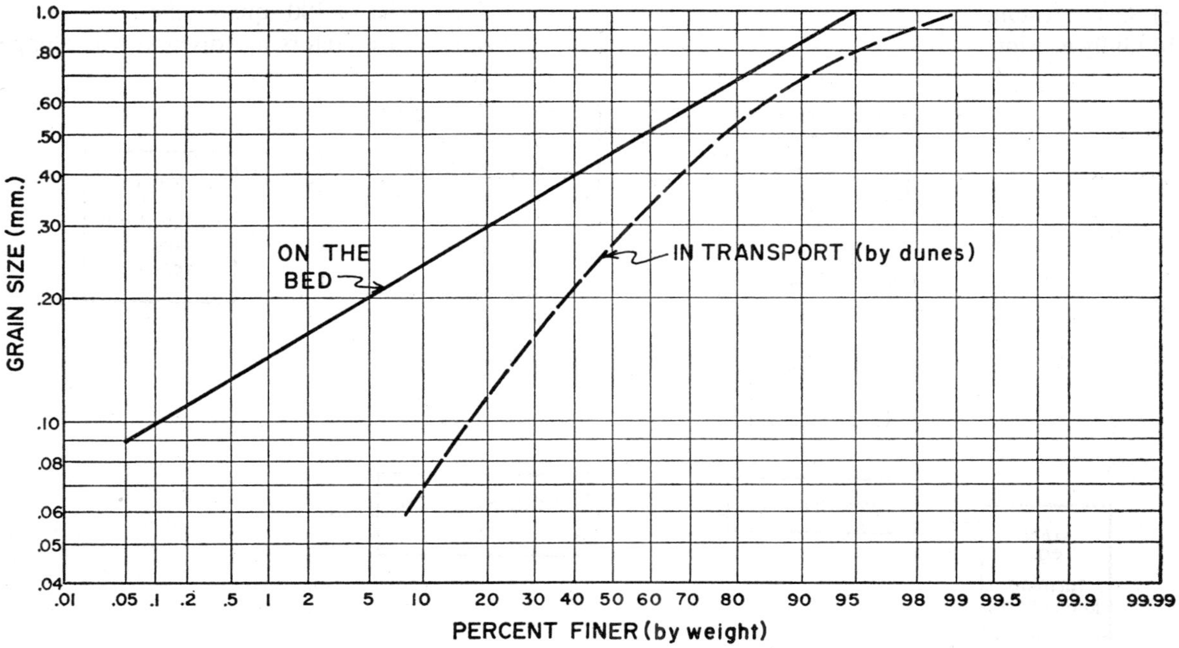

Figure 1 Typical particle size frequencies curves for stream sediments (after Bishop et al).

temperature.[1] This particle size integrates the effects of grain size, specific weight and shape into a single meaningful parameter for sediment transport studies. Researchers at Colorado State University have developed a Visual Accumulation Tube to aid in the determination of the fall diameter distributions for sediment samples.

2.2.2 Particle Size Distribution On the basis of a sieve analysis of fall diameter analysis, of a sediment sample, a cumulative frequency curve for the particle size can be drawn. Figure 1 shows typical particle size frequency curves for a sample taken from a sandy stream bed and for a sample of suspended load over the same bed.[6] The frequency curves are usually plotted on logarithmic-probability paper.

Some important descriptors of the frequency distribution are: (a) the median size or d_{50}, i.e. the size for which 50% by weight, of the sample has smaller particles; (b) the scatter of particle sizes as indicated, for example, by the standard deviation or perhaps the geometric deviation; (c) the characteristic grain roughness which has been associated with the d_{65};[5,7,8] (d) the d_{35} has also been used as a characteristic sediment size.[9]

2.2.3 Bulk Properties The determination of bulk, in place specific weights of sediments is discussed in Section 7.

3. Erosion

Most of the sediment in streams is produced by the following processes:[1]

a) Sheet erosion,
b) Gully erosion,
c) Stream channel erosion,
d) Mass movements of soil (e.g. landslides and soil creep),
e) Erosion to construction works,
f) Solid wastes from municipal, industrial, agricultural and mining activities.

Morisawa,[10] using a system diagram, similar to Figure 2, summarizes the inter-relation of climatic and geologic factors that influence soil erosion and runoff. Figure 2 also shows man's influence on the system.

Langbein and Schumm[3,17] proposed the correlation shown in Figure 3 between annual sediment yield and effective annual precipitation for the United States. The effective precipitation is the adjusted precipitation which would have produced the observed runoff for an annual mean temperature of 50°F.

A recent paper by Saxton *et al.*[11] relates total runoff, surface runoff and land use practices to the sediment yield from loessial watersheds in Iowa. This paper compares erosion and surface runoff from contoured-corn watersheds and from pastured-grass and level-terraced areas. In a 6-year study the contoured-corn areas yielded, annually, about 19,000 tons/sq. mile of sheet erosion plus 3,000 tons/sq. mile of gully erosion while the level-terraced and grassed watersheds yielded about 600 tons/sq. mile. Similarly the surface runoff from the contoured-corn areas was approximately 5 inches compared with 1.5 inches for the level-terraced and grassed areas. The experimental watersheds were of the order of 100 square miles.

Other land use factors are discussed in a paper

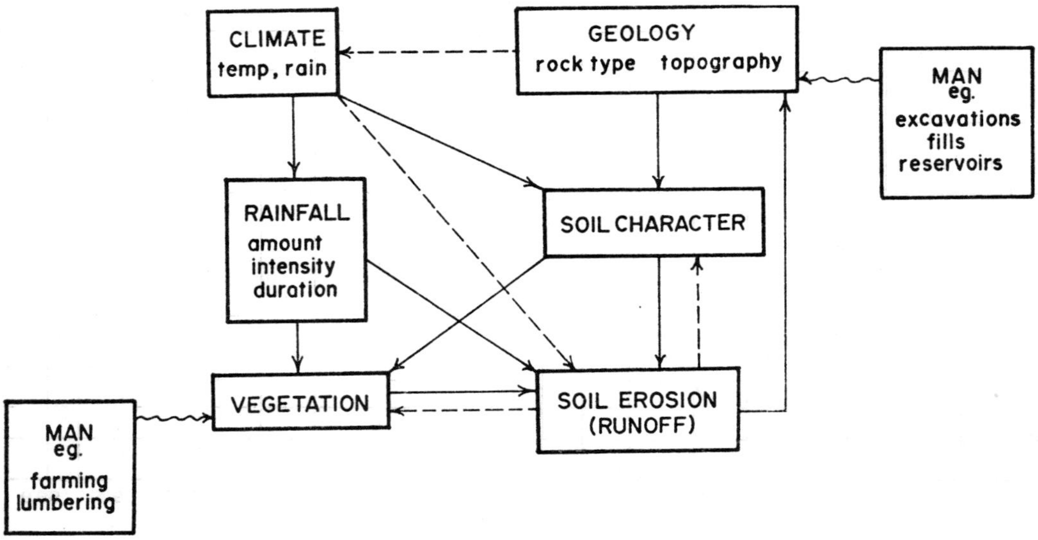

Figure 2 The relationship of climate and geology to soil erosion (adapted from Morisawa).

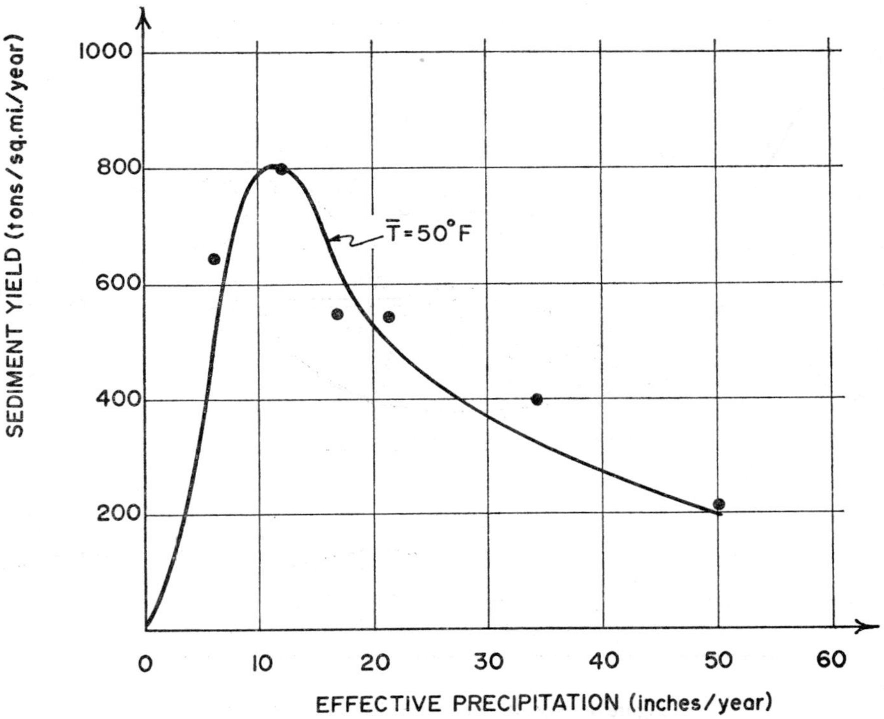

Figure 3 Sediment yield in the United States (after Langbein and Schumm).

by Dawdy[12] who presents sediment yields for the state of Maryland. The annual sediment yield from heavily wooded areas is about 15 tons/sq. mile compared with 200 to 900 for crop land. The annual sediment yields from urban development areas (usually only a few acres) varied from about 1,000 to 140,000 tons/sq. mile.

Curtis[13] obtained annual sediment yields of 390 and 290 for two watersheds (264 and 651 square miles) in the Miami Conservancy District, Ohio.

A number of empirical formulae have been developed[1,14,15] to permit estimation of rates of overland erosion. The U.S. Department of Agriculture developed the universal soil-loss equation (for upland areas),

$$E = RKLSCP, \qquad 3.1$$

where E = soil loss/unit area; R = rainfall runoff factor; K = soil erodibility factor; L = slope length factor; S = slope steepness factor; C_1 = crop management factor and P_1 = erosion control practice factor. Details for estimating the above factors are given by Meyer.[15]

4. Measurement of Sediment Discharge

Samplers have been developed to measure both suspended and bed load in streams. However bed-load samplers are not widely used because of their doubtful accuracy. Generally, only suspended load samples are collected in samplers of the type shown schematically in Figure 4. This sampler is designed so that the intake velocity is nearly the same as the local stream velocity. The extent of the suspended sampled zone is limited by the size of the sampler. Methods of extrapolating these measurements and estimating bed load are discussed in Section 5.

For more details, of sediment measurement techniques and equipment, the reader is referred to the recent articles by Nordin and Richardson,[15] Shen[15] and Karaki,[15] as well as the reference works of Graf[16] and Brown.[1]

In some instances[15] turbulence flumes (a concrete lined reach with baffles to create severe turbulence) have been constructed across a stream channel in order to suspend the bed load and thus to sample it by suspended load techniques.

5. The Mechanics of Sediment Transport in a Stream

5.1 General

The nature of sediment transport in a stream depends on the shear intensity of the flow and the type of bed material. The diagrams in Figure 5 shows the sequence of bed forms (waves) associated with increasing levels of shear on a fine granular bed material.[3] This figure also shows, schematically, the typical changes in the Darcy friction factor and

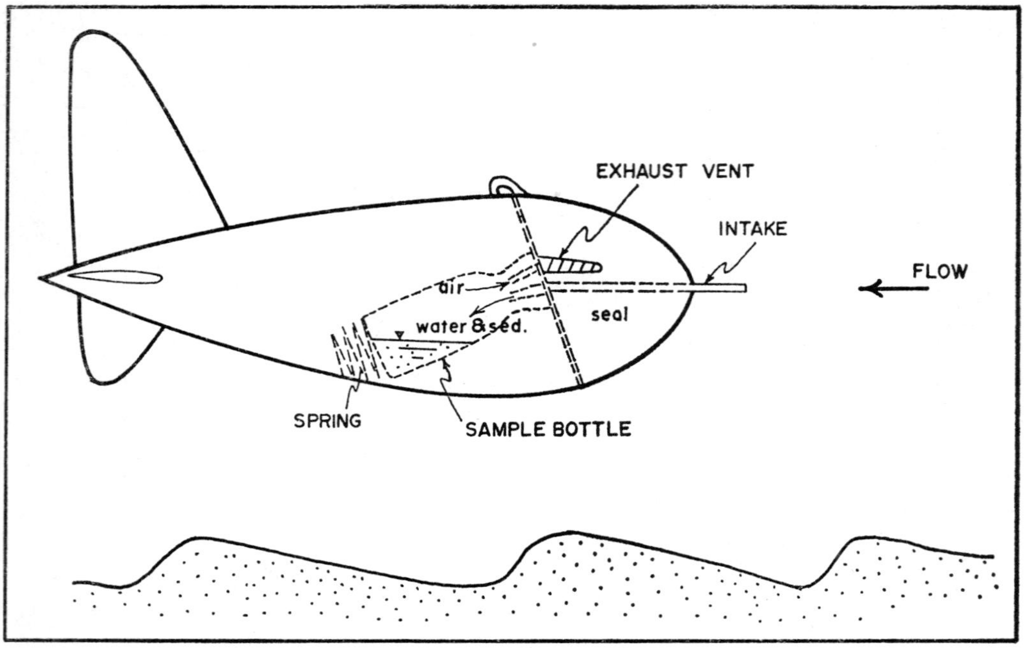

Figure 4 Sketch of a suspended load sampler.

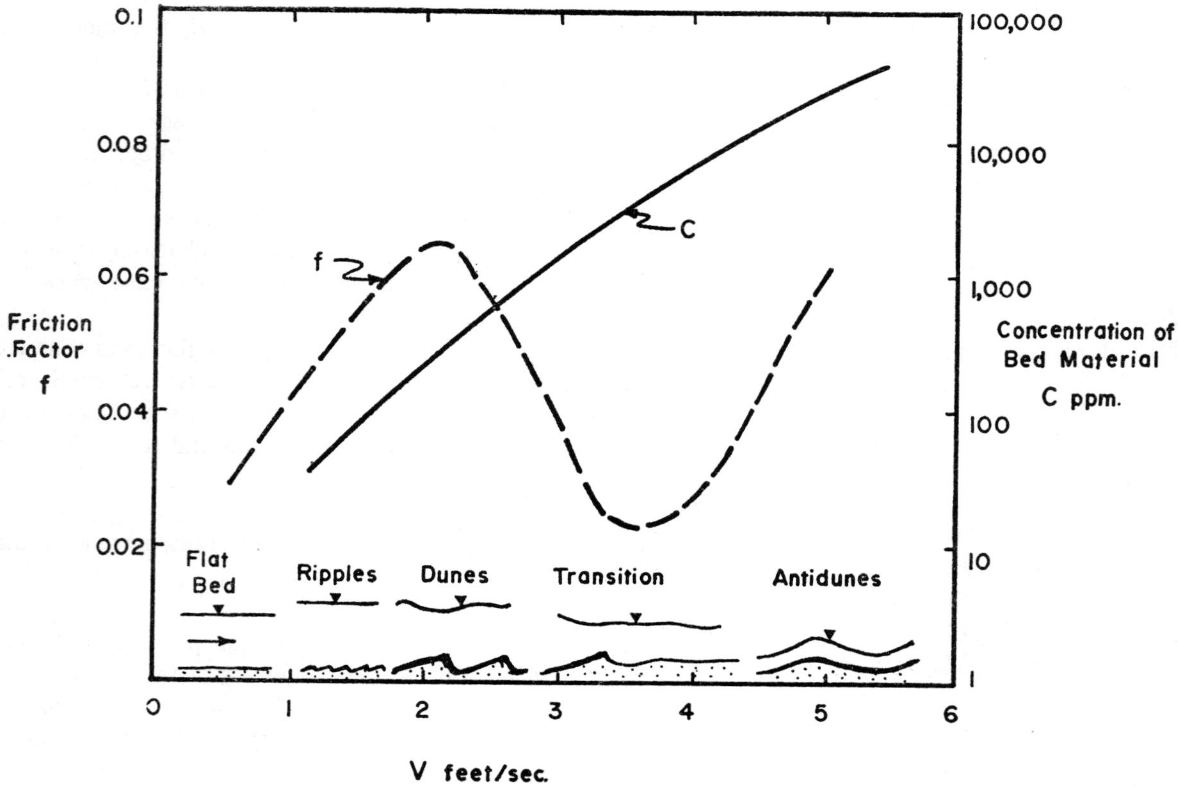

Figure 5 The behaviour of a mobile stream bed (adapted from Leopold, Wolman, and Miller).

the sediment concentration with increasing flow velocity. The primary mode of transport of particles, in the case of ripples,[17] is discrete steps along the bed; however with increasing shear more of the bed material becomes suspended until the particle motion is nearly continuous for anti-dunes.

Dunes and ripples are triangular in shape with relatively flat upstream slopes and steep downstream slopes. The water surface waves are out of phase with the dune formations while ripple formations appear to be independent of the free surface.

Dune wave lengths, λ_d, are related to the depth of flow and in general,

$$\lambda_d > 3 \text{ feet} \qquad 5.1$$

whereas ripple wave lengths λ_r are shorter,

$$2'' \lesssim \lambda_r \lesssim 18''. \qquad 5.2$$

Dune heights, H_d, are related to the depth of flow, with the limiting height approaching the average flow depth. The ratio of dune length to height is given by[17]

$$8 \gtrsim \frac{\lambda}{H_d} \gtrsim 15. \qquad 5.3$$

The maximum ripple height is about 0.1 feet.

Both ripples and dunes progress downstream. The transition from dunes to anti-dunes occurs at a Froude number close to 1.0.

Anti-dunes, as indicated by Figure 5, are in phase with the surface wave. They may be stationary or move upstream. The maximum height of an anti-dune is approximately equal to the flow depth at the trough of the surface wave.

Simons[17,18] on the basis of experimental data, developed the relationship, shown in Figure 6, between stream power and bedform for varying fall diameters. Simons and Richardson[19] also

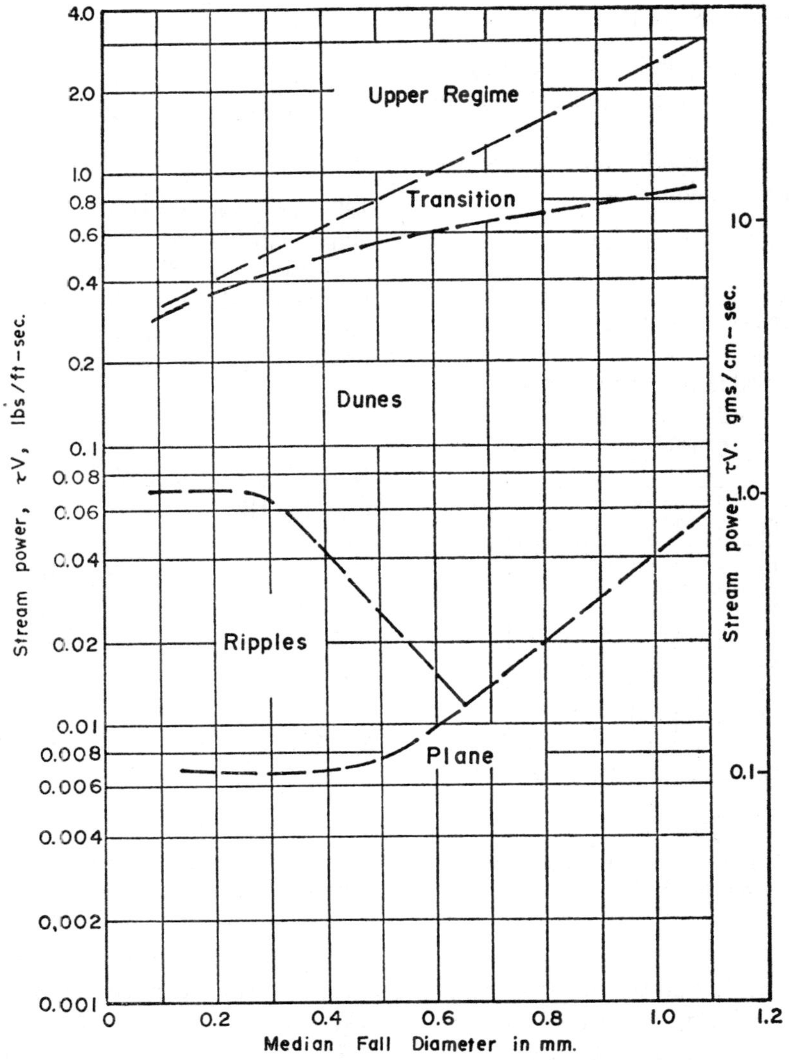

Figure 6 Relation of stream power and median fall diameter to bed form (after Simons).

studied the variation of Chézy's C with bed form. Their results are summarized in Table II.

TABLE II

Chézy C in Sand Channels

Regime	Bed form	$C/\sqrt{g}$ (where C is Chézy C)
Lower regime	ripples d_{50} < .6mm	7.8 to 12.4
	dunes	7.0 to 13.2
	transition	7.0 to 20
Upper regime	plane bed	16.3 to 20
	anti-dune {standing wave	15.1 to 20
	{breaking wave	10.8 to 16.3
	chutes and pools	9.4 to 10.7
	'slug' flow	—

5.2 Initial motion

White in 1940,[20,21] using an analytical approach, showed that, for sufficiently turbulent flow over a granular bed, the critical shear or shear to initiate grain movement is

$$\tau_c = \kappa_c \gamma_f (S_s - 1)\, d, \qquad 5.4$$

in which $\kappa_c \simeq .06$; γ_f = fluid specific weight; S_s = specific gravity of sediment grain; d = grain diameter.

Shields,[21] using an experimental approach, obtained the more general equation

$$\tau_c = \gamma_f (S_s - 1)\, d f(R_*), \qquad 5.5$$

in which $R_* = U_* d/v$; U_* = friction velocity; v = kinematic viscosity; and $f(R_*)$ is defined in Figure 7.

Permissible or allowable tractive stresses for use in channel designs with granular or cohesive boundaries are given by Chow.[7]

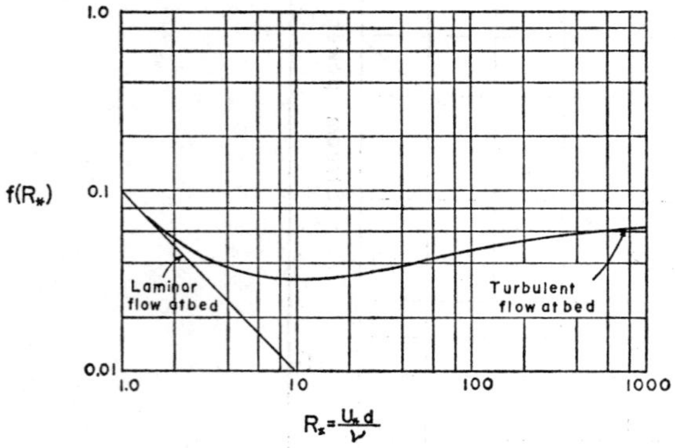

Figure 7 Shields' critical shear function (adapted from Henderson).

5.3 Bed load formulae

When the bed shear, τ_o, due to the flowing stream exceeds the critical shear, τ_c, a part of the bed material starts to move in a layer of the stream near the bed, i.e. the bed layer. Experimental

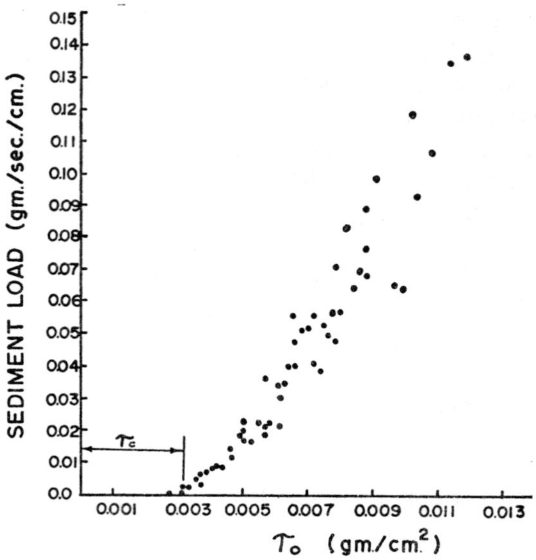

Figure 8 Typical relation of shear and sediment load (adapted from Leopold, Wolman and Miller).

studies[3] indicate that this sediment discharge, known as the bed load, q_B, is a function of the excess of τ_o above τ_c or

$$q_B \propto fcn(\tau_o - \tau_c). \qquad 5.6$$

Figure 8 illustrates a typical experimental relationship between q_B and $(\tau_o - \tau_c)$.

DuBoys in 1879[22] treated the bed material, involved in the bed load, as if it consisted of sliding layers which respond to and distribute the applied stress τ_o. He proposed the relation

$$q_B = C_s \tau_o (\tau_o - \tau_c) \qquad 5.7$$

Both C_s and τ_c depend on particle size as indicated in Table III.

TABLE III

Typical values of C_s and τ_c [after Straub[23, 22]]

d mm	$\frac{1}{8}$	$\frac{1}{4}$	$\frac{1}{2}$	1	2	4
$C_s\ \frac{\text{ft}^6}{16^2 - \text{sec}}$	.81	.48	.29	0.17	0.10	.09
$\tau_c\ \frac{\text{lb}}{\text{ft}^2}$	.016	.017	.022	.032	.051	.09

Note: q_B will have units of ft³/sec/ft. width.

Chang,[1] Schoklitsch,[1,16] MacDougall[1] and Shields[1] have presented bed load formulae similar to Equation 5.7.

The theoretical bed load model developed by Einstein[4,5,8,24] has formed the basis for a number of researches in sediment transport.[6,15,24,36] Einstein utilized: (a) the statistical nature of turbulent flow; (b) the fact that in steady uniform flow there is an equilibrium between the processes of erosion and deposition, i.e. (probability of erosion) = (the probability of deposition); (c) the fact that grains near the bed move in quick "steps" interrupted by "rest" periods; (d) a separate hydraulic radius, R', associated with grain roughness and another hydraulic radius, R'', associated with the bed form.

Einstein obtained the erosion probability function by assuming that the lift force, on a grain, consists of an average component [related to $(U_*)^2$] and a normally distributed random component. Einstein thus obtained the "bed load" equation

$$\frac{A_*\Phi_*}{1 + A_*\Phi_*} = 1 - \frac{1}{\sqrt{\pi}}\int_{-B_*\psi_*-(1/\eta_o)}^{B_*\psi_*-(1/\eta_o)} e^{-t^2\,dt} \qquad 5.8$$

in which

$$\Phi_* = \frac{i_B q_B}{i_b \gamma_s \sqrt{gd^3(S_s - 1)}} \qquad 5.9$$

is Einstein's bed transport function; $A_* = 43.5$; $B_* = 0.143$; $\eta_o = 1/2$;

$$\psi_* = \xi Y \left\{\frac{\log 10.6}{\log \dfrac{10.6X}{\Delta}}\right\}^2 (S_s - 1)\frac{d}{S_e R'} \qquad 5.10$$

in the Einstein flow intensity function; i_B = fraction of q_B in the size range associated with d; d = geometric mean of particle size range being considered; S_e = energy slope; i_b = fraction of bed sediment in specified range; ξ = hiding factor; Y = lift correction factor; $\Delta = d_{65}/\chi$; χ = correction factor for hydraulically smooth flow; $\delta' = 11.6\nu/U_*$;

$$U_*' = \times gR'S_e \qquad 5.11$$

$X = .770$ if $\Delta/\delta' > 1.80$; $X = 1.39\delta'$ if $\Delta/\delta' < 1.80$.

Shen[15] gives an up-to-date review of the modern stochastic approaches to the bed material transport problem.

5.4 The suspended load

5.4.1 Equations of Motion of the Fluid The flow in natural streams is almost always turbulent and may be assumed to incompressible; consequently the applicable equations of motion for the fluid are the Reynolds[25] equations

$$\rho\left[\frac{\partial \bar{U}_i}{\partial t} + \bar{U}_j\frac{\partial \bar{U}_i}{\partial x_j}\right] = \frac{\partial}{\partial x_j}(\sigma_{ji}) + \bar{F}_i, \qquad 5.12$$

in which $\bar{U}_i$ = ensemble mean point velocity in the direction i; σ_{ji} = stress tensor = $\{-\bar{P}\delta_{ji} + \mu\bar{D}_{ji} - \rho\overline{u_iu_j}\}$; $\bar{P}$ = average pressure; δ_{ji} = Kronecker delta; μ = dynamic viscosity; $\bar{D}_{ji}$ = deformation tensor; $-\rho\,\overline{u_iu_j}$ = turbulence or Reynold's Stresses; ρ = fluid density; u_i = random component of velocity in the i direction; $\bar{F}$ = body force in the i direction. The first term in the stress tensor represents the normal stresses due to the average pressure at a point; the second term represents the viscous shear forces; the last term or Reynold's stress has both normal and tangential components. A common method of simplfying equations involves the introduction of an eddy viscosity, ϵ_m such that

$$\rho\epsilon_m\bar{D}_{ji} = -\rho\overline{u_iu_{j(j\neq i)}}. \qquad 5.13$$

The requirement that $(i \neq j)$ in Equation 5.13 eliminates the normal stresses due to turbulence; in order to account for these normal stresses an average turbulence pressure $\bar{P}_t$ is added to $\bar{P}$ thus yielding the simplified stress tensor

$$\sigma_{ji} = -(\bar{P} + \bar{P}_t)\delta_{ji} + (\mu + \rho\epsilon_m)_i\bar{D}_j. \qquad 5.14$$

The fluid continuity equation is

$$\frac{\partial \bar{U}_i}{\partial x_i} = 0. \qquad 5.15$$

Equations 5.12, 5.14 and 5.15 may be solved in a few cases by methods developed to solve the Navier–Stokes equations.

5.4.2 Transport of a Scalar Quantity in Turbulent Flow In an incompressible turbulent fluid the conservation of a scalar quantity requires that the rate of change of a scalar (say $\bar{c}$ units/unit mass of fluid) at a point equals the rate of diffusion of $\bar{c}$ plus the rate of generation of $\bar{c}$ at the point or

$$\frac{D\bar{c}}{Dt} = \frac{\partial}{\partial x_i}\left(h\frac{\partial \bar{c}}{\partial x_i} - \overline{u_ic'}\right) + \bar{F}_c \qquad 5.16$$

in which $c = \bar{c} + c'$; $\bar{c}$ = ensemble average of c; c' = random component of c; D/Dt = substantial derivative; $_c$ is the generation term; h = molecular diffusion coefficient. It is usual to introduce, into Equation 5.16, and 'eddy" transport coefficient ϵ_j, such that

$$-\overline{u_ic'} = \varepsilon_c\frac{\partial \bar{c}}{\partial x_i}. \qquad 5.17$$

Since in most practical problems $\epsilon_c \gg h$, then Equation 5.16 can be reduced to

$$\frac{D\bar{c}}{dt} = \frac{\partial}{\partial x_i}\left[\varepsilon_c\frac{\partial \bar{c}}{\partial x_i}\right] + \bar{F}_c. \qquad 5.18$$

Equations 5.2 and 5.18 are valid for low sediment

concentrations. A review paper by Vasiliev[26] discusses the governing equations which account for various levels of sediment concentrations. For example a first order correction to the Reynold's equation is

$$\rho \frac{D\bar{U}_i}{Dt} = \frac{\partial}{\partial x_j}(\sigma_{ji}) + (1 + r\bar{c})F_i. \qquad 5.19$$

The volume continuity equation is the same as Equation 5.15 while the mass continuity equation becomes

$$\frac{D\bar{c}}{Dt} = -\frac{\partial}{\partial x_i}(\overline{c'u_i}) + \left\{v_s \frac{\partial \bar{c}}{\partial x_3}\right\} \qquad 5.20$$

rate of change diffusion settling out

in which $r = (S_s - 1)$; $\bar{c}$ = average ensemble concentration at a point (mass/mass); v_s = settling velocity; x_3 = vertical coordinate (opposite to the direction of v_s).

5.4.3 The Vertical Concentration Profile There is no general solution for Equations 5.12, 5.15 and 5.18 or 5.19, 5.17 and 5.20; however a few special cases, of practical interest, have been solved.

Using the simplifications which result for steady, uniform flow in two dimensions (as shown in Figures 9 and 10), it is possible to obtain a solution for the vertical, velocity and concentration profiles. The following assumptions are typical of those required to solve Equations 5.12, 5.13 and 5.20

a) $\bar{c} \gg 1$;

b) $\epsilon_c = \beta\epsilon_m$ where $\beta \simeq 1$;

c) $\bar{F}_x \simeq g\rho S_o$;

d) $\dfrac{\partial(\bar{P} + \bar{P}_t)}{\partial x} = 0$;

e) $\tau_o = \rho g S_o D$ and $\tau = \rho g S_o(D - y)$;

f) $\tau = \rho\, l^2 \left(\dfrac{d\bar{U}_x}{dy}\right)^2 = \rho\varepsilon_m \dfrac{d\bar{U}_x}{dx}$ for turbulent flow

g) $l = \kappa y$ where $\kappa \simeq 0.4$.

Chang *et al.*[27] used the above assumptions to obtain: (a) the vertical velocity profile,

$$\bar{U}_x = \frac{2U_*}{\kappa}\left\{\sqrt{1-\varepsilon} - \ln\left(\frac{\varepsilon^{1/2}}{1-\sqrt{1-\varepsilon}}\right) + \frac{1}{3}\right\} + \bar{\bar{U}}_x \qquad 5.21$$

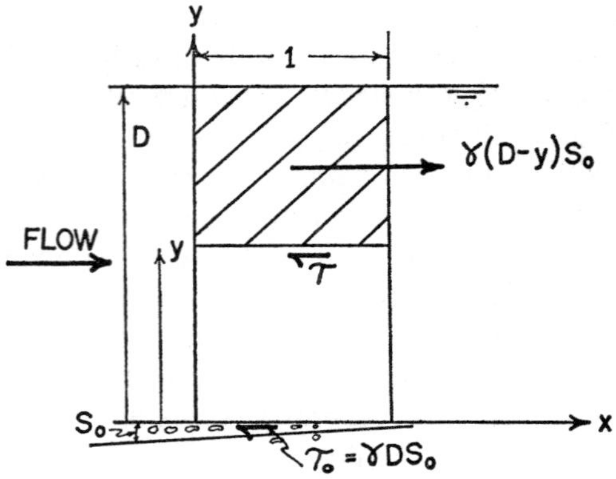

Figure 9 Defining sketch for uniform flow.

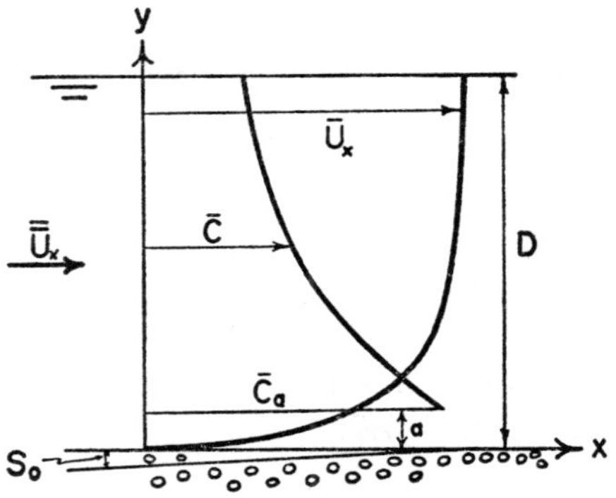

Figure 10 Defining sketch for velocity and concentration profiles.

and (b) the vertical concentration profile

$$\bar{c}(y) = \bar{c}_a\left\{\left(\frac{y}{a}\right)^{1/2}\frac{(D - \sqrt{D-a})}{(D - \sqrt{D-y})}\right\}^{2Z}, \qquad 5.22$$

in which U_* = friction velocity = $\sqrt{gDS_o}$; $\kappa = fcn\,(U_* d/v) \lesssim 0.4$; $\epsilon = y/D$; $\bar{\bar{U}}$ = average velocity in vertical; a = reference height; $Z = v_s/(\beta U_* \kappa)$. Using the Keulegan velocity distributions

$$\bar{U}_x = 5.75\log_{10}\left(\frac{9.05yU_*}{v}\right) \text{(for smooth boundaries)} \qquad 5.23a$$

and

$$\bar{U}_x = 5.75\log_{10}\left(\frac{30.2y}{d_{65}}\right) \text{(for rough boundaries).} \qquad 5.23b$$

Einstein and others[5,1] have obtained a slightly different equation for $c(y)$, i.e.

$$\bar{c}(y) = \bar{c}_a\left[\frac{a(D-y)}{y(D-a)}\right]^Z. \qquad 5.24$$

5.4.4 The Suspended Sediment Load The suspended sediment discharge q_s (weight/unit time/unit width) above a reference level $y = a$ is given by

$$q_s = \gamma \int_a^D \overline{U}_x \bar{c}\, dy, \qquad 5.25$$

where $\overline{U}$ and $\bar{c}$ are given by Equations 5.21 and 5.22 or 5.23 and 5.24.

5.4.5 Longitudinal Dispersion Another problem which has received some attention is that of longitudinal diffusion and dispersion in natural streams and estuaries. Several researchers[16,33,34,35] have sought analytical and numerical solutions for the longitudinal variation in the mean concentration in the vertical, $\hat{c}$.

Considering two dimensional longitudinal dispersion, Equation 5.16 can be approximated by[16]

$$\frac{\partial \hat{c}}{\partial t} + \overline{U}_x \frac{\partial \hat{c}}{\partial x} = E_L \frac{\partial^2 \hat{c}}{\partial x^2} \qquad 5.26$$

in which $E_L \simeq$ coefficient of longitudinal diffusion. A typical[16] value for E_L is

$$E_L = 5.9\overline{U}_* D. \qquad 5.27$$

The solution of Equation 5.26 for initial concentration M_o is

$$\hat{c}(x, t) = \frac{M_o}{\sqrt{4\pi E_L t}} e^{-(x-\bar{\bar{U}}_x t)^2/4E_L t}. \qquad 5.28$$

Other treatments of the dispersion problem may be found in the works of Holley,[28] Householder *et al.*,[29] Chiu *et al.*,[30] Conover *et al.*,[31] Sooky,[32] Fischer,[33] Harleman *et al.*[34] and Sayre.[35]

5.5 The total sediment load

Einstein[5] developed a unified total bed material formulae by converting his computed bed load, q_B to a reference concentration $\bar{c}_a$ at $y = a = 2d$. Inserting $\bar{c}_a$ into Equation 5.24 and 5.25 he obtained an estimate of q_{sB}, the suspended bed material load. Hence the total bed material load per unit width, q_{TB} is

$$\begin{aligned} q_{TB} &= q_B + q_{sB} \\ &= \sum_{\substack{\text{all size}\\\text{ranges}}} i_B q_B (1 + P_e I_1 + I^2) \end{aligned} \qquad 5.29$$

in which $I_1 = K\int_{A_e}^1 (1/y - 1)^Z\, dy$; $I_2 = K\int_{A_e}^1 (1/y - 1)\, \ln y\, dy$; $K = .216 A_e^{Z'-1}/(1 - A_e)^{Z'}$; $A_e = 2d/D$; $P_e = 2.3 \log 30.2\chi d/d_{65}$; $Z' = v_s/(\beta U_* \kappa)$; ($\chi$ see Section 5.3.).

The total sediment load per unit width in a stream ϵ_T is

$$\epsilon_T = \epsilon_{TB} + \epsilon_w, \qquad 5.30$$

where q_w = wash load (fines) which must be obtained independently, e.g. by direct measurement. The Einstein method requires a knowledge of: grain size distribution in the bed; the grain density; the energy slope, S_e; and the water temperature, in order to compute both bed material load and water discharge for a given depth and width of flow.

Colby and Hembree[9,36] modified Einstein's method in order to compute total sediment load (q_T). Their procedure utilizes: the sampled suspended load Q_s; measured discharge; measured depths and sampler depths, the extent of the sampled zone; and all the data used by the Einstein procedure except S_e. Their main modifications are:

a) The finer portion of the total suspended load, Q_s, is based on extrapolation of the actual sampled load Q_s' (using Equations 5.24 and 5.25).

b) The coarser part of the total load (including the bed load) is computed from a simplified Einstein procedure (using a modification of Equation 5.29).

c) Einstein's grain shear velocity U_*' is replaced by an equivalent shear velocity U_m based on the Keulegan equations and the measured discharge.

d) Einstein's flow intensity function ψ_*, is replaced by the larger of

$$\psi_m = 1.65 g d_{35}/(U_m)^2 \quad \text{or} \quad \psi_m = .66 g d/(U_m)^2 \qquad 5.31$$

e) The modified term ψ_m is used to enter Einstein's Equation 5.8 to obtain a bed transport function Φ_*; the modified bed transport function is

$$\Phi_m = \pi_*/2 \qquad 5.32$$

The value of Φ_m is used to compute the bed load associated with a size range d, i.e.

$$i_B q_B \simeq 1200\, d^{3/2} i_B \Phi_m \text{ lb/sec/ft.} \qquad 5.33$$

f) Using the computed bed load for a certain size range, $i_B Q_B$, the measured suspended load in the same size range, $i_s Q_s'$, and Einstein's Equation 5.29 one can obtain a value for Z' in Equation 5.24 which should be better than a Z' based on an estimated v_s.

Bishop, Simons and Richardson[6] simplified the Einstein procedure for determining total bed material load. They introduced a single sediment transport function Φ_T which includes both suspended bed material and bed load. Their flow intensity term is

$$\psi_T = (S_s - 1)\frac{d_{50}}{R'S_e}. \qquad 5.34$$

The experimental relationships shown in Figure 11 were established for actual river sediments of various median sizes. Using Φ_T from Figure 11 the total bed material load per unit width, is

$$q_{TB} = \Phi_T \rho_s (gd)^{3/2}(S_s - 1)^{1/2}. \qquad 5.35$$

The wash load must be added to q_{TB} to obtain the total sediment load.

Colby[37] analysed extension laboratory and field data to establish the empirical relatiosnhip, shown in Figure 12, for the determination of sand discharge. Figure 12 is valid for a water temperature of 60°F and a low to moderate wash load ($\hat{c}$ < 10,000 ppm). Colby provides adjustment coefficients for water temperature and wash load. For example, at a flow depth of 10 feet *a* ± 20°F change in temperature would result in about ∓ 25% change in the sand discharge and an increase in the concentration of fines from 0 to 100,000 ppm could cause up to 10 fold increase in the sand load.

The reader is referred to Graf,[16] Shen[15] and Chang *et al.*[27] for other contributions to the determination of total bed material load.

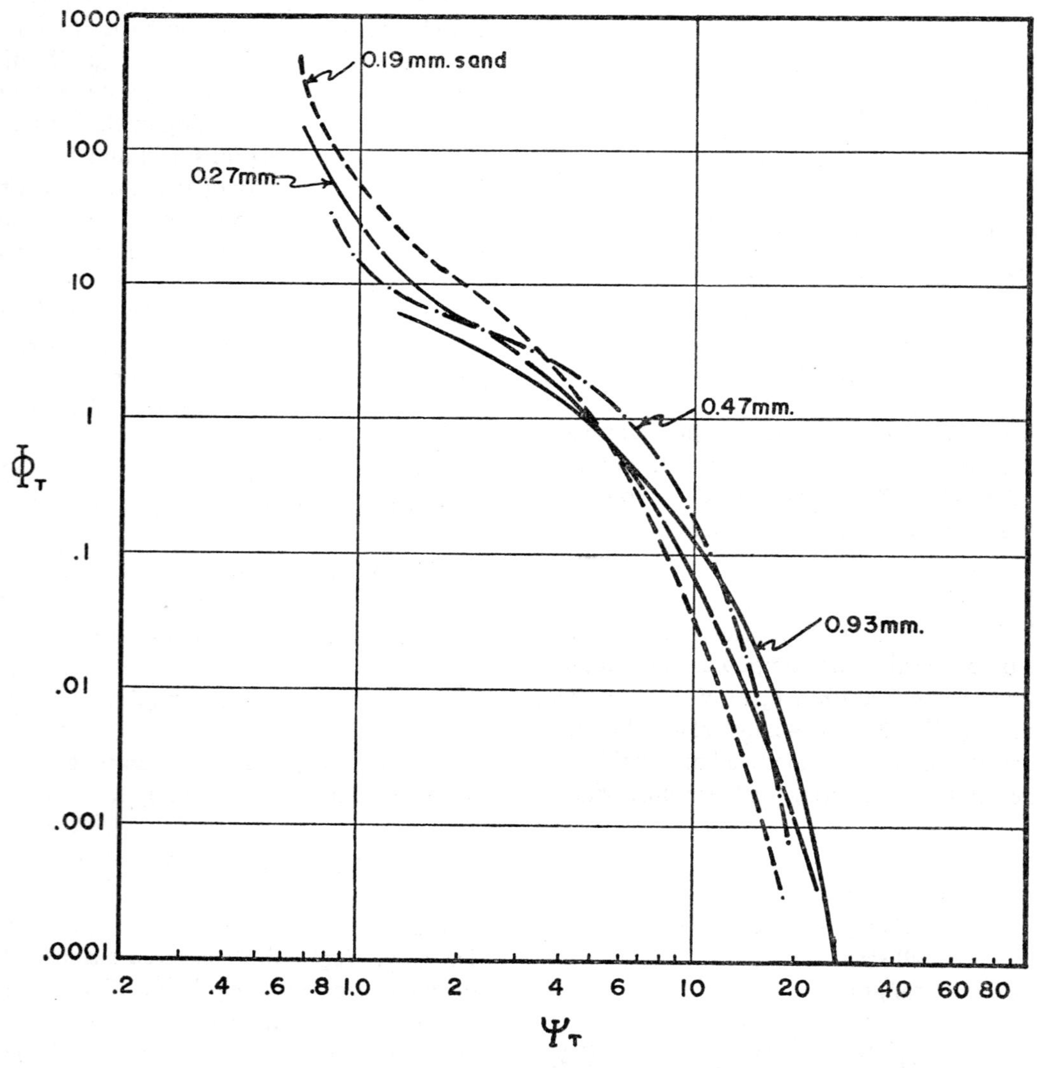

Figure 11 Bed material transport function (after Bishop *et al.*).

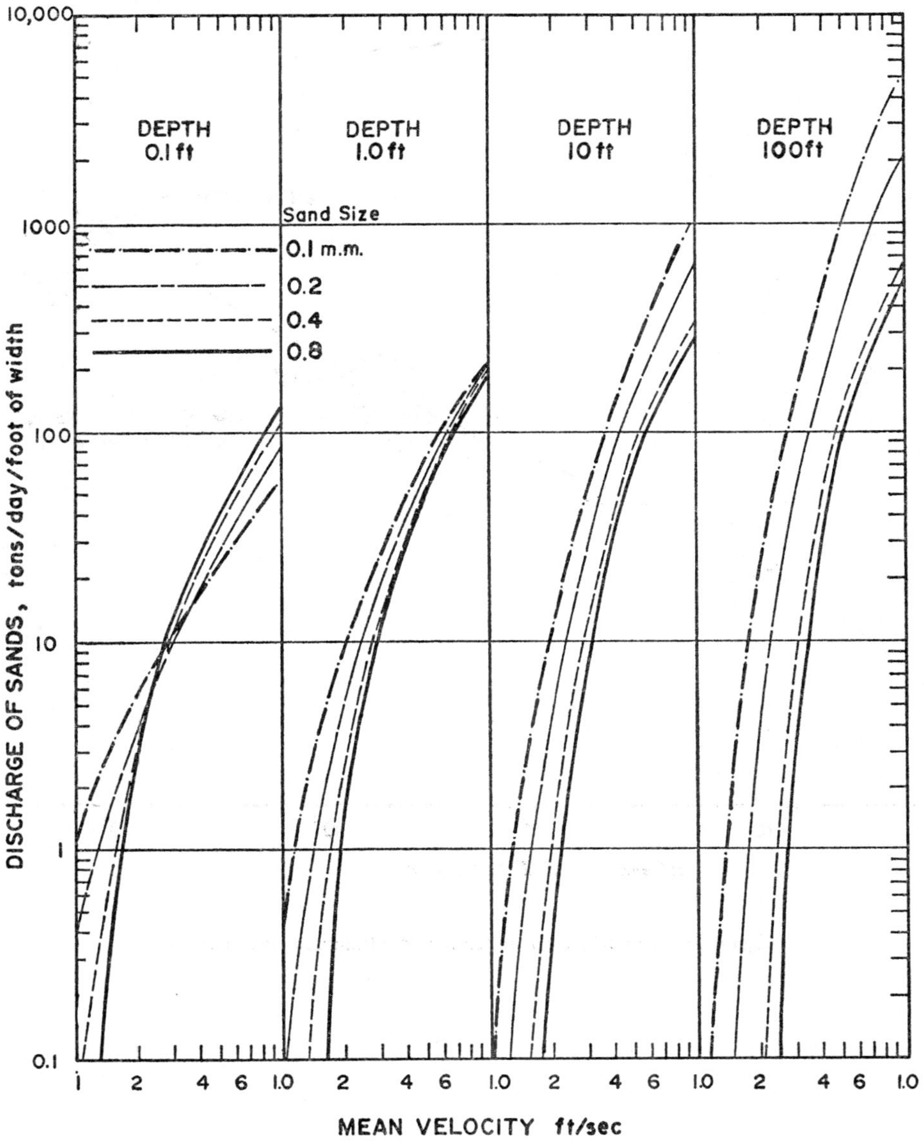

Figure 12 Sand discharge (after Colby).

5.6 The annual sediment transport

In general it is not practical to continuously sample the sediment in a stream; instead, representative samples are taken for various flow conditions and a sediment load verses water discharge or sediment rating curve is established. A typical sediment rating curve is shown in Figure 13. A number of factors contribute to the scatter of data points in Figure 13. The sediment load is out of phase with the discharge hydrograph as illustrated by Figure 14. The sediment load depends on the season of the year.

Using the available stream flows and the sediment rating curve an average annual sediment transport can be estimated.

Often the bed load is not included in the sediment rating curve; if this is the case, the bed load may be computed as discussed in Section 5.3 and added to the annual sediment transport.

6. The Response of a Channel to Changes in it's Sediment Characteristics

6.1 Lane's model

Lane[39] proposed the relationship
(sediment load) × (sediment size) ∝ (stream slope) × (stream flow)
or

$$(Q_s \times d) \propto (S \times Q) \qquad 6.1$$

to describe qualitatively to behaviour of a stream carrying sediment.

Lane used the following terms in referring to

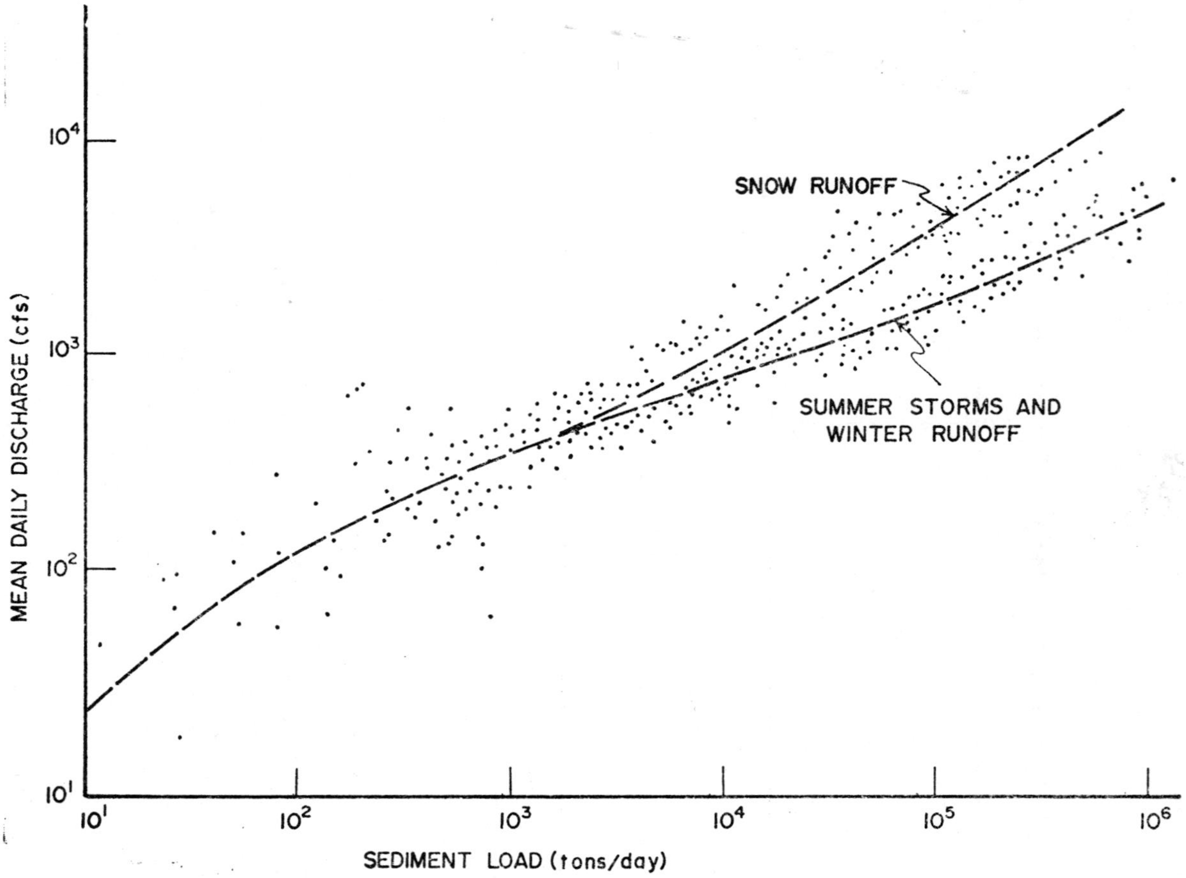

Figure 13 Typical sediment rating curve (adapted from Ref. 38).

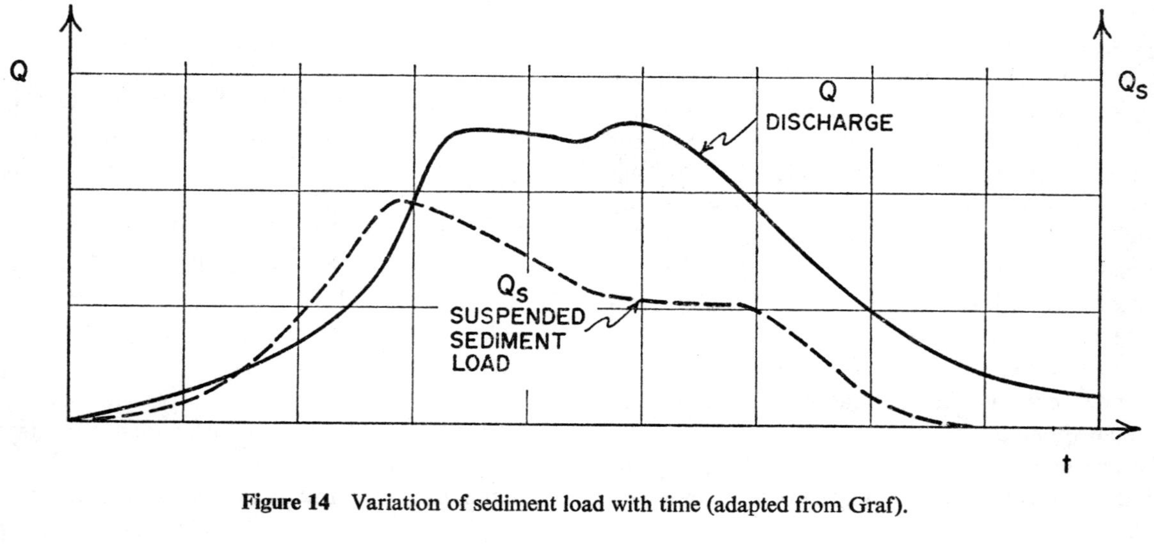

Figure 14 Variation of sediment load with time (adapted from Graf).

streams: (a) "grade" ≡ equilibrium or regime slope; (b) "aggrading" ≡ rising of the stream bed due to deposition; (c) "degrading" ≡ lowering of the stream bed due to scouring; (d) "base level" ≡ the local level to which a stream tends to cut its bed.

Lane contended that there is a natural tendency for a balance between the products in Equation 6.1. For example, if one of the factors, Q_s, is decreased then, in order to balance the equation, the stream slope might also tend to decrease, i.e. degradation. On the other hand an increase in Q_s could lead to an increase in S, i.e. aggradation.

6.2 The regime approach

"The dimensions (width, depth and slope) of a channel to carry a given discharge, with a given silt load, are fixed by nature, i.e. uniquely determined." A channel whose dimensions are so established is said to be in regime.

In the geological sense[3,10] a river system is never really in equilibrium. According to W. M. Davis, who postulated a geomorphological cycle,[3,10] the agents of uplift and gravity (represented mainly by stream erosion) are always opposing each other. However, from the engineering point of view, a stream can be considered to be in "equilibrium" over a period of a few decades if its average behaviour or average dimensions remain unchanged. There are always fluctuations, of the channel geometry, about this average; thus the stream is sometimes said to be in "dynamic equilibrium".

Of course, a stream may be aggrading or degrading (on the average in Engineering time) and thus it is not in equilibrium. The regime theory could be used to predict the ultimate dimensions of a stream that is not in regime.

Kennedy[40] and Lindley[41] collected data from canals in India (Pakistan) and proposed an equation for the non-silting, non-scouring velocity, v,

$$v = C_1 y^n, \qquad 6.2$$

where $C_1 = 8.4$; $n = 0.64$; and y = depth of flow.

Kennedy was followed by Lacey, Inglis and Blench who developed equations for channel slope and width.

Lacey[42,21] introduced the equations:

$$v = 1.17\sqrt{fR} \qquad 6.3$$

$$f = 8\sqrt{d} \qquad 6.4$$

$$v = 16R^{2/3}S^{1/3} \qquad 6.5$$

$$P = 2.67\sqrt{Q} \qquad 6.6$$

in which R = hydraulic radius (ft.); d = medium grain diameter (inches); P = wetted perimeter (ft.); Q = dominant discharge = vPR (cfs.).

The dominant discharge in the case of canal flow is the design flow. In the case of a natural stream it is the channel forming flow which is often taken to be the bank-full discharge[3] which has an approximate return period of, between 1.25 and 2.33, years.

Blench[43] advanced the work of Lacey and introduced bed and side factors to better describe the depth and width of a channel in regime. His equations are:

$$f_b = v^2/y = \text{bed factor} \qquad 6.7$$

$$f_s = v^3/b = \text{side factor} \qquad 6.8$$

$$\text{and} \quad S = \frac{(f_b)^{5/6}(f_s)^{1/12}\nu^{1/4}}{3.63gQ^{1/6}(1 + c/2330)}, \qquad 6.9$$

in which c is the concentration in ppm; b = mean width (ft–sec. units). The recommended f_b is

$$f_b = 9.6\sqrt{d(\text{in.})}(1 + .012c) \qquad 6.10$$

and f_s depends on the cohesiveness of the material in the channel banks. For example, f_s is approximately 0.1, 0.2 and 0.3 for low, medium and high cohesiveness respectively.

The data of Lacey and Blench were mainly from canals, with moderate to low sediment loads ($c < 500$ ppm) and with sand beds and slightly cohesive banks.[17] Simons and Albertson[44,21] have extended the regime equations to make them applicable to the five channel classifications shown in Table IV.

TABLE IV

Canal Classification[44,21]

1) Sand bed and banks.
2) Sand bed and cohesive banks.
3) Cohesive bed and banks.
4) Coarse noncohesive material.
5) Same as for 2, but with heavy sediment loads, 2,000–8,000 ppm.

They proposed the following general equations:

$$P = K_1 Q^{1/2} \qquad 6.11$$

$$b = 0.9P \qquad 6.12$$

$$b = 0.92B - 2.0 \qquad 6.13$$

$$R = K_2 Q^{0.36} \qquad 6.14$$

$$y = 1.21R \quad \text{for} \quad R < 7 \text{ ft.} \qquad 6.15$$

$$y = 2 + 0.93R \quad \text{for} \quad R > 7 \text{ ft.} \qquad 6.16$$

$$v = K_3(R^2S)^m \qquad 6.17$$

$$\frac{C^2}{g} = \frac{v^2}{gyS} = K_4\left(\frac{vb}{\nu}\right)^{0.37} \qquad 6.18$$

in which C = Chézy coefficient; B = surface width; the values of the K's and m are defined in Table V.

TABLE V

Constants in Equations 6.11 *to* 6.18
(ft–sec. units)

Coefficient	Channel type 1	2	3	4	5
K_1	3.5	2.6	2.2	1.75	1.7
K_2	0.52	0.44	0.37	0.23	0.34
K_3	13.9	16.0	—	17.9	16.0
K_4	0.33	0.54	0.87	—	—
m	0.33	0.33	—	0.29	0.29

Schumm[17,45] studied the Great Plains rivers in the U.S. and similar rivers in Australia; he correlated stream geometry with discharge (mean annual flood Q_{ma}) and the percent silt-clay, M, in the channel boundary. Some of his correlations are:

$$\text{Full Bank width} = W = \frac{2.3Q_{ma}^{.58}}{(M)^{.37}} \qquad 6.19$$

$$\text{Width : depth ratio} = \frac{W}{D} = \frac{21Q_{ma}^{.18}}{(M)^{.74}} \qquad 6.20$$

$$\text{Sinuosity} = 0.94M^{0.25}, \qquad 6.21$$

The high correlation of stream geometry and M led Schumm to classify channels (see Table VI) using M as an index to the ratio of coarse load to total load.

TABLE VI

Schumm's Classification

Stream type	Bed load	Mixed load	Suspended load
M	Braided < 5%	5–20%	Meandering > 20%
Coarse load / Total total	> 11%	3–11%	< 3%

Schumm[45,17] associated meandering channels with high values of M and low bed load and braided channels (a relatively straight, steep main channel

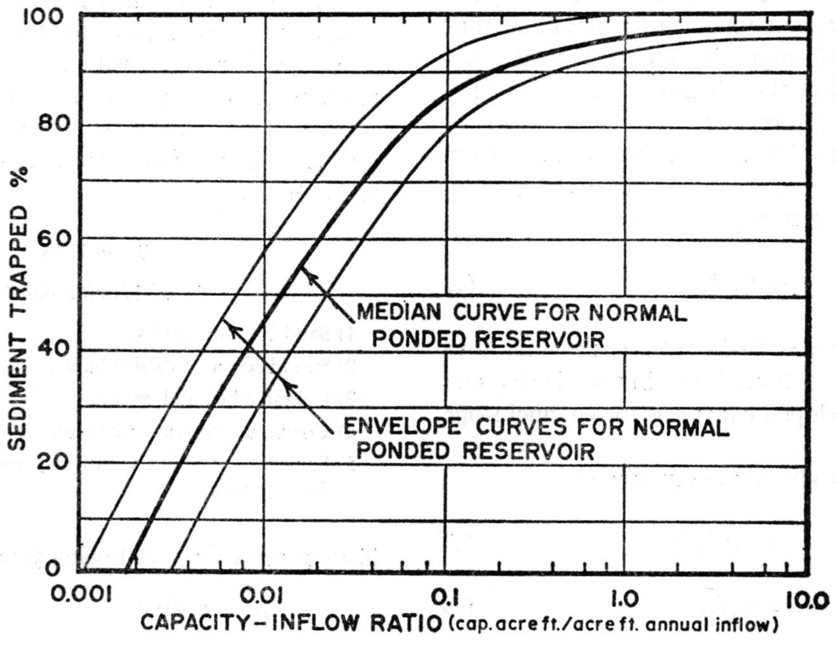

Figure 15 Trap efficiency curve (after Brune).

consisting of a maze of sub-channels sometimes separated by bars or islands) with low values of M and high bed load.

7. Reservoir Sedimentation

A common objective of many sediment transport studies is the prediction of reservoir "siltation" rates. Reservoir siltation depends on: (a) the average annual sediment load entering the reservoir; (b) the grain size distribution of the sediment load; (c) the reservoir trap efficiency; (d) the bulk dry specific weight of the deposited sediments in the reservoir.

The determination of annual sediment yields was discussed in Sections 3 and 5. It is important to predict the possible effects of land development and/or sediment control measures on future sediment yields (see Ref. 46).

An estimate of the percentages sand, silt and clay for the incoming sediment can be obtained on the basis of grain size analyses of the existing load.

Brune in 1953[47,8] presented the trap efficiency curve shown in Figure 15, which applies to reservoirs which normally ponded. Detention type reservoirs would have lower trap efficiencies.

Since annual sediment yield is usually determined in terms of weight it is necessary to know the bulk dry specific weight, and the trapped sediments, in order to estimate the volumetric decrease in reservoir storage. To accomplish this Lane and Koelzer[48,8] developed an equation to describe the change in the bulk dry specific weight, γ_*, of reservoir deposits with time, i.e.

$$\gamma_* = (\gamma^*_{\text{sand}(1)} + K_{\text{sand}} \log_{10}T)X_{\text{sand}} + (\gamma^*_{\text{silt}(1)} + K_{\text{silt}} \log_{10}T)X_{\text{silt}} + (\gamma^*_{\text{clay}(1)} + K_{\text{clay}} \log_{10}T)X_{\text{clay}} \quad 7.1$$

in which T = time in years; X_{sand} = fraction of sand in deposit; $\gamma_{*\text{sand}(1)}$ etc. are the respective bulk dry specific weights at $T \leq 1$ year (see Table VII); K_{sand} etc. are constants (see Table VII).

TABLE VII

Constants for Equation 7.1 (After Lane and Koelzer)

Reservoir operation	Sand		Silt		Clay	
	γ^*	K	γ^*	K	γ^*	K
Normally submerged	93	0	65	5.7	30	16.0
Moderate reservoir drawdown	93	0	74	2.7	46	10.7
Considerable reservoir drawdown	93	0	79	1.0	60	6.0
Reservoir normally empty	93	0	82	0.0	78	0.0

After a period of N years a reservoir will contain deposits varying in age from less than one year to N years with the consequence that the true bulk dry specific weight, γ_*, for the entire deposit should be found by averaging Equation 7.1 over the N year period. Some typical[8] averaged values of $\bar{\gamma}^*$ for various time periods are:

$$N = 10 \text{ years}, \bar{\gamma}_{*10} = \gamma_{*T=1} + .675K$$

$$N = 50 \text{ years}, \bar{\gamma}_{*50} = \gamma_{*T=1} + 1.298K$$

$$N = 100 \text{ years}, \bar{\gamma}_{*100} = \gamma_{*T=1} + 1.588K.$$

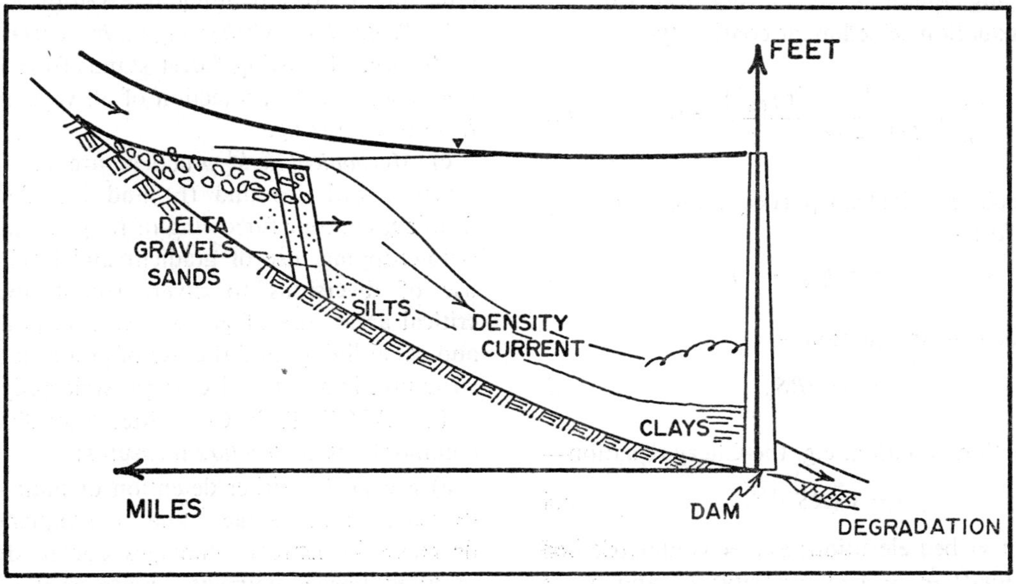

Figure 16 Distribution of deposits in a reservoir.

The decrease in storage (in acre-ft) during an N-year period is given by:

$$\Delta v = \left(\frac{\overline{TE}}{100}\right)\frac{(\overline{SY})(DA) \times N}{\bar{\gamma}_{*N}} \times \left(\frac{2000}{43560}\right) \qquad 7.2$$

in which

$\overline{TE}$ = average trap efficiency in percent;

$\overline{SY}$ = average annual sediment yield in tons/sq. mile;

(DA) = drainage area in sq. miles;

$\bar{\gamma}_{*N}$ = average bulk specific weight for the N-year computation period in lbs/ft^3.

A typical distribution of reservoir sediments is shown in Figure 16. The course sediments (sands and gravels) form a delta at the upstream section of the pond. Finer sediments are deposited downstream from the delta. Very fine sediment (clay particles) may pass through the reservoir or be deposited in the downstream portion of the pond.

8. The Degradation Problem

The response of a stream to changes in its sediment load was described qualitatively in Section 6. The problem of computing the probable rate and extent of degradation downstream from a proposed reservoir has recently received the attention of a number of researchers.[15,49,50]

Numerical estimates of the degrading channel profiles may be obtained by solving, simultaneously, the following equations (see Gessler, Ref. 15):

a) the equation of sediment continuity—

$$\frac{\partial z}{\partial t} + \frac{1}{b(1 - m)}\frac{\partial(q_{TB}b)}{\partial x} = 0 \qquad 8.1$$

b) the bed material transport equation which may have the form—

$$\epsilon_{TB} = C'(\tau_o - \tau_c)^p \qquad 8.2$$

c) the bed shear equation—

$$\tau_o = \gamma RS_e \qquad 8.3$$

d) a friction equation, e.g. the Chézy equation—

$$v = C(RS_e)^{1/2}, \qquad 8.4$$

in which z = bed elevation; q_{BT} = volumetric bed material load; m = bed porosity; C' and p are constants for a given bed material and bed form.

As the bed is scoured, an armouring process occurs due to fact that the finer bed material is more readily removed than the coarser particles in the bed (see Figure 1). This may be accounted for by adjusting τ_c in Equation 8.2.

9. Sediment Control

The adverse effects of excessive sediment loads on reservoirs, navigation channels, harbours and aquatic life may be alleviated by a sediment control programme which may include measures such as prevention of over-land erosion or containment of eroded soil near its source. On the other hand the removal of an established sediment load from a stream may also lead to undesirable consequences such as channel degradation or changes in the established aquatic life.[2]

The ASCE Sedimentation Task Committee[46] have classified sediment control measures under: (a) land treatment, (b) structural.

Land treatment measures are used to reduce wash load (fines) resulting mainly from sheet erosion. Structural measures are most effective for reducing sediment load derived from stream-channel erosion, gully erosion, and sediment associated with mining and construction work.

The main *land treatment* measures are summarized below:[46]

a) *Vegetative treatment* includes changes in the existing land use towards more: use of cover crops and crop rotation, maintenance of effective vegetative cover in critical areas, leaving of straw and stubble in the field, use of long-term hay stands, mulching, pasture planting and re-forestation.

b) *Protecting existing vegetative cover* involves protection of existing forest stands from excessive fire losses and the protection of all vegetated areas from over grazing.

c) *Mechanical field practices* are used in conjunction with (a) and (b) and include contour farming, contour furrowing of range land, contour strip-cropping, use of gradient and level terraces, use of diversions to divert runoff away from critical areas, use of grassed waterways and ditch and canal linings and the use of grade stabilization structures in areas subject to possible gully erosion.

The ASCE Task Committee[46] outlined three commonly used *structure* measures:

a) *Reservoirs*, either detention or multi-purpose, decrease flood stages and consequently may decrease downstream damages due to deposition of flood borne sediments; however it should be remembered that reservoirs themselves create sediment problems which may be just as serious as the problem being solved.

b) *Stream channel improvement and stabilization*—these measures may include straightening, cleaning, deepening and widening of existing channels in order to decrease local flood stages and related sediment damages; again, complications, such as increased channel erosion, can be expected. Other channel improvement methods are: lining the channel on bends and other erodible areas, and providing spur dykes to deflect the flow away from erodible banks.

c) *Debris and sedimentation basins* are usually relatively small reservoirs designed to trap debris and sediment near its source. This method is particularly useful in controlling sediment yields from construction sites or mining operations.

LIST OF SYMBOLS

a = $2d$ = reference distance from the stream bed;
A = flow area;
A_e = a/D;
b = average channel width;
B = top width of channel;
c = point concentration;
$\bar{c}$ = average concentration at a point;
c' = random component of concentration at a point;
$\hat{c}$ = average concentration in the vertical;
C = Chézy coefficient;
C_s = Du Boys' coefficient;
C = constant;
D = flow depth;
$\bar{D}_{ij}$ = deformation tensor;
E_L = coefficient of longitudinal dispersion;
E = erosion rate;
f = friction factor;
$fcn(\ )$ = function of ( );
$f(\ )$ = function of ( );
f = silt factor (Lacey);
f_b = bed factor (Blench);
f_s = side factor (Blench);
F_c = generation term;
F_i = body force;
g = acceleration due to gravity;
h = coefficient of molecular diffusion;
H = height;
i = index in tensor notation;
i_b = portion of material in the bed within a specified size range;
i_B = portion of the bed load in specified size range;
i_s = portion of the suspended load in specified size range;
j = index in tensor notation;
k = constant;
K = constant;
m = porosity;
m = exponent (Simons and Albertson);
M = percent silt-clay;
M_o = initial concentration;
n = exponent;
N = time period;
p = exponent;
P = wetted perimeter
$\bar{P}$ = average pressure
P_t = turbulence pressure;
q_B = bed load/unit width;
q_s = suspended load/unit width;
q_{TB} = total bed material load/unit width;
q_T = total sediment load/unit width;
q_w = wash load/unit width;
Q_s = total suspended load;
Q_T = total sediment load;
Q = water discharge;
R = hydraulic radius;
R' = hydraulic radius associated with grain roughness;
R'' = hydraulic radius associated with bed form;
r = $(S_s - 1)$;
S_s = specific weight of sediment grains,
S_o = bed slope,
S_e = energy slope,
$\overline{SY}$ = average annual sediment yield,
t = time;
T = time period;
u_i = random component of the velocity U,
U_i = instantaneous velocity in direction i;
$\bar{U}_i$ = average velocity in direction i;
U_* = friction velocity;
$\bar{U}_X$ = average point velocity in the x–direction;
$\bar{\bar{U}}_X$ = average velocity in the vertical;
v = stream velocity;
v_s = terminal settling velocity of sediment particles;
w = wash load
W = channel width;
x = coordinate;
y = coordinate;
z = coordinate;
Z = $\frac{vs}{BU^*k}$;
β = $\varepsilon_m/\varepsilon_c$;
γ = specific weight of water;
γ_s = specific weight of sediment grains;
γ_* = bulk dry specific weight of a deposit;
δ' = laminar sub-layer thickness;
δ_{ij} = Kronecker delta;
ε_m = kinematic eddy viscosity;
ε_c = kinematic eddy transport coefficient;
κ = von Karman constant $\simeq$ 0.4;
λ = wave length;
μ = dynamic viscosity;
ν = kinematic viscosity;
ρ = density;
σ_{ji} = stress tensor;
τ_o = bed shear stress;
τ_c = critical shear stress;
Φ = sediment transport function;
ψ = flow intensity function.

REFERENCES

1. Brown, C. B., Sediment Transportation, Chapter XII, *Engineering Hydraulics*, H. Rouse, Editor, J. Wiley and Sons, New York, 1950.
2. Turner, D. J., 'Dams and Ecology', *Civil Engineering*, ASCE, Sept. 1971, pp. 76–80.
3. Leopold, L. B., M. G. Wolman, and J. P. Miller, *Fluvial Processes in Geomorphology*, W. H. Freeman and Co., San Francisco, 1964.
4. Einstein, H. A., 'Formulas for the Transportation of Bed Load', *Trans. ASCE*, Vol. 107, 1942.
5. Einstein, H. A., 'The Bed-Load Function for Sediment Transportation in Open Channel Flows', U.S. Dept. of Agriculture Technical Bulletin No. 1026, 1950.
6. Bishop, A. A., D. B. Simons and E. V. Richardson, 'Total Bed-Material Transport', *Proc. ASCE*, Vol. 91, HY2, March 1965, pp. 175–191.

7. Chow, Ven Te, *Open-Channel Hydraulics*, McGraw-Hill Co., New York, 1959.
8. Chow, Ven Te, *Handbook of Applied Hydrology*, McGraw-Hill Co., New York, 1964.
9. U.S. Bureau of Reclamation, 'Step Method for Computing Total Sediment Load by the Modified Einstein Procedure', Sedimentation Section, Hydrology Branch, July 1955.
10. Morisawa, M., *Streams, Their Dynamics and Morphology*, McGraw-Hill Book Co., New York, 1968.
11. Saxton, K. E., R. G. Spomer and L. A. Kramer, 'Hydrology and Erosion of Loessial Watersheds', *Proc. ASCE*, Vol. 97, HYll, Nov. 1971, pp. 1835–1851.
12. Dawdy, D. R., 'Knowledge of Sedimentation in Urban Environments', *Proc. ASCE*, Vol. 93, HY6, Nov. 1967, pp. 235–245.
13. Curtis, L. W., 'Sedimentation in Retarding Basins', *Proc. ASCE*, Vol. 94, HY3, May 1968, pp. 739–744.
14. Wigham, J. M., 'Sediment Transportation', Section XI, *Handbook on the Principles of Hydrology*, D. M. Gray, Editor, National Research Council of Canada, 1970.
15. Shen, H. W., *River Mechanics*, Vols. I and II, Editor–Publisher H. W. Shen, P.O. Box 606, Fort Collins, Colorado, 1971.
16. Graf, W. H., *Hydraulics of Sediment Transport*, McGraw-Hill Book Co., New York, 1971.
17. Lecture Notes: Summer Institute in Fluvial Geomorphology, Colorado State University, Lecturers S. A. Schumm and D. B. Simons, 1967.
18. Simons, D. B. and E. V. Richardson, 'Forms of Bed Roughness in Alluvial Channels', *Trans, ASCE*, Vol. 128, Part 1, 1963, pp. 284–323.
19. Simons, D. B. and E. V. Richardson, 'Resistance to Flow in Sand Channels', *Proc. XII Congress of the International Association for Hydraulic Research*, Vol. 1, Sept. 1967, pp. 141–150.
20. White, C. M., 'The Equilibrium of Grains on the Bed of a Stream', *Proc. Roy. Soc. A*, Vol. 174, 1940, pp. 322–334.
21. Henderson, F. M., *Open Channel Flow*, The MacMillan Co., New York, (Chapter 10), 1966.
22. Raudkivi, A. J., *Loose Boundary Hydraulics*, Pergamon Press, New York, 1967.
23. Straub, L. G., 'Approaches to the Study of the mechanics of Bed Movement', *Proc. of Hydraulics Conference*, Univ. of Iowa Studies in Engineering, Bulletin 20, 1940.
24. Shen, H. W., (Editor), Sedimentation', Symposium to honor Professor H. A. Einstein, Berkley, California, June 1971.
25. Hinze, J. O., *Turbulence*, McGraw-Hill Book Co., New York, 1959.
26. Vasiliev, O. F., 'Problems of Two-Phase Flow Theory', General lecture XIII Congress of the International Association for Hydraulic Research, Vol. 5–3, Kyoto, 1969.
27. Chang, F. M., D. B. Simons, E. V. Richardson, 'Total Bed-Material Discharge in Alluvial Channels', *Proc. XII Congress of the International Association for Hydraulic Research*, Vol. 1, Fort Collins, Sept. 1967, pp. 132–140.
28. Holley, E. R., 'Unified View of Diffusion and Dispersion' *Proc. ASCE*, Vol. 95, HY2, March 1969, pp. 621–631.
29. Householder, M. K. and V. W. Goldschmidt, 'Turbulent Diffusion and Schmidt Number of Particles', *Proc. ASCE*, Vol. 95, EM6, Dec. 1969, pp. 1345–1369.
30. Chiu, C. L. and K. C. Chen, Stochastic Hydrodynamics of Sediment Transport', *Proc. ASCE*, Vol. 95, EM5, Oct. 1969, pp. 1215–1230.
31. Conover, W. J. and N. C. Matalas, 'Statistical Model of Turbulence in Sediment-Laden Streams', *Proc. ASCE*, Vol. 95, EM5, Oct. 1969, pp. 1063–1081.
32. Sooky, A. A., 'Longitudinal Dispersion in Open Channels', *Proc. ASCE*, Vol. 95, HY4, July 1969, pp. 1327–1346.
33. Fischer, H. B., 'Dispersion Predictions in Natural Streams', *Proc. ASCE*, Vol. 94, SA5, Oct. 1968, pp. 927–943.
34. Harleman, D. R. F. and C. H. Lee, 'Numerical Studies of Unsteady Dispersion in Estuaries', *Proc. ASCE*, Vol. 94, SA5, Oct. 1968, pp. 897–911.
35. Sayre, W. W., 'Dispersion of Silt Particles in Open Channel Flow', *Proc. ASCE*, Vol. 95, HY3, May 1969, pp. 1009–1038.
36. Colby, B. R. and C. H. Hembree, Computation of Total Sediment Discharge', U.S. Geol. Survey, Water Supply Paper 1357, 1955.
37. Colby, B. R., Discharge of Sands and Mean-velocity Relationships in Sand-Bed Streams', U.S. Geol. Survey, Prof. Paper 462·A, 1964.
38. U.S. Bureau of Reclamation, Analysis of Flow Duration, Sediment-Rating Curve Method of Computing Sediment Yield', Sedimentation Section, Hydrology Branch, Denver, Colorado, April 1951.
39. Lane, E. W., The Importance of Fluvial Morphology in Hydraulic Engineering', *Proc. ASCE*, Vol. 81, 1955.
40. Kennedy, R. G., 'The Prevention of Silting in Irrigation Canals', *Minutes of Proc. Inst. of Civil Engineers (U.K.)*, Vol. 119, 1894–95.
41. Lindley, E. S., 'Regime Channels', *Proc. Punjab Eng. Congress*, India, Vol. 7, 1919.
42. Lacey, G., 'A General Theory of Flow in Alluvium', *Proc. Inst. of Civil Engineers (U.K.)*, Vol. 27, Nov. 1946.
43. Blench, T., *Mobile Bed Fluviology*, University of Alberta Press, Edmonton, Alberta, Canada, 1966.
44. Simons, D. B., M. L. Albertson, 'Uniform Water, Conveyance Channels in Alluvial Material', *Proc. ASCE*, Vol. 86, HY5, May 1960, pp. 33–71.
45. Schumm, S. A., 'River Metamorphosis', *Proc. ASCE*, Vol. 95, HY1, Jan. 1969, pp. 255–273.
46. Vanoni, V. A., Chairman of the Task Committee for Preparation of Manual on Sedimentation, 'Sediment Control Methods—Introduction and Watershed Area', (Chap. V), *Proc. ASCE*, Vol. 95, HY2, March 1969, pp. 649–675.
47. Brune, G. M., 'Trap Efficiency of Reservoirs', *Trans. Am. Geophysical Union*, Vol. 34, No. 3, 1953, pp. 407–418.
48. Lane, E. W. and V. A. Koelzer, Report No. 9, 'Density of Sediments Deposited in Reservoirs', U.S. Government and Iowa Inst. of Hydraulic Research, 'A Study of Methods Used in measurement and analysis of Sediment Loads in Streams', 1943.
49. Komura, S. and D. B. Simons, 'River-Bed Degradation Below Dams', *Proc. ASCE*, Vol. 93, HY4, July 1967, pp. 1–14.
50. Komura, S., 'Prediction of River-Bed Degradation Below Dams', *Proc. XIV Congress of International Association for Hydraulic Research*, Vol. 3, C31, Sept. 1971.

J. A. McCorquodale
University of Windsor

SEWAGE: see MUNICIPAL WASTEWATER

SOLID WASTE DISPOSAL: see MANAGEMENT OF SOLID WASTE

SOURCES OF ENERGY: see ENERGY SOURCES—ALTERNATIVES

SOURCES OF POLLUTANTS: see AIR POLLUTION SOURCES

SPILLAGE INTO WATER—TREATMENT

The general subject of treatment of spillage represents a relatively new area of technology that is unique in that it encompasses chemical, mechanical and biological disciplines. There are three major aspects to the problem of oil spillage:

I Prevention of the Spill;
II Containment and Recovery of the Spill;
III Treatment of the Surface Oil.

Although this discussion is mainly directed toward the treatment of the spilled oil, the related areas will also be considered in order to put the overall subject in the correct perspective.

I. Prevention of the Spill

The prevention of oil spillages is the primary consideration

It should be emphasized that prevention is the first consideration and, of course, the most complete solution. In the industrial and governmental communities, the major effort has been directed toward this area. There is extensive ongoing research, for example, ranging from operational areas, e.g. collision avoidance techniques and training to more novel approaches such as the gellation of crude oil. In this latter approach, several chemical systems have been developed to gel the crude oil cargo. This in-situ solidification thereby prevents the release of oil from a damaged cargo compartment that may be in danger of failure.

Details of this gellation system can be found in U.S. Patent 3,634,050.[1] The rigidity of the gelled crude oil can be appreciated by Fig. 1. Other details, such as the effects, of mixing, crude oil type, chemical concentration, temperature, etc., on the strength of the gel have been outlined by Corino.[2] Typical data is shown by Fig. 2 depicting gel strength vs concentration of gelling agent for various typical crude and fuel oils.

Finally, the removal of the oil cargo from a grounded tanker is another area where the threat of the release of a fluid and mobile oil cargo to the marine environment has been mitigated by advances in salvage techniques. The offloading of the grounded SS *General Colocotronis* on a reef off Eleuthera Island in March–April 1969 and the well documented recovery of Bunker C oil from the sunken tanker SS *Arrow* in Chedabucto Bay, Nova Scotia during the winter of 1970[3] are two outstanding examples of this prevention technique.

This latter incident represented a singular achievement in light of the weather conditions encountered during early March in Nova Scotia. Over 6000 tons of viscous Bunker C oil were recovered from the sunken wreck. The salvage team used a hot tap technique to penetrate the tanker cargo tanks and then used a steam traced pumping system to transfer the oil to a barge at the surface.

II. Containment and Recovery of the Spill

If a spill has occurred, it is universally agreed that the recommended procedure is to contain and physically recover it with or without the use of adsorbents. It is obviously the most direct solution to a spill incident, if conditions permit its execution. This approach may entail three processes:

1. Confinement of the spill by spill booms;
2. Recovery of the spill by sorbing agents;
3. Physical removal of the contained oil by oil pickup devices.

Figure 1 Gellation of crude oil to prevent loss from tanker. Expirimental samples of laboratory gelled crude oil.

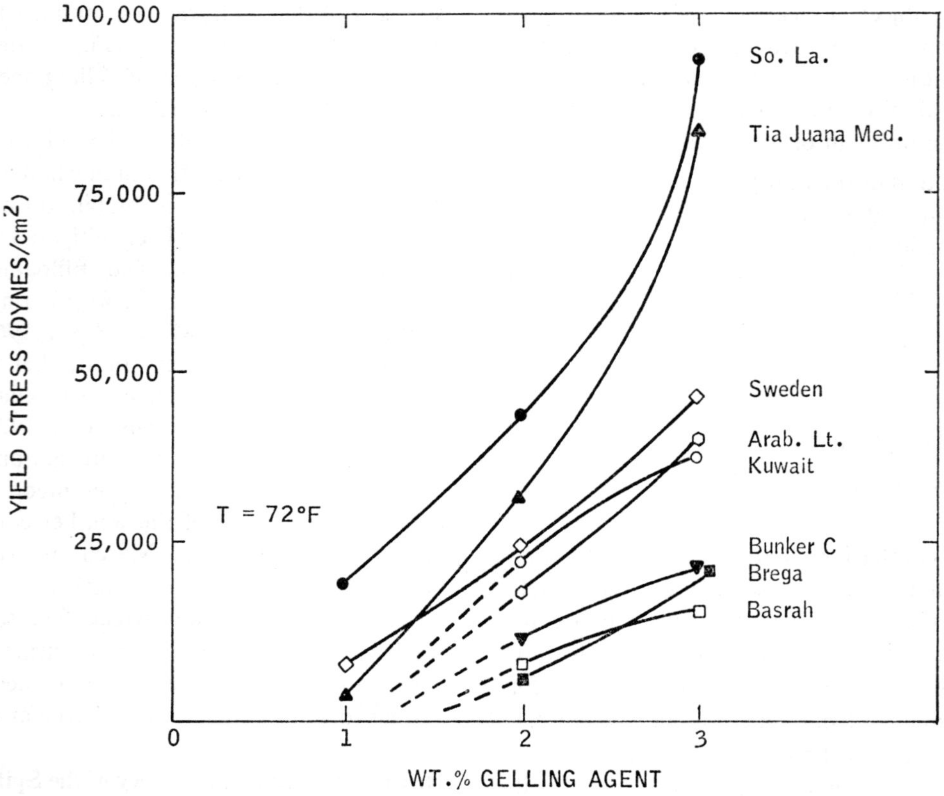

Figure 2 Effect of oil type and gelling agent concentration on gel strength.

These aspects of the recovery approach are interrelated as will be appreciated by the following discussion.

Many oil containment booms are available but are limited to relatively calm seas

There are many oil spill booms commercially available today. A rather concise survey of this area made by Dewling[4] in September 1970 indicated that at that time there were at least 37 different known designs ranging from \$5 to \$45 per foot. Unfortunately, the present state of the art limits these available spill booms to relatively quiescent conditions, i.e., waves of less than two feet and currents of less than 1.5 knots or so. Arthur D. Little, Inc. summarized and described some commercially available spill booms in a report sponsored by the United States Coast Guard.[5]

Although there are variations in the materials of construction, strength, geometry, etc., of these various boom designs, as evidenced by the number available and the range of costs, their general form is quite similar. Almost any type of floating barrier will hold back and contain some amount of oil under quiescent conditions. Indeed, telephone poles have been employed in more than one spill instance as a jury rig emergency measure. To improve the capacity of such a floating barrier, a weighted skirt is hung from the floatation member and a fin is generally extended above it as illustrated in Fig. 3.

Design requirements for spill booms have been published by Lehr and Scherer[6] and Hoult,[7] among others. By a rather cursory inspection of Fig. 3, we may now appreciate some of these requirements such as:

- Sufficient freeboard to prevent overtopping by waves;
- Adequate skirt length below water surface to confine a sufficient quantity of oil;
- Adequate flexibility to permit the boom to bend under wave action and maintain its retention of the oil spill;
- Sufficient mechanical strength to withstand the forces imposed by the environment.

Some of the difficulties of oil retention against the action of a steady current is illustrated in Fig. 3. A discussion of draw down phenomena by Hoult[8] outlines that a gradient in oil thickness, h, is established by the stress imposed by the current flow. There is, based on the fluid dynamics of the contained volume of oil in the presence of a water current, a limiting water velocity above which oil droplets are entrained and flow underneath the barrier.

The deployment of the above described mechanical booms is also an important consideration. In the event of a spill, the speed of response is, of course, most critical. Hence, easily deployed lightweight booms are desirable. However, these desired properties are not necessarily consistent with making booms stronger and more capable of withstanding severe sea conditions. In this regard, a pneumatic boom sometimes called a "bubble barrier" is of interest. As illustrated in Fig. 4, a pipe with a number of spaced small holes is located on the ocean bottom or some distance beneath the surface

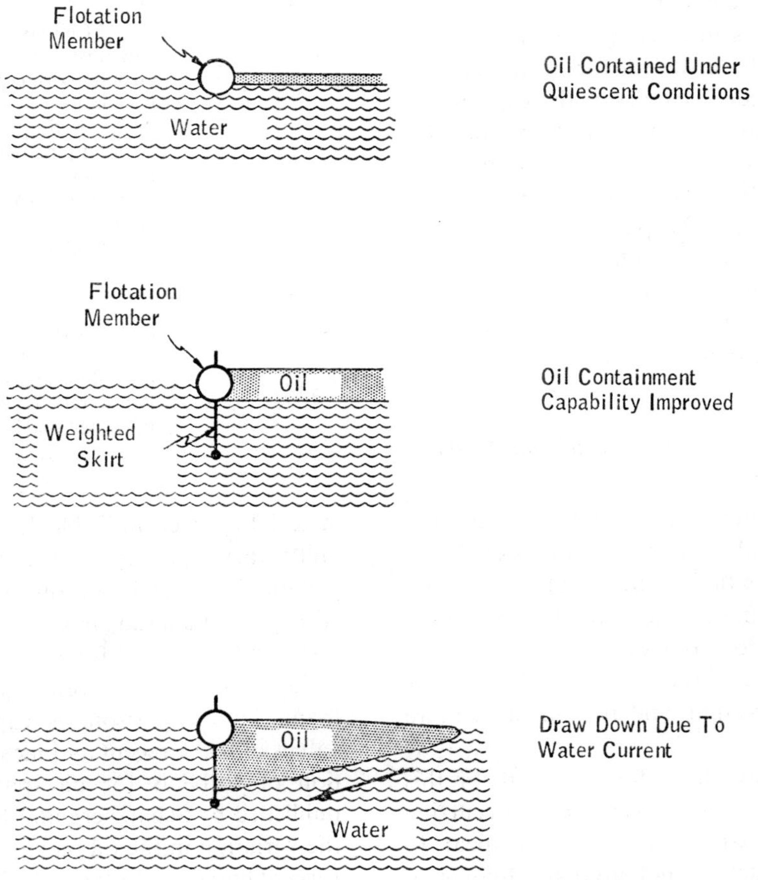

Figure 3 Mechanical boom principle.

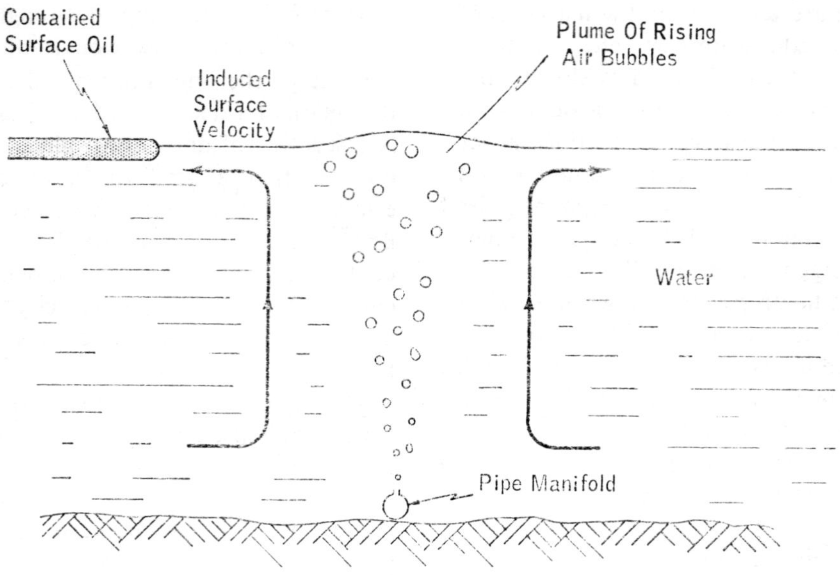

Figure 4 Pneumatic boom principle.

of the water. Air is supplied from a compressor and the small bubbles rising to the surface form a plume. Accordingly, a surface water current is generated to counter the spreading force of the spilled oil.

The potential of the pneumatic boom as a pollution control device is interesting since the system can be permanently installed for instantaneous activation when needed. However, the capacity of the installation is limited by both environmental and economic considerations. For example, the natural current of the water causes the rising air plume to incline. When the plume is inclined 30° from its vertical position, the plume breaks up and the overall effectiveness is diminished. Most installations have been limited to sites such as harbors where the water current is less than one foot per second (0.6 knots).

TABLE 1

Some Oil Absorbent Agents

Natural
Straw
Wood Cellulose
Saw dust
Ground corn cobs
Rice hulls
Peanut hulls
Ground pine bark
Peat moss
Chrome leather Shavings
Perlite
Vermiculite
Synthetic
Polyurethane foam
Urea Formaldehyde foam
Polyethylene fibers
Polystyrene powder
Polyester shavings

The physical recovery of an oil spill can be made easier by use of asorbents

A most direct manner of physically removing the spilled oil is by use of sorbents. These materials are bouyant, and preferentially wetted by and adsorb oil. In essence, they permit this sorbed oil to be physically "picked up" from the water. In addition to making the collection of oil an easier task, the oil is prevented from spreading and remains as a more congealed mass.

Materials that have been found useful for this service vary from simple, naturally occurring materials such as straw, sawdust, and peat to synthetic agents, such as polyurethane foam and polystyrene powder. A list of some available material is given in Table 1. The oil pickup capability varies greatly. For example, values of oil pickup, i.e., weight of oil sorbed per weight of adsorption material, have been reported by Struzeski and Dewling[9] for straw as 3 to 5, although higher values have been reported. Polyurethane foam, by comparison, is capable of oil pickup values of 80. A recent and most complete investigation of sorbents for oil spill removal has been published by Schatzberg and Nagy.[10] Of interest is the variation in the oil pickup capability of a given sorbent based on the type of spilled oil. For example, in Schatzberg's controlled tests, oil pickup by straw was 6.4 for heavy crude oil and 2.4 for light crude oil. For urea formaldehyde foam, however, oil pickup was 52.4 for heavy crude and 50.3 for light crude. Also, some sorbents are much less effective for oil adsorption if contacted by water prior to application to the spill.

Although highly effective sorbents are available as noted above, techniques for harvesting (recovering) the oil soaked sorbent have been limiting. For example, there have been prior instances of oil soaked straw recovery by manual pickup with pitchforks. However, there is development work underway to mechanize this step as well as the application procedure. In this regard, some very practical observations on the use of sorbents have been made by an IMCO subcommittee on Marine Pollution.[11] This guidance manual outlined that "the use of absorbents involves six basic operations, the supply, storage and transportation of the material and then the application, harvesting and disposal of the contaminated absorbent." The manual further observes that some of the early applications of sorbents such as the *Torrey Canyon* and *Santa Barbara* suffered because of the lack of effective and efficient harvesting techniques. It states,

> No method of harvesting was, however, available and the whole of this additional mass together with the oil was blown by the wind on to the coast of Northern France from which it had to be removed almost entirley by hand. In these circumstances, it is doubtful whether use of the material did more than increase the amount of material that had to be handled.

Oil skimming devices are used to physically remove surface oil

Since oil containment booms have a fixed capacity for oil spill containment, it is important to consider means to physically remove the contained oil from the surface. The use of sorbents has been discussed. An alternate approach is to remove the fluid oil by means of skimming devices. This is an area that has shown considerable imagination and innovation.

There are two general classes of such devices—fixed position skimmers and mobile skimmers. An example of a fixed position skimmer is that based on the principle of "Vortex Separation." In this technique, centrifugal force is used to generate a submerged vortex of oil. In essence, oil is drawn down from the surface into this generated vortex where the oil is concentrated and removed. The feasibility of this approach has been investigated by a project sponsored by the Environmental Protection Agency.[12]

Mobile skimmers may be divided into three categories: wier, belt and drum. An extensive summary and description of commercially available skimming devices in these three categories has been prepared by the Edison Water Quality Laboratory.[13] The operating principals are as follows:

- *Weir principle* is based on the simple principal of overflowing a wier to separate the oil from the surrounding water. Their efficiency is highly dependent on calm water and an adequate thickness of oil so that the water intake is minimized.
- *Drum principle and belt principle* are similar in that either a cycling drum or a cycling belt of material is used to selectively adsorb the surface oil film from the water.

The materials used for the surface of rotating drum recovery units have been aluminum and polyurethane. In the case where the drums are aluminum, the oil adheres to the metal surface and is subsequently scraped from the drum for recovery; the best recovery rates have been achieved with higher viscosity oils such as Bunker C. Polyurethane coated cylinders, on the other hand, work best for oils with low viscosity, since these oils can be adsorbed by the polyurethane more rapidly. Oil is removed from the polyurethane by rollers which squeeze or compress it, thus forcing out the oil which has been absorbed.

A variety of materials has been used as the cycling belt on the endless belt type skimmers for contracting and recovering oil from water. Fine mesh wire screen, rubberized fabric, resilient foam, and absorbent cloth or fibers specially treated to repel water are materials used for the oil collection belt. Oil is recovered from the first three materials mentioned above by forced air blowing, scraping and squeezing respectively. The use of absorbent cloth rolls requires burning or burying, while oil can be reclaimed from some absorbent fibre belts by squeezing.

In addition to the above general categories, there have been some additional concepts that show promise, such as a hydraulic skimmer based on the use of water jets[14] and a rotating disc skimmer utilizing a multiple disc unit.[15]

III. Treatment of the Surface Oil

Chemical treatment of surface oil should be considered as an alternate solution

It is generally agreed, as indicated above, that situations can arise where the spill cannot be contained and recovered because sea conditions, weather

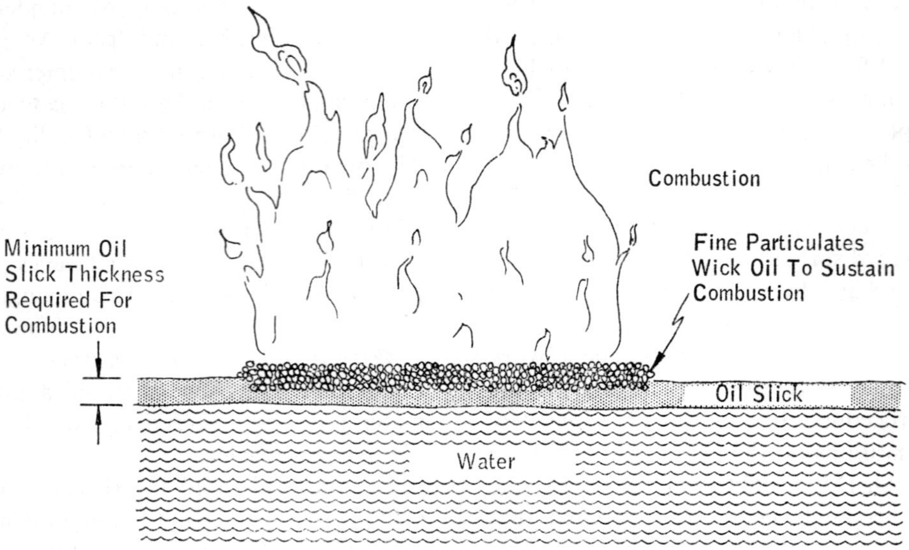

Figure 5 Combustion of oil slick by use of floating particulate material.

state, etc., are beyond the current operating capability of containment devices. There are also instances wherein the logistics of containment and recovery equipment, i.e. containment boom availability and/or deployment time and effort, could indicate chemical treatment as the most practical and expedient handling technique. When physical recovery of the oil pollutant is impractical, there are, in effect, two courses of action possible. In one case, the oil may be permitted to remain as an intact cohesive slick on the surface of the water and possibly reach shore. The alternate course is to "treat" this surface oil—such treatment essentially directed toward the removal of the oil from the water surface and the enhancement of its ultimate removal from the environment. This may be accomplished by:

1) burning;
2) sinking;
3) dispersing.

Burning and sinking are techniques that have not progressed to the same state of commercial development and application as chemical dispersants. In essence, their history of use is relatively limited. The burning technique is based primarily on the use of fine inert particulates. These buoyant particles are applied to the spilled oil and act as a wick permitting the oil to be drawn to the surface of this floating medium by capillary action. In addition to acting as a wick for the oil, the floating layer of particulates act as a barrier so that the combustion zone is insulated from the water. This overall mechanism is shown in Fig. 5. A more detailed description of this mechanism, as well as some field data, have been published by Tully.[16] More recently, a complete review of burning agents for oil spill cleanup was published by Freiberger[17] in which commercial burning agents, as well as natural materials such as straw were discussed. Field experience such as the use of burning agents at Chedabucto Bay during the SS *Arrow* spill are cited. Perhaps one of the more applicable and successful burning experiments was conducted by the U.S.C.G. at the North Slope during 1970 wherein no combustion aid was even used.

Burning represents a surface treatment of an oil spill that is attractive in that the oil is essentially removed from the water. However, some of the negative aspects of this approach that have hampered its widespread acceptance and use may be summarized as follows:

- In many spill instances, there is an obvious concern regarding the combustion of the oil for safety reasons. Spills near harbors, tankers, offshore platforms would create an obvious hazard if set afire.
- A minimum thickness of oil is required to establish combustion.
- Air pollution is a concern in some instances.

There is continuing evaluation and development of burning agents.

Sinking the oil by use of lipophilic (oil compatible) weighting agents such as amine treated sand has been most completedly studied by Pordes and Jongbloed.[18] There has been few commercial applications of this approach since the French Navy employed chalk to sink that part of the *Torrey Canyon* spill threatening the French shoreline. Perhaps the most frequently cited negative aspects for this approach are:

- The logistics of delivering and broadcasting the relatively large volume of sinking agent to the spill site.
- The concern for the bottom dwelling marine life when the oil is sunk to the marine bed.
- The permanency of the sunk oil, i.e. can the oil disassociate from the weighting agent and rise to the surface?

Again, some development effort continues in this area to obtain a better assessment of the above concerns.

At present, therefore, in those instances where the oil cannot be physically recovered, the selection of an approach is generally based on a consideration of the relative merits and debits of permitting the oil to remain as an intact surface slick versus chemically dispersing it into fine droplets.

The ecological and economic damage caused by an untreated oil spill can be extensive

The damage resulting from an untreated oil spill is both visually apparent and extensive. It encompasses both biological as well as property damage. The potential damage may be summarized as follows:

1) Marine fowl, particularly diving birds, are particularly vulnerable to an oil spill. As reported by Nelson-Smith,[19] sea birds are the most obvious victims of an oil spill due to "mechanical damage." The oil penetrates and clogs the plummage which the bird depends upon for water-proofing and heat insulation. For example, a duck with oil-impregnated plummage is under the same stress at a moderate temperature of +59°F as a normal bird would be under a more severe temperature condition at −4°F. Some statistics regarding bird damage have been cited by McCaull.[20] More than 25,000 birds, mostly guillemots and razorbills, were killed after the *Torrey Canyon* grounding. The guillemot casualties equaled the entire breeding stock between the Isle of Wight and Cardigan Bay. Bird losses in the *Santa Barbara* spill, according to the State Department of Fish and Game, totaled 3,500.

2) Shore contamination by beached oil represents biological, as well as property damage. The tendency of oil to cling to shore surfaces, such as beach sand, sea walls, and the resultant property damage, are well established. This is perhaps the most apparent and widely publicized damaging aspect as attested to by lawsuits on the part of tourist interests, property owners, etc. There is also, in a biological sense, a physical smothering effect on some attached, intertidal organisms such as mussels and barnacles. The effects of untreated oil coming ashore is well illustrated by Blumer *et al.*[21] regarding a No. 2 diesel fuel spill from the barge *Florida* in Buzzards Bay, Massachusetts in September 1969. Oil was incorporated into the bottom sediment to at least 10 meters of water depth, testifying to the wetting effect of untreated oil. In this instance, the oil was physically dispersed by the heavy seas but retained its adhesive characteristics. Therefore, it is deduced that the oil droplets probably came into contact with and wetted the upswept, suspended particulates which later settled again to the bottom. Other spill instances depicting the importance of this aspect—that of the incorporation of oil into the sediment—have been reported by Murphy.[22] In the Buzzards Bay and several other spill incidents of distillate fuels cited by Murphy, there has been a significant kill of all marine life in the area since these highly aromatic products are known to be much more toxic than whole crude oil.

3) Persistent tarry agglomerates are formed as the spilled oil weathers at sea. There has been increasing attention directed to the presence of tar-like globules ranging up to 10 cm in diameter in the open sea. As reported by Baker[23] during the voyage of Thor Heyerdahl's papyrus boat, *Ra*, during five separate days, they sailed through masses of these agglomerates whose age could be substantiated by the growth of goose barnacles adhering to them. There have been other incidents reported recently by the International Oceanographic Foundation[24] and a well documented survey was made by the research craft, R.V. *Atlantis*, as reported by Horn *et al.*[25] In this latter investigation, tarry agglomerates were present in 75% of over 700 hauls with a surface skimming (neuston) net in the Mediterrean Sea and eastern North Altantic. The amount of tar in some areas was estimated at 0.5 milliliter in volume per square meter of sea surface.

The behavior of spilled oil at sea

Before consideration of the mechanism of dispersing oil and its associated effects, an understanding of the behavior of spilled oil at sea will be useful. When a volume of oil is spilled onto the surface of water, the oil has a driving force to film out or spread—in essence, a spreading pressure usually expressed as a Spreading Coefficient. This Spreading Coefficient, $S_{o/w}$, is readily quantified and is determined by a balance of the surface tension forces as follows.

$$S_{o/w} = \gamma_w - \gamma_{o/w} - \gamma_o, \qquad (1)$$

wherein:

$S_{o/w}$ is the spreading coefficient for oil on water, ergs/cm^2 or dynes/cm

γ_w is surface tension of water, dynes/cm

γ_o is surface tension of oil, dyqes/cm

$\gamma_{o/w}$ interfacial tension of oil and water, dynes/cm.

By an examination of the force balance shown in Fig. 6, it can be seen that if $S_{o/w}$—the resultant spreading force—is positive, the oil will spread on the water; if negative, it will not spread but remain as a "lens" of liquid. For example, spreading coefficient values for Kuwait Crude on sea water, reported by Canevari,[26] are positive and confirm that for this system the oil readily spreads on the water phase. Garrett[27] has summarized spreading pressures of various oils on sea water that vary

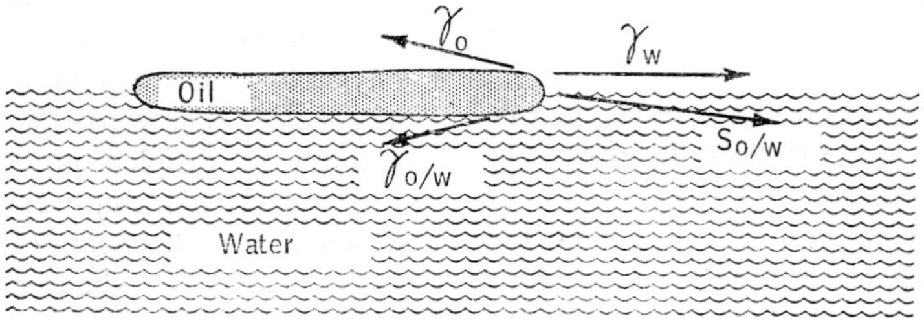

$S_{o/w}$, Spreading Coefficient For Oil On Water,

$$= \gamma_w - \gamma_o - \gamma_{o/w}$$

Measured Value For Kuwait Crude Oil On Sea Water

$$S_{o/w} = 61 - 28 - 22$$
$$= 11 \text{ Dynes/cm}$$

Figure 6 The spreading behavior of spilled oil.

Film Thickness Inches x 10^{-6}	Appearance Of Film	Approx. Gals./Sq. Mile
1.5	Barely Visible	25
3.0	Silver Sheen	50
6.0	First Trace Of Color	100
12.0	Bright Bands Of Color	200
80.0+	Dark Colors	1330+

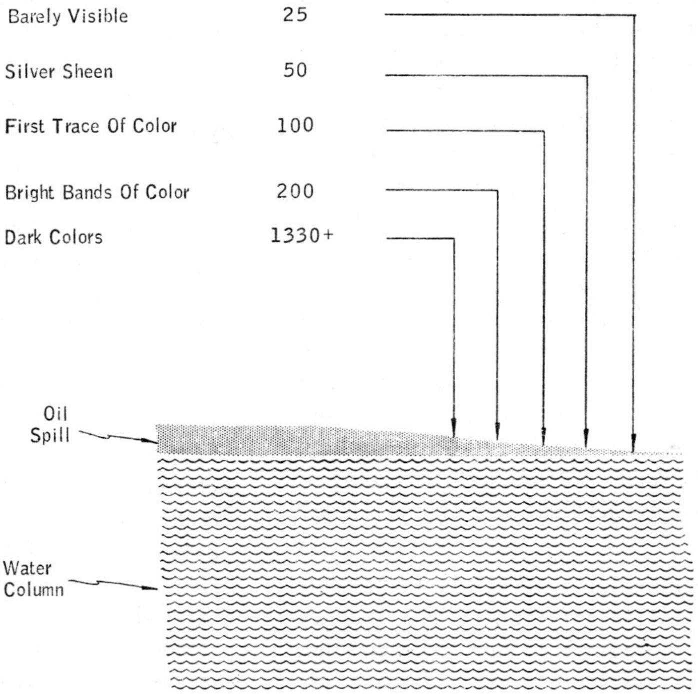

Figure 7 Oil slick appearance during spreading.

from 25 to 33 dynes/cm. Cochran[28] has also published values that generally agree with these levels on sea water. As one can see from Fig. 7, for positive spreading coefficients, the oil is capable of filming out to very thin films. A film thickness of only 3.0×10^{-6} inches representing a spill of 50 gallons of oil distributed over a surface area of one mile will be quite visible as a "flat" silver sheen on the surface of the water.

However, the initial spreading rate of a large volume of spilled oil is based on the volume and density of the oil—in essence, sort of a static head that overcomes other factors such as interfacial tension. Expressions for spreading rate have been derived by Blokker.[29] More recently, Fay[30] has outlined how the rate of spreading for large spills varies with time. Actually, the spreading rate of the oil film will pass through three principal regimes during which specific spreading forces become dominant. Fay identifies these as:

1) The gravity—inertia regime (called "inertial spread");

2) The gravity—viscous regime (called "viscous spread");

3) The surface tension—viscous regime (called "surface tension" spread).

Although a large spill will pass through these three regimes in succession, a small spill of oil, such as one gallon, will adhere to the surface tension regime from the outset.

The mechanism of dispersing surface oil slicks by chemical dispersants

The dispersion of surface oil films as fine oil droplets into the water column is promoted by the use of a chemical dispersant. This oil spill dispersant consists primarily of a surface active agent (surfactant) and a solvent. The solvent is added as a diluent or vehicle for the surfactant. It also reduces the viscosity and aids in the uniform distribution of the surfactant to the oil film.

A surfactant is a compound that actually contains both water compatible (hydrophilic) and oil compatible (lipophilic) groups. Due to this amphiphatic nature, a surfactant locates and arranges itself at an oil–water interface as schematically shown in Fig. 8. The surfactant's molecular structure, e.g. ratio of hydrophilic to lipophilic portion, determines the type of dispersion (oil droplets dispersed in water phase or water droplets dispersed in oil phase), as well as stability of the dispersion. In essence, a surfactant that is principally water soluble disperses oil-in-water and establishes water as the continuous phase; a surfactant that is principally oil soluble, the converse. This is Bancroft's Law,[31]

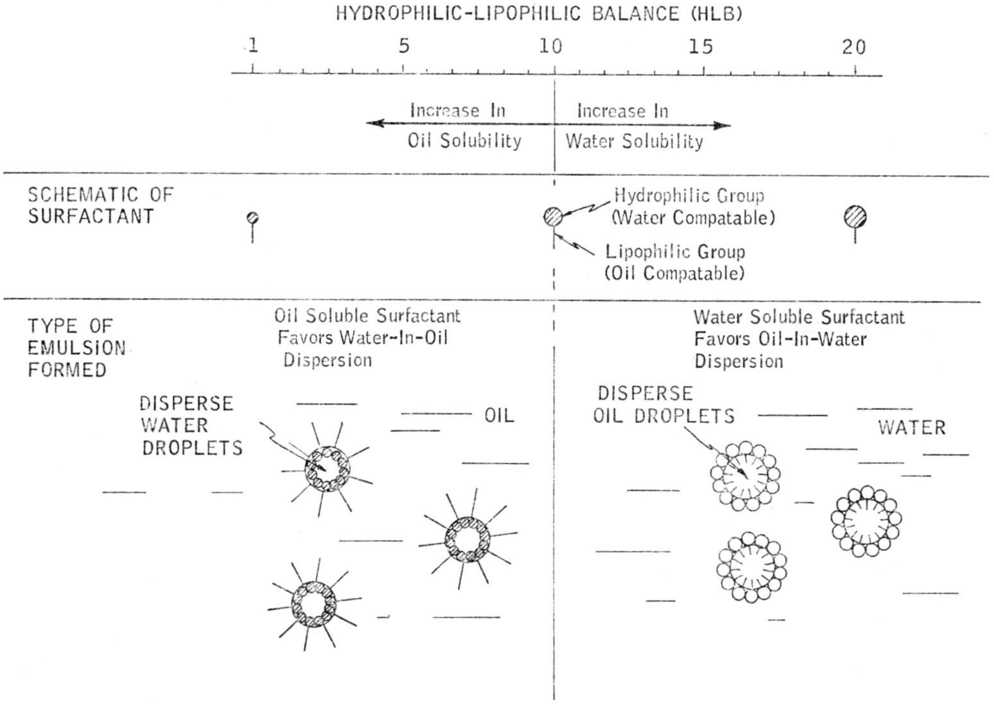

Figure 8 Influences of surfactant structure on type of dispersion.

which has been tested and proven empirically true over the years. A convenient classification for surfactants, therefore, is based on the ratio or balance of the water compatible portion to the oil compatible portion—sometimes referred to as HLB (Hydrophilic–Lipophilic Balance).[32] This relationship between the molecular structure of the surfactant and the emulsion type is also shown in Fig. 8 and the physical concept behind Bancroft's Law may be appreciated. For example, it can be visualized that for a more water compatible surfactant, the physical location of the larger hydrophilic group on the outside of the dispersed oil droplets results in a more effective "fender" to parry droplet collisions and prevent droplet coalescence. The converse, locating the larger portion of the surfactant in the dispersed rather than the continuous phase, would be geometrically awkward and unstable.[33]

The mechanism of oil slick dispersion by the application of chemical dispersants has been covered in some detail by Poliakoff[34] and Canevari,[35,36,37] among others. From the above discussion, one can see that the chemical dispersant (surfactant) will locate at the oil–water interface and reduce interfacial tension. This will then act to increase the spreading tendency of the oil film as shown by Equation (1). More important, it promotes fine droplet formation which can be expressed as:

$$W_K = A_{o/w}\gamma_{o/w}, \qquad (2)$$

where:

W_K mixing energy, ergs

$A_{o/w}$ interfacial area, cm^2

$\gamma_{o/w}$ interfacial tension, dynes/cm

Thus, for the same amount of mixing energy, a reduction of $\gamma_{o/w}$ will result in a corresponding increase in $A_{o/w}$.

It is important to emphasize that, as can be realized from the above discussion, the chemically dispersed oil does not sink. Rather, the surfactant merely enhances small droplet formation for a given amount of mixing energy. Smaller diameter oil droplets have a much lower rise velocity per the familiar Stokes Law. Hence, once the oil is chemically treated, and placed 3 to 5 feet below the surface of the water by the mixing process, it does not rise to the surface as readily, as illustrated by Fig. 9.

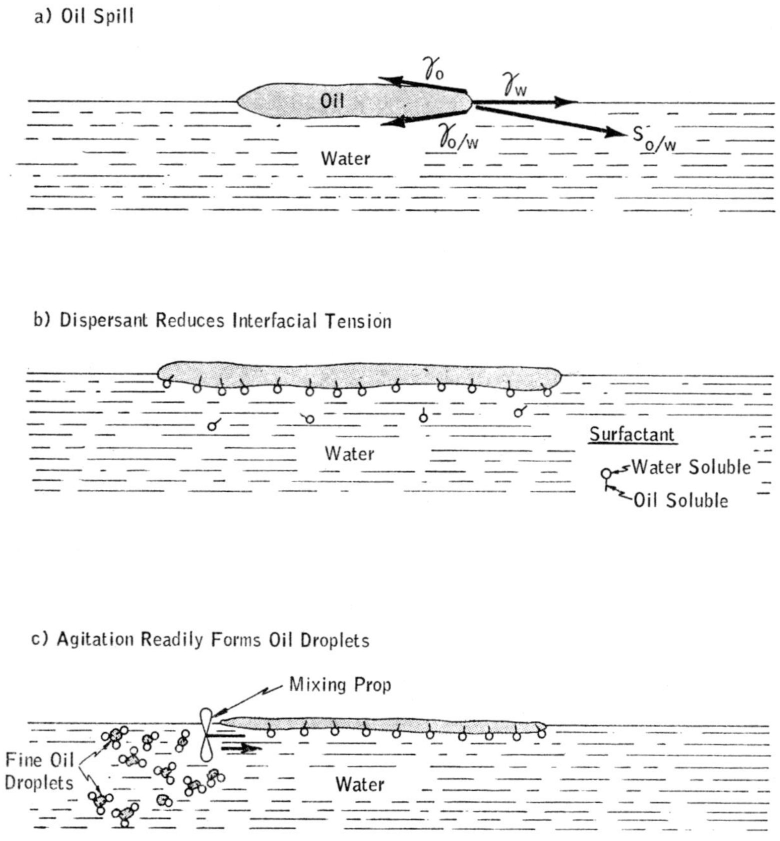

Figure 9 Dispersant enhances droplet formation.

An example calculation to illustrate this effect of surfactants was presented by Canevari.[38] If Equation (2) is applied to a mixture of 100 gallons of sea water and 1 gallon of gasoline, the relationship between droplet size, D, mixing energy, W_K, and interfacial tension, $\gamma_{o/w}$ may be noted as follows:

$\gamma_{o/w}$, Gasoline–Water Interfacial Tension = 48 dynes/cm

wherein:

D, Dispersed Gasoline Droplet Diameter
= 150 microns
n, Number of droplets = 2.14×10^9
$A_{o/w}$ Interfacial area = 151 sq meters
W_K, Work = 48 dynes/cm × 151 m^2
= 7.26×10^7 ergs
= 5.35 ft lbs.

The above 150 micron oil droplet would have a rise rate of approximately 4 inches/min in the water column. If a surfactant is added to the above system that would reduce the interfacial tension to a value of 7 dynes/cm, the resultant oil droplet diameter for the same mixing energy would be 22 microns. This "surfactant stabilized" 22 micron oil droplet would now have a corresponding rise rate of only .086 inches/min[1]

There are many surfactants that will aid in the formation of fine droplets in the above manner. It has already been noted that the surfactant structure (Hydrophilic–Lipophlic Balance) influences the efficiency of the emulsifier. However, a more subtle and less tractable requirement for an effective dispersant is the prevention of droplet coalescence once the fine oil droplets are formed. This is illustrated by Fig. 10 wherein a volume of oil has been dispersed by a chemical surfactant and maintained in suspension by gentle bubbling of air. After 24 hours, there has been no coalescence or separation of these fine oil droplets. In the control sample, with similar volume of oil and mixing energy, the oil separated almost immediately and reformed an intact, cohesive film of oil.

In essence then, an effective dispersant must parry droplet collisions physically. For example, dispersed oil may separate in a sample bottle but even though there may be a "creaming" effect, i.e. oil droplets concentrate near the surface, the droplets should not coalesce to reform an intact slick. It is this same "fendering" action that reduces the

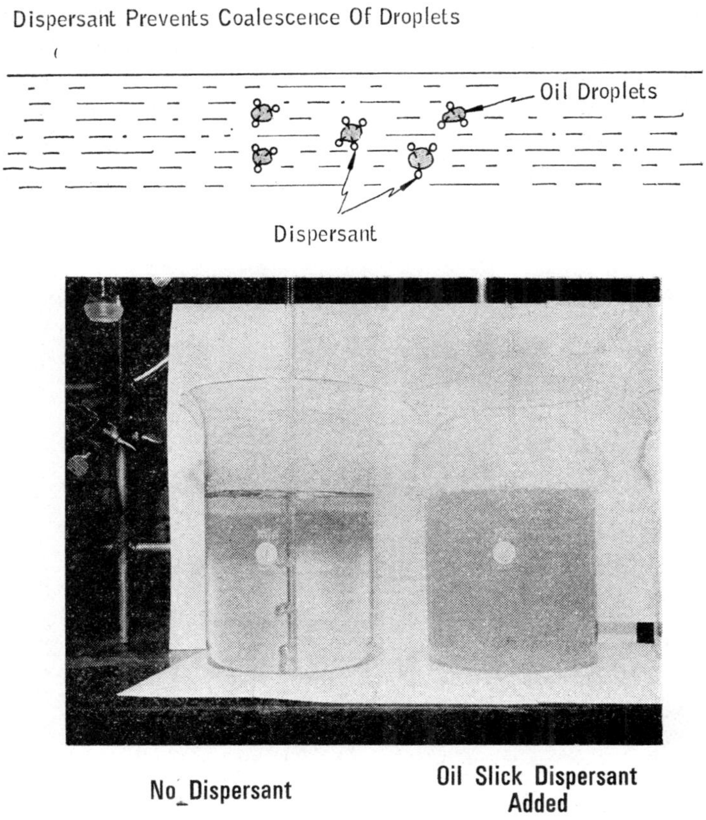

Figure 10 Dispersant maintains oil droplets in suspension with mild agitation.

tendency of the oil droplets to stick to a solid surface.

The physical and environmental incentives for dispersing oil slicks

Consideration of the previous summary of the potential damaging aspects of an untreated and unrecoverable oil spill indicates that the removal of the intact, cohesive mass of oil from the surface of the water yields more than a cosmetic effect as is often claimed. For this alternate approach when conditions do not permit the recovery of the spilled oil, the removal of oil from the surface by dispersing it into fine droplets yields established benefits that can be summarized by the following discussion:

1) Oil properly dispersed with a chemical dispersant will not stick to a solid surface. As previously outlined, the physical fending action of a properly selected surface-active agent prevents the oil droplets from coalescing after dispersion. This same property also inhibits the oil from wetting out on a solid surface. This has become a controversial point and it has actually been claimed that the converse is true. For example, in the First Report of the President's Panel on Oil Spills,[39] it has been stated that such agents cause the oil to "spread into the sand—surfaces which untreated oil would not wet."

A laboratory experiment was conducted to evaluate this aspect. A mixture of 265 cc of sea water 95 cc of beach sand (New Jersey shore area), and 20 cc Kuwait Crude, were placed in a graduate. This represented a vertical cross section of the marine environment after an oil spill. The mixture was then agitated to simulate the possible contact of sediment by the oil when turbulent conditions existed. After mixing, the sample was settled to separate the oil-sand-water phases. In a body of water, either the oil may be driven down into contact with the sandy bottom or the sand may be suspended in the body of water by wave action, such as deduced from the previously cited Buzzards Bay spill. The graduate was then purged with clean water to simulate the return of the environment to a non-contaminated condition.

The experiment was then repeated using 20 cc of Kuwait Crude Oil and 4 cc of a chemical dispersant (5 parts oil/1 part dispersant). As illustrated in Fig. 11, virtually no "treated" oil impregnated the sand. For the experiment with the untreated crude oil, an analysis of the oil content of the sand bed indicated that 11.20 cc of oil remained of the initial 20 cc.

2) Oil removed from surface of water prevents bird damage. The aforementioned hazard to marine fowl that is presented by the surface oil film is clearly eliminated when the oil is dispersed as fine droplets into the water column. These dispersed droplets are placed several feet below the water surface by the mixing process.

3) The fire hazard from the spilled oil is reduced by dispersion of the oil several feet into the water column. The removal of this combustible material from the water's surface and from contact with the atmosphere prevents possible combustion of the spilled oil. This is perhaps the most accepted benefit

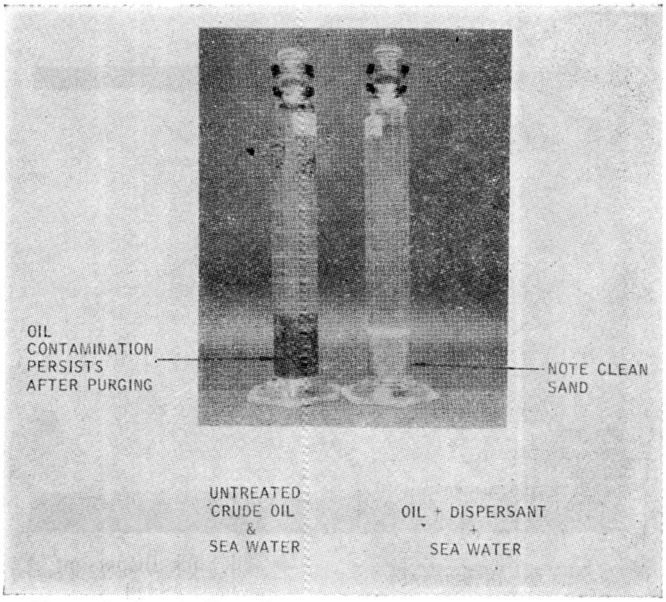

Figure 11 Relative effects of oil and oil + dispersant mixture on marine sediment. Samples shown after agitation and purging.

accruing from the use of dispersants. It has provided the motivation for many past instances of dispersant applications.

4) The rate of biodegradation of the oil is enhanced. This is the historical basis for the dispersion of oil. It is perhaps the most significant contribution of dispersants. The orders of magnitude increase in interfacial area that are generated by the dispersant greatly increases the rate of biodegradation of the oil. ZoBell[40] has reported biodegradation rates that are one or two orders of magnitude higher in laboratory experiments in which the oil is emuslified. Not only is the physical state of the oil, i.e. small droplets, more conducive to bacterial action, but it is also made available to a much larger population of microbial organisms. This particular reference has been one of the most complete treatments of the subject of oil biodegradation to date. Some pertinent items from this publication are summarized as follows:

> The growth of oil-oxidizing bacteria is believed to be beneficial to the food-chain in the sea because such bacteria are eaten by numerous animal species. In discussing the sequence of events in oil-polluted water, Voroshilova and Dianova[41] relate that the water becomes progressively enriched with bacteria. The protozoa in turn are devoured by higher animals. Rodina [42] has reviewed some of the extensive literature on the contribution of bacteria to the nutrition of aquatic animals.
>
> In controlled laboratory experiments, we find that oil-oxidizing bacteria convert an average of 30 to 40 percent of the carbon content of hydrocarbons into bacterial cell substance or protoplasm. Thus for each gram of oil oxidized, from 300 to 400 mg of animal food might be manufactured by bacteria.
>
> The rate at which microorganisms oxidize HCs is influenced largely by the dispersion or solubility of the HCs and by the water temperature. In fact, HCs will not be attacked at all by microorganisms unless there is contact of the HC molecules with water. Since most liquid and solid HCs are only poorly soluble in water, their utilization by microorganisms is dependent upon emulsification, adsorption on solids, or other means of dispersion in water as reported by ZoBell.[40]
>
> Virtually all kinds of oils are susceptible to microbial oxidation. The rate of such oxidation is influenced by the kinds and abundance of microorganisms present, the availability of oxygen, temperature, and the dispersion of the oil in water. Microbial oxidation is most rapid when the hydrocarbon molecule is in intimate contact with water and at temperatures ranging from 15° to 35°C; some oxidation occurs at temperatures as low as 0°C. An average of one-third of the hydrocarbon may be converted into bacterial cells, which provide food for many animals. The remaining two-thirds of the hydrocarbon are oxidized largely to CO_2 and H_2O. In the marine environment, oil persists only when protected from bacterial action.

More recently, a study by Robichaux and Myrick[43] presented the results of a study of the effects of chemical dispersing agents on the rate of microbial destruction of crude oil in aqueous environments. Increased destruction rates of up to 15 times the rate of untreated oil/water mixtures were reported.

5) The formation of persistent tar lumps from an untreated oil spill is prevented. The tarry agglomerates (up to 10 cm dia) found on the ocean surface, as mentioned peviously, represent a small percent residue of the crude oil. If the crude oil had been dispersed into 10 μ to 1 mm diameter droplets, these large residue agglomerates would not have formed and their persistence in the marine environment would have been greatly reduced.

In this regard, Hellmann *et al.*,[44] Federal Institute for Hydrological Research of West Germany, have shown the role that suitable surfactants can play in the prevention of gelataneous water-in-oil emulsions and in the formation of the more desirable oil-in-water dispersion. Dr. Hellmann is one of the foremost researchers of oil spill handling and has applied some basic principles of Surface Chemistry to the problem. Writing in "Tenside", Dr. Hellmann reports:

> The Bundesanstalt für Gewasserkunde has studied the conditions under which spilled oil absorbs water and the problems created by these emulsions with respect to oil fighting. From the viewpoint of costal protection, any approaching *W/O* emulsion is highly undesirable. By the collision of the Greek TMS "MARIA ZILAS" with the German MS "LUTJENBURG" at fire ship Elbe 1 on April 5, 1969, 600 to 700 tons Caribbean crude oil flowed into the water. The oil was drifted over the Suderoogsand and on April 15 was thrown on the beach of St. Peter and Westerhever by a storm tide. The resulting damage would not have occurred if the oil had formed an oil-in-water emulsion or at least a dispersion instead of a water-in-oil emulsion as actually was the case.

The concern regarding the chemical dispersion of oil spills

Clearly then, from a consideration of the foregoing, the removal of oil from the surface of the sea has merits in mitigating the damage resulting from a spill. It is more than a cosmetic, hide-it-from view effect. What then are the negative aspects to their use? What is the ecological price for introducing the chemical dispersant and dispersed oil into the water column?

The major concern regarding the use of dispersants are twofold:

1) The toxic effects of the chemical dispersants. This has been an area of great concern since their use has become significant. There is a basis for this concern. It was highlighted by the investigation by Smith *et al.*,[45] after the *Torrey Canyon* that indicated that in some areas, particularly in the intertidal zone, the chemicals used were more toxic to the marine life than the oil itself. As a result, a very extensive literature search was conducted by

Battelle Memorial Institute.[46] Some of their published findings regarding chemical dispersants (detergents) were:

- Biological effect of all detergents is similar;
- Most authors agree that 5 to 10 ppm will cause death;
- 2 to 3 ppm will cause noticeable pathological symptoms.

As cited above, the specific agents tested did exhibit a high level of toxicity. During this period (1967–1968), the chemical formulations available to disperse spilled oil were derived mainly from cleaning agents, hence the term "detergent" was used quite commonly. To permit these agents to dissolve tar-like residues and perform their cleaning function, an aromatic solvent, such as heavy aromatic naphtha, was generally employed. The short term acute toxicity of aromatic hydrocarbon to marine life is well-known. Blumer[47] states that low boiling aromatics are toxic to man as well as all other organisms and that it was the great tragedy of the *Torrey Canyon* that the detergents used were dissolved in low boiling aromatics. The toxicity of these aromatic solvent constituents were extensively studied by the Marine Biological Laboratory of the U.K. Their acute toxicity was evident since 5 ppm of kerosene extract solvent killed 50% of the Elminius nauplius larvae in 21 minutes. Their analyses of the more common detergents (dispersants) used during the *Torrey Canyon* indicated that they contained some portion of aromatics.

In addition to these toxic aromatic solvents, the surfactants were typically selected from the class of compounds formed by the reaction of hydroxy-containing compounds (e.g. phenol or alcohol) with ethylene oxide. A typical surfactant might be ethoxylated nonylphenol. The number of ethylene oxide groups added to the nonylphenol hydrophobe may be controlled to any desired extent to adjust the degree of water solubility of the material. These types of surfactants, although effective emulsifiers, were quite detrimental to marine life. In fresh water experiments, Marchetti[48] in 1965 indicated that a nonylphenol-ethylene oxide condensate was toxic at concentrations below 10 ppm.

However, during the past several years there has been research directed toward formulating dispersants that would have little effect on marine life. For example, water is now used as the solvent in products where it is compatible with the particular surfactants. High boiling saturated hydrocarbons which are similar to the type of hydrocarbon that occur naturally in the marine environment have a low order of toxicity and are also employed as solvents in some of the more recent dispersants. This modification of the solvent, and the selection of generic types of surface-active agents that are not considered to be chemically toxic, have resulted in the development of dispersants that have greatly reduced toxicity. This can be illustrated by the study of J. E. Portmann,[49] summarized in Table 2.

TABLE II

Development of Low Toxicity Dispersants Illustrated by Portmann Study

Chemical	48 Hour LC_{50}, ppm Brown Shrimp (Crangon Crangon)
Torrey Canyon Dispersant 'A'	8.8
Torrey Canyon Dispersant 'B'	5.8
Torrey Canyon Dispersant 'C'	6.6
Post Torrey Canyon Dispersant 'D'	7,500–10,000
Post Torrey Canyon Dispersant 'E'	3,300–10,000
Post Torrey Canyon Dispersant 'F'	3,300
Nonyl Phenol-Ethylene Oxide	89.5

For example, three dispersant products used during the *Torrey Canyon* spill and identified as Torrey Canyon Dispersants A, B, C, have 48 hr LC_{50} values of 8.8, 5.8 and 6.6 ppm, respectively. These concentrations represent the amount of the specific agent to kill 50% of the test species (Crangon crangon) in 48 hours. The toxicity of a typical *Torrey Canyon* surfactant, ethoxylated nonylphenol is shown at 89.5 ppm. By comparison, the toxicity levels of three dispersant products developed since the *Torrey Canyon*, identified as Post Torrey Canyon Dispersants D, E, F, are 7,500–10,000; 3,300–10,000; and >3,300 ppm, respectively. These concentrations are orders of magnitude greater than the level applied by conventional application in the field. In this regard, the statement that a "completely new family of dispersants has now been developed" was made by Beynon in a presentation to the Workshop on Oil Spill Cleanup in the U.K. during October 1970.[50]

Other agencies have confirmed this finding. Table 3 illustrates results of a recent study by the

TABLE III

Summary of Canadian Fish. Res. Bd. Evaluation of 10 Dispersants

Classification	Number of dispersants	48 hour LC_{50}, ppm Salmon (Salmo Salar L)
Toxic	8	1–100
Moderately toxic	1	100–1000
Slightly toxic	0	1000–10,000
Practically non-toxic	1	>10,000

Fisheries Research Board of Canada entitled, "Toxicity Tests with Oil Dispersants in Connection with Oil Spill at Chedabucto Bay, N.S."[51] Again, the large difference in toxicity due to the surfactant-solvent recipe can be noted in the summary of results (Table 3). These values represent 4 day LC_{50} values in fresh water to Salmon (Salmo salar L) and vary from "Toxic" (1–100 ppm) to "Practically non-toxic" (>10,000 ppm). Over 25 research institutions are known to have conducted studies on these lower toxicity chemicals. Testing by Dr. Molly Spooner,[52,53] among others, has encompassed juvenile species, planktonic life and other very sensitive forms of marine life. Studies such as those by Boyle[54] and Stander[55] have actually surveyed the toxicological effects at sea after application of these new chemical dispersants to actual oil spills.

Clearly then, the concern and conclusion that all chemical dispersants are in themselves inherently toxic is incorrect. Some of the most effective emulsifiers/dispersants available are those derived from and found in the natural environment.

2) The toxic effects of the dispersed oil. When the surface film of oil is dispersed several feet or more into the water column, it is unfortunately made available to other forms of marine life in addition to the hydrocarbon-oxidizing bacteria. Necton and other filter feeders may now come into contact with dispersed oil droplets that they otherwise may have escaped as surface oil.

This is, in effect, the "ecological price" for the cited benefits of dispersing oil. There are published data on the acute toxicity levels of dispersed oil such as that from the State of Michigan[56] presented as Table 4. This does indicate an approximate tolerance level of a thousand ppm or more for dispersed oil. It can also be noted that the toxicity of the chemical is reflected in the toxicity levels for the dispersed oil. In considering a toxic level of 1000 ppm or so for dispersed oil, however, it should be noted that (1) it is unlikely that fish would remain in this inhospitable environment for 96 hours and (2) the dispersed oil has a driving force to dilute itself.

Of greater concern than these short term acute effects is the possibility that the finely dispersed oil droplets represent a more subtle contaminant and may cause long-range detrimental effects. However, it should also be noted that crude oil is a natural rather than man-synthesized material. Wheeler North[57] reported after extensive research into several spill incidents, "Unlike many of the products man liberates into the environment, crude oil is a naturally occurring substance. From time to time it appears on the earth's crust by natural processes of exudation."

However, there is a need to obtain a better assessment of the long term effects of oil on marine life. The short-term toxic effects are apparent in terms of mortality at various concentrations, staining, etc. Possible long-range effects, such as change in behavioral patterns and accumulation of trace amounts of persistent hydrocarbons, are both more nebulous and less known. Concerning the current status of this area, there is extensive research now underway, sponsored by both industry and regulatory groups, to determine these long range effects of spilled oil—both in the untreated and chemically dispersed state—on the marine environment.

In summary, the ultimate use that dispersants might find will be predicated on the determination of the long-range effects of the dispersed oil droplets in the water column. To date, information on the effects of both oil and dispersants has been mainly derived from short-term laboratory experiments. Data on the long-range effects are needed to fill this gap in the scientific knowledge on this subject.

TABLE IV

Toxicity of Dispersants with and Without Crude Oil

Chemical	96 hour TL_M, ppm Fathead Minnow (Pimephales promelas)
Dispersant A	5.6
Dispersant A + Oil	14.0
Dispersant B	14.0
Dispersant B + Oil	27.0
Dispersant C	25.0
Dispersant C + Oil	42.0
Dispersant D	32.0
Dispersant D + Oil	44.0
Dispersant E	56.0
Dispersant E + Oil	75.0
Dispersant F	3200^+
Dispersant F + Oil	1800^+

Note: $\frac{\text{Oil}}{\text{Dispersant}} \quad \frac{2}{1}$

REFERENCES

1. Corino, E. R., E. F. Broderick and G. P. Canevari, "Method of Gelling Tanker Cargoes," U.S. Patent 3,634,050. Issued January 11, 1972.
2. Corino, E. R., "Chemical Gelling Agents and Dispersants." Paper presented to the Third Joint Meeting of the American Institute of Chemical Engineers and the

Puerto Rican Institute of Chemical Engineers, May 20, 1970.

3. Department of the U.S. Navy, "The Recovery of Bunker C Fuel Oil From The Sunken Tanker, SS ARROW . . ." Navships 0994–008–1010, March 1970.
4. Dewling, R. T., Statement of R. T. Dewling, Chief of Research Activities, FWQA, Edison, New Jersey, before the Subcommittee on Aih and Water Polution of the Senate Public Works Committee, on the Environmental Impact of Costal Oil Refineries, Petrochemical Plants. and Ocean Transportation of Oil, in Machias, Maine, on September 9, 1970.
5. Arthur D. Little, Inc., 'Combatting Pollution Created by Oil Spills." Report to the Dept. of Transportation, U.S. Coast Guard, June 30, 1969.
6. Lehr, W. E. and J. O. Scheren, Jr., Design Requirements for Booms. *Proc. of API and FWPCA Joint Conference on Control of Oil Spills*, N.Y.C. New York, December 1969.
7. Hoult, David P., Containment and Collection Devices for Oil Slicks. *Oil on the Sea*, Plenum Press, 1969.
8. Hoult, David P., "Containment of Oil Spills by Physical and Air Barriers." Paper presented to the Third Joint Meeting of the American Institute of Chemical Engineers and the Puerto Rican Institute of Chemical Engineers. May 20, 1970.
9. Struzeski, E. J., Jr. and R. T. Dewling, Chemical Treatment of Oil Spills. *Proc. of API and FWPCA Joint Conference on Control of Oil Spills*, N.Y.C., N.Y., December 15–17, 1969.
10. Schatzberg, Paul and K. V. Nagy, Sorbents for Oil Spill Removal. *Proc. of API and EPA Joint Conference on Prevention and Control of Oil Spills*, Washington, D.C., June 15–17, 1971.
11. Subcommittee on Marine Pollution IMCO, "National Arrangements for Dealing With Oil Pollution Preparation of a Manual for the Guidance of Governments," March 2, 1972.
12. Environmental Protection Agency, Water Quality Office, "Vortex Separation for Oil Spill Recovery Systems," Water Pollution Control Research Series No. 15080 EUU, October 1970.
13. Oil and Hazardous Materials Research Section, Edison Water Quality Laboratory, U.S. Dept. of Interior, "Oil Skimming Equipment," May 1970.
14. Environmental Protection Agency, Water Quality Office, "Concept Development of a Hydraulic Skimmer System for Recovery of Floating Oil." Water Pollution Control Research Series No. 15080 FWP, April 1971.
15. Environmental Protection Agency, Water Quality Office, "Recovery of Floating Oil–Rotating Disk Type Skimmer." Water Pollution Control Research Series 15080 FWN, July 1971.
16. Tully, Paul R., Removal of Floating Oil Slicks by the Controlled Combustion Technique. *Oil on the Sea*, Plenum Press, 1969.
17. Freiberger, Arnold, Burning Agents for Oil Spill Cleanup. *Proc. of the API and EPA Joint Conference on the Prevention and Control of Oil Spills*, Washington, D.C., June 15–17, 1971.
18. Pordes, O. and L. J. Jongbloed, Laboratory Investigations into the Sinking of Oil Spills with Particulate Solids. *Proc. of API and EPA Joint Conference on Prevention and Control of Oil Spills*, Washington, D.C., June 15–17, 1971.
19. Nelson-Smith, A., Effects of Oil on Plants and Animals. *Proc., Seminar on Water Pollution by Oil.* Aviemore, Scotland, May 4–8, 1970.
20. McCaull, Julian, The Black Tide, *Environment*, November 1969.
21. Blumer, M., G. Souza and J. Sass, Hydrocarbon Pollution of Edible Shellfish by an Oil Spill, *Marine Biology*, 1970.
22. Murphy, Thomas A., "Environmental Aspects of Oil Pollution," Paper presented to the Session on Oil Pollution Control, ASCE, Boston, Massachusetts, July 13, 1970.
23. Baker, Norman, The Life and Death of the Good Ship RA, *Sports Illustrated*, April 20, 1970.
24. *Sea Secrets*, International Oceanographic Foundation, Vol 14, No. 4, p. 2, July–August 1970.
25. Horn, Michael H., John M. Teal, and Richard H. Backus, Petroleum Lumps on the Surface of the Sea. *Science*, Vol 168, pp. 245–246, April 10, 1970.
26. Canevari, Gerard P., The Role of Chemical Dispersants in Oil Cleanup. *Oil on the Sea*, Plenum Press, 1969.
27. Garrett, William D., Confinement and Control of Oil Pollution on Water with Monomolecular Surface Films, *Proc. of API and FWPCA Joint Conference on Control* of Oil Spills, N.Y.C., N.Y., December 15–17, 1969.
28. Cochran, Robert A. and Paul R. Scott, The Growth of Oil Slicks and Their Control by Surface Chemical Agents, *J. Petroleum Technology*, July 1971.
29. Blokker, P. C., Paper presented at the Fourth International Conference, Antwerp, June 22–27, 1964.
30. Fay, James A., Physical Processes in the Spread of Oil on a Water Surface, *Proc. of API and EPA Joint Conference on Prevention and Control of Oil Spills*, Washington, D.C., June 15–17, 1971.
31. Bancroft, W. D., *J. Phys. Chem*, Vol 17, p. 501, 1913; Vol 19 p. 275, 1915.
32. Becker, P., *Emulsions: Theory and Practice*, Reinhold Publishing Corp., N.Y., 1957.
33. Canevari, G. P., Some Basic Concepts Regarding the Separation of Oily Water Mixtures, *ASLE Transactions*, p. 190–198, July 1968.
34. Poliakoff, M. Z., "Oil Dispersing Chemicals," Water Pollution Control Research Series ORD-3, Washington, D.C., May 1969.
35. Canevari, Gerard P., The Role of Chemical Dispersants in Oil Cleanup, *Oil on the Sea*, Plenum Press, p. 29–51, 1969.
36. Canevari, Gerard P., General Dispersant Theory. *Proceedings of Joint Conference on Prevention and Control of Oil Spills*, API/FWQA, New York City, Ne York, December 1969.
37. Canevari, Gerard P., Oil Spill Dispersants—Current Status and Future Outlook. *Proc. of API and EPA Joint Conference on Prevention and Control of Oil Spills*, Washington, D.C., June 15–17, 1971.
38. Canevari, Gerard P., Interfacial Properties on Oily Water Clarification. *Water Quality Improvement by Physical and Chemical Processes*. University of Texas Press, Austin and Houston, 1970.
39. First Report of the President's Panel on Oily Spills, Excutive Office of the President, Office of Science and Technology, Washington, D.C., 1970.
40. ZoBell, Claude E., The Occurrence, Effects and Fate of Oil Polluting the Sea, *Int. Journal Air Water Pollution*, p. 173–198, Pergamon Press, 1963.
41. Voroshilova, A. and E. V. Dianova, Bacterial Oxidation of Oil and Its Migration in Natural Waters. *Mikrobiologiya*, **19**: 2–3–210, 1950.
42. Rodina, A. G., Bacteria as Food of Aquatic Animals, *Priroda*, **38**: 23–26, 1949.
43. Robichaux, T. J. and H. N. Myrick, "Chemical Enhancement of the Biodegradation of Oil Pollution." Paper presented at the Offshore Technology Conference, Dallas, Texas, April 19–21, 1971.
44. Hellmann, H. and F. Bruns, "Model Tests for the Formation of Water in Oil Emulsions and Their Importance in Fighting Oil Spills at Sea," Tenside, 7, Vol 1, pp. 11–15, 1970.

45. Smith, J. E., *Torrey Canyon Pollution and Marine Life*. Cambridge University Press, 1968.
46. Oil Spillage Study, Battelle Memorial Institute, Richland, Washington, November 1967.
47. Blumer, Max, The Extent of Marine Oil Pollution, *Oil on the Sea*, Plenum Press, pp. 29–51, 1969.
48. Marchetti, R., Critical Review of the Effects of Synthetic Detergents on Aquatic Life. Stud. Rev. Gen. Fish. Coun, Mediterr. 26, 1965.
49. Portmann, J. E., "The Toxicity of 120 Substances to Marine Organisms," Fisheries Laboratory, Burnham-on-Crouch, Essex, England, September 1970.
50. Beynon, L. R., "Oil Spill Dispersants," Presentation at Workshop on Oil Spill Cleanup, London, England, October 16, 1970.
51. Sprague, John B. and W. G. Carson, "Toxicity Tests with Oil Dispersants in Connection with Oil Spill at Chedabucto Bay, N.S., "Fisheries Research Board of Canada, St. Andrews, N.B., 1970.
52. Spooner, M. F. and G. Malcolm Spooner, "The Problems of Oil Spills at Sea," Marine Biological Association of the U.K., Plymouth, England 1968.
53. Spooner, M. F., "Preliminary Work on the Comparative Toxicities of Some Oil Spill Dispersants and a Few Tests with Oils and COREXIT," Marine Biological Association of the U.K., Plymouth, England 1968.
54. Boyle, C.L., "Oil Pollution of the Sea; Is the End in Sight?" Biological Conservation, July 1969.
55. Stander, G. H., "The Esso Essen Incident." A report of the Division of Sea Fisheries tabled in the House of Assembly (Rep. of So. Africa) on June 19, 1968.
56. "A Biological Evaluation of Six Chemicals Used to Disperse Oil Spills," Department of Natural Resources, State of Michigan (1969).
57. Mitchell, Charles T., Einar K. Anderson, Lawrence G. Jones, and Wheller J. North, What Oil Does to Ecology. *Journal WPCE*, Vol 42, No. 5, Part 1, May 1970, pp. 812–818.

GERARD P. CANEVARI
Esso Research and Engineering

STACK SAMPLING

The quantity of pollutant material present per unit volume of a gas stream can be found from analysis of a representative fraction, or sample, of that gas stream.

Such samples are taken at sources of pollutant generation for one, or both, of two reasons:

1) To determine the quantity of emissions produced by a process under specific operation conditions.

2) To evaluate the performance of equipment; of methods, designed to remove pollutants from gas streams.

Sampling Principles and Techniques

Flow volume in main gas stream

A determination of the volume rate of flow in the parent gas stream is usually made prior to the taking of the pollutant sample itself. This determination is necessary if:

1) Total pollutant emissions, per unit of time, are to be reported for the process being sampled.

$$\text{Total Emissions Per Unit Time} = \text{Volume of Parent Gas Stream Flow Per Unit Time} \times \text{Quantity of Pollutant Present Per Unit Volume of Flow}$$

2) Pollutant sampling is for particulate matter. In sampling for solids, or liquid droplets, it is necessary that the velocity of flow into the sampler be *equal* to the velocity of flow in the main gas stream, at the point of sampling. If this is neglected, the particulate matter captured in the sample will *not* be representative of the particulate matter in the gas stream.

Determination of flow volume

The rate of parent gas stream flow is equal to the product of the average velocity of gas flow across a cross-section of the carrier duct or stack multiplied by the cross-sectional area.

The velocity of flow at any single point in the duct or stack is found through measurements of the gas stream velocity pressure. The velocity pressure is that pressure exerted by the gas stream in the direction of flow of the stream.

The relationship between flow velocity and velocity pressure is given by the equation: $V = [2gh]^{1/2}$, where "h" is velocity pressure in terms of the height of a column of fluid which, because of its weight, would exert an equivalent pressure upon its base. In this basic equation, the equivalent column fluid is identical with the gas stream itself, in density.

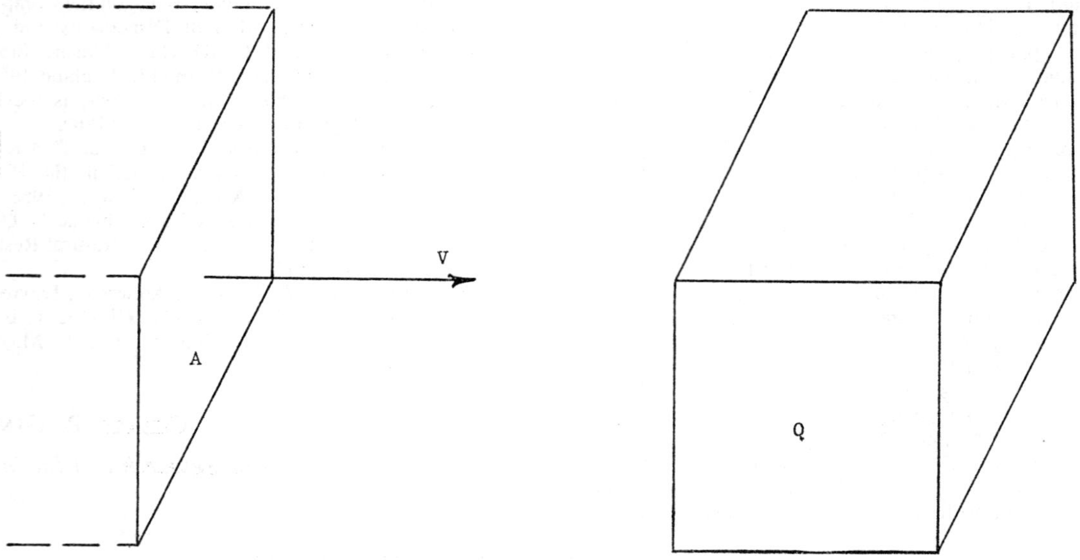

Q = V . A

FLOW VOLUME = AVERAGE VELOCITY . AREA

Figure 1 Volume rate of flow in a stack cross-section.

Since velocity pressures are commonly measured and reported in fluids, such as water or mercury, which generally differ in density from the gas stream being sampled, the basic equation revised becomes:

$$V = \left[2gH_{\text{Fluid}} \times \frac{\text{Density}_{\text{Fluid}}}{\text{Density}_{\text{Gas Stream}}}\right]^{1/2}$$

In this equation, H_{Fluid} is equal to the gas stream velocity pressure in terms of an equivalent column height of measuring fluid. The measuring fluid density can be considered as a constant factor. The density of water, for example, can be taken as 1 GM./CM^3, or 62.45 Lb. Mass/Ft^3 for the range of ambient conditions normally encountered in source sampling. The density of the parent gas stream can be established from the gas law:

$$\text{Density} = \frac{\text{Absolute Static Pressure} \times \text{Molecular Weight}}{\text{Universal Gas Constant} \times \text{Absolute Temperature}}$$

When velocity (V) is measured in feet per second, velocity pressure (H_{Fluid}) is in inches of water, absolute static pressure is in inches of mercury, and absolute temperatures is in degrees Rankine, the equation is written:

$$V = 85.5\left[\frac{T_{\text{Absolute}} \times H_{\text{Fluid}}}{P_{\text{Absolute}} \times \text{Mol. Wt.}}\right]^{1/2}$$

EXAMPLE The velocity pressure of a moving gas stream is measured as 0.25 inches of water. The molecular weight of the gas is 29.8. The absolute static pressure of the gas is equal to 30 inches of mercury, and the gas stream absolute temperature is 540°R. What is the velocity of flow?

$$\text{Answer:} \quad V = \left[\frac{540 \times 0.25}{30 \times 29.8}\right]^{1/2}$$

$$V = 33.2 \text{ feet per second.}$$

Practical velocity pressure measurements

The total pressure exerted by a moving gas stream, in the direction of flow, is made up of the sum of the velocity pressure and the absolute static pressure of the gas. Absolute static pressure results from the random motion of gas molecules—moving, colliding, rebounding, colliding again—not only against themselves, but against any enclosing surface, or any surface immersed in the gas. This molecularly inspired pressure is present not only for stationary bodies of gases, such as the air in a closed room, but also for moving bodies of gases, such as those flowing in a duct or stack.

A pitot tube is a velocity pressure measuring device which is so designed, that when positioned properly in a moving gas stream, the total pressure of the stream impacts upon the open mouth of the instrument. Other, and smaller, openings on the tube sense only the absolute static pressure of the gas stream. The open mouth transmits the total gas pressure to one leg of a fluid filled manometer, or pressure gauge. The smaller openings transmit the absolute static pressure to the other manometer leg. Since each side of the gauge is acted upon, equally, by the absolute static pressure of the gas stream, the net effect is cancellation, with the remaining unbalance between the two manometer legs being a measurement of the velocity pressure.

The standard pitot tube is "L" shaped, with the total pressure opening being at the terminus of the short leg. This opens into an axial chamber which, as described, is connected to one manometer leg. A separate static pressure chamber is concentric to this with, usually, 8 static pressure openings arranged, in a single ring around the tube's circumference, a few inches downstream from the tip. The pitot tube is slender and is made so for least interference with gas stream flow.

Static pressure holes in a standard pitot tube, are quite small, so that if the gas stream contains much particulate matter, there is a tendency for these holes to clog. In this event, a "type S" pitot tube can be employed. Here, the two chambers are straight,

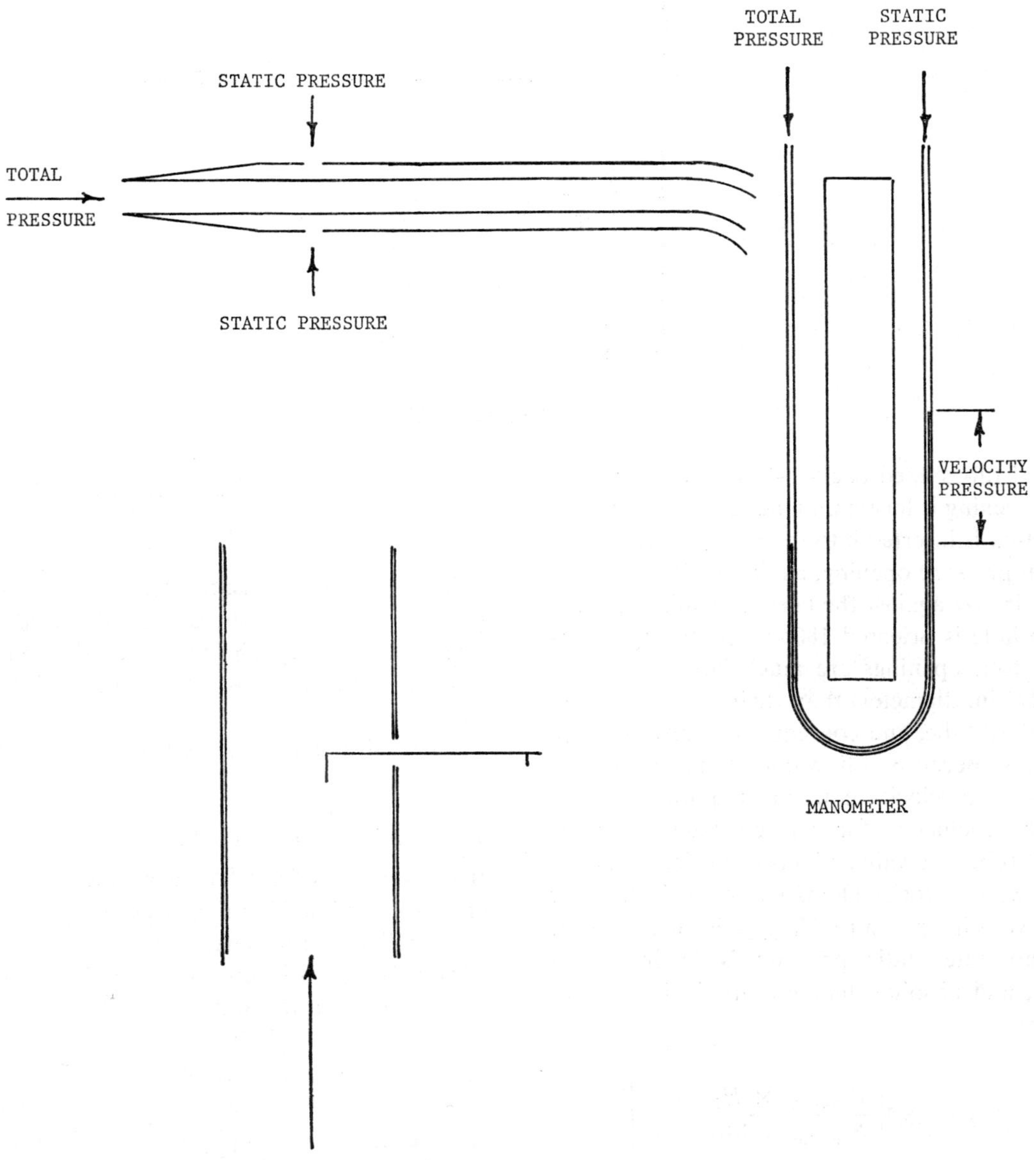

Figure 2 The common pitot tube.

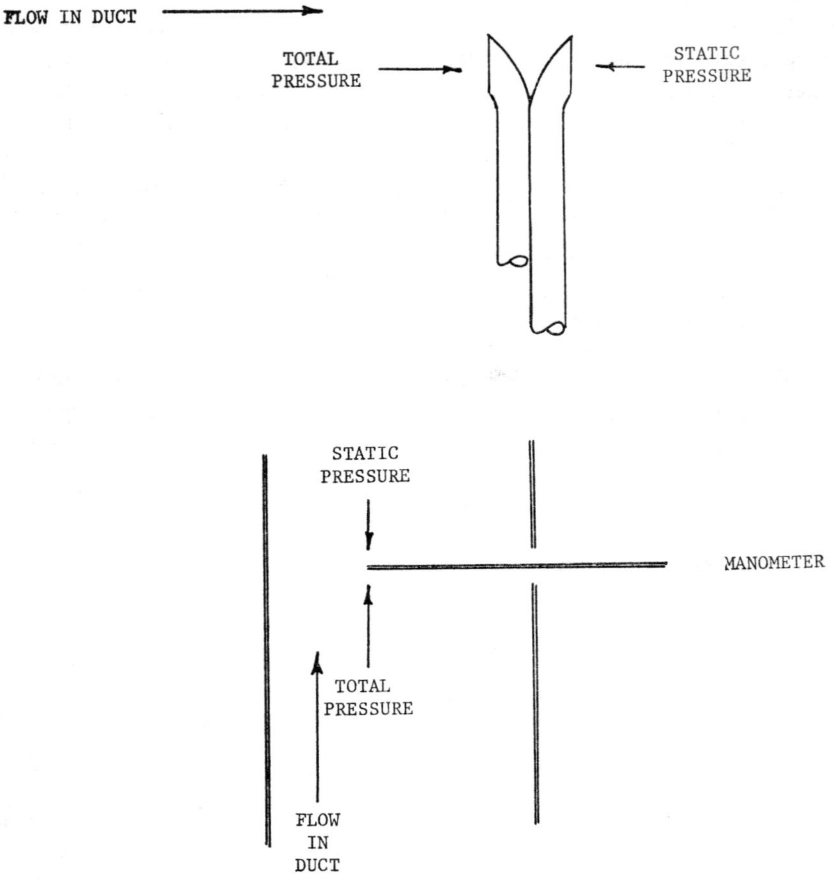

Figure 3 The type "S" pilot.

individual tubes fixed back-to-back. Each pressure seneing opening is located, on its respective tube, at the end that is inserted into the moving gas stream. The total pressure opening, again, is placed so that it faces directly against the current, while the static pressure hole is oriented 180° away, facing downstream. Both openings are much larger (approximately 1/4 in. diameter) than their counterparts in the standard tube, and consequently are less prone to clogging. Because of flow conditions around the "S" tube, the velocity equation requires use of a pitot tube coefficient for correct results. For the "type S" tube, the value of this coefficient is .83.

Thus, when velocity (V) is measured in feet per second, velocity pressure (H_{Fluid}) is in inches of water, absolute static pressure is in inches of mercury, and absolute temperature is in degrees Rankine:

$$V = \text{Cp} \times 85.5\left[\frac{T_{\text{Absolute}} \times H_{\text{Fluid}}}{P_{\text{Absolute}} \times \text{Mol. Wt.}}\right]^{\frac{1}{2}}$$

When using a type "S" pitot,

$$V = .83 \times 85.5\left[\frac{T_{\text{Absolute}} \times H_{\text{Fluid}}}{P_{\text{Absolute}} \times \text{Mol. Wt.}}\right]^{\frac{1}{2}}$$

Since the static pressure openings on the standard pitot tube are not at the tip where total pressure is sensed, a similar coefficient is properly applied here, also. For the standard tube, the value of this coefficient ranges between 0.98 and 1.02. Often, in practical situations, the coefficient is assumed to be unity.

Determining the average gas flow velocity

If the velocity of gas flow across a duct, or stack, cross-section is uniform, then a single pitot measurement will suffice to determine the average velocity of flow for the entire cross-section. Such a condition of flow is a rarity and may be considered nonexistent. In reality, the velocity of flow near the center of the duct will usually exceed the velocities of flow along the boundary walls. Conditions of local turbulence often complicate this relatively simple condition.

Since flow velocities vary across a duct section a

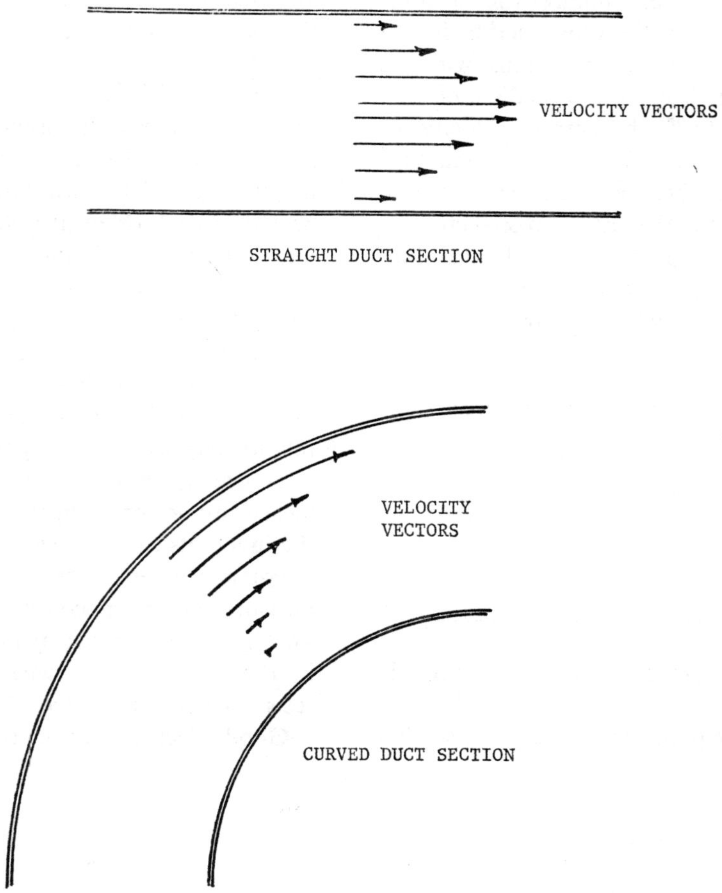

Figure 4 Flow stream lines in a stack or duct.

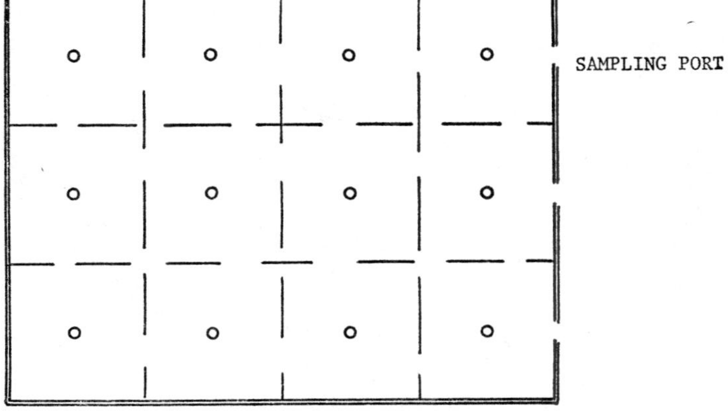

Figure 5 Rectangular section sub-areas.

practical method for determining the average velocity involves dividing the cross-section into a number of small, equal area sub-sections, with the velocity at the geometric center, or median, of each sub-section assumed to be the average velocity for that particular small area. These equal area sub-section velocities can then be averaged to obtain the average velocity for the entire cross-section.

Rectangular ducts are commonly divided into rectangular sub-sections. The minimum number of such sub-sections usually follow the guidelines given below:

Cross-sectional area square feet	Number of sub-sections
Less than 2	4
2 to 25	12
More than 25	20

Ducts of circular cross-section are commonly divided into annular sections of equal area. In these instances, two sample points in each annular section are used, on diameters 90° apart, at the median of the specific annular area.

Practical temperature measurements

In the usual case, a bi-metallic thermocouple is inserted into the gas stream for temperature measurement. The two dissimilar wires are connected to each other at both ends, with the "hot" junction being an intimate, direct, tie between the wires, and the "cold" or reference, junction accomplished through a measuring instrument. When the junctions are at different temperatures, an electrical potential difference will exist between the two locations. This voltage will vary in almost direct relationship with the temperature difference. If the reference junction is made through a voltage measuring device, temperature differences between the junctions can be measured.

Potentiometer instruments can be used to measure the thermocouple voltage by balancing a known battery voltage against it. No current flows in the thermocouple wires, and therefore, their resistance does not affect the readings.

Good electrical contacts at the thermocouple

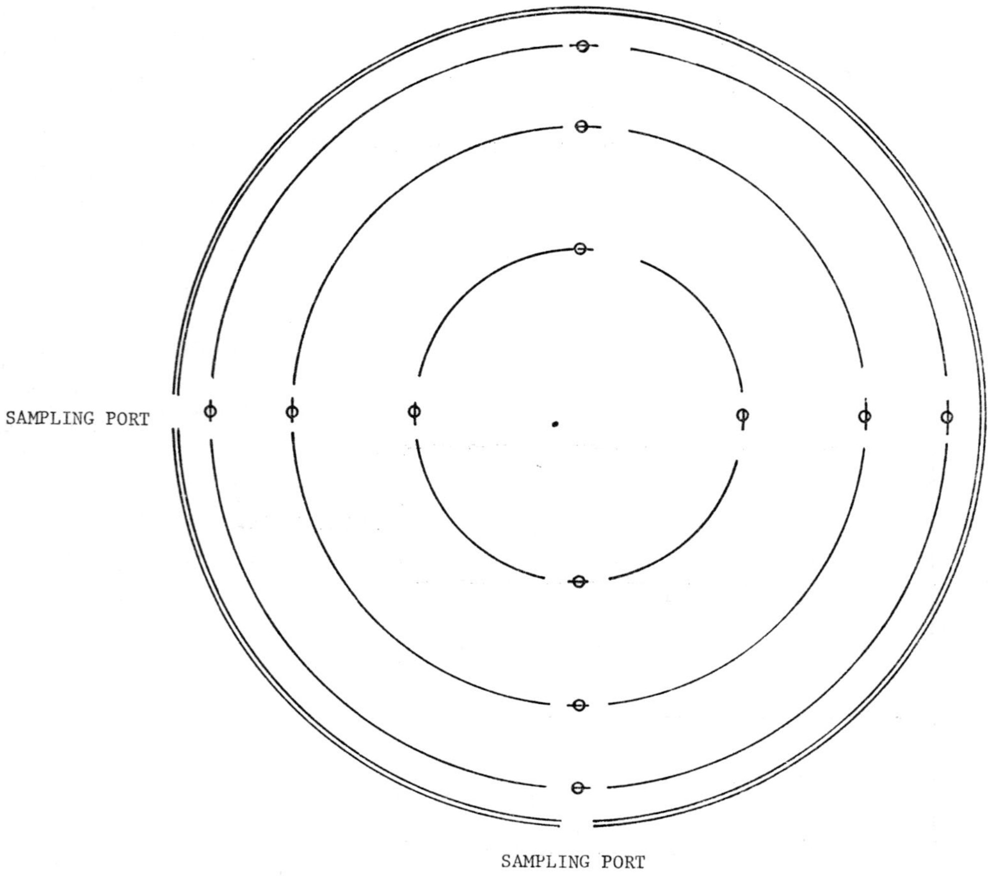

Figure 6 Circular section sub-areas.

junctions are important. The junction which is inserted into the gas stream will have its greatest mechanical strength, and resistance to oxidation, if the two dissimilar wires are welded together at their tips.

The following thermocouple wire combinations are commonly used:

Temperature	Wire combination
Below 500°F	Copper-Constantan
500–1200°F	Iron–Constantan
Above 1200°F	Platinum–Platinum Rhodium Alloy

Since heat from the gas stream can be lost through the duct, or stack wall resulting in cooler gas temperatures near the wall, a temperature traverse of the stack should be made as part of the sampling procedure. This should be similar to the pitot traverse, with temperatures taken at the center or median or each sub-area.

Practical absolute static pressure measurements

The static pressure of the stack, or duct, gas stream is measured relative to the ambient atmospheric pressure. The relative difference is then combined algebraically with the ambient pressure to indicate the absolute stack gas static pressure. If in the duct, or stack for example, the sample point is on the vacuum side of the gas mover or fan, the relative difference will be a negative one and the static pressure measurement should be subtracted from the ambient atmospheric pressure.

The ambient pressure is obtained by use of a barometer. The relative, or gauge, static pressure of the stack gas is obtained by connecting the pitot tube static pressure tap to one leg of a manometer whose other leg is open to the atmosphere.

The manometer, in any of its forms, is simple in construction, easy to read, and has no mechanical nor electrical components to go out of calibration. In addition, it will not be permanently damaged by pressure overloads of any magnitude. The manometer does, however, require periodic replacement of fluid and it is sometimes awkward to use in the fluid, because of the necessity to mount it in an upright, level position.

Mechanical pressure gauges, such as the dial-and-pointer magnehelic gauge, or electrical devices, such as the pressure transducer, can be used in place of the manometer. The pressure transducer's electrical output can be connected to a calibrated recording instrument for a permanent record of the pressures measured.

Practical molecular weight determinations

The apparent molecular weight of a mixture of gases or vapors is equal to the summation of the products of the decimal fractions by volume of each component multiplied by the respective individual component's molecular weight.

If a process is being sampled for the first time, it may be necessary to extract a representative gas fraction for quantitative and qualitative analysis, to determine the apparent molecular weight of the gas, before an accurate calculation of the gas stream flow volume can be made.

If the process sampled is a common combustion process, the analysis of a representative sample for molecular weight determination is usually accomplished by use of an Orsat apparatus, which is designed to produce values for the amounts of carbon monoxide, carbon dioxide, and oxygen present in the sample. The balance of the combustion gas sample is assumed to be nitrogen. The amounts of these gases obtained by the Orsat unit are on a dry basis; the quantity of water vapor present should also be determined, through use of a psychrometer or condenser.

If it is known that the duct or stack gas is air alone, acting as a carrier for particulate matter, a special molecular weight analysis is, of course, not required. The molecular weight of dry air is 28.966.

Sample Extraction

There are two primary techniques for extracting a gaseous sample from a duct or stack gas stream:

1. Limited volume sampling

In this method, a container of limited volume not only serves as a receiver for the gas sample, but generally plays a large part in inducing the sample to leave the parent gas stream. The sample volume is fixed by the physical dimensions of the container, so limited volume sampling must be confined to those instances where the gas of interest is present in sufficient enough quantity so that it may be detected and quantified even though the sample volume is small.

Vacuum displacement is one common method of limited volume sampling. A flask of known volume, valved at one or both ends, is evacuated mechanically. If the flask is to be used dry, evacuation can be carried down to an absolute pressure of one millimeter of mercury or less. If the flask is to contain an absorbing reagent, evacuation should not continue below the vapor pressure of the liquid. After evacuation has been completed, the valves are closed and the flask transported to the sampling point. A suitable probe is connected to the inlet of the flask, with the other end of the probe inserted into the gas stream. Limited volume sampling is meant for gaseous materials alone, so that it is common practice to place a particulate filter between the probe and the flask. Sampling begins when the flask inlet is opened, allowing the sample to enter the container. When the characteristic noise of the sample gases rushing to fill the container ceases, the valvdes are closed.

Both flask and probe must be made of materials which do not react with the stack or duct carrier gas. Glass is often used.

If a dry flask is used, the sample volume extracted will equal the volume of the flask minus the volume occupied by the mass of residual air remaining after the initial evacuation.

If a liquid reagent is used, the sample volume is determined in a similar manner, except that the volume of the flask is reduced by the volume of liquid used minus the quantity of gas absorbed by the liquid. This latter volume must, of course, be determined by analysis of the reagent.

Many flasks used in vacuum displacement techniques can also be used for liquid displacement processes. In this technique, the container is completely filled with a liquid, and all air bubbles are eliminated. A probe is used, again, and to begin samplng both top and bottom valves are opened. The liquid drains from the flask and is replaced in the container by sample gas. The sample volume is equal to the flask volume. If possible, the displacement liquid should be saturated with the sample gas prior to sampling.

In vacuum, or liquid, displacement techniques, the static pressure of the flowing gas stream provides the impetus which moves the sample into the container. With respect to the ambient atmospheric pressure, the static pressure of the main gas stream can be either positive or negative, as long as it exceeds the absolute pressure in the flask. In another form of limited volume sampling, known as "bag" sampling, the static pressure of the duct or stack gas stream must be positive if the gas stream is to provide the impetus for filling the bag. This is because the bag is collapsed prior to sampling, and the entering sample gas must overcome the ambient atmospheric pressure acting on the outer surface of the bag. In another variation of bag sampling, the bag is placed within a box which is alternately pressurized or evacuated to empty or fill the bag.

The advantages of bags over rigid flasks are

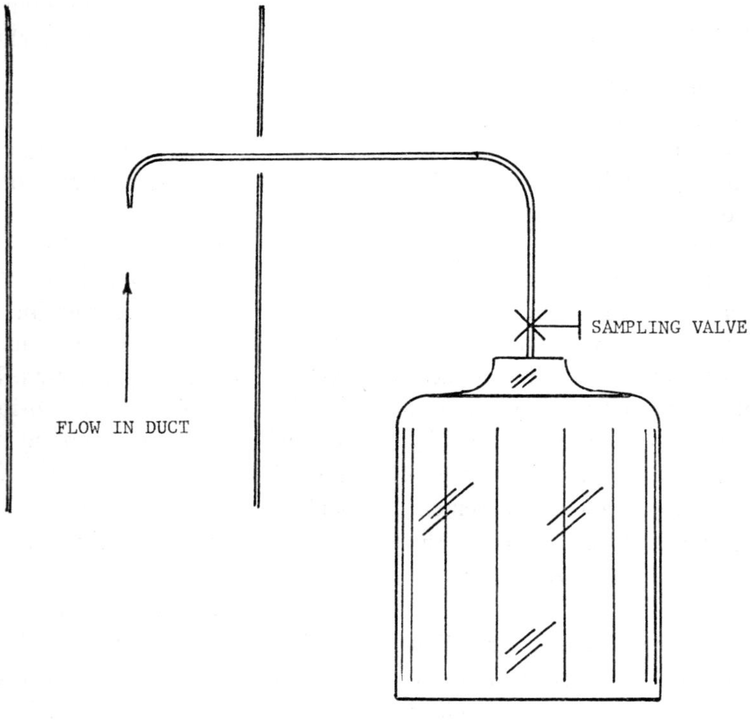

Figure 7 Fixed volume sampling.

numerous: they are inexpensive, easily transported, less prone to damage, and generally more conducive to larger volume sampling.

Bags, however, are not readily cleaned and may not be suited for repeated use. In addition, samples collected must be metered outside the bag as the bag itself is normally not a good gauge of the sample volume.

2. Unlimited volume sampling

In this method of sampling, which is used for the determination of both gaseous and particulate pollutants, the sample gas extracted from the duct or stack is processed to remove special interest materials for analysis, is metered to determine the sample volume, and then is released. Except for the restrictions imposed by the capacities of filters, absorbents, or adsorbents, the volume of sampled gas is not limited.

The typical unlimited volume sampling train includes the following:

a) Nozzle
b) Probe
c) Pollutant remover

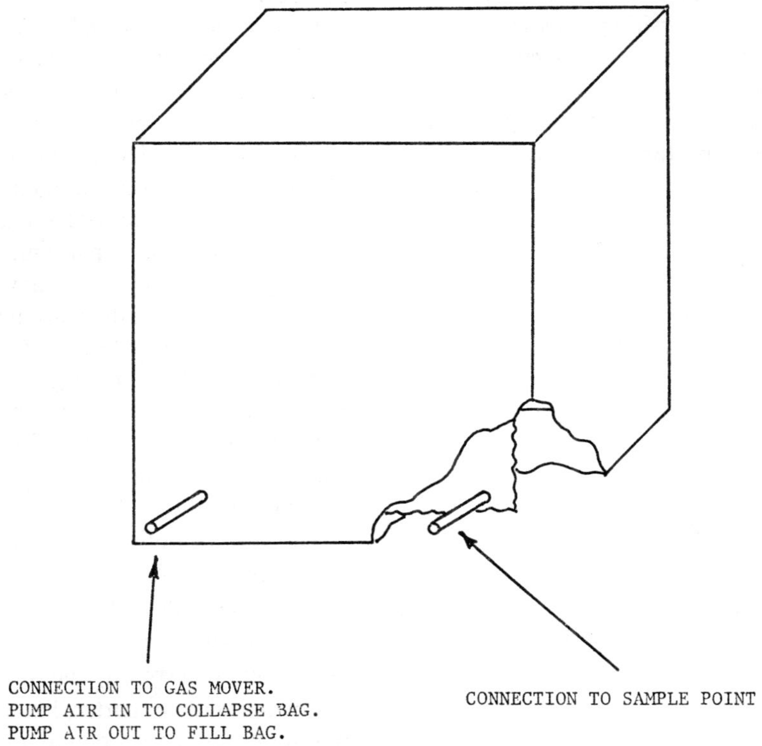

Figure 8 Bag sampling.

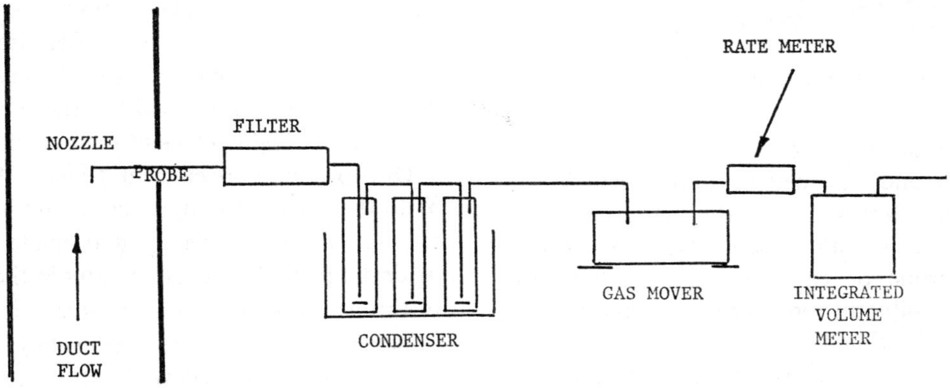

Figure 9 Unlimited volume sampling train.

d) Condenser
e) Gas meter
 1. Integrating volume meter
 2. Rate meter. Essential for particulate sampling.
f) Gas mover.

The nozzle is the entrance to the sampling train and placed within the duct so that it can most easily receive the sample gas. For purposes of sampling pollutant gases, it is essential that the nozzle material does not react with any of the compounds in the duct or stack gas stream. Stainless steel or glass nozzles are commonly used. If sampling is performed for particulate pollutants, it is also essential that the open nozzle face directly opposite to the line of flow of the onrushing stack gas stream with the sample velocity into the nozzle exactly equal to the gas stream velocity at the sample point. This condition is known as isokinetic sampling and is necessary for accurate particulate matter determinations.

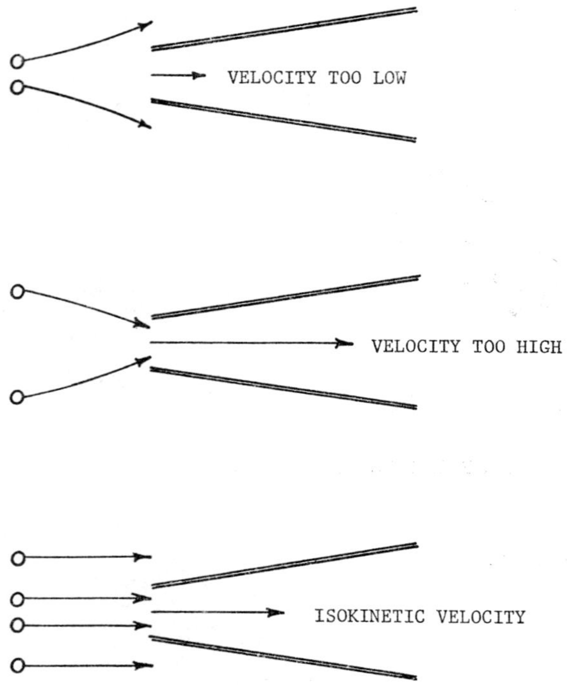

Figure 10 Isokinetic sampling.

The conventional particulate matter nozzle is also sharp edged and designed so that it provides a minimum interference with the pattern of gas stream flow at the sample point. With this type of nozzle, a probe or carrying tube conducts the sample to a pollutant remover outside the duct or stack. For exceptionally large cross-sectional area ducts or stacks, the required probe length may create problems associated with the settling out of particulate matter within the probe. Often, in an attempt to minimize this problem, the pollutant remover is placed within the duct or stack itself, immediately adjacent to the nozzle. With this practice, however, the bulk of the unit may interfere with gas stream flow.

Special nozzles have been designed where in static pressures internal to, and external to, the nozzle are balanced against one another creating an apparently isokinetic condition with a minimum of effort. Because of entry and other frictional losses, however, these "null balance" nozzles must be chosen for specific flow ranges and are susceptible to error.

In addition to nozzles, probes also must be fashioned from non-reactive materials. In addition, if there is a significant moisture content in the sample gas, the probe may have to be heated artificially in order to maintain a temperature above the condensation point. This is important, because an accurate determination of the quantity of pollutant present per unit volume of flow depends just as much upon a valid metering of the volume of flow as it does upon a valid measurement of the quantity of pollutant. Any water vapor which is present in the sample gas should be metered as part of the flow volume. Protection against premature condensation of moisture is another reason why pollutatn removers are sometimes placed into the stack or duct, along with the sampling nozzle.

The type of pollutant removal unit incorporated within the sampling train depends upon the character of the pollutant itself. For gaseous materials, a wide variety of methods are used, including condensation, absorption, and adsorption processes.

For particulate matter, like gaseous material, the pollutant removal technique used in sampling is very often a miniature version of techniques used for pollution control. As an example, small "cyclones" are sometimes used, most often when substantial particulate matter concentrations are expected in the stack or duct gas stream. Because "cyclones" are not high efficiency collectors, it is usual practice to place them in series, within the sampling train, before more highly efficient removal devices.

One form of more efficient device is the impinger. With this unit, the sample gas stream is accelerated through a small opening and made to impinge against a plate. Particulate matter in the sample gas is thrown from the sample stream in the act of impingement. Impingers are usually partly filled with water so that removed particulate matter will not be re-entrained. Impingers, such as the com-

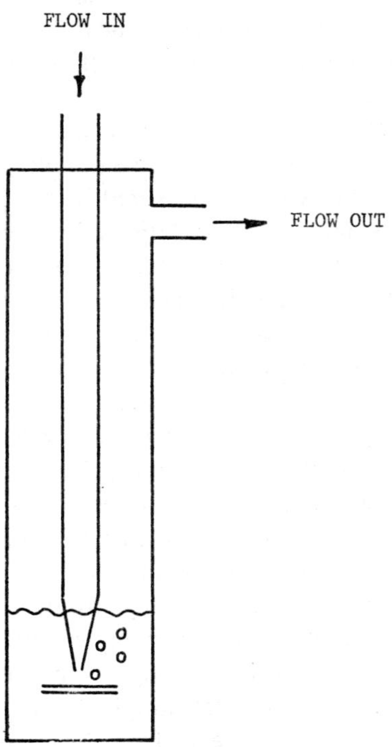

Figure 11 The impinger.

monly used Greenburg–Smith impingers, were originally developed for industrial hygiene work.

It is most common in particulate sampling work to utilize the principle of filtration in the pollutant removal device. A unit very often used because of its particle removing efficiency, compactness, strength, and durability in the field, is the thimble filter. This type of sampling filter is shaped literally like a household thimble, or cup, and is mounted within a cylindrical metal holder. It is so positioned within the holder that the sample gas enters the open end of the thimble to its interior. Under the influence of the partial vacuum created by the gas mover further along in the sampling train, the sample gas is made to pass through the thimble's filtering walls and base into a primarily annular space between the filter and its cylindrical housing. Particulate matter in the sample gas is retained in the thimble's interior, where it is held for later analyses. From the space between the holder and the thimble, the sample gas moves on through the remainder of the sampling train.

Chemical filter papers or porous ceramics are regularly utilized as construction materials for thimble filters. The porous (aluminium) ceramics are used when excessively moist, hot, or corrosive sample gases make it unwise to sample with paper filters.

From the pollutant remover, the sample gas stream next enters a condenser. The purpose of this unit is to remove sample moisture for accurate measurement, and also to minimize the chance that any water present will condense later in one of the flow meters. In addition, condensate which would be liquid at ambient temperatures is sometimes considered as part of the particulate matter collected.

If a supply of flowing cold water is available, a water-cooled counterflow condenser may be used. These metal units provide a small resistance to sample gas flow, and are rugged for field use.

As a general rule, a supply of flowing water is not available, and containers packed in material such as frozen carbon dioxide are common substitutes. Greenburg–Smith impingers partially filled with water are a good container choice, because the small sample gas bubble induced by impingement aids condensation.

If particulate matter is to be sampled isokinetically, it is essential that a sample gas flow rate meter be part of the sample train. Flow rates must be adjusted to match main gas stream velocities. In practice, the same stack or duct cross-sectional area points chosen for pitot tube velocity readings are also chosen as pollutant sample points. If the process sampled is a steady-state one, with both main gas stream flow and pollutant concentration expected to hold constant, the pitot measurements can precede and be separate from the pollutant sampling itself. If the process sampled is not constant, gas velocity readings should be simultaneous with pollutant sampling. This can be accomplished by mounting the pitot tube immediately adjacent to the sampling probe and nozzle. In either case, the

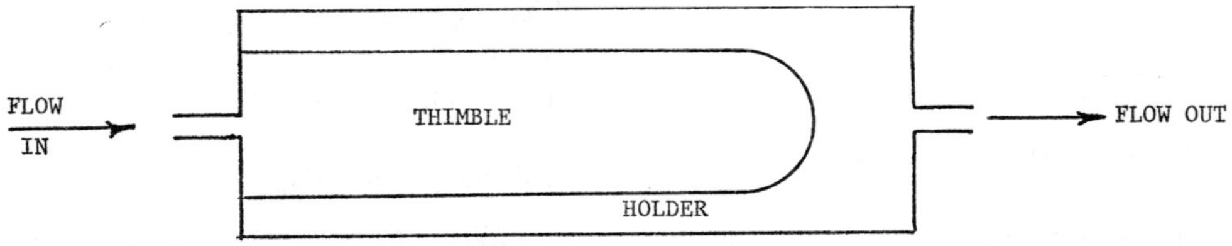

Figure 12 The thimble filter.

sample flow is adjusted so that the rate meter indicates that isokinetic conditions exist at the nozzle.

Rotameters are often used as flow rate meters in sampling trains. In this meter, a float or ball is free to move within a vertical glass tube. The fluid to be metered enters at the bottom of the tube and moves out at the top. The interior of the tube is tapered so that as the float moves upward under the impetus of the fluid, the annular space between the float and the glass wall increases. As this space gets larger, there is less resistance to flow and, consequently, less upward drag of the fluid against the float. At the point where upward drag equals the weight of the float, the float will remain suspended. The greater the flow rate, the higher the float will move. The position of the float in the tube indicates the fluid flow rate. Rotameters are easily read, and offer a small resistance to flow, but they must be mounted vertically, are expensive, and are easily damaged.

A better flow rate meter for stack or duct sampling is the orifice meter. In this unit, a plate containing a sharp edged orifice is placed into the sample gas stream at right angles to the direction of flow. In passing through the restricting orifice, the sampled gas static pressure decreases. The pressure drop is proportionate to the sample flow rate. With a pressure gauge, such as a manometer, available for pressure drop readings, corresponding flow rates can be quickly determined from a calibration curve. The orifice meter is suitable for field work because it is compact, rugged, and can be mounted at any attitude. One disadvantage is that it does, normally, impose a greater resistance to sample flow than does the rotameter.

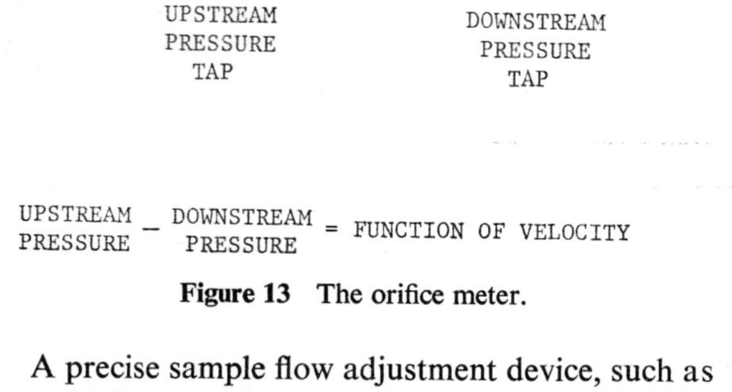

Figure 13 The orifice meter.

A precise sample flow adjustment device, such as a multiple turn valve, must be a part of any particulate matter sampling train. Sample flow rate adjustments must be made quickly and surely to assure isokinetic sampling conditions at all times. This, of course, implies that the relationship is known between sample flow rate, as measured by a rotameter or orifice meter, and sample point main gas stream velocity, as measured by the pitot tube. It is necessary that this relationship be established prior to the beginning of actual pollutant sampling. Important factors which must be considered in the relationship include: stack gas temperature and absolute pressure, meter temperature and pressure, moisture content of the stack gas, moisture remaining in the sample at the meter, nozzle diameter, stack gas velocity, and metered volume rate of flow. Under best circumstances, curves of pitot readings versus sample flow rate meter readings will be available for isokinetic conditions.

A rate meter measures only instantaneous flow conditions and must be complemented in the sample train by an integrating volume meter. This meter measures the total sample volume extracted from the main gas stream from beginning to end of the sample period, excepting the vapor condensed in the condenser unit. In computing the total sample, of course, the condensate must not be ignored.

The most commonly used integrating volume meter is the Dry Gas Meter. This is the unit universally utilized by gas utilities to measure the amount of fuel delivered to their customers. The dry gas meter contains three leather-walled interior chambers; a rotary slide valve alternately allows flow into and out of the central and exterior chambers. A linkage arrangement connects the movable leather partitions to a pointer on a dial, permanently recording the flow passage. If total sample volume at meter conditions is to be recorded, the condensate as vapor at meter conditions of temperature and pressure must be added to the volume recorded by the integrating volume meter. Because the typical dry gas meter is prone to inaccuracies under strong vacuum conditions, it is sound practice to place the meter on the discharge side of the gas mover, with its own discharge to the atmosphere.

The gas mover itself is normally an electric motor driver vacuum pump, although steam or air ejectors can be used for special circumstances, as in the case of an explosive atmosphere.

Problems in Sampling

As indicated earlier, the purpose of sampling is to determine the quantity of pollutant present per unit volume of gas stream. Again, this serves the objectives of determining: (1) the quantity of emissions produced by a process under specific operating conditions, and (2) the performance of equipment or methods designed to remove pollutants from gas streams. To adequately fufill these latter two objectives requires that sampling be undertaken under representative process conditions. If there are process fluctuations during the actual sample taking, the validity of the sample may be in doubt. Very often, when main gas stream pollutant concentrations are low, an extended sample period becomes necesary in order to obtain a sufficient sample size for analysis; if this extended period spans a process change, the sample validity again may be doubtful.

Obtaining a sufficient sample size for analytical purposes is often inhibited by the size of the gas mover available and the resistance of the sample train to the flow of the sample gas. Because of equipment bulk, and flow resistance, sampling in the field is normally confined to flows less than three cubic feet per minute.

Sampling for gaseous pollutants generally provides fewer basic problems to the sampler than is the case for particulate sampling; one reason for this is that the sampling process itself always affects the character of the particulate matter itself. This is usually not the case with gaseous pollutants. Because of agglomeration and similar problems occasioned by sampling, the particulate matter obtained in the sample can be expected to vary in size and other physical characteristics from the particulate matter present in the main gas stream. For weight analyses, and certain chemical analyses, this failing is not drastically important, but for particle size analyses it is all important. Such size analyses are often crucial to epidemiological and other air pollution health effects studies. It should always be borne in mind that the sampling process should be so designed as to produce a sample which is suitable for the analysis techniques which are to be performed, and not vice versa.

In choosing the stack or duct cross-section which is to be sampled, care should be exercised to choose a straight run of stack or duct which can be expected to be not significantly influenced by upstream or downstream bends, restrictions, or discharge points. Any of these can disturb the main gas stream flow, cause eddies, or otherwise produce conditions unsuitable for sampling.

REFERENCES

1. Stern, A. C., "Air Pollution," 2nd ed., Vol. I, II and III, Academic Press, 1968.
2. Air Pollution, *Anal. Chem.*,**43**, 1R (1971); **41** 1R (1969); **39**, 10R (1967).
3. American Soc. for Testing and Materials, Standards of Methods for the Sampling and Analysis of Atmospheres, Part 23, 1971.
4. "Source Sampling Manual," Los Angeles Air Pollution Control District, Los Angeles, Calif., 1963.
5. American Soc. Mechanical Engineers, Power Test Codes, N.Y., 1941.
6. Cooper, H.B.H., Jr., A. T., Rossano, Jr., "Source Testing for Air Pollution Control," Environmental Sciences Services Div., Wilton, Ct., 1970.
7. Environmental Protection Agency, "Standards of Performance for New Stationary Sources," Notice of Proposed Rule Making, *Fed. Reg.*, 36, No. 159, pp. 15704–15722, Aug. 17, 1971.
8. Duprey, R. L., "Compilation of Air Pollutant Emission Factors," Public Health Service Publ. No. 999-AP-42, Washington, D.C., 1968.
9. Brief, R. S., State of the Art of Emmission Testing, *Heating Piping Air Conditioning*, **43**, pp. 93–96, Sept. 1971.
10. Achinger, W. C. and R. T. Shigehaia, A Guide for Selected Sampling Methods for Different Source Conditions, *J. Air Pollution Control Assn.*, **18**, p. 605 (1968).
11. Bloomfield, B., in "*Air Pollution*," Vol. II, 2nd ed., A. C. Stern, ed., Chap. 28, Academic Press, New York, 1968.
12. "Atmospheric Emissions from Sulfuric Acid Manufacturing Processes," Public Health Service Publ. No. 999-AP-13, Raleigh, N.C., 1965.
13. Mulik, J. D., others, An Analytical System, Designed to Measure Multiple Malodorous Compounds Related to Kraft Mill Activities, Presented at TAPPI Water and Air Conference, Apr. 4–7, 1971, Boston, Mass.
14. Sem. G. J., J. A. Borgos and J. G. Olin, "Automatic Monitors of Particulate Mass Emissions from Stationary Fossil-Fuel Combustion Sources," Presented Am. Inst. Chem. Eng. 68th National Meeting, Houston, Tex. Mar. 3, 1971, Paper 68d.

KENNETH L. JOHNSON

Environmental Protection Agency

STATISTICAL METHODS FOR ENVIRONMENTAL SCIENCE

All measurement involves error. Any field which which uses empirical methods must therefore be concerned about variability in its data. Sometimes this concern may be limited to errors of direct measurement. The physicist who wishes to determine the speed of light is looking for the best approximation to a constant which is assumed to have a single, fixed true value.

Far more often, however, the investigator views his data as samples from a larger population, to which he wishes to apply his results. The scientist who analyzes water samples from a lake is concerned with more than the accuracy of the tests he makes upon his samples. Equally crucial is the extent to which these samples are representative of the lake from which they were drawn. Problems of inference from sampled data to some more general population are omnipresent in the environmental field.

A vast body of statistical theory and procedure has been developed to deal with such problems. This paper will concentrate on the basic concepts which underlie the use of these procedures.

Distributions

1. Discrete distributions

A fundamental concept in statistical analysis is the probability of an event. For any actual observation situation (or experiment) there are several possible observations or outcomes. The set of all possible outcomes is the sample space. Some outcomes may occur more often than others. The relative frequency of a given outcome is its probability; a suitable set of probabilities associated with the points in a sample space yield a probability measure. A function x, defined over a sample space with a probability measure, is called a random variable, and its distribution will be described by the probability measure.

Many discrete probability distributions have been studied. Perhaps the more familiar of these is the binomial distribution. In this case there are only two possible events; for example, heads and tails in coin flipping. The probability of obtaining x of one of the events in a series of n trials is described for the binomial distribution by

$$f(x;\theta,n) = \binom{n}{x}\theta^x(1-\theta)^{n-x}, \qquad (1)$$

where θ is the probability of obtaining the selected event on a given trial. The binomial probability distribution is shown graphically in Fig. 1 for $\theta = .5$, $n = 20$.

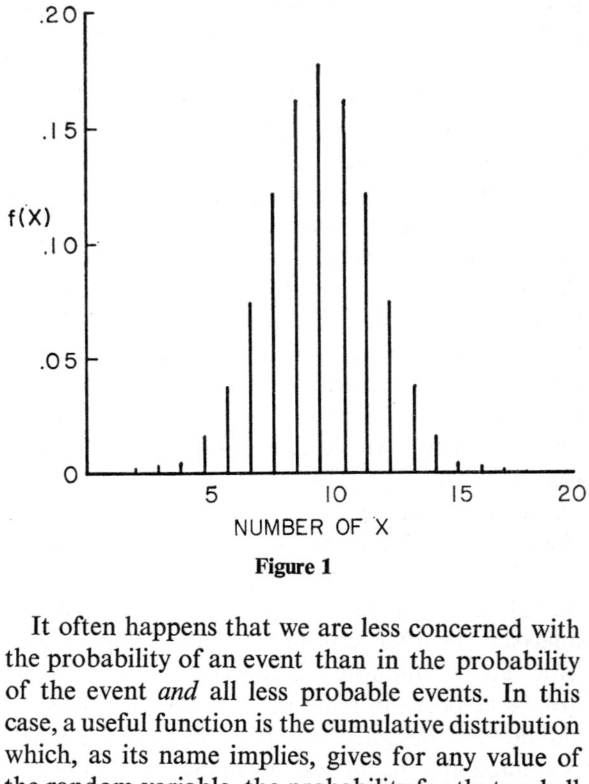

Figure 1

It often happens that we are less concerned with the probability of an event than in the probability of the event *and* all less probable events. In this case, a useful function is the cumulative distribution which, as its name implies, gives for any value of the random variable, the probability for that and all lesser values of the random variable. The cumulative distribution for the binomial distribution is

$$F(x;\theta,n) = \sum_{i=0}^{x} f(x;\theta,n). \qquad (2)$$

It is shown graphically in Fig. 2 for $\theta = .5$, $n = 20$.

An important concept associated with the distribution is that of the moment. The moments of a distribution are defined as

$$\mu_k = \sum_{i=1}^{n} x_i^k f(x_i) \qquad (3)$$

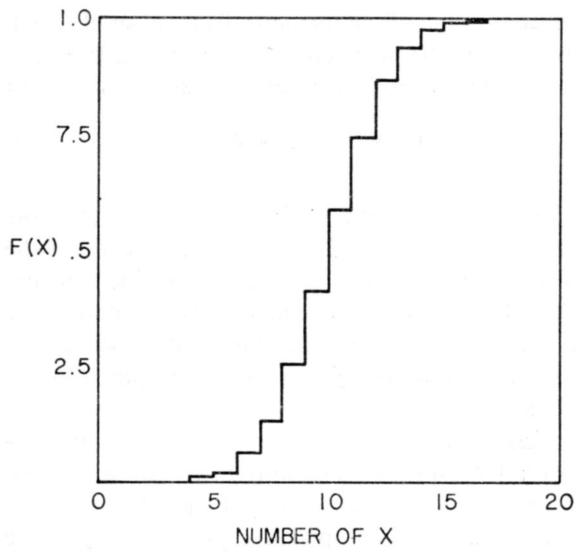

Figure 2

for the first, second, third, etc. moment, where $f(x_i)$ is the probability function for the variable x. Moments need not be taken around the mean of the distribution. However, this is the most important practical case. The first and second moments of a distribution are especially important. The mean itself is the first moment and is the most commonly used measure of central tendency for a distribution. The second moment about the mean is known as the variance. Its positive square root, the standard deviation, is a common measure of dispersion for most distributions. For the binomial distribution the first moment is given by

$$\mu = n\theta \tag{4}$$

and the second moment is given by

$$\sigma^2 = n\theta(1 - \theta). \tag{5}$$

The assumptions underlying the binomial distribution are that the value of θ is constant over trials, and that the trials are independent; the outcome of one trial is not affected by the outcome of another trial. Such trials are called Bernoulli trials. The binomial distribution applies in the case of sampling with replacement. Where sampling is without replacement, the hypergeometric distribution is appropriate. A generalization of the binomial, the multinomial, applies when more than two outcomes are possible for a single trial.

The Poisson distribution can be regarded as the limiting case of the binomial where n is very large and θ is very small, such that $n\theta$ is constant. The Poisson distribution is important in environmental work. Its probability function is given by

$$f(x;\lambda) = \frac{\lambda^x \, e^{-\lambda}}{x!}, \tag{6}$$

where $\lambda = n\theta$ remains constant.
Its first and second moments are

$$\mu = \lambda \tag{7}$$

$$\sigma^2 = \lambda. \tag{8}$$

The Poisson distribution describes events such as the probability of cyclones in a given area for given periods of time, or the distribution of traffic accidents for fixed periods of time. In general, it is appropriate for infrequent events, with a fixed but small probability of occurrence in a given period. Discussions of discrete probability distributions can be found in Freund (1962), among others. For a more extensive discussion, see Feller (1968).

2. Continuous distributions

The distributions mentioned in the previous section are all discrete distributions; that is, they describe the distribution of random variables which can be taken on only discrete values.

Not all variables of interest take on discrete values; very commonly, such variables are continuous. The analogous function to the probability function of a discrete distribution is the probability density function. The probability density function for the standard normal distribution is given by

$$f(x) = \frac{1}{\sqrt{2\pi}} \, e^{-x^2/2}. \tag{9}$$

It is shown in Fig. 3. Its first and second moments are given by

$$\mu = \frac{1}{\sqrt{2\pi}} \int_{-\infty}^{\infty} x \, e^{-x^2/2} \, dx = 0 \tag{10}$$

and

$$\sigma^2 = \frac{1}{\sqrt{2\pi}} \int_{-\infty}^{\infty} x^2 \, e^{-x^2/2} \, dx = 1. \tag{11}$$

The distribution function for the normal distribution is given by

$$F(x) = \frac{1}{\sqrt{2\pi}} \int_{-\infty}^{x} e^{-t^2/2} \, dt. \tag{12}$$

It is shown in Fig. 4.

The normal distribution is of great importance for any field which uses statistics. For one thing, it applies where the distribution is assumed to be the result of a very large number of independent variables summed together. This is a common

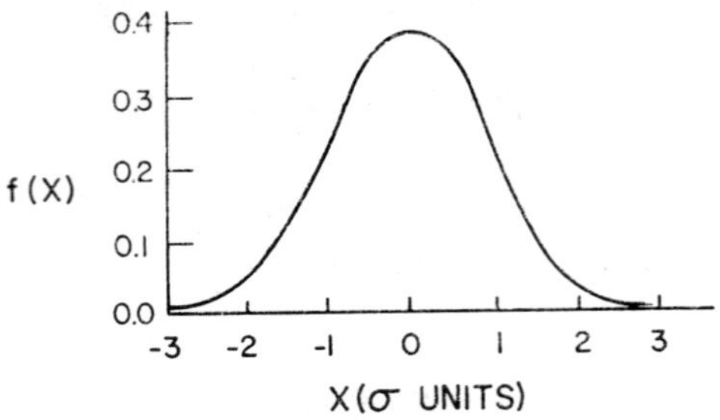

Figure 3

assumption for errors of measurement, and it is often made for any variable affected by a large number of random factors, a common situation in the environmental field.

There are also practical considerations involved in the use of normal statistics. Normal statistics have been the most extensively developed for continuous random variables; analyses involving nonnormal assumptions are apt to be cumbersome. This fact is also a motivating factor in the search for transformations to reduce variables which are described by nonnormal distributions to forms to which the normal distribution can be applied. Caution is advisable, however. The normal distribution should not be assumed as a matter of convenience, or by default, in case of ignorance. The use of statistics assuming normality in the case of variables which are not normally distributed can result in serious errors of interpretation. In particular, it will often result in the finding of apparently significant differences in hypothesis testing when in fact no true differences exists.

The equation which describes the density function of the normal distribution is often found to arise in environmental work in situations other than those explicitly concerned with the use of statistical tests. This is especially likely to occur in connection with the description of the relationship between variables when the value of one or more of the variables may be affected by a variety of other factors which cannot be explicitly incorporated into the functional relationship. For example, the

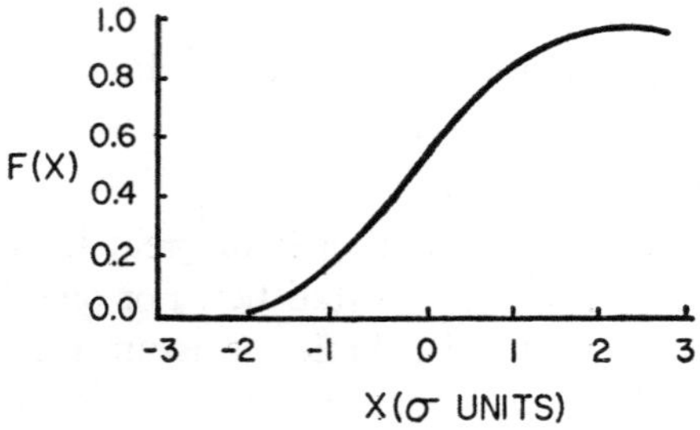

Figure 4

concentration of emmissions from a smokestack under conditions where the vertical distribution has become uniform is given by Panofsky (1973) as

$$C = \frac{Q}{\sqrt{2\pi V D \sigma_y}} e^{-y^2/2\sigma y^2}, \tag{13}$$

where y is the distance from the stack, Q is the emission rate from the stack, D is the height of the inversion layer, and V is the average wind velocity. The classical diffusion equation was found to be unsatisfactory to describe this process because of the large number of factors which can affect it (Panofsky, 1973).

The lognormal distribution is an important nonnormal continuous distribution. It can be arrived at by considering a theory of elementary errors combined by a multiplicative process, just as the normal distribution arises out of a theory of errors

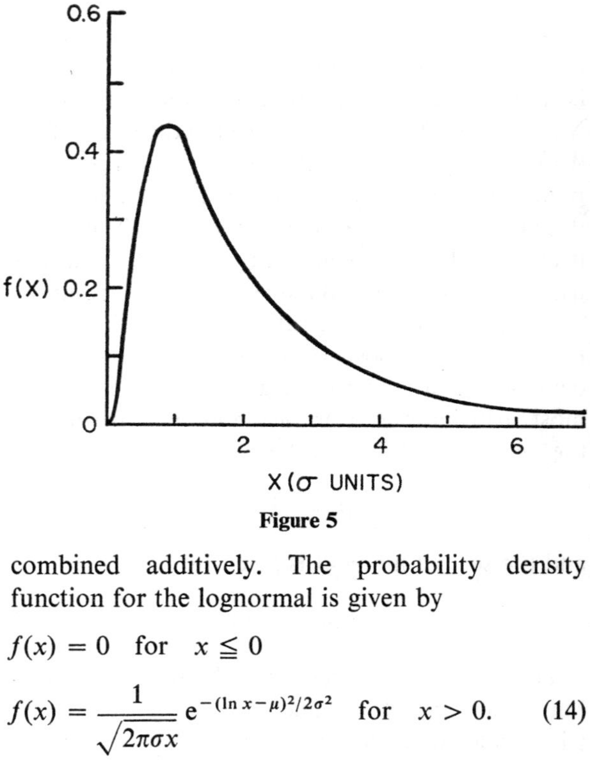

Figure 5

combined additively. The probability density function for the lognormal is given by

$$f(x) = 0 \quad \text{for} \quad x \leqq 0$$

$$f(x) = \frac{1}{\sqrt{2\pi\sigma x}} e^{-(\ln x - \mu)^2/2\sigma^2} \quad \text{for} \quad x > 0. \tag{14}$$

The shape of the lognormal distribution depends on the values of μ and σ^2. It's density function is shown graphically in Fig. 5 for $\mu = 0, \sigma = 0.5$. The positive skew shown is characteristic of the lognormal distribution.

The lognormal distribution is likely to arise in situations in which there is a lower limit on the value which the random variable can assume, but no upper limit. Time measurements, which may extend from zero to infinity, are often described by the lognormal distribution. It has been applied to the distribution of income sizes, to the relative abundance of different species of animals, and has been assumed as the underlying distribution for various discrete counts in biology. As its name implies, it can be normalized by transforming the variable by the use of logarithms. See Aitchison and Brown (1957) for a further discussion of the lognormal distribution.

Many other continuous distributions have been studied. Some of these, such as the uniform distribution, are of minor importance in environmental work. Others are encountered occasionally, such as the exponential distribution, which has been used to compute probabilities in connection with the expected failure rate of equipment. The distribution of times between occurrences of events in Poisson processes are described by the exponential distribution and it is important in the theory of such stochastic processes (Parzen, 1962). Further discussion of continuous distributions may be found in Freund (1962), or most other standard statistical texts.

A special distribution problem often encountered in environmental work is concerned with the occurrence of extreme values of variables described by any one of several distributions. For example, in forecasting floods in connection with planning of construction, or droughts in connection with such problems as stream pollution, concern is with the most extreme values to be expected. To deal with such problems, the asymtotic theory of extreme values of a statistical variable has been developed. Special tables have been developed for estimating the expected extreme values for several distributions which are unlimited in the range of values which can be taken on by their extremes. Some information is also available for distributions with restricted ranges. An interesting application of this theory to prediction of the occurrence of unusually high tides may be found in Pfafflin (1970), and the Delta Commission Report (1960). Further discussion may be found in Gumbel (1954, 1958).

Hypothesis Testing

1. Sampling considerations

A basic consideration in the application of statistical procedures is the selection of the data. In parameter estimation and hypothesis testing sample data are used to make inferences to some larger population. The data are assumed to be a random sample from this population. By random we mean that the sample has been selected in such a way that the probability of obtaining any particular sample value is the same as its probability in the sampled population. When the data are taken care must be used to insure that the data are a random sample from the population of interest; make sure that there must be no biases in the selection process which would make the samples unrepresentative. Otherwise, valid inferences cannot be made from the sample to the sampled population.

The procedures necessary to insure that these conditions are met will depend in part upon the particular problem being studied. A basic principle, however, which applies in all experimental work is that of randomization. Randomization means that the sample is taken in such a way that any uncontrolled variables which might affect the results have an equal chance of affecting any of the samples. For example, in agricultural studies when plots of land are being selected, the assignment of different experimental conditions to the plots of land should be done randomly, by the use of a table of random numbers or some other randomizing process. Thus, any differences which arise between the sample values as a result of differences in soil conditions will have an equal chance of affecting each of the samples.

Randomization avoids error due to bias, but it does nothing about uncontrolled variability. Varibility can be reduced by holding constant other parameters which may affect the experimental results. In a study comparing the smog-producing effects of natural and artificial light, other variables, such as temperature, chamber dilution, etc, were held constant (Laity, 1971). Note, however, that such control also restricts generalization of the results to the conditions used in the test.

Special sampling techniques may be used in some cases to reduce variability. For example, suppose that in an agricultural experiment, plots of land must be chosen from three different fields. These fields may then be incorporated explicitly into the design of the experiment and used as control variables. Comparisons of interest would be arranged so that they can be made within each field, if possible. It should be noted that the use of control variables is not a departure from randomization. Randomization should still be used in assigning conditions within levels of a control variable. Randomization is necessary to prevent bias from variables which are not explicitly controlled in the design of the experiment.

Considerations of random sampling and the selection of appropriate control variables to increase precision of the experiment and insure a more accurate sample selection can arise in connection with all areas using statistical methods. They are particularly important in certain environmental areas, however. In human population studies great care must be taken in the sampling procedures to insure representativeness of the samples. Simple random sampling techniques are seldom adequate and more complex procedures have been developed For further discussion of this kind of sampling, see Kish (1965) and Yates (1965). Sampling problems arise in connection with inferences from cloud seeding experiments which may affect the generality of the results (Bernier, 1967). Since most environmental experiments involve variables which are affected by a wide variety of other variables, sampling problems, especially the question of generalization from experimental results, is a very common problem. The specific randomization procedures, control variables and limitations on generalization of results will depend upon the particular field in question, but any experiment in this area should be designed with these problems in mind.

2. Parameter estimation

A common problem encountered in environmental work is the estimation of population parameters from sample values. Examples of such estimation questions are: What is the "best" estimate of the mean of a population: Within what range of values can the mean safely be assumed to lie?

In order to answer such questions, we must decide what is meant by a "best" estimate. Probably the most widely used method of estimation is that of maximum likelihood, developed by Fisher (1958). A maximum likelihood estimate is one which selects that parameter value for a distribution describing a population which maximizes the probability of obtaining the observed set of sample values, assuming random sampling. It has the advantages of yielding estimates which fully utilize the information in the sample, if such estimates exist, and which are less variable under certain conditions for large samples than other estimates.

The method consists of taking the equation for the probability, or probability density function, finding its maximum value, either directly or by maximizing the natural logarithm of the function, which has a maximum for the same parameter values, and solving for these parameter values, The sample mean, $\hat{\mu} = \left(\sum_{n}^{i=1} x_i\right)/N$, is a maximum likelihood estimate of the true mean of the distribution for a number of distributions. The variance, $\hat{\sigma}^2$, calculated from the sample by $\hat{\sigma}^2 = \sum_{i=1}^{n} (x_i - \hat{\mu})^2/n$, is a maximum likelihood estimate of the population σ^2 for the normal distribution.

Note that such estimates may not be the best in some other sense. In particular, they may not be unbiased. An unbiased estimate is one whose value will, on the average, equal that of the parameter for which it is an estimate, for repeated sampling. In other words, the expected value of an unbiased estimate is equal to the value of the parameter being estimated. The variance is, in fact, biased. To obtain an unbiased estimate of the population variance, it is necessary to multiply σ^2 by $n/(n - 1)$, to yield s^2, the sample variance, and s, $(+\sqrt{s^2})$ the sample standard deviation.

There are other situations in which the maximum likelihood estimate may not be "best" for the purposes of the investigator. If a distribution is badly skewed, use of the mean as a measure of central tendency may be quite misleading. It is common in this case to use the median, which may be defined as the value of the variable which divides the distribution into two equal parts. Income statistics, which are strongly skewed positively, commonly use the median rather than the mean for this reason.

If a distribution is very irregular, any measure of central tendency which attempts to base itself on the entire range of scores may be misleading. In this case, it may be more useful to examine the maximum points of $f(x)$; these are known as modes. A distribution may have 1, 2 or more modes; it will then be referred to as unimodal, bimodal, or multimodal, respectively.

Other measures of dispersion may be used besides the standard deviation. The probable error, p.e., has often been used in engineering practice. It is a number such that

$$\int_{\mu - p.e.}^{\mu + p.e.} f(x)\, dx = 0.5. \qquad (15)$$

The p.e. is seldom used today, having been largely replaced by σ^2.

The interquartile range may sometimes be used for a set of observations whose true distribution is unknown. It consists of the limits of the range of values which include the middle half of the sample values. The interquartile range is less sensitive than the standard deviation to the presence of a few very deviant data values.

The sample mean and standard deviation may be used to describe the most likely true value of these parameters, and to place confidence limits on that value. The standard error of the mean is given by $s/\sqrt{n}$ (n = sample size). The standard error of the mean can be used to make a statement about the probability that a range of values will include the true mean. For example, assuming normality, the range of values defined by the observed mean $\pm$ 1.96 $s/\sqrt{n}$ will be expected to include the value of the true mean in 95% of all samples.

A more general approach to estimation problems can be found in Bayseian decision theory (Pratt *et al.*, 1965). It is possible to appeal to decision theory to work out specific answers to the "best estimate" problem for a variety of decision criteria in specific situation. This approach is well described in Weiss (1961). Although the method is not often applied in routine statistical applications, it has received attention in systems analysis problems and has been applied to such environmentally relevant problems as resource allocation (Liebesman, 1970).

3. *Frequency data*

The analysis of frequency data is a problem which often arises in environmental work. Frequency data for a hypothetical experiment in genetics are shown in Table I. In this example,

TABLE 1

Hypothetical Data on the Frequency of Plants producing Red, Pink and White Flowers in the First Generation of an Experiment in which Red and White Parent Plants were Crossed, assuming Single Gene Inheritance, neither Gene Dominant

		Flower color		
		Red	Pink	White
Number of plants	expected	25	50	25
	observed	28	48	24

the expected frequencies are assumed to be known independently of the observed frequencies. The chi-square statistic, χ^2, is defined as

$$\chi^2 = \sum \frac{(E - O)^2}{E^2}, \qquad (16)$$

where E is the expected frequency and O is the observed frequency. It can be applied to frequency tables, such as that shown in Table I. Note that an important assumption of the chi-square test is that the observations be independent The same samples or individuals must not appear in more than one cell.

In the example given above, the expected frequencies were assumed to be known. In practice this is very often not the case; the experimenter will have several sets of observed frequencies, and will wish to determine whether or not they represent samples from one population, but will not know the expected frequency for samples from that population.

In situations where a two-way categorization of the data exists, the expected values may be estimated from the marginals. For example, the formula for chi-square, for the fourfold contingency table shown below is

	Classification II	
Classification I	A	B
	C	D

$$\chi^2 = \frac{N\left(|AD - BC| - \dfrac{N}{2}\right)^2}{A{\cdot}B{\cdot}C{\cdot}D}. \qquad (17)$$

Observe that instead of having independent expected values, we are now estimating these parameters from the marginal distributions of the data. The result is a loss in the degrees of freedom for the estimate. A chi-square with four independently obtained expected values would have four degrees of freedom; the fourfold table above has only one. The concept of degrees of freedom is a very general one in statistical analysis. It is related to the number of observations which can vary independently of each other. When expected values for chi-square are computed from the marginals, not all of the O–E differences in a row or column are independent, for their discrepancies must sum to zero. Calculation of means from sample data imposes a similar restriction; since the deviations from the mean must sum to zero, not all of the observations in the sample can be regarded as freely varying. It is important to have the correct number of degrees of freedom for an estimate in order to determine the proper level of significance; many statistical tables require this information explicitly, and it is implicit in any comparison. Calculation of the proper degrees of freedom for a comparison can become complicated in specific cases, especially that of analysis of variance. The basic principle to remember, however, is that any linear independent constraints placed on the data will reduce the degrees of freedom. Tables for value of the χ^2 distribution for various degrees of freedom are readily available. For a further discussion of the use of chi-square, see Snedecor. (1967)

4. Difference between two samples

Another common situation arises when two samples are taken, and the experimenter wishes to know whether or not they are samples from populations with the same parameter values. If the populations can be presumed to be normal, then the significance of the differences of the two means can be tested by

$$t = \frac{\hat{\mu}_1 - \hat{\mu}_2}{\sqrt{\frac{s_1^2}{N_1} + \frac{s_2^2}{N_2}}}, \tag{18}$$

where $\hat{\mu}_1$ and $\hat{\mu}_2$ are the sample means, s^2 and s^2 are the sample variances, N_1 and N_2 are the sample sizes, and the population variances are assumed to be equal. This is the **t**-test, for two samples. The **t**-test can also be used to test the significance of the difference between one sample mean and a theoretical value. Tables for the significance of the **t**-test may be found in most statistical texts.

The theory underlying the **t**-test is that the measures of dispersion estimated from the observations within a sample provide estimates of the expected variability. If the means are close together, relative to that variability then it is unlikely that the populations differ in their true values. However, if the means vary widely, then it is unlikely that the samples come from distributions with the same underlying distributions. This situation is diagrammed in Fig. 6. The **t**-test permits an exact statement

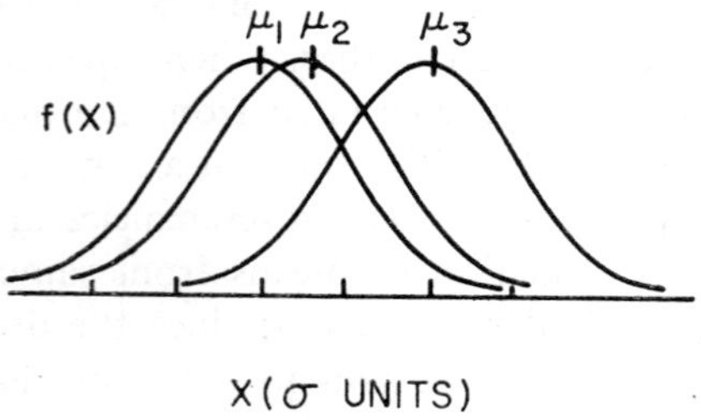

Figure 6

of how unlikely the null hypothesis (assumption of no difference) is. If it is sufficiently unlikely, it can be rejected. It is common to assume the null hypothesis unless it can be rejected in at least 95% of the cases, though more stringent criteria (99% or more) may be adopted if more certainty is needed.

The more stringent the criterion, of course, the more likely it is that the null hypothesis will be accepted when, in fact, it is false. The probability of falsely rejecting the null hypothesis is known as a type I error. Accepting the null hypothesis when it should be rejected is known as a type II error. For a given type I error, the probability of correctly rejecting the null hypothesis for a given true difference is known as the power of the test for detecting the difference. The function of these probabilities for various true differences in the parameter under test is known as the power function of the test. Statistical tests differ in their power and power functions are useful in the comparison of different tests.

Note that type I and type II errors are necessarily related; for an experiment of a given level of precision, decreasing the probability of a type I error raises the probability of a type II error, and vice versa. Thus, increasing the stringency of one's criterion does not decrease the overall probability of an erroneous conclusion; it merely changes the type of error which is most likely to be made. To decrease the overall error, the experiment must be made more precise, either by increasing the number of observations, or by reducing the error in the individual observations.

Many other tests of mean difference exist besides the **t**-test. The appropriate choice of a test will depend on the assumptions made about the distributions underlying the observations. In theory, the **t**-test applies only for variables which are continuous, range from $\pm$ infinity in value, and are normally distributed with equal variance assumed for the underlying population. In practice, it is often applied to variables of a more restricted range, and in some cases where the observed values of a variable are inherently discontinuous. However, when the assumptions of the test are violated, or distribution information is unavailable, it may be safer to use nonparametric tests, which do not depend on assumptions about the shape of the underlying distribution. While nonparametric tests are less powerful than parametric tests such as the **t**-test, when the assumptions of the parametric tests are met, and therefore will be less likely to reject the null hypothesis, in practice they yield results close to the **t**-test unless the assumptions of the **t**-test are seriously violated. Nonparametric tests have been used in meteorological studies because of nonnormality in the distribution of rainfall samples. (Decker and Schickedanz, 1967) For further discussions of hypothesis testing, see Hoel (1962) and Lehmann (1959). Discussions of nonparametric tests may be found in Pierce (1970) and Siegel (1956).

5. Analysis of variance (ANOVA)

The **t**-test applies to the comparison of two means. The concepts underlying the **t**-test may be generalized to the testing of more than two means. The result is known as the analysis of variance. Suppose that one has several samples. A number of variances may be estimated. The variance of each sample can be computed around the mean for the sample. The variance of the sample means around the grand mean of all the scores gives another variance. Finally, one can ignore the grouping of the data and complete the varience for all scores around the grand mean. It can be shown that this "total" variance can be regarded as made up of two independent parts, the variance of the scores about their sample means, and the variance of these means about the grand mean. If all these samples are indeed from the same population, then estimates of the population variance obtained from within the individual groups will be approximately the same as that estimated from the variance of sample means around the grand mean. If, however, they come from populations which are normally distributed and have the same standard deviations, but different means, then the variance estimated from the sample means will exceed the variance as estimated from the within sample estimates.

The formal test of the hypothesis is known as the F-test. It is made by forming the F-ratio.

$$F = \frac{\text{M.S.E.}_{(1)}}{\text{M.S.E.}_{(2)}}. \tag{19}$$

Mean square estimates (M.S.E.) are obtained from variance estimates by division by the appropriate degrees of freedom. The mean square estimate in the numerator is that for the hypothesis to be tested. The mean square estimate in the denominator is the error estimate; it derives from some source which is presumed to be affected by all sources of variance which affect the numerator, except those arising from the hypothesis under test. The two estimates must also be independent of each other. In the example above, the within group M.S.E. is used as the error estimate; however, this is often not the case for more complex experimental designs. The appropriate error estimate must be determined from examination of the particular experimental design, and from considerations about the nature of the independent variables whose effect is being tested; independent variables whose values are fixed may require different error estimates than in the case of independent variables whose values are to be regarded as samples from a larger set. Determination of degrees of freedom for analysis of variance goes beyond the scope of this paper, but the basic principle is the same as previously discussed; each parameter estimated from the data (usually means, for ANOVA) in computing an estimator will reduce the degrees of freedom for that estimate.

The linear model for such an experiment is given by

$$X_{ij} = \mu + G_i + e_{ij}, \tag{20}$$

where X_{ij} is a particular observation, μ is the mean, G_i is the effect the Gth experimental condition and e_{ij} is the error uniquely associated with that observation. The e_{ij} are assumed to be independent random samples from normal distributions with zero mean and the same variances. The analysis of variance thus tests whether various components making up a score are significantly different from zero.

More complicated components may be presumed. For example, in the case of a two-way table, the assumed model might be

$$X_{ijk} = \mu + R_i + C_j + RC_{ij} + e_{ijk}. \tag{21}$$

In addition to having another condition, or main effect, there is a term RC_{ij} which is associated with that particular combination of levels of the main effects. Such effects are known as interaction effects.

Basic assumptions of the analysis of variance are normality and homogeneity of variance. The F-test however, has been shown to be relatively "robust" as far as deviations from the strict assumption of normality go. Violations of the assumption of homogeneity of variance may be more serious. Tests have been developed which can be applied where violations of this assumption are suspected. See Scheffé, (1959; Ch. 10), for further discussion of this problem.

Innumerable variations on the basic models are possible. For a more detailed discussion, see Cochran and Cox, (1957) or Scheffé (1959). It should be noted, especially, that a significant F-ratio does not assure that all the conditions which entered into the comparison differ significantly from each other. To determine which mean differences are significantly different, additional tests must be made. The problem of multiple comparisons among several means has been approached in three main ways; Scheffé's method for post-hoc comparisons; Tukey's gap test; and Duncan's multiple range test. For further discussion of such testing, see Kirk (1968).

Computational formulas for ANOVA can be found in standard texts covering this topic. However, hand calculation becomes cumbersome for problems of any complexity, and a number of computer programs are available for analyzing various designs. The Biomedical Statistical Programs (Ed. by Dixon, 1967) are frequently used for this purpose. A method recently developed by Fowlkes (1969) permits a particularly simple specification of the design problem and has the flexibility to handle a wide variety of experimental designs.

Special Estimation Problems

The estimation problems we have considered so far have involved single experiments, or sets of data. In environmental work, the problem of arriving at an estimate by combining the results of a series of tests often arises. Consider, for example, the problem of estimating the coliform bacteria population size in a specimen of water from a series of dilution tests. Samples from the water specimen are diluted by known amounts. At some point, the dilution becomes so great that the lactose broth brilliant green bile test for the presence of coliform bacteria becomes negative (Fair and Geyer, 1954). From the amount of dilution necessary to obtain a negative test, plus the assumption that one organism is enough to yield a positive response, it is possible to estimate the original population size in the water specimen.

In making such an estimate, it is unsatisfactory simply to use the first negative test to estimate the population size. Since the diluted samples may differ from one another, it is possible to get a negative test followed by one or more positive tests. It is desirable, rather, to estimate the population from the entire series of tests. This can be done by setting up a combined hypothesis based on the joint probabilities of all the obtained results, and using likelihood estimation procedures to arrive at the most likely value for the population parameter, which is known as the Most Probable Number (MPN) (Fair and Geyer, 1954). Tables have been prepared for estimating the MPN for such tests on this principle, and similar procedures can be used to arrive at the results of a set of tests in other situations.

Sequential testing is a problem that sometimes arises in environmental work. So far, we have assumed that a constant amount of data is available. However, very often, the experimenter is making a series of tests, and wishes to know whether he has enough data to make a decision at a given level of reliability, or whether he should consider taking additional data. Such estimation problems are common in quality control, for example, and may arise in connection with monitoring the effluent from various industrial processes. Statistical procedures have been developed to deal with such questions. They are discussed in Wald (1947).

Correlation and Related Topics

So far we have discussed situations involving a single variable. However, it is common to have more than one type of measure available on the experimental units. The simplest case arises where values for two variables have been obtained, and the experimenter wishes to know how these variables relate to one another.

1. Curve fitting

One problem which frequently arises in environmental work is the fitting of various functions to bivariate data. The simplest situation involves fitting a linear function to the data when all of the variability is assumed to be in the Y variable. The most commonly used criterion for fitting such a function is the minimization of the squared deviations from the line, referred to as the least squares criterion. The application of this criterion yields the following simultaneous equations:

$$\sum_{i=1}^{n} Y_i = nA + B\sum_{i=1}^{n} X_i$$

and (22)

$$\sum_{i=1}^{n} X_i Y_i = A\sum_{i=1}^{n} X_i + B\sum_{i=1}^{n} X_i^2 .$$

These equations can be solved for A and B, the intercept and slope of the best fit line. More complicated functions may also be fitted, using the least squares criterion, and it may be generalized to the case of more than two variables. Discussion of these procedures may be found in Daniel and Wood (1971).

2. Correlation and regression

Another method of analysis often applied to such data is that of correlation. Suppose that our two variables are both normally distributed. In addition to investigating their individual distributions, we may wish to consider their joint occurrence. In this situation, we may choose to compute the Pearson product moment correlation between the two variables, which is given by

$$r_{xy} = \frac{\text{cov}(x_i y_i)}{\hat{\sigma}_x \hat{\sigma}_y}, \tag{23}$$

where $\text{cov}(x_i yx)$ the covariance of x and y, is defined as

$$\sum_{i=1}^{n} \frac{(x_i - \hat{\mu}_x)(y_i - \hat{\mu}_y)}{n}. \tag{24}$$

It is the most common measure of correlation. The square of r gives the proportion of the variance associated with one of the variables which can be predicted from knowledge of the other variables. This correlation coefficient is appropriate whenever the assumption of a normal distribution can be made for both variables.

Another way of looking at correlation is by considering the regression of one variable on another. Fig. 7 shows the relation between two variables, for two sets of bivariate data, one with a 0.0 correlation, the other with a correlation of 0.75. Obviously, estimates of type value of one variable based on values of the other are better in the case

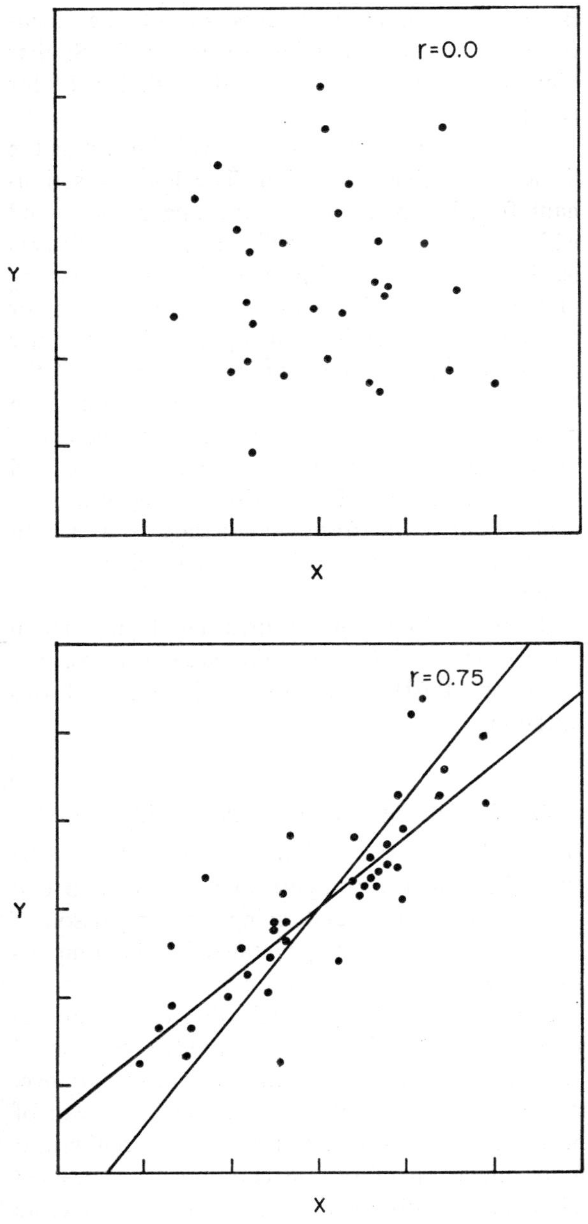

Figure 7

of the higher correlation. The formula for the regression of y on x is given by

$$\frac{y - \hat{\mu}_y}{\hat{\sigma}_y} = \frac{r_{xy}(x - \hat{\mu}_x)}{\hat{\sigma}_x}. \qquad (25)$$

A similar equation exists for the regression of x on y.

A number of other correlation measures are available. For ranked data, the Spearman correlation coefficient, or Kendall's tau, are often used. Measures of correlation appropriate for frequency data also exist. See Siegel (1956).

Multivariate Analysis

Measurements may be available on more than two variables for each experimental unit. The environmental field is one which offers great potential for multivariate measurement. In areas of environmental concern such as water quality, population studies, the study of the effects of pollutants on organisms, to name only a few, there are often several variables which are of interest. The prediction of phenomena of environmental interest, such such as rainfall, or floods, typically involves the consideration of many variables. This section will be concerned with some problems in the analysis of multivariate data.

1. Multivariate distributions

In considering multivariate distributions, it is useful to define the n-dimensional random variable X as the vector

$$X' = [X_1, X_2, \cdots\cdots X_n]. \qquad (26)$$

The elements of this vector will be assumed to be continuous unidimensional random variables, with density functions $f_1(x_1)$, $f_2(x_2)$ . . . . $f_n(x_n)$, and distribution functions $F_1(x_1)$, $F_2(x_2)$ . . . . $F_n(x_n)$. Such a vector also has a joint distribution function

$$F(x_1, x_2, \cdots\cdots x_n) = P(X_1 \leq x_1, \cdots X_n \leq x_n) \qquad (27)$$

where P refers to the probability of all the stated conditions occurring simultaneously.

The concepts considered previously in regard to univariate distributions may be generalized to multivariate distributions. Thus, the expected value of the random vector, X, analogous to the mean of the univariate distribution, is

$$E(X') = [E(X_1), E(X_2), \cdots E(X_n)], \qquad (28)$$

where the $E(X_i)$ are the expected values, or means, for the univariate distributions.

Generalization of the concept of variance is more

complicated. Let us start by considering the covariance between two variables,

$$\sigma_{ij} = E[X_i - E(X_i)]\,[X_j - E(X_j)]. \qquad (29)$$

The covariances between each of the elements of the vector X can be computed; the covariances of the ith and jth elements will be designed as σ_{ij}. If $i = j$ the covariance is the variance of X_i, and will be designed as σ_{ii}. The generalization of the concept of variance to a multidimensional variable then becomes the matrix of variances and covariances. This matrix will be called the covariance matrix. The covariance matrix for the population is given as

$$\sum = \begin{bmatrix} \sigma_{11}\sigma_{12} \cdots \sigma_{1n} \\ \sigma_{21}\sigma_{22} \cdots \sigma_{2n} \\ \cdots\cdots\cdots\cdots\cdots \\ \sigma_{n1}\sigma_{n2} \cdots\cdots \sigma_{nn} \end{bmatrix} \qquad (30)$$

A second useful matrix is the matrix of correlations

$$\begin{bmatrix} r_{11} \cdots\cdots r_{1n} \\ r_{21} \cdots\cdots r_{2n} \\ \cdots\cdots\cdots\cdots \\ r_{n1} \cdots\cdots r_{nn} \end{bmatrix} \qquad (31)$$

If the assumption is made that each of the individual variables is described by a normal distribution, than the distribution of X may be described by the multivariate normal distribution. This assumption will be made in subsequent discussion, except where noted to the contrary.

2. Tests on means

Suppose that measures have been obtained on several variables for a sample, and it is desired to determine whether that sample came from some known population. Or there may be two samples for example, suppose data have been gathered on physiological effects of two concentrations of SO_2 for several measures of physiological functioning, and the investigator wishes to know if they should be regarded as samples from the same population. In such situations, instead of using **t**-tests to determine the significance of each individual difference separately, it would be desirable to be able to perform one test, analogous to the **t**-test, on the vectors of the means.

A test, known as Hotellings's $\mathbf{T}^2$ test, has been developed for this purpose. The test does not require that the population covariance matrix be known. It does, however, require that samples to be compared come from populations with the same covariance matrix, an assumption analogous to the constant variance requirement of the **t**-test.

To understand the nature of $\mathbf{T}^2$ in the single sample case, consider a single random variable made up of any linear combination of the n variables in the vector X (all of the variables must enter into the combination, i.e., none of the coefficients may be zero). This variable will have a normal distribution, since it is a sum of normal variables, and it can be compared with a linear combination of elements from the vector for the population with the same coefficients, by means of a **t**-test. We then adopt the decision rule that the null hypothesis will be accepted only of it is true for all possible linear combinations of the variables. This is equivalent to saying that it is true for the largest value of **t** as a function of the linear combinations. By maximizing $\mathbf{t}^2$ as a function of the linear combinations, it is possible to derive $\mathbf{T}^2$. Similar Similar arguments can be used to derive $\mathbf{T}^2$ for two samples.

A related function of the means is known as the linear discriminant function. The linear discriminant function is defined as the linear compound which generates the largest $\mathbf{T}^2$ value. The coefficients used in this compound provide the best weighting of the variables of a multivariate observation for the purpose of deciding which population gave rise to an observation. A limitation on the use of the linear discriminant function, often ignored in practice, is that it requires that the parameters of the population be known, or at least be estimated from large samples. This statistic has been used in analysis of data from monitoring stations to determine whether pollution concentrations exceed certain criterion values.

Other statistical procedures employing mean vectors are useful in certain circumstances. See Morrison (1967) for a further discussion of this question.

3. Multivariate analysis of variance (MANOVA)

Just as the concepts underlying the **t**-test could be generalized to the comparison of more than two means, the concepts underlying the comparison of two mean vectors can be generalized to the comparison of several vectors of means.

The nature of this generalization can be understood in terms of the linear model, considered previously in connection with analysis of variance. In the multivariate situation, however, instead of having a single observation which is hypothesized to be made up of several components combined additively, the observations are replaced by vectors of observations, and the components by vectors of components. The motivation behind this generalization is similar to that for Hotelling's T^2 test: it permits a test of the null hypothesis for all of the variables considered simultaneously.

Unlike the case of Hotelling's T^2, however, various methods of test construction do not converge on one test statistic, comparable to the F test for analysis of variance. At least three test statistics have been developed for MANOVA, and the powers of the various tests in relation to each other are very incompletely known.

Other problems associated with MANOVA are similar in principle to those associated with ANOVA, though computationally they are more complex. For example, the problem of multiple comparison of means has its analogous problem in MANOVA, that of determining which combinations of mean vectors are responsible for significant test statistics. The number and type of possible linear models can also ramify considerably, just as in the case of ANOVA. For further discussion of MANOVA, see Morrison (1967) or Seal (1964).

4. Extensions of correlation analysis

In a number of situations, where multivariate measurements are taken, the concern of the investigator centers on the prediction of one of the variables. When rainfall measurements are taken in conjunction with a number of other variables, such as temperature, pressure, etc., for example, the purpose is usually to predict the rainfall as a function of the other variables. Thus, it is possible to view one variable as the dependent variable for *a priori* reasons, even though the data do not require such a view.

In these situations, the investigator very often has one of two aims. He may wish to predict one of the variables from all of the other variables. Or he may wish to consider one variable as a function of another variable, with the effect of all the other variables partialled out. The first situation calls for the use of multiple correlation. In the second, the appropriate statistic is the partial correlation coefficient.

Multiple correlation coefficients are used in an effort to improve prediction by combining a number of variables to predict the variable of interest. The formula for three variables is

$$r_{1\cdot 23} = \sqrt{\frac{r_{12}^2 + r_{13}^2 - 2r_{12}r_{13}r_{23}}{1 - r_{23}^2}}. \tag{32}$$

Generalizations are available for larger numbers of variables. If the variables are relatively independent of each other, multiple correlation may improve prediction. However, it should be obvious that this process reaches an upper limit since additional variables, if they are to be of any value, must show a reasonable correlation with the variable of interest, and the total amount of variance to be predicted is fixed. Each additional variable can therefore only have a limited effect.

Partial correlation is used to partial out the effect of one or more variables on the correlation between two other variables. For example, suppose it is desired to study the relationship between body weight and running speed, independent of the effect of height. Since height and weight are correlated, simply doing a standard correlation between running speed and weight will not solve the problem. However, computing a partial correlation, with the contribution of height partially out, will do so. The partial correlation formula for three variables is

$$r_{12\cdot 3} = \frac{r_{12} - r_{13}r_{23}}{\sqrt{1 - r_{13}^2}\sqrt{1 - r_{23}^2}}, \tag{33}$$

where $r_{12.3}$ gives the correlation of variables 1 and 2, with the contribution of variable 3 held constant. This formula may also be extended to partial out the effect of additional variables.

Let us return for a moment to a consideration of the population correlation matrix, *p*. It may be that the investigator has some a priori reason for believing that certain relationships exist among the correlations in this matrix. Suppose, for example there is a reason to believe that several variables are heavily dependent on wind velocity and that another set of variables are dependent on temperature. Such a pattern of underlying relations would result in systematic patterns of high and low correlations in the population matrix, which should be reflected in the observed correlation matrix. If the obtained correlation matrix is partitioned into sets in accordance with the *a priori* hypothesis, test for the independence of the sets will indicate whether or not the hypothesis should be rejected. Procedures have been developed to deal with this situation, and also to obtain coefficients reflecting the correlation between sets of correlations. The latter procedure is known as canonical correlation. Further information about these procedures may be found in Morrison (1967).

5. Other analyses of covariance and correlation matrices

In the analyses discussed so far, there have been *a priori* considerations guiding the direction of the analysis. The situation may arise, however, in which the investigator wishes to study the patterns in an obtained correlation or covariance matrix without any appeal to *a priori* considerations. Let us suppose, for example, that a large number of measurements relevant to weather prediction have been taken, and the investigator wishes to look for patterns among the variables. Or suppose that a large number of demographic variables have been measured on a human population. Again, it is reasonable to ask if certain of these variables show a tendency to be more closely related than others, in the absence of any knowledge about their actual relations. Such analyses may be useful in situations where large numbers of variables are known to be related to a single problem, but the relationships among the variables are not well understood. An investigation of the correlation patterns may reveal consistencies in the data which will serve as clues to the underlying process.

The classic case for the application of such techniques has been the study of the human intellect. In this case, correlations among performances on a very large number of tasks have been obtained and analyzed, and many theories about the underlying skills necessary for intellectual function have been derived from such studies. The usefulness of the techniques are by no means limited to psychology, however. Increasingly, they are being applied in other fields, as diverse as biology (Fisher and Yates, 1964) and archaeology (Chenhall, 1968). Principal component analysis, a closely related technique, has been used in hydrology.

One of the more extensively developed techniques for the analysis of correlation matrices is that of factor analysis. To introduce the concepts underlying factor analysis, imagine a correlation matrix in which the first x variables and the last $n - x$ variables are all highly correlated with each other, but the correlation between any of the first x and any of the second $n - x$ variables is very low. One might suspect that there is some underlying factor which influences the first set of variables, and another which influences the second set of variables, and that these two factors are relatively independent statistically, since the variables which they influence are not highly correlated. The conceptual simplification is obvious; instead of worrying about the relationships among n variables as reflected in their $n(n - 1)/2$ correlations, the investigator can attempt to identify and measure the factors directly.

Factor analysis uses techniques from matrix algebra to accomplish mathematically the process we have outlined intuitively above. It attempts to determine the number of factors, and also the extent to which each of these factors influences the measured variables. Since unique solutions to this problem do not exist, the technique has been the subject of considerable debate, especially on the question of how to determine the best set of factors. Nevertheless, it can be useful in any situation where the relationships among a large set of variables is not well understood..

Additional Procedures

1. Multidimensional scaling and clustering

There are a group of techniques whose use is motivated by considerations similar to those underlying the analysis of correlation matrices, but which are applied, directly to matrices of the distances, or similarities, between various stimuli. Suppose, for example, that people have been asked to judge the similarity of various countries. These judgments may be scaled by multidimensional techniques to discover how many dimensions underlie the judgments. Do people make such judgments along a single dimension? Or are several dimensions involved? An interesting example of this sort was recently analyzed by Wish (1972). Sophisticated techniques have been worked out for such procedures.

Multidimensional scaling has been most extensively used in psychology, where the structure underlying similarity or distance measurements may not be at all obvious without such procedures. Some of these applications are of potential importance in the environmental field, especially in areas such as urban planning, where decisions must take into account human reactions. They are not limited to such situations however, and some intriguing applications have been made in other fields.

A technique related in some ways to multidimensional analysis is that of cluster analysis. Clustering techniques can be applied to the same sort of data as multidimensional scaling procedures. However, the aim is somewhat different. Instead of looking for dimensions assumed to underlie the data, clustering techniques try to define related clusters of stimuli. Larger clusters may then be identified, until a hierarchical structure is defined. If the data are sufficiently structured, a "Tree" may be derived.

A wide variety of clustering techniques have been explored, and interest seems on the increase (Johnson, 1967). The procedures used depend upon the principles used to define the clusters. Clustering techniques have been applied in a number of different fields. Biologists have used them to study the relationships among various animals; for example, a kind of numerical taxonomy (Johnson, 1967).

The requirements which the data must meet for multidimensional scaling and clustering procedures to apply are usually somewhat less stringent than in the case of the multivariate procedures discussed previously. Multidimensional scaling in psychology is often done on data for which an interval scale of measurement cannot be assumed. Distance measures for clustering may be obtained from the clustering judgments of a number of individuals, which lack an ordinal scale. This relative freedom is also useful in many applications where the order of items is known, but the equivalence of the distances between items measured at different points is questionable.

2. Stochastic processes

A stochastic or random process is any process which includes a random element in its description. The term stochastic process is frequently also used to describe the mathematical description of any actual stochastic process. Stochastic models have been developed in a number of areas of environmental concern.

Many stochastic processes involve space or time as a primary variable. Bartlett (1960) in his discussion of ecological frequency distributions begins with the application of the Poisson distribution to animal populations whose density is assumed to be homogeneous over space, and then goes on to develop the consequences of assuming heterogeneous distributions, which are shown to lead to other distributions, such as the negative binomial. The Sutton equation for the diffusion of gases applied to stack effluents, a simplification of which was given earlier for a single dimension (Strom, 1968) is another example of a situation in which statistical considerations about the physical process lead to a spatial model, in this case, one involving two dimensions.

Time is an important variable in many stochastic models. A number of techniques have been developed for the analysis of time series. Many of the concepts we have already considered, such as the mean and variance, can be generalized to time series. The autocorrelation function, which consists of the correlation of a function with itself for various time lags, is often applied to time series data. This function is useful in revealing periodicities in the data, which show up as peaks in the function. Various modifications of this concept have been developed to deal with data which are distributed in discrete steps over time. Time series data, especially discrete time series data, often arise in such areas as hydrology, and the study of air pollution, where sampling is done over time. Such sampling is often combined with spatial sampling, as when meterological measurements are made at a number of stations.

An important consideration in connection with time series is whether the series is stationary or non-stationary. Stationarity of a time series implies that the behavior of the random variables involved does not depend on the time at which observation of the series is begun. The assumption of stationarity simplifies the statistical treatment of time series. Unfortunately, it is often difficult to justify for environmental measurements, especially those taken over long time periods. Examination of time series for evidence of non-stationarity can be a useful procedure, however; for example, it may be useful in determining whether long term climatic changes are occurring (Quick, 1973). For further discussion of time series analysis, see Anderson (1971).

Stochastic models of environmental interest are often multivariate. Mathematical models applied to air pollution may deal with the concentrations of a number of pollutants, as well as such variables as temperature, pressure, precipitation, and wind direction. Special problems arise in the evaluation of such models because of the large numbers of variables involved, the large amounts of data which must be processed for each variable, and the fact that the distributions of the variables are often nonnormal, or not well known. Instead of using analytic methods to obtain solutions, it may be necessary to seek approximate solutions; for example, by extensive tabulation of data for selected sets of conditions, as has been done in connection with models for urban air pollution (Moses and Conrad, in press).

The development of computer technology to deal with the very large amounts of data processing often required has made such approaches feasible today. Nevertheless, caution with regard to many stochastic models should be observed. It is common to find articles describing such models which state that a number of simplifying assumptions were necessary in order to arrive at a model for which computation was feasible, and which then go on to add that even with these assumptions the computational limits of available facilities were nearly exceeded, a combination which raises the possibility that excessive simplfication may have been introduced. In these circumstances, less ambitious treat–

ment of the data might prove more satisfactory. Despite these comments, however, it is clear that the environmental field presents many problems to which the techniques of stochastic modelling can be usefully applied.

Additional Considerations

The methods outlined in previous sections of this paper represent a very brief introduction to the statistics used in environmental studies. It appears likely that the importance of some of these statistical methods, particularly analysis of variance, multivariate procedures, and the use of stochastic modelling, will increase as the environmental field develops. Individuals who are working in the environmental field should also be aware of the impact of computer techniques on statistical computations. An enormous amount of work has been done in this area and much more will be done in the future. However, many statistical texts available today do not explicitly deal with the use of computers for the use of statistical procedures. Some exceptions are Daniel and Wood (1971) and Cooley and Lohnes (1971) who devote extensive discussion to the methods and problems associated with the computerization of statistical techniques. Such computerization is particularly important in the environmental field where very large amounts of data may be collected and can only be efficiently processed by computer space methods.

Acknowledgements—The author is greatly indebted to Dr. E. B. Fowlkes for his many valuable suggestions and comments regarding this paper and to Dr. J. M. Chambers for his critical reading of sections of the paper.

REFERENCES

Aitchison, J. and J. A. Brown, *The Lognormal Distribution*. Cambridge: Cambridge Univ. Press, 1957.

Anderson, T. W., *The Statistical Analysis of Time Series*. New York: John Wiley and Sons, Inc., 1971.

Bailey, N. T. J., *The Elements of Stochastic Processes; with Applications to the Natural Sciences*. New York: John Wiley and Sons, Inc. 1964.

Bartlett, M. S., *An Introduction to Stochastic Processes*, 2nd ed., Cambridge: Univ. Press, 1966.

Bartlett, M. S., *Stochastic Population Models in Ecology and Epidemiology*. London: Methuen and Co., Ltd.: New York: John Wiley and Sons, Inc., 1960.

Bernier, J., On the Design and Evaluation of Cloud Seeding Experiments Performed by Electricité de France. In *Proceedings of the Fifth Berkeley Symposium on Mathematical Statistics and Probability*, Vol. 5, Lecam, L. M. and Neyman, Jerzy, Eds. Berkeley: University of California Press, 1967, p.35.

Chenhall, R. G., The Impact of Computers on Archaeological Theory. *Computers and the Humanities*, **3**, 1968, p. 15.

Cochran, W. G. and G. M. Cox, *Experimental Designs*, 2nd ed., New York: John Wiley and Sons, Inc., 1957.

Computation Laboratory Staff, *Tables of the Cumulative Binomial Probability Distribution*. Cambridge, Mass.: Harvard University Press, 1955.

Cooley, William W. and Paul R. Lohnes, *Multivariate Data Analysis*. New York: John Wiley and Sons, Inc., 1971.

Cramér, H., *The Elements of Probability Theory*. New York: John Wiley and Sons, Inc., 1955.

Cramér, H., *Mathematical Methods of Statistics*. Princeton, N. J.: Princeton University Press, 1946.

Daniel, C. D. and F. S. Wood, *Fitting Equations to Data*. New York: John Wiley and Sons, Inc., 1971.

Decker, Wayne L. and Paul T. Schickedanz, The Evaluation of Rainfall Records from a Five Year Cloud Seeding Experiment in Missouri. In *Proceedings of the Fifth Berkeley Symposium on Mathematical Statistics and Probability*, Vol. 5, Lecam, L. M. and Neyman, Jerzy, Eds. Berkeley: Univ. of California Press, 1967, p.55.

Rapport Delta Commissie, Beschouwingen over Stormvloeden en Getijbeweging, III 1 S Bigdragen Rijkwaterstaat (The Hague, 1960).

Dixon, W. J., ed. *Biomedical Computer Programs*. Univ. of California Publications in Automatic Computation No. 2, Berkeley: Univ. of Calif. Press, 1967.

Fair, G. M. and J. C. Geyer, *Water Supply and Waste-Water Disposal*. New York: John Wiley and Sons, Inc., 1954.

Feller, Wm., *An Introduction to Probability Theory and Its Applications*, 3rd ed., Vol. 1, New York: John Wiley and Sons, Inc., 1968.

Fisher, R. A., *Statistical Methods for Research Workers*, 13th ed., New York: Hafner, 1958.

Fisher, R. A. and F. Yates, *Statistical Tables for Biological, Agricultural and Medical Research*, 6th ed., New York: Hafner, 1964.

Fowlkes, E. B., Some Operators for ANOVA Calculations. *Technometrics*, **11**, 1969, p.511.

Freund, J. E., *Mathematical Statistics*. Englewood Cliffs, N. J.: Prentice-Hall, Inc., 1962.

General Electric Company, Defense Systems Department, *Tables of the Individual and Cumulative Terms of Poisson Distribution*. Princeton, N. J.: Van Nostrand, 1962.

Gumbel, E. J., *Statistics of Extremes*. New York: Columbia University Press, 1958.

Gumbel, E. J., *Statistical Theory of Extreme Values and Some Practical Applications*. Applied Mathematics Series No. 3, National Bureau of Standards, Washington, D.C.: U.S. Govt. Printing Office, 1954.

Harman, H. H., *Modern Factor Analysis*. 2nd. ed., Chicago: University of Chicago Press, 1967.

Hoel, P. G., *Introduction to Mathematical Statistics*, 3rd ed., New York: John Wiley and Sons, Inc., 1962.

Johnson, S. C., Hierarchical Clustering Schemes. *Psychometrika*, **32**, 1967, p.241.

Jolicoeur, P. and J. E. Mosimann, Size and Shape Variation in the Painted Turtle: A principal component analysis, *Growth*, **24**, 1960, p.339.

Kirk, R. E., *Experimental Design: Procedures for the Behavioral Sciences*. Belmont, Calif: Brooks, Cole, 1968.

Kish, Leslie, *Survey Sampling*. New York: John Wiley and Sons, Inc., 1965.

Laity, J. L., A Smog Chamber Study Comparing Blacklight Flourescent Lamps with Natural Sunlight. *Environmental Science and Technology*, **5**, 1971, p. 1218.

Lehmann, E. L., *Testing Statistical Hypotheses*. New York: John Wiley and Sons, Inc., 1959.

Lieberman, G. J. and D. B. Owen, *Tables of the Hypergeometric Probability Distribution*. Stanford, Calif.: Stanford Univ. Press, 1961.

Liebesman, B. S., *Decision Theory Applied to a Class of Resource Allocation Problems*. Doctoral Dissertation, School of Engineering and Science, New York University, 1970.

MacInnis, C. and J. R. Pfafflin, Municipal Waste Water *The Encyclopedia of Environmental Science and Engineering*, Vol. 2, New York: Gordon and Breach, Inc., 1976

Molina, E. C., *Poisson's Exponontial Binomial Limit*. New York: Van Nostrand Company, Inc., 1942.

Morrison, D. F., *Multivariate Statistical Methods*. New York: McGraw-Hill Book Co., 1967.

Moses, H. and J. M. Conrad, Urban Air Pollution Modelling. *The Encyclopedia of Environmental Science and Engineering*, Vol. 2, New York: Gordon and Breach, Inc., 1976.

Panofsky, Hans, Meteorology of Air Pollution. *The Encyclopedia of Environmental Science and Engineering*, Vol. 1, New York: Gordon and Breach, Inc., 1976.

Parzen, Emanuel, *Stochastic Processes*. San Francisco: Holden-Day, Inc., 1962.

Pfafflin, J. R., A Statistical Approach to the Prediction of Recurrent Intervals of Abnormally High Tides. *Ocean Engineering*, **2**, 1970, p.33, Pergamon Press, Great Britain.

Pierce, A., *Fundamentals of Nonparametric Statistics*. Belmont, Calif.: Dickenson Pub. Co., 1970.

Pratt, J. W., Howard Raiffa and R. Schlaifer, *Introduction to Statistical Decision Theory*. New York: McGraw-Hill Book Co., 1965.

Quick, Michael C, Hydrology. *The Encyclopedia of Environmental Science and Engineering*, Vol. 1, New York: Gordon and Breach, Inc., 1973.

Romig, H. G., *50–100 Binomial Tables*. New York: John Wiley and Sons, Inc., 1953.

Scheffé, H., *The Analysis of Variance*. New York: John Wiley and Sons, Inc., 1959.

Scheffé, H., A Method for Judging All Contrasts in the Analysis of Variance, *Biometrika*, **40**, 1953, p.87.

Seal, Hilary L. *Multivariate Statistical Analysis for the Biologist*. London: Methuen and Co., Ltd., 1964.

Siegel, S., *Nonparametric Statistics for the Behavioral Sciences*. New York: McGraw-Hill, 1956.

Snedecor, G. W. and W. G. Cochran, *Statistical Methods*, 6th ed., Ames: The Iowa State University Press, 1967.

Strom, Gordon H., Atmospheric Dispersion of Stack Effluents. *Air Pollution*, Vol. 1, Stern, A. C. Ed., 2nd ed., New York: Academic Press, 1968.

Tables of the Binomial Probability Distribution. National Bureau of Standards Applied Mathematics Series No. 6. Washington, D.C.: U.S. Govt. Printing Office, 1950.

Wald, A., *Sequential Analysis*. New York: John Wiley and Sons, Inc., 1947.

Weiss, L., *Statistical Decision Theory*. New York: McGraw-Hill Book Co., 1961.

Wish, Myron, Nine Dimensions of Nation Perception: Cross-Cultural and Intertask Variation. *Proceedings, 80th Annual Convention, APA*, **1972**.

Yates, Frank, *Sampling Methods for Censuses and Surveys*, 3rd ed., New York: Hafner, 1965.

SHEILA M. PFAFFLIN
Bell Telephone Laboratories

SULFUR REMOVAL

Treatment of the Fossil Fuels

This paper deals with the series of sulfur containing pollutants and with the ways and means currently being employed to limit their discharge into the air. More than 30 million tons of sulfur dioxide are now being discharged annually in the United States. More than 75% of this total results from fuel burning.

Sulfur oxides can be classified among the most serious air pollutants. A 1969 study, conducted by the National Air Pollution Control Administration, stated

> . . .Adverse health effects were noted when 24-hour average levels of sulfur dioxide exceeded 300 mg/m^3 (0.11 PPM) for three to four days; also when the annual mean level of SO_2 exceeded 115 mg/m^3 (0.03 PPM).

Many major urban areas have or are instituting regulations designed to limit the sulfur dioxide concentration in the ambient air. The near term goal is a 24-hour mean level of 0.03 PPM. The primary action being taken is to limit the allowable sulfur content of the fossil fuels burned. For example, in California, regulations have been in effect for several years, limiting the use of fuel oil containing more than 0.5% sulfur. In the New York City area, a maximum allowable fuel oil sulfur level of 1% was implemented in 1969. Within the next few years, however, the use of coal may increase significantly.

And yet, without some significant change, the amount of sulfur dioxide emitted in the United States will almost double in the next decade due to increased energy demands (approximately 3.5% annually) and increased sulfur concentrations found in the more remote crudes sources.

The hydrocarbon and power industries must, therefore, strike a delicate balance between the public's dual requirement of increased quantities of cleaner fuel. More fuel must now be desulfurized more completely and/or more sulfur dioxide must be removed from stack gases.

Against the backdrop of this dilemma, the first portion of this article concerns itself with a survey of current desulfurization techniques in use throughout the petroleum, natural gas and coal industries.

Treatment of stack gases to effect sulfur removal will be discussed separately in the remaining portion.

Processes involving the basic fuels

The two most commonly combusted energy sources are coal and fuel oil having typical sulfur ranges of 1–4% and 3–4% respectively; a 3% S oil produces the same SO_2 emission as a low sulfur coal when based on a comparable energy release. Technically, fuel oil desulfurization is possible, economically it has not been practical.[5A] Hydrogenation, solvent extraction, absorption and chemical reaction are being attempted; but no satisfactory technique has been found which can compete with process for removing sulfur from the flue gases. Finfer[6] claims a possible sulfur reduction from 2.5 to 0.5% might cost 20 cents per barrel by a hydrodesulfurization process. Coal contains sulfur which may be combined with either the organic or inorganic (pyritic and sulfate) matter. The organics may be removed by various cleaning processes, but little reduction in organic sulfur has been found to occur. Currently an extraction process, followed by hydrogenation, is being tried. Some coals have been reduced to S contents below 2%,[7A] and typical sulfur reduction estimates are in the range of 20–40% reduction.[8A] Even if these reduced levels are achieved, a need for further removal of S from the flue gases will exist.

I Fuel Oil Desulfurization (General)

Before the ecological need for fuel oil desulfurization was recognized, oil stocks were desulfurized for a number of other reasons:

1) To avoid poisoning and deactivation of platinum catalysts used in most catalytic reforming processes.

2) To reduce sulfurous acid corrosion of home burner heating equipment.

3) To demetalize crude stocks (sulfur removal from crude is generally accompanied by a concomitant removal of such trace metals as sodium, vandium and nickel).

4) To recover pure sulfur.

5) To reduce or eliminate final product odor.

By definition, hydrodesulfurization is the removal of sulfur by a catalytic reaction with hydrogen to form hydrogen sulfide. As carried out in the petroleum industry, the hydrodesulfurization process is not a specific chemical reaction. Various types of sulfur compounds (mercaptans, sulfides, polysulfides, thiophenes) with varying structures and molecular weights are treated. Obviously, they react at various rates. In addition, during the course of desulfurization, non-sulfur containing molecules may be hydrogenated and in some cases cracked.

The flow design of hydrosulfurization process systems is relatively simple. Preheated oil and hydrogen under pressure are contacted with catalyst. The effluent from the reactor is passed to one or more separators to remove most of the effluent hydrogen and light hydrocarbon gases produced in the operation. These gases are generally recycled with or without prior removal of light hydrocarbons by absorption. The separator liquids may be stripped, rerun or otherwise treated to obtain hydrogen sulfide free products of the desired boiling range.

Except in the case of residuum processing, plant design options are few in number and relatively simple. For example, in the processing of distillates, correlation systems have been developed which relate degree of desulfurization to about three parameters which define the charge stock, reactor temperature, pressure, feed space velocity, hydrogen rate and a catalyst activity parameter.

When residuum stocks are considered, however, generalizatons are not so easily made. The wide variance in residuum properties (i.e. atmospheric or vacuum type, viscosity, Conradson carbon content, metals content and the paraffinic or aromatic nature of residuum) makes each case a special one as far as process design. But the main stumbling blcok seems to be catalyst poisoning due to metals deposition on catalyst surface. As the degree of deposition increases, catalyst efficiency drops, reducing overall desulfurization yields. Catalyst must then be regenerated or replaced, thus adding to overall cost of the particular system employed.

An alternative to desulfurization exists, that being the use of naural low sulfur fuel oils. They may be used alone or in blends with higher sulfur content material. The major source of low sulfur fuel oil is North African crudes, principally from Lybia and Nigeria, and some Far Eastern crude from Sumatra. Fuels made from these crudes will meet even very low sulfur regulations calling for 0.5% sulfur or less. However, the highly waxy nature of these paraffinic materials makes handling difficult and costly. Therefore, the blend becomes a more palatable course of action.

Blends of natural low-sulfur fuel oils with other higher sulfur fuels oils will be adequate in some case to meet more moderate sulfur regulations. The fuel oil fractions of North African crudes contain about 0.3% S. Thus significant amounts

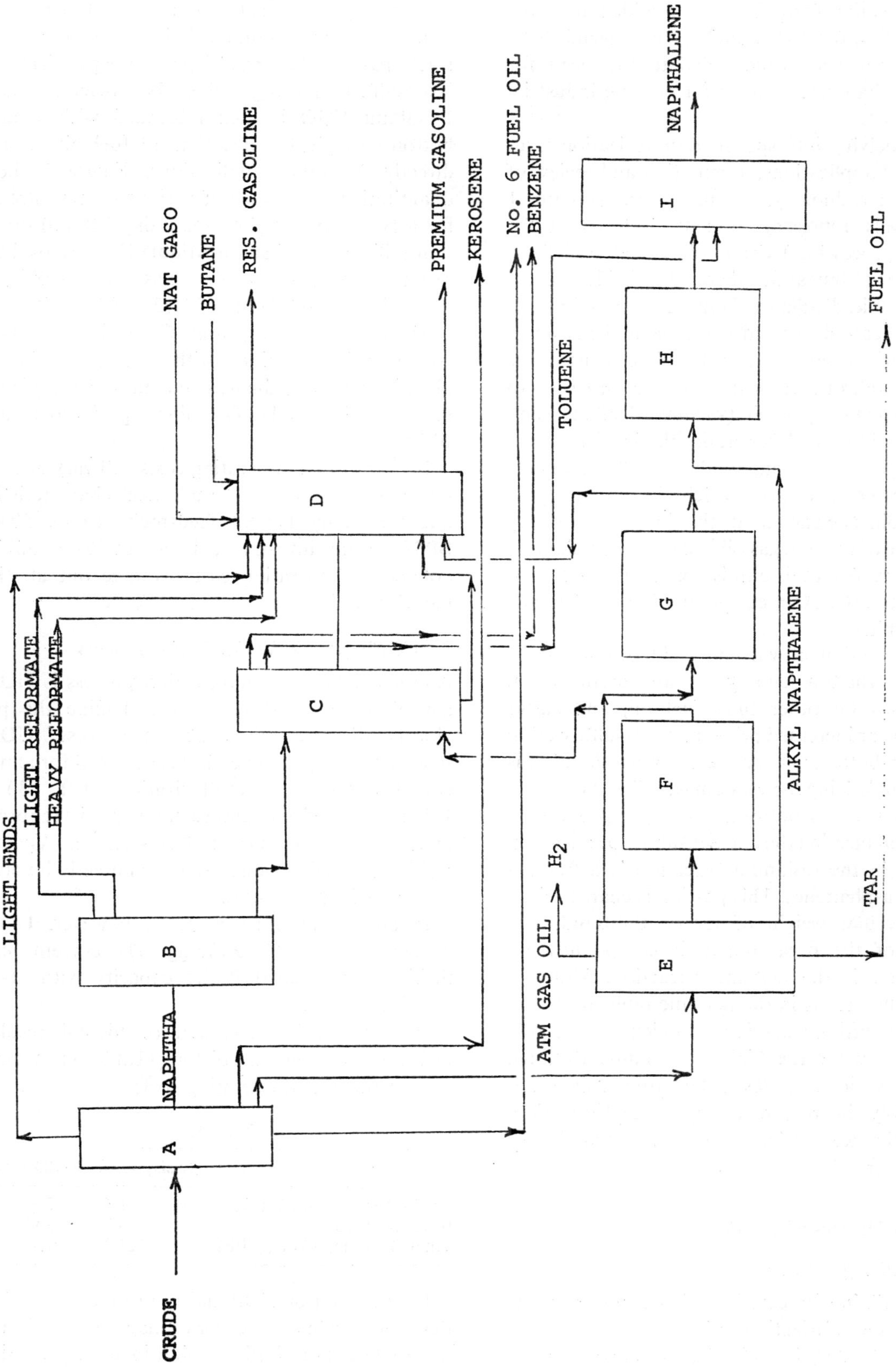

Figure 1 General flowsheet—crude oil processing. A—crude distillation; B—catalytic reformer; C—BTX extraction; D—gasoline pool; E—pyrolysis; F,G,H—hydrotreater; I—hydrodealkylation.

of higher sulfur fuel oils can be added to make blends calling for 1–2% sulfur. These blends have physical properties which obviate the need for specialized handling (a must for existing industrial installations).

Before delving into specific desulfurization technology and applications, a definition and review of pertinent terminology, is in order. (Figure 1 schematically represents a general flowsheet for crude oil processing.) Crude oil, as received from the source is first atmospherically distilled. Light ends and mid-distillates from this operation are further processed to yield gasolines and kerosene. Atmospheric residuum can be directly used for No. 6 fuel oil, or further fractionated (*in vacuo*) to produce vacuum gas oil (vacuum distillate) and vacuum residuum. After atmospheric distillation, the average crude contains about 50% of atmospheric tower bottoms, which is nominally a 650°F + oil. The vacuum distillation yields roughly equal parts of vacuum gas oil and vacuum residuum. The bottoms from this unit is nominally a 975°F + oil, although the exact cut point will vary for each vacuum unit.

Desulfurization of vacuum residuum would be applicable where a refinery has use for the virgin vacuum gas oil other than fuel oil, and sulfur restrictions or increased prices make desulfurization of vacuum bottoms attractive. Another situation is where desulfurizing the vacuum gas oil and blending back with vacuum bottoms no longer produces a final fuel oil meeting the current sulfur specification.

Present in the residuum (vacuum) is a fraction known as asphaltenes. This portion is characterized by a molecular weight of several thousand. The majority of the organo-mettalic compounds are concentrated in the asphaltene fraction. Although many of the metals in the periodic table are found in trace quantities, vanadium and nickel are usually present in by far the highest amounts. Residual oils from various crudes differ from each other considerably in regard to hydrodesulfurization. These differences reside to a great extent in the asphaltene fraction.

IA Light Oil Desulfurization

The G O-Fining process

The G O-Fining Process is designed for relatively complete desulfurization of vacuum gas oils, thermal and catalytic cycle oils, and coker gas oil. It represents an extremely attractive alternative where a lesser degree of sulfur removal from the fuel oil pool and/or a very low sulfur blending stock is required. The feed to the G O-Finer System is atmospheric residuum. This stream is vacuum fractionated and the resulting vacuum gas oil (VGO) is desulfurized using a fixed bed reactor system. Resultant VGO is then reblended with vacuum bottoms to yield a desulfurized fuel oil or used directly for other applications. Figure 2 shows quantitative breakdown of various process streams for a 50,000 barrel per stream day (BPSD) operation utilizing a 3% sulfur Middle East atmospheric residuum feed. The process has the capability of producing 49,700 BPSD of 1.72% S fuel oil.

There are currently four G O-Fining units in commercial operation, with five more in the planning stages (estimated start-up—1972) this will bring total installed G O-Fining capacity to 375,000 BPSD.

Investment and operating costs will vary depending on plant location and crude stock characteristics, but for many typical feedstocks (basis 50,000 BPSD) total investment is about 5.45 million dollars and operating costs average out at 21 ¢/ barrel fuel oil.

2 *UOP's gas oil desulfurization process*

Another light oil desulfurization process is UOP's gas oil desulfurization scheme. Unlike the previously discussed G O-Fining process, UOP's scheme (already commercial) is designed for almost complete (~90%) desulfurization of a 630 to 1050;F blend of light and vacuum gas oils (approximate sulfur content of feed—1.5%). Vacuum residuum is neither directly nor indirectly involved anywhere in the process.

In almost all other respects, however, UOP's process parallels G O-Fining. The current plant facility is of 30,000 BPSD capacity with above mentioned feed.

One year performance data of this unit resulted in following economic picture (Table A) in terms of investment and operating cost:

TABLE A

(Basis; 40,000 BPSD plant)		
Feed sulfur content, Wt %	1.6	2.8
Investment, 10^6 $	3.7	3.9
Total Operating Costs, ¢/BBL	23.3	27.1

Comparison of UOP and G O Finer costs show that both are in same order of magnitude and differ markedly only in initial capital investment. This is in part attributable to the fact that a G O-Fining facility requires atmospheric residuum fractionation whereas UOP's does not.

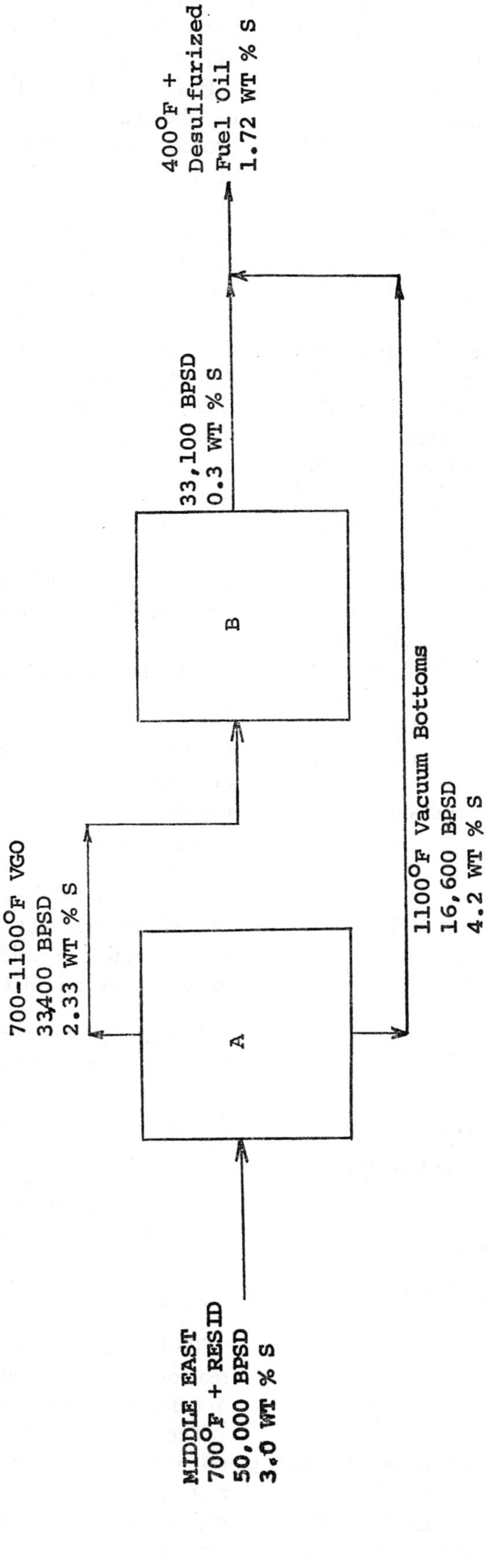

Figure 2 The G O-Fining process.

Stocks of high-sulfur content are difficult to crack catalytically because all or most of the catalysts now in commercial use are poisoned by sulfur compounds. In recent years the trend has been toward processes that remove these sulfur compounds more or less completely. The high sulfur contents of petroleum stocks are mainly in the form of thiophenes and thiophanes and these can be removed only by catalytic decomposition in the presence of hydrogen. The Union Oil Company has developed a cobalt molybdate desulfurization catalyst capable of handling the full range of petroleum stocks encountered in refining operations. Even the more refractory sulfur compounds associated with these stocks are removed. This catalyst exhibited excellent abrasion resistance and heat stability, retaining its activity and strength after calcination in air at temperature as high as 1470°F.[2] Cobalt molybdate may be considered a chemical union of cobalt oxide and molybdic oxide, Co O · Mo O_3. The high activity of this compound is due to an actual chemical combination of these oxides with a resultant alteration of the spacing of the various atoms in the crystal lattice.[1A] Catalyst life is two to five years. Catalyst poisons consisted of carbon, sulfur nitrogen and polymers. Regeneration is accomplished at 700 to 1200°F using air with steam or flue gases.

The fundamental reactions in desulfurization are as follows:

General Reaction

$$C_nH_mS_p + xH_2 \rightarrow C_nH_{m+2x-2p} + pH_2S$$

Desulfurization of ethyl mercaptan

$$C_2H_5SH + H_2 \rightarrow C_2H_6 + H_2S \qquad \Delta H = -19.56 \text{ kg cal/mole}$$

Desulfurization of diethyl sulfide

$$(C_2H_5)_2S + 2H_2 \rightarrow 2C_2H_6 + H_2S \qquad \Delta H = -36.54 \text{ kg cal/mole}$$

Desulfurization of thiophene

$$C_4H_4S + 4H_2 \rightarrow C_4H_{10} + H_2S \qquad \Delta H = -73.26 \text{ kg cal/mole}$$

Desulfurization of amylene

$$C_5H_{10} + H_2 \rightarrow C_5H_{12} \qquad \Delta H = -33.48 \text{ kg cal/mole.}$$

The change in heat content for all these reactions is negative, indicating that they take place with evolution of heat. The sulfur content in Middle East Gas Oil, a typical feed, is 1.25% by weight. The pilot plant data shows that the heat effect is not serious and the whole process can be treated as isothermal.

Hoog[24] explained the chemical reaction process on the catalyst. The reaction is postulated to proceed on the surface of the catalyst by interaction of the sulfur-bearing molecules and hydrogen atoms formed through activated absorption of hydrogen molecules. Oil molecules are more strongly absorbed than hydrogen molecules, and therefore may preferentially cover part of the surface, leaving less surface available for dissociation of hydrogen molecules. In the presence of diluent, namely, N_2, it can also compete for free sites on the surface, and accordingly may cause a reduction in the concentration of hydrogen on the surface, thus giving the lower rate constant when working with H_2–N_2 mixture.

Conversion of the sulfur compounds to hydrogen sulfide and saturated hydrocarbons occurs by cleavage of the sulfur to carbon bonds; essentially no C—C bonds are broken.

IB Residuum Desulfurization

1) *The H-Oil process* (*Cities Service*)

In order to meet the need for an efficient method of desulfurizing residual oils without the complexities encountered in the myriad of existing fixed bed catalytic systems, cities service developed what is now known as the H-Oil System.

Although fixed bed catalytic reactors had been extensively used for desulfurizing distillate oils, desulfurization of residual oil in a fixed bed reactor presented several difficulties:

1) the high temperature rise through the bed tended to cause hot spots and coking,

2) the presence of solids in the feed and the formation of tar-like coke deposits on the catalyst tended to cause a gradual build-up of pressure drop over the catalyst bed and

3) because of the relatively rapid deactivation of the catalysts, system shut down for catalyst replacement occurred often, on the order of six times yearly.

To overcome these problems an ebbulated bed reactor was designed. Figure 3 is a simplified drawing of reactor workings.

The feed oil is mixed with the recycle and makeup hydrogen gas and enters the bottom of the reactor. It passes up through the distributor plate which distributes the oil and gas evenly across the reactor.

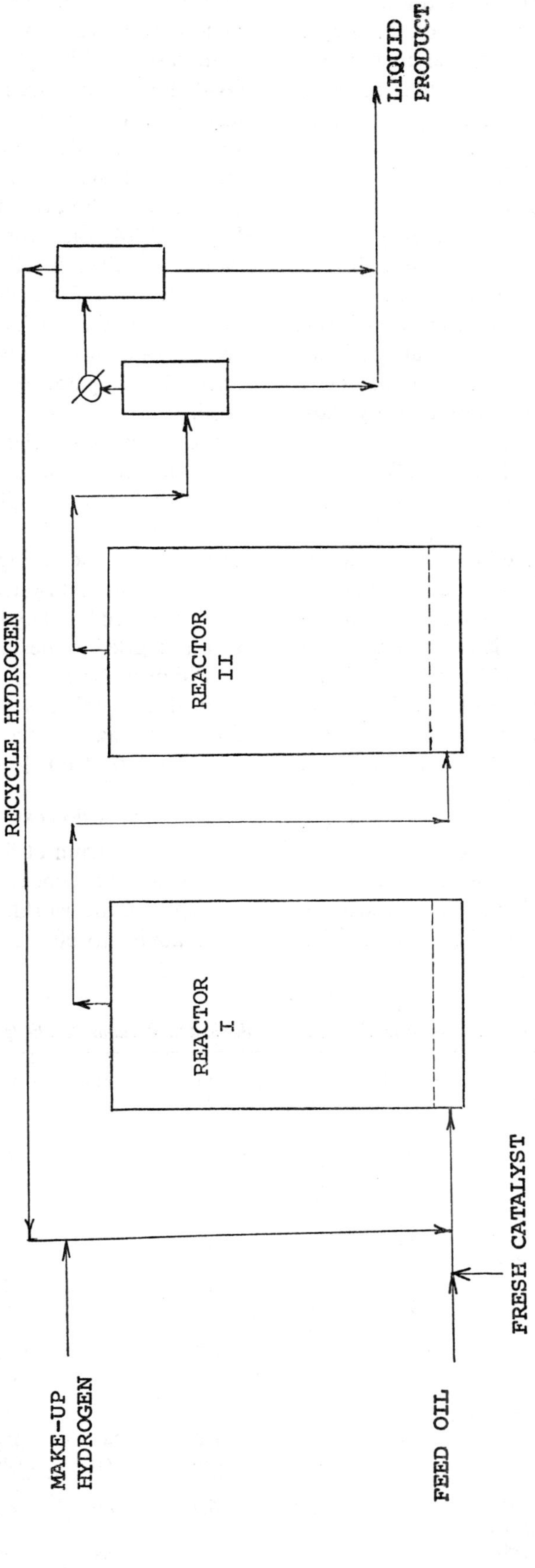

Figure 3 The H-oil process.

The reaction zone consists of a liquid phase with gas bubbling through and with the catayst particles suspended in the liquid, and in random motion. It is a backmixed, isothermal reactor, with a temperature gradient between any two points in the reactor no greater than 5°F.

Due to the catalyst suspension in liquid phase, catalyst particles do not tend to adhere to one another, causing blockage of flow. Any solids present in the feed pass directly through the reactor. Reactor pressure drop is constant.

One of the more important aspects of the ebbulated bed reactor system is that periodic shutdowns for catalyst replacement is not necessary. Daily catalyst replacement results in a steady state activity.

Table B shows examples of H-Oil desulfurization performance with atmospheric and vacuum residuals. In addition, investment and operating cost data are shown to illustrate the important effect of feed stock characteristics on overall economics.

Cases 1–3 describe processing of three atmospheric residual feeds. The Kuwait Residuum treated in case 1 is a high sulfur oil containing relatively low metals content (60 PPM). Therefore, the rate of catalyst deactivation is low and operating conditions are set to minimize hydrocracking and maximize desulfurization. In fact, only 2–3% naphtha and 9–10% middle distillate are produced. The actual chemical hydrogen consumption is fairly close to the estimated needed to remove the sulfur. For many atmospheric residuals which are not too high in metals, this case is typical to give maximum production of low sulfur fuel oil at minimum conversion and hydrogen consumption.

In case 2, although metals content is also low (~40 PPM), hydrogen consumption is exceptionally high. This is due to the fact that conversion was not minimized and 7% naphtha and 13% middle-distillate was produced by hydrocracking.

Case 3 is characteristic of high metals content (~320 PPM) oils from that area. As noted previously, catalyst deactivation increases with metals content. Therefore, catalyst addition rates are higher, resulting in increased operating costs. To compensate for the reduced catalyst activity, higher operating temperatures and/or residence times are used.

Cases 4–6 summarize vacuum residua operations. Desulfurization rates for vacuum residua are lower than for amospheric. The asphaltenes and metallic compound's reside in the vacuum residuum, consequently increasing catalyst deactivation rates and therefore catalyst costs per barrel. In all the cases depicted (4–6) hydrogen consumption, relative to that needed for desulfurization, is high indicating that high sulfur content of feed precludes setting of operating conditions to minimize conversion. In fact, naphtha production ranges from 7–15%, mid-distillates from 15–23%.

2) *The Isomax processes*

A broad spectrum of fixed bed desulfurization and hydrocracking processes are now in operation throughout the world. They are characterized by their ability to effectively handle a wide range of

TABLE B

H-OIL Desulfurization of Atmospheric and Vacuum Residuals

Type-Feed (A-atmos) (V-vacuum)	Case 1 A	Case 2 A	Case 3 A	Case 4 V	Case 5 V	Case 6 V
Source	Kuwait	W. Texas	Venezuela	Kuwait	W. Texas	Venezuela
Feedstock data						
Sulfur (Wt %)	3.8	2.5	2.2	5.0	2.2	2.9
Vanadium and nickel (PPM)	60	40	320	90	55	690
975°F+						
Vol %	45	45	52	80	70	75
sulfur, Wt %	5.3	3.2	2.8	5.3	2.7	3.2
Yield, quality (400°F+)						
Vol %	99.3	96.2	94.2	94.7	92.9	92.9
% S	0.9	0.4	0.9	1.8	0.6	1.2
Chemical H_2 consumption (SCF/BBL)						
For S removal (est.)	290	210	140	340	170	200
Total	490	670	470	660	640	920
Economics						
Capital inv, $\$X10^6$	6.7	7.8	6.9	7.9	8.3	8.9
OP cost, ¢/BBLFeed (20,000 BPSD UNIT)	33	40	39	44	46	65

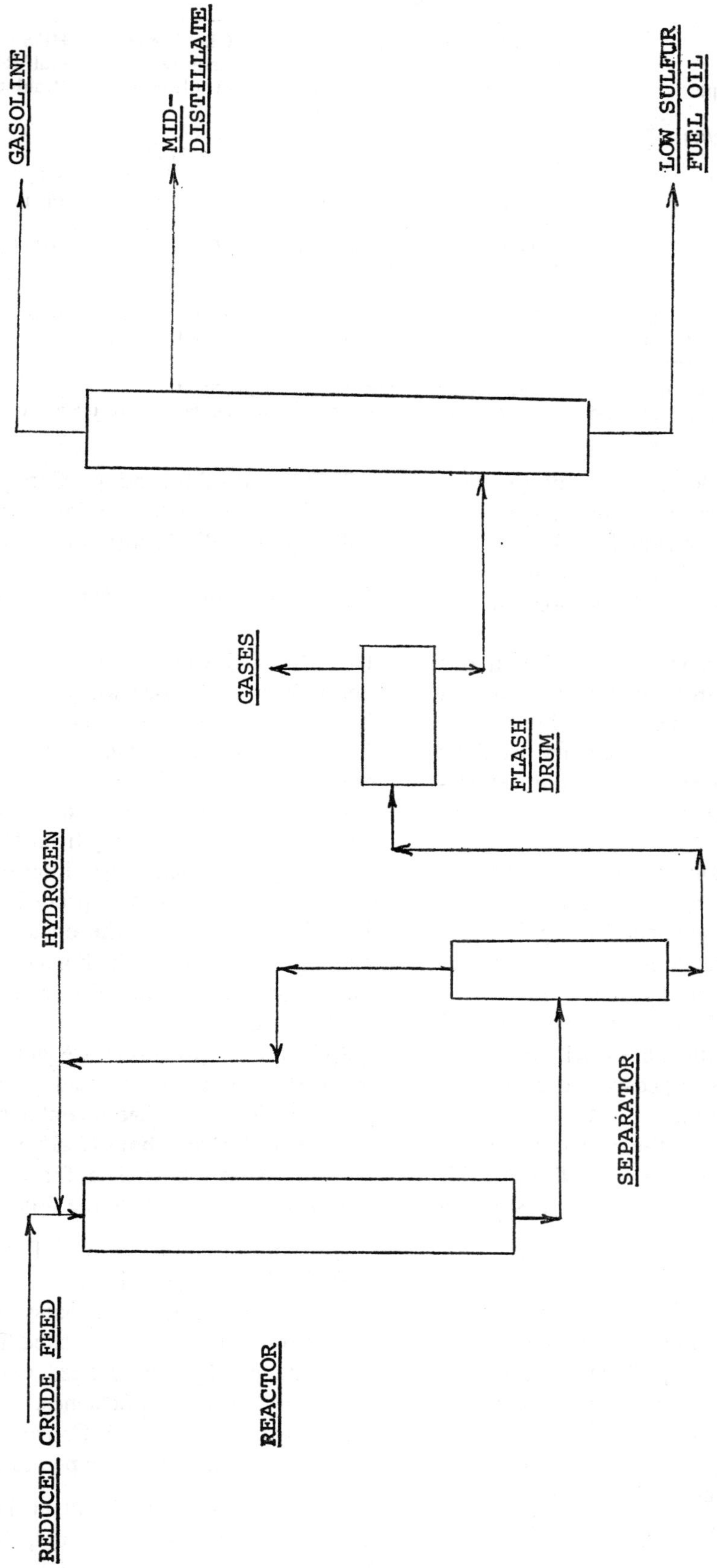

Figure 4 RCD isomax.

TABLE C

Process	RCD Isomax	RDS Isomax	CDS Isomax	HDS
Licensers	UOP	Chevron	Chevron	Gulf R&D
General feed type	Atmospheric residuum	Atmospheric residuum	Whole crude	Residuum
Feed characteristics				
Name	Kuwait	Arabian light	Arabian light	—
Sulfur content	3.9	3.1	1.7	5.5
Process diagram	Figure 4	Figure 5	Figure 6	Figure 7
Fuel oil product				
Quantity (BPSD)	40,000	40,000	40,000	40,000
Sulfur content	1.0	1.0	1.0	2.2
Economics				
Investment[a] (millions)	9.7	24.5	16.7	10.0
Operating costs[b] (¢/BBL)	51	40–60	40–60	—

[a] Includes only cost for Isomax reactor/distillation and auxiliary equipment.
[b] Includes utilities, labor, supervision, maintainence, taxes, insurance, catalyst, hydrogen, etc.

crude feedstocks. In addition, some of the processes are capable of directly desulfurizing crude oil while others treat only residual stocks.

Rather than discuss each process individually, a comparative summary of the major ones is presented in Table C.

There are many other processes which in one way or another effect a reduction in the amount of sulfur burned in our homes and businesses. All of them use some type of proprietary catalytic system, each with its own peculiar optimum operating ranges with regard to feed composition and/or reactor conditions.

The hydrodesulfurization process is still relatively expensive (25–75¢/BBL) by petroleum processing standards. The capital investment for large reactors which operate at high pressures and high temperatures, the consumption of hydrogen during the processing and the use of large volumes of catalyst with a relatively short life all contribute to the costs. In addition, processing costs also depend on the feedstock characteristics.

But when one considers the awesome annual alternative of 30 million tons of sulfur dioxide being pumped into the atmosphere, the cost seems trifling indeed.

II Desulfurization of Natural Gas

Approximately 33% of the natural gas in the United States and over 90% of that processed in Canada is treated to remove normally occurring hydrogen sulfide. The recovered sulfur, which now accounts for about 25% of the free world's production is expected to increase in the future.

Current processes may be classified into four major categories:

1) Dry Bed—Catalytic Conversion,
2) Dry Bed—Absorption—Catalytic Conversion,
3) Liquid Media Absorption—Air Oxidation,
4) Liquid Media Absorption—Direct Conversion.

Dry bed catalytic conversion (the Modified Claus Process)

The Modified Claus Process is used to remove sulfur from acid gases whch have been extracted from a main sour gas stream. The extraction is done with one of the conventional gas treating processes such as amine or hot potassium carbonate.

The process may be used to remove sulfur from acid gas streams containing from 15 to 100 mole % H_2S. The basic schemes use either the once through process or the split stream process. Figure 8 shows flow characteristics of the once through scheme, which in general gives the highest overall recovery and permits maximum heat recovery at a high temperature level.

Split stream processes are generally employed where H_2S content of the acid gas is relatively low (20–25 Mole %) or when it contains relatively large amounts of hydrocarbons (2–5%).

Pertinent design criteria for dry bed catalytic conversion plants include the following:

1) Composition of Acid Gas Feed,
2) Combustion of Acid Gas,
3 For a Once Through Process, Retention Time, of Combustion Gases at Elevated Temperatures,
4) Catalytic Converter Feed Gas Temperature,
5) Optimum Reheat Schemes,
6) Space Velocity in the Converters,
7) Sulfur condensing Temperatures.

The sulfur from a Claus Plant may be produced in various forms, such as liquid, flaked or prilled. Form of choice is determined by transportation mode and end usage.

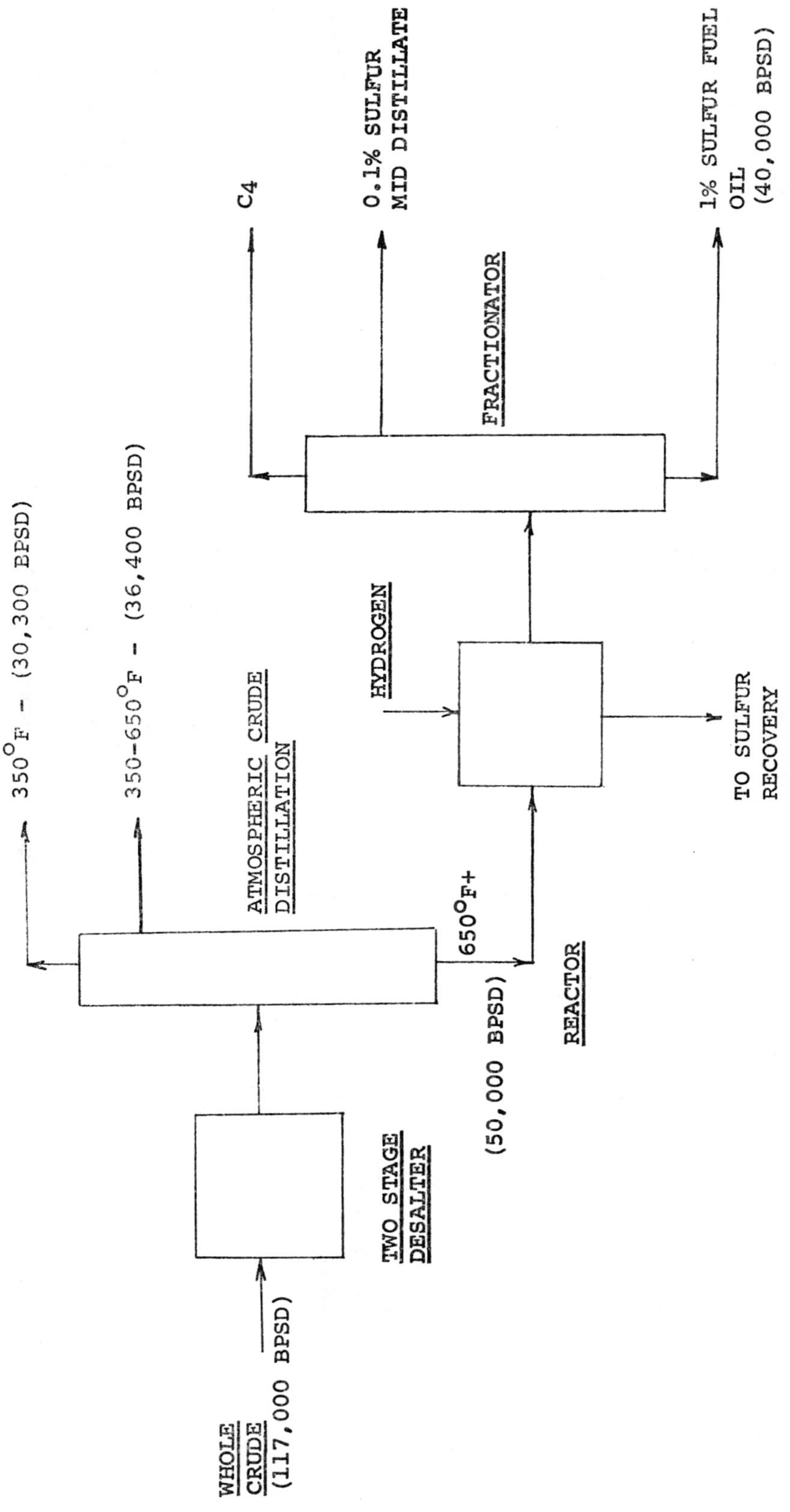

Figure 5 RDS isomax.

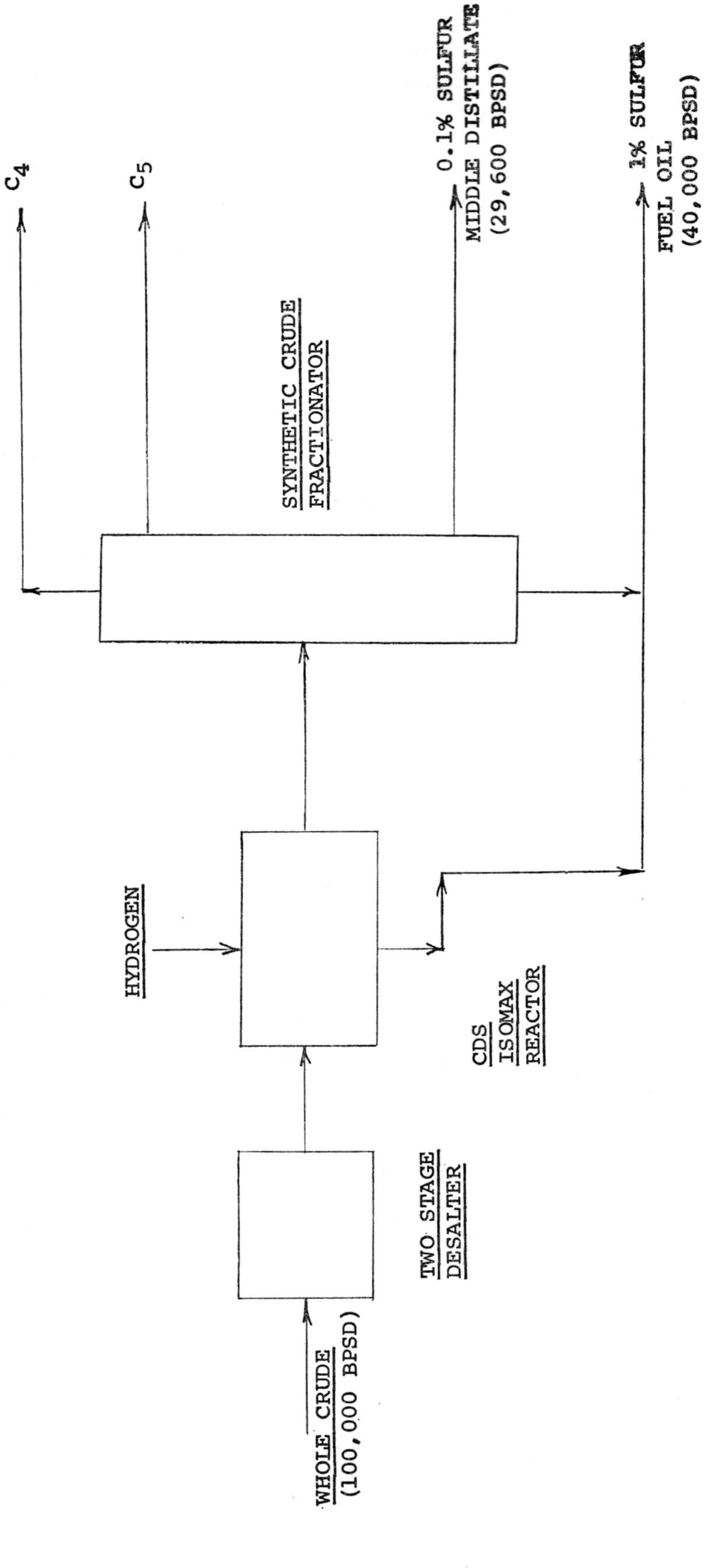

Figure 6 CDS isomax.

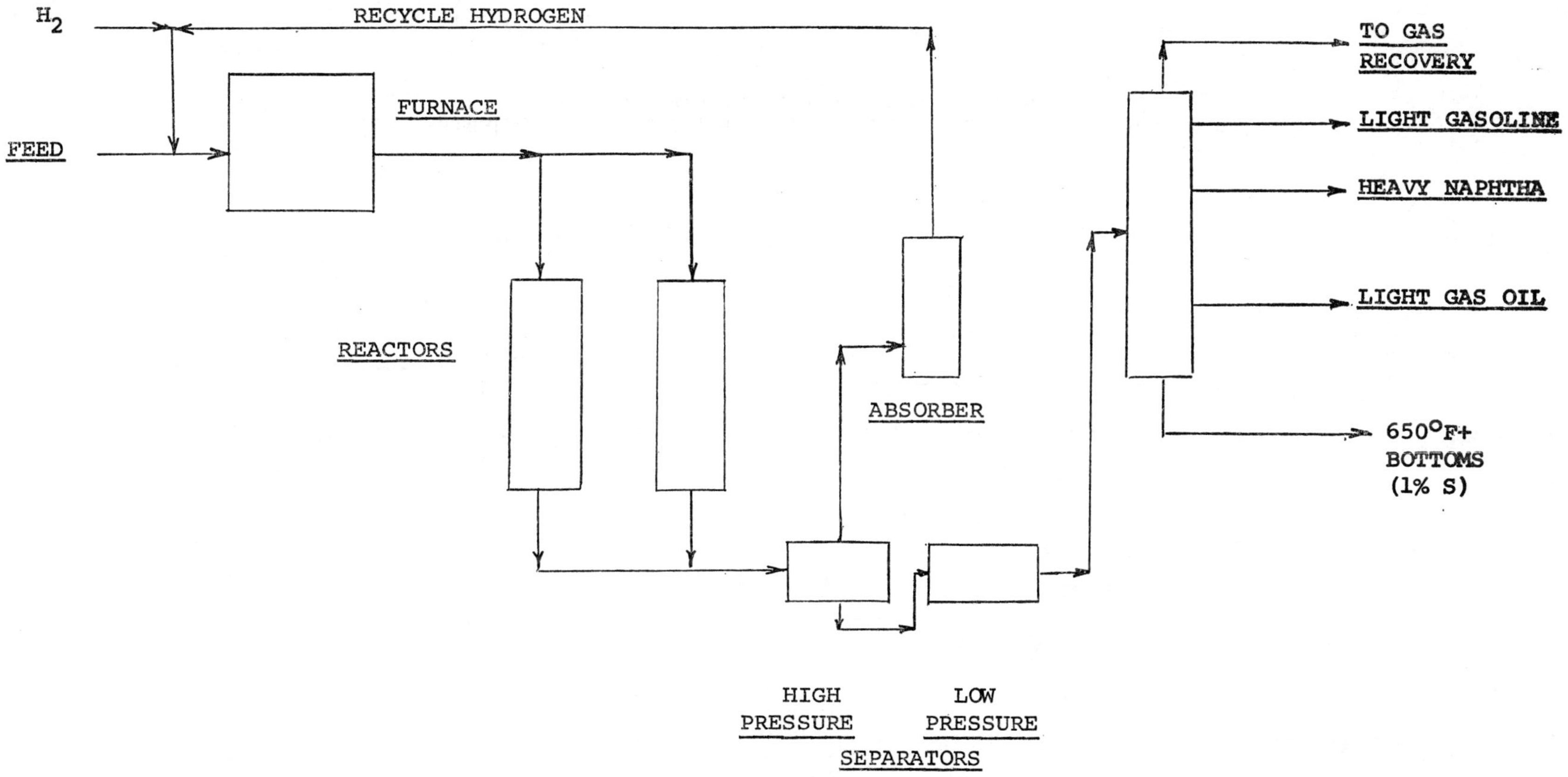
H2
RECYCLE HYDROGEN
FEED
FURNACE
REACTORS
ABSORBER
HIGH
PRESSURE
LOW
PRESSURE
SEPARATORS
TO GAS
RECOVERY
LIGHT GASOLINE
HEAVY NAPHTHA
LIGHT GAS OIL
650°F+
BOTTOMS
(1% S)

Figure 7 HDS.

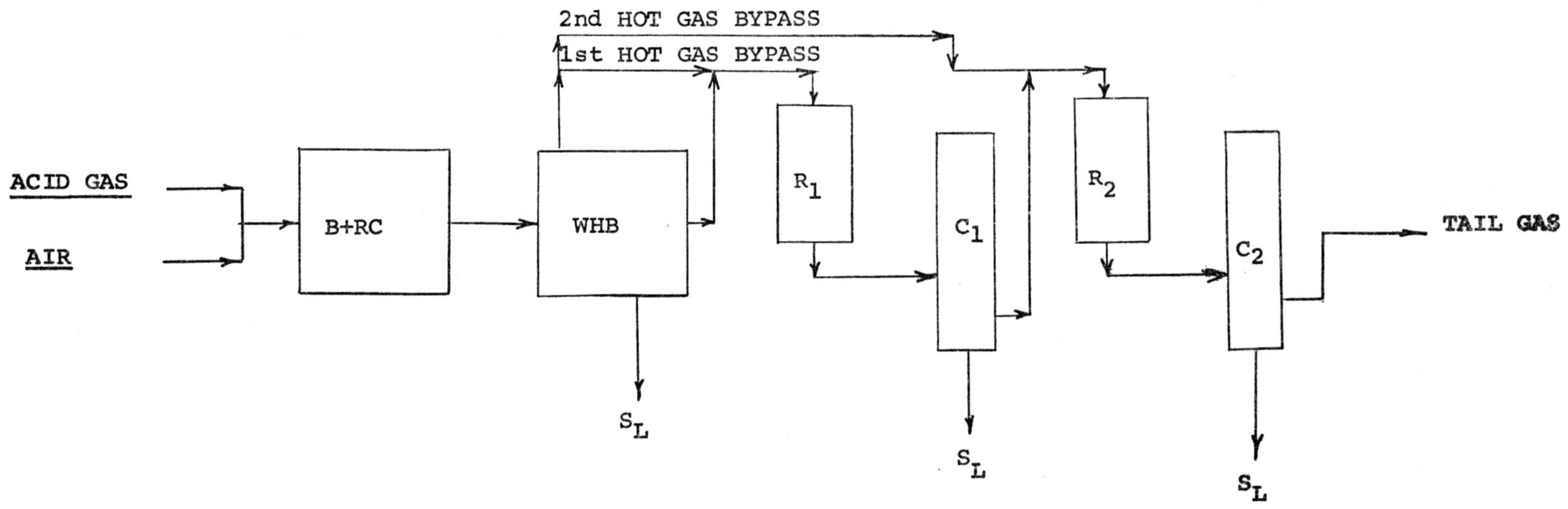

Figure 8 Modified Claus process. B + RC—burner + reaction chamber; WHB—waste heat boiler; R—catalytic converter; C—condenser; S_L—liquid sulfur.

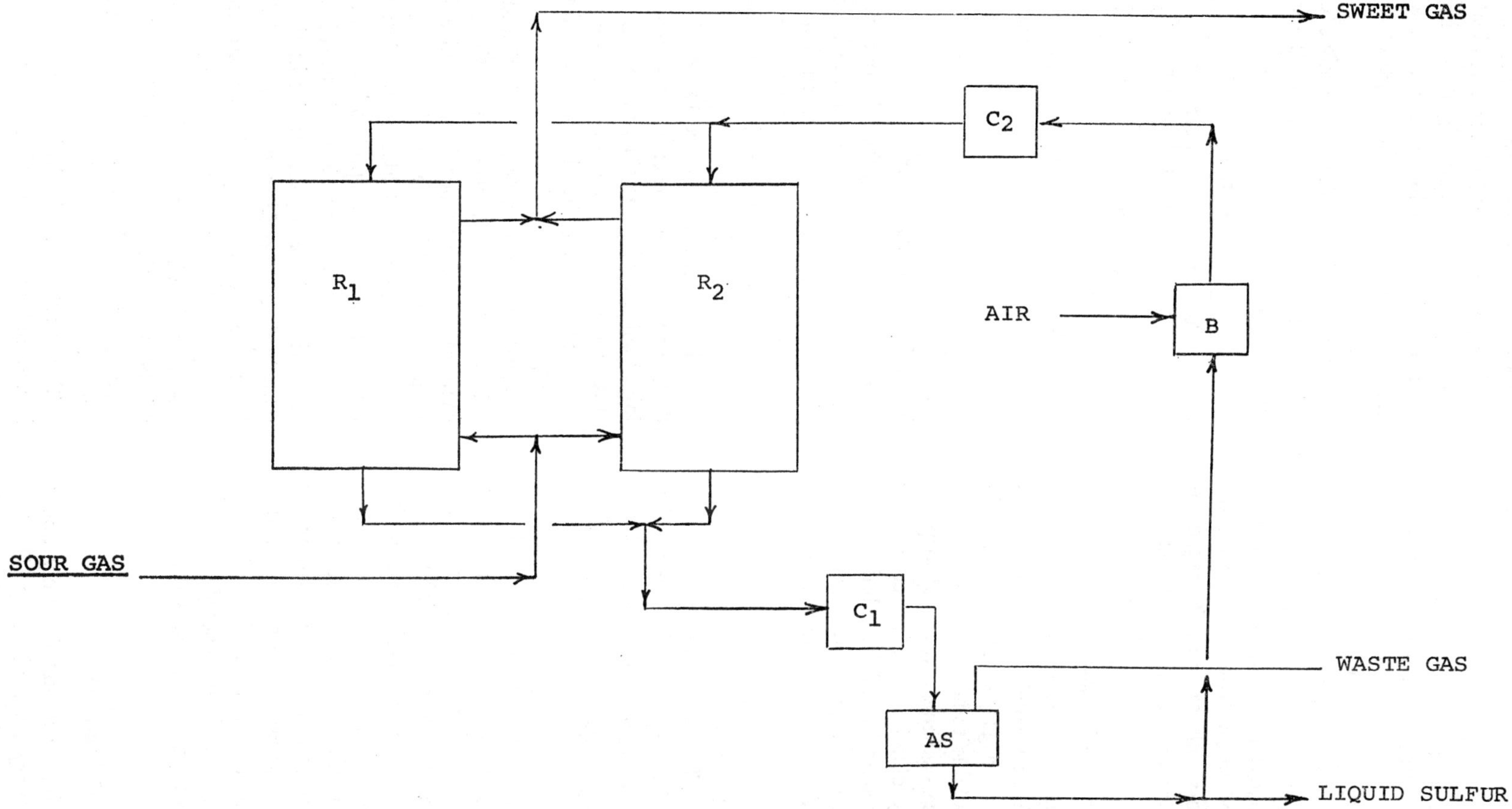

Figure 9 Haines process. R—Zeolite bed absorbers; C_1—sulfur condenser; C_2—Arial cooler; AS—accumulator/separator; B—sulfur burner.

Dry bed absorption—catalytic conversion (Haines Process)

In the Haines Process (see Figure 9), sulfur is removed from sour natural gas using zeolites or molecular seives.

Hydrogen sulfide is absorbed from the gas on a bed of zeolites until the bed becomes saturated with H_2S. The bed is then regenerated with hot SO_2 bearing gases, generated from burning a part of the liquid sulfur production. The zeolite catalyzes the reaction of H_2S form sulfur vapor. The regeneration effluent gases are cooled and sulfur is condensed.

Liquid media absorption—air oxidation

Most commonly in use in Europe for removal and recovery of sulfur from manufactured gases such as coal gas or coke-oven gas, several processes in this category are available today.

Typically, the process scheme involves absorption of H_2S in a slightly alkaline solution containing oxygen carriers. Regeneration of the solution is by air oxidation. The H_2S is oxidized to elemental sulfur. Figure 10 shows the typical processing scheme.

The air also acts as a flotation agent for the sulfur which is collected at the regenerated solution surface as a froth. The sulfur sludge is either filtered or centrifuged to yield a sulfur cake which may be recovered as a wet paste or dry powder.

Liquid media absorption—direct conversion (Townsend Process)

The Townsend Process is perhaps one of the newest sulfur removal processes on the scene today. Still in formative stages of development, its potential advantages point to it directly challenging the other conventional system containing an amine plant, a dehydration plant and a claus sulfur plant. The Townsend plant offers the added advantage of recovering a higher percentage of the sulfur.

The Townsend Process uses an aqueous solution of an organic solvent such as triethylene glycol to contact the sour gas and simultaneously sweeten the gas, dehydrate the gas and convert the gas to elemental sulfur.

III Desulfurization of Coal

Although coal burning accounts for only about 1/4 of the nation's energy, approximately 2/3 of all the sulfur dioxide emitted in the United States is traceable to its usage. And since coal supplies far outstrip gas and oil reserves, interest in coal desulfurization is great.

Presently, however, there are no processes sufficiently developed, either technically or commercially, which have any significant impact on the industry. The following is therefore, a brief summary of the more pertinent processes currently under evaluation.

A typical high-sulfur, bituminous coal (4.9%) sulfur may be characterized by the composition shown in Table D.

TABLE D

Coal Analysis (on dry basis)	
Volatile combustible matter	42%
Ash	10%
Fixed carbon	48%
Moisture	—
Sulfur breakdown (by %—forms available)	
Sulfate	0.33
Pyritic	2.53
Organic	2.04
	4.9%

The solvent refine process

Solvent refined coal (SRC) is one name among others given to a reconstituted coal which has been dissolved, filtered, and separated from its solvent. It is free of water, low in sulfur, very low in ash, and sufficiently low in melting point that it can be handled as a fluid.

In the process (see Figure 11), coal is ground to 80% through a 200 mesh screen and slurried in an initial solvent oil. The slurry is pumped to a pressure of 1,000 lb/sq. in. and passed upwards through a heater to bring the slurry to a temperature of 45°C.

The flow rate is between a half and one space velocity. As the material leaves the heater, more than 90% of the carbon in the coal is in solution. (Anthracite coal is an exception.)

A small amount of hydrogen is introduced into the slurry prior to preheating. The hydrogen prevents repolymerization of the dissolved coal. A portion of the organic sulfur in the coal unites with hydrogen to form hydrogen sulphide, which is later separated as a gas. The unutilized hydrogen is recycled back to the preheater. After the coal has been dissolved, the ash is filtered at a pressure of about 50 lb/sq. in. The pyritic sulfur leaves the process mixed with the other separated mineral matter.

The filtrate or coal solution, now greatly reduced in ash and sulfur is flash evaporated to obtain the necessary recycle solvent. It has been demonstrated that no make up solvent is required. In fact, an excess of solvent oil, released from the coal structure itself during solvation is recoverable, if desired.

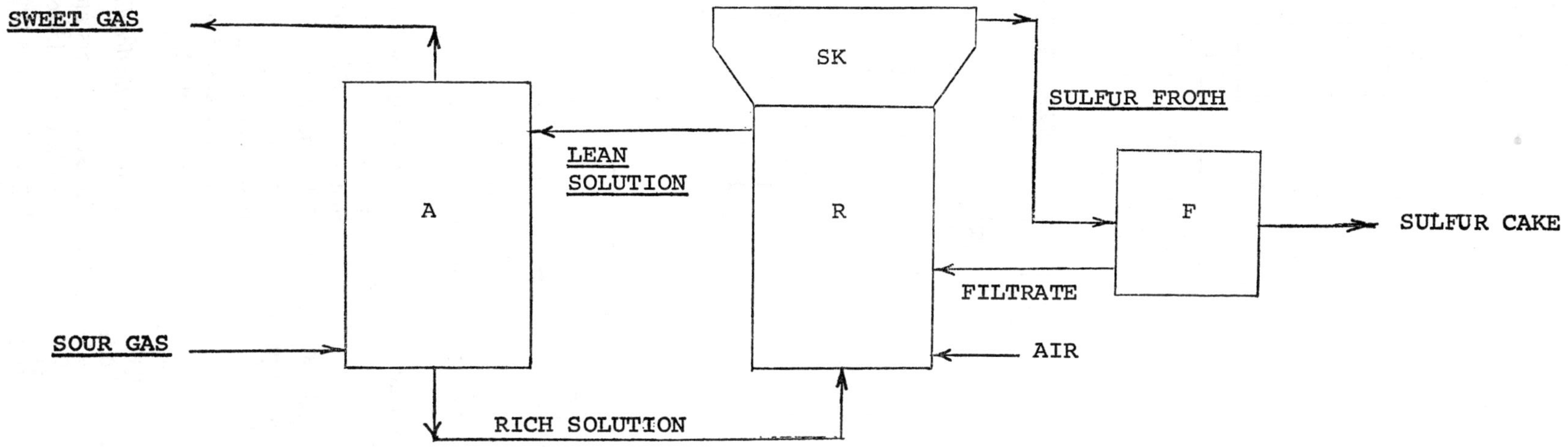

Figure 10 Liquid media absorption. A—absorber; R—regenerator; SK—skim tank; F—filter.

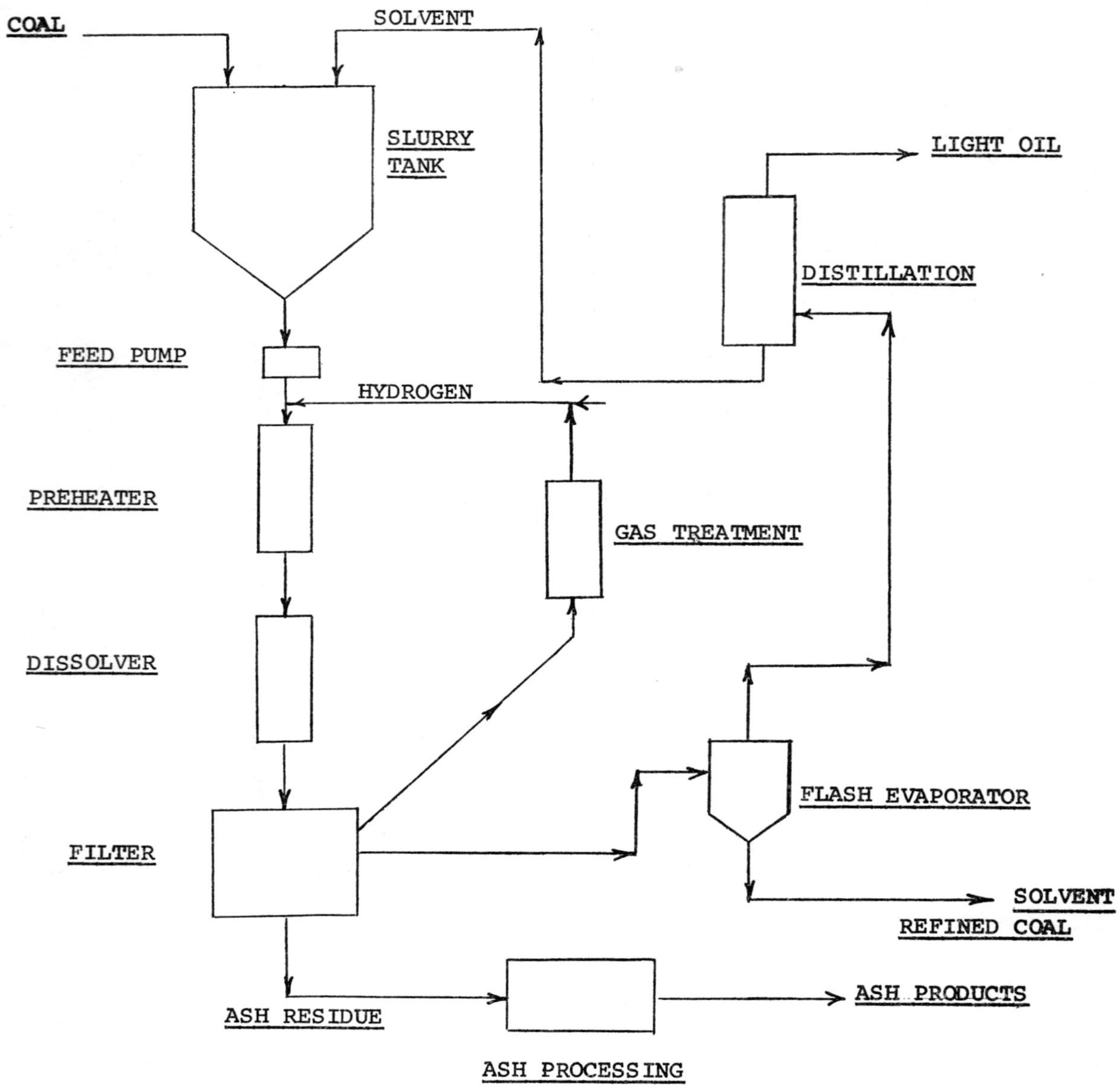

Figure 11 Solvent refine coal process.

The remaining hot liquid residue is discharged and cooled to form a hard, brittle solid of solvent refined coal.

Table E shows a comparative analysis of a raw coal (% S—3.27%) and the solvent refined process, along with rough economies.

TABLE E

	Raw coal	Solvent refined coal
Ash	6.91%	0.41
Carbon	71.31	89.18
Sulfur	3.27	0.95
Volatile matter	44.0	51.0
Heat content (BTU/LB)	13978	15956
Cost ($/Ton)	3.32	9.92
Cost (¢/MMBTU)	12.00	31.00

Obviously, solvent refined coal represents a marked improvement over the raw starting material. Sulfur content is reduced by about 30%, Ash content by 93% and heating value (in BTU/LB) is significantly increased. However, the cost of these improvements is 19¢/MM BTU's, or the processing cost. On an average, national basis, the cost is about 14¢.

Devolatilization/carbonization to a low sulfur char

United Engineers and Company have investigated the use of a fluidized bed desulfurization process. Figure 12 shows general flow scheme for the labe scale process.

Ground coal (1/16″) is introduced into the

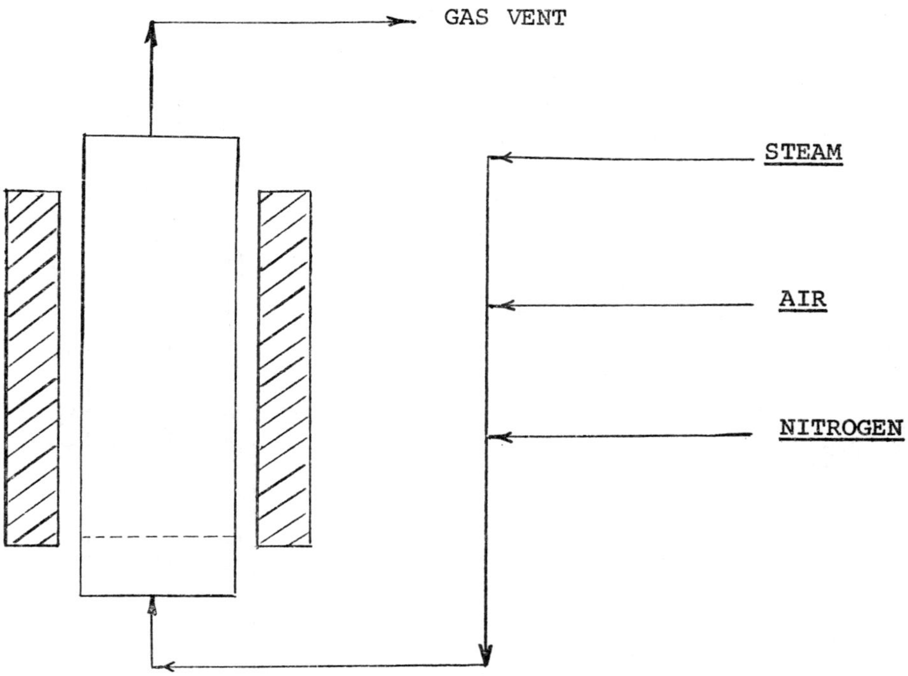

Figure 12 Fluidized bed desulfurization.

heated, tubular reactor. Gas flow is then adjusted to maintain bed fluidity. Reactor temperatures approach 950°F.

The char is then removed through the bottom of the reactor.

The factors most directly affecting desulfurization are particle size, reactor residence time, reaction temperature and fluidizing velocity. Figure 13 summarizes relationships between extent of desulfurization (expressed as the ratio of sulfur in char to that in feed-ΔS) and above mentioned parameters.

Other processes, in various stages of development include causticized fluidized bed desulfurization, gasification to high and low BTU Gases and extraction of pyritic sulfur from raw coal. The Bureau of Mines, bituminous coal research and others have sought to remove sulfur (pyritic) by washing, using various techniques including centrifugation, flotation and magnetic separation methods. None of these has the potential to remove more than half the sulfur and each leads to significant product losses.

Treatment of Effluent from Stacks

Since, in the United States, about 30 million tons per year of SO_2 are emitted to the atmosphere,[4] there is a great incentive not only to remove but to recover sulfur usually as liquid SO_2, sulfuric acid, elemental sulfur or ammonium sulfate. A critical summary of the existing technology is described below in two parts, namely, the wet and dry processes.

Sulfur dioxide removal

a) Wet processes 1. Dimethylaniline (DMA) process—An equation format may be used to describe the steps depicted in Figure 14.

1) $\text{Waste gas (Rich } SO_2) + \text{DMA (Lean } SO_2) \xrightarrow[\text{Absorber}]{} \text{Waste Gas (Lean } SO_2\text{, DMA)} + \text{DMA(Rich } SO_2)$

2a) $\text{DMA (Rich } SO_2) + \text{Steam} \xrightarrow[\text{Stripper}]{q} \text{Steam (Rich } SO_2) + \text{DMA}$

b) $\text{Waste Gas (Lean } SO_2\text{, DMA) } Na_2CO_3 \xrightarrow[\text{Absorber}]{} Na_3CO_2(SO_2) + \text{Waste Gas (DMA)}$

3a) $\text{Steam (Rich } SO_2) \xrightarrow[\text{Dehydrator}]{-q} H_2O(l) + SO_2\ (l)$

b) $\text{Waste Gas (DMA)} + \text{dil. } H_2SO_4 \xrightarrow[\text{Absorber}]{} \text{Waste Gas} + \text{dil. } H_2SO_4\text{(DMA)}.$

Three other processes follow similar schemes to that for DMA with a different absorbent being used in place of DMA. These are the *Sulfidine Process* which uses a mixture of xylidine and water,[9a] the *Ammonia Process* which uses ammonium sulfate, and the *Basic Aluminum Sulfate Process.* In the ammonia process, ammonium bisulfate is formed in addition to sulfite.

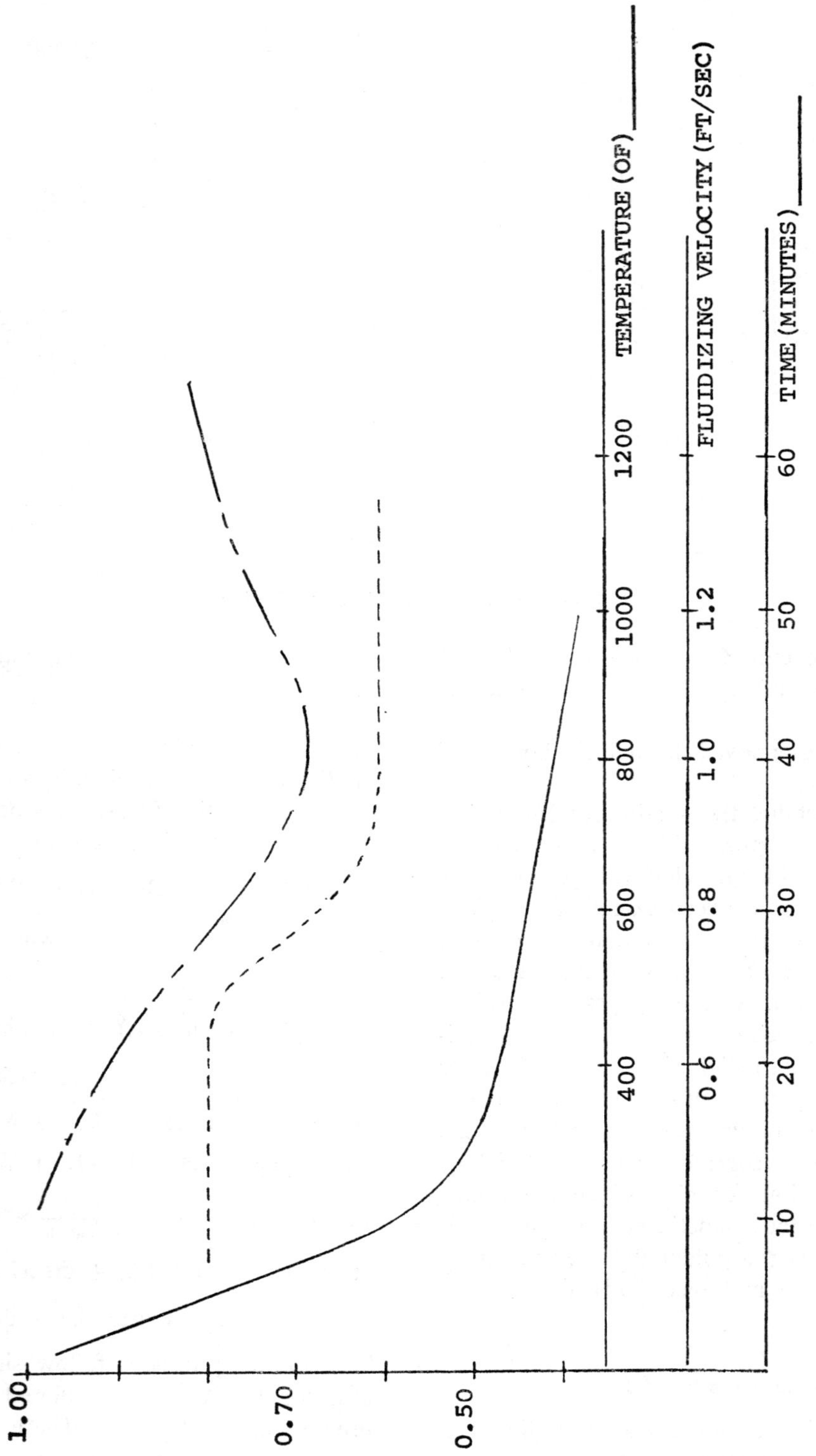

Figure 13 Extent of reaction.

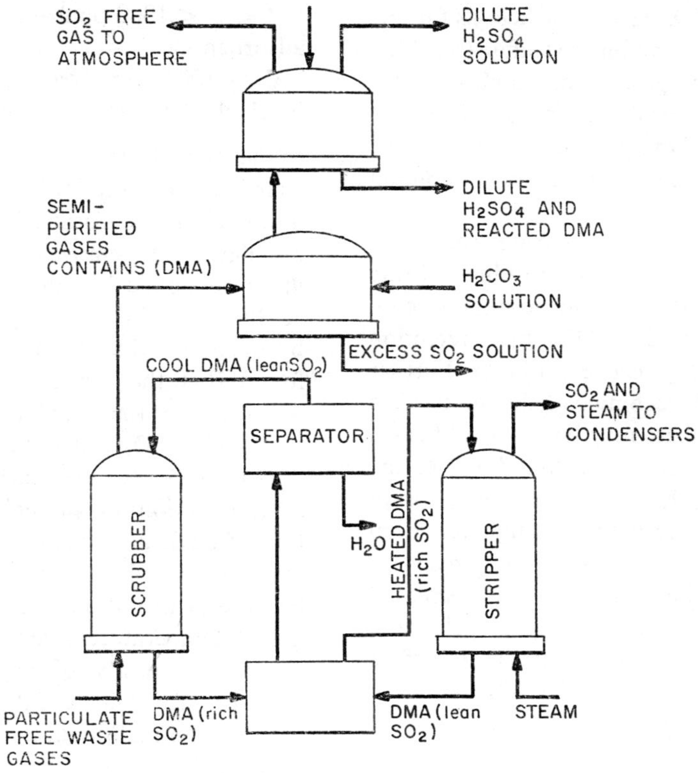

Figure 14 DMA process.

Instead of using steam to regenerate the adsorbent, chemical means may be employed. Zinc oxide will react with sulfite solutions and precipitate zinc sulfite. The SO_2 is driven off by calcination reforming the oxide.[10a] Adsorption contact areas are kept high by using bubble towers, packed towers and wood grid towers.

In the *Ammonia–Sulfuric Acid Process*, the sulfuric acid reacts with the sulfite–bisulfate solution producing SO_2 for recovery. It works with high removal from low (0.1%) inlet SO_2 concentrations.[10b]

The *Alkaline or Hard Water Process* is used near very large water sources which have Na, Mg and Ca compounds in them. Of course, the potential of H_2O pollution exists.

In the *Lime Process* SO_2 is absorbed by a suspension of $CaOH_2$, calcium sulfite and sulfate in water;

$$Ca(OH)_2 + SO_2 \rightarrow \underset{\text{sulfite}}{CaSO_3} + H_2O$$

$$2CaSO_3 + O_2(\text{dissolved}) \rightarrow \underset{\text{sulfate}}{2CaSO_4}.$$

The sulfate precipitates out on the suspended sulfate particles. The product may be marketed as gypsum.

SO_2 is a desirable end product of most of the physical processes used in the manufacture of H_2SO_4, elemental sulfur or sulfonated compounds.[9a]

A major unresolved problem with scrubbing is that the cooled less-buoyant escaping gases descend rapidly to ground level with much less dispersion than for hot dry gases. Some wet processes are already used in the United Kingdom (Battersea and Bankside power plants along the Thames river) with attempts to remove the wet gases at higher temperature levels to prevent the problem of SO_2 descent. Field *et al.*[10] have presented cost estimates for three of the most important scrubbing processes, limestone, ammonia and sodium sulfite; an average cost of about $1.80/ton coal is calculated.

2. Catalytic absorption of sulfur dioxide to produce dilute sulfuric acid—In this process dilute sulfuric acid is produced by injecting ozone into the flue gas and scrubbing it in a packed tower using a dilute sulfuric acid solution containing manganese ions. Unidentified gaseous contaminants in the flue gas reduce the efficiency of the manganese-ozone catalytic process. The manganese catalyst probably is being poisoned by these contaminants since no change in the efficency of the process results when the manganese concentration is changed. The process can be optimized by reducing retention time in the scrubber and increasing the ozone efficiency.

3. Ammoniation of dilute sulfuric acid as formed in process 2 to produce ammonium sulfate (scrubber solution)—Unidentified gaseous contaminants also adversely affect this process. In addition, the economic feasibility of the process depends on the relationship between ammonia cost and ammonium sulfate value.

4. Acidulation of rock phosphate slurry by absorption of sulfur dioxide to produce citrate soluble phosphate fertlizer—This process is considered unfeasible because of the high retention times and the low SO_2 recovery (50%). Further study of the process is recommended. The particle size of the rock phosphate may be a critical factor. If the particle size is too large, "blinding" of the phosphate rock by the formation of gypsum around the particle may result at high retention times. This can explain the reduced SO_2 recovery with increased retention time and the increased SO_2 recovery with increased slurry recycle rate. The high recycle rate supplies a greater rock surface area per unit time to react with the SO_2. Also, the addition of ozone to the slurry might improve the SO_2 recovery.

5. Reaction of manganese dioxide slurry and sulfur dioxide to produce manganese sulfate; the manganese sulfate is calcined to regenerate MnO_2 and release SO_2 which is used to produce high grade sulfuric acid—When the gases containing sulfur dioxide and oxygen are scrubbed with the manganese dioxide slurry, sulfuric acid is also formed. The acid extracts impurities such as iron oxide from the pyrolusite ore, which interfere with the reaction between MnO_2 and SO_2. The formation of sulfuric acid in the scrubbing liquor can be prevented by maintaining a concentration of the lower manganese oxides to neutralize it. Also, the removal of these impurities prior to the recovery of the manganese sulfate has not been considered in the economic analysis of this process.

b) Dry processes Dry processes are those which remove sulfur dioxide from the stacks' effluent without humidifying the flue gases. The primary dry processes are adsorption and catalytic reaction on solid surfaces and combination of these.

1. Adsorption with activated charcoals and metallic oxides—Turk[11] critically reviewed various adsorption schemes and suggested the use of adsorbent oxides and impıegnated charcoal adsorbents which may selectvely remove desired polar pollutants. He recommended the following limits for recovery and regeneration:

$O < C < 2$ ppm—no recovery of sorbate, no regeneration

$2 < C < 1000$ ppm—destroy sorbate, regenerate adsorbent

$C > 1000$ ppm—recover sorbate and regenerate in which: C is concentration of gaseous pollutant.

In the Reinluft process[12] a moving bed of adsorbent char is used as the initial stage for recovering SO_2 ultimately in the form of sulfuric acid. Johswich[12] calculates SO_2 removal by activated adsorption is more economical than by wet process methods. A Bureau of Mines Study[13] compared adsorption by metallic oxides with impregnated carbons and found that the former gave significantly greater removal rates than the latter; adsorption capacities of 23–33 g SO_2/100 g adsorbent as compared to 8 g SO_2/100 g for best carbon adsorbent at 130°C. Also operation was possible at higher temperatures for the oxide adsorbent but the carbon adsorbents were destroyed at elevated temperatures (330°) because of oxidation. It is important to operate at higher temperature levels (those of flue gases) to lower the density of any unrecovered SO_2. In instances for which SO_2 recovery is complete, however, an additional thermal energy benefit may be gained from cooling the flue gases. The two most promising adsorbents, *alkalized alumina* and *manganese oxide* have regeneration processes which differ according to differences in the form in which sulfur is recovered. By treating saturated alkalized alumina at 600;C with producer gas, hydrogen sulfide and/or carbonyl sulfide will evolve; the latter can then be converted over bauxite catalyst to elemental sulfur. Additional alkalized alumina material has been published by the Bureau[14] and includes such operating parameters as residence time, use of baffles, gas velocity and particle size variation. Carbon dioxide, water vapor and nitrogen oxides were found to have little effect on SO_2 adsorption. For manganese oxide adsorbent addition of NaOH followed by electrolysis is advised especially for power plant installations or areas of low energy cost. For both oxide adsorbents retention of activity was confirmed for a complete cycle or a number of cycles. Molecular sieve adsorbents were also tested and the best of these had capacities equivalent to the impregnated carbon adsorbents, but significantly lower capacity than the best oxide adsorbents. Copper oxide impregnated into UOP alumina appears to be structurally stronger than the other oxides but less adsorbent.[14a] An economic evaluation of the adsorption method[15] led to estimated costs of $1.54–£2.18/ton of coal. A fluidized bed process for removal of hydrocarbons by a fluidized charcoal adsorbent[16] has been used successfully, but no such process has yet been employed for SO_2 removal from the flue gases.

2. Catalytic oxidation—The catalytic oxidation of SO_2 over vanadium pentoxide is familiar because of its application to the manufacture of sulfuric acid by the contact process. At a given temperature, the equilibrium conversion level to SO_3 is reduced as the gas mixture becomes more diluted; this is just the problem faced in handling flue gases where SO_2 is at a relatively low concentration. Eklund[17] has made a thorough study of the kinetics of the oxidation over commercial V_2O_5 at temperatures in the range of 420–550°C and determined an empirical reaction rate expression of the type proposed by Hougen and Watson,[18] but his SO_2 concentration range was 1–5 vol. %. The Bureau of Mines,[13] in addition to the adsorption studies previously mentioned, has considered using an oxidation catalyst and has tested various V_2O_5 catalyst preparations. The catalysts, promoted with K_2O_5, enhanced the reaction rates and hence conversions at temperatures as low as 370°C (lower than contact process) for a sample of 0.35% SO_2. The Bureau has not made extensive studies of the oxidative method because they feel elemental sulfur is a more suitable end product than H_2SO_4 from the standpoint of storage, transportation and perhaps market. Goldman *et al.*[19] studied the kinetics of SO_2 oxidation for comparison of fluidized and fixed bed reactors and found a significant reaction rate advantage for the fluid bed case. At one atmosphere concentrations of SO_2 were reduced about 25% more in fluid beds than in fixed beds at comparable velocities. The concentration levels at the reactor inlet, although not explicitly stated, were apparently much higher than those encountered in air pollution work. Dixon and Longfield[20] have very thoroughly reviewed SO_2 oxidation studies for relatively high SO_2 concentration levels for both V_2O_5 and platinum catalysts. The only low SO_2 concentration investigation (less than 0.10 vol. %) using V_2O_5–K_2O catalysts was that of Napier and Stone,[21] who obtained high fractional conversions (92–98%). They agreed well with the Bureau of Mines' studies which were run at intermediate SO_2 levels (.35 vol. %) and somewhat lower temperatures. Also, Napier and Stone found that lower residence times would be required at low SO_2 concentrations than at the conditions normally encountered in the contact process and that H_2O vapor and CO_2 have no adverse effect on catalyst activity. The experiments were performed at 430°C with a 4.3 g catalyst bed and linear gas velocities of about 24 cm/sec. An economic evaluation[15] of the oxidation process indicated possible costs in the neighborhood of \$1.75–3.02/ton coal.

Palumbo and Fraas[23] discussing dischage removal showed

> that a damped, or pulsed, high frequency current is more effective than direct current in sulfur removal. Since the data include only the initial and final compositions, nothing can be said of the mechanism of the reaction. The low concentration of nitrogen oxides in the SO_2 tests is explained on the basis that the ionization energy of N_2 is higher than SO_2, a conclusion corroborated by the increased nitrogen oxide formation with the higher electric field intensities in the 1 in. diameter tube.
>
> Although it is too early to indicate the feasibility of adapting the discharge process to SO_2 removal, the use of nitrogen oxides as catalytic agents for SO_2 to SO_3 conversion may have more tangible prospects. Since the electrical discharge formation of nitrogen oxides is easily turned off and on, the process is of particular significance to power plants where dump energy is available. The nitrogen oxides formed by this intermittent surplus of electrical energy would be accumulated and used continuously for SO_2 to SO_3 conversion. Even though the electrical discharge synthesis of nitrogen oxides is now closely competitive to the high pressure ammonia synthesis process, further increase in efficiency is possible with a pulsed waveform and the use of CO_2 as a reaction promoter.

Additional discussions on the status of dry recovery processes may be found in review articles.[21a,21b] Another technique of particular noteworthiness is the Squires fluid bed dolomite process[21c] including regeneration of the solid for cyclic use while recovering the sulfur.

Paper Waste Gases

Pulp and pulp mill wastes can be treated in various specal ways[25] to remove the sulfur compounds. The sulfur from gaseous pulp mill effluents is mainly in the form of SO_2, H_2S, CH_3SH $(CH_3)_2S$, and $(CH_3)_2S_2$.[26] It is reported that 10–25 lbs. of CH_3SH are formed for every ton of pulp produced. The main source of odor from the pulp mill is the bivalent sulfur compounds. The elimination of odor in sulfite and kraft pulp mills is discussed briefly[27,28] and particular discussion of the gas phase oxidation of H_2S, and CH_3SH is also reviewed.[29,30] H_2S can be converted to SO_2 with O_3 in an O_2–N_2 mixture and CH_3SH can also be converted to SO_2 with O_2 at 201–275°C. For the reaction of CH_3SH, the effect of the ratio of CH_3SH to O_2, temperature, and the reaction time has been discussed.

Conclusion

As the papers considered here suggest, SO_2 is highly reactive and reacts in a wide variety of ways. A good many processes are technically feasible, but at what cost? This is, certainly, an all important engineering question and there seems to be no general answer. The absorption and oxidation afford high recovery and help clean our environment of sulfur. But to be economical they cannot be an accessory to a plant, they have to be an integral unit accounted for while designing. When H_2SO_4 or $(NH_4)_2SO_4$ is end-product, the market study is extremely important.

The process to be selected depends very much on the SO_2 concentrations of flue gases and total volume to be handled. If the volume to be handled is small and a liquid reactant like dimethylaniline or xylidine or ammonium sulfite is economically available, the plant may as well opt for that. The process can have variations, easily, if economical. For instance there is a patented process which after scrubbing with manganese oxide solutions, instead of precipitating and heat-decomposing $MnSO_4$, reacts it with caustic soda to form Na_2SO_4. That is electrolyzed to give H_2SO_4 and NaOH, whereas manganese oxide is regenerated from its hydroxide.

The solution of this problem, in general, seems to be specific for individual companies, involving their "economics."

REFERENCES

1. Goldsmith, Jr., *Air Pollution, Volume I*, edit. A. C. Stern, Academic Press, 357–65 (1962).
2. Nonhebel, G., *Gas Purification Processes*, George Newhes Ltd., London, 834 (1964).
3. Southern California Edison Company—Analysis of Stack Gases (1963).
4. Rohrman, F. A. and J. H. Ludwig, Extrapolated, *Chem. Eng. Prog.*, **61**, #9, 59 (1965).
5. Gilpin, A., *Control of Air Polution*, Gordon Butterworth (1963).
6. Finfer, E. Z., *J. Air Poll. Control Ass.*, **15**, 485–8 (1965).

6a. Squires, A. M., *Chem. Eng.*, Nov. 6, 260–8 (1967).

7. Zimmerman, R. E., *Chem. Eng. Prog.*, **62**, #10, 61–6 (1966).
8. Harris, R. D. and R. G. Moses, "Coal Desulfurization," at *MECAR Symposium*, Feb. 24, 1966.
9. Ranz, W. E., *Air Pollution, Volume II*, edit. A. C. Stern, Academic Press, New York (1962).

9a. Francis, W., *Power and Works Engr.*, **41**, 17,25,37,75, 102 (1946).

10. Field, J. H., L. M. Brunn, W. P. Haynes, and H. E. Benson, *JAPCA*, **7**, 109–115 (1957).

10a. Johnstone, H. F. and H. E. Silcrox, *I & EC*, **39**, 808 (1947).

10b. Dean, R. S. and R. E. Swain, *U.S. Bureau of Mines Bull.*, 453 (1944).

11. Turk, A., *Air Pollution*, Volume III, edit. A. C. Stern, Academic Press, New York, 497–518 (1968).
12. Johswich, F. *Brenstoffe Warme Kraft*, **14**, 105–115 (1962).
13. Bienstock, D., J. H. Field and J. G. Meyers, R.I. No. 5735 Bur. of Mines, 29 pp. (1961); R.I. No. 7021, 52 pp. (1967).
14. *ibid*, *ASME J. of Eng. for Power*, Paper No. 63 Pwr–14, Oct. 28 (1963).

14a. McCrea, D. H., A. J. Farney and J. G. Myers, *JAPCA*, **20**, 819–24 (1970).

15. Katell, S., *Chem. Eng. Prog.*, **62**, #10, 67–73 (1966).
16. Etherington, L. D., R. J. Fritz, E. W. Nicholson and H. W. Scheeline, *CEP*, **52**, 274 (1956).
17. Eklund, Rolf-Bertil, Ph.D. Diss. #115, Uppsala (Almquist, Stockholm), 83 pp. (1956).

17a. Tarbuttan, G. *et al.*, *I & EC*, **49**, 392–395 (1957).

18. Hougen, O. A. and K. M. Watson, *Chem. Proc. Principles*, Vol. III John Wiley (1959).
19. Goldman, M., L. N. Canjar and R. B. Beckmann, *J. Appl. Chem.*, **7**, 274 (1957).
20. Dixon, J. K. and J. E. Longfield, *Catalysis*, Vol. VII, ed P. H. Emmett, Reinhold (1960).
21. Napier, D. H. and M. H. Stone, *J. Appl. Chem.*, **8**, 781–86 (1958).

21a. Squires, A. M., Chem. Eng., Dec. 18, 101 (1967).

21b. Hangebranch, R. P. and P. W. Spaite, *JAPCA.*, **18**, 5 (1968).

21c. Squires, A. M. and R. A. Graff, *JAPCA*, **21**, 272 (1971).

22. Levey, R. P., Jr., U.S. Patent No. 3164440 (Jan. 5, 1965).
23. Palumbo, F. J. and F. Fraas, *JAPCA*, **21**, 143 (1971).
24. Hoog, H., J. *Inst. Petrol.*, **36**, 738 (1950).
25. Nemerow, N. L., *Theories and Practices of Industrial Waste Treatment*, Addison-Wesley Publ. Co., Mass., 378–383 (1963).
26. Kesler, R. B., "Modern Methods of Monitoring Gaseous Pulp Mill Effluents for Sulfur Compounds," Paper presented at *Technical Intl. Congress on Automated Analysis*, Chicago, Ill., June, (1969).
27. Harkness, A. C. and F. E. Murray, Gas Phase Oxidation of Methyl Mercaptans, *Int. J. Air & Water Poll.*, 10, 245–51 (1966).
28. Caddle, R. D. and M. Ledford, "Reaction of Ozone with Hydrogen Sulfide," *Int. J. Air & Water Poll.*, **25–30** (1966).
29. Morgan, J. P., "Odor Control in Kraft Pulp Mill," *Chem.* **26**, 6 (9), 30–34, Sept. (1970).
30. Ghisoni, P., "Elimination of Odors in a Sulfide Pulp Mill," *Tappi*, **37**, (5), 201–205, May (1954).

ADDITIONAL READING ON FOSSIL FUELS

1A. Buckingham, P. A. and H. R. Homan. *Hydrocarbon Processing*, August 1971, 121–125.

2A. Paradis, Gould, Bea and Reed, *Chemical Engineering Progress*, August 1971, 57–62.

3A. Moritz, K. H. and H. R. Savage, *Chemical Engineering Progress*, August 1971, 63–70.

4A. Mounce, W. and R. S. Rubin, *Chemical Engineering Progress*, August 1971, 81–85.

5A. Radford, H. D. and R. G. Rigg, *Hydrocarbon Processing*, November 1970, 187–191.

6A. Read, D., C. H. Watkins and Eckhouse, *Hydrocarbon Processing*, June 1965, 155–162.

7A. Yamato, M. and C. H. Watkins, *Hydrocarbon Processing*, May 1968, 131—134.

8A. Goar, B. G., *Hydrocarbon Processing*, September 1968, 248–252.

9A. Siegmund, C. W., *Hydrocarbon Processing*, February 1970, 89–95.

10A. Schuman, S. C., Desulfurization of Petroleum Stocks, Stocks, Joint Symposium Division of Petroleum Chemistry, American Chemical Society, September 1968, D19–D29.

11A. Wall, J. D., *Hydrocarbon Processing*, December 1970, 67–73.

DOMINICK P. BARTENOPE, *Charles Pfizer Co.*
EDWARD N. ZIEGLER *Polytechnic Institue of New York.*

SYSTEMS MODELING FOR WATER POLLUTION CONTROL

The attention of the reader is directed to "Modeling of River and Estuary Water Quality," which appears in Volume 1 of the Encyclopedia of Environmental Science and Engineering.

I. Optimization Studies

Clearly, the ultimate objective of modeling water quality systems is to devise control strategies for optimizing some water quality parameter. All the techniques available have been used at various times, including linear and other types of programming, Pontryagin's Minimum and Maximum Principles, and others.

Smith and Morris, 1969, have performed optimization studies in the Delaware River, under the sponsorship of the Delaware Estuary and Bay Water Quality Sampling and Mathematical Modeling Project.

In order to improve water quality in the river, the waste sources located along the river could be called upon to improve their individual degrees of treatment prior to disposal.

Five different sets of quality criteria were drawn up ranging from letting the river remain in its then present condition (but not getting worse), labelled "Objective Set V" by the authors, to the maximum feasible enhancement of the river, using present technology, Objective Set I.

The objectives subsequently approved by the Delaware River Basin Commission as a desirable aim fell between Set II and Set III.

Each objective set was composed of 12 water quality parameters of which DO was the most important.

Three alternative control programs were considered.

A. Uniform treatment

Every waste source on the river would have to treat its waste to the same level, even though, in some places the water quality achieved would be far higher than the objective set required. Such a program would be easy to administer since no polluter would feel discriminated against. However, in terms of total economic cost to the river basin, the program would be inefficient.

B. Cost Optimization

An individual polluter would have to increase the degree of treatment he gave his waste only to the extent that the sum of individual expenditures was minimized, while at the same time the river quality criteria were satisfied. This program takes into account the fact that unit costs of waste treatment differ from source to source.

This program would be most efficient since the basin-wide costs would be minimized, and the excess DO along the river would also be minimal.

However, administration would be difficult, since no polluter ordered to treat his waste to 90% BOD removal would take kindly to seeing his neighbor get away with less, or none at all.

C. Zone optimization

The estuary is divided into zones, in each of which uniform treatment is required. The treatment level in each zone is then chosen to achieve the water quality goals at minimum overall cost. Obviously, the total basin-wide cost must be greater than for the previous program. However, this one is also clearly more easy to administer.

All three programs were subjected to the same constraints. Namely, in no case can the DO in any river section drop below the present level, even if better than the legal standard, and no effluent source may treat waste to a level lower than at present.

For each waste source, a cost curve was constructed relating cost of treatment to lbs./day of additional BOD removed.

In all three programs, the object was to find

$$\text{MIN} \sum_{k=1}^{M} C_k(f_k),$$

where C_k was the cost to the kth source of providing for the removal of f_k lbs./day of BOD additional. Minimization was performed subject to the requirement

$$\sum_{j=1}^{N} A_{ij} f_j \geqslant B_i; \quad i = 1, 2, 3 \ldots N, \qquad \text{I.1}$$

where f_j is the sum of all the f_k discharged into the jth river section, A_{ij} is the transformation from BOD input into the jth section to DO level in the ith section, and B_i is the increment in DO required in the ith section.

The A_{ij} were obtained from the steady-state river model of Thomann, 1963. (See Section II of "The Modeling of River and Estuary Water Quality.")

A further constraint is

$$0 \leqslant f_k \leqslant U_k;\ k = 1, 2, 3, \ldots M, \qquad \text{I.2}$$

where U_k is the maximum technically feasible BOD removal rate for source k.

The above problem, as it stands, can be solved by linear programming to yield program B, "Cost Minimization." The "Revised Simplex Method" systematically searches for the "best" solution, thereby eliminating the complete enumeration of all possible solutions in order to find the optimum.

Program A, "Uniform Treatment," requires an additional constraint. Let S be the uniform level of treatment finally determined (as percent BOD removed), P_k the percent BOD currently removed at source k, and T_k the raw waste BOD discharge rate of source k, before any treatment. Then the constraint

$$f_k = \begin{cases} (S - P_k)T_k, & \text{for} \quad P_k < S \\ 0 & \text{for} \quad P_k \geqslant S \end{cases} \qquad \text{I.3}$$

ensures that all sources achieve the treatment level S, while none which already treat to a higher level than S are allowed to back off. Instead of applying this last constraint to the entire river, program C, "Zone Optimization," applies individual ones to separate zones. Thus, in zone z, the required degree of treatment is S_z, and

$$f_k = \begin{cases} (S_z - P_k)T_k, & \text{for} \quad P_k < S_z \\ 0 & \text{for} \quad P_k \geqslant S_z. \end{cases} \qquad \text{I.4}$$

As special cases of program C, if the number of zones is one, the program becomes "Uniform Treatment," and if the number of zones equals the number of pollution sources, the program becomes "Cost Minimization."

In the case of program C, linear programming was not feasible because of non-linearities in the constraint functions. The method adopted was to construct a band of possible solutions between a set of upper and lower levels. Then, a search technique was applied within the band to yield all feasible solutions satisfying the DO goal.

Using four geographical zones, results were computed which confirmed that, for all objective sets, the total program costs maintained the sequence:

Uniform Treatment
Zone Optimization
Cost Minimization,

in descending order.

Graves *et al.* (1971), present a non-linear programming model to minimize the total cost of pollution abatement structures along a stream, subject to the constraint that the water quality in any river section is better than some given set of quality goals.

The authors start with the basic Streeter-Phelps equations for a segmented river, and they introduce the complexity that the reaeration rate constant and the (constant) velocity in each segment are functions of the streamflow in that segment. Thus, for segment k:

$$k_{2k} = g_k Q_k^{h_k} \qquad \text{I.5}$$

$$U_k = y_k Q_k^{z_k}. \qquad \text{I.6}$$

Parameters g_k, y_k, h_k and z_k must be estimated for each river segment.

Assuming these relationships, the DOD and DO deficit concentrations in segment k, L_k and D_k, are no longer linear combinations of the initial values L_k^B and D_k^B.

When dividing a river into segments for such a study, a new segment is begun when one of the following occurs:

1) An effluent discharge enters.
2) An incremental flow enters (groundwater, a tributary, etc.).
3) An augmentation flow enters, or a diversion leaves.
4) River parameter values change.

There are assumed to be S polluters and m waste treatment plants along the reach, and each of the S can pipe effluent directly to any of the n river segments or any of the m plants. Each of the m can pipe treated waste to any of the n segments. This piping system allows for regional waste treatment plants and for bypassing.

To use the water quality equations, we must know the BOD and DO deficit concentrations at the beginning of each segment. L^B and D^B are the weighted averages of the concentrations of all the flows into segment k, namely:

1) Advection from segment $(k - 1)$.
2) Effluent discharged into k.
3) Incremental flow into k.
4) Augmentation flow in k.

$$L_k^B = [L_{k-1}Q_{k-1} + L_k^E Q_k^E + L_k^I Q_k^I + L_k^A Q_k^A]/Q_k \qquad \text{I.7}$$

$$D_k^B = [D_{k-1}Q_{k-1} + D_k^E Q_k^E + D_k^I Q_k^I + D_k^A Q_k^A]/Q_k. \qquad \text{I.8}$$

where:

$$Q_k = Q_{k-1} + Q_k^E + Q_k^I + Q_k^A$$

and

$Q_k^E = Q_k^F + Q_k^T$ = flow from polluters plus flow from treatment plants

$Q_k^F = \sum_{j=1}^{S} f_{kj}$ = sum of flows into k from all S polluters.

$L_k^F = \left[\sum_{j=1}^{S} L_j^P f_{kj} \right] \Big/ Q_k^F$ = mean BOD concentration in untreated inputs.

$D_k^F = \left[\sum_{j=1}^{S} D_j^P f_{kj} \right] \Big/ Q_k^F$ = mean DO deficit concentration in untreated inputs

$Q_k^T = \sum_{j=1}^{m} t_{kj}$ = sum of flows into k from all m plants.

$L_k^T = \left[\sum_{j=1}^{m} L_j^{pr} t_{kj} \right] \Big/ Q_k^T$ = mean BOD concentration in treated inputs.

$D_k^T = \left[\sum_{j=1}^{m} D_j^{pr} t_{kj} \right] \Big/ Q_k^T$ = mean DO deficit concentration in treated inputs.

If r_j is the fraction of BOD removed in waste treatment plant j:

$$L_j^{pr} = (1 - r_j) \left[\sum_{i=1}^{S} L_i^P p_{ji} \right] \Big/ \sum_{i=1}^{S} p_{ji},$$

where p_{ji} is the flow from polluter i to plant j.

$D^{pr} + \left[\sum_{i=1}^{S} D^P p_{ji} \right] \Big/ \sum_{i=1}^{S} p_{ji}$, assuming that there is no change in DO concentration in passing through a treatment plant.

Hence:

$$L_k^E = [L_k^F Q_k^F + L_k^T Q_k^T]/Q_k^E$$
$$D_k^E = [D_k^F Q_k^F + D_k^T Q_k^T]/Q_k^E.$$

If $k > 1$, the Streeter–Phelps equations must be applied to all segments i, for $i < k$, to obtain correct values of L_k^B and D_k^B.

Q_k^I will be some fixed constant to account for groundwater, tributaries, water supply diversions, industrial diversions and any other fixed inflow and outflow. Equations I.7 and I.8 are not correct when flow is diverted. In that case L_k^I and D_k^I are river values.

Augmentation flow will be some function of reservoir size.

Water quality constraints are of the form:

$$D_k - D_k^* - \Delta D_k \leqslant 0 \qquad \text{I.9}$$

D_k = DO deficit at the end of segment k.
D_k^* = DO deficit before any structures other than those existing are built.
ΔD_k = change in DO deficit that the decision-maker wants.

Rewrite as:

$$D_k - D_k^* \leqslant \Delta D_k \quad k = 1, \ldots\ldots n. \qquad \text{I.10}$$

If $\Delta D_k < 0$, water quality is constrained to improve in segment k.
If $\Delta D_k > 0$, water quality is allowed to drop in segment k, if it is necessary for reducing costs.
e.g., ΔD_k values can be set so that 5 mg./l. of DO must be maintained in every segment ("Uniform river standard").
Or the river could be zoned with different standards.
The objective is to minimize the total cost:

$$TC = C^P + C^{TP} + C^R \qquad \text{I.11}$$

subject to the constraints of Equation I.10, where:

C^P = total cost of all pipelines constructed in the river basin,

C^{TP} = total cost of all treatment plants constructed in the river basin,

C^R = total cost of all reservoirs constructed in the river basin.

To keep the mathematics consistent with reality, two more constraints are needed:

a) total flow from the *j*th polluter in pipes to treatment plants and river segments must equal the total flow available at that polluter.

$$\sum_{i=1}^{n} f_{ij} + \sum_{i=1}^{m} p_{ij} = Q_j^{PL}; \quad j = 1, \ldots\ldots S, \qquad \text{I.12}$$

where Q^{PL} is total effluent from polluter j.
(Otherwise, we could set f_{ij} and p_{ij} to zero for all i and j and get an unpolluted river at zero cost.)

b) Consistent flow into and out of each treatment plant.

$$\sum_{j=1}^{S} p_{kj} = \sum_{i=1}^{n} t_{ik}; \quad k = 1, \ldots\ldots m. \qquad \text{I.13}$$

The problem has $(n + s + m)$ constraints, the first n of which are non-linear inequalities, while the rest are linear equality constraints for flow conservation. The objective function is also non-linear, since cost functions for pipelines, waste treatment plants and reservoirs are non-linear.

Davidson and Bradshaw, 1967, have considered the effects of temperature on stream quality, using a Pontryagin model.

The source and sink terms in the oxygen material balance are all temperature sensitive, and it is theoretically possible to derive the *best* temperature profile in a polluted stream, so that the DO concentration is maximized at each point in the stream downstream from a source of organic pollution.

The model is deterministic, one-dimensional and steady state, and it defines a slow moving, medium sized stream in the summer, the flow regime being plug flow. Although stochastic effects, diurnal variations, meteorological stresses, etc., are the rule, not the exception, neglecting them still permits meaningful mathematical expressions for BOD and DO to be set up in order to uncover the important optimization variables and their interactions.

A Pontryagin model is an optimization problem with three main elements:

1) Performance equations, in this case continuous, deterministic BOD and DO equations. These are time-variable Streeter–Phelps equations with an added term representing photosythesis minus algal respiration, time-smoothed. In addition, all parameters which are temperature-dependent are included in the equations as their respective temperature functions.

Thus the performance equations are written in the form:

$$\frac{dL}{dt} = f_1(L, T) \qquad \text{I.14}$$

$$\frac{dc}{dt} = f_2(c, L, T), \qquad \text{I.15}$$

where T is temperature and f_1 and f_2 are the functional forms of the BOD and DO equations, respectively. (Dispersion was neglected.)

2) A decision variable, in this case temperature. The stream is assumed to be perfectly mixed, with no variation with depth. T is restricted to the range 0–60°C.

3) An objective function. The temperature profile is specified to maximize the DO concentration throughout the stream for some specified upstream boundary condition.

Applying the Maximum Principle of Pontryagin (Pontryagin, 1965) gave a very complex optimizing algorithm, which proved difficult to run on the computer. The authors programmed an analog computer to draw isothermal DO profiles for various values of temperature by solving equations I.14 and I.15. Then, for a given value of time, they selected that particular isothermal profile having the greatest value of DO concentration at that time. A series of time values thus yielded a series of best temperature values. It was admittedly not the most accurate method.

Computations were performed on a hypothetical stream. The study showed that low temperature was beneficial in the upper reaches of the stream, but after about four flow days, higher temperatures were beneficial. It was also found that if photosynthesis and respiration were neglected, low temperature was best throughout.

Tarassov *et al.* (1969), have studied the problem of artificially aiding stream reoxygenation. Artificial in-stream aeration of polluted rivers is a logical alternative to in-plant abatement or low-flow augmentation, especially where high DO is needed for fish passage and to relieve anaerobic conditions.

The problem is to minimize the relative cost of operating a river aeration installation for several competing design criteria.

Consider a segment of an industrially polluted river of medium size.

Conditions:
Inlet DO 6.0 mg./1.
Inlet BOD 30.0 mg./1.
Saturation DO 9.0 mg./1.
BOD removal coefficient 0.16 day^{-1}.
Natural reaeration coefficient 0.66 day^{-1}.

Assumptions:
No second stage DO, photosynthesis (no distinction between day and night) and benthos.
Plug flow, with stream velocity 1.0 mile/day.
Channel uniform in cross-section.
Steady-state.

Objectives:

1) To meet a legally required minimum DO of 6.0 mg./1.

2) To meet objective 1. with minimum cost.

It is evident that, without artificial aeration, the DO curve will sag well below the 6.0 mg./1. level.

It was decided to use a performance index of the "integral quadratic" form, which is found very often in the literature of optimal control.

$$J = C_1 \int_0^{t_f}\int_0^{x_f} [6.0 - c(t, x)]^2 \, dt \, dx + C_2 \int_0^{t_f}\int_0^{x_f} [v(t, x)]^2 \, dt \, dx. \qquad \text{I.16}$$

The first term is the weighted cost of the integral of the square of the difference between the required DO concentration (6 mg./1.) and the actual DO concentration, $c(t, x)$.

C_1 is the unit cost of this term, with dimensions

$$\$/(\text{mg./1.})^2 \text{ (day) mile.}$$

The second term is the total cost of the square of the control effort to be expended. Here C_2 is the unit cost, with dimensions

$$\$/(\text{mg./1./day})^2 \text{ (day) (mile).}$$

We want to find the policy $v(t, x)$ and the corresponding DO profile $c(t, x)$ for which J has a global stationary minimum with respect to the weights C_1 and C_2, over a time period t_f and distance x_f.

For a physical meaning of the above objective function, one can say that the squared terms reflect the idea that most irreversible processes have entropy-producing terms which are proportional to the square of the driving force for the process.

The mathematical meaning of the objective function is not clear. It is to be noted that the function equals zero whenever the specified DO is reached, i.e., $c(t, x)$ is 6.0 and the corresponding value of $v(t, x)$ is zero. Whenever $c(t, x)$ is not 6 mg./1., J should always be positive definite. This ensures that J has a minimum. The corresponding value of $v(t, x)$ when $c(t, x)$ is not the specified value is also positive definite. It can be further noted that the integral–quadratic function has a special tradition in the control field which cannot be ignored. This type of index for linear systems such as this yields stable numeric solutions that converge rapidly because it happens to be a Liapunov function for these systems.

The weights C_1 and C_2 need not be given values. It is their ratio that is important.

The aerator device is envisaged as a pipeline laid along the river bed, with spargers at 100 ft. intervals. For a five mile line, such an arrangement approximates a continuous discharge of air or oxygen. Thus x_f is 5 miles, and for the given stream velocity, t_f is 5 days.

We assume that no foaming occurs, and that the local effect on *natural* reaeration is small.

Each sparger is connected to the optimizing controller, so that the intensity of oxygen uptake at each, denoted functionally by $v(t, x)$, could be varied in real time and space.

Three types of control are envisioned:

1) Each sparger operated independently so that oxygen uptake will vary "continuously" in magnitude with both time and distance.

2) At any instant, all spargers discharge the same quantity, which is variable only with time.

3) At any point along the river, the sparger discharge is constant, the magnitude varying only with distance.

The mathematical formulation is as follows:

$$\frac{\partial L}{\partial t} = -k_1 L - U\frac{\partial L}{\partial x} \qquad \text{I.17}$$

$$\frac{\partial c}{\partial t} = -k_2 c + k_2 c_s - k_1 L - U\frac{\partial c}{\partial x} + v(t, x). \qquad \text{I.18}$$

At $t = 0$, $\partial L/\partial t = 0$ and $\partial c/\partial t = 0$ (with $v = 0$) for all x.

At $x = 0$, $L = L_0$ and $c = c_0$ (with $v = 0$) for all t.

In optimal control theory parlance, these system equations are identified as being of the quasilinear, first order, multivariable, distributed parameter genre, with $v(t, x)$ as the control function.

Using a perturbation of the cost functional, equation I.16, the necessary condition of optimality generates a scalar Hamiltonian function H, a set of costate system equations and associated initial and boundary conditions.

$$H = -C_1(c_{sp} - c)^2 - C_2(v)^2 + P_1\frac{\partial L}{\partial t} + P_2\frac{\partial c}{\partial t}, \qquad \text{I.19}$$

where $\partial L/\partial t$ and $\partial c/\partial t$ are given by equations I.17 and I.18, c_{sp} is the specified DO concentration, and P_1 and P_2 are costate variables defined by:

$$\frac{\partial P_1}{\partial t} = -\frac{\partial H}{\partial L} = k_1 P_1 + k_1 P_2 - U\frac{\partial P_1}{\partial x} \qquad \text{I.20}$$

$$\frac{\partial P_2}{\partial t} = -\frac{\partial H}{\partial c} = -2C_1(c_{sp} - c) + k_2 P_2 - U\frac{\partial P_2}{\partial x}. \qquad \text{I.21}$$

P_1 and P_2 both are zero at $t = t_f$ *or* $x = x_f$.

The system of equations I.16 through I.21 constitute the optimization algorithm or mathematical programming algorithm for distributed parameter systems of the quasilinear, first order type, with multiple variables.

Taking C_2/C_1 as 0.5, J was normalized by setting $C_1 = 1$, and the following values were obtained. Values of J are proportional to the true cost.

Control type	Min. J	A	B
1	33.3	17.7	15.6
2	37.2	22.4	14.8
3	34.9	19.1	15.8

$$A = \iint (c_{sp} - c)^2 \, dt \, dx \quad B = 0.5\iint (v)^2 \, dt \, dx.$$

It appears that control type 1 is the best. However, bear in mind that the cost functional (equation I.16) did not reflect the capital cost of installation, only the operating cost.

In this problem, optimal control theory was used to determine a start-up control policy limited to the transient regime. Davidson and Bradshaw, 1970, present the steady-state design, based on the system labeled "type 3" in the previous paper. This was oxygen uptake constant with time, but varying with distance.

The objective function is:

$$J(W) = \tfrac{1}{2}\int_0^{t_f}[a_1(c_{sp} - c)^2 + a_2(W)^2]\,d\,. \qquad \text{I.22}$$

$W(t)$ is a function representing the amount of artificially induced oxygen uptake from point to point in the river. Its form is to be determined by the form of the optimal control solution. Variable t, in this case, is the time of travel to a given point from the beginning of the five mile reach.

For the physical significance of $\int a_2(W)^2 dt$, suppose that the scalar $W(t)$ is proportional to voltage or current needed to deliver the air to the river. Then its square is proportional to the power required, and the integral of the square is proportional to the energy expended in the time interval $(0, t_f)$. Coefficient a_2 converts expended energy to dollars.

The term $(c_{sp} - c)$ defines the deviation of actual DO from required DO. By squaring, we penalize deviations greater than 1 ppm more than those less than 1 ppm. Coefficient a_1 is the cost conversion factor, and is approximated from cost data for the removal of BOD in treatment plants. Thus a_1 reflects the cost for prior reduction of BOD before discharge to the river, and forces us to use $W(t)$ optimally, as a treatment alternative.

Parameters a_1 and a_2 physically oppose each other, so that $J(W)$ reflects an extremum (a minimum) for a chosen $W(t)$. The 1/2 factor was introduced for mathematical convenience.

Whipple *et al.* (1969), used a ratio a_2/a_1 of 1/4, for a c_{sp} of 4.0. They showed that an estimate of \$785,000 for enhanced waste treatment was directly comparable to a cost of \$194,000 for induced, staged aeration to achieve the same objective.

The performance equations were Streeter–Phelps, modified to include net oxygen production by photosynthesis. They are categorized as lumped-parameter, deterministic equations. For such systems, there are two generally used methods for the solution of optimal control problems. These are Pontryagin's Minimum (or Maximum) Principle, and Dynamic Programming. Both give exactly the same results, but the Pontryagin method gives a solution that is more tractable mathematically, and the results are more clearly interpretable physically.

The approach is to rewrite the system equations (including the objective function) in matrix form, and then finding the unconstrained m so that the scalar Hamilton function

$$H = \langle \lambda^T \rangle \dot{\mathrm{X}}(\mathrm{X}, \mathrm{m}) \qquad \text{I.23}$$

is minimized and constant along the optimal path.

$\mathrm{m} = [W(t)]$, a single-element vector

$$\mathrm{X} = \begin{bmatrix} L \\ c' \end{bmatrix}, \quad \text{where } c' = c - c_s - \frac{\langle P - R \rangle}{K_a}$$

and adjoint vector λ is given by $d\lambda/dt = -\partial H/\partial \mathrm{X}$. The brackets $\langle\ \rangle$ indicate time-smoothed values. For H to be constant along the optimal path means:

$$\frac{\partial H}{\partial \mathrm{m}} = 0.$$

The complete set of matrix equations constitute the minimum principle formulation of the optimal control law problem.

II Probabilistic Studies

Most existing water quality models are deterministic, therefore water quality standards are usually set in terms of *mean* BOD and DO levels. But BOD and DO levels are seen to vary markedly. If DO falls below a certain critical level for an extended length of time, irreversible damage is possible, even though the *mean* concentration is within acceptable limits.

More effective standards should use DO probability distributions. This implies knowledge of mean DO, whereas knowing the mean DO yields no knowledge of the probability distribution. The percentage of the time that the DO concentration can be expected to fall below any given level can be determined from the DO probability distribution.

To make a mathematical analysis of an estuary, it is necessary to make certain idealizations of the physical system. Those discussed in this article and "The Modeling of Rivers and Estuary Water Quality" are the ones generally acceptable in the literature. Assume that BOD and DO concentrations are uniform across the estuary cross-section. This is the "sectionally homogeneous" model, and analysis is one-dimensional. The stream velocity is assumed to be a known function of time, $Q = Q(t)$. At each location in the reach, $Q(t)$ is the same. The only restriction on $Q(t)$ is that it be integrable. Tidal velocity is described as a sinusoidal function plus additional freshwater flow. The latter may vary from season to season, but is assumed constant during a season.

Five major factors operate in an estuary:

1) BOD and DO are both decreased by bacterial action in first-order reactions. The reaction rate

coefficient is k_1 day^{-1}. It is assumed that some oxygen is always present.

2) DO is increased by reaeration in a reaction of the first order with respect to the DO deficit, which is the difference between the actual DO concentration and the saturation concentration. The reaction rate coefficient is k_2 day^{-1}.

3) BOD is also decreased by sedimentation and adsorption on rocks, at a rate which is assumed to be proportional to the concentration, i.e., a first-order reaction, with a rate coefficient k_3 day^{-1}.

4) Pollution is increased by runoff, etc., along the watercourse, at a rate L_a mg./1./day, independently of the amount present in the stream.

5) DO is decreased at a constant rate D_B mg./1./day, being the net effect of benthal demand, photosynthesis and plant respiration.

The channel cross-section and all physical parameters are assumed constant throughout the stretch. Diffusion of BOD and DO is described by the standard diffusion coefficient.

Thayer and Krutchkoff (1967), based their work on this model, with the further assumption that BOD and DO concentrations change in discrete quanta, Δ , whose value is a parameter of the individual stream. The determination of the value of Δ is given later.

A change of size Δ in a concentration is a change of one "state." When the BOD concentration is L_m, it is said to be in the state m, where $m = L_m/\Delta$. The oxygen deficit state n corresponds to $D_n = n\Delta$.

This work derives time and distance probability distributions of BOD and DO from a single point pollution source. The effect of several sources is obtained by superposition. In probabilistic terms, this implies that the net distribution is a convolution of the individual distributions.

The variations in BOD and DO seen in an estuary stem from two totally different causes:

1) Randomness of the mechanisms which act on the pollutants. (Similar to those met in streams.)

2) Non-random velocity changes in an estuary· (Not met in streams.)

The random component has been considered for streams by Thayer and Krutchkoff (1967). A similar analysis is applicable to an estuary, as has been shown by Custer and Krutchkoff (1969).

Their model considers diffusion as an additional random process, not confounded with tidal motion. It considers first the bacterial and sedimentation mechanisms. Runoff, benthic demand, photosynthesis, etc., are handled separately.

Consider the Brownian motion of a non-conservative particle. It is certain that the particle will move in time δt; and the forces acting on it can be summarized into two components:

1) The symmetric random forces described as "diffusion."

2) Non-symmetric diift, "velocity," which, in an estuary, is a function of time.

For a non-conservative particle, absorption must also be considered.

Consider, now, the motion of a unit of BOD of size Δ. In each δt it moves forward a distance δx along the positive axis with probability $p(t)$, or backward a distance δx with probability $q(t)$. This is assumed to be the only motion possible. However, during each δt, the unit may be absorbed with constant probability r.

Then
$$p(t) + q(t) + r = 1 \qquad \text{II.1}$$
for all t.

Let $u(m, n)$ be the probability that, after n steps (i.e., at time $n\delta t$), the BOD unit is in location $m\delta x$.

This can happen in two ways:

1) A unit at $(m - 1)\,\delta x$, at time $(n - 1)\,\delta t$, takes a positive step.

2) A unit at $(m + 1)\,\delta x$, at time $(n - 1)\,\delta t$, takes a negative step.

Thus $u(m, n + 1) = u(m - 1, n)\,p(n\,\delta t) + u(m + 1, n)\,q(n\,\delta t)$.

for $-\infty < m < \infty\,,\ 0 < n < \infty$.

An analogous relation can be written for DO deficit. This approach finally leads to the equations:

$$f(x, t \mid t_0) = \frac{1}{2\sqrt{\pi E(t - t_0)}} \left\{\exp\left[-\frac{[x - V(t)]^2}{4E(t - t_0)}\right]\right\} e^{-(k_1+k_3)(t-t_0)} \qquad \text{II.2}$$

$$g(x, t \mid t_0) = \frac{k_1}{2(k_2 - k_1 - k_3)} \cdot \frac{1}{\sqrt{\pi E(t - t_0)}} \cdot \left\{\exp\left[-\frac{[x - V(t)]^2}{4E(t - t_0)}\right]\right\} \times [e^{-(k_1+k_3)(t-t_0)} - e^{-k_2(t-t_2)}] \qquad \text{II.3}$$

$f(x, t/t_0)$ is the continuous probability density function for BOD, conditional on $t > t_0$, time of entry.

$g(x, t, t_0)$ is the same, for DO.

$V(t) = \int_0^t U(\tau)\alpha\tau$, where $U(t)$ is the velocity function.

E is the d iffusion coefficient.

It should be pointed out that this method yields approximatons to $u(m, n|n_0)$ and $v(m, n, n_0)$, as δt has a physical value and, despite the suggestiveness of the notation, does not approach zero. The approximations to u and v for any $t = n\delta t$ are found by evaluating f and g, respectively, and multiplying by $2\delta x$.

The preceding analysis gives the probability of a unit of BOD or oxygen deficit released at time t_0 being at a location x after a further time t.

Recall that δt is the time required to release an amount Δ. A continuous release is simulated by releasing Δ at each interval δt, with the first release at $t_0 = 0$ and the last release at $t_0 = t$, where t is the time of interest. Hence the probability of a given concentration at x after t is the convolution of individual probabilities.

The authors show that the BOD and DO are distributed as Poisson distributions with parameters m_1 and m_2 respectively, where:

$$m_1 = \frac{2W}{A\Delta}\int_0^t f(x, t \mid \tau)\, d\tau \qquad \text{II.4}$$

$$m_2 = \frac{2W}{A\Delta}\int_0^t g(x, t \mid \tau)\, d\tau \qquad \text{II.5}$$

W is the pollution entry rate and A is the estuary cross-sectional area.

Δ is defined by:

$$\Delta = \frac{W\delta t}{A\delta x}. \qquad \text{II.6}$$

These Poisson distributions do not include the effects of the initial concentrations L_a and D_B. They alone give rise to BOD and DO distributions which are Poisson, with parameters ρ_1 and ρ_2, where

$$\rho_1 = L_a/\Delta(k_1 + k_3) \qquad \text{II.7}$$

$$\rho_2 = D_B(k_1 + k_3) + k_1 L_a/\Delta k_2(k_1 + k_3). \qquad \text{II.8}$$

Therefore the overall BOD and DO distributions are the convolutions of the two sets, and hence are Poisson, also, but with parameters $(m_1 + \rho_1)$ and $(m_2 + \rho_2)$.

The model provides information at continuous points in time, not just at tidal slack. This is made possible by treating the diffusion coefficient independently of tidal effects. Secondly, the entire BOD and DO probability distributions are obtained, therefore the percentage of time that the DO will be below any given concentration is readily obtainable. Hopefully, these results will enable regulatory agencies to set emission standards in ways which will maintain the desired wates quality at minimum cost.

O'Connor and Thomann (1966), have reviewed the work previously done in this field. They point out that a number of researchers have incorporated a Markovian aspect into a river's flow by assuming a "lag-one" serial correlation between successive flows and the waste discharge. The approach requires developing a transition matrix from historical data.

This matrix provides the computational scheme to go from a river flow Q_t at time t to the flow Q_{t+1} at time $t + 1$, one time unit later. The stationary probability vector (i.e., the steady-state distribution of flows) is computed variously.

Thomas and Burdon (1963) divide a stream into a finite number of reaches and consider each segment a queue, in which the flow is assumed to be temporarily halted before proceeding to the next reach. Output of one queue is input to the next, and the relation between the upper reach output and the input and storage of that reach is formulated as a first-order Markov process. Monthly flow routings are used exclusively, and a non-conservative pollutant is interacted with the hydrologic system. The final step to be taken is that of interacting the waste discharge with DO.

Another approach (Loucks, 1966; Loucks and Lynn, 1966) utilizes the Streeter–Phelps equations, i.e., for a freshwater stream with zero dispersion. As in the previously mentioned work, a first order Markov process is used to describe the probability distributions of streamflows. In this case, daily streamflows are used, and therefore the applicability of a lag-one model may be questionable, especially during the low flow months. During the late summer and early fall, streamflows usually persist well beyond one day. Nevertheless, for each streamflow and waste water flow, the system parameters are assumed to be known. Various models can then be constructed under different assumptions of autocorrelation in waste water flow and cross-correlation between sewage flow and stream flow.

At a somewhat different level, a number of investigations have been made of recorded water quality and temperature data, with a view to determining its deterministic and stochastic components by means of Fourier analysis and variance spectra analysis. Fourier analysis of recorded data yields information in terms of sinusoidal functions. Variance spectra analysis of recorded data is a frequency analysis of the data's variance. (Refer, for instance, to Thomann, 1967(A); DiToro and O'Connor, 1969.)

Thomann (1967B), carries this approach further into a hypothetical problem.

Assume that we know the auto-correlation of the waste load input or its Fourier transform, the power spectral density. Knowing the impulse response and frequency transfer function of the (linear) system, we can input the spectral density of the wasteload. Then we must determine the correlation function and spectral density of the output, in this case the DO profile.

This has been done (Solodovnikov, 1960) and the result is quoted here.

$S_L(\omega)$ is the power spectrum of the stream BOD at the discharge point due to the waste load.
The output DO deficit spectrum is:

$$S_D(\omega) = [A(\omega)]^2 S_L(\omega), \qquad \text{II.9}$$

where $A(\omega)$ is the amplitude characteristic of the stream.

For variance calculations, note that, for any variable x, the total variance equals the integral of the power spectral density over all values of frequency. Thus

$$\sigma_x^2 = \frac{1}{2\pi}\int_{-\infty}^{\infty} S_x(\omega)\, d\omega. \qquad \text{II.10}$$

The integral of the spectrum is therefore equal to the total variance. If the amplitude A happens not to be a function of the input frequency ω, then integrating equation II.9 over ω gives:

$$\sigma_D = A^2\, \sigma_L. \qquad \text{II.11}$$

It can be shown that non-tidal river amplitude characteristics are indeed independent of the input frequency. From this, it can be further shown that the BOD output variance is:

$$\sigma_L^2(x) = e^{-2k_r(x/u)}\sigma_{LO}^2 \qquad \text{II.12}$$

and the DO deficit variance is

$$\sigma_D^2(x) = \left[\frac{k_d}{k_d - k_r}\left(e^{-k_r(x/u)} - e^{-k_a(x/u)}\right)\right]^2 \sigma_{LO}^2. \qquad \text{II.13}$$

In estuaries, however, the amplitude characteristic is frequency-dependent because the tidal dispersion term is not zero.

It is not yet possible to apply this approach completely to a stream because of the lack of continuous water quality data and the number of waste sources discharging variable waste flows.

III Thermal Pollution

With the ever-increasing demands for electric power, and the continuing construction of power stations to satisfy those demands, has come the widespread recognition of the environmental changes caused by the discharge of waste heat into natural water bodies. The literature expressing these concerns is vast, and we mention as a very small sample indeed—Jaske *et al.*, (1970); Kolflat (1970); Jimeson and Adkins (1971).

All discharges of heated water will contribute to physical and biological changes in the receiving water body. These changes can be beneficial, detrimental, or insignificant, depending upon the ecology of the particular water body, the desired uses of that body, and the amount of heat discharged.

As the temperature of water is raised, the capacity of the water to hold oxygen is decreased. Thus, the amount of dissolved oxygen is decreased and the amount of dissolved oxygen available at saturation levels is less. (Dissolved oxygen is required for respiration of fish and most living organisms, for effective bacterial decomposition of organic matter, and for chemical oxidation.) Furthermore, the addition of heat to a water body can cause stratification because of the reduced density of the water at increased temperatures.

It is convenient and economical to utilize water as the principal agent in the dissipation of waste heat. Unfortunately, water provides the environment for many species of organisms. The increasing need for heat dissipation in supplying the growing demands for electricity and the resulting demands for large cooling water supples for steam-electric plants have resulted in a number of studies, mostly in laboratories, of the effects of thermal discharges on aquatic life. However, predictions as to the effects of both temperature changes and maximum temperatures at actual installations still cannot be made with certainty, especially if the changes are gradual, are not far from ambient temperatures, occur for only a short time, or affect limited areas or volumes of large water bodies.

Temperature changes normally play an important and highly regulatory role in the growth of aquatic plants, and in the growth and physiology of fish and other cold-blooded aquatic animals. Reproductive cycles, digestive rates, respiration rates, and other processes occurring in the bodies of aquatic animals are temperature-dependent. Thus, thermal requirements are among the most difficult to define specifically.

All aquatic species have an optimum temperature range. If the environmental temperature varies above or below this range, the chances of survival for that species decrease. However, fish do have the ability to avoid undesirable temperatures. For some aquatic species, the effect produced by the warming of initially cold water could be beneficial, but the chances of survival of this same species would be progressively reduced if the temperature is further increased, especially if the change is rapid. Since different species are favored by different temperatures, a warming trend may lead to the population decline of one species and the growth of another. Rapid change in temper-

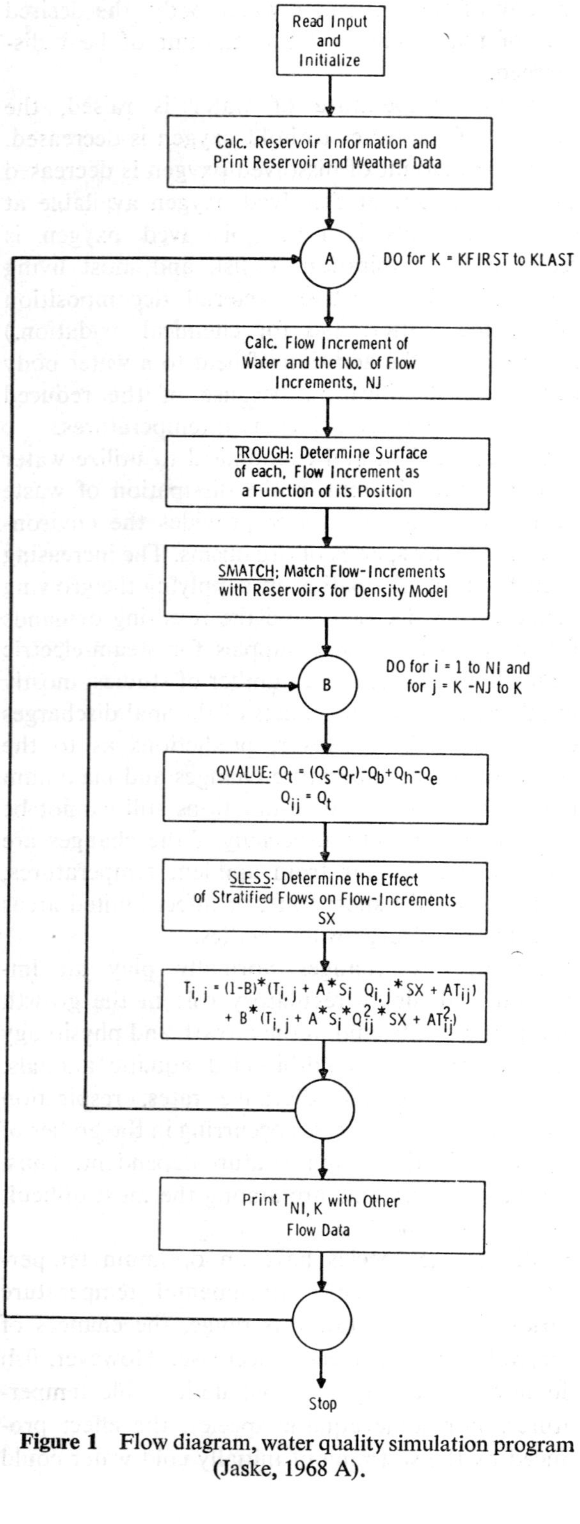

Figure 1 Flow diagram, water quality simulation program (Jaske, 1968 A).

ature caused by thermal plant start-up and shut-down can be lethal to organisms in the affected area.

In order to determine the distribution of temperatures in a river downstream of a thermal discharge, a group at Battelle Memorial Institute's Pacific Northwest Laboratory have developed a special computer program, named COLHEAT. (See, for example, Jaske, 1968A; Jaske, 1968B; Jaske, 1968C; Jaske, 1969.) This approach has been applied in studies on the Columbia River below the Grand Coulee Dam, on the Illinois River for determining the effects of thermal discharges from the Dresden II and III nuclear power plants, and numerous others.

Figure 1 is a flow diagram of the COLHEAT system. On the basis of previous studies, a river is modeled by dividing it into an "inner trough" and an "outer trough," each assumed to be travelling at a uniform speed. The boundary between the troughs is the contour that is actually moving at the river's average velocity. 53% of the cross-section lies in the inner trough and has 52% of the surface area. By using this concept, the model assumes the intermittent transport, mixing, etc. of water in terms of the ratios of the mean velocities of the two regions. The total volume considered in each mass is that associated with a single day's travel time. Hence, the number of days of exposure to the surface interaction is a function of the system volume divided by the travel time. The fundamental difference equation is applied to each region as the internal energy changes are computed. The surface absorbs or loses heat, changes temperature and thus changes the air–water reactions. This calls for iterative computation, since the model's heat balance involves the internal energy of the outlet stream.

The resulting flow model solves the general equations resulting from the very general expression:

$$T_{ij} = [(1 - B)(T_{i-1,j-1} + \Delta T_{ij}^{(1)}) + B(T_{i-1,j-2} + \Delta T_{i,j-i}^{(1)})] + \Delta T_{ij}^{(2)} \quad \text{III.1}$$

T_{i0} = average temperature, °C, of water entering the system during the ith time interval.

T_{ij} = average temperature, °C, of water at the start of the jth flow increment and the end of the ith time increment.

$\Delta T_{ij}^{(1)}$ = temperature change, °C, during the first half of the ith time interval in the jth flow increment (determined from surface heat exchange and advected energy, i.e., the heat budget).

$\Delta T_{ij}^{(2)}$ = temperature change, °C, during the second half of the ith time interval in the jth flow increment.

B = fraction of the water in the inner, fast-moving, trough.

The model can now handle an entire regional flow system, for studying future conditions resulting from accident or normal industrial growth. It can operate in either the temperature, or concentration mode. For the temperature mode, required input data are:

1) Water temperature at the inlet end.

2) Flow discharge at the outlet end.

3) Water temperature at the outlet end (optional, for statistical comparison where available).

4) Meterological parameters (wind velocity for the time period, mean air temperature, dew point, sky cover in tenths, short wave radiation).

5) River (or reservoir) dimensions reduced to equivalent cross-sections (volume, surface or bottom areas are derived).

6) Advected heat quantities (megawatts per time increment).

If daily average data are available, then the time increment is one day; if hourly average data available, then one hour can be used.

In the concentration mode, temperature and surface heat computations are optionally replaced with inlet and outlet concentrations, and allowance is made for bottom deposition if it is significant to the result. The river cross-section information remains unchanged, and, unless temperature conditions cause material changes in the flow regime, the weather parameters can be neglected. The advected material quantities become weight units (or curies) per time increment.

The COLHEAT system has a number of advantages and disadvantages. Advantages are:

1) It requires no statistical data base.

2) It requires only a relatively short record for verification.

3) It needs no time-of-travel estimates or dye studies.

4) It can determine the influence of overlapping weather conditions.

5) It is applicable to any turbulent stream.

6) It can study heat and the concentration of conservative and non-conservative substances concurrently.

7) Every significant coefficient in the program is readily adjustable.

8) It makes possible "reconnaisance" studies with preliminary survey data.

Disadvantages of the COLHEAT system are:

1) It requires a large computer.

2) It requires a relatively good knowledge of the stream bottom profiles, etc.

3) The program is complex.

4) A particular set of meteorological data will usually cover only a part of a river system under study. Hence, the program must be run with different data for individual regions.

5) The program output is not readily adaptable for output display.

Such a model as this assumes the instantaneous mixing with the river flow of the heated effluent from the power plant. This is admissible when considering the "far field" effects at some distance from the discharge point. However, regulatory agencies are becoming increasingly stringent in their standards for the maximum permissible surface temperature rise at the actual outfall. In order to establish this, recourse has been made to models such as that described in QLM (1969).

When a jet of heated effluent is discharged into a receiving water body at some depth below its surface, it rises as plume to the surface, and then spreads laterally and longitudinally. This rising behavior is caused by both initial momentum flux and the net buoyant force due to the lower density of the jet. The initial momentum flux is due to the fact that the jet has a higher velocity than the surrounding ambient water.

Reduction in temperature occurs by entrainment of ambient water into the jet as it approaches the surface. This phenomenon is called jet dilution and occurs by turbulent transport mechanisms. This dilution proceeds until the relative velocity between the jet and surrounding water is reduced to zero.

The relative motion between the plume and the ambient water develops shear stresses. Turbulence is generated and mixing takes place first around the periphery of the jet and finally throughout the whole jet. This results in a continual growth in jet size, a decrease in jet temperature, and an increase in density of the heated jet as it nears the surface.

Entrainment of ambient water which possesses horizontal momentum causes the plume to move in the direction of the predominant current. The introduced heat is then ultimately lost to the atmosphere through the water surface.

The characteristics of a submerged jet can be analyzed by application of the principle of conservation of momentum. The mathematical development is concerned, therefore, with rates of momentum flow, i.e., the momentum per unit time across an inlet or outlet section of the jet volume.

The problem is formulated based on the following assumptions:

1) The momentum at any point along the jet axis is reduced in proportion to the amount lost through drag forces.

2) The jet is axially symmetric along its entire length.

3) Jet expansion continues indefinitely.

4) Boundary effects are neglected and an infinite source of water is available for dilution.

5) Variations in jet temperatures and velocities due to microscale turbulence fluctuations are neglected.

A momentum inventory equation is written along each co-ordinate axis for an infinitesimal volume:

Rate of Momentum Input − Rate of Momentum Output + Forces acting on Jet and Momentum Flow Gained or Lost = Time Rate of Accumulation of Momentum Within Jet

For the steady state condition, the right side of this equation is equal to zero.

These balances are used to develop five independent equations with eleven unknown variables. Geometric and flow relationships are used to develop seven additional equations, resulting in 12 equations and 12 unknowns. These equations are programmed for solution on a digital computer.

The mathematical model is used to predict the coordinates of the rising plume and, at any point on the axis of this plume, the jet size, velocity, dilution, density and temperature. Model inputs include port size, initial jet velocity, jet orientation, discharge water salinity, maximum plant temperature rise, ambient water temperatures, water salinity and runoff.

In order to be absolutely certain that a given power station cooling water discharge does not contravene state or federal regulations, thermal jet models of the kind just described are not accurate enough. They serve to establish the orders of magnitude of the various design parameters, but the trend at this time is toward verification by means of hydraulic models. These must include, not only the discharge equipment itself, but a substantial part of the adjacent water body, as well.

Biguria *et al.* (1969) and Ahlert *et al.* (1970), have studied the problem where the thermal source is not a jet, as in the previous model. That is, its velocity at the discharge is not greater than the stream velocity. However, they do not assume instantaneous mixing. For a channel of uniform cross-section, with no secondary flows, the steady-state energy balance yields this equation:

$$\rho c_p v_x \frac{\partial T}{\partial x} = \frac{\partial}{\partial x}\left(\varepsilon_{hx}\frac{\partial T}{\partial x}\right) + \frac{\partial}{\partial y}\left(\varepsilon_{hy}\frac{\partial T}{\partial y}\right) + \frac{\partial}{\partial z}\left(\varepsilon_{hz}\frac{\partial T}{\partial z}\right). \qquad \text{III.2}$$

where:

ρ = specific gravity of water
c_p = specific heat of water at constant pressure
v_x = stream velocity
T = temperature
x = coordinate distance along the river
z = coordinate distance across the river
y = coordinate distance vertically (i.e., depth)
ϵ_h = thermal eddy diffusivity in a coordinate direction.

In the "short-time" region (about one to 2 depths distance from the source), the authors quote solutions for the temperature distributions from a point source at midstream and mid-depth, and from a vertical line source. The solutions are in non-dimensional forms, and employ exponential terms, and a parameter representing the ratio of effluent flow to river flow.

In the "long-time" region, the temperature distribution is obtained by a finite-difference solution of the following equation:

$$v_x \frac{\partial T}{\partial x} = \varepsilon_z \frac{\partial^2 T}{\partial z^2} + \varepsilon_y \frac{\partial^2 T}{\partial y^2} + \frac{\partial \varepsilon y}{\partial y} \cdot \frac{\partial T}{\partial y} + \frac{\partial \varepsilon_z}{\partial z} \cdot \frac{\partial T}{\partial z}, \qquad \text{III.3}$$

where ϵ = momentum eddy diffusivity in a co-ordinate direction.

For more on temperature distributions see the next section.

IV Lakes and Reservoirs

There is comparatively little literature on mathematical modeling of lake systems, per se. For example, at the fourth symposium on water resources research, held at Ohio State University, in October 1969, entitled "Systems Analysis for Great Lakes Water Resources," the main emphasis was, as the name implies, on water resource management. However, a number of papers, such as Paulik (1969): Dugan *et al.* (1969); Randles *et al.* (1969), dealt with the modeling of a lake, or part of one, as an entity, but did not delve into specific mathematical forms.

O'Connor and Mueller (1970) undertook a simple mathematical analysis to describe water quality changes in the Great Lakes. They assumed that each lake was completely mixed, which is reasonably valid over the time scale of interest—one year.

The mass balance of a non-conservative substance with a first-order rate of decay or increase yields:

$$\frac{\partial c}{\partial t} = \frac{W(t)}{V} - \frac{c}{t_0} - kc, \qquad \text{IV.1}$$

where:

V = volume of a lake
$W(t)$ = discharge of domestic and industrial waste
t_0 = detention time, Q/V, in a lake
Q = flow out of a lake
c = annual average concentration of a substance
k = rate constant for decay or increase of a substance.

Define the parameter α, where:

$$\alpha = k + \frac{1}{t_0}. \qquad \text{IV.2}$$

For a conservative substance, $k = 0$ and $\alpha = 1/t_0$.

For a series of n lakes, where the output of one is the input to the next (assuming each is completely mixed), the mass balance for the nth lake is:

$$\frac{dc_n}{dt} + \alpha_n c_n = \frac{Q_{n-1}}{V} c_{n-1}. \qquad \text{IV.3}$$

The solution for the nth lake due to waste input into the ith lake is:

$$c_n = \frac{1}{V_n}(\alpha_{n-1}\alpha_{n-2}\cdots\alpha_i)\left(e^{-\alpha_n t}\int_0^t e^{\alpha_n t}\,dt\right)$$

$$\left(e^{-\alpha_{n-1}t}\int_0^t e^{\alpha_{n-1}t}\,dt\right)(\ldots)\left(e^{-\alpha_i t}\int_0^t e^{\alpha_i t}\,dt\right) \qquad \text{IV.4}$$

α_i is the previously defined parameter for the ith lake.

As an example of the use to which equation IV.4 can be put, in relation to the Great Lakes, consider a constant waste discharge into the first lake (Superior). What is its effect on water quality in the third lake (Huron)? The answer given by equation IV.4 is:

$$c_3 = \frac{W_0}{\alpha_3 V_3}\left[(1 - e^{-\alpha_3 t}) - a_1(e^{-\alpha_1 t} - e^{-\alpha_3 t}) + a_2(e^{-\alpha_2 t} - e^{-\alpha_3 t})\right], \qquad \text{IV.5}$$

where $$a_1 = \frac{\alpha_3\alpha_2}{(\alpha_3 - \alpha_1)(\alpha_2 - \alpha_1)}$$

and $$a_2 = \frac{\alpha_1\alpha_3}{(\alpha_3 - \alpha_2)(\alpha_2 - \alpha_1)}.$$

The authors proceeded to apply the model to chlorides. Utilizing the simplified hydrology of Figure 2, they first simulated past history, back to the year 1900. Figure 3 gives comparisons of ob-

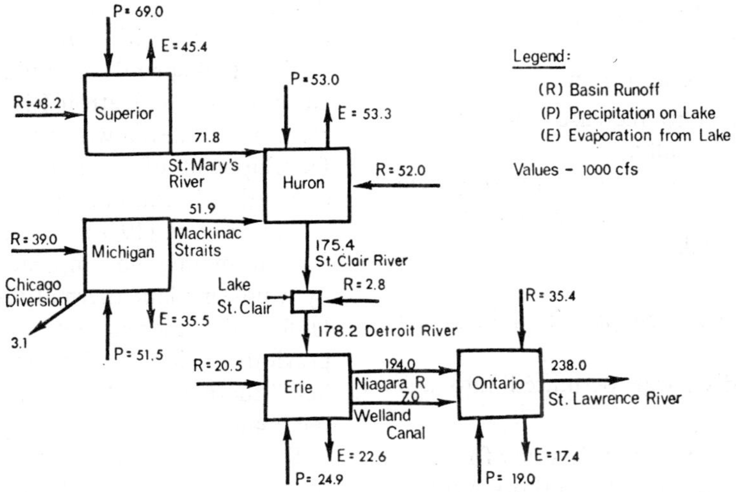

Figure 2 Hydrology of the Great Lakes (O'Connor and Mueller, 1970).

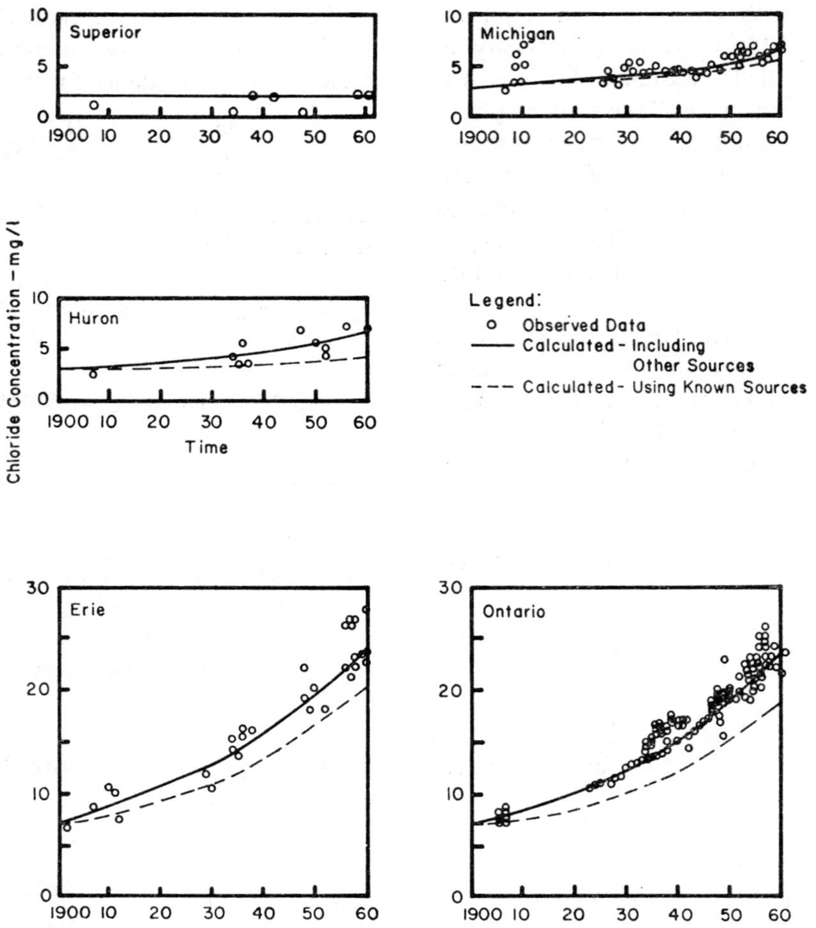

Figure 3 Comparison of observed and calculated chloride concentration (O'Connor and Mueller, 1970).

served and calculated chloride concentrations for all five lakes, for the period 1900–1960.

Each lake had five chloride inputs:

1) Municipal
2) Industrial
3) Road de-icing salt (in run-off)
4) "Other sources"
5) Inflow from the lake upstream.

Item 3 was assumed to increase linearly with time, the others exponentially.

Next, lake chloride concentration was projected to the year 2000, under three possible control regimes for any given lake:

1) No control
2) No industrial discharge permitted into that lake alone.
3) No industrial discharge permitted into any lake.

Figure 4 gives the results of this study for lakes Michigan, Erie and Ontario. The authors went to considerable effort to represent the various chloride sources realistically, and the model shows promise for establishing control patterns of the kind described.

Rumer (1970), has reported on experiments performed on a hydraulic model of Lake Erie. From these, an empirical approach was developed utilizing a transition probability matrix for predicting the spread of pollutants in the western basin due to the Detroit River inflow. Good agreement was achieved with experimental observations. Development of a mathematical model for lake circulation is continuing.

Lawler *et al.* (1968), has developed a lake model for determining the temperature distribution caused by a power plant thermal discharge into the lake. Unlike the thermal jet model described in the previous section, the lake model describes the "far field" thermal profile, i.e., at some distance beyond the point where initial mixing has been completed.

The basic system is shown in Figure 5, where the source, shown as a vertical slotted pipe, is essentially a vertical line source.

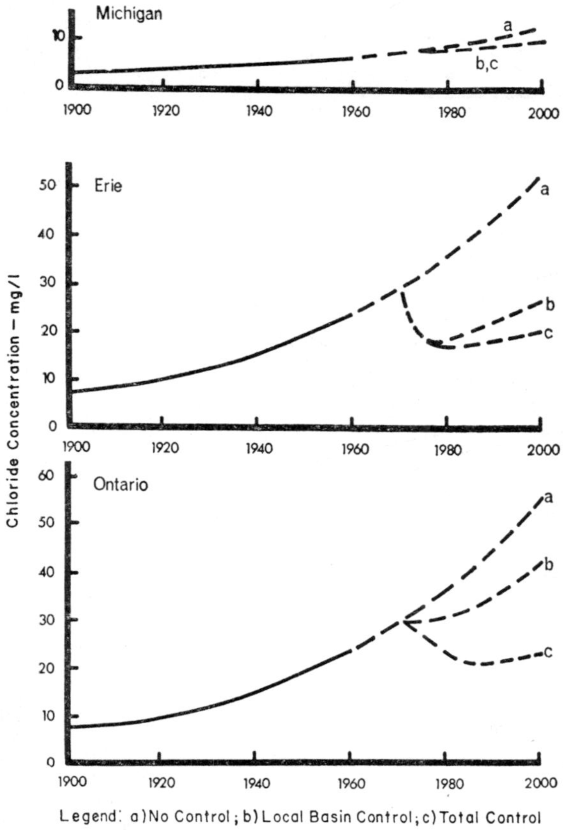

Figure 4 Effect of removal of industrial chlorides (O'Connor and Mueller, 1970).

The heated liquid is discharged symmetrically, the lake boundaries are presumed not to influence the motion, and the scale is long term behavior rather than short term fluctuations. Under these conditions, $\hat{E}_r$, the radial diffusion coefficient and U_r, the radial velocity are independent of the polar angle, θ, and the temperature gradient in the angular direction, $\delta\Delta T/\delta\theta$, will be zero. The angular velocity is also zero and the angular heat flux, q_0, is zero.

The vertical heat flux at the lake's surface must equal the rate of heat dissipation to the atmosphere. The heated layer is presumed to be very stable, due to the inherent density stratification, and vertical mixing with the lower, colder water, is neglected, so the vertical heat flux, q_z, at $z = -D$, is zero.

A temperature gradient in the z direction, within the heated layer, must exist, due to the surface loss. This is not treated explicitly in this model, so that $\Delta T(r)$, the temperature rise at any distance r from the point of discharge, must be interpreted as an average value over the depth D.

The surface heat flux can be written as:

$$q_z \big|_{z=0} = \bar{K}\Delta T, \qquad \text{IV.6}$$

where ΔT is the surface temperature rise over the ambient surface water temperature (rather than the equilibrium temperature) and $\bar{K}$ is a surface heat dissipation coefficient. Then, neglecting entrainment by the heated flow of surrounding lake water, the steady-state energy balance equation is:

$$\frac{1}{r}\frac{\mathrm{d}}{\mathrm{d}r}\left(r\hat{E}_r\frac{\mathrm{d}\Delta T}{\mathrm{d}r}\right) - U_r\frac{\mathrm{d}\Delta T}{\mathrm{d}r} - \frac{\bar{K}}{\rho c_p D}\Delta T = 0. \qquad \text{IV.7}$$

Boundary conditions are:

$$\Delta T\big|_{r=0} = \Delta T_p \qquad \text{IV.8}$$

$$\Delta T\big|_{r=\infty} = 0. \qquad \text{IV.9}$$

The first recognizes that the vertical line, $r = 0$, is the centerline of the discharge, where the temperature rise is that across the condensers. The second presumes that the temperature rise will have decayed to negligble proportions before the boundaries of the lake have been reached.

In order to obtain an estimate of the long range temperature change in a lake due to projected increases in power plant cooling water discharges, Lawler (1971), has devised a simple and conservative model. It assumes that there is complete mixing in the horizontal plane of the lake's surface, over a sufficient depth (small) to support the lake throughput. A steady-state heat balance over the lake then gives:

$$\Delta T = \frac{H}{\rho c_p Q + KA_s} \qquad \text{IV.10}$$

where:

ΔT = lake surface temperature increase, °F.
H = lake heat load, Btu/day.
ρ = density of lake water, lbs./cu. ft.
cp = specific heat of lake water, Btu/lb./°F.
Q = lake outflow, cfd.
K = overall surface heat transfer coefficient, Btu/sq. ft./day/°F.
A_s = lake surface area, sq. ft.

The literature on mathematical modeling in reservoirs (that is, as entities, and not as parts of water resource systems) appears to be devoted very largely to thermal effects.

It is recognized that thermal stratification takes place in reservoirs. The inflow will vary in temperature at different times in the year and establish stable levels in a reservoir, with the coldest water at the bottom and warmest at the top. (This pattern is destroyed, of course, at times of seasonal turnover.)

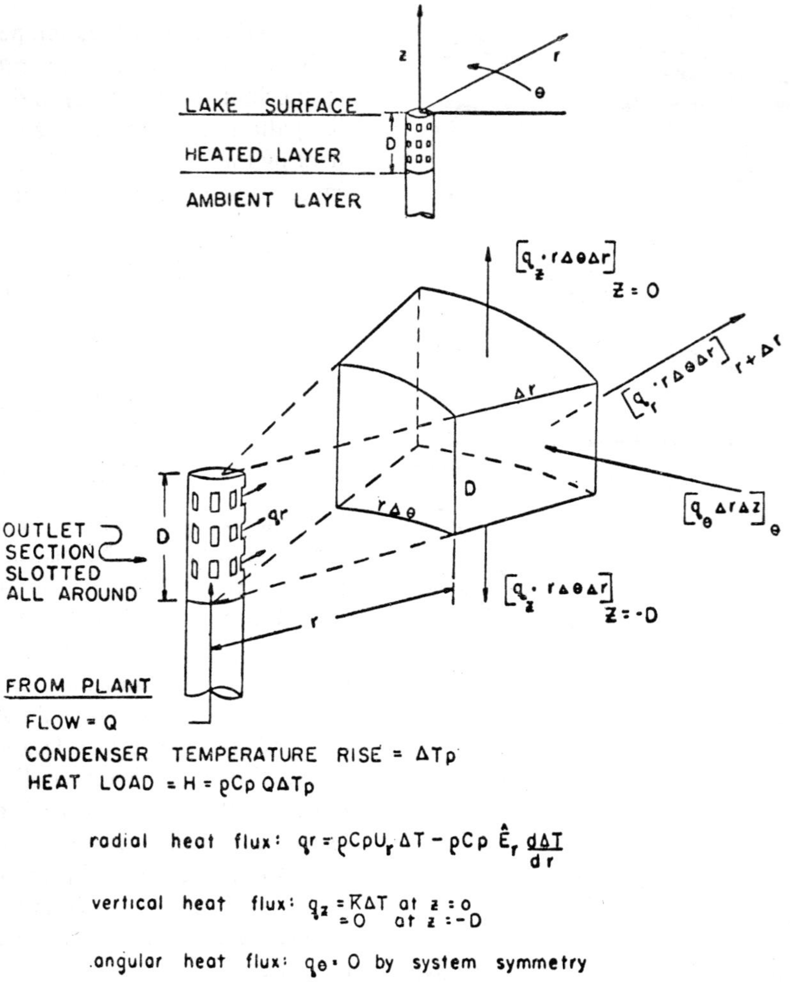

Figure 5 Thermal discharge to a lake—energy balance Development (Lawler *et al.*, 1968).

Thermal stratification has its uses, however. By controlled releases of reservoir water, from selected elevations, the river temperatures downstream can be modified (Delay and Seaders, 1966; Wunderlich and Elder, 1968). Both of the papers cited describe special techniques, partly graphical, for predicting reservoir stratification profiles.

For analytical developments, refer to Orlob *et al.* (1969), and Markofsky and Harleman (1971).

Experience with prototype reservoirs indicates that there are three distinct classes, each of which requires a different type of solution for determining its internal energy (temperature) distribution. These classes are:

1) The DEEP reservoir, characterized by horizontal isotherms.

2) The WEAKLY-STRATIFIED reservoir, characterized by isotherms which are tilted along the longitudinal axis of the reservoir.

3) The COMPLETELY-MIXED reservoir, whose isotherms are vertical.

By their definitions, it is apparent that the deep reservoir solution and the competely mixed reservoir solution are one-dimensional. They differ, of course, in that the solution is taken along the vertical axis for the deep reservoir and along the longitudinal axis for the completely-mixed one. In contrast, the solution of the weakly stratified reservoir is two-dimensional.

The single most important parameter determining into which class a reservoir will fall, and hence the type of solution required, is the densimetric Froude number, defined as:

$$F = \frac{LQ}{DV}\sqrt{\frac{\rho_0}{g\beta}}, \qquad \text{IV.11}$$

where:

L = reservoir length
Q = volumetric discharge through the reservoir
D = mean reservoir depth
V = reservoir volume
ρ_0 = reference density
β = average density gradient in the reservoir
g = gravitational constant.

Orlob *et al.* (1969), give densimetric Froude numbers for five reservoirs in the Columbia River system. Two deep ones, Hungry Horse and Detroit, have F numbers 0.0026 and 0.0030, respectively. Two completely-mixed ones, Priest Rapids and Wells, have F numbers 2.4 and 3.8. The fifth, Lake Roosevelt, is weakly-stratified, with an F number of 0.46. The value of the Froude number as a reservoir index is clear, although the transition values between classes are still not established. Orlob *et al.* (1969), deals with the deep and weakly-stratified classes, not with completely-mixed reservoirs.

For the deep reservoir, an expression was derived for the amount of turbulent energy that is available for mixing:

$$ME = WE_0\, e^{-\alpha d} + A_\tau\left(\frac{\partial u}{\partial z}\right)^2 + gA(z,t)\frac{1}{\rho}\frac{\partial \rho}{\partial z}, \qquad \text{IV.12}$$

where:

WE_0 = energy input per unit volume per unit time at the water surface
α = decay constant
d = depth below the water surface
A_τ = eddy viscosity coefficient
z = elevation
u = mean horizontal velocity at z
$A(z, t)$ = eddy conductivity coefficient
g = gravitational constant
ρ = water density at z.

$A(z, t)$ is a function determined by the temperature profile in the reservoir. A number of different functional forms for it were tested, and the one finally selected was:

$$A(z,t) = A_0\, e^{-\eta(z_s - z)}; \quad z_E < z \qquad \text{IV.13A}$$

$$A(z,t) = bE^{-\alpha} \quad ; \quad z_H < z < z_E \qquad \text{IV.13B}$$

$$A(z,t) = c \quad ; \quad z < z_H \qquad \text{IV.13C}$$

where:

A_0 = value of the eddy conductivity coefficient at the surface
a, b, c = constants evaluated from temperature profiles
E = "gravitational stability" of a stratified water body
z_s = elevation of reservoir surface
z_E = elevation at which $E \simeq 10^{-6}$ meters^{-1}
z_H = elevation at which $E = (b/c)^{1/a}$
η = constant.

The parameter E is given by:

$$E = -\frac{1}{\rho}\frac{\partial \rho}{\partial z} \qquad \text{IV.14}$$

and the value of η is chosen so that:

$$e^{-\eta(z_s - z)} = \frac{b}{A_0}(10^{-6})^{-a}. \qquad \text{IV.15}$$

The reservoir depth down to z_E is that depth theoretically affected by wind mixing.

In addition to the mixing energy, the deep reservoir model includes functions describing withdrawal under several different control regimes. As an example, operating the reservoir outlets on a daily basis in such a manner as to produce a prescribed net outflow temperature. The authors conclude that caution is still needed in evaluating the various parameters required for computation and in application of the model generally.

A weakly stratified reservoir model was developed from the deep one by segmenting the reservoir and considering each segment individually as a deep reservoir. The segments are coupled to one another by the requirement for conservation of heat and mass in the reservoir as a whole. The longitudinal flow in the reservoir was considered to be a density current, whose elevation was established on the basis of its mean temperature and the elevation at which that temperature existed in the reservoir. It was concluded that the model's accuracy was adequate except during the cooling period in the fall of the year.

Markofsky and Harleman (1971), also considered deep reservoirs. They deveoped a one-dimensional water quality mathematical model, which incorporated the internal flow pattern predicted for a stratified reservoir from the temperature model of Huber and Harleman (1968). The water quality parameter of the rivers and streams entering the reservoir are assumed to be known. After initial mixing, the entering water seeks its own density level within the horizontal stratification field. The outflow from the reservoir is assumed to come from a withdrawal layer whose vertical thickness is a function of the time dependent vertical temperature–density gradient. The water quality model is designed to predict the concentration of particular water quality parameters in the outflow water as a function of time. In the case of non conservative pollutants, the model incorporates generation and decay rates for the substance under consideration.

The temperature model is:

$$\frac{\partial T}{\partial t} + v\frac{\partial T}{\partial y} = \frac{1}{A}\frac{\partial}{\partial y}\left[A(D_M + E)\frac{\partial T}{\partial y}\right] + q_i\left[\frac{T_i - T}{A}\right] - \frac{P\phi_m}{\rho C_p A} - \frac{(-1)}{\rho C_p A}(1-\beta)\phi_0\, e^{-\eta(y_s - y)}\left(-\eta A + \frac{\partial A}{\partial y}\right), \quad \text{IV.16}$$

where:

T = temperature, °C
T_i = inflow temperature, C
t = time, minutes
v = vertical convective velocity, cm/min
y = vertical distance, elevation, cm
y_s = surface elevation, cm
A = horizontal cross-section, sq. cm
D_M = diffusivity of mass, sq. cm./min
E = turbulent diffusivity of heat, sq. cm./min
q_i = inflow rate per unit vertical distance, sq. cm./min
P = reservoir perimeter
ϕ_m = heat flux from heat transfer through reservoir sides, cal./sq. cm./min
ρ = density, gm./cu. cm
c_p = specific heat cal./gm. °C
β = fraction of solar radiation absorbed at water surface
ϕ_0 = solar radiation heat flux, cal./sq. cm./min
η = radiation absorption or extinction coefficient, cm^{-1}.

In order to formulate a solution of equation IV.16, two boundary conditions are needed in y, and an initial condition in t.

The initial condition is provided by the iso thermal state of a reservoir in the spring. Taking t as zero in the spring:

$$T = T_0 \text{ at } t = 0, \text{ all } y, \quad \text{IV.17}$$

where T_0 = initial uniform temperature, °C.

The boundary condition for y at the surface is that the heat absorbed due to the incoming radiation, ϕ_0, and atmospheric radiation, ϕ_2, minus surface losses, ϕ_L, must equal the amount of heat diffused into the reservoir from the surface. Thus, at $y = y_s$:

$$\rho c_p(D_M + E)\left.\frac{\partial T}{\partial y}\right|_{y=y_s} = \beta\phi_0 + \phi_2 - \phi_L. \quad \text{IV.18}$$

The boundary condition for y at the bottom is that, there, the temperature changes very little during the year. Thus:

$$\frac{\partial T}{\partial y} = 0 \quad \text{at } y = y_b, \quad \text{all } t. \quad \text{IV.19}$$

Governing equations for the water quality model are:

$$\frac{\partial L}{\partial t} + v\frac{\partial L}{\partial y} = -k_1 L + (u_i L_i - u_i L)\frac{B(y)}{A(y)} \quad \text{IV.20}$$

$$\frac{\partial c}{\partial t} + v\frac{\partial c}{\partial y} = -k_1 L + (u_i c_i - u_i c)\frac{B(y)}{A(y)}, \quad \text{IV.21}$$

where:

L = BOD concentration
c = DO concentration
u_i = interfacial velocity, cm./min.

The surface has been assumed to be DO saturated. Additionally, it has been assumed that there is no net producton of BOD in the surface zone (assumed to be euphotic). Thus, there can be no transfer of BOD across the free surface, and the

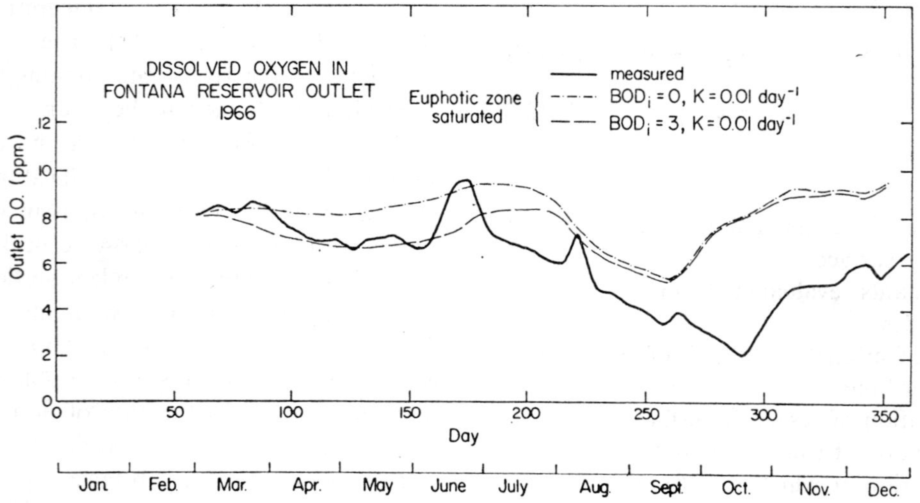

Figure 6 Outlet DO concentrations for Fontana reservoir (Markofsky and Harleman, 1971).

surface boundary conditions are:

$$\frac{\partial L}{\partial y} = 0 \quad \text{at} \quad y = y_s \qquad \text{IV.22}$$

$$c = c_{SAT} \quad \text{at} \quad y = y_s. \qquad \text{IV.23}$$

Since there is assumed to be no transfer of mass across the reservoir bottom, the bottom boundary conditions are:

$$\frac{\partial L}{\partial y} = 0 \quad \text{at} \quad y = y_b \qquad \text{IV.24}$$

$$\frac{\partial c}{\partial y} = 0 \quad \text{at} \quad y = y_b. \qquad \text{IV.25}$$

Equations IV.16, IV.20 and IV.21 are solved simultaneously, in finite-difference form.

This model has been applied to the Fontana Reservoir, which is located on the Little Tennessee River in North Carolina. Figure 6 shows measured and computed values of DO concentration in the outflow over a typical year. Computed values are sensitive to the various assumptions made, but the possibilities for this model appear to be good.

REFERENCES

Ahlert, R. C., G. Biguria and J. Tarbell, *Water Resources Research*, **6**, 614 (1970).

Biguria, G., R. C. Ahlert and M. Schlanger, *Chemical Engineering Prog.* Symposium Series No. 97, **65**, 86 (1969).

Custer, S. W. and R. G. Krutchkoff, *Journal Sanitary Engineering Div., ASCE*, **95**, 865 (1969).

Davidson, B. and R. W. Bradshaw, *Environmental Science and Technology*, **1**, 618 (1967).

Davidson, B. and R. W. Bradshaw, *Water Resources Research*, **6**, 383 (1970).

Delay, W. H. and J. Seaders, *Journal Sanitary Engineering Div., ASCE*, **92**, 115 (1966).

DiToro, D. M. and D. J. O'Connor, American Association of Profs. in Sanit. Eng. 4th Annual Workshop, June 1969.

Dugan, P. R., J. I. Frea, and R. M. Pfister, Proceedings 4th Symposium on Water Resources Research, Water Resources Center, Ohio State University, October 1969.

Graves, G. W., D. Pingry and A. B. Whinston, Army Research Office Report AROD-6368.15-M, February 1971.

Huber, W. C. and D. R. F. Harleman, M.I.T. Hydrodynamics Laboratory Technical Report No. 112, October 1968.

Jaske, R. T., *Chemical Engineering Prog.* Symposium Series No. 90, **64**, 1 (1968A).

Jaske, R. T., U.S.A.E.C. Report BNWL-728, April 1968 B.

Jaske, R. T., U.S.A.E.C. Report BNWL-733, April 1968 C.

Jaske, R. T., U.S.A.E.C. Report BNWL-SA-2737, December 1969.

Jaske, R. T., J. R. Fletcher and K. R. Wise, U.S.A.E.C. Report BNWL-SA-3052, February 1970.

Jimeson, R. M. and G. G. Adkins, *C.E.A.*, **67**, 65 (1971).

Kolflat, T. D., Proceedings ASME Winter Annual Meeting, 1970, 70-WA/PID-5.

Lawler, J. P., Private communication, 1971.

Lawler, J. P., J. L. Leporati and P. J. Lawler, 5th Annual Environmental Health Research Symposium, Albany, N.Y., May 1968.

Loucks, D. P., ASCE National Water Resource Engineering Meeting, Denver, Colo., May 1966.

Loucks, D. P. and W. R. Lynn, *Water Resources Research*, **2**, No. 3 595–605 (1966).

Markofsky, M. and D. R. F. Harleman, EPA Publication 16130 DJH 01/71, January 1971.

O'Connor, D. J. and J. A. Mueller, *Journal Sanitary Engineering Div., ASCE*, **96**, 955 (1970).

O'Connor, D. J. and R. V. Thomann, Proceedings IBM Scientific Computing Symposium on Environmental Sciences, November 1966.

Orlob, G. T., L. A. Roesner and W. R. Norton, EPA Public. 16130 EXT 12/69, 1969.

Paulik, G. J., Proceedings 4th Symposium on Water Resources Research, Water Resources Center, Ohio State University, October 1969.

Pontryagin, L. S., *The Mathematical Theory of Optimum Process*, Interscience, New York (1965).

Quirk, Lawler and Matusky Engineers (QLM), "The Effect of Submerged Discharge of Indian Point Cooling Water on Hudson River Temperature Distribution," Report Prepared for Con-Edison Co. of New York, October 1969.

Randles, C. I., Ting Y. Li, K. S. Shumate and S. R. Stollmack, Proceedings 4th Symposium on Water Resources Research, Water Resources Center, Ohio State University, October 1969.

Rumer, R. R., Jr., Civil Engineering Reports 18.1 and 18.2 Faculty of Eng. and Appl. Science, State University of New York, Buffalo, N.Y., August 1970. FWPCA Grant No. WP-00837.

Solodovnikov, V. V., *Introduction to the Statistical Dynamics of Automatic Control Systems*, Dover Publications, Inc., New York, 1960.

Smith, E. T. and A. R. Morris, *Journal* WPCF, **41**, 1635 (1969)

Tarassov, V. J., J. H. Perlis and B. Davidson, *Water Resources Research*, **5**, 563 (1969).

Thayer, R. P. and R. G. Krutchkoff, *Journal Sanitary Engineering Div., ASCE*, **93**, 59 (1967).

Thomann, R. V., *Journal Sanitary Engineering Div., ASCE*, **89**, 1 (1963).

Thomann, R. V., *Journal Sanitary Engineering Div., ASCE*, **93**, 1 (1967).

Thomann, R. V., Proceedings IBM Scientific Computing Symposium on Water and Air Resource Management., October (1967B).

Thomas, H. A. and R. P. Burdon, "Operations Research in Water Quality Management—Final Report to Public Health Service, Dept. of H.E.W.," Harvard University, Division of Eng. and Appl. Phys. (Feb 1963).

Wilenitz, Israel, "Modeling of River and Estuary Water Quality," *Encyclopedia of Environmental Science and Engineering*, Vol. 1, Gordon and Breach, Inc., New York, 1976.

Whipple, W., Jr., *et al.*, "Instream Aeration of Polluted Rivers," Water Resources Research Institute, Rutgers University, August 1969.

Wunderlich, W. O. and R. A. Elder, *Chemical Engineering Prog.* Symposium Series No. 90, **64**, 82 (1968).

ISRAEL WILENITZ

Quirk, Lawler and Matusky Engrs.

T

TEACHING OF ENVIRONMENTAL STUDIES:
see ENVIRONMENTAL EDUCATION

THE TERRESTRIAL SYSTEM

Space-vehicle Earth was so superbly well designed, equipped and supplied as to have been able to sustain human life aboard it for at least two million years—despite humanity's comprehensive ignorance which permitted a fearfully opinionated assumption of an infinitely extensive planar *World.* Humanity also spontaneously misassumed that its local pollution could be dispelled by the world's infinite extensiveness. Humanity also misassumed that an infinite succession of new and pleasing varieties of abundant, vital resources would be disclosed progressively as man exhausted first one and bespoiled another of the as yet known valuable, because vital, resources. Man must learn in a spontaneously self-enlightening manner to discard many, if not most, of yesterday's false premises, and axioms only believingly accepted; and he must, on his own, discard false premises and learn that only the non-sense Universe is reliable and that a lunatic is not a crazy man but one so sane, well informed, well coordinated, self-disciplined cooperative and fearless as to be the first Earthian human to have been ferried to a physical landing upon the Moon and thereafter to have been returned safely to reboard his mother space-vehicle "Earth".

Long, long ago—little bands of humans seeking fish and fruits, or following animals, frequently became permanently lost and separated from one another. Endowed with the procreative urge, those of the few males and females surviving in company inbred for generations in their respective remotenesses utterly unaware of one another's tribes and separate tribal evolution—and thus evolved a plurality of superficial differences in appearance through special chromosomic concentration brought about by the special characteristics of the survival adaptation process. Thus have developed hundreds of only superficially different types, some very numerous and powerful, some successfully monopolizing specific land areas and others as yet wandering. In their ignorance, all of humanity's national governments assume, misinformedly, that there is not and never will be enough of the vital resources to support all or even a large number of humans, *ergo*, that they must automatically fight one another to the death to discover which government might survive. Often to encourage their respective peoples, political leaders evolve partly expedient and partly idealistic ideologies suitable to their viewpoints, but all the ideologies misassume an only-you-or-me—not both—survival premise as having no axiomatic alternative. Because of the invisibility of 99.9 percent of the source information that contradicts the assumption of a fundamental inadequacy of resources, the probability is that if man is left exclusively to political contriving he will become embroiled in approximately total self-destruction. While the top speed of the intercontinental ballistic rocket is many times that of a bullet, its 20,000 m.p.h. is as nothing beside radar-sight's speed of

70,000,000 m.p.h. The speed of information is now so swift that for the first time in history the lethal missile is no longer faster than man's ability to apprehend both its coming and its specific course—twenty minutes before it can reach him. But the ability to see it coming does not confer the capability to dodge it. Now every one of the opposed political systems' swiftest rocketry attacks can be detected so far in advance that each and every side can dispatch, retaliatorily, not only its full arsenal of atomic warheads but also all its rocket-borne chemical and biological warfare missiles. All opposed sides can and will retaliate automatically *in toto*, thus bringing about approximately total human destruction of vast millions immediately, with the balance to be destroyed soon thereafter by the radiational, biological and chemical contamination.

As in our industrio-social age we now design everything *except* the astro-vehicle paraphernalia, all the metals that have ever been mined and put to use have an average quarter century recycling, invention-to-obsolescence periodicity which includes the scrap, melt, redesign and re-use cycling time. All the metals ever mined and so put to use are now invested in structures and machines that, if operated at full capacity, could take care of only forty-four percent of humanity. The rate at which we have been finding and mining new metals is far slower than the rate of increase of human population. This means that if we freeze the world's design standards at their present levels, which are far below the standards of the astro-vehicle technology, 56 % of humanity, which means humanity's political majority, is doomed to premature demise, and to want and suffering enroute to that early death. There is nothing that politics, per se, can do to alter that condition; only a design revolution—such as that which is already "made to order" in the potentially thousandfold performance per pounds, minutes and kilowatts advancement to be realized by the astro-vehicle industry—can change those fundamental conditions of humanity overnight from failure to comprehensive world-around, human success.

Between 1900 and 1969 our space-vehicle Earth's passengers have experienced an increase of from less than 1% of its total population to 41% of total world population now enjoying a standard of living superior to that either experienced or dreamed of by any monarch before 1900. During that time the material resources per each world man were continually decreasing so that the advancement was not accomplished by exploiting more resources. This historical forty-folding of the percentage of humanity's "haves" can only be explained as the fall-out of ever higher performance per pound technology as developed for the ships of the world's water and air oceans. That an over-night advancement from 40 to 100% is possible can be understood when we realize that the technological fall-out into our domestic economy of ships of extra-terrestrial astrogation have not had time to have important effect on the standard of living because their technological fall-out has not yet had time to occur.

It seems eminently clear that we not only must put our space programs on highest priority of attention and resource investment but that all humanity must be accredited and financed to enter into a new re-educational system that is geared to develop our most prominent awareness, that we indeed *are in space* and that all of our concern is with the fact that our space-vehicle Earth and its life-energy-giving Sun, and the tide-pumping Moon can provide ample sustenance and power for all humanity's needs to be derived from our direct energy income without further robbing our fossil fuels energy savings account. In reality, the Sun, the Earth and the Moon are nothing else than a most fantastically well-designed and space-programmed team of vehicles. All of us *are*, always *have been*, and so long as we exist, *always will be—nothing else but—astronauts*. Let's pull our heads out of the brain benumbing, mind frustrating, misinformedly conditioned reflexes. If it is going to be "All ashore who's going ashore," once more intent to return to nonspace DOWN HERE ON EARTH, humanity is doomed.

But there is hope in sight. The young! While the university students are intuitively skeptical of the validity of any and all evolution-blocking establishments, *ergo*, negatives, the high school age youth thinks spontaneously and positively in astro and electromagnetic technology and their realistic uses. The young of all age levels abhor hypocrisy. They are bored with obsolete UP and DOWN dancing, with bureaucratic inertia, bias of any kind or fear-built security. They disdain white, gray, black and blue lies. The students and school children around the world have idealistic compassion for all humanity. There is a good possibility that they may take over and sucessfully operate SPACE-SHIP EARTH.

How may we use our intellectual capability to higher advantage? Our muscle is very meager as compared to the muscles of many animals. Our integral muscles are as nothing compared to the power of a tornado or the atom bomb which society contrived—in fear—out of the intellect's fearless discoveries of generalized principles governing the fundamental energy behaviors of physical universe.

In organizing our grand strategy we must first discover where we are now; that is, what our present navigational position in the universal scheme of evolution is. To begin our position-fixing aboard our Spaceship Earth we must first acknowledge that the abundance of immediately consumable, obviously desirable or utterly essential resources have been sufficient until now to allow us to carry on despite our ignorance. Being eventually exhaustible and spoilable, they have been adequate only up to this critical moment. This cushion-for-error of humanity's survival and growth up to now was apparently provided just as a bird inside of the egg is provided with liquid nutriment to develop it to a certain point. But then by design the nutriment is exhausted at just the time when the chick is large enough to be able to locomote on its own legs. And so as the chick pecks at the shell seeking more nutriment it inadvertently breaks open the shell. Stepping forth from its initial sanctuary, the young bird must now forage on its own legs and wings to discover the next phase of its regenerative sustenance.

My own picture of humanity today finds us just about to step out from amongst the pieces of our just one-second-ago broken eggshell. Our innocent, trial-and-error-sustaining nutriment is exhausted. We are faced with an entirely new relationship to the universe. We are going to have to spread our wings of intellect and fly or perish; that is, we must dare immediately to fly by the generalized principles governing universe and not by the ground rules of yesterday's superstitious and erroneously conditioned reflexes. And as we attempt competent thinking we immediately begin to reemploy our innate drive for comprehensive understanding.

The architects and planners, particularly the planners, though rated as specialists, have a little wider focus than do the other professions. Also as human beings they battle the narrow views of specialists—in particular, their patrons—the politicians, and the financial and other legal, but no longer comprehensively effective, heirs to the great pirates'—now only ghostly—prerogatives. At least the planners are allowed to look at *all* of Philadelphia, and not just to peek through a hole at one house or through one door at one room in that house. So I think it's appropriate that we assume the role of planners and begin to do the largest scale comprehensive thinking of which we are capable.

We begin by eschewing the role of specialists who deal only in parts. Becoming deliberately expansive instead of contractive, we ask, "*How* do we think in terms of *wholes*?" If it is true that the bigger the thinking becomes the more lastingly effective it is, we must ask, "How big can we think?"

One of the modern tools of high intellectual advantage is the development of what is called general systems theory. Employing it we begin to think of the largest and most comprehensive systems, and try to do so scientifically. We start by inventorying all the important, known variables that are operative in the problem. But if we don't really know how big "big" is, we may not start big enough, and are thus likely to leave unknown, but critical, variables outside the system which will continue to plague us. Interaction of the unknown variables inside and outside the arbitrarily chosen limits of the system are probably going to generate misleading or outrightly wrong answers. If we are to be effective, we are going to have to think in both the biggest and most minutely-incisive ways permitted by intellect and by the information thus far won through experience.

Can we think of, and state adequately and incisively, what we mean by universe? For universe is, inferentially, the biggest system. If we could start with universe, we would automatically avoid leaving out any strategically critical variables. We find no record as yet of man having successfully defined the universe—scientifically and comprehensively—to include the nonsimultaneous and only partially overlapping, micro-macro, always and everywhere transforming, physical and metaphysical, omni-complementary but nonidentical events.

Man has failed thus far, as a specialist, to define the microcosmic limits of divisibility of the nucleus of the atom, but, epochally, as accomplished by Einstein, has been able to define successfully the physicial universe but not the metaphysical universe; nor has he, as yet, defined total universe itself as combining both the physical and metaphysical. The scientist was able to define physical universe by virtue of the experimentally-verified discovery that energy can neither be created nor lost and, therefore, that energy is conserved and is therefore finite. That means it is equatable.

Einstein successfully equated the physical universe as $E = Mc^2$. His definition was only a hypothetical venture until fission proved it to be true. The physical universe of associative and disassociative energy was found to be a closed, but nonsimultaneously occurring, system—its separately occurring events being mathematically measurable; i.e., weighable and equatable. But the finite physical universe did not include the metaphysical weightless experiences of universe. All the unweighables, such as any and all our thoughts and all the abstract mathematics, are weightless. The metaphysical aspects of universe have been thought by the physical scientists to defy "closed system's" analysis. I have found, however, as we shall soon witness, that total universe including both its physical and metaphysical behaviors and aspects are scientifically definable.

Einstein and others have spoken exclusively about the physical department of universe in words which may be integrated and digested as *the aggregate of nonsimultaneous and only partially overlapping, nonidentical, but always complementary, omni-transforming, and weighable energy events.* Eddington defines science as "the earnest attempt to set in order the facts of experience." Einstein and many other first-rank scientists noted that science is concerned exclusively with "facts of experience."

Holding to the scientists' experiences as all important, I define universe, including both the physical and metaphysical, as follows: *The universe is the aggregate of all of humanity's consciously-apprehended and communicated experience with the nonsimultaneous, nonidentical, and only partially overlapping, always complementary, weighable and unweighable, ever omni-transforming, event sequences.*

Each experience begins and ends—ergo, is finite. Because our apprehending is packaged, both physically and metaphysically into time increments of alternate awakeness and asleepness as well as into separate finite conceptions such as the discrete energy quanta and the atomic nucleus components of the fundamental physical discontinuity, all experiences are finite. Physical experiments have found no solids, no continuous surfaces or lines—only discontinuous constellations of individual events. An aggregate of finites is finite. *Therefore, universe as experimentially defined, including both the physical and metaphysical, is finite.*

It is therefore possible to initiate our general systems formulation at the all inclusive level of universe whereby no strategic variables will be omitted. There is an operational grand strategy of General Systems Analysis that proceeds from here. It is played somewhat like the game of "Twenty Questions," but G.S.A. is more efficient—that is, is more economical—in reaching its answers. It is the same procedural strategy that is used by the computer to weed out all the wrong answers until only the right answer is left.

Having adequately defined the whole system we may proceed to subdivide progressively. This is accomplished through progressive division into two parts—one of which, by definition, could not contain the answer—and discarding of the sterile part. Each progressively retained live part is called a "bit" because of its being produced by the progressive binary "yes" or "no" bi-section of the previously residual live part. The magnitude of such weeding operatons is determined by the number of successive bits necessary to isolate the answer.

How many "bi-secting bits" does it take to get rid of all the irrelevancies and leave in lucid isolation that specific information you are seeking? We find that the first subdividing of the concept of universe—bit one—is into what we call a *system. A system subdivides universe into all the universe outside the system (macrocosm) and all the rest of the universe which is inside the system (microcosm) with the exception of the minor fraction of universe which constitutes the system itself.* The system divides universe not only into macrocosm and microcosm but also coincidentally into typical conceptual and nonconceptual aspects of universe—that is, an overlappingly-associable consideration, on the one hand, and, on the other hand, all the nonassociable, nonoverlappingly-considerable, nonsimultaneously-transforming events of non-synchronizable disparate wave frequency rate ranges.

A thought is a system, and is inherently conceptual—though often only dimly and confusedly conceptual at the moment of first awareness of the as yet only vaguely describable thinking activity. Because total universe is nonsimultaneous it is not conceptual. Conceptuality is produced by isolation, such as in the instance of one single, static picture held out from a moving-picture film's continuity, or scenario. Universe is an evolutionary-process scenario without beginning or end, because the shown part is continually transformed chemically into fresh film and reexposed to the ever self-reorganizing process of latest thought realizations which must continually introduce new significance into the freshly written description of the ever-transforming events before splicing the film in again for its next projection phase.

Heisenberg's principle of "indeterminism" which recognized the experimental discovery that the act of measuring always alters that which was being measured turns experience into a continuous and never-repeatable evolutionary scenario. One picture of the scenario about the caterpillar phase does not communicate its transformation into the butterfly phase, etc. The question, "I wonder what is outside the outside-of-universe?" is a request for a single picture description of a scenario of transformations and is an inherently invalid question. It is the same as looking at a dictionary and saying, "Which word is the dictionary?" It is a meaningless question.

It is characteristic of "all" thinking—of all system's conceptioning—that all the lines of thought interrelationships must return cyclically upon themselves in a plurality of directions, as do various great circles around spheres. Thus may we interrelatedly comprehend the constellation—or system—of experiences under consideration. Thus may we comprehend how the special-case economy demonstrated by the particular system considered also discloses the generalized law of energy conservation of physical universe.

To hit a duck in flight a hunter does not fire his gun at the bird where the gunner sees him but ahead of the bird, so that the bird and the bullet will meet each other at a point not in line between the gunner and the bird at time of firing. Gravity and wind also pull the bullet in two different directions which altogether impart a mild corkscrew trajectory to the bullet. Two airplanes in nighttime dogfights of World War II firing at each other with tracer bullets and photographed by a third plane show clearly the corkscrew trajectories as one hits the other. Einstein and Reiman, the Hindu mathematician, gave the name *geodesic lines* to these curvilinear and *most economical lines of interrelationship between two independently moving "events"*—the events in this case being the two airplanes.

A great circle is a line formed on a sphere's surface by a plane going through the sphere's centre. Lesser circles are formed on the surfaces of spheres by planes cutting through spheres but not passing through the sphere's centre. When a lesser circle is superimposed on a great circle it cuts across the latter at two points, A and B. It is a shorter distance between A and B on the great circle's shortest arc than it is on the lesser circle's shortest arc. Great circles are geodesic lines because they provide the most economical (energy, effort) distances between any two points on a spherical system's surface; therefore, nature, which always employs only the most economical realizations must use those great circles which, unlike spiral lines, always return upon themselves in the most economical manner. All the system's paths must be topologically and circularly interrelated for conceptually definitive, locally transformable, polyhedronal understanding to be attained in our spontaneous—ergo, most economical—geodesicly structured thoughts.

Thinking itself consists of self-disciplined dismissal of both the macrocosmic and microcosmic irrelevancies which leaves only the lucidly-relevant considerations. The macrocosmic irrelevancies are all the events too large and too infrequent to be synchronizably tuneable in any possible way with our consideration (a beautiful word meaning putting stars together). The microcosmic irrelevancies are all the events which are obviously too small and too frequent to be differentially resolved in any way or to be synchronizably-tuneable within the lucidly-relevant wave-frequency limits of the system we are considering.

How many stages of dismissal of irrelevancies does it take—that is, proceeding from "universe" as I defined it, how many bits does it take—lucidly to isolate all the geodesic interrelations of all the "star" identities in the constellation under consideration? The answer is the formula $\frac{N^2 - N}{2}$ where N is the number of stars in the thought-discerned constellation of focal point entities comprising the problem.

"Comprehension" means identifying all the most uniquely economical inter-relationships of the focal point entities involved. We may say then that:

$$\text{Comprehension} = \frac{N^2 - N}{2}$$

This is the way in which thought processes operate with mathematical logic. The mathematics involved consist of topology, combined with vectorial geometry, which combination I call "synergetics"—which word I will define while clarifying its use. By questioning many audiences, I have discovered that only about one in three hundred are familiar with synergy. The word is obviously not a popular word. Synergy is the only word in our language that means *behavior of whole systems unpredicted by the separately observed behaviors of any of the system's separate parts or any subassembly of the system's parts.* There is nothing in the chemistry of a toenail that predicts the existence of a human being.

I once asked an audience of the National Honors Society in chemistry, "How many of you are familiar with the word, synergy?" and all hands went up. Synergy is the essence of chemistry. The tensile strength of chrome-nickel, steel, which is

Underlying Order in Randomness

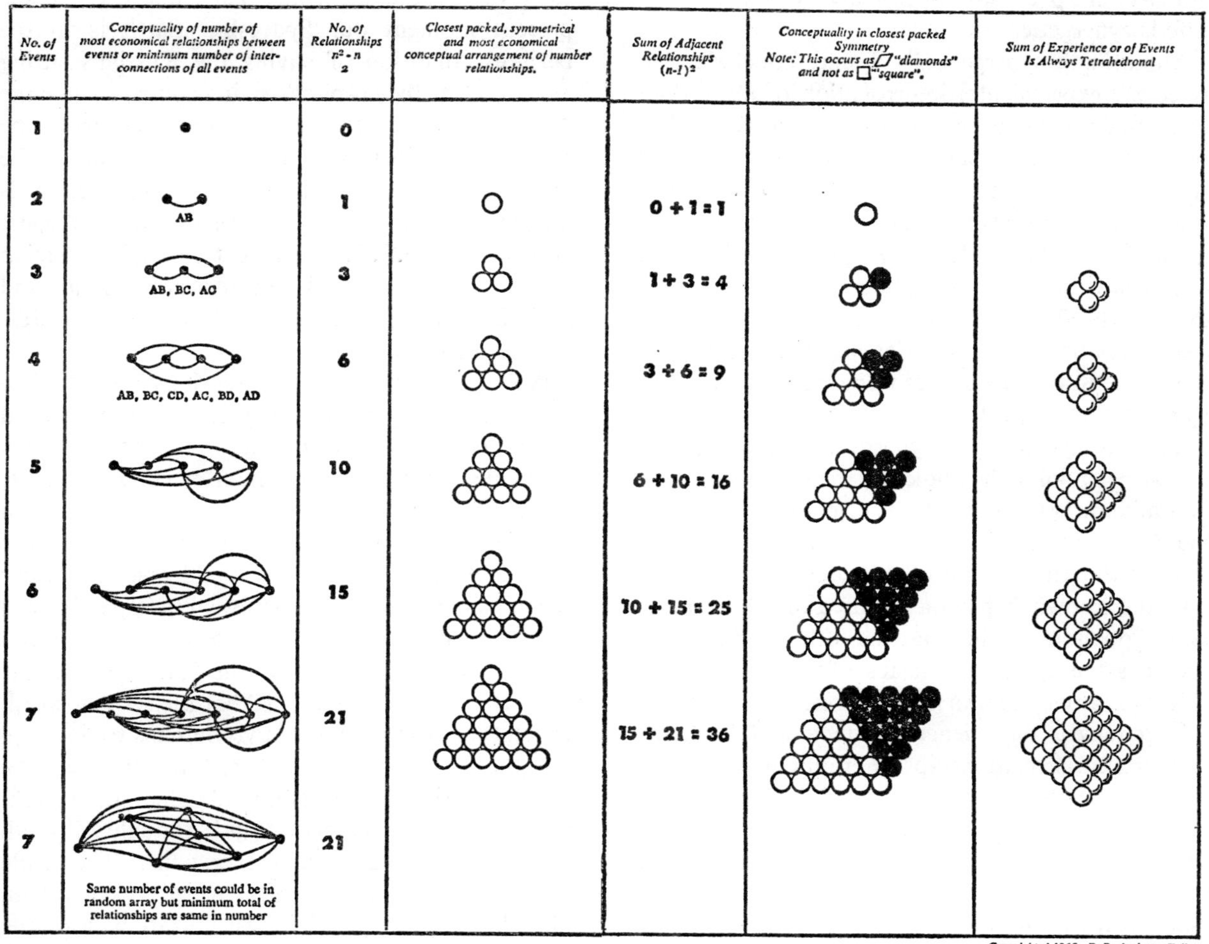

No. of Events	Conceptuality of number of most economical relationships between events or minimum number of interconnections of all events	No. of Relationships $\frac{n^2 - n}{2}$	Closest packed, symmetrical and most economical conceptual arrangement of number relationships.	Sum of Adjacent Relationships $(n-1)^2$	Conceptuality in closest packed Symmetry Note: This occurs as ▱ "diamonds" and not as □ "square".	Sum of Experience or of Events Is Always Tetrahedronal
1		0				
2	AB	1		0 + 1 = 1		
3	AB, BC, AC	3		1 + 3 = 4		
4	AB, BC, CD, AC, BD, AD	6		3 + 6 = 9		
5		10		6 + 10 = 16		
6		15		10 + 15 = 25		
7		21		15 + 21 = 36		
7	Same number of events could be in random array but minimum total of relationships are same in number	21				

approximately 350,000 pounds per square inch, is 100,000 P.S.I. greater than the sum of the tensile strengths of each of all its alloyed together, component, metallic elements. Here is a "chain" that is 50% stronger than the sum of the strengths of all links. We think popularly only in the terms of a chain being no stronger than its weakest link, which concept fails to consider, for instance, the case of an endlessly interlinked chain of atomically self-renewing links of omni-equal strength or of an omni-directionally interlinked chain matrix of ever renewed atomic links in which one broken link would be, only momentarily, a local cavern within the whole mass having no weakening effect on the whole, for every link within the matrix is a high frequency, recurring, break-and-make restructuring of the system.

Since synergy is the only word in our language meaning behavior of wholes unpredicted by behavior of their parts, it is clear that society does not think there are behaviors of whole systems unpredicted by their separate parts. This means that society's formally-accredited thoughts and ways of accrediting others are grossly inadequate in comprehending the nonconceptual qualities of the scenario "universal evolution."

There is nothing about an electron alone that forecasts the proton, nor is there anything about the Earth or the Moon that forecasts the coexistence of the Sun. The solar system is synergetic—unpredicted by its separate parts. But the interplay of Sun as supply ship of Earth and the Moon's gravitationally produced tidal pulsations on Earth all interact to produce the biosphere's chemical conditions which permit but do not cause the regeneration of life on Spaceship Earth. This is all synergetic. There is nothing about the gases given off respiratorily by Earth's green vegetation that predicts that those gases will be essential to the life support of all mammals aboard Spaceship Earth, and nothing about the mammals that predicts that the gases which they give off respiratorily are essential to the support of the vegetation aboard our Spaceship Earth. Universe is synergetic. Life is synergetic.

Sumarizing synergetically I may conclude that since my experimental interrogation of more than one hundred audiences all around the world has shown that less than one in three hundred university students has ever heard of the word synergy, and since it is the only word that has that meaning it is obvious that the world has not thought there are any behaviors of whole systems unpredictable by their parts. This is partially the consequence of over-specialization and of leaving the business of the whole to the old pirates to be visibly conducted by their stooges, the feudal kings or local politicians.

There is a corollary of synergy which says that the known behavior of the whole and the known behavior of a minimum of known parts often makes possible the discovery of the values of the remaining parts as does the known sum of the angles of a tiiangle plus the known behavior of three of its six parts make possible evaluating the others. Topology provides the synergetic means of ascertaining the values of any system of experiences.

Topology is the science of fundamental pattern and structural relationships of event constellations. It was discovered and developed by the mathematician Euler. He discovered that all patterns can be reduced to three prime conceptual characteristics: to *lines; points* where two lines cross or the same line crosses itself; and *areas*, bound by lines. He found that there is a constant relative abundance of these three fundamentally unique and no further reducible aspects of all patterning

$$P + A = L + 2$$

This reads: the number of points plus the number of areas always equals the number of lines plus the number constant two. There are times when one area happens to coincide with others. When the faces of polyhedra coincide illusionarily the congruently hidden faces must be accounted arithmetically in formula.

Thus man has developed an externalized metabolic regeneration organism involving the whole of Spaceship Earth and all its resources. Any human being can physically employ that organism, whereas only one human can employ the organically integral craft tool. All 91 of the 92 chemical elements thus far found aboard our spaceship are completely involved in the world-around industrial network. The full family of chemical elements is unevenly distributed, and therefore our total planet is at all times involved in the industrial integration of the unique physical behaviors of each of all the elements. Paradoxically, at the present moment our Spaceship Earth is in the perilous condition of having the Russians sitting at one set of the co-pilot's flying controls while the Americans sit at the other. France controls the starboard engines, and the Chinese control the port engines, while the United Nations controls the passenger operation. The result is an increasing number of U.F.O. hallucinations of sovereign states darting backwards and forwards and around in circles, getting nowhere, at an incredibly accelerating rate of speed.

All of humanity's tool extensions are divisible into two main groups: the craft and the industrial tools. I define the craft tools as all those tools which could be invented by one man starting all alone, naked in the wilderness, using only his own experience and his own integral facilities. Under these isolated conditions he could and did invent spears, slings, bows, and arrows, etc. By industrial tools I mean all the tools that cannot be produced by one man, as for instance the S.S. *Queen Mary*. With this definition, we find that the spoken word, which took a minimum of two humans to develop, was the first industrial tool. It brought about the progressive integration of all individual generation-to-generation experiences and thoughts of all humanity everywhere and everywhen. The Bible says, "In the beginning was the word"; I say to you, "In the beginning of industrialization was the spoken word." With the graphic writing of the words and ideas we have the beginning of the computer, for the computer *stores* and retrieves information. The written word, dictionary and the book were the first information storing and retrieving systems.

The craft tools are used initially by man to make the first industrial tools. Man is using his hands today most informatively and expertly only to press the buttons that set in action the further action of the tools which reproduce other tools which may be used informatively to make other tools. In the craft economies craftsman artists make only end or consumer-products. In the industrial economy the craftsman artists make the tools and the tools make the end or consumer-products. In this industrial development the mechanical advantages of men are pyramided rapidly and synergetically into invisible magnitudes of ever more incisive and inclusive tooling which produces ever more with ever less resource investment per each unit of end-product, or service, performance.

As we study industrialization, we see that we cannot have mass production unless we have mass consumption. This was effected evolutionarily by the great social struggles of labor to increase wages and spread the benefits and prevent reduction of the numbers of workers employed. The labor movement made possible mass purchasing; ergo, mass production; ergo, low prices on vastly improved products and services, which have altogether established entirely new and higher standards of humanity's living.

Our labor world and all salaried workers, including school teachers and college professors, are now, at least subconsciously if not consciously, afraid that automation will take away their jobs. They are afraid they won't be able to do what is called "earning a living," which is short for earning the right to live. This term implies that normally we are supposed to die prematurely and that it is abnormal to be able to earn a living. It is paradoxical that only the abnormal or exceptional are entitled to prosper. Yesterday the term even inferred that sucess was so very abnormal that only divinely ordained kings and nobles were entitled to eat fairly regularly.

It is easy to demonstrate to those who will take the time and the trouble to unbias their thoughts that automation swiftly can multiply the physical energy part of wealth much more rapidly and profusely than can man's muscle and brain-reflexed—manually-controlled production. On the other hand humans alone can foresee, integrate, and anticipate the new tasks to be done by the progressively automated wealth-producing machinery. To take advantage of the fabulous magnitudes of real wealth waiting to be employed intelligently by humans and unblock automation's postponement by organized labor we must give each human who is or becomes unemployed a life fellowship in research and development or in just simple thinking. Man must be able to dare to think truthfully and to act accordingly without fear of losing his franchise to live. The use of mind fellowships will permit humans comprehensively to expand and accelerate scientific exploration and experimental prototype development. For every 100,000 employed in research and development, or just plain thinking, one probably will make a breakthrough that will more than pay for the other 99,999 fellowships. Thus, production will no longer be impeded by humans trying to do what machines can do better. Contrariwise, omni-automated and inanimately powered production will unleash humanity's unique capability—its metaphysical capability. Historically speaking, these steps will be taken within the next decade. There is no doubt about it. But not without much social crisis and consequent educational experience and discovery concerning the nature of our unlimited wealth.

Through the universal research and development fellowships, we're going to start emancipating humanity from being muscle and reflex machines. We're going to give everybody a chance to develop their most powerful mental and intuitive faculties. Given their research and development fellowship, many who have been frustrated during their younger years may feel like going fishing. Fishing provides an excelent opportunity to think clearly; to review one's life; to recall one's earlier frustrated and abandoned longings and curiosities. What we want everybody to do is to *think* clearly.

We soon will begin to generate wealth so rapidly that we can do very great things. I would like you to think what this may do realistically for living without spoiling the landscape, or the antiquities or the trails of humanity throughout the ages, or despoiling the integrity of romance, vision, and harmonic creativity. All the great office buildings will be emptied of earned living workers, and the automated office-processing of information will be centralized in the basements of a few buildings. This will permit all the modernly mechanized office buildings to be used as dwelling facilities.

When we approach our problems on a universal, general systems basis and progressively eliminate the irrelevancies, somewhat as we peel petals from an artichoke, at each move we leave in full visibility the next most important layer of factors with which we must deal. We gradually uncover *you* and *me* in the heart of now. But evolution requires that we comprehend each layer in order to unpeel it. We have now updated our definitions of universe by conforming them with the most recent and erudite scientific findings such as those of Einstein and Planck. Earlier in our thinking we discovered man's function in universe to be that of the most effective metaphysical capability experimentally evidenced thus far within our locally observable phases and time zones of universe. We have also discovered that it is humanity's task to comprehend and set in order the special case facts of human experience and to win therefrom knowledge of the *a priori* existence of a complex of generalized, abstract principles which apparently altogether govern all physicially evolving phenomena of universe.

We have learned that only and exclusively through use of his mind can man inventively employ the generalized principles further to conserve the locally available physical energy of the only universally unlimited supply. Only thus can man put to orderly advantage the various, local, and otherwise disorderly behaviors of the entropic, physical universe. Man can and may metaphysically comprehend, anticipate, shunt, and meteringly introduce the evolutionarily organized environment events in the magnitudes and frequencies that best synchronize with the patterns of his successful and metaphysical metabolic regeneration while ever increasing the degrees of humanity's space and time freedoms from yesterday's ignorance sustaining survival procedure chores and their personal time capital wasting.

Now we have comprehended and peeled off the layers of petals which disclosed not only that physical energy is conserved but also that it is ever increasingly deposited as a fossil-fuel savings account aboard our Spaceship Earth through photosynthesis and progressive, complex, topsoil fossilization buried ever deeper within Earth's crust by frost, wind, flood, volcanoes, and earthquake upheavals. We have thus discovered also that we can make all of humanity successful through science's world-engulfing industrial evolution provided that we are not so foolish as to continue to exhaust in a split second of astronomical history the orderly energy savings of billions of years' energy conservation aboard our Spaceship Earth. These energy savings have been put into our Spaceship's life-regeneration-guaranteeing bank account for use only in self-starter functions.

The fossil fuel deposits of our Spaceship Earth correspond to our automobile's storage battery which must be conserved to turn over our main engine's self-starter. Thereafter, our "main engine," the life regenerating processes, must operate exclusively on our vast daily energy income from the powers of wind, tide, water, and the direct Sun radiation energy. The fossil-fuel savings account has been put aboard Spaceship Earth for the exclusive function of getting the new machinery built with which to support life and humanity at ever more effective standards of vital physical energy and reinspiring metaphysical sustenance to be sustained exclusively on our Sun radiation's and Moon pull gravity's tidal, wind, and rainfall generated pulsating and therefore harnessable energies. The daily income energies are excessively adequate for the operation of our main industrial engines and their automated productions. The energy expended in one minute of a tropical hurricane equals the combined energy of all the U.S.A. and U.S.S.R. nuclear weapons. Only by understanding this scheme may we continue for all time ahead to enjoy and explore universe as we progressively harness evermore of the celestially generated tidal and storm generated wind, water, and electrical power concentrations. We cannot afford to expend our fossil fuels faster than we are "recharging our battery," which means precisely the rate at which the fossil fuels are being continually deposited within Earth's spherical crust.

We have discovered that it is highly feasible for all the human passengers aboard Spaceship Earth to enjoy the whole ship without any individual interfering with another and without any individual being advantaged at the expense of another, provided that we are not so foolish as to burn up our ship and its operating equipment by powering our prime operations exclusively on atomic reactor generated energy. The too-shortsighted and debilitating exploitation of fossil fuels and atomic energy are similar to running our automobiles only on the self-starters and batteries and as the latter become exhausted replenishing the batteries only by starting the chain reaction consumption of the atoms with which the automobiles are constituted.

We have discovered also why we were given our intellectual faculties and physical extension facilities. We have discovered that we have the inherent capability and inferentially the responsibility of making humanity comprehensively and sustainably successful. We have learned the difference between brain and mind capabilities. We have learned of the superstitions and inferiority complexes built into all humanity through all of history's yesterdays of slavish survival under conditions of abysmal illiteracy and ignorance wherein only the most ruthless, shrewd, and eventually brutish could sustain existence, and then for no more than a third of its known potential life span.

This all brings us to a realization of the enormous educational task which must be successfully accomplished right now in a hurry in order to convert man's spin-dive toward oblivion into an intellectually mastered power pullout into safe and level flight of physical and metaphysical success, whereafter he may turn his Spaceship Earth's occupancy into a universe exploring advantage. If it comprehends and reacts effectively, humanity will open an entirely new chapter of the experiences and the thoughts and drives thereby stimulated.

Most importantly we have learned that from here on it is success for all or for none, for it is experimentally proven by physics that "unity is plural and at minimum two"—the complementary but not mirror-imaged proton and neutron. You and I are inherently different and complementary. Together we average as zero—that is, as eternity.

Now having attained that cosmic degree of orbital conceptioning we will use our retro-rocket controls to negotiate our reentry of our Spaceship Earth's atmosphere and return to our omni-befuddled present. Here we find ourselves maintaining the fiction that our cross-breeding World Man consists fundamentally of innately different nations and races which are the antithesis of that cross-breeding. Nations are products of many generations of local inbreeding in a myriad of remote human enclaves. With grandfather chiefs often marrying incestuously the gene concentrations brought about hybrid nationally-unique physiological characteristics which in the extreme northern hibernations bleached out the human skin and in the equatorial casting off of all clothing inbred darkly tanned pigmentation. All are the consequence only of unique local environment conditions and super inbreeding.

The crossbreeding world people on the North American continent consist of two separate *input* sets. The first era input set consists of those who came with the prevailing winds and ocean currents eastward to the North, South, and Central Americas by raft and by boat from across the Pacific, primarily during an age which started at least thirty thousand years ago, possibly millions of years ago, and terminated 300 years ago. The eastbound trans-Pacific migration peopled the west coasts of both South and North America and migrated inland towards the two continents' middle ground in Central America and Mexico. In Mexico today will be found every type of human characteristic and every known physiognomy, each of which occur in such a variety of skin shades from black to white that they do not permit the ignorance-invented "race" distinctions predicated only superficially on extreme limits of skin color. The second or west-bound input era set of crossbreeding world man now peopling the Americas consists of the gradual and slower migration around the world from the Pacific Ocean westward into the wind, "following the sun," and travelling both by sea through Malaysia, across the Indian Ocean up the Persian Gulf into Mesopotamia and overland into the Mediterranean, up the Nile from East Africa into the South and North Atlantic to America—or over the Chinese, Mongolian, Siberian, and European hinterlands to the Atlantic and to the Americas.

Now both east and westbound era sets are crossbreeding with one another in ever-accelerating degree on America's continental middleground. This omni reintegration of world man from all the diverse hybrids is producing a crossbred people on the Pacific Coast of North America. Here with its aerospace and oceans penetrating capabilities, a world type of humanity is taking the springboard into all of the hitherto hostile environments of universe into the ocean depths and into the sky and all around the earth.

Returning you again to our omni-befuddled present, we realize that reorganization of humanity's economic accounting system and its implementation of the total commonwealth capability by total world society, aided by the computer's vast memory and high speed recall comes first of all of the first-things-first that we must attend to make our space vehicle Earth a successful man operation. We may now raise our sights, in fact must raise our sights, to take the initiative in planning the world-around industrial retooling revolution. We must undertake to increase the performance per pound of the world's resources until they provide all of humanity a high standard of living. We can no longer wait to see whose biased political system should prevail over the world.

You may not feel very confident about how you are going to earn your right to live under such world-around patronless conditions. But I say to you the sooner you do the better chance we have of pulling out of humanity's otherwise fatal nose dive into oblivion. As the world political economic emergencies increase, remember that we have discovered a way to make the total world work. It must be initiated and in strong momentum before we pass the point of no return. You may gain great confidence from the fact that your fellow men, some of them your great labor leaders, are already aware and eager to educate their own rank and file on the fallacy of opposition to automation.

I have visited more than 300 universities and colleges around the world as an invited and appointed professor and have found an increasing number of students who understand all that we have been reviewing. They are comprehending increasingly that elimination of war can only be realized through a design and invention revolution. When it is realized by society that wealth is as much everybody's as is the air and sunlight, it no longer will be rated as a personal handout for anyone to accept a high standard of living in the form of an annual research and development fellowship.

I have owned successively, since boyhood, fifty-four automobiles. I will never own another. I have not given up driving. I began to leave my cars at airports—never or only infrequently getting back to them. My new pattern requires renting new cars at the airports as needed. I am progressively ceasing to own things, not on a political-schism basis, as for instance Henry George's ideology, but simply on a practical basis. Possession is becoming progressively burdensome and wasteful and therefore obsolete.

Why accumulate mementos of far away places when you are much more frequently in those places than at your yesterday's home, nation, state, city and street identified residences, as required for passport, taxing, and voting functions? Why not completely restore the great cities and buildings of antiquity and send back to them all their fragmented treasures now deployed in the world's museums? Thus, may whole eras be reinhabited and experienced by an ever increasingly interested, well-informed, and inspired humanity. Thus, may all the world regain or retain its regenerative metaphysical mysteries.

I travel between Southern and Northern hemispheres and around the world so frequently that I no longer have any so-called normal winter and summer, nor normal night and day, for I fly in and out of the shaded or sunflooded areas of the spinning, orbiting Earth with ever-increased frequency. I wear three watches to tell me what time it is at my "home" office, so that I can call them by long distance telephone. One is set for the time of day in the place to which I am next going, and one is set temporarily for the locality in which I happen to be. I now see the Earth realistically as a sphere and think of it as a spaceship. It is big, but it is comprehensible. I no longer think in terms of "weeks" except as I stumble over their antiquated stop-and-go habits. Nature has no "weeks." Quite clearly the peak traffic patterns exploited by businessmen who are eager to make the most profit in order to prove their right to live causes everybody to go in and out of the airport during two short moments in the twenty-four hours with all the main facilities shut down two-thirds of the time. All our beds around the world are empty for two-thirds of the time. Our living rooms are empty seven-eights of the time.

The population explosion is a myth. As we industrialize, down goes the annual birth rate. If we survive, by 1985, the whole world will be industrialized, and, as with the United States, and as with all Europe and Russia and Japan today, the birth rate will be dwindling, and the bulge in population will be recognized as accounted for exclusively by those who are living longer.

When world realization of its unlimited wealth has been established there as yet will be room for the whole of humanity to stand indoors in greater New York City, with more room for each human than at an average cocktail party.

We will oscillate progressively between social concentrations in cultural centers and in multi-deployment in greater areas of our Spaceship Earth's as yet very ample accommodations. The same humans will increasingly converge for metaphysical intercourse and deploy for physical experiences.

Each of our four billion humans' shares of the Spaceship Earth's resources as yet today amount two-hundred billion tons.

It is also to be remembered that despite the fact that you are accustomed to thinking only in dots and lines and a little bit in areas does not defeat the fact that we live in omni-directional space-time and that a four dimensional universe provides ample individual freedoms for any contingencies.

So, planners, architects, and engineers, take the initiative. Go to work, and above all co-operate and don't hold back on one another or try to gain at the expense of another. Any success in such lopsidedness will be increasingly short-lived. These are the synergetic rules that evolution is employing and trying to make clear to us. They are not man-made laws. They are the infinitely accommodative laws of the intellectual integrity governing universe.[2]

The preceeding material has been excerpted from the work of Dr. R. Buckminster Fuller[1,2] with permission of the author.

REFERENCES

1. American Scholar, Spring, 1968.
2. *Operating Manual for Spaceship Earth*, S.I.V. Press, Carbordale, Ill. 1969.

R. Buckminster Fuller
Southern Illinois University

THERMAL EFFECTS ON FISH ECOLOGY

Of all environmental factors that influence aquatic organisms, temperature is the most all-pervasive. There is always an environmental temperature while other factors may or may not be present to exert their effects. Fish are, for all practical purposes, thermal conformers, or obligate poikilotherms. That is, they are able to exert little significant influence on maintaining a certain body temperature by specialized metabolic or behavioral means. Their body temperature thus fluctuates nearly in concert with the temperature of their aquatic medium (although particularly large, actively-moving fish such as tuna have deep muscle temperatures slightly higher than the water). Intimate contact at the gills of body fluids with the outside water and the high specific heat of water provide a very efficient heat exchanger that insures this near identity of internal and external temperatures.

Every response of fish, from incubation of the egg to feeding activity, digestive and metabolic processes, reproduction, geographic distribution, and even survival, proceeds within a thermal range dictated by the immediate environment. As human activities change this thermal environment, such as through deforestation, damming or thermal discharges from power stations, the activities of indigenous fish species must also change. Depending upon the magnitude and rates of the thermal changes, there may be minor readjustments of the rates of metabolism and growth, or major changes in the distribution of species and of the functioning of the affected aquatic ecosystems.

In our recent environmental awareness, we have coined the phrase "thermal pollution" for extensive thermal changes to natural aquatic environments that are believed to be detrimental to desired fish populations. The key to controlling "thermal pollution" is a firm understanding of how temperature affects fish, and of the circumstances that truly constitute pollution.

The subject of thermal effects on fishes has been given critical scientific review periodically over the past 25 years. (e.g. Fry, 1947; Bullock, 1955; Brett, 1956; Fry, 1964; Fry, 1967 and Brett, 1970). Scientific knowledge as a basis for controlling pollution is clearly more advanced in this area than than for almost any other environmental factor. This knowledge has been applied to the context of thermal modifications by electricity generating stations in two symposium volumes (Parker and Krenkel, 1969; Krenkel and Parker, 1969) and by Cairns (1968), Clark (1969), Parker and Krenkel (1969) and Coutant (1970 and 1972). The voluminous scientific literature on temperature effects on fishes may be easily searched for specific information in bibliographies by Kennedy and Mihursky (1967), Raney and Menzel (1969) and annual literature reviews by Coutant (1968, 1969, 1970, 1971) and Coutant and Goodyear (1972). Readers seeking more than a general review are advised to read these materials.

While fish must conform to water temperature, they have evolved mechanisms other than body temperature regulation to deal with vicissitudes of temperature fluctuations that occur geographically, seasonally and daily. That such mechanisms exist became apparent when fish physiologists realized that at any one temperature a fish may survive or die, be hyperactive or be numbed into activity, be stimulated to migrate or be passive, be sexually mature or remain immature, all depending upon the state of previous temperature exposures. Temperature affects organisms not only by absolute level (as in physics and chemistry) but also by change. Like light, temperature can exert effects through daily or seasonal patterns that exhibit a special quality beyond that of absolute level*.

The functional properties of temperature acting on fish can be summarized as follows: Temperature can act as a lethal agent that kills the fish directly, as a stressing agent that destroys the fish indirectly, as a controlling factor that sets the pace of metabolism and development, as a limiting factor that restricts activity and distribution, as a masking factor that interacts with other environmental factors by blocking or altering their potential expression, and as a directing agent in gradients

*Clear distinction must be made between *heat* which is a quantitative measure of energy of molecular motion that is dependant upon the mass of an object or body of water and *temperature* which is a measure (unrelated to mass) of energy intensity. Organisms respond to temperature, not to heat.

that stimulate sensory perception and orient activity. Each of these properties can be visualized as acting on two levels—on the individual fish and on the population of any one fish species.

Temperature as a Lethal Agent

Mass mortalities of fish in nature have often been reported, but usually the causes are obscure. Fish rarely die in places and at times when proper field instrumentation is operating or when trained observers are at hand. Many deaths probably go unnoticed, for scavengers may act quickly or water currents disperse carcasses (particularly of small fishes). The most common reports are of cold kills brought about by particularly severe winters or rapid drops in temperature (e.g. summaries by Brett, 1970). It is well known among fishery biologists that the abundance of a species reproduced in any one year varies tremendously, a fact that many scientists have attributed in part to deaths from unfavorable temperatures at early life stages when the fish are too small to be recognized as constituting a "fish kill".

Studies of temperature tolerance in fishes began in the last century. The early method of determining the lethal end-point (generally the cessation of opercular movements) by slow heating or cooling was generally supplanted in the 1940's by a more precise method of direct transfer to a series of preset temperatures in which the rates of dying of individual fish and the statistical variation among many individuals could be obtained. These experiments demonstrated the importance of recent past history of the fish, both the controlled holding temperature imposed in the laboratory prior to testing (acclimaton), and the seasonal environmental temperature when fish were tested directly from field collections (acclimatization).

These experiments also showed that each species of fish (and often each distinct life stage of one species) has a characteristic range of temperature that it will tolerate that is established by internal biochemical adjustments made while at the previous holding temperature (Figure 1). Ordinarily (for purposes of comparison) the upper and lower ends of this range are defined by survival of 50% of a sample of individuals similar in size, health and other factors, for a specified length of time, often one week. The tolerance range is shifted upward by long-term holding (acclimation) in warmer water, and downward by acclimation to cooler water. This accommodation is limited, however, at the lower end by freezing point of water (for species in

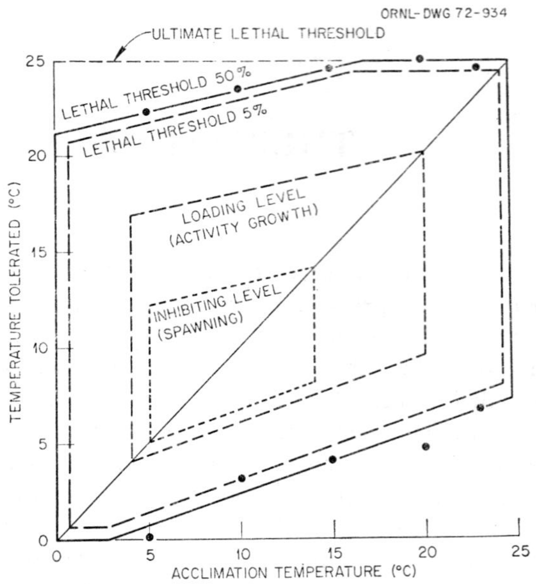

Figure 1 Upper and lower lethal temperatures for young sockeye salmon with various acclimation temperatures, plotted to show the ranges of tolerance, and within these ranges more restrictive requirements for activity, growth or spawning. (Reproduced by permission from Coutant, 1972.)

temperate latitudes) and at the upper end by an ultimate lethal threshold. The graphic representation (Figure 1) is a geometric figure for which an area can be computed. The areas (as degrees squared) provide conveneient measures of the relative overall sensitivity of tolerance among different species and life stages (a small area or zone on the graph signified high thermal sensitivity).

It is not surprising that rough species such as carp and goldfish were found to have large thermal tolerance zones.

Outside the thermal tolerance zone, premature death is inevitable and its onset is a function of both temperature and time of exposure (thermal resistance). Death occurs more rapidly the farther the temperature is from the threshold (Figure 2), an attribute common to the action of toxicants, pharmaceuticals, and radiation. The duration of survival of half of a test population of fish at extreme temperatures can be expressed as an equation based on experimental data for each acclimation temperature:

$$\log \text{survival time}_{(\text{min})} = a + b\,(\text{Temp}_{(°\text{C})}),$$

in which a and b are intercept and slope of the linear regression lines in Figure 2. In some cases the time–temperature relationship is more complex than this semilogarithmic model, but this expression is the most generally applicable and is the one most generally accepted by the scientific

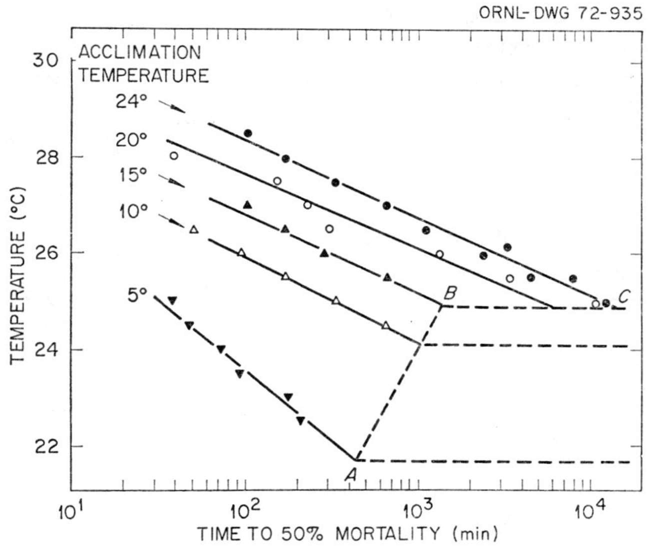

Figure 2 Median resistance times to high temperatures among young chinook salmon acclimated to the temperatures indicated. Line A–B denotes rising lethal threshold levels with increasing acclimation temperature. This rise ceases at higher acclimation temperatures. (Reproduced by permission from Coutant, 1972.)

community. The equation defines the average rate of dying at any extreme temperature.

The thermal resistance equations allow prediction of fish survival (or death) in zones where human activity induces extreme high temperatures. For example, juvenile salmon and trout were found to pass through warm mixing zones of thermal discharges to the Columbia River during their seaward migration (Becker *et al.*, 1971). The thermal exposure was a complex pattern of rapid temperature rise (often to temperatures beyond the tolerance zone) followed by a slow decline as the heated effluent mixed with the cooler river. By using the equation-expressed rates of dying at each of the temperatures briefly experienced, and the length of time the fish were exposed to each incremental temperature, the ability of the fish to survive the exposure was estimated and compared with actual field exposures. Similar predictions can be made for proposed thermal discharges, and corrective engineering can be selected before the project is constructed. Similar predictions can be made for circumstances where fish may become acclimated to warm water (e.g. in a discharge canal) and then be cooled rapidly and face a potential cold kill. This predictive methodology is further described by Coutant (1972).

Temperature as a Stressing Factor

Death need not come to fish directly from temperature or its change. In natural ecological systems death often comes as the result of a secondary agent acting upon a fish weakened by some stress such as temperature. This secondary agent is often disease or predator. A potentially lethal high temperature will, for example, induce loss of equilibrium before the physiological death point is reached, and equilibrium loss (going "belly-up") in a natural environment is an open invitation to predators. In fact, ongoing research indicates that stress from relatively small temperature changes (both up and down) will induce selective predation on the stressed fish. The effect appears to follow a time-temperature pattern similar to that for death, with stress appearing after shorter exposures and lower temperatures than required for death directly. The predictability developed for lethal responses can be applied to these stressing conditions as well, if we wish to prevent "ecological death."

Temperature as a Controlling Factor

a) Metabolism

Within the zone of thermal tolerance of any species (Figure 1), the most important contributor to survival and success in nature is the dynamic cycle of energy intake, conversion and utilization for activity, development (the differentiation of cells) and growth (multiplicaton of cells and storage of energy reserves). Since the time that Fry (1947) observed that environmental temperature controls energy metabolism, there has been extensive research

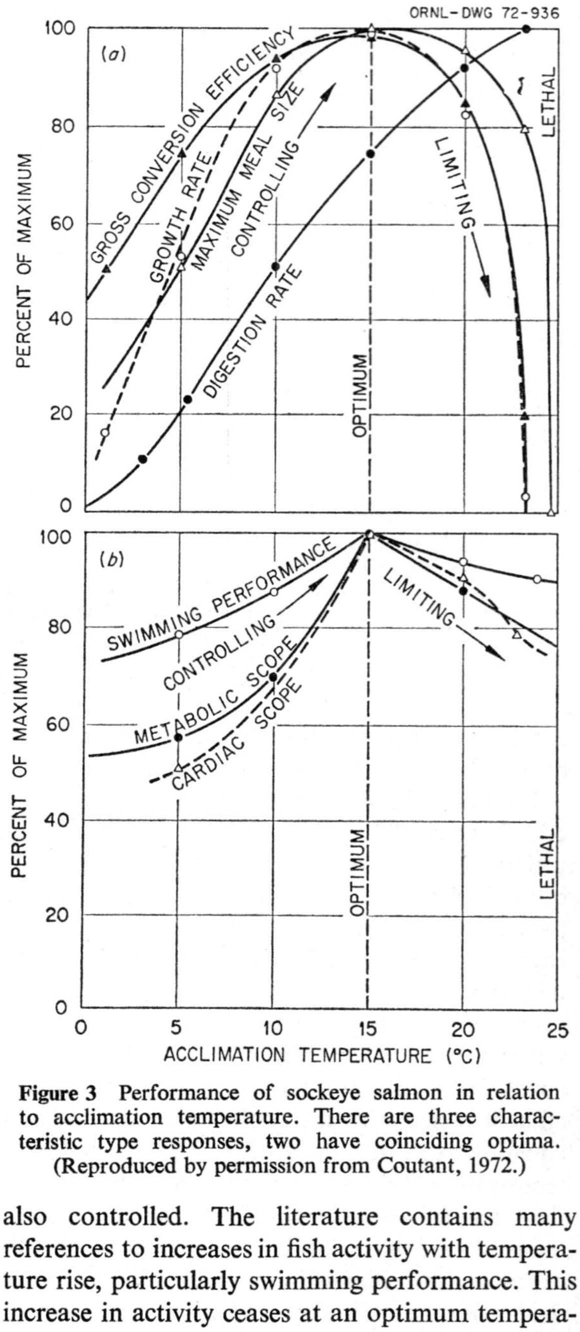

Figure 3 Performance of sockeye salmon in relation to acclimation temperature. There are three characteristic type responses, two have coinciding optima. (Reproduced by permission from Coutant, 1972.)

in this area of fish physiology and biochemistry. This research has yielded important generalizations about the temperature responses of fish, and the physiological and biochemical "reasons" for these responses.

Metabolic processes are basically chemical in character. Among the most significant vital chemical reactions are the actions of the living catalysts (enzymes) which control the oxidation of organic food materials. Most enzymes show an optimum temperature at which they reach a maximum rate of catalytic activity. This is sometimes higher than the upper lethal threshold for the whole fish. The aggregate of many metabolic reactions also exhibits a temperature optimum, or point of maximum rate, which is often remarkably similar for various functions involved, for example digestion, development and locomotion (Figure 3). Through genetic selection, the optimum has become different for any two species. Below the optimum, the maximum rate possible is controlled by water temperature. These rates can be quite different for various functions. It should be noted that the optimum temperature and the maximum metabolic rates at any given temperature may be quite different during embryonic development and during the lifetime of the fully-developed fish.

Of the various methods that have been used to measure metabolic rates (see Brett, 1971), the most often measured has been the rate of oxygen consumption. This provides an instantaneous measure of enzyme activity so long as no oxygen debt, or delayed oxidation of certain chemical compounds, is accumulated. Three levels of metabolic rates have been commonly recognized for fish: (1) *Standard metabolic rate*, representing that fraction which is just necessary to maintain vital functions of a resting fish, (2) *routine metabolic rate* which also includes the energy demands of routine, spontaneous activity, and (3) *active metabolic rate* which represents the maximum level of oxygen consumed by a working (swimming) fish. The amount of energy available for active work (or growth) is termed the *metabolic scope* for activity, and it is the difference between active and standard metabolic rates. Each of these is related to temperature in a different way. The most important measure for a fish's ability to cope with the overall environmental demands in the metabolic scope, which has an optimum temperature (Figure 3).

b) Activity

As temperature controls the metabolic rate which provides energy for activity, that activity, then, is also controlled. The literature contains many references to increases in fish activity with temperature rise, particularly swimming performance. This increase in activity ceases at an optimum temperature that appears to coincide with the temperature of maximum metabolic scope (Figure 3).

c) Growth

Temperature is one of the principal environmental factors controlling growth of fishes, others being light and salinity. There recently has been a considerable amount of laboratory experimentation to separate these often-correlated influences on growth.

Whenever there is abundant food, increasing temperature enhances growth rate up to an optimum (Figure 3) above which there is a decline. Low temperatures generally retard growth, although organisms residing habitually in cold areas such as the arctic have evolved metabolic compensations that allow good growth even at low extremes. Optimum growth appears to occur at about the same temperature as maximum metabolic scope. Restriction of food generally forces the optimum growth temperature toward cooler levels and restricts the maximum amount of growth attainable (Brett *et al.*, 1969).

Temperature as a Limiting Factor

As the previous discussion implied, there comes a point (the optimum) on a rising temperature scale at which increased temperature no longer speeds processes but begins to limit them. In contrast to the gradual increase in performance with temperature rise exhibited at sub-optimum temperatures, the responses at levels above optimum often show a precipitous decline (Figure 3). Performance is often reduced to zero several degrees below temperatures which would be directly lethal in the relatively short period of one week. One of the most significant of thermal limitations from the standpoint of a fish's overall success in his environment is upon net growth rate for the population. If a majority of individuals of the species cannot sustain positive growth, then the population is likely to succumb. While it is probably unnecessary for populations to grow at maximum rates, there must be a thermal maximum for prolonged exposures of any fish species that is less that the established lethal levels at which growth limitation becomes critical for continued population survival. The requirement for sustained growth may be one of the most important mechanisms of geographic limitations of species. Intensive research in this area is needed to establish rational upper temperature standards for water bodies.

Temperature as a Masking Factor

All other environmental factors, such as light, current, or chemical toxins, act upon fish simultaneously with a temperature regime. With so much of a fish's metabolic activity dependent upon temperature, both immediate and previous, it is little wonder that responses to other environmental factors change with differing temperature. The interactions are seemingly infinite, and the general impression that one obtains is that temperature is masking a clear-cut definition of the response pattern to any other environmental parameter.

This pessimism overstates the case, however. Two-factor experimentation is routine today, and interactions of temperature and a variety of pollutants are now becoming clear. For instance, research in Britain has shown that the effect of increased temperature on the toxicity of poisons to fish is generally to reduce their time of survival in relatively high lethal concentrations, but median *threshold* concentrations for death may not be markedly changed, or may even be increased (Ministry of Technology, 1968). An increase in temperature of 8 °C reduced the 48 hr LC_{50} (median lethal concentration) to rainbow trout by a factor of 1.8 for zinc (i.e. increased toxicity) but increased it (i.e. reduced toxicity) by about 1.2 for phenol, by 2.0 for undissociated ammonia, and by 2.5 for cyanide. The effect of temperature on ammonia toxicity is further expressed by changing the dissociation of ammonia in water and thus the percentage of actively toxic ammonia available. For estuarine and marine fishes temperature–salinity interactions are of special importance, and are receiving increased research attention.

Temperature as a Directing Agent

a) Gradient responses

Numerous observations of fish in horizontal and vertical thermal gradients both in the laboratory and under field conditions have demonstrated preferred or selected temperatures. There are wide differences among species, and some differences among life stages of any one species. The preferred temperature is dependent upon recent prior thermal history, but continuous exposure to a gradient (in which metabolic acclimation gradually takes place) results in a "final preferendum". Preferred ranges have been shown to coincide with the species-specific optimum temperature for maximum metabolic scope for activity, and thus the directive mechanism would appear to have survival value.

Many fish have a delicate sense for temperature discrimination. The threshold for teleosts (bony fish) appears to be on the order of ± 0.05°C, although elasmobranchs (sharks, rays) have a threshold quite a bit higher (about ± 0.8°C). Orientation responses have generally been elicted by differences of about 0.5°C (Brett, 1971). Many fish are very capable of detecting undesirable temperatures and of avoiding water masses that are potentially detrimental to them.

b) Directive cues

A mechanistic response to temperature gradients is often overridden by seasonal influences and special behavior patterns involving temperature-orientated activities such as migration. The seasonal response to a specific temperature has been shown to have great importance for reproductive activity of a large number of fishes.

The sequence of events relating to gonad maturation, spawning migration, courting behavior, release of gametes, and subsequent development of egg and embryo represents one of the most complex phenomena in nature. While temperature cues appear critical in many cases, the interactions with other factors such as seasonal light intensity are still not clearly understood. Advance or retardation of reproduction has been closely related to temperature of the months preceeding spawning in such fish as the cod *Gadus morhua*. The difference in the effect of temperature governing a rate phenomenon (controlling or limiting) and temperature acting as or releasing factor is clearly shown in cases where falling temperatures induce spawning, as in the Pacific salmon.

Temperature appears to confine spawning to a narrower range than most other functions. The average range for spawning of marine fish is one-quarter to one-third that for the lethal range (Brett, 1971).

Summary

From this brief introduction, we can see that temperature is probably the preeminent master factor in the lives of fish. No study of fish in relation to their environment ("fish ecology") would be meaningful without consideration of thermal relationships. This review can direct the curious to more comprehensive treatises. From a different perspective, there are few environmental modifications that man could make to aquatic systems that would be so assured of causing some ecological change as temperature. Within limits, fish possess effective mechanisms for adapting to thermal changes, for such changes are a normal part of their existance. Man must be careful not to exceed these limits, however, if he wishes to preserve a productive commercial and recreational fishery.

REFERENCES

Becker, C. D., C. C. Coutant and E. F. Prentice, 1971. Experimental drifts of juvenile salmonids through effluent discharges at Hanford. Part II. 1969 Drifts and Conclusions. USAEC Rept. BNWL-1529, Battelle Northwest, Richland, Washington.

Brett, J. R., 1956. Some principles in the thermal requirements of fishes. *Quarterly Review of Biology* **31**(2): 75–87.

Brett, J. R., 1970. Temperature—Animals—Fishes. O. Kinne, Ed., in *Marine Ecology*, Vol. 1. Environmental Factors, Part 1. pp. 515–560.

Brett, J. R., 1971. Energetic responses of salmon to temperature. A study of some thermal relations in the physiology and freshwater ecology of sockeye salmon (*Oncorhynchus nerka*). *American Zoologist* **11**: 99–113.

Brett, J. R., J. E. Shelbourn and C. T. Shoop, 1969. Growth rate and body composition of fiingerling sockeye salmon, *Oncorhynchus nerka*, in relation to temperature and ration size. *J. Fish. Res. Bd. Canada* **26**: 2363–2394.

Bullock, T. H., 1955. Compensation for temperature in the metabolism and activity of poikilotherms. *Biol. Rev.* **30**(3): 311–342.

Cairns, John, Jr., 1968. We're in hot water. *Scientist and Citizen* **10**(8): 187–198.

Clark, J. R., 1969. Thermal pollution and aquatic life. *Sci. Amer.* **220**(3): 18–27.

Coutant, C. C., 1968. Thermal pollution—Biological effects a review of the literature of 1967. *J. Water Poll. Cont. Fed.* **40**(6): 1047–1052.

Coutant, C. C., 1969. Thermal pollution—Biological effects a review of the literature of 1968. Battelle-Northwest, Richland, Wash.; BNWL-SA-2376, *J. Water Poll.* Cont. Fed. **41**(6): 1036–1053.

Coutant, C. C., 1970. Thermal Pollution—Biological effects a review of the literature of 1969. Battelle-Northwest, Richland, Wash.; BNWL-SA-3255, *J. Water Poll. Cont. Fed.* **42**(6): 1025–1057.

Coutant, C. C., 1970. Biological aspects of thermal pollution. I. Entrainment and discharge land effects. CRC Critical Reviews in *Environmental Control* **1**(3): 341–381.

Coutant, C. C., 1971. Thermal pollution—Biological effects. In: A review of literature of 1970 on wastewater and water pollution control. *J. Water Poll. Cont. Fed.* 43(6): 1292–1334.

Coutant, C. C., 1972. Biological Aspects of Thermal Pollution. II. Scientific basis for water temperature standards at power plants. CRC Crit. Rev. in *Envir. Control* (in press).

Coutant, C. C. and C. P. Goodyear 1972. Thermal effects. In A Review of the literature of 1971 on wastewater and water pollution control. *J. Water. Poll. Cont. Fed.* **44**(6): 1250–1294.

Fry, F. E. J., 1947. Effects of the environment on animal activity. Univ. Toronto Stud. Biol. Ser. No. 55. Publ. Ont. Fish. Res. Lab. No. 68: 1–62.

Fry, F. E. J., 1964. Animals in aquatic environments: Fishes (Chap. 44). Handbood of Physiology, Section 4: Adaption to the Environment. Amer. Physiol Soc., Wash. D. C.

Fry, F. E. J., 1967. Responses of vertebrate poikilotherms to temperature. In *Thermobiology*, A. H. Rose (ed.) Academic Press, London. pp. 375–409.

Kennedy, V. S. and J. A. Mihursky, 1967. Bibliography on the effects of temperature in the aquatic environment. Univ. of Maryland, Nat. Res. Inst. Cont. No. 326. 89 p.

Krenkel, P. A. and F. L. Parker, 1969. *Biological Aspects of Thermal Pollution*, Vanderbilt Univ. Press, Nashville, Tennessee.

Ministry of Technology, U. K., 1968. Water pollution research 1967. p. 63.

Parker, F. L. and P. A. Krenkel, 1969b. Thermal pollution: Status of the art. Dept. of Envir. and Water Res. Eng., Vanderbilt Univ. Rept. No. 3.

Parker, F. L. and P. A. Krenkel, 1969a. *Engineering Aspects of Thermal Pollution*. Vanderbilt Univ. Press, Nashville, Tennessee.

Raney, E. C. and B. W. Menzel, 1969. Heated effluents and effects on aquatic life with emphasis on fishes: A bibliography. Ichthyological Associates Bull. No. 2 prepared with Cornell Univ. Water Resources and Marine Sciences Center and Philadelphia Electric Company. 470 p.

CHARLES C. COUTANT
Oak Ridge National Laboratory

U

URBAN AIR POLLUTION MODELING†

I. Introduction

The undesirable effects of air pollution emphasize the need for understanding the role played by the atmosphere in affecting the levels of pollutant concentration. With a constant rate of emission into the atmosphere, concentrations on the ground may be 1000 times greater under the poorest conditions than under the most favorable ones. For this reason, the role of meteorology in air pollution has been receiving increasing attention.

A mathematical air pollution model may serve to gain insight into the relation between meteorological elements and air pollution. It may be likened to a transfer function where the input consists of both the combination of weather conditions and the total emission from sources of pollution, and the output is the level of pollutant concentration observed in time and space. The mathematical model takes into consideration not only the nature of the sources, (whether they are distributed or point sources) and the levels of concentration at the receptors, but also the atmospheric processes which take place in transforming the concentrations at the sources of emission into those observed at the receptor or monitoring station. Among such processes are photochemical action, adsorption either on aerosols or ground objects, and of course, eddy diffusion.

There are a number of areas in which a valid and practical model may be of considerable value. For example, the operators of an industrial plant which will emit sulfur dioxide want to locate it in a particular community. Knowing the emission rate as a function of time, the distribution of wind speed, wind direction, and atmospheric stability, the location of SO_2-sensitive industrial plants, and the spatial distribution of residential areas, it is possible to calculate the effect the new plant will have on the community. As air quality standards are developed, one may intelligently place limits on the amount of emission allowed to any industrial group.

In large cities, such as Chicago, Los Angeles, or New York during strong anticyclonic conditions with light winds and low dispersion rates, pollution levels may rise to a point where health becomes affected; eyes smart, hospital admissions for respiratory ailments increase, and in some cases even death results. To minimize the effects of air pollution episodes, advisories or warnings are issued by government officials. Tools for determining, even only a few hours in advance, that unusually severe air pollution conditions will arise are invaluable. The availability of a workable urban air pollution model plus a forecast of the wind and stability conditions could provide the necessary information.

In long range planning for a growing community, it may be desirable to zone some areas for industrial activity and others for residential use in order to minimize the effects of air pollution. Not only the average sized community, but also the larger megalopolis could profitably utilize the ability to compute concentrations resulting from given emissions using a model and suitable weather data. In addition, the establishment of an air pollution climatology for a city or state which can be used in the application of the model would represent a step forward in assuring clean air.

For all these reasons, a number of groups have been devoting their attention to the development of mathematical models for determining how the atmosphere disperses materials.

II. History of Mathematical Model Development

The pioneer in this work is Dr. Francois N. Frenkiel[1] who developed a mathematical model for

† Sponsored by the U.S. Energy Research and Development Administration.

the city of Los Angeles. After Frenkiel's early work, the problem was taken up by the Meteorology Group of the Public Health Service at the Robert A. Taft Sanitary Engineering Center in Cincinnati, Ohio under the direction of Mr. Robert A. McCormick. The Meteorology Group of the Robert A. Taft Sanitary Engineering Center is now Office of Air Progress of the Environmental Protection Agency located at Research Triangle Park, North Carolina.

Turner[2] laid the foundation for daily operational models in his development of the Nashville model. Later this group performed an extensive air pollution study of the St. Louis area. Turner extended and improved his Nashville model for application to this investigation. Pooler[3] has carried out nine series of measurements over St. Louis to study the nature of urban atmospheric diffusion. Clarke[4], another member of the team, used measurements over Cincinnati to produce a rather simple model for this area. Still another group, Miller and Holzworth,[5] developed a new model which depends heavily on the mixing layer concept. Schiermeier[6] carried out further tests and refinements on the Clarke model for St. Louis, Kussman[7,8] tested and refined both the Clarke model and Miller and Holzworth model for New York City.

Simultaneously, work on air pollution models progressed at a number of universities: (1) a group at the University of Florida[9] developed a model for the city of Jacksonville, Florida, (2) Pennsylvania State University[10] developed a model for Johnstown, Pennsylvania, (3) New York University[11] developed a very sophisticated model for New York City. New York City has over 100 wind measuring stations. This group obtained substantial amounts of data on the variation of SO_2 as well as temperature with height by means of a helicopter.

An advance in this problem resulted from the work at the Travelers Research Center,[12] performed by Professor Franklin I. Badgley, on leave from the University of Washington, Dr. Glenn Hilst and other staff members. They developed a model for the state of Connecticut. Concentration measurements are currently being obtained to test this model. The theory was developed to a rather high degree. Hilst and Bowne[13] of the Travelers Research Center carried out another study to develop a diffusion model over Fort Wayne, Indiana based on an elevated line source emitted from an aircraft.

An urban model study outside of the United States has been that of Fortak for the city of Bremen.[14] He also was concerned with the SO_2 problem.

A listing of the investigations dealing with urban air pollution models on which this paper is based is given in Table I. The tabulation gives the authors, locations and pollutants used. To allow an assessment of the magnitude of each program, Tables II, III and IV are presented. Table II shows the duration of the study, the date of publication, and information on the amount of data obtained. Table III provides information on the size of the meteorological and pollution monitoring stations, while Table IV presents characteristic features of the model: sample duration, nature of the grid networks, and effective plume heights.

One of the most extensive efforts in the development of an urban air pollution model for SO_2 is that of the Argonne National Laboratory made in collaboration with the City of Chicago and sponsored both by the Department of Health, Education, and Welfare and the Atomic Energy Commission. Available for this study are over three years of data consisting of 15-minute readings from eight stations providing information on SO_2 concentrations, wind speed, and wind direction. Details and the results on its program are discussed elsewhere,[15–18]

The above models were designed to provide daily

TABLE I
Investigators, Locations and Pollutants of Urban Air Pollution Models

Investigators	Location	Pollutant
Frenkiel	Los Angeles, California	Number of contaminants including ozone. (All not specified.)
Turner	Nashville, Tennessee	SO_2
Clarke	Cincinnati, Ohio	SO_2, NO_x
Fortak	Bremen, Germany	SO_2
Hilst and Bowne	Fort Wayne, Indiana	Fluorescent particles
Pooler	St. Louis, Missouri	Fluorescent particles
Miller and Holzworth	Washington, D.C. Los Angeles, Calif. Nashville, Tennessee	NO_x NO_x SO_2
Davidson	New York, New York	SO_2
Koogler, Shotes, Danis and Harding	Jacksonville, Fla.	SO_2
Panofsky and Prasad	Johnstown, Pa.	Particulates
Hilst, Badgley, Yocum and Bowne	Connecticut	Hydrocarbons, CO, NO_x, SO_2 and particulates
Lamb and Neiburger	Los Angeles, Calif.	Carbon monoxide (CO)
Martin	St. Louis, Mo.	SO_2
Roberts, Croke and Kennedy	Chicago, Ill.	SO_2

TABLE II

Investigations, Amounts of Data, Period of Study and Publication Dates of Urban Air Pollution Models

Investigator	Date of publication	Period of study	No. of observations pollutants
Frenkiel	April 1956	Sept. 1956	
Turner	February 1964	Oct. 1958–Mar. 1959	1036 24-hr readings 2710 2-hr readings
Clarke	September 1964	Jan.–May 1962	33 days
Fortak	February 1966	Jan.–Dec. 1962	
Hilst and Bowne	July 1966	Mar. 1964–Feb. 1966	21 experiment periods (days) 70 releases
Pooler	December 1966	May 1963–Mar. 1965	43 experiments
Miller and Holzworth	January 1967	a. Los Angeles, May 1963 b. Nashville, Oct. 1958–Mar. 1959 c. Washington, D.C., 1962–1964	35 test days 31 test days 41 test days
Davidson	March 1967	1963–1967	9 experiment periods 5 days per period
Koogler, Sholtes, Danis and Harding	April 1967	Dec. 1965–Jan. 1966	12 days, 111 observations
Panofsky and Prasad	June 1967	Oct. 1964–Nov. 1964 July 1965–Aug. 1965 Oct. 1965–Nov. 1965 Jan. 1966–Feb. 1966	
Hilst, Badgley, Yocum and Bowne	October 1967	(Source inventory—1967)	None
Lamb and Neiburger	1971	15-hour period on Sept. 23, 1966	Hourly CO concentrations
Martin	June 1971	Not stated; model applied to seasonal averages	Not stated
Roberts, Croke and and Kennedy	1970	Jan. 1967	2328 hourly average values of SO_2 concentration

TABLE III

Investigators, Monitoring Stations and Monitoring Grids of Urban Air Pollution Models

Investigator	Number of monitoring stations	Micrometeorological measurements
Frenkiel	1	Used available published data, no special measurements.
Turner	32 stations making 24-hour measurements 7 stations making 2-hour measurements	Wind speed and direction at 10 meters—four stations.
Clarke	1	
Fortak	None	Weather Service—Bremen Airport, no special instrumentation.
Hilst and Bowne	25 sequential samplers 250 rotorod samplers 10 Gelman tape samplers 13 rotorods on 244-meter tower 23 rotorods on tethered barrage balloon 4 rotorods on 61-meter tower	Wind and temperature measurements at ten stations: six in the city and four in the rural surroundings. One 244-meter tower with temperature and wind measurements at 12.2, 30.5, 61, 91 and 213 meters; one 61-meter tower with wind and temperature measurements at 15.2, 22.9, 30.5, 47.2 and 53 meters; two wiresondes and one modified radiosonde; one aircraft to measure turbulence and also temperature by conventional and infrared means.
Pooler	60 rotorod samplers 30 membrane filter samplers 10 drum-pulsed samplers	Three stations at periphery of city with aerovanes and hygrothermographs on KMOX–TV tower; three levels for measurements of wind, temperature, and vertical temperature gradient. Wind measurements with pilot balloons and also at tracer release site. Free and tethered radiosonde soundings, tetroon soundings.
Miller and Holzworth	Los Angeles, 9 NO_x stations Nashville, 7 SO_2 stations Washington, 1 CAMP station	Weather Bureau—surface and upper air sounding of temperature and wind for each city.
Koogler, Sholtes, Danis and Harding	11	Five wind stations, 1 TV tower for temperature at 100, 200, 300, 450 and 750 feet.
Davidson	32 fixed ground stations 3 mobile ground stations 1 helicopter 1 helicopter	Over 100 anemometers, pibals and helicopter.
Panofsky and Prasad	10	Two 150-ft. TV towers for wind and temperature. One 75-ft. tower for wind. Two additional anemometers—airway station data.

TABLE III (*continued*)

Investigator	Number of monitoring stations	Micrometeorological measurements
Hilst, Badgley, Yocum and Bowne	None	Weather Bureau stations and Department of Defense stations in Connecticut and adjoining states.
Lamb and Neiburger	13	Wind speed and direction at 32 stations; morning sounding to determine inversion base altitude.
Martin	40	Weather Service joint frequency distribution of hourly meteorological conditions; mixing heights from nearest rawinsonde station.
Roberts, Croke and Kennedy	8	Wind speed and direction from eight monitoring stations; standard weather data from O'Hare and Midway airports; stability, wind speed and direction, solar radiation from Argonne National Laboratory tower; radiosonde data from Peoria, Ill. and Green Bay, Wisc. to determine mixing layer height.

TABLE IV
Time per Sample, Grid Size, and Effective Plume Rise

Investigator	Time per sample (hrs.)	Grid (miles)	Effective plume height
Frenkiel	—	—	—
Turner	24 2	9×11 mile monitoring grid 17×16 mile inventory grid	20 meters
Clarke	2-hr values used to obtain 24-hr averages	Irregular source grid Single monitoring station Computing grid: 1. 22.5 sectors of a circle with monitoring station at center and radius 1 km. 2. 22.5 annular sectors bounded by arcs of concentric circle with 1 km and 4 km radii; also for 4 and 10 km radii.	30 meters—SO_2 20 metres—NO_x
Fortak	—	Source grid: 1 km square subdivided into 100 subsquares. Computing grid: 480×800 meters rectangularly arranged in a 50×50 grid network.	Domestic—15 m Small emitters—25 m (less than 1 kgm/hr)
Hilst and Bowne	10 Gelman tape samplers—5 min 25 sequential samplers—30 min Rotorod samplers—variable (depends on wind speed)	5 parallel lines, 1/2 mile between sampling, 50 samples per line.	—
Pooler	1	Group I arcs: 0.5, 2 and 4.5 mi with 6° spacing Group II arcs: 1.25, 2.5 and 5 mi with 6° spacing Group III arcs: 10 mi with 3° spacing In later experiments, the 4.5 and 5 mi had 3° spacing.	—
Miller and Holzworth	Los Angeles-: 2hr Nashville: 2-hr Washington, D.C.: 4-hr	Los Angeles: Details of Monitoring Grid not given Same as Turner's for 2-hr samples Single CAMP station	—
Davidson	1	1-mi square, 50×50 sq. mi	Space heating, hot water 30.5 m
Koogler, Sholtes, Danis and Harding	24	1-mi square, 15×15 sq. mi	Δh w $\frac{1.5V_s d+aQ_H}{u}$ at 2000 m For distance from source >2000 m $\Delta h = \frac{1.5V_s d+aQ_H}{u}\frac{x^{2/3}}{2000}$
Panofsky and Prasad	12 12	—	—
Hilst, Badgley, Yocum and Bowne	—	5000-ft squares over area of State of Connecticut	—
Lamb and Neiburger	1	107 line sources, 2.5 miles long; 198 rectangular areas about 2×2 miles	1 meter (auto exhaust only)

TABLE IV (*continued*)

Investigator	Time per sampler (hrs)	Grid (miles)	Effective plume height
Martin	24	36 point sources; 204 area sources about 1×1 miles.	For area sources: unstated average height. For point sources: actual stack height plus plume rise correction as obtained from Holland with modification suggested by Briggs.
Roberts, Croke and Kennedy	1-hr averages based on four 15-minute values	56 point sources; about 222 area sources 1×1 miles.	For point sources: actual stack height for wind speeds over 15 mph; otherwise, $\Delta H = KQ_s^{1/4}/U$, where ΔH is plume rise (ft) Q_s is heat emission rate from stack (BTU/hr) U is wind speed (mph) at height of stack and 0.870 (unstable—Class 3) $K =$ 0.354 (neutral—Class 4) 0.222 (stable—Class 5) For area sources: varying average heights (dependent on source types).

or hourly values of concentrations at selected points over a city. Models to provide monthly or seasonal values of pollution concentrations have also been devised. Pooler,[19] Meade and Pasquill,[20] and Martin[21] describe such models. Pooler calculated monthly averages of SO_2 concentration for Nashville using a network of 123 lead peroxide candles. Meade and Pasquill had available the data from a 15-station network also equipped with lead peroxide candles. Their model determined seasonal averages of SO_2 concentrations in the vicinity of the Staythorpe electric power station in England. Martin used 40 stations from St. Louis to validate his model.

III. Components of an Urban Air Pollution Model

A mathematical urban air pollution model comprises four essential components. The first is the source inventory. One must know what materials, how much, from what location, and at what rate they are being injected into the atmosphere or what is being brought into a community across the boundaries. The second involves the measurement of contaminant concentration at representative parts of the city, sampled properly in time as well as space. The third is the meteorological network, and the fourth is the meteorological algorithm or mathematical formula which describes how the source input is transformed into observed values of concentration at the receptors. See Figure 1. The difference between what is actually going on in the atmosphere and what we think goes on, based on our measured sources and our imperfect mathematical formulations as well as our imperfect sampling of air pollution levels, causes discrepancies between the observed and calculated values.

Also of importance is the verification procedure. The remainder of this paper is devoted to these four components and the verification procedures.

Accounts may be found in the literature of a number of investigations which do not have the four components of the mathematical urban air pollution model mentioned above, namely, the source inventory, the mathematical algorithm, the meteorological network, and the monitoring network. Some of these have one or more of the components missing. An example of this kind is the theoretical investigation such as that of Lucas[22] who developed a mathematical technique for determining the pollution levels of sulfur dioxide produced by the thousands of domestic fires in a large city. No measurements are presented to support this study. Another is that of Slade[24] who discusses a megalopolis model. Smith[24] also presented a theoretical model which is essentially an urban box model. Another is that of Bouman and Schmidt,[25] on the growth of pollutant concentrations in the cities during stable conditions. Three case studies, each based on data from a different city, are presented to support these theoretical results. Studies relevant to the urban air pollution problem are the pollution surveys such as the London survey,[26] the Japanese survey,[27] and that of the Capitol region in Connecticut.[28] In these studies, analyses are made

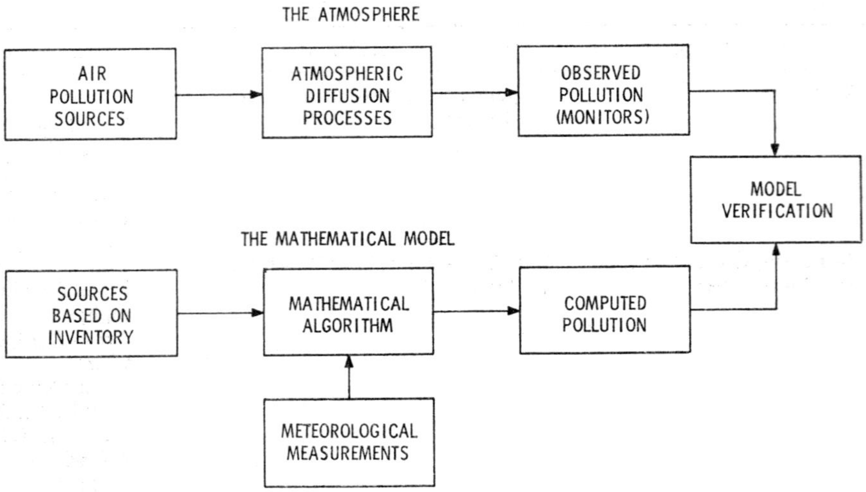

Figure 1 Schematic diagram of an urban air pollution model.

of pollution measurements; and in some cases meteorological as well as source inventory information are available; but in most cases, the mathematical algorith for predicting pollution is absent. Another study of this type is one on suspended particulate and iron concentrations in Windsor, Canada by Munn *et al.*[29] Early work on forecasting urban pollution is described in two papers: one by Scott[30] for Cleveland, Ohio and the other by Kauper *et al.*[31] for Los Angeles, California. A comparison of urban models has been made by Wanta[32] in his refreshing artcle which discussed the relation between meteorology and air pollution.

IV. The Source Inventory

In the development of an urban air pollution model, two types of sources are considered: (1) individual point sources, and (2) distributed sources. The individual point sources are often the large coal-burning power generating station stacks or the stacks of large buildings such as the Chicago Merchandise Mart. Any chimney stack may serve as a point source, but some investigators have placed lower limits on the emission rate of a stack to be considered a point source in the model. Fortak,[14] for example, considers a source as an individual point source if it emits 1 kgm of SO_2 per hour, while Koogler *et al.* uses a 10-kgm-per-hour criterion.[9] In addition, when ground concentrations are calculated from the emission of an elevated point source, the effective stack height must be determined, i.e., the actual stack height plus the additional height due to plume rise.

Information concerning emission rates, emission schedules, or per cent of sufur is customarily obtained by means of a source inventory questionnaire. It is usual to find the answering rate of such questionnaires quite low. A municipality with licensing power, however, has the advantage of being able to force disclosure of information provided by a source inventory questionnaire since the license may be withheld until the desired information is furnished. Merely the awareness of this capability is sufficient to result in gratifying co-operation. The City of Chicago has received a very high percentage of returns from those to whom a source inventory questionnaire was submitted.

Information on distributed sources may be obtained in part from questionnaires, and, in part, from an estimate of the population density. Population density data may be derived from census figures or from an area survey employing aerial photography.

In addition to knowing where the sources are. one must have information on the rate of emission as a function of time. Information on the emission for each hour would be ideal, but nearly always one must settled for much cruder data. Usually one has at his disposal for use in the calcuations only annual or monthly emission rates. Corrections for diurnal patterns may be applied, i.e., more coal is burned in the morning when people arise than during the latter part of the evening when most retire. Roberts[15] has referred to the relationship describing fuel consumption (for domestic or commercial heating) as a function of time, e.g., the hourly variation of coal use, as the "janitor function." Consideration of changes in hourly emission patterns with season is, of course, also essential.

In addition to the classification involving point sources and distributed sources, the source inventory information is often stratified according to broad general categories to serve as a basis for estimating source strengths. The nature of the pollutants—e.g., whether it be sulfur dioxide or lead—influences the grouping. Frenkiel[1] has described his sources as those due to: (1) automobiles, (2) oil and gas heating, (3) incinerators, and (4) industry; Turner[2] has used the categories: (1) residential, (2) commercial, and (3) industrial; the Connecticut model[12] considers these classes: (1) automobiles, (2) home heating, (3) public services, (4) industrial, and (5) electric power generation. (Actually, the Connecticut model had a number of subgroups within these categories.) In general, each investigator used a classification tailored to his needs and one which facilitated estimating the magnitude of the distributed sources.

Source inventory information is difficult to acquire to the necessary level of accuracy; nevertheless, it forms an important component of the urban air pollution model.

V. The Mathematical Equations

Mathematical equations of urban air pollution models describe the processes by which pollutants injected into the atmosphere are diluted. The mathematical algorithm—the backbone of any air pollution model—can be conveniently divided into three major components: (1) the source emissions subroutine, (2) the chemical kinetics subroutine, and (3) the diffusion subroutine which includes meteorological parameters. Although each of these components may be treated as an independent entity for the analysis of an existing model, their interrelations must be considered when the model is constructed. For example, an exceedingly rich and complex chemical–kinetic subroutine when combined with a similarly complex diffusion program may lead to a system of non-linear differential equations so large as to preclude a numerical solution, if possible, on even the largest of computer systems. Consequently, in the development of the model, one must "size" the various components and generate subroutines of compatible complexity and precision.

In the most general case, the system to be solved consists of equations of continuity or mass balance for each specific chemical species to be considered in the model. For a concise description of such a system and a cogent development of the general solution, see Lamb and Neiburger.[33] The appropriate equations, their associated boundary conditions and initial values are given in Table V, entry 12.

TABLE V

Basic Equations

1. Frenkiel
   Equation not given
2. Turner

$$\frac{\chi}{Q} = \frac{1}{u\pi(\sigma_y+402)\sigma_z} \exp\left(-\frac{1}{2}\frac{y^2}{(\sigma_y+402)^2} - \frac{1}{2}\frac{(z-h)^2}{\sigma_z^2}\right) \exp\left(-\frac{0.693}{T_{1/2}}t\right)$$

3. Clarke

$$\frac{\chi}{Q} = \frac{2}{u\sqrt{2\pi}\sigma_z[(\pi/8)x]} \exp\left(-\frac{1}{2}\frac{z^2}{\sigma_z^2}\right) \exp\left(-\frac{0.693}{T_{1/2}}t\right),$$

   where x = distance from source
4. Fortak
   Gaussian
5. Hilst and Bowne

$$D(x-x_0, 0) = \frac{Q}{\sqrt{2\pi}u[\sigma_{z0}+a(x-x_0)]} \exp\left(-\frac{1}{2}\frac{z_0^{2}e^{-2\lambda(x-x_0)}}{[\sigma_{z0}+a(x-x_0)]^2}\right)$$

   $D(x-x_0, 0)$ = dosage at a distance from line source of $x-x_0$
   σ_{z0} = standard deviation of concentration at release level
   a and λ = constants
6. Pooler

$$\frac{\chi}{Q} = \frac{1}{\pi u(\sigma_y+80)(\sigma_z+30)} \exp\left(-\frac{1}{2}\frac{y^2}{(\sigma_y+80)^2} - \frac{h^2}{2(\sigma_z+30)^2}\right)$$

7. Miller and Holzworth

$$\frac{\chi}{Q_A} = \frac{u}{s} {}_{50}\int^{t_L} {}_{50}\int^{t_L} \frac{2dtdt}{\sqrt{2\pi}\sigma_z} + {}_{t_L}\int^{t_s} {}_{t_L}\int^{t_s} 1_z L dtdt$$

   χ = average concentration
   Q_A = area source strength

Table V (*continued*)

t_L = time for plume to reach mixing layer height (L)
t_s = time of travel from most distant source
s = distance from edge of city
T = temperature, °F
a and b = constants

8. Davidson
Gaussian

9. Koogler, Sholtes, Danis and Harding

$$\frac{\chi}{Q} = \frac{1}{u\pi(\sigma_y+402)\sigma_z} \exp\left(-\frac{1}{2}\frac{y^2}{(\sigma_y+402)^2} - \frac{1}{2}\frac{(z-h)^2}{\sigma_z^2}\right) \exp\left(\frac{-0.693t}{T_{1/2}}\right)$$

10. Panofsky and Prasad

1. $\chi = \dfrac{2Q}{\sqrt{2\pi} u w \sigma_z}$

2. $\chi = \dfrac{a}{uR_v} \Sigma \dfrac{Q}{3_y p}$

3. $\sigma_z = b\sigma\theta x_p$

w = width of valley floor
R_v = range of vertical angle of bivane
$p \sim 1$ in neutral cases
$p > 1$ in unstable cases
a and b = constants
σ_θ = standard deviation of azimuth angle fluctuations

11. Hilst, Badgley, Yocum and Bowne

$$\frac{\chi}{Q} = \frac{1}{\pi\sigma_y\sigma_z u} \exp\left(-\frac{1}{2}\frac{y^2}{\sigma^2} - \frac{h^2}{2\sigma_z^2}\right)$$

12. Lamb and Neiburger

$$\frac{\partial C}{\partial t} + U(x,y,t)\frac{\partial C}{\partial x} + V(x,y,t)\frac{\partial C}{\partial y} = \mathscr{L}C + f(t)C + S(x,y,z,t)$$

Boundary Conditions:

$C(x,y,z,0) = I(x,y,z)$

$\lim\limits_{x,y \to \pm\infty} C(x,y,z,t) = 0$

$\dfrac{\partial}{\partial z} C(x,y,0,t) = 0; \qquad \dfrac{\partial C}{\partial z} = -\beta C$ at $z = h$,

where

$C = C(x,y,z,t)$ = mean concentration of contaminant
$I(x,y,z)$ = initial concentration distribution
β = ground level ($z = h$) absorption coefficient
$U(x,y,t)$ = x—component of the surface wind
$V(x,y,t)$ = y—component of the surface wind
$f(t)$ = temporal dependence of chemical processes in which reaction speed is proportional only to concentration of pollutant
$S(x,y,z,t)$ = emissions source function
$\mathscr{L}$ = differential operator describing time rate of change of mass concentration due to action of turbulence
Inversion base is taken at $z = 0$.

13. Martin

$\chi(\rho,L,S) = [2Q/(2\pi)^{\frac{1}{2}}\, \sigma_z(\rho,L)u(S)(2\pi\rho/16)] \,.\, \exp[-P(H/\sigma_z(\rho,L))^2]$

$\chi(\rho,L,S) = Q/Mu(S)(2\pi\rho_z 16)$ (inversion)

where

$\chi(\rho,L,S)$ = average ground-level concentration (g/m³) for a particular combination of meteorological conditions at any receptor point at distance ρ within the given sector due to a point source with emission rate Q (g/sec)
$u(S)$ = wind speed (m/sec) representative of a wind speed class (S)
H = effective source height (m)
$\sigma_z(\rho,L)$ = standard deviation (m) of the vertical concentration distribution for a ground-level emission; it is a function of ρ and atmospheric stability class (L)
M = height of the upper limit to vertical mixing (m)
Equations for long-term average concentration at receptor is given in text (section VII, B.4)

Table V (*continued*)

14. Roberts, Croke and Kennedy

$$\chi(x,y,z,M) = \sum_{N=1}^{M} QM-N+1 \int_{(N-1)\Delta}^{N\Delta} dT \left(- \left[\frac{(x-UT)^2}{2\sigma_x^2} + \frac{y^2}{2\sigma J^2} + \frac{z^2}{2\sigma_z^2} \right) \right] \cdot \left(\exp(-0.639 T_z T^{\frac{1}{2}})/(2\pi)^{\frac{3}{2}} \sigma_x(T) \sigma_y(T) \sigma_z(T) \right),$$

where

$\chi(x,y,z,M)$ = concentration at time $t = M\Delta$
M = number of fundamental time intervals over which discrete transfer function is integrated
N = iteration integer
Δ = fundamental time increment
$Q(t)$ = piecewise constant pollutant release function
T = delay time, i.e. time interval since release occurred
U = steady mean wind velocity
σ_x = dispersion coefficient in x-direction, etc.
$T_{\frac{1}{2}}$ = characteristic half-life of removal process.

The mathematical formulation used to describe the atmospheric diffusion process that enjoys the widest use is a form of the Gaussian equation, also referred to as the modified Sutton equation. In its simplest form for a continuous ground level point source, it may be expressed as

$$\frac{\chi}{Q} = \frac{1}{\pi u \sigma_y \sigma_z} \cdot \exp\left(- \frac{y^2}{2\sigma_y^2} - \frac{z^2}{2\sigma_z^2} \right) \qquad (1)$$

χ = concentration in grams/meter^3

Q = source strength in grams per second

u = wind speed at the emission point in meters/second

σ_y = the perpendicular distance in meters from the centerline of the plume in the horizontal direction to the point where the concentration falls to 0.61 times the centerline value

σ_z = the perpendicular distance in meters from the centerline of the plume in the vertical direction to the point where the concentration falls to 0.61 times the centerline value

π = 3.1416

x,y,z = spatial coordinates—downwind, cross-origin at the point source.

Any consistent system of units may be used.

From an examination of the variables it is readily seen that several kinds of meteorological measurements are necessary. The wind speed, u, appears explicitly in the equation; the wind direction is necessary for determining the direction of pollutant transport from source to receptor.

Further, the values of σ_y and σ_z depend upon atmospheric stability which in turn depends upon the variation of temperature with height, another meteorological parameter. At the present time, data on atmospheric stability over large urban areas are uncommon. Pasquill has developed Table VI for use with Figures 2 and 3, as a substitute for stability measurements to determine values of σ_y and σ_z. Turner[2] has proposed a modification of the Pasquill diagrams for the same purpose. Panofsky and Prasad[10] have used the range of the direction swings of a wind vane as a substitute of values of σ_y and σ_z.

The temperature variation with height may be obtained by means of thermal elements mounted on radio or television towers. Tethered or free balloons carrying suitable sensors may also be used. Helicopter soundings of temperature have been used for this purpose in New York City, Cincinnati, Ohio and elsewhere. There is litte doubt that as additional effort is devoted to the development of urban air pollution models, adequate stability measurements will become available. In a complete study, measurements of precipitation, solar radiation, and net radiation flux may be used to advantage. Another meteorological variable of importance is the hourly temperature for hour-to-hour predictions or the average daily temperature for 24-hour calculations. The source strength, Q, when applied to an area source consisting of residential units burning coal for space heating, is a direct function of the number of degree hours or degree days. The number of

TABLE VI
Key to Stability Categories

Surface wind speed (at 10 m), m sec^{-1}	Day: Incoming solar radiation: Strong	Day: Incoming solar radiation: Moderate	Day: Incoming solar radiation: Slight	Night: Thinly overcast or $\leq 4/8$ low cloud	Night: $\geq 3/8$ cloud
<2	A	A–B	B		
2–3	A–B	B	C	E	F
3–5	B	B–C	C	D	E
5–6	C	C–D	D	D	D
>6	C	D	D	D	D

The neutral class, D, should be assumed for overcast conditions during day or night.

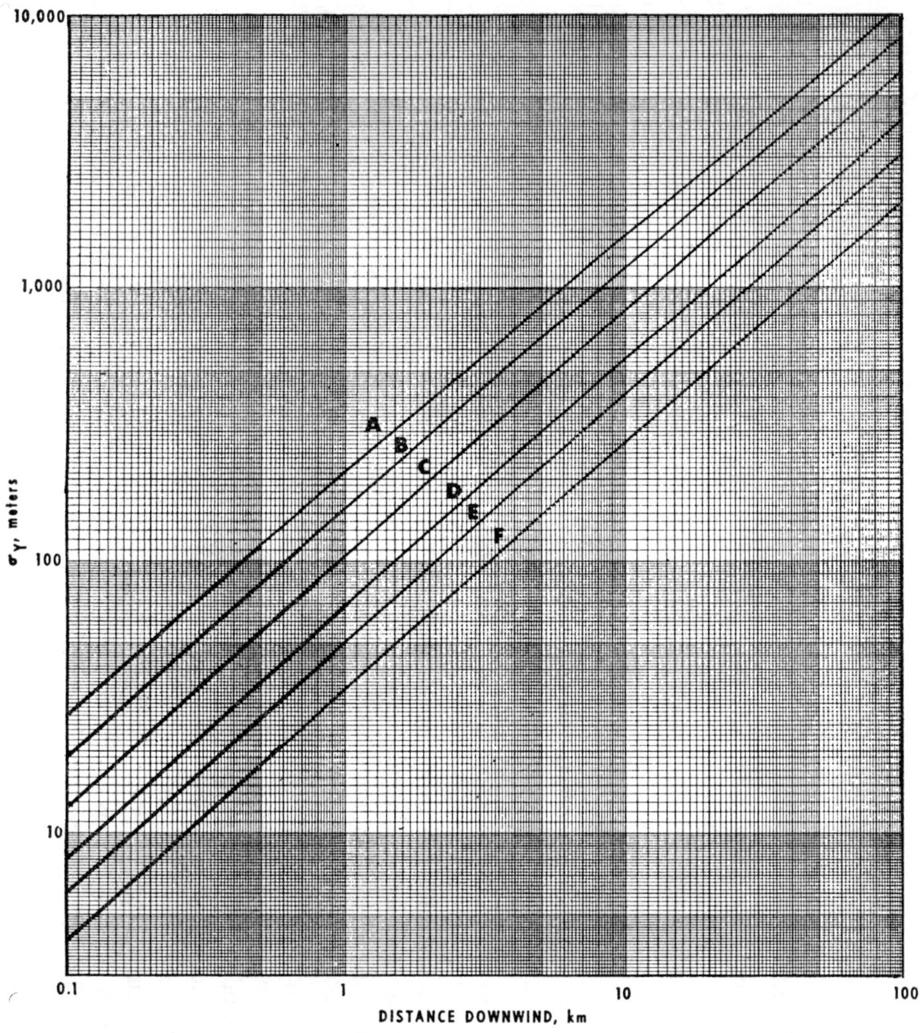

Figure 2 Variation of σ_y as a function of downwind distance from a source. Stability classes A–F are explained in Table VI. (After Turner.[40])

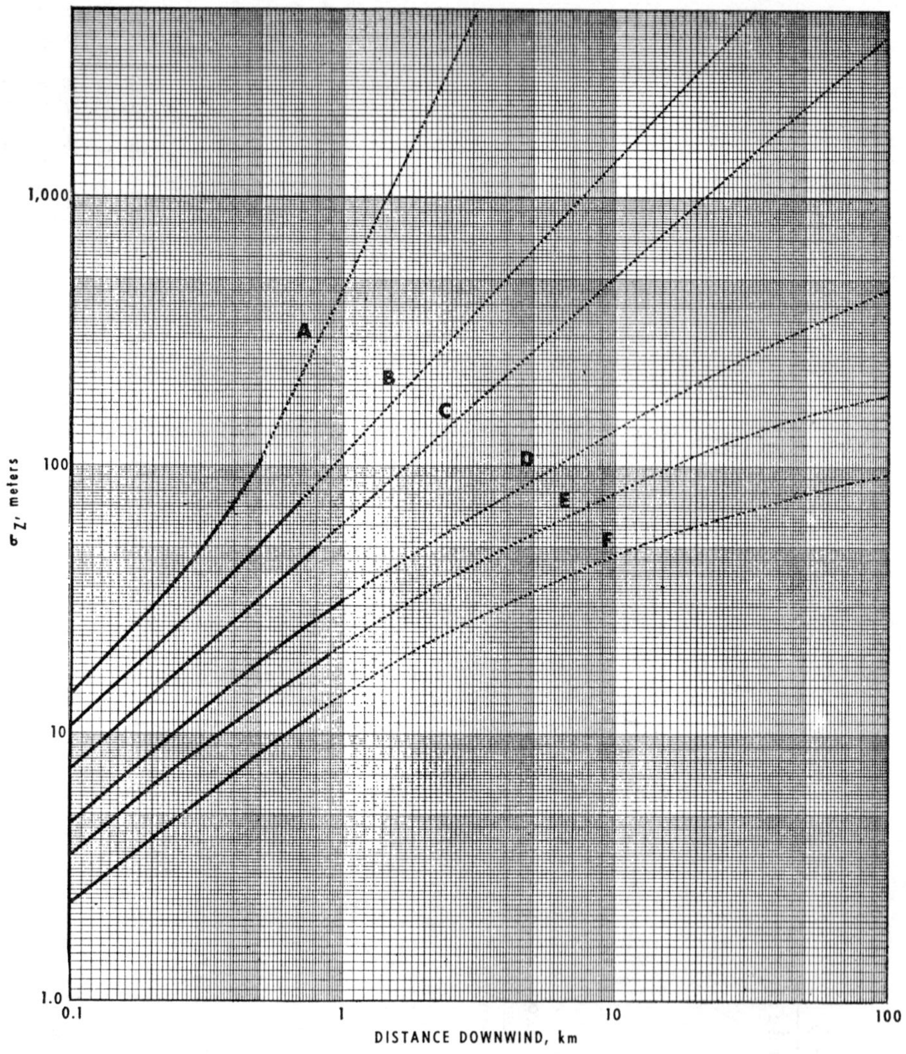

Figure 3 Variation of σ_z with downwind distance from the source. Stability classes A–F are explained in Table VI. (After Turner.[40])

degree days is defined as the difference between the average temperature for the day and 65°. If the average temperature exceeds 65°, the degree day value is considered zero. An analogous definition applies for the degree hour. Turnerz[4] points out that in St. Louis the degree day or degree hour values explain nearly all the variance of the output of gas as well as of that of steam produced by the public utilities.

VI. The Use of Grids

In the development of a mathematical urban air pollution model, two different grids may be used: one based on existing pollution sources and the other on the location of the instruments which form the monitoring network.

A. The pollution source grid

In this country, grid squares one mile on a side are frequently used, such as was done by Davison, Koogler and Turner. Fortak of West Germany used square, 100 × 100 metres. The Connecticut model is based on a 5000-foot grid, and Clarke's Cincinnati model on sectors of a circle. Sources of pollution may be either point sources such as the stacks of a public utility, or distributed sources such as the sources representing the emission of many small homes in a residential area. The map of Fig. 4 shows the pollution source grid for the City of Chicago.

B. The monitoring grid

In testing the model, one resorts to measurements obtained by instruments at monitoring stations. Such monitoring stations may also be located on a grid. Further, this grid may be used in the computation of concentrations by means of the mathematical equation, e.g., concentrations are calculated for the midpoints of the grid squares. The emission grid and monitoring grid may be identical or they may be different. For example, Turner used a source grid of 17 × 16 miles, but a measurement grid of 9 × 11 miles. In the Connecticut model, the source grid covers the entire state, and calculations based on the model also cover the entire state. Fortak used 480 × 800 meter rectangles.

VII. Types of Urban Air Pollution Models

A. The source-oriented model

In applying the mathematical algorithm, one may proceed by determining the source strength for a given point source and then calculating the isopleths of concentration downwind arising from this source. The calculation is repeated for each area source and point source. Contributions made by each of the sources at a selected point downwind such as the midpoint of square 15 in Figure 5, are then summed to determine the calculated value of the concentration. Isopleths of concentration may then be drawn to provide a computed distribution of the pollutants.

In the source-oriented model, detailed information is needed both on the strength and on the time variations of the source emissions. The Turner model[2] is a good example of a source-oriented model.

It must be emphasized that each urban area must be "calibrated", to account for the peculiar characteristics of the terrain, buildings, forestation and the like. Further, local phenomena such as lake-breezes and mountain–valley effects may markedly influence the resulting concentrations. Specifically, one would have to determine such relations as the variation of σ_y and σ_z with distance or the magnitude of the effective stack heights. A network of pollution monitoring stations is necessary for this purpose. The use of an algorithm without such a calibration is likely to lead to disappointing results.

B. The receptor-oriented model

Several types of receptor-oriented models have been developed. Among these are the Clarke mode, the regression model, the Argonne tabulation prediction scheme, and the Martin model.[21]

1) *The Clarke model*

In the Clarke model,[4] one of the most well-known, the receptor or monitoring station is located at the center of four concentric circles having radii of 1, 4, 10 and 20 kilometers respectively. These circles are divided into 16 equal sectors of $22\frac{1}{2}°$. See Figure 6. A source inventory is obtained for each of the 64 (16 × 4) annular sectors. Also for the 1-km radius circle and for each of the annular rings, a chart is prepared relating χ/Q (the concentration per unit source strength) and wind speed for various stability classes and for various mixing heights. The algorithm such as given in Table V for the Clarke model may be used. An example of such a chart is shown in Figure 7. In refining his model,[35] Clarke considers, separately, the contributions to the concentration levels made by transportation, industry and commerce, space heating and strong point-sources such as utility stacks. The following equations are then used to calculate the pollutant

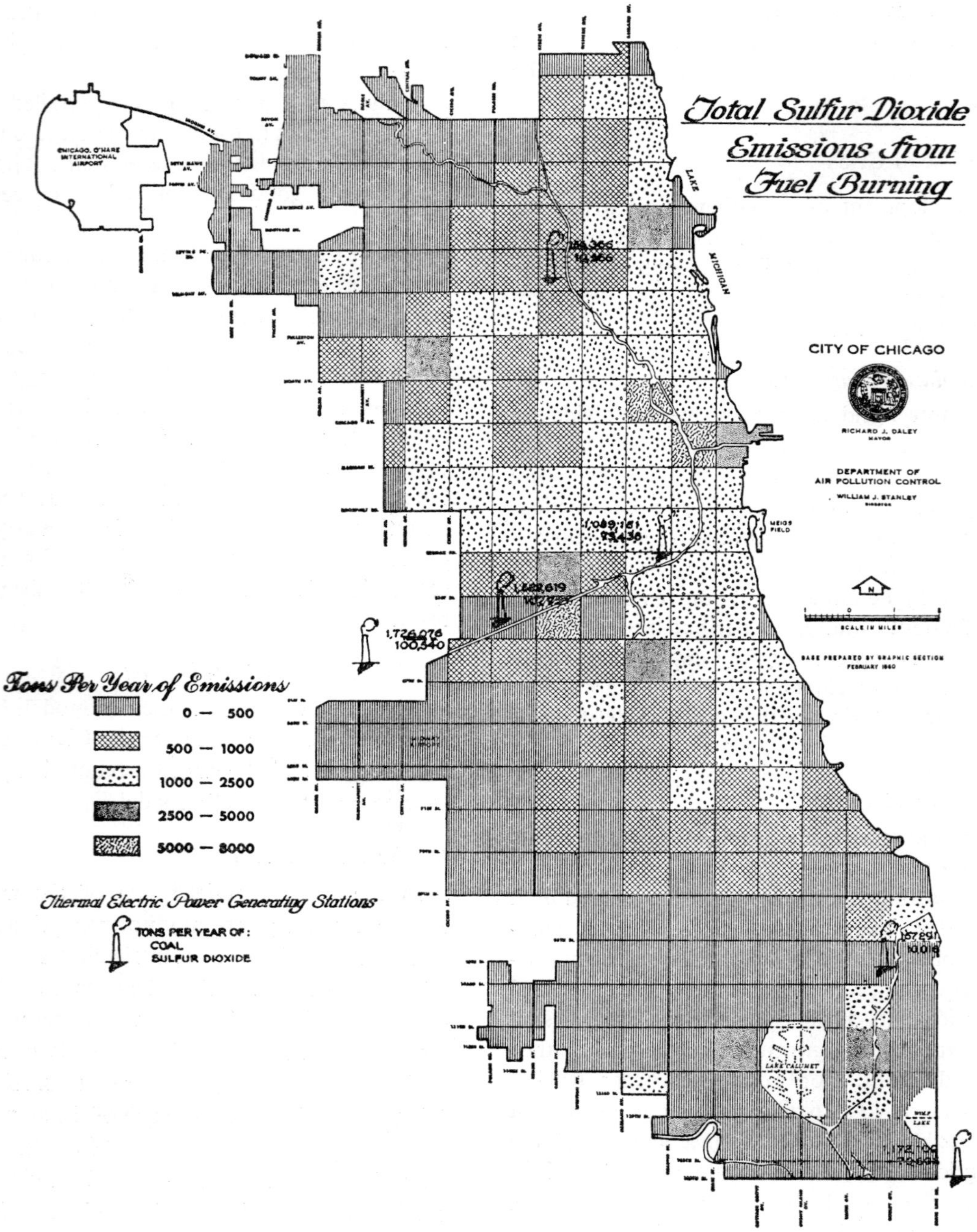

Figure 4 Example of a source inventory map.

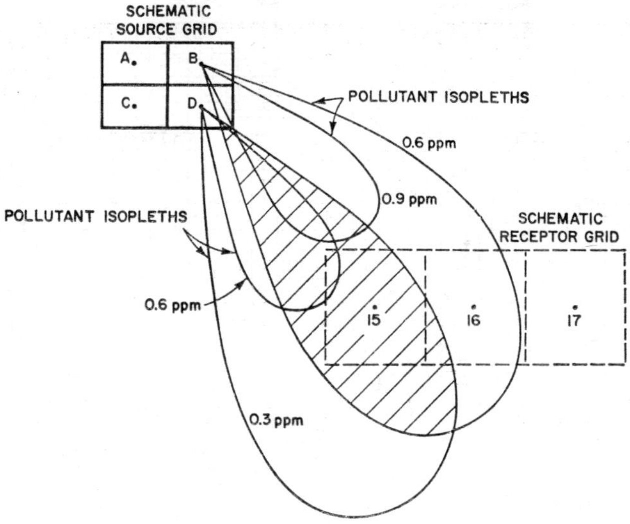

Figure 5 Schematic diagram of calculation techniques for source-oriented model. Sources are located at A, B, C and D of source inventory grid. A section of the monitoring grid is given by squares 15, 16 and 17. The concentration enclosed by the 0.6 ppm isopleth of source B and the 0.3 ppm isopleth of source D contribute a concentration exceeding 0.9 ppm for square 15. See hatched area.

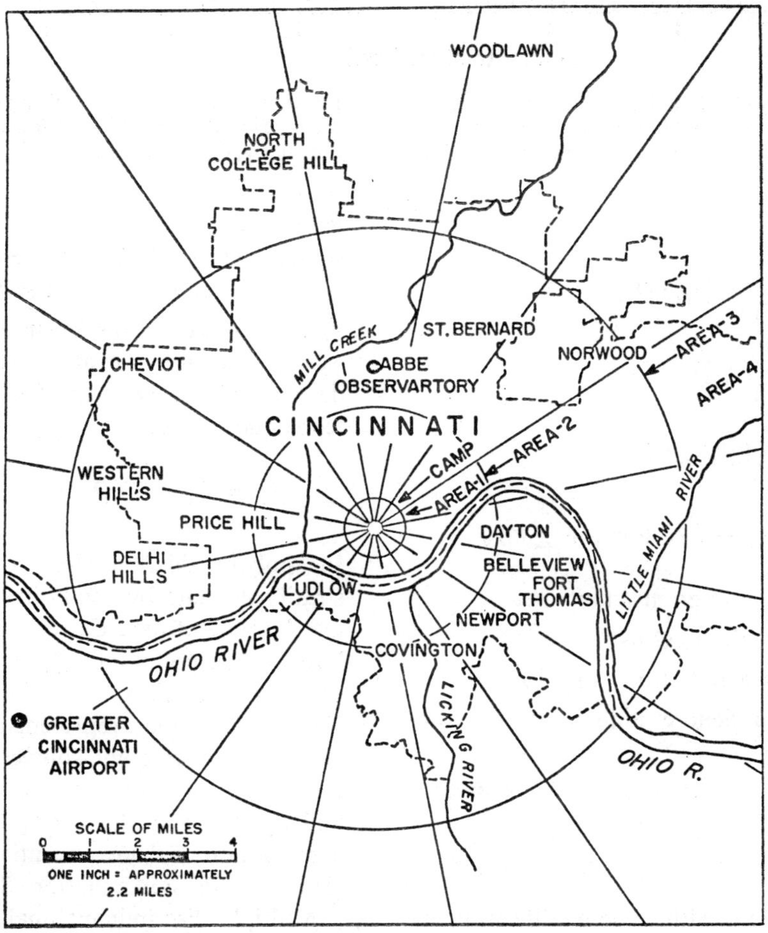

Figure 6 Greater Cincinnati area showing standard emission areas in the form of sectors of the innermost circle or annular sectors of the other circles. (After Clarke.[4])

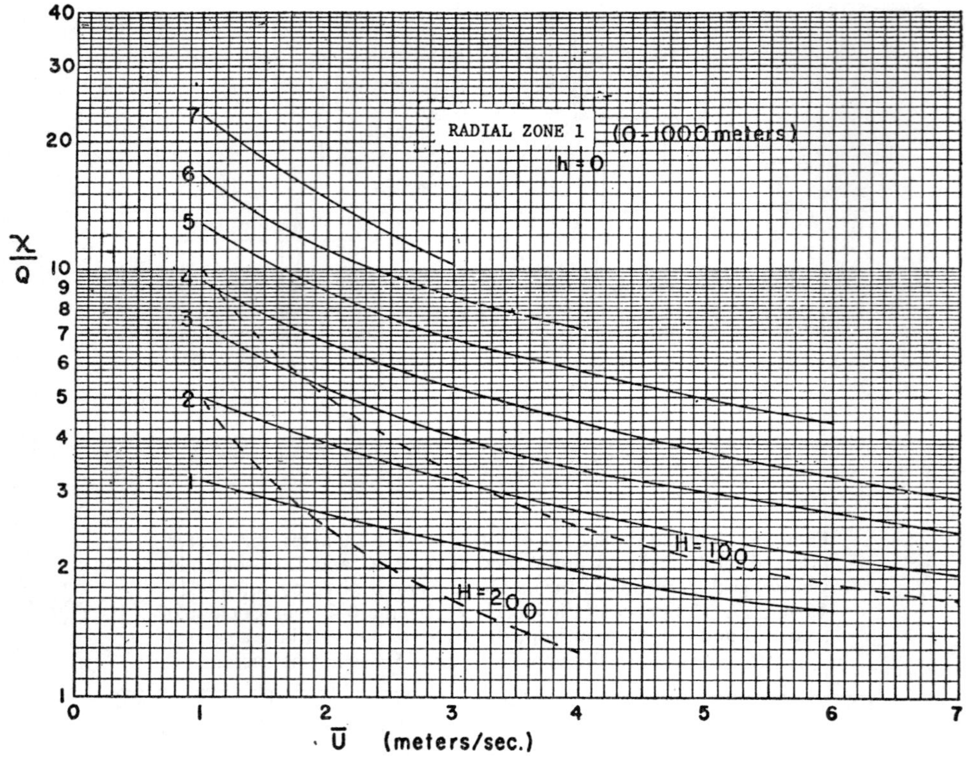

Figure 7 Relative concentrations (X/Q) as a function of wind speed (u), mixing depth (H), and stability classes for ground level sources. The stability classes 1–7 are analogous to the classes A–F discussed previously, (After Clarke.[35])

concentration.

$$\chi_T = \sum_{i=1}^{4} (\chi/Q)_{Ti} \cdot Q_{Ti}$$

$$\chi_I = \sum_{i=1}^{4} (\chi/Q)_{Ii} \cdot Q_{Ii}$$

$$\chi_S = \sum_{i=1}^{4} (\chi/Q)_{Si} \cdot Q_{Si}$$

$$\chi_{\text{Total}} = a\chi_T + b\chi_I + c\chi_S + \sum_{i=1}^{n} k_i \chi_p$$

χ = concentration in grams/cubic meter

Q = source strength in grams/sec

T = subscript to denote transportation sources

I = subscript to denote industrial and commercial sources

S = subscript to denote space heating sources

p = subscript to denote point sources

i = refers to the annular sectors.

The above equations with some modification are taken from Clarke's report.[35] Values of the constants a,b,c are determined from information concerning the diurnal variation of the transportation, industrial and commercial, and space heating sources. The coefficient, k_i, represents a calibration factor applied to the point sources.

2) The linear regression-type model A second example of the receptor-oriented model is one developed by Roberts and Croke[1]; using regression techniques. Here,

$$\chi = C_0 + C_1Q_1 + C_2Q_2 + \sum_{i=1}^{n} k_iQ_i.$$

In applying this equation, it is necessary first to stratify the data by wind direction, by wind speed, and by time of day. C_0 represents the background level of the pollutant; Q_1 represents one type of source such as the commercial and industrial emissions and Q_2 may represent contributions due to large individual point sources. It is assumed that there are n point sources. The coefficients C_1 and C_2 and k_i represent the $1/\sigma_y\sigma_z$ term as well as the contribution of the exponential factor of the Gaussian type diffusion equation. See Equation 1.

Multiple discriminant analysis techniques[1]; for individual monitoring stations may be used to determine the probability that pollutant concentrations fall within a given range or that they exceed a given critical value such as 0.3 ppm. Meteorological variables, such as temperature, wind speed, and stability are used as the independent variable in the discriminant function.

3) The Martin model A diffusion model specifically suited to the estimation of long-term average values of air quality has been developed by Martin.[2] The basic equation of the model is the Gaussian diffusion equation for a continuous point source. It is modified to allow for a multiplicity of point sources and a variety of meteorological conditions.

The model is receptor-oriented. The equations for the ground level concentration within a given $22\frac{1}{2}°$ sector at the receptor for a given set of meteorological conditions (i.e., wind speed and atmospheric stability) and a specified source are listed in Table V. The assumption is made that all wind directions within a $22\frac{1}{2}°$ sector—corresponding to a 16-point compass—occur with equal probability.

In order to estimate long-term air quality, the single point-source equations cited above are evaluated to determine the contribution from a given source at the receptor for each possible combination of wind speed and atmospheric stability. Then, using Martin's notation, the long-term average is given by

$$\chi = \sum_N \sum_L \sum_S F(D_n, L, S) \cdot \chi(\rho_n, L, S),$$

where D_n indicates the wind direction sector in which transport from a particular source (n) to the receptor occurs; ρ_n is the distance from a particular source to the receptor; $F(D_n,L,S)$ denotes the relative frequency of winds blowing into the given wind direction sector (D_n) for a given wind speed class (S) and atmospheric stability class (L); N is the total number of sources. The joint frequency distribution $F(D_n,L,S)$ is determined by the use of hourly meteorological data.

A system of modified average mixing heights based on tabulated climatological values is developed for the model. In addition, adjustments are made in the values of some mixing heights to take into account the urban influence. Martin has also incorporated the exponential time decay of pollutant concentrations since he compares his calculations with measured sulfur dioxide concentrations for St. Louis, Mo. The pertinant parameters of this model are given in Tables I, II, III and IV.

4) The Tabulation Prediction Scheme This method, developed at the Argonne National Laboratory, consists of developing an ordered set of combinations of relevant meteorological variables and presenting the percentile distribution of SO_2 concentrations for each element in the set. An example of the tabulation is shown in Table VII. In this table, the independent variables are wind direction, hour of day, wind speed, temperature and stability. The 10, 50, 75, 90, 98 and 99 percentile values are presented as well as the minimum and the maximum values. Also presented are the interquartile range and the 75–95 percentile ranges to provide a measure of dispersion and of skewness respectively.

Since the meteorological variables are ordered, it is possible to look up any combination of meteorological variables just as one would look up a name in a telephone book or a word in a dictionary. This method, of course, can be applied only as long as the source distribution and terrain have not changed appreciably. For continued use of this method, one must be cognizant of changes in the sources as well as changes in the terrain due to new construction.

In preparing the tabulation, the data are first

TABLE VII

Season: Dec., Jan., Feb. Precipitation: No. TAM Station *Period of Data: Jan.* 1, 1966–*Dec.* 31, 1967

Wind direction degrees	Hour of day (CST)	Wind speed mph	Temperature °F	Stability °C/100 m	Percentile values of SO_2 concentrations (ppm) Min.	10	25	50	75	90	95	98	99	Max.	No. of cases
300–350	08–11	4–7	10–19	>2	0.10	.12	.15	.20	.35	.50	.85	1.00	1.20	1.50	85
300–350	08–11	4–7	10–19	1.9–0.0	0.08	.10	.13	.15	.30	.40	.70	.90	1.10	1.20	90
300–350	08–11	4–7	20–29	>2	0.05	.10	.12	.15	.20	.30	.35	.40	.50	.70	92
300–350	08–11	4–7	20–29	1.9–0.0	0.05	.08	.10	.11	.12	.15	.15	.20	.25	.35	81

stratified by season and also by the presence or absence of precipitation. Further, appropriate group intervals must be selected for the meteorological variables to assure that within each grouping the pollution values are not sensitive to changes in that variable. For example, of the spatial distribution of the sources, one finds that the pollution concentration at a station varies markedly with changes in wind direction. If one plots percentile isopleths for concentration vs. wind direction, see Figure 8, one may choose sectors in which the SO_2 concentrations are relatively insensitive to direction change. A similar chart to determine time bands during which SO_2 concentrations are insensitive to the hour of the day is shown in Figure 9. With the exception of wind direction and hour of day, the meteorological variables of Table VII vary monotonically with SO_2 concentration.

The tabulation prediction method has advantages over other receptor-oriented techniques in that (1) it is easier to use, (2) it provides predictions of pollution concentrations more rapidly, (3) it provides the entire percentile distribution of pollutant concentration to allow a forecaster to "fine tune" his prediction based on synoptic conditions, and (4) it takes into account nonlinearities in the relationships of the meteorological variables and SO_2 concentrations. In a sense, one may consider the tabulation as representing a nonlinear regression hypersurface passing through the data which represent points plotted in n-dimensional space. The analytic form of the hypersurface need not be determined in the use of this method.

The disadvantages of this method are that (1) it is necessary to have the use of a large digital computer in constructing the tables, (2) at least two years of meteorological data are necessary, (3) changes in the emission sources degrade the method, and (4) the model could not predict the effect of adding, removing or modifying important pollution sources; however, it can be designed to do so.

Where a network of stations is available such as exists in New York City, Los Angeles, or Chicago, then the receptor-oriented technique may be applied

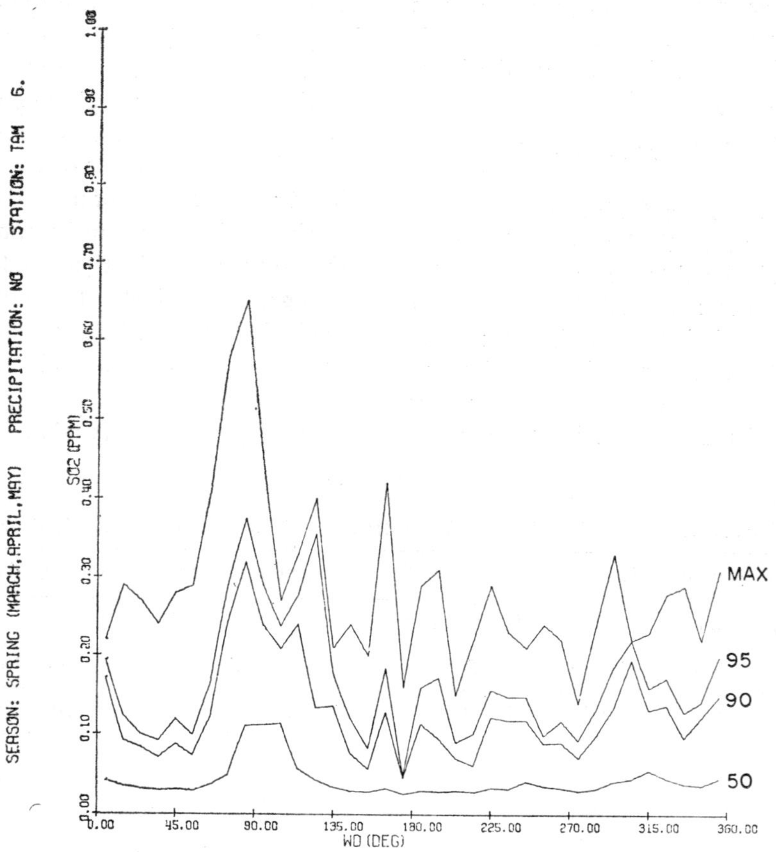

Figure 8 SO_2 concentration (ppm) vs. wind direction for the spring season, March, April, May of 1966 and 1967. Chicago Air Pollution Control Telemetered Automatic Monitoring Station No. 6. No precipitation was occurring. The 50th, 90th, 95th, and 100th percentile curves are shown.

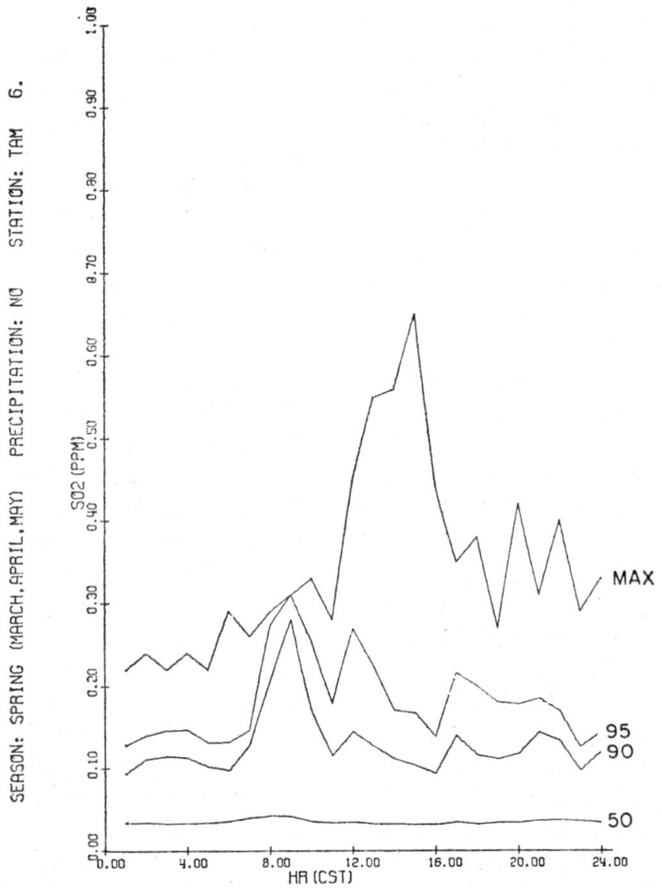

Figure 9 SO_2 concentration (ppm) vs. time of day for the spring season, March, April, May or 1966 and 1967. Chicago Air Pollution Control Telemetered Automatic Monitoring Station No. 6. No precipitation was occurring. The 50th, 90th, 95th, and 100th percentile curves are shown.

to each of the stations to obtain isopleths of concentration similar to that obtained in the source-oriented model.

It would be ideal to have a source-oriented model which could be applied to any city, given the source inventory. Unfortunately, the nature of the terrain, general inaccuracies in source strength information and the influences of factors such as synoptic effect or the peculiar geometries of the buildings produce substantial errors. Similarly, a receptor-oriented model, such as the Clarke model or one based on regression techniques must be tailored to the location. Every urban area must therefore be "calibrated" whether one desires to apply a source-oriented model, or a tabulation prediction scheme. The tabulation prediction scheme, however, does not require detailed information on the distribution and the strength of emission sources.

Perhaps, the optimum system would be one which would make use of the advantages of both the source-oriented model with its prediction capability concerning the effects of changes in the sources and the tabulation prediction scheme which could provide the probabilty distributions of pollutant concentrations. It appears possible to develop a hybrid system by developing means for appropriately modifying the percentile entries when sources are modified, added or removed. The techniques for constructing such a system would, of course, have general applicability.

5) The Fixed-Volume Trajectory Model In the trajectory model, the path of a parcel of air is predicted as it is acted upon by the wind. The parcel is usually considered as a fixed-volume chemical reactor with pollutant inputs only from sources along its path; in additon, various mathematical constraints placed on mass transport into and out of the cell make the problem tractable. Examples of this technique are discussed by Worley.[36] In this model, derived pollution concentrations are known only along the path of the parcel considered. Consequently, its use is limited to the "strategy planning" problem. Qlso, intitial concentrations at the origin of the trajectory and meteorological variables along it must be well known since input errors along the path are not averageable but, in fact, are propagated.

6) The Basic Approach Attempts have been made to solve the entire system of three-dimensional time-dependent continuity equations. The ever-increasing capability of computer systems to handle such complex problems easily has generated renewed interest in this approach. The most ambitious treatment to date is that of Lamb and Neiburger[33] who have applied their model to carbon monoxide concentrations in the Los Angeles basin. However, chemical reactions—although allowed for in their general formulation—are not considered because of the relative inertness of CO. Nevertheless, the validity of the diffusion and emission subroutines are still tested by this procedure. Details of this work are summarized in Tables I through V.

The model of Freidlander and Seinfeld[37] also considers the general equation of diffusion and chemical reaction. These authors extend the Lagrangian similarity hypothesis to reacting species and develop, as a result, a set of ordinary differential equations describing a variable-volume chemical reactor. By limiting their chemical system to a single irreversible bi-molecular reaction of the form A+B−C, they obtain analytical solutions for the ground-level concentration of the product as a function of the mean position of the pollution cloud above ground level. These solutions are also functions of the appropriate meteorological variables, namely, solar radiation, temperature, wind conditions, and atmospheric stability. Their model has not been field tested.

VIII. Adaption of Basic Equation to Urban Air Pollution Models

The basic equation, Equation 1, is the continuous point source equation with the source located at the ground. It is obvious that the sources of an urban complex are for the most part located above the ground. The basic equation must, therefore, be modified to represent the actual conditions. Table V shows the mathematical algorithms used by various authors and includes appropriate modifications of Equation 1. In addition, a source-oriented model developed by Roberts *et al.*[18] to allow for time-varying sources of emission is discussed below (see section VIII, F.).

A. Chemical kinetics—removal or modifications of pollutions

In the chemical kinetics portion of the model, many different approaches ranging in order from the extremely simple to the very complex have been tried. Obviously the simpest approach is to assume no chemical reactions are occurring at all. Although this assumption may seem contradictory to our intent and an oversimplification, yet it applies to any pollutant that has a long residence time in the atmosphere. For example, the reaction of carbon monoxide with other constituents of the urban atmosphere is so small that it can be considered inert over the time span for which the model is valid (at most, a few hours).

Considerable simplification of the general problem can be effected if chemical reactions are not included and all variables and parameters are assumed to be time-independent (steady-state solution). In this instance, a solution is obtained that forms the basis for most diffusion models extant—the normal bivariate or Gaussian distribution for the downwind diffusion of effluents from a continuous point source. Its use allows steady-state concentrations to be calculated both at the ground and at any altitude. Many modifications to the basic equation to account for plume rise, elevated sources, area sources, inversion layers, and variations in chimney heights have been proposed and used. Further discussion of these topics is deferred to sections VIII, B through E.

The second level of chemical-kinetic complexity assumes first-order or psuedo-first-order reactions are responsible for the removal of a particular pollutant; as a result, its concentration decays exponentially with time. In this case, a characteristic residence time or half-life describes the temporal behavior of the pollutant. Often the removal of pollutants by chemical action is included in the Gaussian diffusion model by simply multiplying the appropriate diffusion equation by an exponential term of the form $\exp(-t/T)$, where T represents the half-life of the pollutant under consideration. Equations employing this procedure are developed below. The interaction of sulfur dioxide with other atmospheric constituents has been treated in this way by many investgators; for examples, see Roberts, *et al.*[18] and Martin.[21] Chemical reactions are not the only removal mechanism for pollutants. Some other processes contributing to their disappearance may be absorption by plants, soil bacteria action, impaction on surfaces, and washout. To the extent that these processes are simulated by or can be fitted to an exponential decay, the above approximation proves useful and valid.

If one makes the assumption that the removal rate is directly proportional to the amount of pollutant present then

$$\frac{d\chi}{dt} = -\lambda\chi$$

or integrating between the indicated limits, one has

$$\int_{\chi_0}^{\chi} \frac{d\chi}{\chi} = -\int_{o}^{t} \lambda \, dt$$

or

$$\chi = \chi_o \, e^{-\lambda t} = \chi_o \exp - \frac{0.693t}{T_{1/2}},$$

where

χ = concentration of pollutant

t = time

λ = decay constant

$T_{1/2}$ = removal time for one-half of the pollutant

Thus Equation 1 may be modified to read

$$\chi = \frac{Q}{\pi u \sigma_y \sigma_z} \exp\left(-\frac{y^2}{2\sigma_y^2} - \frac{z^2}{2\sigma_z^2}\right) \exp\left(-\frac{0.693t}{T_{1/2}}\right). \quad (2)$$

The half-life or the half residence time of pollutants such as CO, CO_2, and SO_2 are not well known. In urban air pollution models, a value for SO_2 of four to six hours has often been used.[2] Since chemical reaction rates are markedly influenced by temperature, e.g., a doubling for every 10°C rise in temperature, the residence time must also be a function of temperature if chemical reactions are involved.

This approach is overly simple since no specific chemical interactions between polutants need be considered. One simply adjoins the appropriate temporal dependence to a solution that depends upon the given emission sources. However, to develop a model applicable to photochemical smog, these simple techniques cannot be used. Photochemical smog involves the sunlight-induced interactions of nitrogen oxides and hydrocarbons from various sources with each other and the ambient atmosphere into which they are released. As a result, a large conglomeration of hydrocarbons, oxidants, and other compounds in various physical states are produced. A set of reaction equations to describe the chemistry for the entire system cannot be written because of compositional uncertainties in the mixture, particularly of the hydrocarbons. But even more, no one really knows what reactions are in fact occurring in any given smog system. As one might expect, there is general accord on the so-called inorganic reactions:

$$NO_2 + h\nu - NO + O$$

$$O + O_2 + M \rightarrow O_2 + M$$

$$NO + O_2 - NO_2 + O_2.$$

These three reactions appear in almost every chemical kinetic model. On the other hand, many different sets of equations describing the subsequent reactions have been proposed. For example, Hecht and Seinfeld[38] recently studied the propylene–NO[6]–air system and list some 81 reactions that can occur. Any attempt to find an analytical solution for a model utilizing all these reactions and even a simple diffusion sub-model will almost certainly fail. Consequently, the number of equations in the chemical kinetic subroutine is reduced by resorting to a "lumped parameter" stratagem. Here, three general types of chemical processes are identified: (a) a chain-initiating process involving the inorganic reactions cited above as well as subsequent interactions of product oxidants with source and product hydrocarbons to yield (b) chain-propagating reactions in which free radicals are produced; these free radicals in turn react with the hydrocarbon mix to produce other free radicals and organic compounds, to oxidize NO to NO_2, and to participate in (c) chain-terminating reactions; here, non-reactive end products (for example, peroxyacetylnitrate) and aerosol production serve to terminate the chain. In the lumped-parameter representation, reaction rate equations typical of these three categories (and usually selected from the rate-determing reactions of each category) are employed with adjusted rate constants determined from appropriate smog chamber data. An attempt is usually made to minimize the number of equations needed to fit well a large sample of smog chamber data. See, for examples, the studies of Friedlander and Seinfeld[37] and Hecht and Seinfeld.[38] Lumped-parameter subroutines are primarily designed to simulate atmospheric conditions with a simplified chemical kinetic scheme in order to reduce computing time when used with an atmospheric diffusion model.

B. Elevated sources and plume rise

With the origin of the coordinate system at the ground, but the source at a height, h', Equation 2 becomes

$$\frac{\chi}{Q} = \frac{1}{\pi u \sigma_y \sigma_z} \exp\left(-\frac{y^2}{2\sigma_y^2} - \frac{(z-h')^2}{2\sigma_z^2}\right) \exp\left(-\frac{0.693t}{T_{1/2}}\right). \quad (3)$$

Of course, materials emitted from a stack do not necessarily stay at the same level. The plume may rise because of its buoyancy and momentum. The height of plume rise, $h = h' + Bh$. There are numerous formulas for calculating plume rise.[39] Equation 3 then becomes

$$\frac{\chi}{Q} = \frac{1}{\pi u \sigma_y \sigma_z} \exp\left(-\frac{y^2}{2\sigma_y^2} - \frac{(z-h)^2}{2\sigma_z^2}\right) \exp\left(-\frac{0.693t}{T_{1/2}}\right). \quad (4)$$

C. Mixing of pollutant under an inversion lid

When the lapse rate in the lowermost layer, i.e.. from the ground to about 200 meters, is near adiabatic but a pronounced inversion exists above this layer, the inversion is believed to act as a lid preventing the upward diffusion of pollutants. The pollutants below the lid are assumed to be uniformly mixed. By integrating Equation 4 with respect to z and distributing the pollutants uniformly over a height, H, one obtains

$$\frac{\chi}{Q} = \frac{1}{2\pi u \sigma_y H} \exp\left(-\frac{y^2}{2\sigma_y^2}\right) \exp\left(-\frac{0.693t}{T_{1/2}}\right). \quad (5)$$

Those few measurements of concentration with height which do exist, do not support the assumption that the concentration is uniform in the lowermost layer. One is tempted to say that the mixing layer thickness, H, may be determined by the height of the inversion; however, during transitional conditions, i.e., at dawn and dusk, the thickness of the layer containing high concentrations of pollutants may differ from that of the layer from the ground to the inversion base.

The thermal structure of the lower layer as well as pollutant concentration as a function of height may be determined by helicopter soundings.

D. The area source

When pollution arises from many small point sources such as small dwellings, one may consider the region as an area source. Preliminary work on the Chicago model[16,1]; indicates that contributions to observed SO_2 levels in the lowest tens of feet substantially from dwellings exceeds that emanating from tall stacks such as power generating stacks. For a rigorous treatment, one should consider the emission Q as the emission in units per unit area per second, and then integrate Q along x and along y for the length of the square. Downwind, beyond the area source square, the plume may be treated as originating from a point source. This point source is considered to be at a virtual origin upwind of the area source square. As pointed out by Turner,[40] the approximate equation for an area source

$$\frac{\chi}{Q} = \frac{\exp\left(-\frac{y^2}{[2\sigma_y(x_{yo}+x)]^2} - \frac{(z-h)^2}{2\sigma_z^2}\right) \exp\left(-\frac{0.693t}{T_{1/2}}\right)}{\pi u [\sigma_y(x_{yo}+x)]\sigma_z}$$

where $\sigma_y(x_y + x)$ represents the standard deviation of the horizontal crosswind concentration as a function of the distance $x_y + x$ from the virtual origin. Since the plume is considered to extend to the point where the concentration falls to 0.1 that of the centerline concentration, $\sigma_y(x_{yo}) = S/403$ where $\sigma_y(x_{yo})$ is the standard deviation of the concentration at the downwind side of the square of side length S. The distance, x_{yo}, from the virtual origin to the downwind side of the grid square may be determined from Figure 2, and is that distance for which $\sigma_y(x_{yo}) = S/4.3$. The distance x is measured from the downwind side of the grid square. Other symbols have been previously defined.

E. Correction for variation in chimney height

In any given area, chimneys are likely to vary in height above ground, and the plume rises vary as well. The variation of effective stack height may be taken into account in a manner similar to the handling of the area source. To illustrate, visualize the points representing the effective stack height projected onto a plane perpendicular to the ground and parallel both to two opposite sides of the given grid square and to the horizontal component of the wind vector. The distribution of the points on this projection plane would be similar to the distribution of the sources on a horizontal plane.

Based on Turner's discussion,[40] the equation for an area source and for a source having a Gaussian distribution of effective chimney heights may be written as

$$\frac{\chi}{Q} = \frac{\exp\left(-\frac{y^2}{2[\sigma_y(x_{yo}+x)]^2} - \frac{(z-h)^2}{2[\sigma_y(x_{zo}+x)]^2}\right) \exp\left(-\frac{0.693t}{T_{1/2}}\right)}{\pi u[\sigma_y(x_{yo}+x)][\sigma_z(x_{zo}+x)]},$$

where $L_z(x_{zo}+x)$ represents the standard deviation of the vertical crosswind concentration as a function of the distance $x_{zo}+x$, from the virtual origin. The value of $L(x_{zo})$ is arbitrarily chosen after examining the distribution of effective chimney heights and the distance x_{zo} represents the distance from the virtual origin to the downwind side of the grid square. The value x_{z_0} may be determined from Figure 3 and represents the distance corresponding to the value for $\sigma_z(x_{z_0})$. The value of x_{y_0} usually differs from that of x_{z_0}. The other symbols retain their previous definition.

In determining the values of $\sigma_y(x_{y_0}+x)$ and $\sigma_z(x_{z_0}+x)$ one must know the distance from the source to the point in question or the receptor. If the wind direction changes within the averaging interval, or if there is a change of wind direction due to local terrain effects, the trajectories are curved. There are several ways of handling curved trajectories. In the Connecticut model, for example, analytic forms for the trajectories were developed. The selection of appropriate trajectory or stream line equations (steady state was assumed) was based on the wind and stability conditions. In the St. Louis model, Turner[41] developed a computer program using the available winds to provide pollutant trajectories. Distances obtained from the trajectories are then used in the Pasquill diagrams such as in Figures 2 and 3 to determine the values of $\sigma_y(x_{y_0}+x)$ and $\sigma_z(x_{z_0}+x)$.

F. Time-dependent emissions (the Roberts model)

The integrated-puff transport algorith of Roberts, *et al.*[18]—a source-oriented model—uses a three-dimensional Gaussian puff kernel as a basis. It is designed to simulate the time-dependent or transient emissions from a single source. Concentrations are calculated by assuming that dispersion occurs from Gaussian diffusion of a puff whose centroid moves with the mean wind. Time-varying source emissions as well as variable wind speeds and directions are approximated by a time series of piecewise continuous emission and meteorological parameters. In addition, chemical reactions are modelled by the inclusion of a removal process describable by an exponential decay with time.

The Roberts basic dispersion equation is given in Table V, entry 14.

The usual approximation for inversion lids of constant height—namely, uniform mixing arising from the superposition of an infinite number of multiple source reflections—is made. Additionally, treatments for lids that are steadily rising or steadily falling and the fumigation phenomenon are incorporated.

Output consists of calculated concentrations for a given source for each hour of a 24-hour period. The concentrations can be obtained for a given receptor or for a uniform horizontal or vertical grid of up to 1000 points.

The preceding model also forms the basis for two other models—one whose specific aim is the design of optimal control strateges, and a second which repetitively applies the single-source algorithm to each point and area source in the model region. Pertinent parameters of the model are also given in Tables I through V.

IX. Meteorological Measurements

Wind speed and direction data measured by the Weather Bureau were used by most investigators, even though some had a number of stations and towers of their own. New York City had an extensive meteorological wind network consisting of over 100 anemometers as well as pilot balloons to provide information on wind variation with height. Smaller programs made use of one or two anemometers.

Pollutants were measured for periods of one hour, two hours, twelve hours, or twenty-four hours. Twelve and twenty-four hour samples of pollutants such as SO_2 leave much to be desired, since many features of their variations with time are obscured. Further, one often has difficulty in determining a representative wind direction or even a representative wind speed for such a long period.

The total amount of data available varies considerably in the eleven studies. Frenkiel's study was based on data for one month only. A comparatively large amount of data was gathered by Davidson, but even these in truth represent a small sample. The most extensive study is the one carried out by the Argonne National Laboratory and the City of Chicago in which 15-minute readings of SO_2 for eight stations and wind speed and direction for at least thirteen stations are available for a three-year period.

In the application of the mathematical equations, one is required to make numerous arbitrary decisions: for example, one must choose the way to handle the vertical variation of wind with height when a high stack, *circa* 500 feet, is used as a point source; or how to test changes in wind direction or stability when a change occurs half-way through the one-hour or two-hour measuring period. In the case of an elevated point source, Turner in his St. Louis model, treated the plume as one originating from the point source up to the time of a change in wind direction and as a combination of an instantaneous line puff and a continuous point source thereafter. The occurrence of precipitation presents serious problems since adequate diffusion measurements under these conditions are lacking. Further, the chemical and physical effects of precipitation on pollutants are only poorly understood. In carrying forward a pollutant from a source, one must decide on how long to apply the calculations. For example, if a two-mile per hour wind is present over the measuring grid and a source is ten miles away, must one take account of the transport for a total of five hours.

Determining a representative wind speed and wind direction over an urban complex with its variety of buildings and other obstructions to the flow is frequently difficult since the horizontal wind field is quite heterogeneous. This is so for light winds, especially during the daytime when convective processes are taking place. With light wind conditions, the wind direction may differ by 180° within a distance of one mile. Numerous wind stations are necessary to depict the true wind field. With high winds, those of the order of 20 mph, the wind direction is quite uniform over a large area so that fewer stations are necessary. It appears that an adequate number of measurements to handle the light wind condition was lacking in all of the studies except the one in New York City.

X. Methods for Evaluating the Mathematical Model

To determine the effectiveness of the mathematical model, validation tests must be applied. These usually include a comparison of observed and calculated values. Validation tests are necessary not only for updating the model because of changes in the source configuration or modification in terrain characteristics due to new construction, but also for comparing the effectiveness of the model with any other which may be suggested. Of course, the primary objective is to see how good the model really is, both for incident control as well as for long range planning.

A. Scatter diagrams and correlation measures

Of the validation techniques appearing in the literature, the most common involves the preparation of a scatter diagram relating observed and calculated values (Y_{obs} vs. Y_{calc}). See Figure 10.

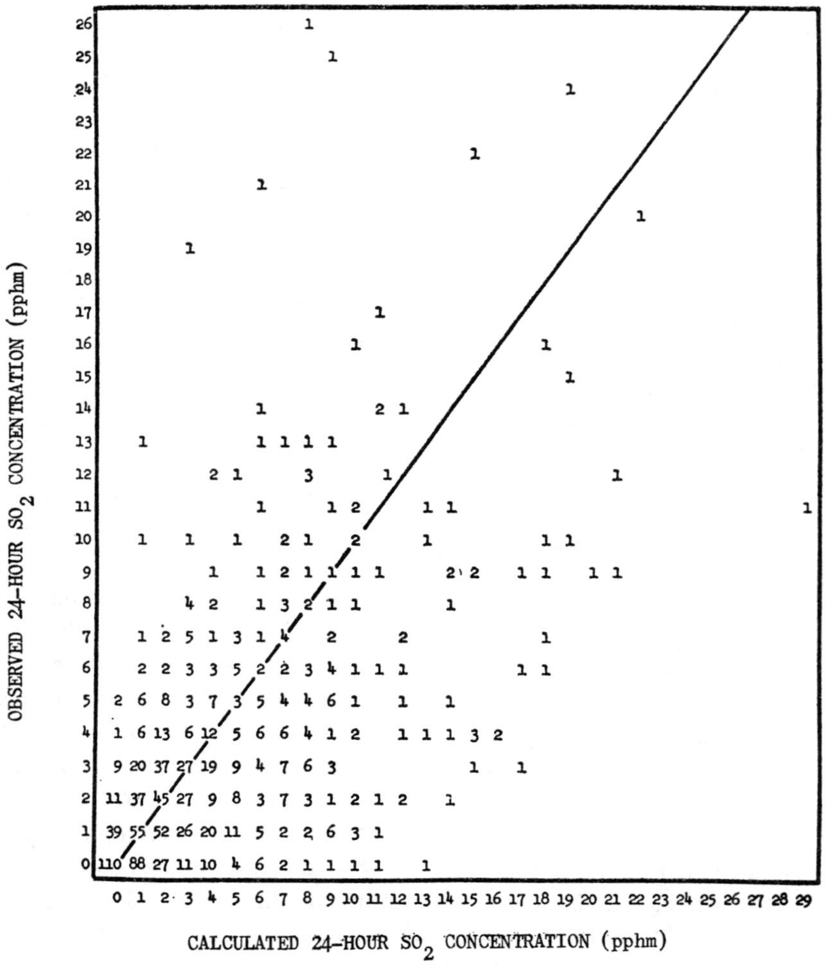

Figure 10 Scatter diagram showing calculated 24-hour SO_2 concentrations vs. observed 24-hour SO_2 concentrations in pphm. Numbers refer to number of observations or number of points at the indicated position of the chart. (After Turner.[2])

The degree of scatter about the 45° line provides a measure of the effectiveness of the model. At times, one finds that a majority of the points lies either above the line or below the line, indicating systematic errors.

It is useful to determine whether the model is equally effective at all concentration levels. To test this, the calculated scale may be divided into uniform bandwidths and the mean square of the deviations about the 45° line calculated for each bandwidth. Another test for systematic error as a function of bandwith consist of an examination of the mean of the difference between calculated and observed values for $Y_{calc} < Y_{obs}$ and similarly for $Y_{calc} > _{obs}$.

The square of the linear correlation coefficient between calculated and observed values or the square of the correlation ratio for non-linear relationships represent measures of the effectiveness of the mathematical equation. For a linear relationship between the dependent variable, e.g., pollutant concentration, and the independent variables.

$$R^2 = 1 - \frac{S_y^2}{\sigma_y^2} = 1 - \frac{\text{unexplained variance}}{\text{total variance}}$$

$$= \frac{\sigma_y^2 - S_y^2}{\sigma_y^2} = \frac{\text{explained variance}}{\text{total variance}},$$

where R^2 = the square of the correlation coefficient between observed and calculated values, S_y^2 = the average of the square of the deviations about the regression line, plane, or hyperplane, and σ_y^2 is the variance of the observed values.

B. Contingency tables

A variation of the scatter diagram is the contingency table shown in Table VIII. To determine whether such a table can be explained by chance, a χ-square test may be applied.

Two variations of the contingency table have been found useful[42] as illustrated in Table IX and X. In the first table, (Table IX), each entry of Table VIII is divided by the sum of its respective column, and multiplied by 100, e.g., $60 = 9/15 \times 100$ for the entry in row 2, column 2. The table provides the percentage frequency distribution of the observed values given the forecast concentration value and indicates the fraction of forecasts which were verified.

TABLE VIII
Contingency Table for SO_2 Concentration Forecasts

Observed SO_2 Conc. (ppm)	Forecast SO_2 Concentrations (ppm) <0.3	0.3–0.5	>0.5	Total
<0.3	6	2	2	10
0.3–0.5	3	9	4	16
>0.5	7	4	5	16
Total	16	15	11	42

TABLE IX
Per Cent of Time each Forecast Concentration of SO_2 Occurred as Indicated

Observed SO_2 conc. (ppm)	Forecast SO_2 concentrations (ppm) <0.3	0.3–0.5	>0.5
<0.3	37	13	18
0.3–0.5	19	60	37
>0.5	44	27	45
Total	100	100	100

In Table X, a similar calculation is made, but this time each entry of Table VIII is divided by the sum of its respective row and multiplied by 100. This provides information on the relative effectiveness of the model as a function of the observed value. It is especially important to see how well the model works for each portion of the observed range of concentration values. A useful model should be particularly effective for high concentration values.

One must consider the magnitude of the range of variables. If the range of observed pollution values is small or the distribution about the mean is small because only a small sample was used, misleading results may be obtained. If the range is small because the pollution values are always small and vary but little, then there is no need for sophisticated calculations. Forecasting presents no problem, and the citizens are fortunate.

C. Skill scores

Another model validation measure is the Heidtke skill score[42] which may be expressed as

$$\frac{\text{No. of correctly calculated values}}{\text{Total no. of calculated values}} - \frac{\text{No. of expected hits}}{\text{No. of expected hits}}$$

$$\text{Skill Score} = \frac{V - E}{T - E}$$

TABLE X
Per Cent of Time each Observed Category of SO_2 Concentration was Forecast as Indicated

Observed SO_2 conc. (ppm)	Forecast SO_2 concentrations (ppm) <0.3	0.3–0.5	>0.5	Total
<0.3	60	20	20	100
0.3–0.5	19	56	25	100
>0.5	44	25	31	100

V = number of calculations which are verified

E = expected hits according to some criterion

T = total number of calculations.

The expected value E may be calculated in a number of different ways depending on whether the forecast equation is compared to pure chance, persistence, climatology, or some other forecast scheme.

The skill score is subject to manipulation since there is leeway in deciding what constitutes a correct calculated value. In practice, one indicates that concentrations will fall within a given bandwidth rather than that a specified value will occur. The width of the band selected subjectively, therefore, determines the magnitude of the skill score.

A cruder way of presenting the effectiveness of a model is to indicate the ratio of hits within a given band to the total number of calculations, e.g. 8/10 of the calculations fell within 0.03 ppm of the observed value.

D. Effectiveness of model as a function of a particular variable

Let us assume that the calculation based on the model was verified if the calculated value and the observed value differ by 5 pphm or less. We may then determine the per cent of calculated values which exceeded, were verified or were less than the values in the observed band. Also, we may stratify the data in accordance with a particular variable, e.g., wind speed. Then for each wind speed group interval, we may compute the per cent of calculated values which were greater than, were verified, or were less than the observed band values. When a plot is made of these percentages as a function of wind speed intervals as seen in Figure 11, we have an indication of the relation between the effectiveness of the model and a particular variable. Further, the data may be stratified according to two or more variables such as would be the case if the computation of Figure 11 were carried out for data with the wind direction in the 270–315° sector, i.e., stratification by wind direction as well as speed. Stratification may be extended to include stability and temperature. Multiple stratification is limited by the amount of data available since too small a number of cases in each cell of the multidimensional space may result.

If the observed concentration is a function of several variables, viz, wind speed, wind direction, temperature, and stability, then by stratifying the data, the effect of each variable may be studied, For example, consider only data where the wind direction ranges from 270° to 315° and the atmosphere is very stable, then we may plot observed concentration versus temperature for a wind speed band of 1–4 mph. On the same graph, a similar plot

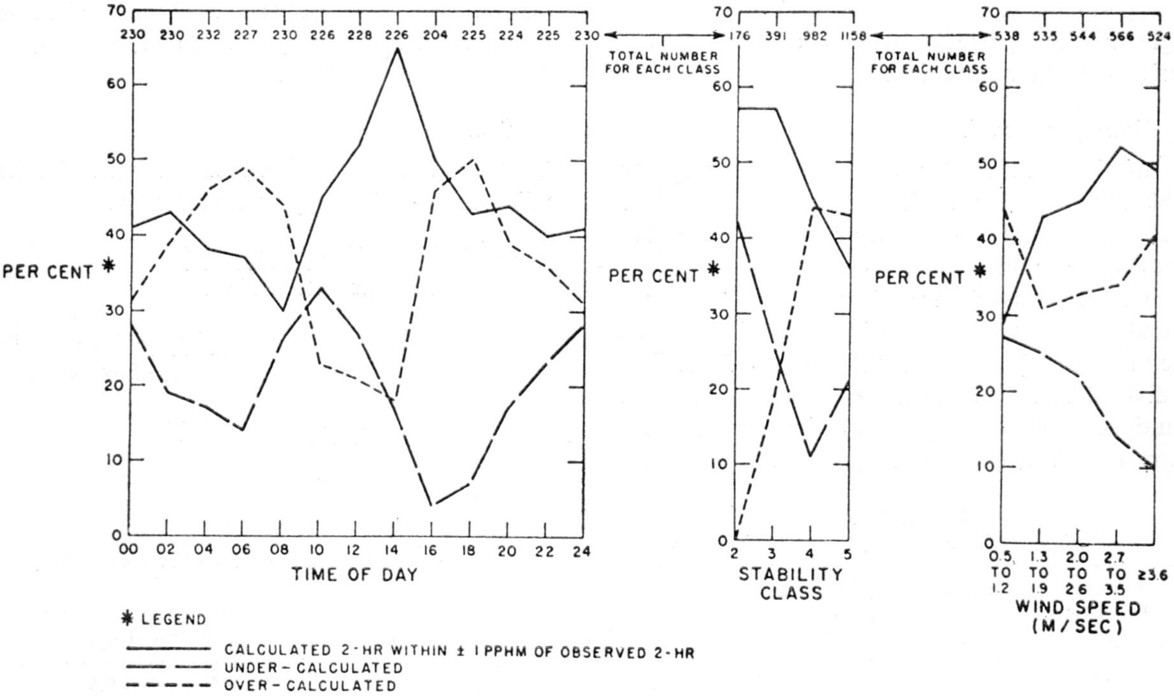

Figure 11 Accuracies of calculations with ±1 pphm vs. time of day. (After Turner.[2]) Number of cases shown near top of chart.

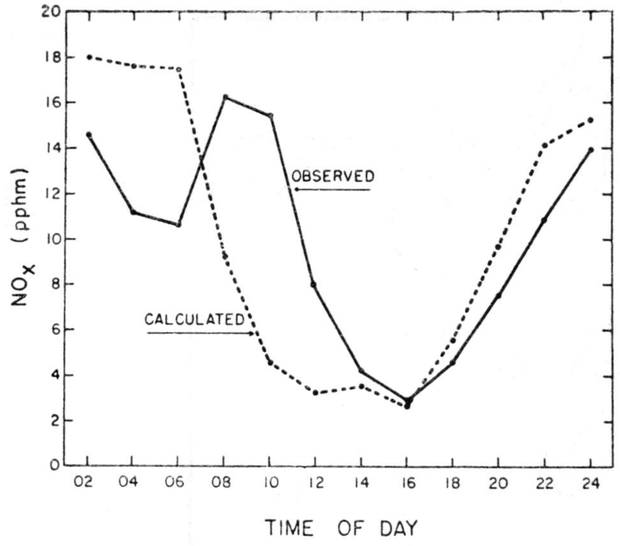

Figure 12 Average diurnal calculated and observed values of oxides of nitrogen. (After Clarke.[14])

can be made for calculated concentrations so that the observed and calculated values may be compared. Graphs can be made for other combinations of variables.

A comparison of observed and calculated values of the oxides of nitrogen for each hour of the day is shown in Figure 12. No other data stratification is involved in this figure.

E. Spatial and temporal variation of pollutants—isopleth charts

The pollutant concentrations as well as the meteorological variables are functions of the three space coordinates, x, y, and z, and time, t. Thus we have a five-dimensional system

$$F(x,y,z,t,0) = 0,$$

where ϕ is a meteorological or pollutant variable. By holding two dimensions fixed, let us say t and z, we may draw isopleths of ϕ as a function of x and t in a horizontal plane. Q vertical cross-section may be obtained by holding y and t constant.

Davidson[11] has made detailed soundings of SO_2 and temperature using a helicopter to obtain vertical cross-sections. Although time, t, was not constant, the variables were assumed to vary slowly with time. A cast study as shown in Figure 13 provides an enlightening picture of the layering of warm air.

Isopleths on a horizontal plane may be drawn for observed values with calculated values plotted at the stations or drawn for calculated values with the observed values plotted. Another possibility is to draw isopleths of ratios of observed to calculated values. See Figure 14. Such charts are valuable

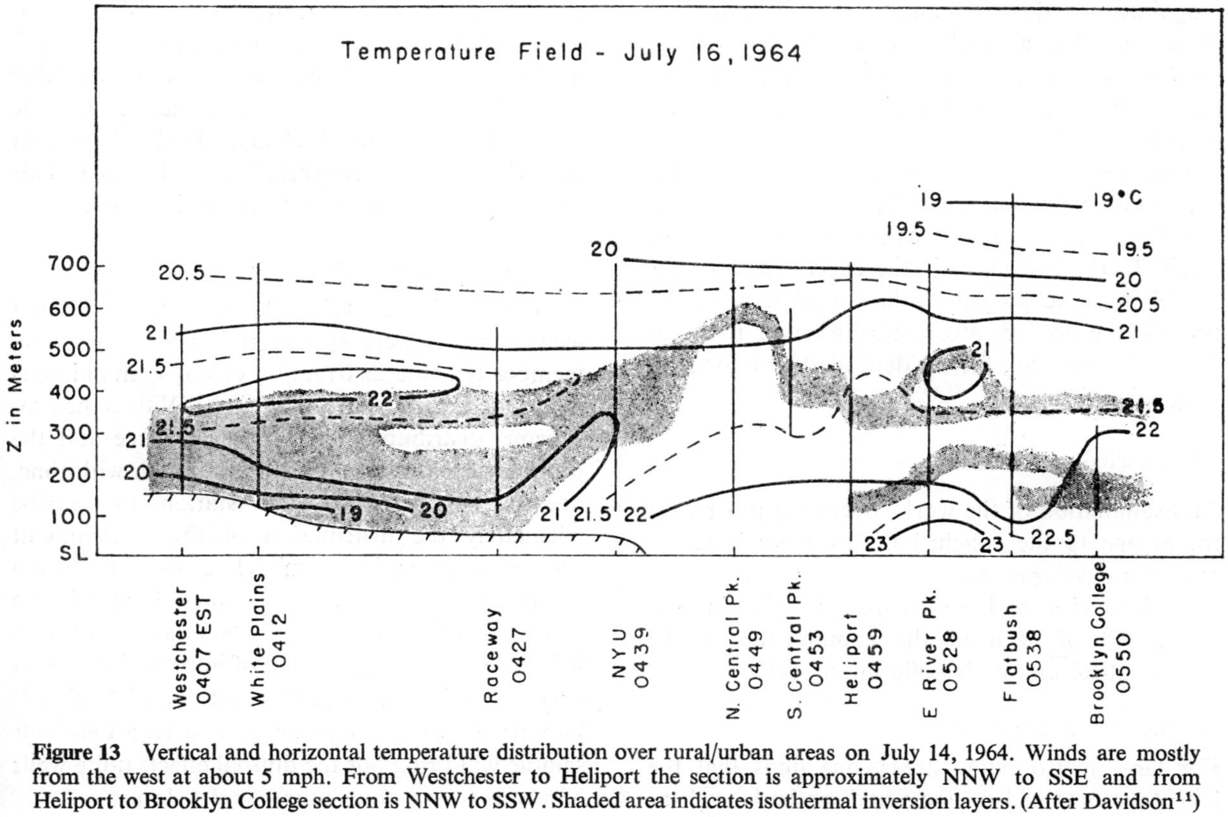

Figure 13 Vertical and horizontal temperature distribution over rural/urban areas on July 14, 1964. Winds are mostly from the west at about 5 mph. From Westchester to Heliport the section is approximately NNW to SSE and from Heliport to Brooklyn College section is NNW to SSW. Shaded area indicates isothermal inversion layers. (After Davidson[11])

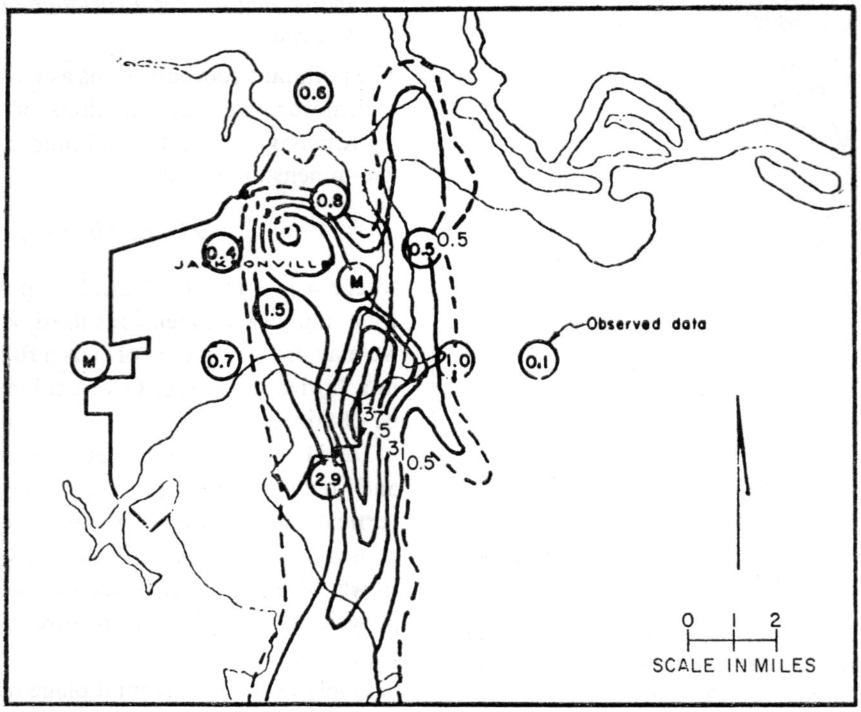

Figure 14 Observed and computed SO_2 concentrations for January 20, 1966. (After Koogler.[9])

since they call attention to areas of high concentrations as well as to the shape of these areas, e.g., elongated, diffuse, or circular. The location and magnitude of the maximum is clearly indicated. When one plots a number of such isopleth charts, each for a different wind direction, the effect of large sources on the pollution pattern becomes evident.

Thus there are a number of ways of presenting the results of a comparison between observed and calculated values and of calculating measures of merit. In the last analysis the effectiveness of the model must be judged by how well it works to provide the needed information whether it be for day-to-day control, for incident alerts, or for long range planning.

XI. Concluding Remarks

An examination of the work covered in this report forces one to the conclusion that there is ample room for development.

Inadequacies and shortcomings exist in our assessment of each of the components of the mathematical urban air pollution model.

A. The source inventory

For large metropolitan areas, one finds that the inventory obtained by the usual methods such as questionnaires is often out of date upon its completion. A continual updating is necessary. However, in a receptor-oriented model, the requirement for a detailed source inventory is relaxed. Further, by developing a receptor-oriented "anomaly" model, one may further reduce the error resulting from inadequate source information. In the "anomaly" type model, changes in the dependent variable over a given period are calculated. This interval may be one, two, four, or six hours.

B. Pollutant measurements

An examination of Table II, shows that pollutant measurements were sparse. It is necessary to remember that the distribution of any contaminants is a function of space and time. With a heterogeneous distribution of sources in space and the pronounced variation in source strength with time, one can hardly expect a few stations to describe adequately the distribution of the contaminant sources. Further, in the models to date, no group has measured the variation of the pollutant in the vertical continuously. In the New York study, a helicopter provided this kind of information, but at best, it was fragmentary. Also, the averaging time is important. A one-hour sample or even a two-hour sample will bring out the diurnal effects quite well; however, twenty-four hour samples do not.

C. Meteorological measurements

The amount of weather data is inadequate. Since the concentrations at a given receptor are markedly affected by the wind direction, the wind field must be known. One must consider not only the horizontal variation of wind speed and direction near the surface, but also the variation with height, the shear. The orientation of the mean air flow over a city has an additional effect. When the winds are perpendicular to the long axis of a rectangular-shaped city then the residence time of materials over the city is relatively short. If the winds are along the long axis, there will be greater accumulations on the downwind side.

In most of the studies, information on the stability was obtained only indirectly. Measurements of the vertical variation of temperature with height was only rarely obtained. In the New York study, the helicopter did obtain such information.

Measurements of the mixing layer depth was for the most part absent. This information can be obtained by remote probing techniques such as lidar or radar, by balloons, or by aircraft or helicopters. However, the mixing layer depth is an essential parameter in determining the volume over which the material will be mixed, and is of importance in forecasting levels of atmospheric concentrations.

D. The mathematical algorithm

Most of the studies have been based on the simple Gaussian model with suitable corrections such as those for the variation of stack heights, plume rise, or removal rates of the contaminant. Changes in the wind direction or stability during the measuring interval were either ignored or treated crudely. The selection of adequate values for the adjustable parameters was well nigh impossible because of the lack of good measurements.

E. Validation techniques

The literature shows that efforts to validate the effectiveness of a model are fraught with difficulties. The calculated values of skill scores may be of questionable significance since they involve considerable subjectivity in the selection of the band-with representing a forecast hit or in the technique for calculating the expected values. Further, skill scores based on the entire range of pollutant values are not completely useful since it may be trivial to forecast low values of pollutant concentration, but may be extremely important to know when high values will occur to prevent damage to property or the onset of respiratory difficulties. The model should therefore be geared for maximum effectiveness at the high end of the scale, e.g., levels of SO_2 exceeding 0.5 ppm. Similar problems are encountered in forecasting low ceilings or frost since only one end of the scale of variables is of interest.

Acceptable statistical procedures were at times violated. Where concentration data from several stations were available, these were lumped together to provide a large sample. This is in general unacceptable especially where pronounced heterogeneity in the areal distribution of concentration existed. Further, in time series of pollutant concentrations, autocorrelation effects must be considered in asesssing the number of independent measurements for use in significance determinations.

XII. Future Considerations

If mathematical modeling is to be effective, it is essential that information be available on the space-time distribution of both the pollutant and the necessary meteorological variables. By considering concentration changes with time and using the receptor-oriented approach, one may minimize the influence of the source inventory, but in the last analysis, source inventory information is necessary for any model. In the validation procedure, one must consider the occurrence of systematic errors, i.e., readings consistently too high or too low compared to the calculated values. Similarly, large deviations between calculated and observed values should be carefully investigated. The selection of an appropriate sampling time is most important.

In conclusion, although the efforts made to date on the problem are commendable, the results are still not as good as is desired. The continued effort in the development of an urban air pollution model is necessary, and hopefully will provide the needed tools for handling urban air pollution problems.

REFERENCES

1. Frenkiel, F. N. (1956). Atmospheric Pollution in Growing Communities. Smithsonian Report for 1956, pp. 269–299.
2. Turner, D. Bruce (1964). A Diffusion Model for an Urban Area. *J. Applied Meteorology*, **3**, No. 1, February 1964, pp. 85–91.
3. Pooler, Francis, Jr. (1966). A Tracer Study of Dispersion over a City. *J. Air Pollution Control Association*, **16**, No. 12, December 1966, pp. 677–681.
4. Clarke, John F. 1964). A Simple Diffusion Model for Calculating Point Concentrations from Multiple Sources. *J. Air Pollution Control Association*, **14**, No. 9, September 1964, pp. 347–353.
5. Miller, Marvin E. and George C. Holzworth (1967). An Atmospheric Model for Metropolitan Areas. *J. Air*

Pollution Control Association, **17**, No. 1, January 1967, pp. 46–50.
6. Schiermeir, F. A., private communication.
7. Kussman, A. S. (1967). *Status of SO_2 Concentration Forecasts and Computations*, WBO, New York, (unpublished).
8. Kussman, A. S. (1968). Atmospheric Diffusion Model for Metropolitan Areas as Applied to New York City, (unpublished).
9. Koogler, J. B., R. S. Sholtes, A. L. Danis, and C. I. Harding, (1967). A Multivariable Model for Atmospheric Dispersion Prediction. *J. Air Pollution Control Association*, **17**, No. 4, April 1967, pp. 711–214.
10. Panofsky, H. A. and B. Prasad (1967). The Effect of Meteorological Factors on Air Pollution in a Narrow Valley. *J. Applied Meteorology*, **6**, No. 3, June 1967, pp. 494–499.
11. Davidson, Ben (1967). A Summary of the New York Urban Air Pollution Dynamics Research Program. *J. Air Pollution Control Association*, **17**, No. 3, March 1967, pp. 154–158.
12. Hilst, G. R. F., F. I. Badgley, J. B. Yocum and N. E. Bowne, (1967). The Development of a Simulation Model for Air Pollution Over Connecticut. A Final Report to the Connecticut Research Commission, Vol. I and II. The Travelers Research Center, Inc., Hartford, Connecticut, October 1967.
13. Hilst, G. R. and N. E. Bowne, (1966). A Study of the Diffusion of Aerosols Released from Aerial Line Sources Upwind of an Urban Complex. A Final Report to the U.S. Army Dugway Proving Ground, Vol. I, The Travelers Research Center, Inc., Hartford, Connecticut, July 1966.
14. Fortak, H. (1966). Rechnerische Ermittlung der SO_2— Grundbelastung aus Emissiondaten, Anwendung auf die Verhaltnisse des Stadtgebietes von Bremen mit Abbildungsteil, Institut fur theoretische Meterologie der freien Universitat Berlin.
15. Croke, E., J. Carson, F. Clark, A. Kennedy, and J. Roberts (1968). Chicago Air Pollution System Model, First Quarterly Progfress Report, Argonne National Laboratory, ANL/ES–CC–001, February 1968.
16. Croke, E. J., J. E. Carson, D. F. Gatz, H. Moses, F. L. Clark, A. S. Kennedy, J. A. Gregory, J. J. Roberts, R. P. Carter, and D. B. Turner (1968) Chicago Air Pollution System Model, Second Quarterly Progress Report, Argonne National Laboratory, ANL/ES–CC–002, May 1968.
17. Croke, E. J., J. E. Carson, D. F. Gatz, H. Moses, A. S. Kennedy, J. A. Gregory, J. J. Roberts, K. Croke, J. Anderson, D. Parsons, J. Ash, J. Norco, and R. P. Carter (1968). Chicago Air Pollution System Model, Third Quarterly Progress Report, Argonne National Laboratory, ANL/ES–CC–003, October 1968.
18. Roberts, J. J., E. S. Croke, and A. S. Kennedy (1970). An Urban Atmospheric Dispersion Model. *Proceedings of the Symposium on Multiple Source Urban Diffusion Models*, pp. 6–1 to 6–70. Also see: Chicago Air Pollution Systems Analysis Program, Final Report, Argonne National Laboratory, ANL/ES–CC–009, February 1971, pp. 198–209.
19. Pooler, Francis, Jr. (1961). A Prediction Model of Mean Urban Pollution for Use with Standard Wind Roses. *Int. J. Air and Water Pollution*, Pergamon Press, **4**, Nos. 3/4, pp. 199–211.
20. Meade, P. J., and F. Pasquill (1958). A Study of the Average Distribution of Pollution Around Staythorpe. *Int. J. Air Pollution*, Pergamon Press, **1**, pp. 60–70.
21. Martin, D. O. (1971). An Urban Diffusion Model for Estimating Long Term Average Values of Air Quality. *J. Air Pollution Control Association*, **21**, pp. 16–19.
22. Lucas, D. H. (1958). The Atmospheric Pollution of Cities. *Int. J. Air Pollution*, Pergamon Press, **1**, pp. 71–86.
23. Slade, David H. (1967). Modeling Air Pollution in the Washington, D.C. to Boston Megalopolis. *Science*, **157**, No. 3794, pp. 1794–1307.
24. Smith, M. E. (1961). *International Symposium for Chemical Reaction of the Lower and Upper Amtosphere*, San Francisco. Advance Papers, Stanford Research Institute, pp. 273–286.
25. Bouman, D. J. and F. H. Schmidt (1961). On the Growth of Ground Concentrations of Atmospheric Pollution in Cities During Stable Conditions. *Beitrage zur Physik der Atmosphare*, **33**, No. 3/4, Akademische Verlagsgesellschaft, m.b.H, Frankfurt am. Main.
26. Commins, B. T. and R. E. Waller (1967). Observations from a Ten-Year Study of Pollution at a Site in the City of London. *Atmospheric Environment*, Pergamon Press, **1**, pp. 49–68.
27. Canno, D., S. Fukui, H. Ikada, and Y. Ono (1959). Atmospheric SO_2 Concentrations Observed in Keihin Industrial Center and Their Relation to Meterological Elements. *Int. J. Air and Water Pollution*, **1**, No. 3, pp. 234–240.
28. Yocum, J. E., D. A. Chisholm, G. F. Collins, J. A. Farrow, R. M. Gagosz and J. C. Magyar (1967). Air Pollution Study of the Capitol Region, December 1967. Travelers Research Center Service Corporation, Hartford, Connecticut, Prepared for the Capitol Region Planning Agency.
29. Munn, R. E., D. A. Thomas and A. R. W. Cole (1969). A Study of Suspended Particulate and Iron Concentration in Windsor, Canada. *Atmospheric Environment*, **3**, No. 1, pp. 1–10.
30. Scott, H. J. (1954). Cleveland Cooperative Meteorological and Air Pollution Program, Paper No. 54–A–166, Presented at Annual Meeting of the American Society for Mechanical Engineers, New York, New York, November 28 through December 3, 1954.
31. Kauper, E. J., D. F. Hartman, and C. J. Hopper (1961) Smog Forecasting in the Los Angeles Basin, Air Quality Report No. 37, Air Pollution Control District, County of Los Angeles.
32. Wanta, R. C. (1967). Meteorology and Air Pollution, Chapter 7 of *Air Pollution*, Vol. 1, edited by A. C. Stern, Academic Press, Inc., New York.
33. Lamb, R. G. and Morris Neiburger (1971). An Interim Version of a Generalized Urban Air Pollution Model. *Atmospheric Environment*, Pergamon Press, **5**, pp. 239–264.
34. Turner, D. Bruce (1968). The Diurnal and Day-to-Day Variations of Fuel Usage of Space Heating in St. Louis, Missouri. *Atmospheric Environment*, Pergamon Press, **2**, pp. 339–351.
35. Clarke, J. F. (1967). Forecasting Pollutant Concentrations, U.S. Weather Bureau Forecasters Training Course, Silver Spring, Maryland.
36. Worley, F. L., Jr. (1971). Report on Mathematical Modeling of Photochemical Smog. Prepared for presentation to the Panel on Modeling, NATO/CCMS Pilot Project on Air Pollution, Paris, France, July 26–27, 1971.
37. Friedlander, S. K. and J. H. Seinfeld (1969). A Dynamic Model of Photochemical Smog. *Environmental Science and Technology*, **3**, pp. 1175–1181.
38. Hecht, T. A. and J. H. Seinfeld (1972). Development and Validation of a Generalized Mechanism for Photochemical Smog. *Environmental Science and Technology*, **6**, pp. 45–57.
39. Moses, H. and J. E. Carson (1968). Stack Design Parameters Influencing Plume Rise. *J. Air Pollution Control Association*, **18**, No. 7, July 1968.

40. Turner, D. Bruce (1967). Workbook of Atmospheric Dispersion Estimates, Public Health Service Publication, No. 999–AP–26, Environmental Health Series, Department of Health, Education and Welfare.
41. Turner, D. Bruce, private communication.
42. Panofsky, H. A. and G. W. Brier (1958). *Some Applications of Statistics to Meteorology*. The Pennsylvania State University Press, University Park, Pennsylvania, 244 pages; Meteorology of Air Pollution, *Encyclopedia of Environmental Science and Engineering*, Vol. 1, Gordon and Breach, Inc., New York, 1976.

HARRY MOSES
Argonne National Laboratory
CONRAD J. MASON
University of Michigan

URBAN PLANNING

Although there are a number of excellent definitions of Urban Planning available, the clearest insight comes from examining the elements or steps used in the formulation of an Urban Plan.

The main elements are:

Data Collection,

Data Analysis,

Goal Formulation (value judgments),

Plan Making (including alternatives),

Plan Implementation,

Feed Back,

Plan Revision.

These elements indicate the stages necessary in the formulation of an Urban Plan, and the last two in particular indicate the iterative and dynamic nature of an Urban Plan. Many of these elements are self-explanatory but some discussion of a few of them may help to clarify the Planning Process.

The collection of data involves population, land use, types of structures, condition of structures, influence of land use on the environment, nonconforming land use, etc. This data can be collected from a variety of sources such as census data, city records and field surveys. The data can then be assembled in a variety of ways possibly using decennial periods, which can show the changes that are taking place. Upon analysis of the data trends can be seen quite readily and forecasts can be easily made over the next decade or two. At this point, the question can be asked, is this the direction that the city should develop in terms of the total environment and the well-being of the inhabitants as a whole? It is clearly the direction that the present urban dynamics will carry the city over the near term if no controls are to be employed.

The answer to this dilemma is the essence of true urban planning, and in simple terms the solution lies in encouraging the healthy existing trends and discouraging the others. This should be done with a few broad sweeping policies (not a series of short term stopgap measures) developed through thorough consultation with a wide cross-section of the community. To be effective, this must be followed by a well-organized public information service on a continuing basis. The development of these broad-sweeping policies will require some value judgments which, to be successful, must reflect the values of the community at large not just those of the planners or the entrepreneurs. This is difficult to do when we realize that we must not discourage capital investment, but encourage it and direct it to areas that are in the best interests of the entire community, while at the same time develop the city in an orderly fashion that will keep public works improvement costs within reasonable limits. What this all leads up to is the need for a Master Plan for the entire area, preferably covering all the contiguous property in the region not just that within the present city limits.

In the Province of Ontario in Canada, official Master Plans are prepared for planning areas on the initiation of a municipality, or more than one municipality when they form, in the opinion of the Minister of Municipal Affairs a complete planning area. An official plan is prepared by a planning board appointed by the municipality, but members of the municipal council may not compose a majority of the planning board members. The official Plan is developed following a survey of the physical, social and economic conditions within the planning area. Maps, statistics and other materials are prepared, and public meetings are held as well as consultations with all local boards. Finally, an official Plan is completed and submitted to the municipal council for adoption. Upon municipal ratification, the Plan is submitted to the Minister of Municipal Affairs for study by the Public Service of Ontario. The Minister, in consultation with the council of the municipality, will negotiate settlement of such modifications as seems necessary. The Minister may then approve the Plan and it then becomes the official plan for the planning area. Amendments to an official plan are made from time to time in much the same way.

The official Plan provides an orderly pattern of development for the municipality that, if careully prepared, will protect the environment, and keep the costs of expanding municipal services within reason. With respect to private investment, although there is some loss of freedom regarding where certain structures can be located, investors are quick to recognize the protection afforded their investments due to the order that can follow a well-prepared official Plan.

This particular mechanism is not being proposed as a model for others to follow, and it isn't that unique in North America. However, it provides a reasonably workable arrangement. Irrespective of how an official Plan may be prepared, such a Plan is a necessary guide to the orderly development of a community.

In the following sections, the importance of such an official or master Plan will be outlined with respect to the development of a wide variety of municipal services and on controlling pollution of the environment.

Water Supply and Distribution

The importance of a water supply that is dependable, abundant and of high quality[1] cannot be overemphasized. A city can overcome a lot of difficulties, but an insufficient or unsafe water supply is not one of them. If the city in question does not suffer from the basic handicaps indicated above, it should respond nicely to proper urban planning. The following points should indicate a few of the input requirements for proper water supply planning, and one of the most serious implications of urban sprawl.

First of all it is absolutely essential to have a well considered master plan showing land use in various areas, population densities and other elements discussed earlier under Master Plan. It is only with this kind of information that adequate treatment and distribution facilities can be developed in an orderly manner and at least cost to the city.

Secondly, an interesting point that should be more properly considered at the master plan stage as well as later, in water distribution, according to, nations cities,[2] if the demand doubles in a fixed area due to increased density or to a higher industrial or commercial use, all that is necessary is to expand the pipe diameter by about forty percent. This is true since the pipe cross-sectional area increases with the square of the radius. However if the demand doubles due to doubling the service area, we require, among other things, double the pipe line mileage. To this you add an increase in the cross-section of the old system at its base to transmit the extra load to the new extension, and increase pressure at the load centre to maintain adequate pressure at the fringes, which may require pipe joint upgrading to withstand this increased pressure. This provides a sobering look at the extreme cost of urban sprawl when it is allowed to develop uncontrolled and unplanned. When you consider sewers and other services in the same light it is more understandable why so many are unable to satisfy their dream, a single family detached home in the suburbs.

Sewage Collection and Treatment

A sewage treatment plant requires a considerable area, preferably with gently sloping topography, in a somewhat isolated location, near a body of receiving water, hopefully downwind from the residental areas and downstream from the water treatment plant intake. Although these are not the only considerations they are sufficient in themselves to greatly limit the number of acceptable locations. Once built its influence will be felt with respect to further urban development for many years to come, so great care should be taken in its location.

The sewage collector system, like the water distribution system, is extremely sensitive to gross errors in planning. Once again the importance of a master plan is easily demonstrated in the design of a collector system.

The best and most economic sewage collector system flows by gravity, avoids pumping as much as possible, as well as extremely flat or steep grades. For these reasons among others, ravines and ridges are generally best left undeveloped. They happen to be easily turned into very excellent recreational areas in most cases. Also the ravines can very often serve as an important part of the storm drainage system. In order to keep grades within reasonable limits and to minimize excavation, it is wise to run streets generally in the direction of the contour lines and avoid unnecessary cross contour streets where slopes are steep.

The Urban Land Institute[3] (Ch. 5), suggests that due to new sewer cleaning techniques, sewers can be quite successfully built as long radius curves instead of a series of short straight chords with an expensive manhole at each intersection. In addition they suggest the use of vertical curves to avoid unnecessary turbulence at manholes instead of the usual uniform grade between manholes, where grades are steep.

It should be noted that the topography bears little relationship to political boundaries and a regional approach[4] to sewer and sewage treatment planning is the most rational.

Drainage and Flood Storage

In the design of drainage facilities, several factors create serious problems for the drainage engineer, that good planning can in large measure overcome. The problem of determining appropriate runoff coefficients for various areas is facilitated by a carefully prepared master plan. Knowing such things as land use, intensity of use, population density, percentage of land coverage, etc., will remove much of the guess work for the drainage specialist. The problem of designing a system that will handle large storms without danger to the public, with a minimum of inconvenience, and at a reasonable cost is a real challenge. Perhaps the most interesting innovation in this area is the suggestion of the Urban Land Institute[3] (Ch. 3), that our cities have two separate and complete drainage systems: a primary system and a secondary system. The primary system consists of the normal drainage conduits and structures, while the secondary system is the route followed by the flood or runoff waters when the primary system is overloaded. The secondary system has all too often received very little design attention. In order to improve the secondary system and thus minimize the cost of the primary system while at the same time lessen flood hazards the following design considerations are suggested.

1) Utilization of the streets hydraulic capacity to handle a large portion of the runoff without seriously impairing vehicular access.

2) Controlling inlet capacities in order to allow not only some reduction in the size of primary facilities, but to attenuate flood peaks.

3) Design flat factory and commercial building roofs to temporarily retain a controlled amount of rainfall by limiting the capacity of the connections to the primary sewer system.

4) Utilization of the ravines and other low lying areas which are normally used for recreational purposes, as a temporary flood storage system. This will do little permanent damage to the recreational aspects, and it will pay big dividends in reducing the cost of the primary drainage system, and reduce downstream flooding by evening out the flow.

5) When employing flood plain storage, it is necessary to incorporate flood plain regulations[5] particularly with respect to location of buildings, public safety and proper maintenance.

The utilization of a carefully planned approach to the design of secondary drainage systems can reduce over-all costs, increase public safety, and is worthy of serious consideration.

Air Pollution

Air pollution is the most insidious of all forms of pollution from one standpoint at least. Although you can partially avoid the direct danger of most other forms of pollution, you must breathe the air that happens to be at hand.

With respect to planning and air pollution we know that industries can easily be separated into groups that pollute and those that do not pollute. They can further be subdivided into air polluters and others. Now the air polluters can be located in industrial sites where the prevailing wind can carry the pollutants in such a direction as to create the least nuisance. This is best done at the master plan stage when industrial zoning is being considered. Even if these industries are taking every precaution to control their emissions, locating them in designated areas is not only a wise precaution, but it enables the air pollution enforcement branch to police the problem more effectively.

As fossil fuels become more scarce and expensive, and particularly in northern areas where auxiliary heating is required much of the year, central heating for large sections of the city should be investigated. In Sweden where it has proven its worth, not only is fuel consumption down by one third, but air pollution can almost be eliminated from this source, due to improved combustion and the use of air pollution control devices, at the central heating plant. Even if the fuel economy was ignored the reduction in air pollution would make central heating feasible in many areas.

Refuse Collection and Disposal

The total refuse production[5] in most North American cities on a per capita basis is three quarters of a ton per annum. Of this refuse about 75 % is combustible with a calorific value of about 5000 B.T.U.'s per pound.

Regarding the collection phase, other than improvements in the design of collection vehicles little has changed. It is still a rather labour intensive operation. On the other hand the disposal of refuse along with the associated field of waste reclamation and recycling is one of the most dynamic technological areas. The possibilities for the innovative engineer are almost limitless.

Although many ideas are being advanced, including making structural or paving blocks out of garbage, at the moment four principal methods with several variations are being used.

1) Land fill,
2) Municipal incineration,
3) Garbage grinding,
4) Composting.

Of the four the first two are the most popular and provided they are operated correctly, and on a large enough scale, they are economically viable and create no serious nuisance. However, if carelessly operated the land fill may have blowing paper, harbour rats, produce gas, uneven settlement, etc., and the incinerator may smoke, produce odor, or have a fly ash fall out problem. Generally speaking the land fill is used where haul distances are not too great and suitable inexpensive land is available for fill sites. Whereas incineration is used where land is unavailable, too expensive or haul distances to fill sites are too great.

Garbage grinding, either by home units or municipally, will place a heavy burden on the sewage treatment plant, in fact to operate well the plant should be designed with garbage grinding in mind. Composting is effective, however unless suitable dependable markets for the compost can be developed, it will continue to be too expensive.

All of the methods can, and some require an auxiliary scavenging operation that may produce a little bit of revenue (rags, metals, glass, etc.). In the case of incineration and composting, sewage sludge may be added. However composting heavy metals from industrial wastes may prove to be a problem. The incineration may be used to fire boilers and produce steam or hot water for heating or other purposes.

The keys to proper refuse disposal are first to pick an economic method and locate the facility in an area where the possible nuisance, and thence complaints, will be minimal. Or in the case of a large city more than one method may be required, i.e. incineration in the core and land fill in the suburbs. And secondly operate the facilities in the recommended manner and there should be very few problems.

Noise and Visual Pollution

In the last century noise levels that urban man could be expected to be exposed to have increased from 60 decibels for speech, to 120 decibels for a pneumatic chipping hammer and 150 decibels for a rocket engine. The increase has been nearly a decibel per year.[6] Experiments have shown that 160 decibels can kill small fur bearing animals. The same level can deafen a man for life, and in some cases pierce his eardrums as well. It is clear we are reaching the upper limit of the audio insult a man can endure.

The decrease in property value due to the climbing noise levels near jet airports has prompted the Federal Housing Authority to deny mortgage insurance in areas subject to this form of blight. It should also be noted that expressways are having the same effect on property values as the flight paths around airports. It is clear that planners are paying more attention to this problem and it is just as important to zone out residential development in such areas as it is to control building heights.

Once again the master plan stage is where major decisions regardng sensible zoning, allowance for future expansion and other related matters should be made, with respect to airports, noisy industry and the inevitable expressways.

Professor Richards suggests that where possible, flight paths should be directed over water as a means of minimizing much of the problem. Where this is not possible golf courses, other recreational areas, or purely rural uses work well. This will allow for expansion if and when necessary without serious expense or dislocation, and will avoid most of the aforementioned problems.

A less acute problem but one receiving attention in recent years is the visual pollution not only of the city but the whole countryside as well, caused by billboards and garish neon signs. For years every bare wall, side of a barn or elevated knoll has been a challenge to the advertising men. Movements to keep advertising within bounds are beginning to gain momentum. The free and easy period when advertisers could outrage our sensibilities, and disfigure our buildings and landscape may be drawing to a close.

Regulations limiting sign sizes, overhangs, height above ground, and location can be expected to receive more attention by city planners as the ground swell of public indignation rises. The visual pollution of modern advertising is not far removed from that of other forms of litter and must be dealt with accordingly.

Combined Effects of Pollution

There are obviously great difficulties involved in pinpointing the exact level of a water, air, noise or other pollutant beyond which a specific illness, be it physical or mental, will develop, even if we base it on an average person of average health. In addition we realize that the danger to the old, the very young, and the infirm varies greatly due to their different tolerance levels. This makes the task not only of setting tolerance levels, but even tolerance ranges almost impossible. Now we arrive at an even bigger stumbling block. If we do set tolerance levels or ranges for a variety of pollutants, the combined effect of a multitude of pollutants may be considerably more or in more cases less than their sum total.[12] What about the combination of two chemicals that although rather innocent taken separately combine to form a toxic substance? How much noise, air pollution, water pollution and littered streets in addition to his normal daily problems can a man take before he becomes physically or mentally ill? It is this serious problem that appears to lie midway between the physical and social scientist, one that requires very serious and immediate attention.

Recreation and Parks

The recreation industries are among our most rapidly expanding, since we work little more than 60% of that at the turn of the century and have two days off work per week and two to three times the annual vacation of that period. Golf and skiing are no longer sports restricted to the wealthy. Every area of recreation is rapidly expanding to fulfill the needs of a large, somewhat affluent middle class. The ingredients are there, time and sufficient money to enjoy it. But what about the other five days per week and fifty weeks per year What do we presently offer the recreationally minded citizen in the modern city? In most cities the answer is very little indeed.

Rather than outline standards[10,11] regarding parks and other facilities, equipment, sizes, location, population served etc., only the more general considerations and areas of greatest need will be discussed. For the most part our parks are little more than blocks of land not occupied by buildings. How often do you see old people sunning themselves, or snoozing in the shade of our treeless parks? How about young mothers with small children, do they use the parks? In far too many cases the park consists of a treeless block with a fence around it, filled with blown paper and other rubbish. About as inviting as the exercise lot at the penitentiary. About the only uses many of these parks are put to, is Little League baseball and gangwars. This situation is simply unacceptable in the 1970's, and the more progressive cities are beginning to recognize their responsibilities to all the citizens.

Parks must be designed to appeal to all walks of life. Teeter-totters and swings have only limited interest to the young. But masses of rock, concrete pipes, blocks, wooden mazes and other interesting masses of concrete, wood or steel never cease to appeal to the imaginative world of the small child. A clump of trees, a few benches, a tree lined walk appeal to older people and mothers with young children. A picnic bench under a shady tree, or benches near a reflecting pool all have an attraction to a wide variety of people. If we simply examine the parks we have now, we will find a few that are always attracting crowds while others lie deserted. Examine these parks and ask yourself why is one used and another one not used. Usually the answer can be felt through the pores of the skin it's so obvious. With this kind of information let's set about renovating our parks and strike some balance, and try and serve the needs of the under ten and over twenty-five age groups a little better.

The needs of the increasing number of older retired people are being sadly neglected. Not only do our parks not interest them, but the types of community facilities that they enjoy most, are not available to the majority of them and in particular the urban poor. Occasionally we see excellent examples of community centres for older people, sometimes as a project by some service club, but more often in the retirement areas that the more affluent go to in the sunny south for their retirement years. The cities must give more attention to the ever increasing number of older retired citizens, and provide some facilities to help make their lives a little richer.

Finally a word on planning and parks. In almost every city, we see examples of low lying river land, steep ridges, or lake shore, that has been either developed when it shouldn't have been, or was developed improperly. A properly conceived master plan would withhold these lands from development and make them into the beautiful parks that many of the truly famous cities are noted for the world over. Urban life need not be as ugly and vicious as it has become in many contemporary cities, and careful planning of parks and recreational areas is one tool to use in humanizing the city.

Geological and Grading Problems

In urban design and development, especially since the development of density zoning[3] which allows clustering of buildings around open space, we have an excellent opportunity to minimize grading and to avoid difficult geological problems by working around them. If the area is such that geological problems are known or suspected to exist, enough geological data[9] should be generated to fully outline the situation. With this information, the design engineer can avoid the worst of the problem, thus keeping costs and the risk to human life to a minimum. This data will indicate where blasting is necessary to where it can be avoided by changes in the location of structures, or revisions in the proposed grading of the area.

A proper geological investigation can locate fault zones, expansive soils, and areas requiring special sub-drain design, to mention a few of the most serious problems. The solutions range from abandoning the project for economic or other reasons, to a wide variety of possible engineering remedies. To find these conditions in the planning stage, although at times a real inconvenience, is certainly preferable to the disastrous situation that can occur when they lie undiscovered or are only discovered when the project is in its final stages.

Even when the geological problems are insignificant, proper planning of clearing and grading can have a tremendous impact on the environment and avoid the mile upon mile of subdivisions that result from the wholesale rape of the land by bulldozer. In general, areas of low density will only permit a minimal amount of expensive grading, while areas of high density will support maximum grading. Intelligent planners subscribe to this thesis, disturb the natural beauty of an area as little as possible, for every unnecessary change has its cost. This cost may be measured from the engineering and construction viewpoint or from the ecological and environmental aspect. To accomplish the above goal, structures should be so grouped on the more easily and safely developed portion of the topography leaving the remainder to be intelligently utilized for the common good of the inhabitants.

When considering even minimal grading, it will involve the loss of trees and shrubs, as most trees are very sensitive to either cutting or filling of even a foot or so, in the area of their root systems. When filling around a tree, even with the trunk protected by a well, an experienced horticulturist should be consulted regarding the maximum depth of fill the particular type of tree will tolerate.

The importance of careful planning based on proper information regarding the geology and soil conditions in the area is undeniable. And when this information is combined with a strong desire to destroy as little of the natural beauty as possible, not only will over-all costs be reduced, but we can produce communities that are beautiful the day they are completed. How much nicer than the subdivisions of the fifties that are just gradually becoming livable environments today, almost twenty years later.

Municipal Easement Planning

Residential streets are challenging enough to design attractively, without overhead wires, within the street right-of-way. Most municipalities require overhead wires be carried at the back of lots wherever possible. To a lesser but increasing extent they are being placed underground within the street right-of-way, in order to provide the necessary easements in such a manner as to keep capital and maintenance costs of utilities as low as possible. Some design factors[8] are suggested for proper planning of easements.

1) Easements should be located along rear or side lot lines where possible, and if it is necessary (in the case of deep lots) run easements across them. Access must be provided to every parcel of land.

2) In certain situations such as lake or river front lots, the right-of-way may prove to be the best location for the easement, but buried utilities are recommended in such cases.

3) Easements should be twenty feet wide along rear lot lines, and in the case of side lot lines, ten feet minimum width, the width normally being split between adjacent lots.

4) Easements should be continuous from block to block where possible, providing ingress and egress from streets along rear and side lot lines.

5) Easements should be aligned as much as possible, keeping offsets from block to block (which require guys and anchors) to a minimum. Generally an angle greater than ten degrees will require a guy structure.

6) For lots facing curvilinear streets, the rear lot lines and thence the easements, should be straight chords extending over several lots, and at least 120 feet long, to minimize the number of poles.

7) At the ends of long blocks when up to four lots face the short side street, the rear lot line for these lots should be straight, providing a straight easement to service these lots.

8) Easements should require that no permanent structures be built on or across them, and should confer tree trimming and removal rights within the easements.

9) Controlled planting and landscaping using shrubs that attain mature heights of no more than sixteen feet are recommended to simplify line clearance problems.

10) In exceedingly long blocks, a pedestrian way of sufficient width to allow vehicular access to the easement at mid-block is recommended.

Easements properly located can improve the environment, and reduce maintenance and the inconvenience of interrupted service.

Land Subdivision and Land Development

Land subdivision and development are of vital importance to the city, as they represent a high proportion of the new development within the city each year. It is from this area that most of the new housing stock as well as other much needed structures come into the market. And if we can't do an improved job on these new developments, there is little hope for our cities in the future. There is already so much lack of planning from the past, and old worn-out neighborhoods that need help, that we can ill afford to add to the problem by being careless with the new development.

With this in mind, let's look at ways and means of accomplishing proper municipal goals with regard to new development. One of the most important tools we can use is a carefully prepared master plan, indicating the land use and other data for each of the developed areas. Also the adjacent undeveloped areas are given future land uses based on their suitability for those uses, and bearing in mind the orderly development and the effects of these areas on the total environment of the whole urban complex. Within the context of the master plan, suitable land for every use should be available in sufficient quantity to attract private capital so necessary in the development and redevelopment of the city.

Regulations and bylaws regarding the day-to-day implementation of the master plan should be prepared with the utmost care. They must clearly outline the important criteria to be adhered to in the development or subdivision of the various areas —such general considerations as land use, population density, building height, etc., and the more specific regulations concerning building codes and construction standards. These regulations must be developed with the express purpose of providing a high quality development along with a good environment, and not to simply be restrictive and thence discourage innovative development.

Regulations regarding land use and density of occupation must not be so rigid as to exclude the more exciting approaches to urban living, otherwise there may be a proliferation of adequate (just within the law) but somewhat conventional unexciting developments. The key to successful contemporary development seems to be the provision of a wide variety of good quality accommodation in every area. Apartments, row houses, condominiums, single family dwellings and others, in a park-like setting with plenty of open space designed for active and passive recreation. Developments of this type appeal to all walks of life and appear to have the variety and the excitement that the downtown rows of apartment buildings and the suburban subdivisions lack.

The idea that apartment buildings are the only answer for housing people in the downtown areas and that the single family ranch home is the only answer in suburbia, is gradually giving way to a more cosmopolitan approach to urban living. There is no reason why we cannot provide privacy on one hand, excitement on the other, and good wholesome living for all, at densities several times greater than we have in the conventional suburbs. To do this, we require architectural innovation, and much more careful use of space. To provide decent housing and at the same time an interesting high quality environment, such kinds of housing alternatives must be developed, for every year fewer people can afford the half acre ranch home in suburbia and the costly services that go with such developments.

Urban Transport

This section will be primarily concerned with overall planning alternatives open to the urban planner. The design,[13,14] geometric layout[15,16] and other considerations involved in the implementation of the over-all policy must be sought elsewhere.

With respect to local streets, we must try and preserve the integrity of the neighbourhood wherever possible. Although there are many definitions of neighbourhood, one of the most appropriate is the territory serviced by an elementary school, or a school complex. To accomplish the goal of preserving the neighbourhood several tools are available. First, try and separate pedestrian and vehicular travel as much as possible. The judicious use of cul-de-sacs and court developments may be of use. Secondly, avoid carving neighbourhoods into pieces with careless placement of expressways and large collector streets. Thirdly, avoid as much of the gridiron system as is possible, thus avoiding many dangerous and unnecessary intersections. Fourthly, don't build local street surfaces wider than twenty-six feet[3] and if adequate off-street parking is available they can be narrower. Twenty-six feet is wide enough for parking and through traffic, and to build them any wider will not increase capacity but will encourage speeding to a dangerous level. Finally, avoid putting arbitrary curves in streets (which look best on plans or from the air). Use curves to fit the topography and to preserve the natural beauty of the area.

Regarding collector streets a number of points are pertinent. A collector street should have limited access and egress to function properly. Some local streets should intercept several other small streets and carry this flow to the collector street. In this way the collector can pick up or lose traffic at controlled points rather than every three hundred feet, which is often the case when the collector intercepts every local street, and this leads to chaos. Since collector streets carry considerable traffic load, it is unwise to have lots fronting on them, for the mutual benefit of the home owner and the traffic flow. Have the lots front onto adjacent streets inside the subdivisions and make these lots about 20% deeper with a buffer of shrubs and trees between the back of the lots and the collector street. Never allow commercial ribbon development to spring up along collector streets, as this will ruin the traffic carrying capacity of the street, and produce a marginal development that will surely flounder and start a serious blight.

With respect to throughways and expressways, the scope of this problem is so great that only a few of the major consequences will be outlined. Much of the problem arises from too many people using the expressway for about four hours out of twenty-four, two in the morning and two in the late afternoon. Any scheme which could flatten out these two peaks would help tremendously; or systems that can safely allow some central lanes to be used one way in the morning and the opposite way in the afternoon. In any event the cost of an expressway is not limited to the many millions of dollars per mile to construct them. The loss of tax producing real estate may be in the neighbourhood of 25 acres per mile and 80 acres per interchange. To this can be added the total disruption of the neighbourhoods when the expressways are placed in an arbitrary way, or on purely economic grounds. The resulting decrease in value of these adjacent properties is a cost whose full impact won't be felt for some years. But it produces a blight that will exact its full cost ultimately. As for the downtown area, the expressway places a very heavy stress on parking as well as the old street pattern which was never designed for this influx of traffic. It's like putting a young athlete's heart into an 80-year old man's body with hardened and constricted arteries; the prognosis is poor. When a modern city (on a land surface area basis) is 70% streets, expressways and parking space (vehicles) and 30% buildings (people), how much farther can one go with this imbalance? Surely a point will be reached at which the remaining attractions will not have the drawing power to fully employ the existing roadway. Although such a situation represents a balance of sorts, is this what sane human beings call a balanced urban environment? Does it have any human scale?

In the area of public transport, let us look at one form, the subway. The subway is fast, cheap, and efficient in a rigid sort of way. If a city has one or more axes of high population density a subway will be quite economical. It can move as many people per track as about 16 lanes of expressway if automobiles are the mode of transport being compared. When built below ground, they hardly disturb neighbourhoods at all and the pollution compared with the 16 lanes of expressway is negligible. They do attract a great deal of apartment building along their axis if zoning will allow it, and they can give the central business district a real shot in the arm in many cases. When properly connected with other surface transport and railway lines servicing outside towns and cities, they can reduce downtown congestion a great deal while increasing commercial activity. The whole aspect of public transport requires very careful planning, and in areas comprising a number of municipalities that have grown into a metropolitan area, it should be a metropolitan, not a local responsibility.

Urban Planning in the Future,

There are many problems confronting planners today that will require new techniques, new forms of governmental cooperation, and new laws and regulations in the statute books, if they are to be effectively dealt with in the future. Let us briefly examine some of the changes that are likely to take place in the latter part of this century with respect to effective urban planning.

It is likely that the computer will be more successfully employed in the storage of data that can be used by a variety of municipal departments. This would do away with the large amount of individual data collection (much of which is overlapping) that is presently being done in most cities. Also the use of computers and mathematical models for forecasting[17,18] and aiding planners in establishing realistic goals should soon become more reliable. The experiments conducted in the United States to date have had only limited success, partly due to the complex nature of the urban system, and partly due to a lack of experienced personnel and a reluctance on the part of others to make use of these techniques. Certainly the field of computer technology as applied to urban problems is pregnant with possibilities and the next decade should see a great amount of progress in this area.

There is a great need for up to date information regarding the public's position on a variety of urban problems and what solutions to these problems would they consider most effective. The difficulty and cost of getting up to date information on a continuing basis regarding public opinion is a very real and serious problem. Surely the computer can be employed to advantage in quickly and cheaply compiling and analyzing such data taken from a sample of statistically significant size. Up to now most cities operate either in a vacuum or they are using very old and unreliable information. With one family in five or six moving every year, often to another city, information a few years old does not have much relevance.

The whole concept of private property and the fact that it is such a speculative commodity operates to the detriment of the community at large. When we realize the finite nature of available land the difficulties presented when trying to assemble large enough tracts or blocks of land to allow a co-ordinated well balanced approach to planning, we can see that changes in the powers of eminent domain and condemnation are surely not far off. Certainly ways must be found to assemble large blocks of land without running the price up to the sky,[19] and when the alternative is a continuation of the piecemeal development that we have seen in recent years a remedy must surely be found as soon as possible.

The structure of municipal taxation, and the relationship of municipal, state or provincial and federal taxation is an area receiving a lot of attention in recent years. There appears to be some attempt on the part of the federal government to come to the relief of the city in a variety of ways. Funds for urban renewal, pollution clean up and, more recently, education. Rather than dwell in this area that is so contemporary and amply covered in the news media let's look at the municipal tax structure and in particular a somewhat revolutionary idea in this area.[2]

We should tax land more and improvements less. This would reduce the disproportionate tax load borne by good homes and business buildings while placing more burden on properties that are simply being held for speculative purpoes. It would encourage developments to proceed rather than languish on the drawing boards. It would also lead to much more private development of the slum and obsolete areas in our cities. Surely it is worth serious consideration as at least one alternative to the present system.

An area that is adding considerable cost to new construction is the multiplicity of, in many cases, rather minor variations in building codes, and other regulations. A unified approach to building codes, electrical, plumbing and other regulations would in no way reduce safety but would allow the building industry to make full use of their ability to reduce costs through the more wide spread standardization of a variety of building modules and self contained units. Whether mass production would add to the beauty of the home is difficult to answer but it would certainly give more for the construction dollar. These are the areas that seem to be most ripe for change; there are others, but it is difficult to see any movement on the horizon toward them. One that seems to offer a great deal of benefit is the use of central heating and cooling in our cities. Central heating in the northern part of the U.S.A. and in Canada can offer many benefits due to the fact that fuel costs are cut considerably and the pollution produced by a central heating plant is almost negligible compared with the thousands of individual systems. Sweden has pioneered in this area and we in North America could find this very beneficial as well. The utilization of central cooling in the southern states is another idea that might be feasible. Surely overall costs shoud be less and the constant drone of individual units in windows and back yards is a factor worthy of consideration. It is certain that these are only a few of the deveopments one can expect in the future, but a move in these directions would certainly have far reaching effects on the city of the future.

REFERENCES

1. U.S. Department of Health, (1962). Education and Welfare, "Public Health Service Drinking Water Standards", Washington, D.C.
2. National League of Cities (1968). "Nations Cities, Urban Affairs Portfolio", Washington, D.C.
3. Urban Land Institute (1967). "New Engineering Concepts in Community Development", Technical Bulletin No. 59, Washington, D.C.
4. Grava, S. (1969). "Urban Planning Aspects of Water Pollution Control", Institute of Urban Environment, Columbia University.
5. Logan, J. A., P. Oppermann and N. E. Tucker (1961). *Proceedings of the First Conference on Environmental Engineering and Metropolitan Planning*, Northwestern University Press.
6. Gordon, M. (1963). *Sick Cities*, Penguin Books, Baltimore, Maryland.
7. Richards, E. J. (1961). "Noise at Airports", *Proceedings of the Institution of Civil Engineers*, Vol. 20, London.
8. Department of Municipal Affairs (1969). Community Planning Branch, "Easement Planning for Utility Services".
9. Urban Land Institute (1968). "Engineering Geology—Its Importance in Land Development", Technical Bulletin No. 63.
10. American Society of Civil Engineers (1969). "Urban Planning Guide", Manuals and Reports on Engineering Practice, No. 49, Chapter 6.
11. Shivers, J. S. and G. Hjelte (1971). *Planning Recreational Places*, Fairleigh Dickinson University Press.
12. Grimm, S. N. (1961). *Physical Urban Planning—System of General Concepts abd Principal Features*, Syracuse University, New York.
13. Baerwald, J. E. (1965). *Traffic Engineering Handbook*, Institute of Traffic Engineers, Washington, D.C. 3rd Ed.
14. Hewes, L. I. and C. H. Oglesby. (1963). *Highway Engineering*, John Wiley and Sons.
15. Manual of Geometric Design Standards for Canadian Roads and Streets (1971). Roads and Transportation Association of Canada.
16. A Policy on Arterial Highways in Urban Areas (1962). American Association of State Highway Officials. Washington, D.C.
17. A. G. Wilson (1970). *Forecasting Planning*, P. Cowan, Editor. Developing Patterns of Urbanization. Sage Publications.
18. J. W. Forrester (1969). *Urban Dynamics*. M.I.T. Press.
19. John Fisher (1969). "Planning for the Second America". Harper's, pp. 21–26.

JAMES P. HARTT
University of Windsor

URBAN RUNOFF

Introduction

An understanding of the subject of urban runoff requires some knowledge of a myriad of scientific and engineering disciplines such as meteorology, hydrology, hydraulics, economics, statistics, chemistry, biology and mathematics. This situation has arisen as urban engineers have had to deal with an increasingly complex set of problems surrounding the task of safely conveying accumulated precipitation from inhabited areas to selected receiving waters. Thus, whereas initially, the assignment for the engineer was to develop an utilize a methodology to deal with the quantity of runoff under a variety of circumstances, he must now also be concerned with the qualitative or pollution control aspects of storm water discharges.

Consideration of the latter facet of the problem has derived from the fact that a recreation oriented public is now seeking out virtually every body of water capable of supporting aquatic sports. Because of their relative accessibility, water courses in the vicinity of metropolitan areas have been major targets of today's outdoorsman. Unfortunately, many, if not most, of these bodies of water display easily perceptible characteristics of pollution due to the variety of discharges from industry, commerce, and municipal water pollution control facilities, and wind blown debris from almost every human activity. Where the city's "bath water" flows down the storm sewer, the incremental pollution load is frequently sufficient to depress receiving water quality conditions to a point that the water is no longer suitable for human enjoyment.

The basic task of routing accumulated precipitation away from areas where flooding entails serious property damage or loss of life has been with man ever since he began to urbanize some 5000 years ago. Although there exists ample evidence that ancient civilizations utilized closed conduits for this purpose, the American heritage, which derived principally from North European practices, was to continue to employ natural drainage courses. Precipitation residue, along with other wastewaters, generally flowed over the surface to streams, gullies and washes.

However, disasterous flooding experiences led to a recognition of the need for hydraulically adequate storm water facilities. There remains little evidence as to the original techniques used to estimate the quantities of water to be conveyed by the sewerage system. However, in the last half-century statistical methods for analyzing rainfall records have been scientifically researched, and the hydrological aspects of the subject have been refined to the point where a routine engineering methodology now exists (see "Hydrology" by M. C. Quick in this publication).

Solutions to existing urban stormwater management problems could undoubtedly be relatively straightforward if it were possible to develop entirely new systems. However, the economic burden imposed by such an approach would be intolerable for most communities. In 1966 it was estimated that replacement of San Francisco's storm sewer system would cost in the range of $1.5 billion, or $2000 per capita. Consequently, the engineer must accommodate the results of decisions made as long as a century ago when he develops contemporary solutions to current storm water problems.

One of the "givens" in many urban areas is the existence of a combined sewer system. Combined means that both sanitary sewage and storm water are conveyed in the same pipe. This type of system dates from an era in which sewage treatment was considered to be either unnecessary or economically unfeasible. Sewerage systems were constructed for purposes of conveying any and all liquid wastes to points of convenient discharge. In most cases the location was coincidentally quite near the city limits.

The advent of the era of sewage treatment required a resolution of the problem of what to do with the large quantities of runoff water during periods of rainfall. The typical solution was to construct high flow bypasses upstream of the sewage treatment plant. This means that during wet weather, large amounts of sanitary sewage in addition to residue deposited in the sewers during dry weather are discharged untreated along with the storm water runoff. Needless to say, when this occurs, virtually every receiving water quality requirement is grossly violated. Thus, one of the major current tasks is to develop means to control the quality of such discharges. This effort is being supported by the Storm and Combined Sewer Overflow Program of the Federal Environmental Protection Agency.

The urban drainage is complicated by a host of utilities-related activities in major metropolitan areas. The City of San Francisco was faced with a tremendous task of sewer relocation during the construction of rapid transit facilities. Moreover, the sewer system had to remain functional during the transition period. New York City has embarked on a program of sewer replacement (many of the city's sewers are over 100 years old) which will entail expenditues in the range of $100 million per year. Needless to say, excavation in a Manhattan street is not viewed with pleasure by the occupants of vehicles which must detour to other already congested streets.

Runoff Quantity

It is intuitively obvious that rainfall and runoff are closely related, and yet there are many phenomena which affect the element of water between the time it ceases to be rain and the point of discharge to the receiving lake, stream or estuary. Figure 1 is a simplified diagram showing the important mechanisms which influence the rate and total quantity of runoff from precipitation in urban areas.

Rainfall

There are several types of rainfall which any municipality might expect to experience from time to time, and discussion of them is beyond the scope of this paper. However, in the main the engineer is concerned with the more intense storms which occur with less frequency than moderate or light rainfall. It would be virtually impossible to design a storm sewer of sufficient capacity to handle the runoff from the most intense rainfall which might be expected in the infinite future. As a consequence the municipal engineer uses charts prepared from statistical analyses of historical rainfall records and he generally selects a time interval (return period of from five to 25 years, with 10 years being a typical value. That is to say, if future precipitation patterns follow those of the period of historical record, then the capacity of the sewer system will be inadequate on the average of once every 10 years. There are no known recent study results to indicate that this practice is valid in terms of minimizing expenditures (the sum of the costs of the sewer system and the computed potential costs of flood damage), and this area remains in need of further research.

Rainfall intensity, I, is related to return period, R, and duration, t, by the following approximate relationship:

$$I = \frac{K(R)^x}{(t)^y}, \tag{1}$$

where the coefficient K, and the exponents, x and y, are unique for each geographical area. Plots of

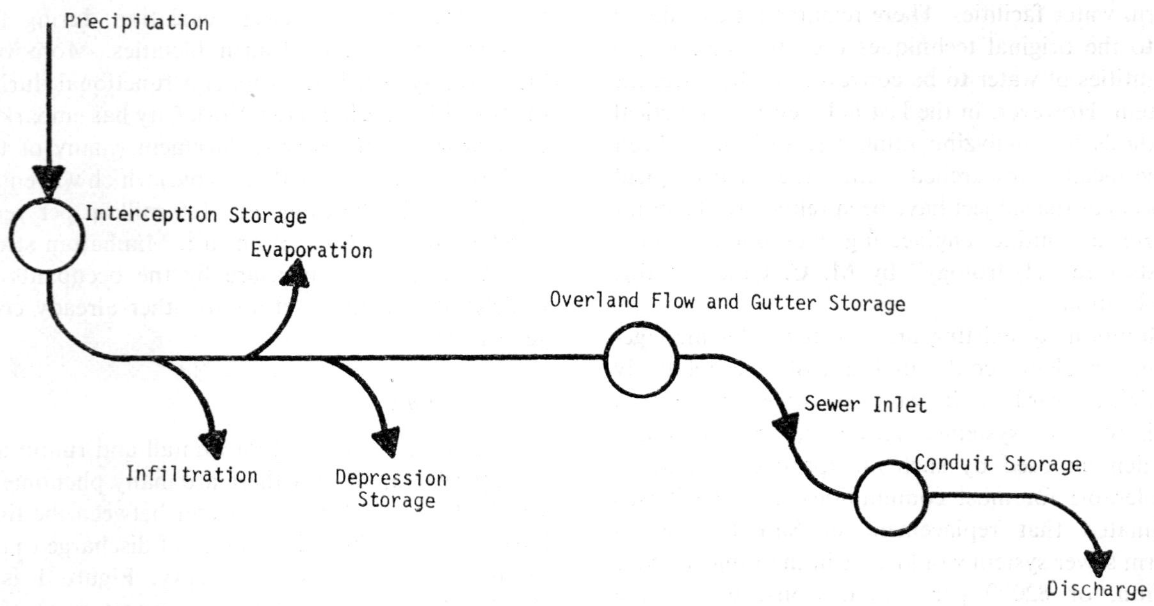

Figure 1 Phenomena affecting the rate of urban runoff.

intensity–duration–frequency (return period) relationships for San Francisco and New York are shown in Figures 2 and 3, respectively. The predominance of thundershower activity in New York, as contrasted with the cyclonic nature of storms experienced in San Francisco, means that New York storm sewers must be designed for more intense precipitation. The five-year, 60-minute rainfall intensity in New York City is approximately two inches per hour, whereas in San Francisco it is only 0.7 inches per hour.

Effective rainfall—losses and dispersion

In most urban areas rainfall intercepted by vegetation and lost through evaporation during precipitation is rarely of importance. Investigations of infiltration have shown that infiltration approaches a steady minimum rate after one or two hours.

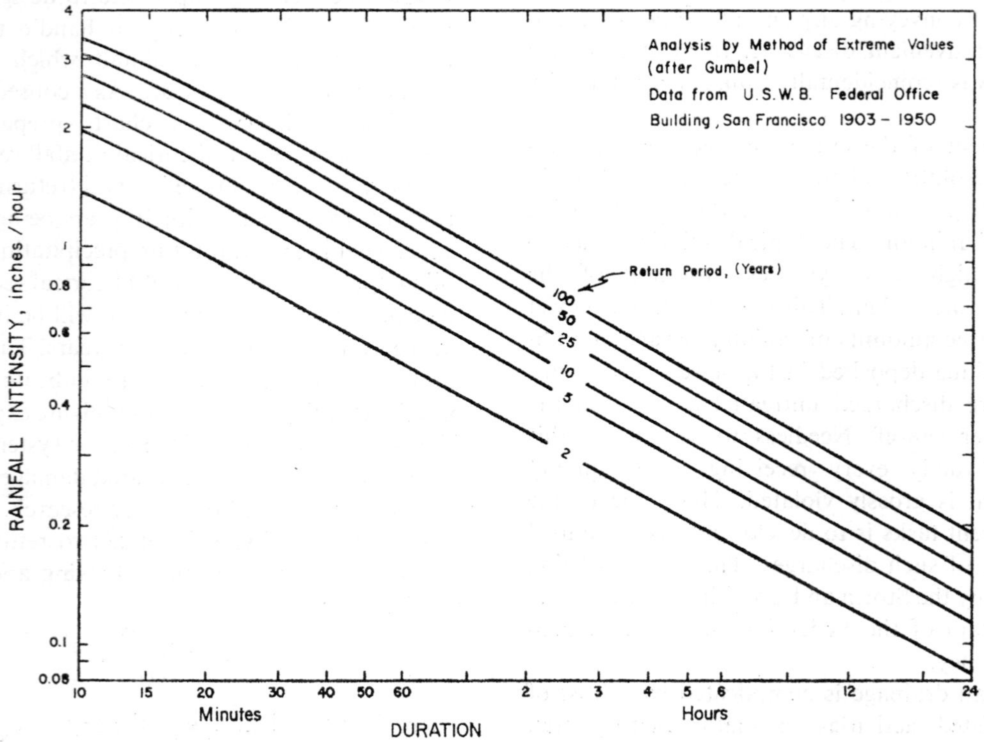

Figure 2 Rainfall intensity–duration–frequency relationships, San Francisco, California.

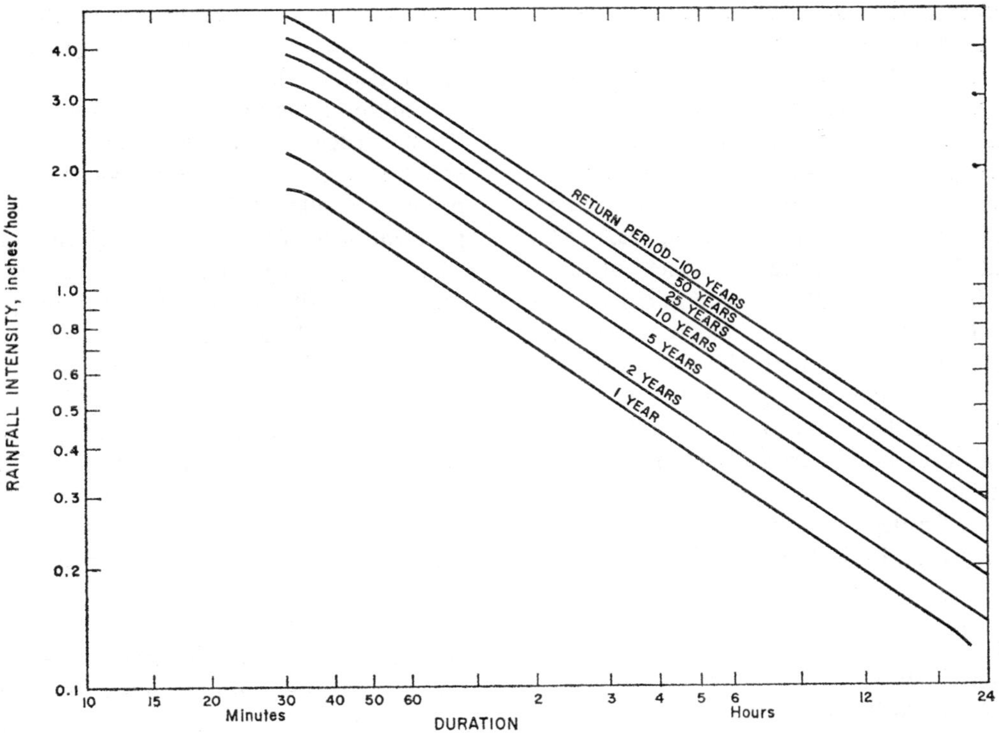

Figure 3 Rainfall intensity–duration–frequency relationships, Spring Creek, New York.

Infiltration is also affected by antecedent precipitation. High-intensity rains of short duration occurring after a dry spell often produce little, if any, runoff. A standard infiltration curve[1] can be used to compute losses due to infiltration. For urban areas, infiltration losses are approximately 10% of the precipitation rate. Depression storage values for different land surfaces depend on their roughness and slope.

Of more importance to the engineer is the dispersion of the peak flow rate due to the interim storage phenomena, such as overland flow, gutter, and conduit storage. These storage mechanisms impose a delay on the instantaneous flow rate, causing the peak flow rate to be attenuated and the duration of flow to be extended. Generally speaking, the larger the drainage system, the longer the time of travel of the flood wave and the more the attenuation of the peak flow rate.

The rational method

The "rational method" of analysis for storm sewer design, which is widely used in the engineering profession, commences with the simple formula:

$$Q = CIA \tag{2}$$

where:

Q = flow rate in cubic feet per second (cfs).

C = a coefficient,

I = the design rainfall intensity in inches per hour,

A = the area of the sewer system in acres.

Because the product, IA, in acre–inches per hour is equivalent to the volume flow rate of cubic feet per second (within 1%), the coefficient, C, is a decimal fraction with a value in the range of 0.4 to 0.8 for urban systems.

Given the drainage area, A, the engineer must select appropriate values for C and I. Beginning with the latter, as shown in equation (1), I is a function of both return period and the duration of rainfall. Assuming that the return period can be established (by tradition or other means), then the engineer must decide on the duration. In this respect it has been widely accepted that intensity–duration relationships are such that peak rates of runoff are attained when the entire tributary area contributes to the discharge in a given conduit. The time interval (or time delay) for this to occur is called "the time of concentration," t_c. By estmating the time of travel of the flood wave across the surface and in the storm sewer system, the engineer can calculate the time required for the uppermost sectors of the drainage basin to contribute to the flow, and therefore he has defined the time of concentration. The remaining step is to utilize a plot such as Figure 2 or 3, fixing t_c on the abscissa, moving vertically to the desired return period, R, and then horizontally to the left to read off the appropriate value of I.

Unfortunately, the assumption of a partially filled conduit is usually made, whch commonly puts the velocity of travel of the flood wave in the range of 5 to 10 feet per second. Actually, it has been frequently observed that short periods of extremely intense rainfall result in full sewer pipes, which means that the sewer has been exhausted of reservoir capacity and has reached a terminal rate of discharge. The latter fact is not widely recognized. However, with a fixed conduit size and essentially a fixed head, a pipe flowing full has an easily calculated, fixed flow rate. This is another area where applied research is critically needed.

Most textbooks on hydrology,[1,2] provide a methodology for determining the value of the runoff coefficient, C. Typical suggested values are as follows:

Urban residential	
Single houses	0.3–0.4
Garden apartments	0.5
Commercial and industrial	0.9
Parks	0.1–0.3
Asphalt and concrete	0.8–0.9

Having selected R, computed t_c (which includes a surface flow, or inlet, time of 5 to 10 minutes), graphically determined I, and selected C, the engineer then computes the design discharge for the sector of the drainage basin. Beginning with the upper reaches, he successively incorporates more and more of the area, moving down the trunk of the storm sewer. This means that as the area to be analyzed gets larger, the design rainfall intensity becomes smaller (t_c increases), and therein lies the problem of the full pipe as described above.

Actual peak runoff rates as a function of peak rainfall intensity for a 500 acre drainage basin in New York City are shown in Figure 4. It is apparent that for this drainage basin, the runoff coefficient is in the range of 0.75. Note that for dry antecedent conditions and low rainfall intensity, the runoff coefficient is much lower. This fact has little implication for storm sewer design, but is extremely important for quality control considerations, which might involve flow-through treatment facilities.

Hydrographic methods

Both Los Angeles and Chicago developed hydrographic methods for analysis of storm sewer requirements.[1] Both methods incorporate empirically determined factors, based on long term observations of rainfall runoff-relationships. The methodology essentially amounts to a synthesis of hydrographs from rationally selected precipitation events and the routing of the computed flows through the system. In this respect the procedures are more rational than the so-called "rational

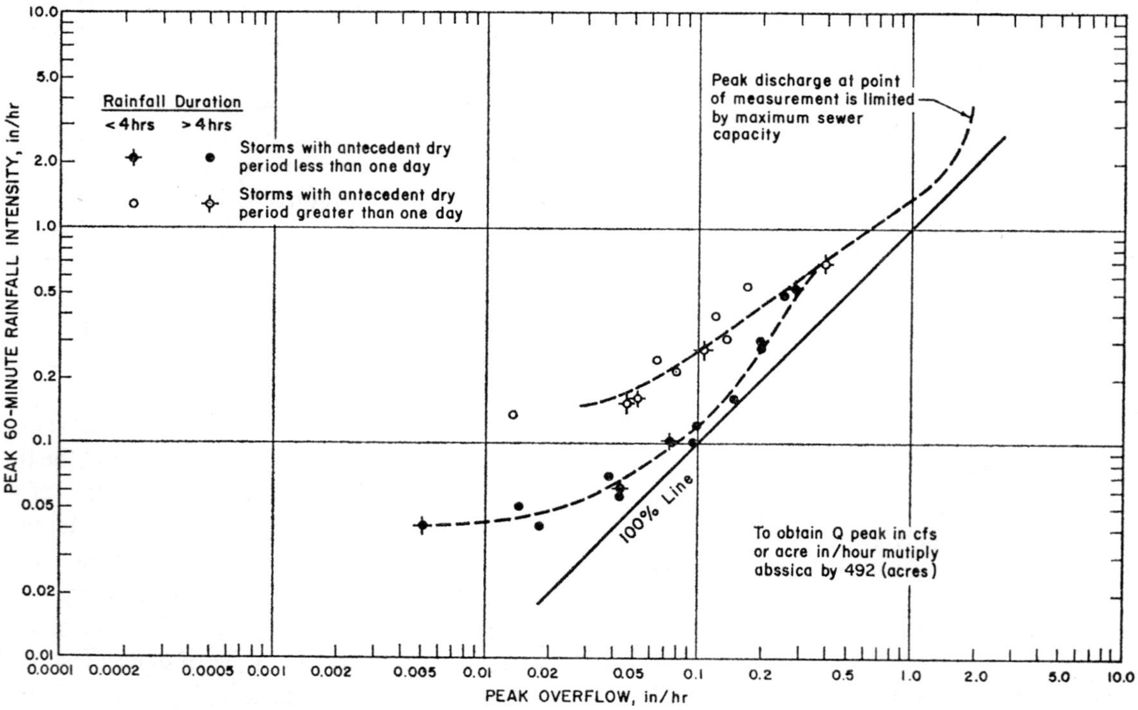

Figure 4 Peak overflow vs. peak 60-minute rainfall intensity, Hendrix Creek outfall sewer.

method. However, the application of the methodology in other areas is somewhat tedious.

A simpler hydrographic method, called the Inlet Method, has been developed by researchers at Johns Hopkins University.[1] The group found that strong correlations could be developed between the maximum five-minute peak rate of discharge to the storm sewer inlet. Their basic equation is similar to equation (2):

$$Q_p = C_p I_5 A, \qquad (3)$$

where:

Q_p = the peak inlet rate of flow, cfs,

C_p = a peak runoff coefficient,

I_5 = the 5-minute average precipitation rate, in/hr.

A = the tributary area, acres.

The value of C_p was found to be principally a function of the imperviousness of the tributary area, although rainfall intensity is also important. For an I_5 value of 5 inches per hour, the following C_p values were determined:

Percent imperviousness	C_p
20	0.3
40	0.4
50	0.6
60	0.75
70	1.0

The procedure involves routing synthetic triangular hydrogaphs of base, $2T$, and height, Q_p, where T is the duration of intense rainfall (of which the period of I_5 is the beginning). The discharge at the design point is computed from the empirically derived relationships:

$$Q_0 = Q_p[2T/(2T+0.8L/V), \qquad (4)$$

where:

Q_0 = the contributed discharge at the design point, cfs,

L = the length of the sewer from the inlet to the design point, ft,

V = the velocity of flow, fps.

The values of the individual Q_0 s are then added to obtain a total discharge at the design point.

This method has been found to give extremely accurate results in Baltimore and Philadelphia. However, its validity for other cities has yet to be established. It appears that if the method is utilized in conjunction with adequate rainfall records, it does not have the shortcoming of ignoring the full pipe situation implicit in the rational method.

Linear system approximation

As pointed out above, the design of urban storm sewerage systems is a well developed technology. Through the utilization of well known methods, such as the rational formula, Gumbel's analysis, and Manning's formula, it is a relatively straightforward task to establish the capacity requirements of various elements of the system. This is not to say that there do not exist technical difficulties in the preparation of such designs, but there is a wealth of experience to indicate that the aforementioned techniques, when properly used, result in adequate facilities. On the other hand, we have now entered an era in which hydrologic and hydraulic considerations are no longer exclusively the controlllng factors in urban sewerage system design. With the advent of treatment facilities for combined sewer overflows, it has become necessary to reexamine the fundamental precepts embodied in the analytical methods and to ascertain their applicability in the modified drainage situation.

Because of the need to prevent damage from flood waters, the engineer has traditionally been concerned with peak rates of runoff. He has usually selected for design purposes a rainfall intensity having a statistical recurrence interval of something in the range of five to ten years (frequently using Gumbel's analytical methods) and coupled this with an empirically derived runoff factor to compute design peak runoff rates. In general, because of the nature of rainfall intensity–duration–recurrence interval relationships, the system cost increase associated with the selection of a five-year return interval over and against a two year period is a relatively small percentage.

On the other hand, the design of storm and combined sewer overflow treatment facilities such that the treatment parameters would be based on the design runoff of the sewerage system would be prohibitively expensive. Some lesser flow rate must be employed. The question is: what flow rate? In order to answer this question properly, an analysis of the performance of the facility under various flow conditions must be carried out, and a picture of the expected frequencies of the range of flows must be developed. Furthermore, the water quality requirements of the receiving waters must be coupled with the anticipated effects of the facility discharges under the conditions imposed by the various rates of flow. Subsequently, it may be possible to arrange trade-offs between the size of the facilities and treatment process variables, or to optimize treatment schemes in already constructed facilities.

The Spring Creek Auxiliary Water Pollution Control Project, which was carried out by the Department of Water Resources of the City of New York with a grant from EPA's Storm and Combined Sewer Program, included one of the first successful approaches to the development of routine techniques for synthesizing complete discharge hydrographs.[3]

Various mathematical techniques were utilized in conjunction with simulation modeling with a digital computer. The results of these efforts consist of a set of mathematical models capable of producing accurate outflow hydrographs from either the drainage system or the treatment facility along with other important characteristics, such as water level in the treatment facility, flow-through velocity, effective residence time, and storage volume. Comprehensive monitoring of storm and combined sewer overflows was conducted for purposes of verifying the modeling results.

Model selection Rainfall–runoff relationships have been studied by hydrologists and drainage engineers for many years. The engineering literature contains countless methods designed to yield the hydrography of urban surface runoff when given the input storm hyetograph and catchment structures. These range from the simple Rational Methods to the ultra-detailed Hydrograph Method. To a varying degree, all these methods lean upon empirical relationships. Recently, many attempts have been made to simulate surface runoff using mathematical models by solving the differential equations of momentum and continuity.

Both empirical and numerical methods have their advantages and disadvantages. Empirical methods have in general gained popularity because of their simplicity. However, uncertainty often arises as to the physical implications and the generality of the various coefficients required. Numerical methods which rely upon the equations of motion are sometimes favored because of their clearly defined physics. Furthermore, computer hardware and software technologies have progressed to the point where it is both possible and economically feasible to utilize this approach. However, difficulties often encountered in the use of this method (as well as any other mathematical model) arise from the fact that performance of the model depends greatly upon the control parameters such as the physiographic characteristics of the drainage system.

Experience has shown that the physical parameters of a drainage system (especially an old one) are extremely difficult to predict. Debris and trash on the street gutters and changes in the sewer line make it difficult for a modeling engneer to "assume" these factors by studying drainage maps and sewer construction plans which may have been prepared many years ago.

In the Spring Creek Project, before construction of the drainage quantity–quality model for future water quality predictions, both empirical and numerical models were evaluated. It was decided that a semi-empirical approach would be most suitable for the project's needs. This conclusion was based upon the fact that a large amount of monitoring data (both quantity and quality) had been obtained in the Spring Creek drainage area.

Two types of rainfull–runoff model were developed. Their principles of computation are different only in the portion that simulates the process from effective rainfall hyetograph (ERH) to direct runoff hydrograph (DRH). Other portions which simulate infiltration losses, land use effects and quality parameters are essentially the same. In the ERH–DRH stage of the first model, the quasi-instantaneous unit hydrograph principle was used. This model is more applicable to drainage systems where extensive monitoring data area avilable and requires less time and expense than the second model. The second model embodies the principles of kinematic wave propagation for both overland and channel flows. The results discussed in this paper are mainly obtained from the first model.

Urban Drainage Basin—A Quasi-Liner System Figure 5 is a schematic diagram showing various components of the precipitation–overflow sequence for a typical urban drainage system in which the receiving water is affected by tidal action. The rainfall–runoff relationship has been for many years treated as a linear process. Recent investigators have studied the nonlinearity of runoff distribution by techniques such as the generalized functional series, and they have found that some nonlinearities are caused by seasonal variations. However, before any definite and quantitative relationships are established, the present computational model still assumes that an urban drainage system is a linear system. Adjustments were made by using measured summer storm discharges.

According to linear system theory, input–output relationship can often be descrbed by the convolution integral:

$$Y(t) = \int_{-\infty}^{\infty} W(t, \tau) \cdot X(\tau)\, d\tau, \qquad (5)$$

where $X(\tau)$ is the input and $Y(t)$ the resulting output.

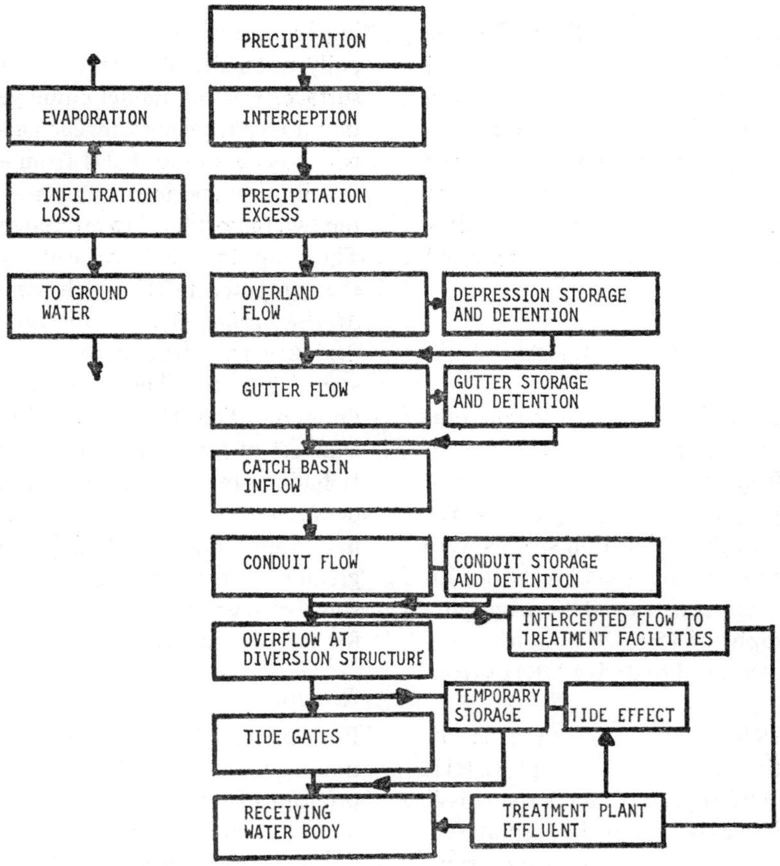

Figure 5 Precipitation–overflow relationships.

As the function of the two variables, $W(t,\tau)$ is called the weighting function of the system.

If a linear system is described by a convolution integral, then the output $Y(t)$ at a given time t is a weighted sum of the values of the input over the integral from negative to positive infinity. That is, the contribution to the output from the input is a weighted value of $X(\tau)$, where the weighting is provided by the weighting function $W(t,\tau)$. Applying this to the rainfall–runoff process, a hydrograph can be predicted for any given effective hyetograph if the weighting function is known.

Unit Hydrograph and Instantaneous Unit Hydrograph In order to derive the weighting function, it is necessary to introduce the unit hydrograph (UH) theory and instantaneous unit hydrograph (IUH). The unit hydrograph of a drainage basin is defined as a hydrograph of direct runoff from one inch of effective rainfall generated uniformly over the basin area at a uniform rate during a specific period of time or duration. (The word "unit" is often misinterpreted as one inch of "unit depth"). In essence, linearity (superposition) and time invariance are the two fundamental principles of the unit hydrograph.

If the duration of the effective precipitation becomes infinitesimally small, the resulting unit hydrograph is called an "instantaneous unit hydrograph" which is, expressed by $U(0,t)$ or $U(t)$. By the principle of superposition, when an effective rainfall function $I(\tau)$ of duration t_0 is applied, each infinitesimal element of this effective rainfall hyetograph (ERH) will produce a direct runoff hydrograph (DRH) equal to the product of $I(\tau)$ and the IUH expressed by $U(t-\tau)$. Thus, the ordinate of the DRH at time t is

$$Q(t) = \int_0^{t' \leq \tau_0} U(t - \tau) \cdot I(\tau)\, d\tau. \tag{6}$$

One can easily see that Equation (6) is equivalent to Equation (5). Equation (6) is also known as the Duhamel integral, in which $U(t-\tau)$ is a kernel function, $I(\tau)$ is the input function, and $t' = t$ when $t < t_0$ and $t' = t_0$ where $t > t_0$.

One important difference between the two is that the system described by Equation (6) (usually called a causal or a physically realizable system) cannot anticipate what the future input will be. In other words, the weighting function of a causal system is zero for $\tau < t$, that is, future values of the input are weighted zero.

For a given drainage basin, the ordinate at time t of the UH having a unit duration of Δt_0 is represented by $U(\Delta t_0,t)$, where t is any time after the beginning of effective rainfall. The effective rainfall for a given storm may be considered to consist of n blocks of different intensity I_i and of duration equal to Δt_0 where the subscript i denotes the number representing a block. By the principle of linearity, the ordinate of the direct-runoff hydrograph (DRH) for the given storm may be expressed as:

$$\sum_{i=1}^{n} U[\Delta t_0, t - (i - 1)\Delta t] I_i \Delta t. \quad (7)$$

Equation (7) is a summation form of the convolution integral, and it describes the principle of computing DRH from ERH for each drainage sub-basin. Measured hydrographs (DRH) for each sub-basin from isolated short-duration storms were used to compute unit hydrographs. A basic 20-minute hydrograph was constructed by averaging several unit hydrographs of 15 to 20 minutes duration. This basic UH was used to derive DRH's from computed ERH's.

Determination of ERH From TRH In order to determine the effective rainfall hyetograph (ERH) from the total rainfall hyetograph (TRH), the "loss" function for the drainage basin must be formulated. Loss parameters include interception, evaporation, infiltration, depression storage, etc. The relative importance of each loss component depends principally upon the physical characteristics of the land surface. For the model employed in this investigation, loss parameters are each assigned to a function which generates an ERH from any TRH. Land use distribution and imperviousness of each surface are the two factors used to estimate the loss parameters. These input values have been adjusted by comparing the computed DRH s with measured DRH s.

Model Verification In the use of models for each drainage area the computational methods were the same, but the basic characteristics were quite different. The Hendrix drainage basin was the smallest of five which were extensively monitored. It had more impervious areas (75%) and a small depression storage (0.05 inches). Thurston Basin had approximately 40% impervious area and a greater depression storage (0.2 inches). Comparisons between measured and computed hydrographs for the two basins are shown in Figures 6 and 7.

Remarks

Refinement of these urban runoff models is continuing with the intent of developing "packaged programs for routine use on smaller computers and remote computer terminals. The assumption of a linear system appears to be thoroughly justified, and this approach promises to provi de much needed

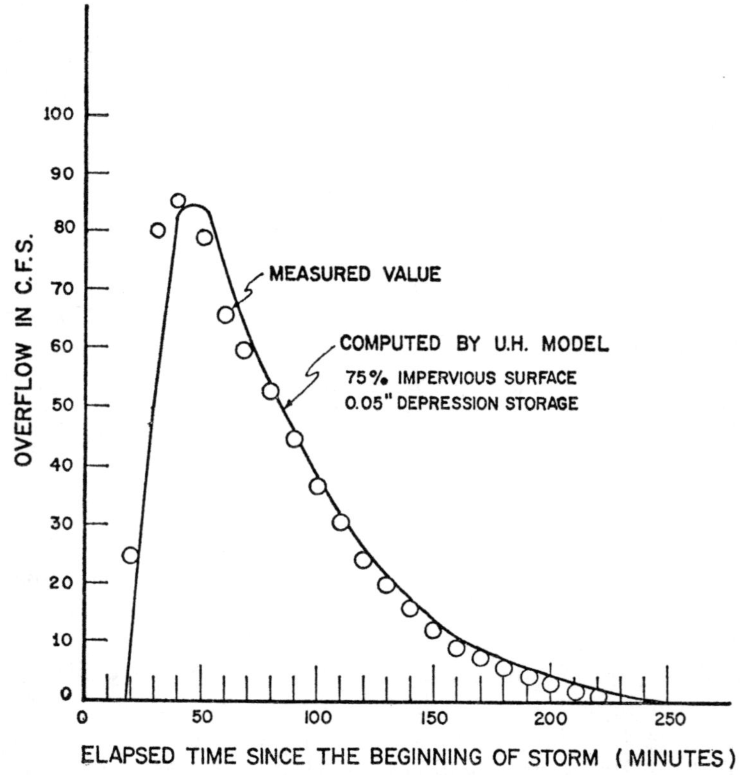

Figure 6 Hendrix drainage basin. Comparison between computed overflow and measured values—June 25, 1969.

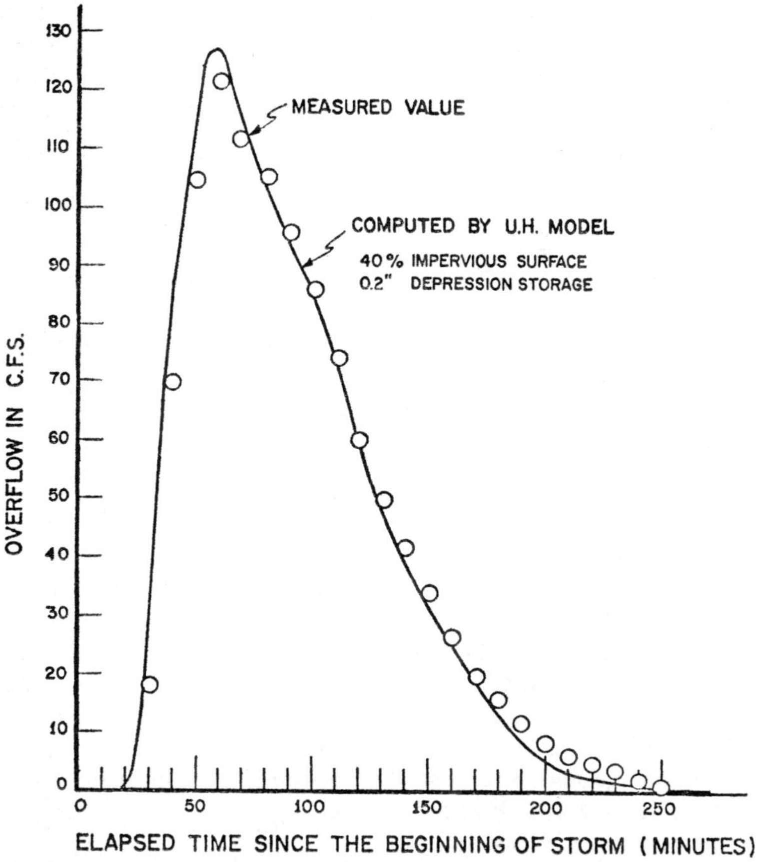

Figure 7 Thurston drainage basin. Comparison between computed overflow hydrograph and measured values—September 27, 1970.

versatility and speed in the analysis of urban storm systems. The following section includes a description of the use of the model to facilitate analyses of urban runoff quality.

Runoff Quality

Results of field Monitoring

Combined Sewers Until recently, investigation of the quality characteristics of combined sewer overflows had not received a great deal of attention in the United States. Only scattered reports appear in the sanitary engineering literature and these are in general devoted to the hydraulic and hydrologic aspects of combined sewers. Very few of the reported studies have incorporated an evaluation of the quality characteristics of combined sewer overflows and in few instances have comprehensive monitoring programs been conducted.

The characteristics of combined sewer overflows have been analyzed to various degrees by a number of investigators. In most cases, however, it is not possible to develop a scientific explanation of system behavior from the reported data.

Palmer[4] published results from a series of observations in Detroit. His conclusion was that combined sewer overflows in that City have the following "average" characteristics:

Constituent	Concentration
Total Coliforms (MPN)	43,000 per ml
5-day BOD	50 mg/l
suspended Solids	250 mg/l
Volatile Suspended Solids	100 mg/l

Dunbar and Henry[5] have published similar data from several locations. These data are presented in Table I.

TABLE I

Characteristics of Combined Sewer Overflows[5]

City	Coliform (MPN/ml)	Total solids (mg/l)	Suspended solids (mg/l)	BOD (mg/l)
Buffalo N.Y.	—	—	172–1220	—
Buffalo N.Y.	—	498–754	158–544	100–162
Buffalo N.Y.	—	461–785	126–436	121–127
Toronto Ont.	230–24,000	—	130–930	40–260
Toronto Ont.	700–35,000	—	17–580	0–100
Welland Ont.	2100	850–960	167–426	220–614

Limited data on suspended solids discharges in combined sewer overflows have been published by Romer and Klashman.[6] They report the following data from Sheffield and Heywood, England:

Time after commencement of overflow (Hours)	Suspended solids (mg/l) Sheffield[a]	Heywood[b]
0	592	2380
1	602	1100
2	671	690
3	1701	500
4	1259	380
5	1335	830
6	1012	280
7	1006	180
8	979	—
9	417	—
10	401	—
11	263	—

[a] 0.11 inch of rain.
[b] Heavy rain for 4 hours.

Romer and Klashman[6] reported on several combined sewer overflows which were monitored in the Albany Street sewerage system (860 acres) in Buffalo, New York, in 1936 on 24 May, 23 July and 19 August. The rainfall, discharge and suspended solids concentrations for the first two overflows are shown in Figure 8—discharge and suspended solids concentrations for the third storm were as follows:

Time after commencement of overflow (hours)	Discharge (mgd)	Suspended solids (mg/l)
0	25.3	208
1	120.6	964
2	104.0	1220
3	56.7	696
4	37.6	364
5	28.6	172

Mass discharges, mass discharge coefficients and flow weighted means for these storms are as follows:

	Flow-weighted concentrations (mg/l)		Mass discharges (lbs/acre)		Mass discharge coefficients (lbs/acre-inch)	
Date	SS	VSS	SS	VSS	SS	VSS
24 May 36	1018	559	11	6	230	126
23 July 36	1917	791	61	25	433	179
19 Aug 36	871	10	197	—	—	—

Romer and Klasham[6] also reported the results of an overflow from the Bergen Basin drainage system in New York City which was monitored on 3 August 1961 (Figure 8). Previously, rains of 0.80 inch on 29 July and 2.59 inch on 31 July had flushed the system, yet concentrations of 300 mg/l suspended solids were observed. The Bergen Basin drainage system discharges to Jamaica Bay and has a drainage area of 2699 acres. Mass discharges, mass discharge coefficients and flow-weighted means for this overflow were calculated as follows:

Flow-weighted concentrations (mg/l)		Mass discharges (lbs/acre)		Mass discharge coefficients (lbs/acre-inch)	
SS	VSS	SS	VSS	SS	VSS
166.9	65.2	11.4	4.5	37.8	14.8

Total discharge for this storm was 2,964,000 cubic feet.

In 1963 Gameson and Davidson[7] published results of one of the first known attempts at a comprehensive study of the variations in quantity and quality of combined sewer overflows. Figure 9 is a plot of a data summary presented by Gameson and Davidson (Table 6 of that paper). The data plotted represent long term weighted averages, hence the usually reported very sporadic initial readings are not indicated.

During 1966–67 a comprehensive study[8] of two combined sewer drainage systems in the City of San Francisco by Engineering-Science, Inc., ended with the following conclusions:

1) Analyses of the data collected during the study indicate that the concentration of various constituents in the overflows follow a distinct pattern and it was postulated that the observed pattern could be divided into three phases, each of which is dominated by a single phenomenon. The initial phase was most probably caused by a flushing of sewage in the lower reaches of the sewerage system and in general initial overflows had the characteristics of raw sewage. During the second phase, a systematic scouring of materials in the sewer and on the surface appeared to take place, and an increase in the concentrations of the various pollutional constituents had been observed in most instances. Subsequently the concentrations dropped to a steady level, which constituted the third phase. The combination of relatively unpolluted surface runoff and the normal sewage flow made up the discharges during the third phase.

2) The time of decrease to a steady level, or decay time, was found to be remarkably constant and virtually independent of the system physiography and the meteorological conditions. Profiles of pollutant concentration time histories are shown in Figures 10, 11, 12, 13 and 14.

3) The mass discharges of the various constituents in primary treatment effluent, combined sewer overflows and urban surface runoff are

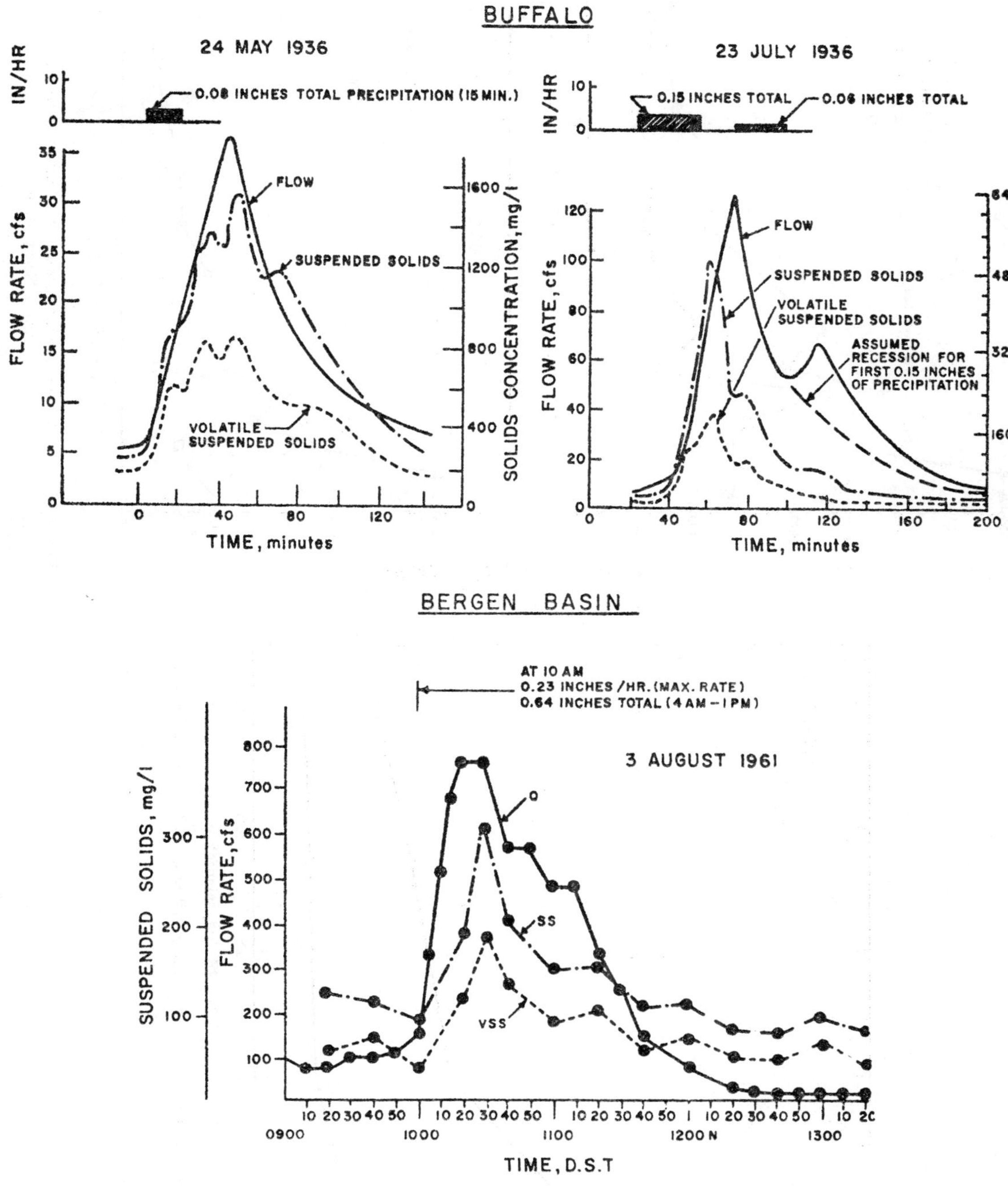

Figure 8 Combined sewer overflows in Buffalo, New York and Bergen Basin, Queens' New York.

shown in Table II. Differences between the discharges of combined sewer overflows and (estimated) urban storm runoff were, in most cases, relatively very small. This seemed to indicate that the separation of sewers would not result in a significant reduction in the incidence or magnitude of pollution of receiving waters.

4) The receiving water studies demonstrated that in waters proximate to combined sewer outfalls were significantly affected by wet weather discharges. A principal factor in this regard was bacteriological pollution. Coliform concentrations averaged 5×10^4 per ml. in the overflows monitored in San Francisco. It was concluded that disinfection of combined sewer overflows would be necessary if receiving waters were to meet recreational water quality requirements.

Combined sewer overflow monitoring in the Jamaica Bay Project[3] verified most of the conclusions developed in the San Francisco studies. However, it became readily apparent that overflow phenomena are more complex than had been

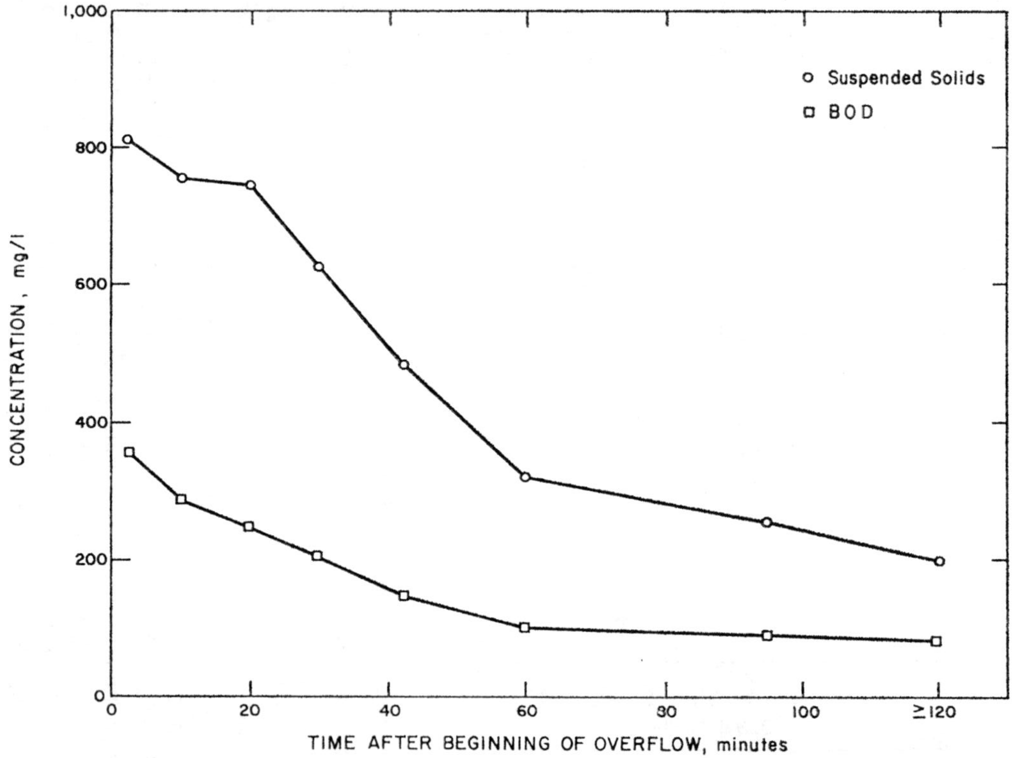

Figure 9 Constituent concentration variations in combined sewer overflows, Northampton, England.

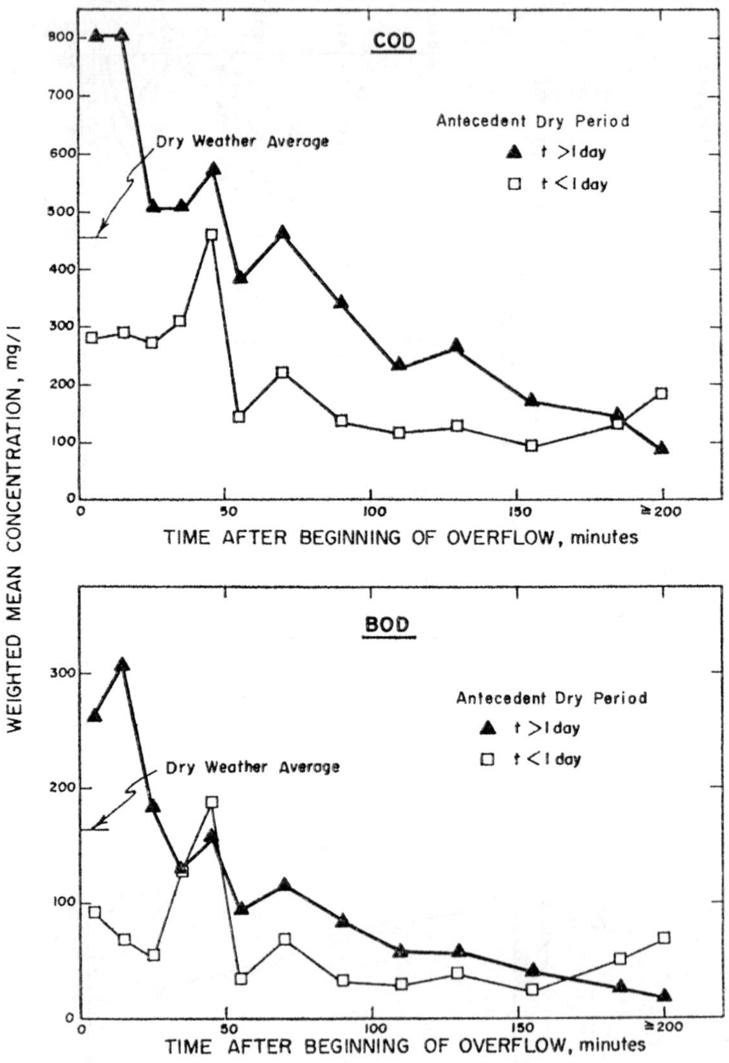

Figure 10 Constituent concentration variations in combined sewer overflow—Selby Street.

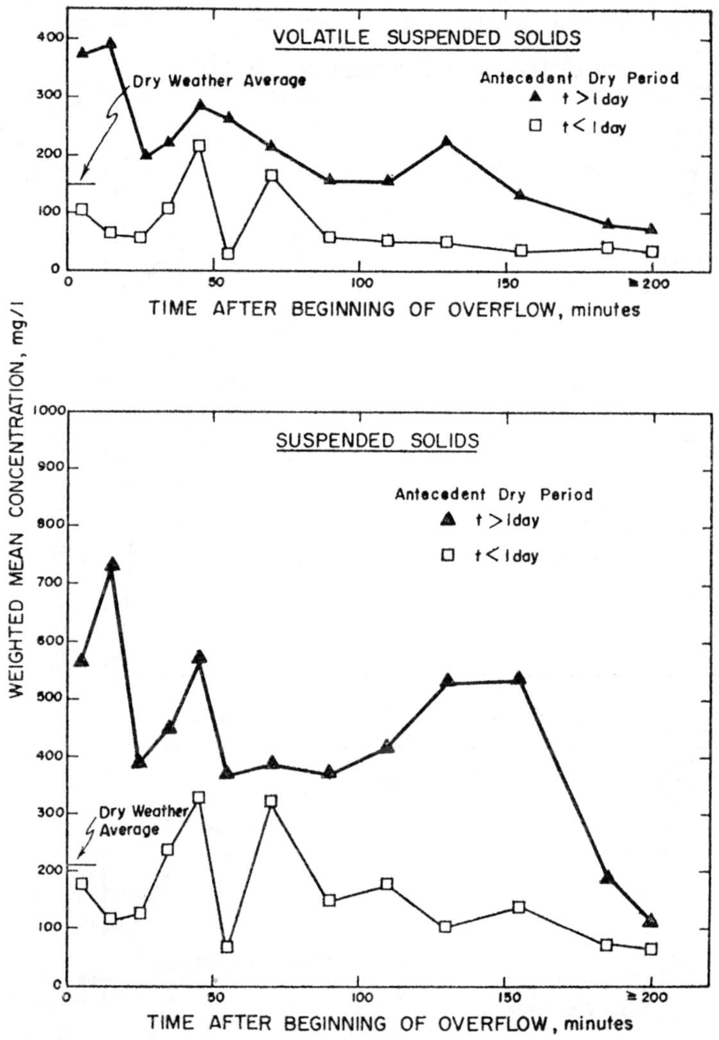

Figure 11 Constituent concentration variations in combined sewer overflows—Selby Street.

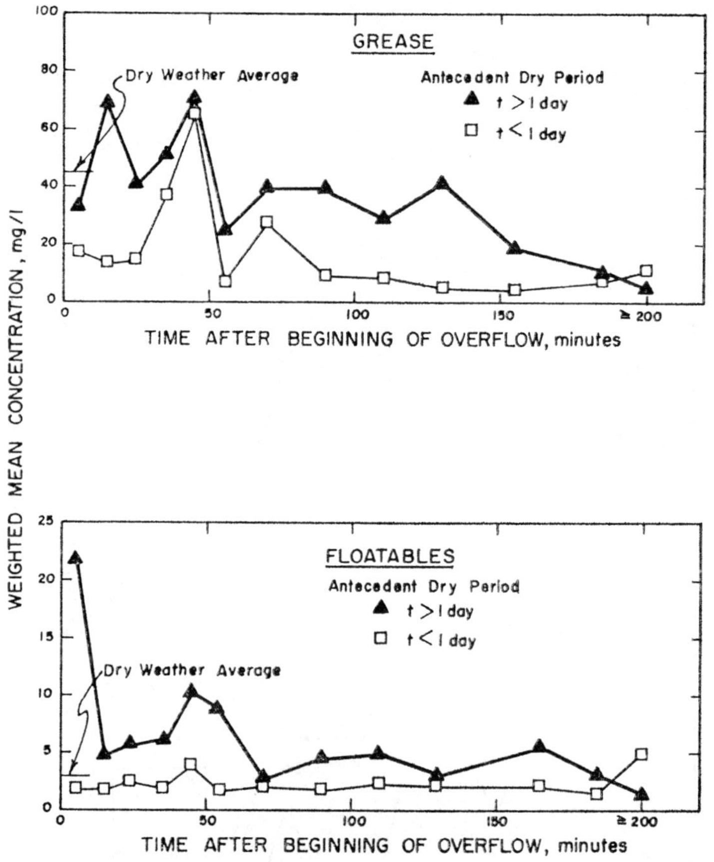

Figure 12 Constituent concentration variations in combined sewer overflows—Selby Street.

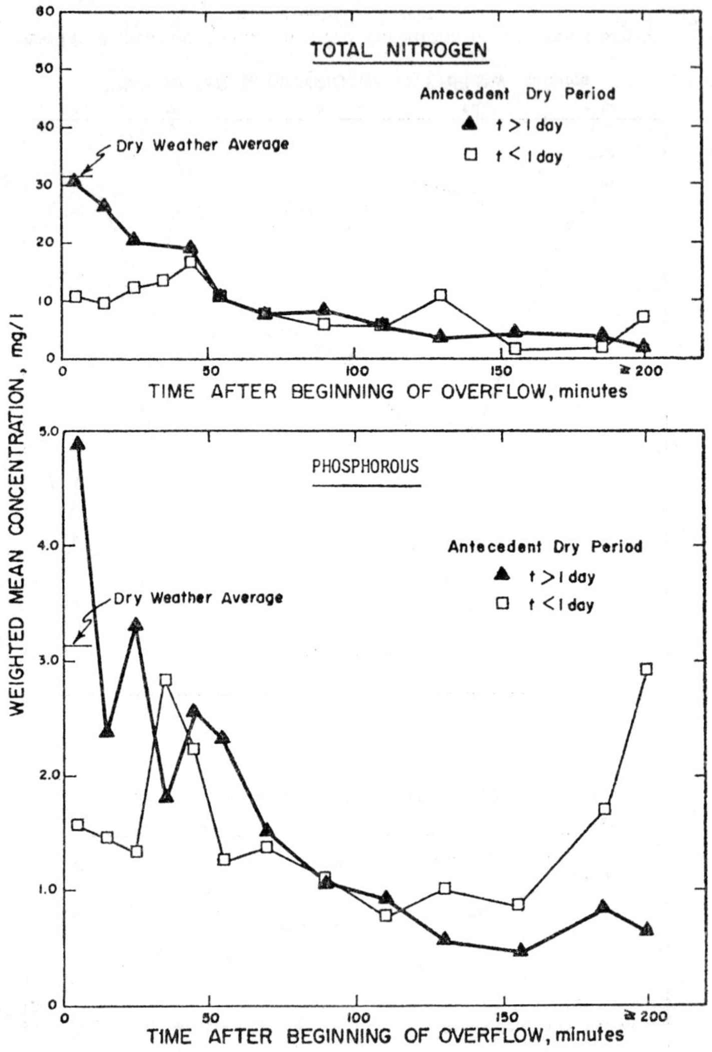

Figure 13 Constituent concentration variations in combined sewer overflows—Selby Street.

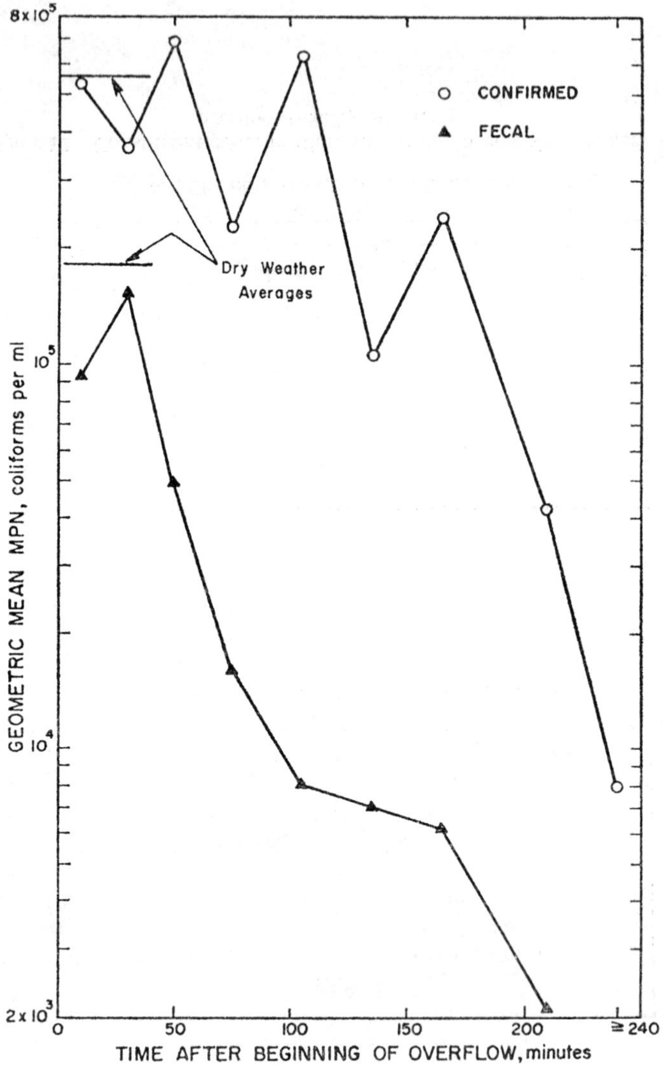

Figure 14 Coliform MPN variations in combined sewer overflows—Selby Street.

TABLE II

Masses of Constituents in Wet Weather Discharges from Urban Areas

Constituent	Storm runoff in Cincinnati		Combined sewer overflow, San Francisco			
			Selby System		Laguna System	
	lb/acre-yr[a]	lb/acre-inch runoff	lb/acre-yr[c]	lab/cre-inch runoff	lb/acre-yr[d]	lb/acre-inch runoff
BOD	33	2.01	101	8.1	136	9.50
COD	240	14.0	447	35.8	480	33.5
SS	730	45.6	632	50.7	540	37.5
VSS	160	10.0	218	17.5	224	15.6
N	8.9	0.56	10.6	0.85	15.6	1.09
PO_4	2.5	0.16	2.4	0.19	3.2	0.23
Grease (HEM)	—	—	36.5	2.92	40.7	2.83

[a] Weibel *et al.*[44]
[b] Calculated with an annual runoff of 16 inches.
[c] Calculated with an annual runoff of 12.5 inches.
[d] Calculated with an annual runoff of 14.4 inches.

TABLE III

Characteristics of Jamaica Bay Combined Sewer Overflows

Drainage basin	N. Conduit	Paerdegat	Spring Creek	Hendrix Cr.	Thurston
Area-acres	1382	5730	1874	492	1980
Approximate runoff% Coefficient—Percent	50	30	40	60	25
Pollutant Concentrations[a] (mass discharge coefficients)					
Biochemical oxygen demand					
avg.	40	23	21	34	25
σ	20	16	12	11	10
Chemical oxygen demand					
Avga.	103	—	54	81	76
σ	30	—	31	21	27
Suspended solids					
avg.	108	22	67	52	57
σ	78	12	59	23	34
Grease (HEM)					
Avg.	13.7	6.3	8.6	11	6.6
σ	6.6	5.8	8.4	8	2.8
Organic nitrogen					
Avg.	34.0	2.5	3.2	3.4	2.8
σ	1.8	0.6	1.3	1.2	1.2
Soluble phosphorous	0.94	0.18	0.66	0.92	0.55
σ	0.62	0.01	0.57	0.43	0.30
Bacteriological Quality					
Coliforms (10^5/ml)	3.6	—	11.4	4.7	5.0
Fecal coliforms (10^5/ml)	0.3	—	1.9	0.3	0.5
Fecal strep (10^3/ml)	12.0	—	11.1	—	3.8

[a] Units are: pounds per acre-inch of runoff. To convert to mg/l, multiply by 4.45.

thought. The data in Table III demonstrate the variability of average concentrations of several pollutants, as determined from extensive monitoring of combined sewer overflows from five rather large urban drainage basins. Furthermore, combined sewer overflows in the Jamaica Bay area displayed much higher concentrations of pollutants than had been found in San Francisco. This fact ultimately led to the conclusion that it would be inappropriate to attempt to develop predictive generalizations based solely on the accumulated monitoring data. That is, it is apparent that combined sewer systems are sufficiently diverse to consider each to be unique (within certain limits), and it was decided to develop procedures for quantitating the characteristics of a combined sewer system so that predictive analyses could be carried out. The methods are discussed in the section entitled, "Time Variant Characteristics of Combined Sewer Overflows."

Storm Water A number of investigators have recognized that urban storm runoff itself is a significant factor in pollution associated with combined sewer overflows.[9–13] Table IV, prepared by the

TABLE IV

Characteristics of Surface Runoff from Urban Areas[44]

Constituent	Seattle Washington	Oxney, England	Moscow, U.S.S.R.	Leningrad, U.S.S.R.	Stockholm, Sweden	Pretoria, S. Africa Park area	Business district
BOD (mg/l)	10	100 (max)	18–285	36	17–80	30	34
COD (mg/l)					18–3100	29	28
Total solids (mg/l)					30–8000		
Suspended solids (mg/l)		2045	1000–3500	14,541			
Coliform (MPN/100 ml)	16,000				40–200,000	240,000	230,000
Org. –N (mg/l)	9.0 (max)					5.4	3.5
NO_3 –N (mg/l)	2.8 (max)						
Soluble P (mg/l)	784 (max)						
Total P (mg/l)	1400 (max)						
Fixed residue (mg/l)					210–2420		
Dissolved solids (mg/l)						228	154

Public Health Service[14] summarizes certain of the findings. Examination of Table IV leads to the conclusions that significant quantites of major pollutional constituents are entrained in runoff from urban areas. However, there have been few attempts to assess the relative contribution of surface runoff to the aggregate pollutional content of combined sewer overflows. Interest in such information is more than academic. As a prerequisite to the design of control systems or treatment processes for combined sewer overflows, it is essential that the problem be well understood in terms of the character of the major inputs.

Studies on the causes and remedies of water pollution from surface drainage of urban areas were recently completed by the American Public Works Association in Chicago.[15] It was found that in representative urban residential areas street litter accumulates at an average of 1.05 tons per acre per year. Of this total approximately 70% is dust and dirt, as determined from analyses of street sweepings. These data were extrapolated to New York, where the average runoff is about 25 acre-inches per acre per year, assuming that street litter is washed away with storm runoff. The results of this analysis indicate that the suspended solids content of urban surface runoff should average 300 to 370 mg/l from street litter alone.

Weibel[16] has presented results from a monitoring of urban surface runoff in Cincinnati, and his study has represented the most comprehensive effort of this nature undertaken to date. Data were collected over a two year period using automated sampling equipment. During this period a wide range of meteorological conditions were experienced, and the conclusions developed are probably applicable to urban areas of similar characteristics.

Table V illustrates Weibel's calculations of mean concentrations of various constituents in urban land runoff as a function of time. It was not evident that there was a significant relationship between antecedent dry period and the quality of urban surface runoff.

Based on his hydrologic and urban runoff quality data, Weibel calculated the annual mass discharge of various constituents in urban surface runoff. These values are shown below.

Constituent	Annual discharge (lbs/acre per year)
Suspended solids	730
Volatile suspended solids	160
Chemical oxygen demand (COD)	240
Biochemical oxygen demand (BOD)	33
Total Kjeldahl nitrogen	8.9
Phosphate (PO_2)	2.5

Weibel concluded that urban surface runoff cannot be neglected in considering waste loadings from urban sources.

Table VI compares the characteristics of combined sewer overflows and storm sewer overflows in Oakland, California.[14] Both storm water and combined sewer overflows contain substantial pollutional loads as measured by the classical standards Differences seem to be most significant with respect to the number of coliforms present as might be expected.

Rainfall Although the common conception of rainfall is that it is "pure" water, analysis of accumulated precipitation at several sites in the United States have disproved this notion. Emissions from industry, automobiles, and agricultural activities are but a few of the sources of pollutants which are entrained in droplets of rain. Although there are

TABLE V

Mean Concentrations of Constituents in Urban Land Runoff, Cincinnati, Ohio[16]

Constituent	Time after start of runoff 0–15 min	15–30 min	30–60 min	60–120 min	120 min and over
SS, mg/l	390	280	190	200	160
VSS, mg/l	98	69	47	58	38
COD, mg/l	170	130	110	97	72
BOD, mg/l	28	26	23	20	12
Total Nitrogen –N, mg/l	3.6	3.4	3.1	2.7	2.3
PO_4 total soluble as PO_4) mg/l)	0.99	0.86	0.92	0.83	0.63

TABLE VI

Characteristics of Combined Sewer Overflows and Storm Water at Oakland[44]

Determination	Combined sewer overflows (14 samples from various station)			Storm sewer flows (21 samples from various stations)		
	Minimum	Maximum	Average	Minimum	Maximum	Average
DO (mg/l)	2.4	9.6	6.9	0	13.2	7.3
BOD (mg/l()	13	153	59	3	1,700	87
Total solids (mg/l)	132	1,327	400	726	726	1,401
Vol. solids (mg/l)	83	291	144	168	168	168
Susp. solids (mg/l,	60	1,120	203	16	4,400	618
Coliform (MPN/ml)	2,300	2,400,000	293,000	4	70,000	11,800
Chlorides (mg/l)	619	619	619	300	10,260	5,100
Oil and grease (mg/l)	8	66	33	2	162	32
Sand (mg/l)	0	276	76	7	868	158
pH	6.8	7.4	7.1	6.3	7.8	6.9

no conclusive data to support the hypothesis, it has been suggested that conditions are worse in the vicinity of major metropolitan areas. The importance for analysis of urban runoff problems lies in the fact that without treatment urban drainage waters cannot be of better quality than the precipitation which initiates the entire process.

A partial, chemical analysis of rainwater collected at a site near Jamaica Bay[3] is presented in Table VII. It is of importance to note that the concentrations of nitrogen (N) and phosphorus are both sufficient to promote eutrophication or algal "blooms" in receiving waters.

Similar, but more comprehensive data were obtained by Weibel, *et al.*[1] from two sites in Ohio. Their analyses (Table VII), also showed significant concentrations of organic chlorides, which were interpreted to be residues of chlorinated hydrocarbon pesticides.

TABLE VII
Chemical Quality of Rainwater 26*th Ward WPCF Raingauge*

Date	Total rainfall (inches)	Total Kjeidahl–N (mg/l)	NH_3–N (mg/l)	NO_3–N (mg/l)	Total –P (mg/l)
10 June 69	0.61	0.3	0.1	0.51	0.12
03 July 69	0.36	1.5	0.2	1.65	0.9
18 July 69	0.52	0.6	0.2	0.58	—
Averages	—	0.8	0.17	0.77	0.16

Time variant characteristics of combined sewer overflows

Approach As indicated above, monitoring data support the conclusion that the aggregate parameter of lb./acre-inch cannot be assumed uniform over all urban drainage basins. Tracking the time history of pollutant concentrations over entire overflow events can yield a better perception of the unique factors of any combined sewer drainage basin effecting the temporal variations in quality of system waste streams. Such analysis permits a

TABLE VIII
Constituents in Rainfall, Averages[11]

Constituent	Cincinnati, Ohio[a]	Coshocton, Ohio[b]
SS, mg/l	13	11.7
COD, mg/l	16	9.0
ΣN, mg/l[c] (N)	1.27	1.17
Inorg. N., mg/l[d] (N)	0.69	0.86
Hydrolyzable PO_4, mg/l	0.24	0.08
Org. Cl^-, μg/l	0.28	0.22

[a] August 1963–December 1964.
[b] November 1963–March 1964.
[c] Arithmetic sum of the four forms of nitrogen.
[d] Inorg. N = arithmetic sum of NH_3, NO_2, and NO_3.

qualitative definition of the basin hydrologic, hydraulic, sewer network, diversion structure, systems operations, and receiving water characteristics affecting the shape of the pollutograph.

In the Jamaica Bay Project, a predictive model was developed to examine the time history of suspended solids and coliform concentrations under various storm conditions. The model was used to predict the operating efficiency of the Spring Creek Auxillary Water Pollution Control Facility (combined sewer overflow treatment) under various storm conditions and chlorination practices. During the development of the model, coliform pollutographs based on monitored storms were useful in verifying and tuning the model. Once this was accomplished, the model was used to generate additional pollutographs for various input conditions. Thus, the pollutographs were constructed using dual approaches:

1) Time varying pollutant concentrations for monitored storms were plotted for several overflow parameters.

2) Time varying coliform concentrations for various rainfall intensities and durations were generated using the drainage basin models.

The number of basins monitored permits a qualitative assessment of the impact of the various factors previously mentioned; however, the scope of the study was not designed to detail the extent to which each factor affects the shape of an individual pollutograph.

Time Varying Concentrations of Pollutants Early peak concentrations of pollutants are partially due to the flushing of material deposited in the sewer. Sewer characteristics (slope, roughness, diameter) create a situation where the velocity required to scour and re-suspend deposited debris is reached early in the runoff event, normally before peak flow is reached. The attainment of maximum scour velocity coupled with limited sources of deposited material causes peak concentrations of pollutants to be reached prior to the realization of peak discharge.

In general, peak parameter concentrations occur early in the storm (mostly before peak discharge). Washing of streets and scouring of the sewers contribute large amounts of pollutants early in the storm. As overflow continues, pollutant levels decrease as surface and sewer washings become source limiting and levels are indicative of dilution of dry weather flow.

The length of the antecedent dry weather period plays a major role on the location of peak concentrations as well as the shape of the pollutograph. The longer the dry period preceding a storm, the greater the opportunity for accumulation of material on the surface and in the sewer.

The significance of the peak parameter concentrations preceding the peak overflow lies in the possibilities of caputre and/or treatment of only a portion of the wastewater. If sharp peaks occur early in an overflow, capture and subsequent treatment at a parent facility may be the optimum approach. If the pollutographs are flat or show little change in concentration throughout an overflow, separate, continual treatment may hold some advantages.

The effects of antecedent dry periods are clear. Considerations which can be extracted from the relationship between antecedent dry period and overflow quality are

1) Improved street cleaning and/or sanitation practices may decrease the contributions from surface washings, especially during long dry periods.

2) In design of sewers, consideration should be given to increased slopes to prevent deposition in the sewer. Little is known of the tradeoffs between increased sewer construction costs (due to steep slopes) and the necessity to capture/treat deposited material re-suspended during overflow.

3) It may be feasible to operate future auxillary water pollution control facilities differently depending on antecedent dry weather periods, the objective being to minimize the impact of overflows at minimum cost.

Time Varying Concentrations of Pollutants for Simulated Storms At any particular time during an overflow, the concentration of coliform bacteria is the result of the following processes

1) The mixing and dilution of the domestic sewage flow by stormwater. This is a constant process and is continuous throughout the overflow.

2) The re-suspension of coliforms by bottom scouring. The contribution by ths process is a function of the sewer system "memory" (the temporal and spatial distribution of deposited material as a function of sewer characteristics). This process is more pronounced when the sewer invert elevation is low with respect to the discharge control point.

3) The washing of coliforms from street gutters and urban land surfaces. This process is maxmum during the early part of a storm, but its impact at the overflow is continuous throughout most storms due to delays caused by conduit time.

The effect of sewer "memory" will increase if a treatment/capture basin is constructed near the outfall. When a treatment basin of given weir crest elevation is constructed, the permanent storage-induced settling will occur not only in the basin but up into the system. This settling is induced by decreasing velocity due to the basin filling process.

Deposited material may be routinely removed from the treatment basin, but normally no provision will be made for cleaning the affected portion of the sewer system. The beginning of runoff from the next storm will generate sufficiently velocity to to transport a bed load, but unless the storm is of sufficient magnitude, re-suspension of particulates will not occur. However, the movement of the bed load will be enough to re-suspend coliforms in the sediment by the cascade of turbulent eddies and dispersion due to the vertical non-uniformity of the velocity profile. This dichotomy of behavior in coliform and suspended solids transport causes the different characteristic shapes of their respective pollutographs and difficulties in modeling the SS behavior pattern.

Coliform Profiles For any particular instance during an overflow, the amount and concentration of coliform bacteria are the combined results of the following processes

1) Coliforms contained in the dry weather flow are being mixed and diluted by the stormwater. At any given time, t, the resulting coliform concentration is equal to the product of the dry weather concentration and flow rate divided by the sum of the dry and wet weather flow rates as shown in

$$C'_{(t)} = \frac{C_{D(t)}q_{D(t)}}{q_{D(t)} + q_{S(t)}}, \tag{8}$$

where:

C_D = dry weather coliform concentration,

q_D = dry weather flow rate, and

q_s = wet weather flow rate.

$C'_{(t)}$ is the concentration component which is caused by dilution alone. The characteristic shape of $C'_{(i)}$ is an inversed Gaussian curve (skewness and peakedness depending upon the storm hydrograph) each end asymptotically approaching the dry weather concentration.

2) The second contributing component is derived from sewer scouring. The amount of contribution depends greatly on the "memory" of the sewer system. This effect is more pronounced when the sewer system has a low elevation and is equipped with tide gates. If a storm begins during a high-tide condition, the ponding effect will cause a major portion of the solids to settle out in the trunk sewers. The prolonged tidal recession and dewatering process will not have the ability to carry away the settled solids and bacteria. Qualitatively speaking, the coliform concentration contributed by this process is proportional to the scouring velocity and limited by the concentration available. The amount of scouring is proportional to the n'th power of the flow. Therefore, the concentration contributed from the scouring action is

$$C''_t = \alpha S(q_S + q_D)_t^{n-1}, \tag{9}$$

where:

S = coefficient; function of storage factor and sewer slope,

$\alpha = 0$ when $t_{max} < t_i < \infty$, or

$\alpha = 1$ when $t_0 < t_i < t_{max}$.

The characteristic shape of the concentration curve from this component rises expoentially as the storm hydrograph rises but drops sharply when the available concentration is exhausted.

3) Another important source of coliforms is the street gutters. The amount contributed from street gutters is highly variable due to the different street cleaning frequencies, pet populations and antecedent dry periods involved. The graph of the amount contributed from this source has the same shape as the overflow hydrograph due to the early impact of the storm causing most of the pollutants in the street gutters to be carried into the sewer system. The curve is proportional to the k'th power of the hydrograph resulting from the first few effective storm impulses (first 10 to 20 minutes) divided by the first power of the hydrograph itself, as shown in Equation (10).

$$C'''_t = W\frac{(q_S)_t^k}{(q_S)_t} = W(q_S)^{k-1}, \tag{10}$$

where

$(q_S)_t$ = ordinate of the storm hydrograph at time, t,

W = coefficient varying with street cleaning frequency, basin geometry and population density, and

k = varies from 1.5 to 2.0.

Combining the effects of dilution (Equation (8)), scouring (Equation (9)), and street gutters, (Equation (10)) yields:

$$C_t = \left(\frac{C_D q_D}{q_D + q_S}\right)_t + \alpha S(q_S + q_D)_t^{n-1} + W(q_S)_t^{k-1}. \tag{11}$$

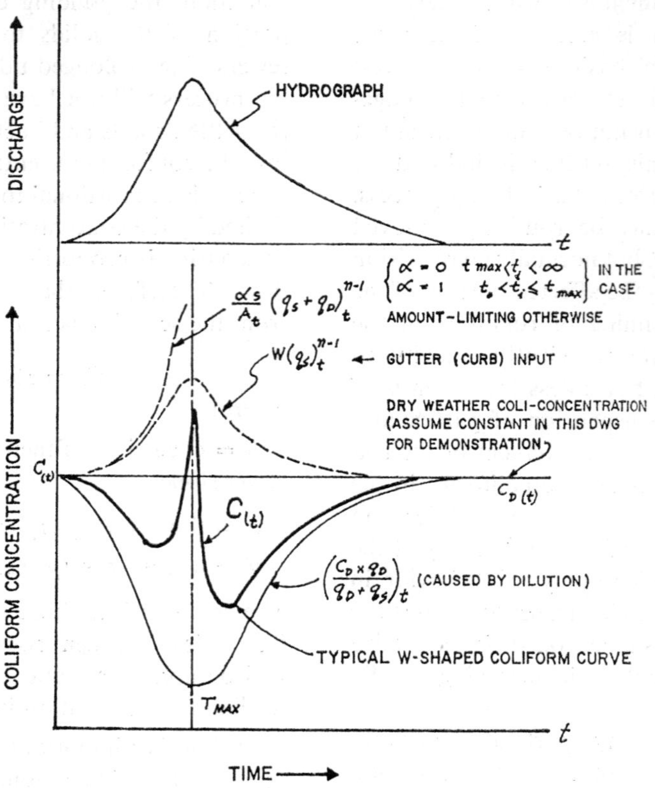

Figure 15 Definition sketch, coliform analysis.

For a typical storm, the time history of coliform concentration, C_t, will exhibit the W-shaped curve shown in Figure 15. Coliform data taken at the five CSO monitoring sites in the Jamaica Bay Project confirmed this configuration. An approximation of the powers in Equation (11) has been made from close scrutiny of the measured coliform concentration curves. For all the drainage systems monitored, n is approximately equal to 3.0 and k to 2.0. Coefficients S and W vary with the drainage system because of the basin and sewer network characteristics.

On 3 July 1969 the same storm was monitored at North Conduit, Spring Creek and Thurston Basin. This storm, and a storm occurring on 2 February 1970 monitored at Hendrix, were used to derive the values of S and W for each basin.

Comparisons between the computed and observed values of coliform concentrations along with approximations of S and W yielding the "best fit" curve for North Conduit basin are presented in Figure 16. Upper and lower 95% coliform confidence limits were computed for each observed MPN value and these are shown on each graph.

In comparing the computed curve with the measured curve it should be remembered that points identified on the measured curve do not necessarily reflect turning points of the true coliform distribution. Periodic sampling produces the discontinuities shown, but the short time between samples decreases the possibilities of the true curve being much different than the measured curve. In addition, the values of S and W will vary slightly for each discrete storm in a given drainage basin. However, the magnitude of the coefficients will not change the basic shape of the computed curve. Furthermore, the relative influence of the powers, n and k, on the shape and magnitude of the curve is much greater than that caused by S and W. These powers were found to be the same for all monitored drainage basins.

All computed curves agree quite well with the observed values. Using $S = 10$ and $W = 100$ for North Conduit, the agreement is excellent. In the case of Thurston Basin, the values of $S = 3$ and $W = 0$ produced close agreement. In Hendrix Creek, $S = 20$ and $W = 10$ yielded desirable results, and in Spring Creek good results were achieved with $S = 50$ and $W = 1000$.

Higher S values were indicative of pronounced scouring effects, and high W values indicate large contributions from surface washing. The relatively high S value of Spring Creek is caused by the low

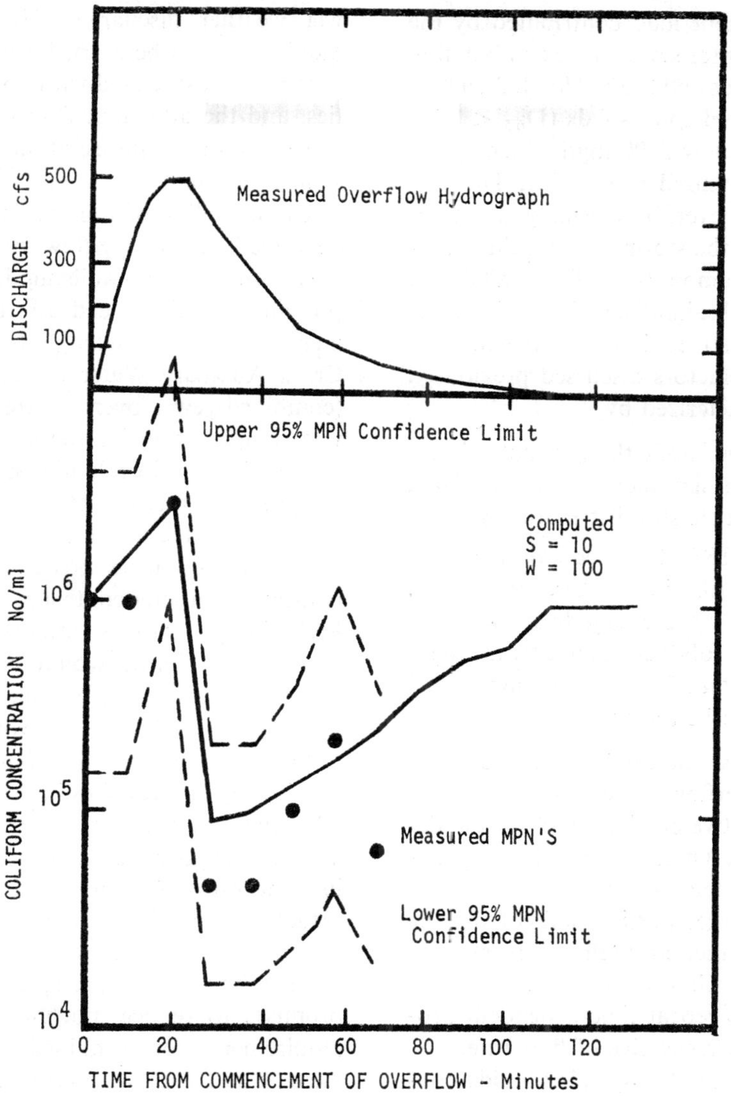

Figure 16 Coliform concentration profile, North Conduit Blvd. (New York), July 3, 1969.

sewer elevations which causes ponding and subsequent scouring of large amounts of pollutants. The flat land surface effects the size of W for Spring Creek. With these constants evaluated, and knowledge of their relationship to sewer and surface characteristics, estimates for other areas becomes relatively easy. In addition, a minor amount of monitoring (two to three periods) of a system would permit excellent evaluation of these parameters.

Suspended Solids Profiles The total suspended solids (TSS) curves are quite similar to the coliform curves when dilution and scouring are considered. For the average storm, the solids concentration contributed by dilution of the dry weather flow is less significant than the portions contributed by scouring and street washings. However, for prolonged storms, the significance of the dilution contribution increases. In those systems having significant ponding and downstream effects, the "memory" effect of the sewer system is also quite important.

The most reliable method of computing sediment transport presently available is the Einstein method. The entire method and equations are too lengthy to be presented here, but in essence, the method provides a means of computing the transport rate of a given particle size (D_{65}) under various flow rates for channels of fixed bed slope. Rating curves for the Spring Creek and Thurston Basin Interceptor sewers leading to the diversion structures were used to estimate the peak solids concentration during a storm overflow. For example, at the beginning of a storm, the total sediment load contributed by the North Conduit interceptor sewer is the combination of total suspended solids and the bed load. At a flow of 200 cfs. the estimated total solids ($D_{65} < 0.25$) transport is approximately 2300 mg/l which agrees very well with the measured peak value. The TSS curve of most storm overflows usually decreases from the beginning of the storm because the scouring power exceeds the amount of solids available in the sewer and the initial rainfall usually washes most of the solids from the streets into the system.

Considering all the factors discussed previously, the TSS curve is characterized by

1) In the early stage, both the amount of TSS and the mean particle size increase substantially. At the same time, particle size distribution widens.

2) After the peak TSS, the mean particle size decreases and the distribution becomes narrower.

It was concluded that a drainage basin with unpaved areas will supply solids continuously throughout runoff. The TSS data from all five monitored basins indicated this to be the case.

Analyses showed that the total suspended solids discharged during overflow were directly proportional to the total effective precipitation (area under overflow hydrograph). Direct proportionality implies that higher flow has greater scouring power and ability to carry larger particle solids from the surface. The San Francisco (Selby Street) data reflect this situation. That is, concentrations of pollutants appeared to repeat time-dependent profiles with each storm, irrespective of flow rate.

The time history of total suspended solids concentrations varies from basin to basin. By averaging all the monitored TSS pollutographs, it was found that TSS increase exponentially from an average of 120 mg/l to the peak, then decrease exponentially back to 120 mg/l. The exception was Paerdegat Basin where pre- and post-overflow values are much lower.

Remarks

Sufficient reliable monitoring data have now been accumulated to clearly demonstrate that both combined sewer overflows and urban stormwater discharges are significant sources of water pollution. Despite the fact that the information available leads to the conclusion that each drainage basin has enough individual characteristics to preclude making any *a priori* judgements as to the qualitative nature of its storm flows, techniques have been developed to facilitate engineering assessments. Granted, these procedures require monitoring of wet weather discharges. However, the required monitoring can be carried out for a small fraction of the costs associated with pollution control facilities, and the attendant field inspections frequently provide valuable information on the nature of the sewerage system.

The modeling of time variant concentrations of combined sewer overflow pollutants, which followed from the hydraulic modeling described in the preceding section, lead to further mathematical analyses of the predicted performance of the Spring Creek Auxiliary Water Pollution Control Facility (combined sewer overflow treatment). The facility was completed during the last year of the Jamaica Bay Project, and evaluative monitoring results are not yet available. Nonetheless, it became apparent that through the use of the hydraulic-water quality model it would be possible to employ on-line real-time computer control of the treatment facility. Preliminary analyses indicated that substantial savings in chlorine would be possible, and that overall improved performance might be expected because human judgement would be obviated.

The scheme called for continuous precipitation monitoring at three sites in the drainage basin, with telemetery of the data to the control computer. This would give about 45 minutes lead time for influent flow estimates, with periodic checks of actual flow against predicted flow. Chlorination rates would be set accordingly. Computational schemes have not yet been perfected, but the method promises to reduce much of the projected labor requirements for combined sewer overflow treatment. The following section covers this aspect in more detail.

Engineering Implications

As pointed out in the introductory section of this paper, there exists widespread concern for the quality of receiving waters in urban areas. This concern has been well articulated by the Office of Water Resources Research in its publication *A National Urban Water Resources Research Program:*[8]

The value of water for environmental enhancement and recreation is well recognized. City dwellers have traditionally gone to the country for relaxation, aesthetic enjoyment, fishing, boating and swimming. Indeed, they are doing so in ever larger numbers, thereby creating the mixed blessings of increased auto traffic and heightened pressure on rural and wilderness areas. The conscious use of urban water to make a city environment capable of satisfying a larger part of the needs of tranquility and recreation is not likely to diminish noticeably the appeal of seaside and mountain resorts because a change of pace and surroundings is itself a basic human need. But it can make the adjustments of millions of people to the restrictions of urban living easier and more rewarding.

The pollution aspects of storm drainage present several situations that so far appear as dilemmas. It seems certain that they cannot efficaciously be resolved without substantial breakthroughs of a technological character or, in the alternative, without drastic policy and financial decisions that have not yet been seriously contemplated.

For example, the combined sewer problem has received much attention in recent years, but no solutions are yet visible. Many years ago municipal engineers consolidated wastewater and stormwater runoff in a single set of sewers as an economical expedient. Both could flow into streams and be forgotten together. The system was considered to be an excellent example of efficiency and ingenuity until government officials and the general public began to rebel at massive discharges of raw or inadequately treated liquid wastes. It was then that it began to seem a little less felicitous to suffer through the periodic discharge of combined sewer overflows. Whenever a significant rain occurs in many of our largest urban centers, some sewage is discharged raw into receiving waterways because the tremendous volumes of combined stormwater and liquid wastes cannot be retained or contained for long enough to permit treatment plants constructed and operated at great expense to do their job.

It is possible to say that there shall be separate waste and storm sewer systems installed in new communities or subdivisions and that urban renewal should include separation of combined sewers. Such decisions have been made in a number of places, but we are still left with the existing legacy of billions of dollars in combined facilities. It is not only the cost of the sewers themselves that must be counted. Even more, it is the cost of tearing up such large installations in heavily developed, high real estate value areas and of constructing additional and alternative collection and disposal lines. While some research is underway, it would seem that it must be continued and even increased until solutions, or at least sufficiently ameliorative techniques, including operational improvements in present facilities, can be found for coping with combined runoffs and overflows.

Treatment vs. storage of storm flows

The alternative concepts of continuous treatment and storage have been recognized for some time. The Federal Water Pollution Control Administration published the proceedings of a seminar held in 1969,[19] and an overview was presented by the Director of the Storm and Combined Sewer Program, William Rosenkranz

1) First of all, there is likely to be no single method of either control or treatment applicable as a complete answer to combined sewer problems. I believe that it it is safe to say that this is true even when considering sewer separation as a corrective measure. We have to think in terms of individual outfall control and treatment. Over-all systems which would achieve control over individual drainage areas is of great importance. Systems which can handle the entire problem for a given community or even perhaps a metropolitan area must be considered and evaluated. In other words, drainage area approach must be applied when investigating solutions to overflow problems. While the point source control or treatment application must also be utilized, they will fail unless the entire drainage area problems are assessed. This is applicable to the entire community or metropolitan area as well as the individual portions within the area. Proper planning must consider and evaluate all of the different kinds of treatment that might be utilized in an integrated control/treatment system. We need to carefully examine the compatibility of the methodology used in order to properly develop integrated and coordinated systems.

2) The concept of storage that we use in our program involves any kind of storage that you want to talk about—concrete tanks, design and construction of buildings or modification of roof designs to permit use of roof-top storage, off-shore storage by means of retention basins, underwater bags, many surface ponds, deep tunnels or lined caverns—many different methods and in many different configurations. Each of these methods may have a particular application to a given situation due to the geology of the area, the topography of the land, the location of the sewers, type of receiving waters, water quality required and many other factors.

3) Engineering studies must consider all potential alternatives when seeking to determine what is *most* applicable, what is efficient and what is economical. In order to achieve an "optimal" system physical control by storage must be considered in conjunction with potentially applicable treatment methods. This would include as possible solutions the use of storage or surge basins in combination with screening, dissolved air flotation, bio-disc treatment, high rate biological filtration or any other treatment configuration. In-system flow control, flood routing in the system, and storage of waste waters from the system - off the system. In other words, remove wastewater from the system—perhaps even in the upper portions of the drainage area for feedback into the system when the storm is over. Improved regulators, remote control, surge tanks combined with existing or expanded sewage treatment plants, surface storage or retention basins and microstrainers should be examined as possibilities.

Essentially the only alternatives available for management of combined sewage flows are treatment and immediate discharge, or storage followed by subsequent treatment and discharge. The primary objective of storage is to capture that portion of a sewage flow which has the highest concentrations of undesirable constituents. A key objective in the operation of treatment facilities is to stabilize the hydraulic or constituent loading rates in the feed stream at an optimum level to achieve maximum efficiency from the unit. It follows from these observations that the use of storage as a management alternative would be most efficacious where the greatest percentage of the total-storm pollutant emission occurs early in the storm, and the use of treatment as a management alternative would be most desirable where the pollutant concentration in the feed stream to the treatment facility remains in the range of concentrations in which the performance of the treatment facility is optimal.

Time-concentration profiles of pollutants and overflow hydrograph profiles of combined sewage overflows have an important role in the evaluation of whether treatment or storage is desirable, because the profiles can be used to define the rate of accumulation of pollutants and flow over the course of a combined sewage flow. The general characteristics of the time-concentration profiles for constituents in combined sewage overflows, and the basic factors that influence the shapes of overflow hydrographs and time-concentration profiles have been discussed in the previous section.

The role of modeling in the management of treatment alternatives should be clear. The complex interaction between hydraulic-quality parameters and random components (systems noise) of the system warrant model usage to achieve the most efficient and economical management process. Because the optimal treatment scheme for each parameter is not identical, a model can successfully weigh the alternatives and tradeoffs involved in deriving the overall optimal scheme. Various shapes and volumes of the treatment basins can be investigated, considering all the waste input streams (parameters) and constraints, and evaluating each selected alternative configuration against cost.

Pollutographs and cumulative emission curves generated by the model provide valuable information in alternatives selection. The pollutographs depict the time history of concentrations for an overflow event. This information can be used to determine when peak parameter concentration occurs in relation to the hydrograph peak. The effects of scouring can also be immediately determined from the pollutograph.

Assessment of urban runoff quality control technology

At this point in time it is impossible to accurately establish the most promising means of urban runoff (storm and combined sewer) quality control. Several prototype control schemes have been under investigation during the past decade, but a comprehensive evaluation of the results of these investigations has yet to be made.

Both Boston and Chicago have considered deep tunnel storage.[19] San Francisco has constructed a dissolved air flotation (continuous treatment) facility,[20] which is now being evaluated. Submerged rubber storage tanks were utilized in a study in Washington, D.C.,[21] and the costs of retention (storage) basins for Halifax, Nova Scotia have been estimated by Waller.[22] Microstraining of combined sewer overflows has been proposed based on studies in Philadelphia,[23] and vibratory fine screening was tested in Portland, Oregon.[24] As mentioned previously, the city of New York has constructed a continuous flow treatment facility for a 2000 acre drainage basin.[3,25] The facility will include removal of settleable solids and chlorination of the facility effluent. A novel approach of controlled in-system storage with the use of real-time computer control has been implemented in Minneapolis-St. Paul.[26] All of the reported installations and proposed facilities have been justified either on the basis of actual or estimated performance efficiencies or economic considerations. Yet, the primary objective of receiving water quality management has seldom been considered as the principal goal. Thus, what is needed now is the development of a methodology which will effectively relate the following factors for the selection of proper control procedures for any urban drainage area

1) The characteristics of the receiving waters;

2) Existing and potential uses of the receiving waters;

3) Land use characteristics in the vicinity of the point of stormwater discharge;

4) Sewer system characteristics;

5) Drainage area land use and population density; and

6) Precipitation patterns.

Optimization in Treatment Facility Design and Operation

The development of an operational model is important for two reasons

1) the model can be used to find the best operational method for a designed facility based on monitoring of various influent characteristics, and

2) the model will enable guidelines to be set for future design considerations.

Because of the interaction between the hydraulic-quality parameters and the random components involved, the most efficient and economical approach is to consider each essential parameter in an orderly way of means of modeling. This approach was used in the Jamaica Bay Study in New York.[25]

The optimal treatment scheme for one constituent is not always the best when other pollutants are considered. Compromises usually have to be made. The problem is to minimize the inefficiencies. For example, flow turbulence in a treatment system is essential to the effectiveness of chlorination, but it greatly reduces the solids removal efficiency. Shape and volume of a treatment basin should be studied by trial with all important input parameters and constraints considered and evaluated against cost.

The purpose of a coliform disinfection model is to find the "optimal" dosing scheme. The optimal dosing scheme is defined as the minimization of the time integral of the control vector (dosage) subject to specified constraints based on predetermined performance characteristics. In other words, it is the time history of the required minimal dosage for a given storm such that the resulting coliform concentration at the beginning of basin overspill is exactly equal to that of the receiving water quality standard, and that such a level remain throughout the entire spillover process.

A desirable process control system is one in which the controllable input is regulated by a control mechanism according to some given criterion through a continuous monitoring of the output. However, this cannot be accomplished here due to the following difficulties

1) Input and output quality cannot be monitored *in situ* during the process in order to regulate the controllable input for the desired results.

2) From the time and point of dosing, both contact time and coliform decay rate are unknown, because the contact time depends on the future input quantity and the decay rate depends on the future input quality.

There are two solutions to these problems. First, indirect measurements can be made by relating the unmeasurable variables (pollutant concentrations) to a measurable quantity (inflow rate) by means of mass discharge coefficients. After a sufficient number of trials, an appropriate dosing rate can be obtained for typical summer storms.

The second solution is to close the "information gap" by means of a predictive model and several transfer functions. This control scheme is shown in Figure 17. It can be shown that an optimal solution exists under this scheme because all the parameters needed for evaluating overflow quality at any given instant are within the time domain of prediction.

This procedure can be demonstrated with the help of Figure 18. The numbered blocks represent unit input (TRH and ERH to the drainage system) and the family of S-shaped curves gives the corresponding resultant output from the drainage basin. These S-curves can be either the cumulative inflow to the treatment basin (same as the routed outflow from the drainage basin) or the cumulative pollutographs (same as a routed cumulative mass pollutant outflow from the combined sewer system).

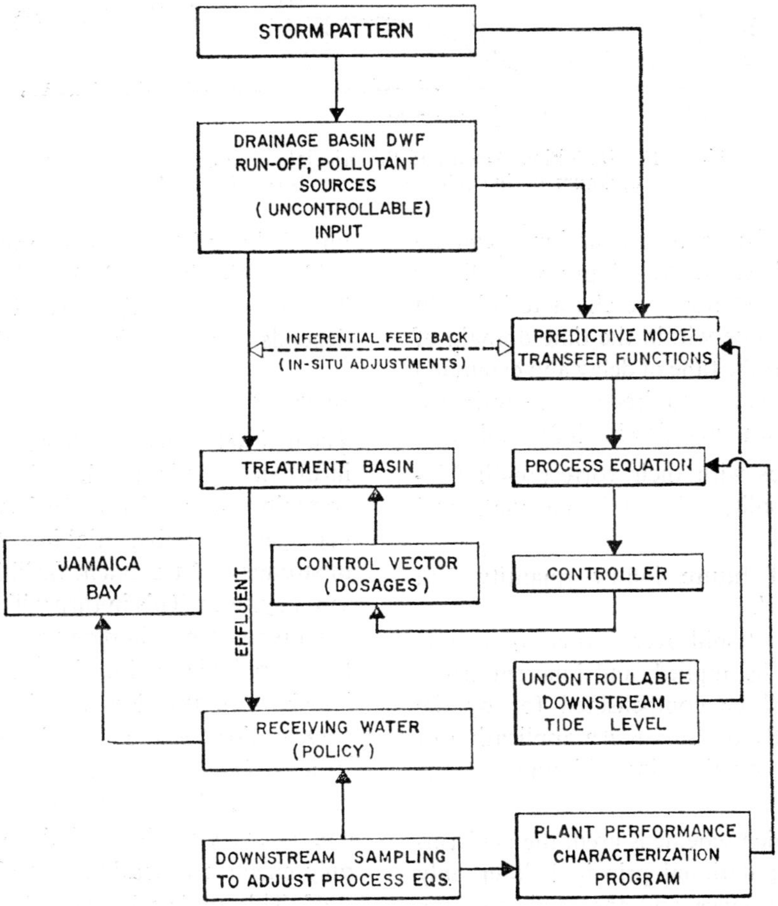

Figure 17 A real-time computer-controlled stormwater treatment system.

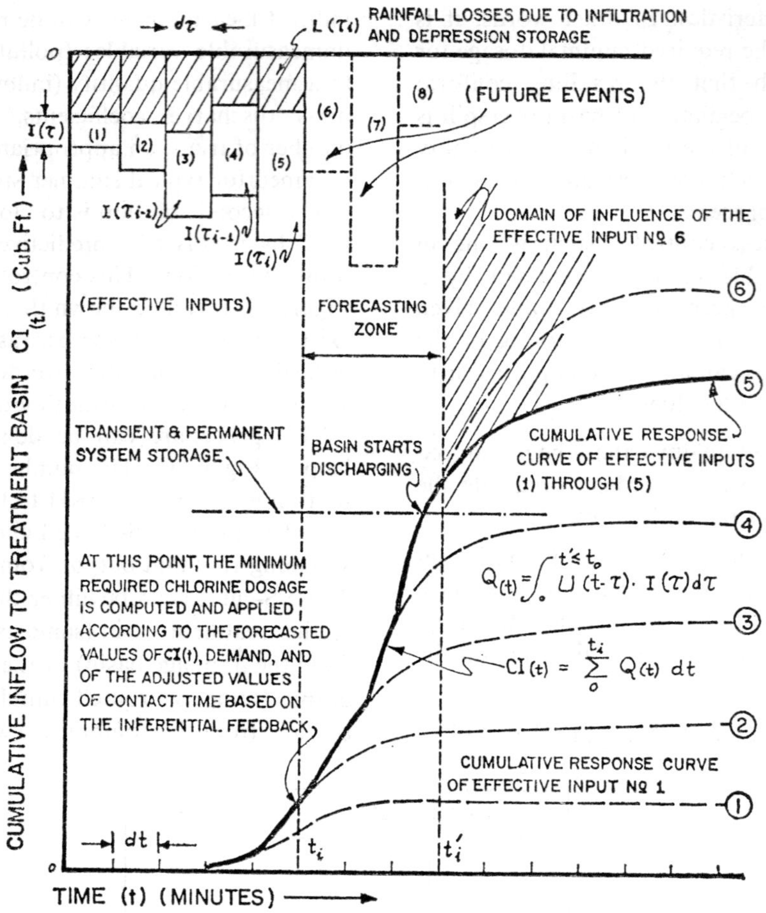

Figure 18 Definition sketch and the principle of computation of the optimum dosing scheme using a forecasting model.

At time, t_i, the future treatment input can be predicted up to time, t_i'. Any input to a linear system with a delayed response characteristic will effect only the response within the time domain of influence, starting at the time of delay and extending to infinity. Therefore, the required dosage at time, t_i can be computed with the following information

1) previous doses with their corresponding inflow quantity, quality, demand, residual, and residual decay, and

2) the predicted future inflow quantity and quality up to time t_i'.

If the basin does not spill over at time, t_i' a flow-weighted dose will be applied, and inherent errors in this dosage will be compensated for by the $(t_i'+n\Delta t)$th dose. By the successive application of this technique, the actual dosing will approach the optimal path.

Regardless of which scheme is used, the performance and the computational principal differ only slightly. The performance and the quality of the controlling technique is dependent mainly on the knowledge of the process equation derived from field monitoring and the plant characterization. The accuracy of the second method of control depends on the preciseness of the predictive model.

Remarks

The maintenance and enhancement of water quality in urban areas is a task which will require a large commitment to efforts of urban runoff control and management. Substantial investments will be made in storage and treatment facilities and in improved sewer systems. This in turn will demand that a more comprehensive technology assessment be made and that a reliable engineering methodology be developed for the selection of optimum control facilities.

Operation of the facilities once they are constructed is another area that will require further research. It has been demonstrated that on-line computer control is a technique which promises not only effective operation, but also minimization of staff. This topic will undoubtedly receive a great deal of attention during the coming decade.

REFERENCES

1. Jens, S. W. and M. B. McPherson (1964). "Hydrology of Urban Areas", in *Handbook of Applied Hydrology* (V. T. Chow, Ed.), McGraw-Hill.
2. Lihsley, R. K. and J. B. Franzini (1955). *Elements of Hydraulic Engineering*, McGraw-Hill.
3. Final Report—Year I, *Spring Creek Auxiliary Water Pollution Control Project*, (Jamaica Bay Project) Bureau of Water Pollution Control, Dept of Water Resources, City of New York, 1970. (Final report in production.)
4. Palmer, C. L. (Feb. 1950). "The Pollutional Effects of Storm Water Overflows from Combined Sewers", *Sewage and Industrial Wastes*, **22,** No. 2, 154.
5. Dunbar, D. D. and J. G. F. Henry (Jan. 1966). "Pollution Control Measures for Storm Waters and Combined Sewer Overflows", *J. Water Poll. Cont. Fed.*, **38** (1), 9.
6. Romer, H. and L. M. Klashman (March and April 1963). "How Combined Sewers Affect Water Pollution —Parts I and II", *Public Works.*
7. Gameson, A. L. H. and R. N. Davidson (1963). "Storm Water Investigations at Northampton," *J. and Proc. Inst. of Sewage Purification*, Part 2, p. 105.
8. "Characterization and Treatment of Combined Sewer Overflows," Report to Federal Water Pollution Admin. by the City and County of San Francisco. Prepared by Engineering-Science, Inc. (November 1967).
9. "Report on Sanitary Sewerage Systems, Iowa City, Iowa," Veenstra and Kimm, Des Moinse, Iowa, 1963.
10. "Engineering Report—Sewer Separation and Sewage Treatment for City of Kansas City, Kansas," Truman Schhep, Kanas City, Kansas, 1953.
11. "Report on Master Plan for Trunk Sewers and Sewage Treatment Facilities for Kansas City, Missouri," Black and Veatch, Kansas City, Mo., 1958.
12. "Sanitary Sewers and Storm Drainage, Kendallville, Indiana," Clyde E. Williams and Associates, South Bend, Ind., 1963.
13. "City of Lafayette, Indiana—A Master Plan for Sewers," Henry B. Steeg and Associates, Indianapolis, Ind., 1963.
14. "Pollutional Effects of Stormwater and Overflows from Combined Sewer Systems: A Preliminary Appraisal." U.S. Public Health Service Publ. No. 1246, November 1964.
15. "Water Pollution Aspects of Urban Runoff," report by American Public Works Assoc. to the Federal Water Pollution Control Admin., WP–20–15 (January, 1969).
16. Weibel, S. R., R. J. Anderson and R. L. Woodward (July 1964). "Urban Land Runoff as a Factor in Stream Pollution," *J. Water Poll. Cont. Fed.*, **36** (7), 914.
17. Weibel, S. R., *et al.* (1966). *Pesticides and Other Contaminants from Rainfall and Runoff as Observed in Ohio*, Cincinnati Water Research Laboratory, Federal Water Pollution Control Administration.
18. *A National Urban Water Resources Research Program* Office of Water Resources Research, U.S. Dept. of Interior, 1971.
19. *Combined Sewer Overflow Seminar Papers*, Federal Water Pollution Control Administration, U.S. Dept. of Interior, November 1969.
20. "Treatment of Combined Sewer Overflows by the Dissolved Air Flotation Process—Phase I, Preconstruction Studies," Dept. of Public Works, City and County of San Francisco and Engineering-Science, Inc., April 1970.
21. *Control of Pollution by Underwater Storage*, Federal Water Pollution Control Administration, U.S. Dept. of Interior, December 1969.
22. Waller, D. H. (1971). "Cost and Performance of Retention Basins in the Treatment of Wet Weather Sewage Flows," Dept. of Civil Engineering, Nova Scotia Technical College, Halifax, Nova Scotia.
23. Diaper, E. and G. Glover (October 1971). "Microstraining of Combined Sewer Overflows," *J. Water Poll. Cont. Fed.* **43** (10), 2101.
24. *Combined Sewer Overflow Abatement Technology*, Federal Water Quality Administration, U.S. Dept. of Interior, June 1970.
25. *Final Report—Spring Creek Auxiliary Water Pollution Control Project* (Jamaica Bay Project), Bureau of Water Pollution Control, Dept. of Water Resources, City of New York, 1972.
26. Anderson, J. J. (August 1968). "Real Time Computer Control of Urban Runoff," *Proceedings, A.S.C.E. Hydraulics Division Conference.*

DAVID W. ECKHOFF
University of Utah
DAVID S. K. LIU
The RAND Corporation

VEHICLE POLLUTION: see AUTOMOTIVE POLLUTION

WASTES OF INDUSTRY: see LIQUID WASTES OF INDUSTRY

W

WASTEWATER: PHYSICAL AND CHEMICAL TREATMENT

Introduction

The characteristics of domestic and industrial wastewaters having significance in water pollution control, disposal, and reuse are (a) soluble organics resulting in dissolved oxygen depletion in streams and estuaries and/or causing taste and odour, (b) organic suspended solids resulting in dissolved oxygen depletion, (c) inert suspended solids causing turbidity and resulting in bottom sediments, (d) toxic substances and heavy metal ions, (e) oil and floating materials, (f) acids and alkalis, and (g) dissolved salts, particularly nutrients like phosphorus and nitrogen.

The conventional wastewater treatment practices have been oriented to the removal of grit and floating matter followed by the removal of suspended and dissolved organic matter. The removal of suspended matter has been achieved by sedimentation, and the bulk of the soluble organic matter is removed by biological oxidation. These processes, when carried out in combination, have proven to be economical and effective means for removing organic matter from wastewaters. However, there are certain disadvantages associated with them. These include:

i) the biological process requires considerable operating control and often generates operating problems of complex nature,

ii) the biological process is easily upset and requires time to regain efficient operation, and

iii) many wastes containing certain industrial wastes do not respond to biological treatment or alternatively require a good pretreatment.

In recent years, physical-chemical treatment of wastewater has been studied on laboratory as well as pilot plant scales.[1–8] This type of treatment is used either as an advanced treatment to the effluent after secondary treatment or as a substitute for the conventional biological treatment. In latter case, it is found to produce effluent of a quality at least equal to that produced by good conventional biological treatment. The chemical process usually used is the chemical coagulation for removal of phosphates and non-soluble organic materials, whereas the physical process is usually the activated carbon adsorption for removal of soluble organic materials.

Historical Development of Physical-Chemical Processes

The first study on the treatability of raw wastewater by physical-chemical process were reported by Rudolfs and Trubnick[1] in 1935. In this study, solids were removed by chemical coagulation with ferric chloride followed by adsorption of dissolved impurities with activated carbon.

Stander and Van Vuuren[2] investigated the treatment of raw wastewater in a pilot plant where solids removal was achieved by primary sedimentation and chemical coagulation with lime, and adsorption with activated carbon. Rizzo and Schade[3] also have reported results on the pilot plant treatment of raw wastewater with chemical coagulation and anionic polymer and adsorption with activated carbon.

Zuckerman and Molof[4] studied the efficiency of a treatment system in which raw wastewater was lime clarified at high pH and then carbon treated. Their results showed that the chemical oxygen demand, COD, values of the final effluent were significantly lower than those associated with good conventional treatment. Moreover, they concluded that the removal of soluble organics with activated carbon is enhanced because of the hydrolytic breakdown of high molecular weight organic compounds, at a higher pH value, which are absorbed more readily by carbon.

Weber, *et al.*,[5] investigated the chemical clarification of primary effluent with ferric chloride followed by activated carbon adsorption. Their results showed that 65 percent of the organic matter present in primary effluent was removed by chemical treatment with ferric chloride. Overall removal of biochemical oxygen demand, BOD, was reported as being consistently in the range of 95 to 97 percent. Final effluent from the system contained approximately 5 mg/l BOD as compared to 30 mg/l for the same wastewater treated conventionally.

In another study, Villiers *et al.*,[6] showed that the treatment of primary effluent by lime clarification and activated carbon, in a steady flow system, produced an effluent with total organic carbon, TOC, averaging 11 mg/l and turbidity averaging less than two. Phosphate and suspended solids removal were consistently 90 percent or better. These product characteristics are comparable to those associated with product from well operated conventional treatment plants.

Shuckrow[7] has developed a sewage treatment process involving chemical coagulation for suspended solids removal, followed by adsorption of soluble organics on powdered carbon. The advantages cited for this process are (i) a total treatment time of less than one hour, (ii) a high quality effluent, (iii) lower initial plant cost, (iv) ability to remove nitrogen and phosphorous, and (v) a final sludge reduction to sterile ash in a centrifuge–incineration process combined with a chemical regeneration step to recover both the coagulant and the carbon. While the estimated operational costs are high, the overall costs during a 20 year plant life are considered to be significantly less than costs for comparable biological facilities.

South Tahoe Public Utility District has been operating successfully a 7.5 million gallons per day plant for treating the secondary effluent by physical and chemical treatment processes.[8]

Ecodyne Corporation's first complete physical-chemical treatment plant in Rosemount, Minn., with 1–2 mgd peak capacity, consists of bar screening, phosphate removal with sludge recirculation, dual media filtration, carbon adsorption to remove dissolved organics, secondary filtration, and ammonia removal by ion exchange with zeolite. The plant includes facilities for regenerating the carbon and recovering ammonia and regenerate brine from the ion-exchange system.[9]

The flow charts for some of these processes are shown in Figures 1 to 3. Table I shows the partial list of full-scale plants using or planning to use chemical phosphorus removal.[10] These physical

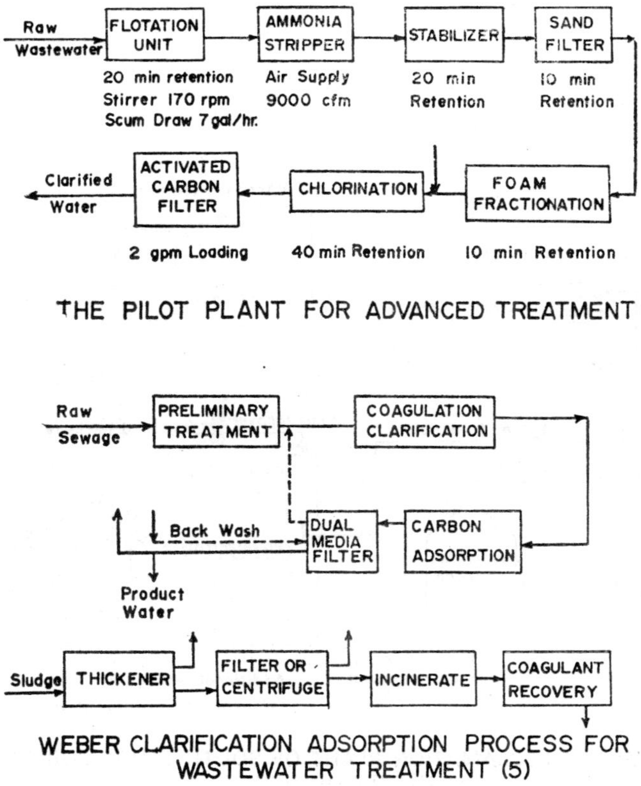

Figure 1 Schematics of different physical-chemical wastewater treatment systems.

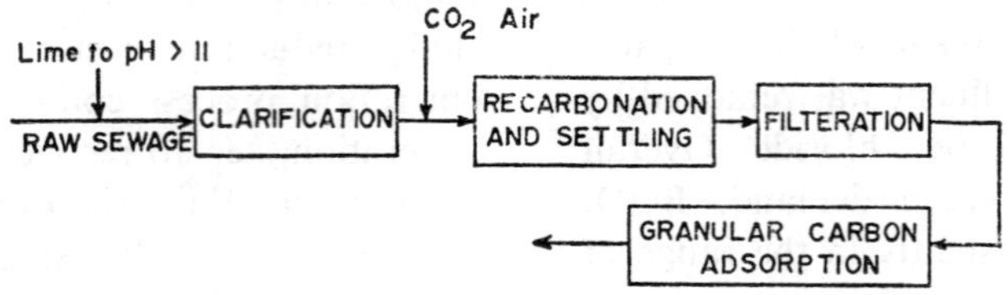

ZUCKERMAN-MOLOFF SCHEMATICS OF PHYSICAL-CHEMICAL TREATMENT SYSTEM (4)

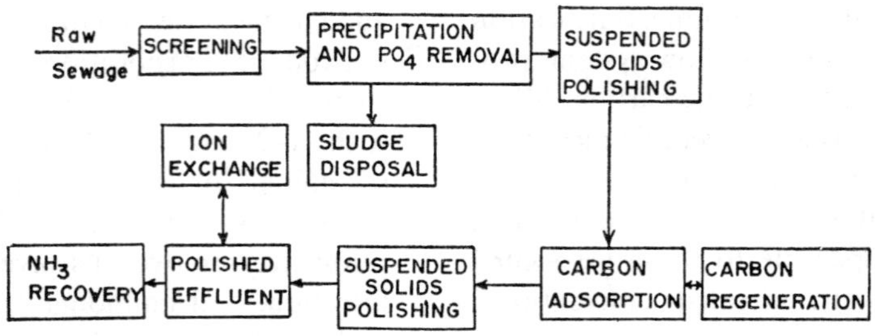

FLOW CHART FOR ECODYNE PHYSICAL-CHEMICAL SEWAGE TREATMENT PLANT AT ROSEMOUNT (9)

Figure 2 Schematics of different physical-chemical wastewater treatment systems.

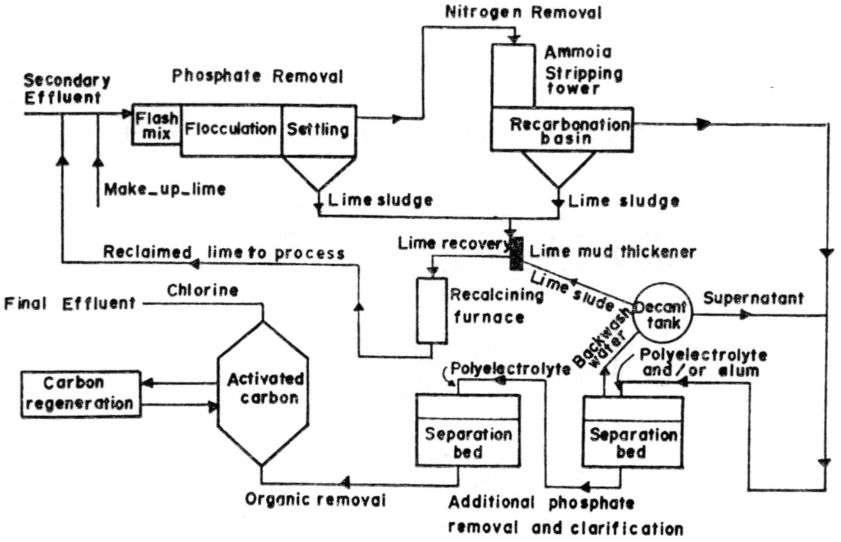

WATER RECLAMATION PLANT OF SOUTH TAHOE PUBLIC UTILITY DISTRICT[8]

Figure 3 Schematics of different physical-chemical treatment systems.

TABLE I
Partial List of Full-Scale Plants Using or Planning To Use Chemical Phosphorus Removal

Stage where treatment performed	Flow mgd	Chemicals
PRIMARY TREATMENT		
Detroit, Mich.	600	Steel Manufacturing Waste Pickle Liquor—mostly ferrous with ferric chloride
Rochester, N.Y.	100	Lime
Grand Rapids, Mich.	45	Ferric Chloride + Polymer
Bay City, Mich.	12	Ferric Chloride
Rocky River, Ohio	10	Aluminum Sulfate + Polymer
SECONDARY TREATMENT		
Milwaukee, Wis.	80	Ferrous Sulfate
Chicago South Creek Plant, Ill.	30	Aluminum Sulfate
Metro Seattle, Wash.	20	Aluminum Sulfate
TERTIARY TREATMENT		
South Lake Tahoe, Calif.	7.5	Lime
Piscataway, Maryland	5	Lime

Source: Technology Transfer, Environmental Protection Agency, Washington, D.C.[10]

and chemical operations are essentially the same whether used independently or in combination with other conventional wastewater treatments. Therefore their description is applicable to both the removal of impurities from biologically treated or raw wastewaters.

Process Description

The following important unit operations and unit processes involved in the physical and chemical treatment of wastewater are discussed in detail.

A) Chemical Coagulation, Flocculation, and Sedimentation: These operations result in reducing suspended and collodial solids, phosphates, organic matter, colour and certain toxic substances.

B) Filtration: This is employed for the removal of finely divided suspended material carried over from primary or secondary clarification. This may or may not be preceded by chemical coagulation. Since great percentages of phosphates and organic matter are present in suspended form, removal of these constituents will also be achieved during filtration.

C) Air Stripping: For removal of ammonia.

D) Ion Exchange: For the removal of phosphates, nitrogen and total dissolved solids.

E) Reverse Osmosis: For the removal of organic and inorganic substances.

F) Electrodialysis: For the removal of inorganic salts.

G) Carbon Adsorption: For reduction in organic matter.

H) Others: Foam Stripping, etc.

A. Chemical coagulation, flocculation and sedimentation

The use of chemical treatment appeared early in the development of sewage and wastewater treatment. Aluminum sulfate, lime, and ferrous sulfate, when used in the manner usually adopted for water clarification, were successful in producing an effluent of quality better than that obtained by plain sedimentation. An effluent that is generally fairly clear, with only very fine suspended or colloidal solids but with practically all of the dissolved solids remaining, can be produced. Under most favourable conditions and with skilled operation, suspended solids, SS, may be reduced in amount up to 90% and biochemical oxygen demand, BOD, up to 85%. However, the cost of the coagulants and the difficulty of disposing of the bigger amount of the sludge produced by this process caused it to be abandoned. The revival of chemical treatment can be attributed to a number of factors which accumulated as a result of continuous investigations and re-evaluation of the process. These are (i) the decrease in cost of chemicals, particularly the ferric salts, which seem to be most efficient, (ii) better understanding of floc formation and the factors affecting it, (iii) the development of methods of sludge filtration and processing which overcome in part the difficulty of greater sludge bulk, and (iv) the establishment of the relationship between eutrophication in streams and nutrients, particularly phosphorous, nitrogen oxides and organic matter. This relation desires the need of final effluent wastes free of such pollutants regardless of the cost of additional treatment.

The settling velocities of finely divided and colloidal particles in wastewaters are so small that removing them in a settling tank under ordinary conditions is impossible unless very long detention periods are provided. Therefore, it has been necessary to devise means to coagulate these very small particles into larger ones which will have higher settling velocities. The aggregation of dispersed particles in wastewater is induced by addition of chemical coagulants to decrease the effects of the stabilizing factors, viz, hydration and zeta potential, and by agitation of the medium to encourage collisions between particles.

Because of the greater amount of suspended matter in sewage, the doses for chemical coagulants must be considerably greater. Therefore, in order to keep the cost down, it is important that the chemical reaction involved with each coagulant should be known and enhanced and that optimum pH values be obtained by adjustment with acid or lime to get more efficient coagulation and clarification with least sludge production.

Coagulation Coagulation is a process in which chemicals are added to an aqueous system for the purpose of creating rapid-settling aggregates out of finely divided, dispersed matter with slow or negligible settling velocities. The potential applications of this process in treating wastewater are: (i) direct coagulation of organic matter present mostly as colloidal particles in wastewater, (ii) the removal of colloidal substances prior to such tertiary treatment processes as ion exchange, carbon adsorption, and sand filtration, (iii) the removal of colloidal precipitates formed in phosphate precipitation processes, (iv) the removal of dispersed microorganisms after a brief bio-oxidation processes.

The majority of colloids in domestic wastewater or in organic wastes are of hydrophilic nature, that is, they have an affinity for water. This affinity of hydrophilic particles for water results from the presence of certain polar groups such as —OH, —COOH, and —NH; on the surface of the particles. These groups are water soluble and, as such, attract and hold a sheath of water firmly around the particle. The primary charge on hydrophilic colloidal particles may arise from ionization of the chemical groups present at the surface of the particles, e.g., carboxyl, amino, sulfate, and hydroxyl. This charge is dependent upon the extent to which these surface groups ionize, and thus, the particle charge depends upon the pH.

The precise zeta potential which yields optimum coagulation must be determined for a given wastewater by actual correlation with jar test or plant performance. The control point has been reported to be in the range of 0 to -10 millivolts when raw sewage is coagulated by alum. It is important that coagulants contribute polyvalent ions of charge opposite to the zeta potential of the dispersion. On a molar basis bivalent ions seems to be about 10 to 50 times and trivalent ions about 300 to 700 times as effective as monovalent ions for destabilization of dispersions in wastewater.[11]

Since most dispersions encountered in wastewaters are stabilized by negative charges, coagulants required are polyvalent cations such as aluminum, ferric, ferrous or calcium. Organic polyelectrolytes are also effective coagulants. Dispersions stabilized principally by electrostatic force are in general amenable to coagulation in as much as addition of small doses of suitable electrolytes may effect significant change in zeta potential of the particles. The most widely used chemicals for coagulation of wastewater are the salts of aluminum and iron. Lime alone has also been used for precipitation of phosphates.

Aluminum Sulfate In order to form flocs, aluminum sulfate requires the presence of alkalinity which if naturally present in wastewater in the form of bicarbonate, would lead to the following reaction:

$$Al_2(SO_4)_3 \,.\, xH_2O + 3(HCO_3)_2 \longrightarrow 2Al(OH)_3 + 3CaSO_4 + xH_2O + 6CO_2 \downarrow . \qquad (1)$$

In case of insufficient alkalinity in the wastewater, lime is generally added and the reaction with alum becomes:

$$Al_2(SO_4)_3 \,.\, xH_2O + 3(Ca(OH)_2 \longrightarrow 2\,Al(OH)_3\downarrow + 3CaSO_4 + xH_2O. \qquad (2)$$

In the presence of phosphates, the following reaction also occurs:

$$Al_2(SO_4)_3 + 2PO_4 \longrightarrow 2AlPO_4 \downarrow + 3SO_4. \qquad (3)$$

The aluminum hydroxide floc is least soluble at a pH of approximately 7.0. The floc charge is positive below pH 7.6 and negative above pH 8.2.[12] The solubility of $AlPO_4$ is related to the pH and the equilibrium constant for the salt. Rohlich[13] had observed that the optimum phosphate removal from sewage effluent, is at pH 7.1 to 7.7 with an alum dose of 200 mg/l. Generally at pH above 6.3, the phosphate removal occurs either by incorporation in a complex with aluminum or adsorption on the aluminum hydroxide flocs. According to Yuan and Hsu,[14] the reaction mechanism for precipitation of phosphates by aluminum hydroxide is very complex. He has proposed that the positively charged hydroxy–aluminum polymers are the species which account for the precipitation of phosphates and that effective phosphate precipitation can occur only when the positive charges on the polymers are completely neutralized. It is also reported that the effectiveness of aluminum is related to the nature and concentration of the foreign components present and also the amount of phosphate to aluminum ratio.

Alum has been used extensively for phosphate removal in raw wastewaters. Bench-scale tests of alum addition were conducted at Springfield, Ohio,[15] and Two Rivers, Wisconsin.[16] Raw wastewater at Springfield required an average Al : P weight ratio of 1.9 : 1 to achieve 80% removal, while at Two Rivers the average ratio was 0.93 : 1 to obtain phosphate removal of 85%. The stoichiometric Equation 3 indicates that, each pound of phosphorous requires 0.87 lb. of aluminum for complete precipitation.

Ferrous Sulfate and Lime If ferrous salts are used for wastewater coagulation, addition of a small amount of base, usually sodium hydroxide or lime is essential. The required dosage is related to the alkalinity of water. Ferrous sulfate reacts with calcium bicarbonate in water, but this reaction is much delayed and therefore cannot be relied on.[17] Caustic alkalinity, due to the addition of lime to the wastewater, produces a speedy reaction. The lime is added first, and the following reaction takes place:

$$FeSO_4 . 7H_2O + Ca(OH)_2 \rightarrow Fe(OH)_2 \downarrow + CaSO_4 + 7H_2O. \quad (4)$$

The ferrous hydroxide, $Fe(OH)_2$, is not an efficient floc, but it can soon be oxidized by the dissolved oxygen in wastewater as follows:

$$4Fe(OH)_2 + O_2 + 2H_2O \rightarrow 4Fe(OH)_3 \downarrow . \quad (5)$$

An insoluble hydrous ferric oxide is produced over a pH range of 3 to 13. The floc charge is positive in the acid range and negative in the alkaline range, with a mixed charge over a pH range of 6.5 to 8.0.

This process is usually cheaper than the use of alum, but needs greater skill to dose with the two chemicals.

Ferric Chloride It has been used successfully for wastewater coagulation because it works well in wider pH ranges.[17,18] The reactions of ferric chloride with bicarbonate alkalinity and lime are respectively:

$$2FeCl_3 + 3Ca(HCO_3)_2 \rightarrow 2Fe(OH)_3 \downarrow + 3CaCl_2 + 6CO_2 \quad (6)$$

$$2FeCl_3 + 3Ca(OH)_2 \rightarrow 2Fe(OH)_3 \downarrow + 3CaCl_2. \quad (7)$$

Wuhrmann[19] was successful in removing phosphates from sewage effluent by precipitation with a mixture of ferric salt and lime. The ferric dosages varied between 10 and 20 mg/l and the lime dosages from 300 to 350 mg/l in order to raise the pH to value between 8 and 8.3. The actual required lime dosage is related to the alkalinity of the water. According to Wuhrmann, the dominant reaction product between the phosphate ion and the ferric ion at pH above 7 is believed to be $FePO_4$ with a solubility product of about 10^{-23} at 25°C. The sufficient excess of ferric ion for the formation of a well-flocculating hydroxide precipitate which includes the $FePO_4$ particles and acts as an efficient adsorbent for other phosphorus compounds.

It has been reported that efficient phosphorus removal (85–90%) requires the stoichiometric amount of iron (1.8 mg/l Fe per mg/l P) to be supplemented by at least 10 mg/l of iron for hydroxide formation. Also, the use of anionic polymer is considered desirable in order to produce a clear supernatant.[20,21]

Lime Lime reacts with the bicarbonate alkalinity of wastewater to form calcium carbonate which precipitates.

$$Ca(OH)_2 + Ca(HCO_3)_2 \rightarrow 2CaCO_3 \downarrow + 2H_2O. \quad (8)$$

Normally 70–90 percent of the phosphorus in domestic sewage is in the form of orthophosphates or polyphosphates which may hydrolize to orthophosphates. The remaining phosphorus is present in the form of organic-bound phosphorus. The removal of phosphorus can be achieved by direct adsorption on the surface of calcium carbonate particles. Orthophosphate can also be precipitated in the alkaline range by reaction with calcium salts to form hydroxyapatite, according to the reaction

$$10Ca^{++} + 6H_3PO_4 + 20OH^{-} \rightleftharpoons Ca_{10}(PO_4)_6(OH)_2 \downarrow + 18H_2O. \quad (9)$$

Schmid and McKinney[22] observed that hydroxyapatite was present in insoluble form at a pH value above 9.5. They also found that, at pH values of 9.5 or less, phosphorus was absorbed onto the growing faces of calcium carbonate particles, thereby inhibiting their growth. Buzzell and Sawyer[23] have shown that at pH levels of 10 to 11 in the primary sedimentation tanks, BOD removal of 55 to 70 percent, nitrogen removal of 25 percent, phosphates removal of 80 to 90 percent, and coliform removal of 99 percent can be expected. Bishop, *et al.*,[24] have reported that precipitation of domestic wastewater with lime removed approximately 80% of the TOC, BOD, and COD, 91% of the SS, 97% of the total phosphorus and 31% of the total nitrogen. Phosphates from secondary effluent have been removed successfully at Lake Tahoe by precipitation with lime.[8] Albertson and Sherwood[25] found that by recirculating calcium phosphate solids, previously formed by addition of lime, it was possible to reduce the lime dosage by about 50%.

Lanthanum Using pure solutions of ortho– and condensed phosphates and also secondary effluent, Recht *et al.*[26] investigated the precipitation of phosphates from water with lanthanum. They found that residual phosphates in all tested cases were considerably lower over a much broader pH range than with aluminum salts. La^{+++}, unlike Al^{+++}, were effective at natural wastewater pH levels, 7 to 8, and, at a pH of 7, orthophosphate removal was directly proportional to the amount of La^{+++} added.

In wastewater treatment practices, it is detrimental to form large floc particles immediately in the flocculation step because it reduces the available floc surface area for adsorption of phosphorus. Therefore, it is essential to maintain fine pinpoint flocs in order to get a maximum phosphate removal by surface adsorption and this can be achieved by minimizing the time of their flocculation. This is not the case if the goal is one of colloidal solids removal, as is often in water treatment.

The progress of coagulation and flocculation processes in wastewater treatment can be summarized in the following three steps and illustrated with Figure 4.

I) As the coagulant dissolves, positive aluminum and ferric ions become available to neutralize the negative charges on the colloidal particles including organic matter. These ions may also react with constituents in solution such as hydroxides, carbonates, phosphate, sulfides or organic matter to form complex gelatinous precipitates of colloidal dimensions that are termed microflocs. This is the first stage of coagulation, and for greatest efficiency a rapid and intimate mixing is necessary before second reaction takes place.

II) After the positively-charged ions have neutralized a large part of the colloidal particles and the zeta potential has been reduced, the resulting flocs are still too small to be seen or to settle by gravity. The treatment thereafter should be 'flocculation', slow stirring so that very small flocs may agglomerate and grow in size until they are in proper condition for sedimentation. Some evidence[27] suggests that aggregation of microflocs with dispersed waste constituents is the most important mechanism affecting coagulation in water treatment.

III) During the third phase, surface adsorption of particles takes place on the large surface area provided by the floc particles. Some of the bacteria will also become entangled in the floc and carried to the bottom of the tank.

Table II shows the average values of mineral doses added to wastewater, phosphorus removal achieved, and the corresponding references to the studies.[28,29] Figures 5 and 6 demonstrate how existing equipments in wastewater treatment plants can be used for adoption to the addition of chemical salts.[29]

Sedimentation Sedimentation basins are important components in water and wastewater treatment systems, and their performance greatly depends upon their proper design. In chemical

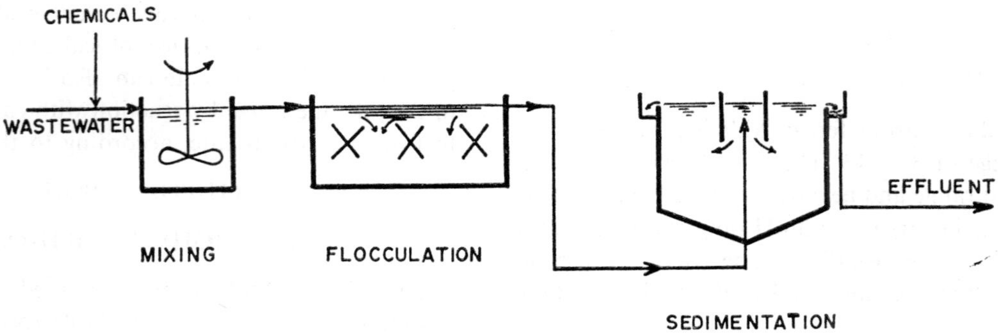

Figure 4 The progress of coagulation and flocculation processes in wastewater treatment.

treatment of wastewater, the separation of chemically-coagulated floc depends on the characteristics of the floc in addition to other factors considered in design of the conventional primary and secondary clarifiers. The field experience indicates that the usual values for surface overflow rates used in separating chemical floc in water treatment practices must be reduced in order to obtain a good efficiency in the removal of floc from chemically coagulated wastewater.[5,30-32] In wastewater treatment practices, the recommended overflow rate for removal of alum floc is 720 gallons per day/sq. ft., while with use of lime or iron salts, it can be increased up to 1020 gallons per day/sq. ft.

B. Filtration

The process of filtration has been adopted recently to remove solids from wastewater, whereas the filtration of sludges has been practices for a long time. Filtration of wastewater can be accomplished by the use of (i) microscreens, (ii) diatomaceous earth filters, (iii) sand filters, or (iv) mixed media filters. The filtration of sludges, on the other hand, is achieved by sand beds or vacuum filters.

TABLE II

Studies on Phosphorus Removal by Chemical Coagulation

Type of study	Coagulant dose C mg/1	Base mg/1	Polymer mg/1	% removal of phosphorus
Plant	15–25 $FeCl_3$	30–50 NaOH	0.3 Dow A 23, anionic	68–80
Plant	15–25 $FeCl_2$	30–50 NaOH	0.3 Dow A 23, anionic	75–93[a]
Laboratory	10 Fe^{++}	30 CaO	0.7 Dow A 23, anionic	80
Plant	21 $FeCl_3$	—	0.26 Dow A 23, anionic	89.7[a]
Plant	90 $FeCl_3$	—	0.5 Atlas Atlasep 2A2, anionic	91
Laboratory	60 $FeCl_2$	80 CaO	—	>80
Plant	40 Alum	—	—	81.5[a]
Plant	220 Alum	Sufficient CaO for pH adjustment	—	100[a]
Plant	300 Alum	—	—	91.5[a]

[a]Secondary treatment provided. Removal values are for entire plant.
Source—References 28 and 29.

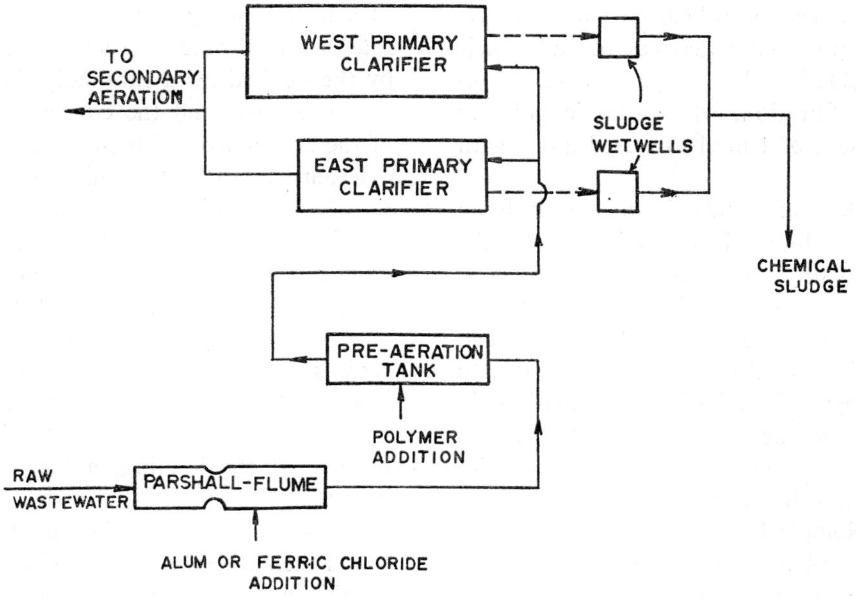

Figure 5 Lebanon, Ohio primary treatment and chemical feeding schematic.

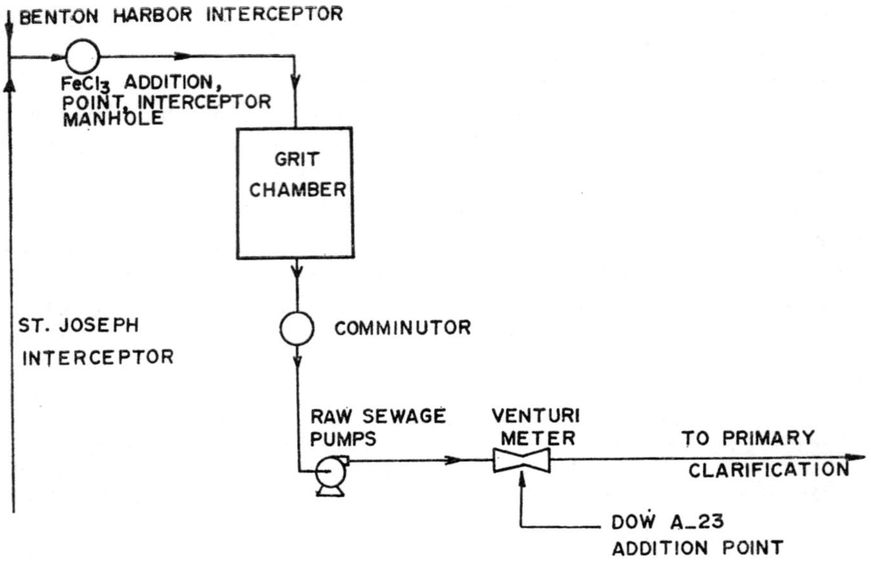

Figure 6 Schematic of pretreatment of plant flow at Benton-Harbour St. Joseph wastewater disposal plant.

The filtration characteristics of the solids found in a biological treatment plant effluent, are greatly different from those of the floc formed during chemical coagulation for the removal of organic matter and phosphates. Tchobanoglous and Eliassen[33] have noted that the strength of the biological floc is much greater than that of the flocs resulting from chemical coagulation. Accordingly, biological floc can be removed with coarser filter medium at higher filtration rates than can the weaker chemical flocs which may shear and penetrate through the filter more readily.

Lynam, *et al.*[34] had observed that the chemical floc strength can be controlled, to some degree, with the use of polymers as coagulant aids. Their experiments yielded higher suspended solids removal ratio by filtration, when anionic polymer A-21 at the dosage of 1 mg/l was used along with the alum.

The filterability of solids in a conventional biological plant effluent is dependent upon the degree of flocculation achieved in the biological process. For example, filtration of the effluent from a trickling filter plant normally cannot yield more than 50% removal of the SS present due to the poor degree of biological flocculation in trickling filters. On the other hand, the activated sludge is capable of much higher degree of biological flocculation than the trickling filter process. The degree of biological flocculation achieved in an activated sludge plant was found to be directly proportional to the aeration time and inversely proportional to the ratio of the amount of organic material added per day to the amount of suspended solids present in the aeration chamber.[35] It has also been reported that up to 98 percent of the suspended solids, found in the effluent from a domestic sewage treatment plant, with 24 hr. aeration time, could be removed by filtration without the use of coagulants.[36]

Microscreening Microscreens are mechanical filters in which flow is passed through a special metallic filter fabric placed around a drum. The filter traps the solids and rotates with the drum to bring the fabric under wash-water sprays fitted on the top of the machine, in order to wash the solids to a hopper for gravity removal to disposal. The rate of flow through the microscreen is determined by the applied head (normally limited to about 6 inches or less) and the concentration and nature of the suspended solids in the effluent.

Extensive tests at the Chicago Sanitary District[34] showed that microscreens with 23 μ aperature could reduce the suspended solids and BOD of a good quality activated sludge effluent, 20–25 mg/l SS and 15–20 mg/l BOD, to 6–8 mg/l and 3.5–5 mg/l respectively. It was noted that the microscreens were more responsive to suspended solids loading than to hydraulic loading and that the maximum capacity of the microscreens was reached at the loading of 0.88 lb/ft^2/day at 6.6 gpm/ft^2.

Diatomaceous earth filtration Diatomite filters found their widest application in the production of potable waters, where the raw water supply was already of a relatively good quality, i.e., of low turbidity. Operating characteristics of diatomite filters can now be predicted under a wide range of operating conditions by utilizing different mathematical models.[37,38] Several investigators have studied the filtration of secondary effluent by diatomite filters whose ability to produce an excellent quality effluent is well established.[39-41] However, the extremely high cost and their inability to tolerate significant variations in suspended solids concentration, limit the usage of diatomite filters in sewage treatment practices.

Sand filtration Sand filters have been operated as slow sand filters or as rapid sand filters made with one or more media. *A slow sand filter* consists of a 6–15 in. thick layer of 0.4 mm. sand supported on a layer of a coarser material of approximately the same thickness. The underdrainage system under the coarser material collects the filtrate. The rate of flow through the filter is controlled at about 75 US gal. per square feet per day. This rate is continued until the head loss through the bed becomes excessive. Then the filter is thrown out of service, allowed to partially dry, and 1–2″ of the sand layer which includes the surface layer of sludge is manually scraped from the top for washing. *Disadvantages of slow sand filtration system are* (i) the filters may become inoperative during the cold winter weather, unless properly housed, (ii) slow sand filters are not effective due to the rapid clogging of filters. The frequency of cleaning filters varies from once to twice a month,[42] (iii) the cost of slow sand filtration is three times the cost of rapid sand filters and twice the cost of microscreens,[43] and (iv) large space requirement.

Rapid sand filters consist of about 15″ thick layer of 0.5–0.65 mm size sand supported on coarser gravel. The rate of filtration ranges between 2–3 US gallons/min/square foot. At this high filtration rate, the filter beds need backwashing when the head loss becomes excessive.

Lynam, *et al.*[34] has reported the results of detailed tests conducted on filtration of secondary effluent from an activated sludge plant of the Chicago Sanitary District. The filter bed was 0.58 mm sand of 11 in. depth and filtration rate was 3 gpm/sq. ft. He analysed the data in terms of both hydraulic and suspended solids loadings. Poor correlations were obtained between effluent quality and hydraulic loading, effluent quality and solids loading, and solid removal and hydraulic loading. However, an excellent correlation existed between suspended solids loading and suspended solids removals. It was also observed that the sand filtration of alum-coagulated solids was no better than that of uncoagulated solids and the optimum suspended solids removal was obtained by alum and polymer coagulation in combination with sand filtration.

Multi-media filtration The limitation of the single medium rapid sand filter follows from its behavior as a surface filtration device. During filter backwashing, the sand is graded hydraulically, with the finest particles rising to the top of the bed. As a result, most of the material removed by the filter is retained at or very near the surface of the bed. When the secondary effluent contains relatively high solids concentrations, the head loss increases very rapidly and suspended solids clog the surface in only a few minutes. One approach to increase the effective filter depth is the use of dual media beds consisting of discrete layer of coarse coal placed above a layer of fine sand. *The design data for a typical dual-media filter are shown in Table III.*

More recently, the concept of mixed-media filters has been introduced in order to achieve a filter performance which very closely approaches an ideal one. In this case a third, very heavy fine material, garnet with specific gravity of 4.2 or ilmenite, with specific gravity of 4.5, is placed beneath the coal and sand. Conley and Hsiung[44] have suggested the figures shown in Table IV for optimum design. The selection of media for any filtration application should be based on the floc characteristics.

Moving-bed filters These types of filters have been put in the market recently by Johns-Manville Corporation.[45] It is a continuous sand filter in which influent wastewater passes through the bed and becomes product water. Solid trapped on the filter face and within the bed, move with the filter media, counter current to the liquid. Solids and small amounts of filter media regularly removed from the filter face are educted to the filter media tower without stopping operations. Solids are scrubbed from the media and discharged as a waste sludge, while the washed media is fed back into the bed.

The filter medium usually used is 0.6 to 0.8 mm

TABLE III

Design Data for a Typical Dual-Media Filter Bed

Characteristics	Sand	Anthrafilt
Depth	10–15in.	10–20in.
Effective size of filtering material	0.4–1.0mm	0.8–2.0mm
Sp. gravity of filtering material	2.6	1.6

TABLE IV
Design Data for Typical Multi-Media Filter Beds

Type of application	Garnet size	Garnet depth	Silica sand size	Silica sand depth	Coal size	Coal depth
Very heavy loading of fragile floc.	−40 +80	8 in.	−20 +40	12 in.	−10 +20	22 in.
Moderate loading of very strong flocs	−20 +40	3 in.	−10 +20	12 in.	−10 +16	15 in.
Moderate loading of fragile flocs	−40 +80	3 in.	−20 +40	9 in.	−10 +20	8 in.

Note: Size −40 +80 means particles passing No. 40 and retained on No. 80 US sieves.

sand with a maximum sand feed rate of 12 in./hour and maximum filtration rate of 2100 gallons per day/sq. ft. The advantages claimed[45] for this system are (i) automatic and continuous operation, (ii) the filter allows much higher and variable solids loadings than permissible with a sand band, and (iii) through efficient use of coagulant chemicals, the system has the flexibility to reuduce turbidity, phosphorus, suspended solids, and BOD to desired level.

C. *Air stripping*

In domestic wastewaters, most of the nitrogen is present either as ammonia or in organic form which gets converted to ammonia during biological degradation. When the carbon concentration in wastewater becomes low, and the nitrifying bacteria are populous, this ammonia can be oxidized by bacteria to nitrites and nitrates in presence of dissolved oxygen. The stripping process can be employed either before or after secondary treatment for removing high levels of nitrogen that is present as ammonia. If it is to be used as pretreatment prior to a biological system, enough nitrogen (N : BOD = 5 : 150) must be left in the effluent to satisfy nutritional requirement.[46]

In wastewater, ammonium ions exist in equilibrium with ammonia and hydrogen ions:

$$NH_4^+ \rightleftharpoons NH_3 + H^+. \qquad 10$$

At pH levels of 6 to 8, ammonia nitrogen is mostly present in the ionized form NH_2^+. Increasing the pH to above 10, all the nitrogen changes to an ammonia form which is removable by agitation. The stripping of ammonia from wastewater is carried out with air. In this operation, wastewater is agitated vigorously in a forced-draft countercurrent air stripping tower when the ammonia is driven out from solution and leaves with the air exhausted from the tower. The efficiency of ammonia removal in stripping process depends upon the pH, air flow rate, tower depth, and hydraulic loading to the tower.

Slechta and Culp[8] have shown experimentally that the efficiency of ammonia stripping process is dependent on the pH of the wastewater for pH values up to 10.8. However no significant increase in ammonia removals was achieved by elevating the pH above 10.8, Figure 7. Kuhn[47] had come to the same conclusion. It has also been reported that the efficiency of the ammonia stripping process depends on maximizing the air–water contact and drop increasing the rupture and reformation within the stripping tower. Higher ammonia removals and lower air requirements were obtained with a 1.5 by 2 in. packing than with a 4 by 4 in. packing. Increased tower depth, which provides additional air–water contact, resulted in greater ammonia removals and lower air requirements. 90%, 95% and 98% removals of ammonia was obtained at an air flow rates of 250, 400, and 800 cu. ft./gal. respectively.[8] Figure 8 shows the relationships between different variables involved in the air stripping process. Because ammonia stripping is conducted at an alkaline pH, lime is used for pH adjustment of influent to the tower. Considerable removal of phosphorous, at this pH is also achieved.

D. *Ion exchange*

The ion-exchange process has been adopted successfully in wastewater treatment practice for removing most of the inorganic dissolved salts. However, the cost of this method for wastewater treatment can not be justified unless the effluent water is required for multiple industrial or municipal reuse.

Gaffney *et al.*[48] have reported that the modified DESAL Process, developed for treating acid mine drainage water, Figure 9, can be applied successfully to the treatment of secondary sewage effluent. This process consists of passing secondary sewage plant effluent upflow through an ion-exchange unit filled with a weak base anion exchange resin, amberlite IRA–68, operated on a bicarbonate cycle. The effluent with a pH of 6.0 is then treated with a

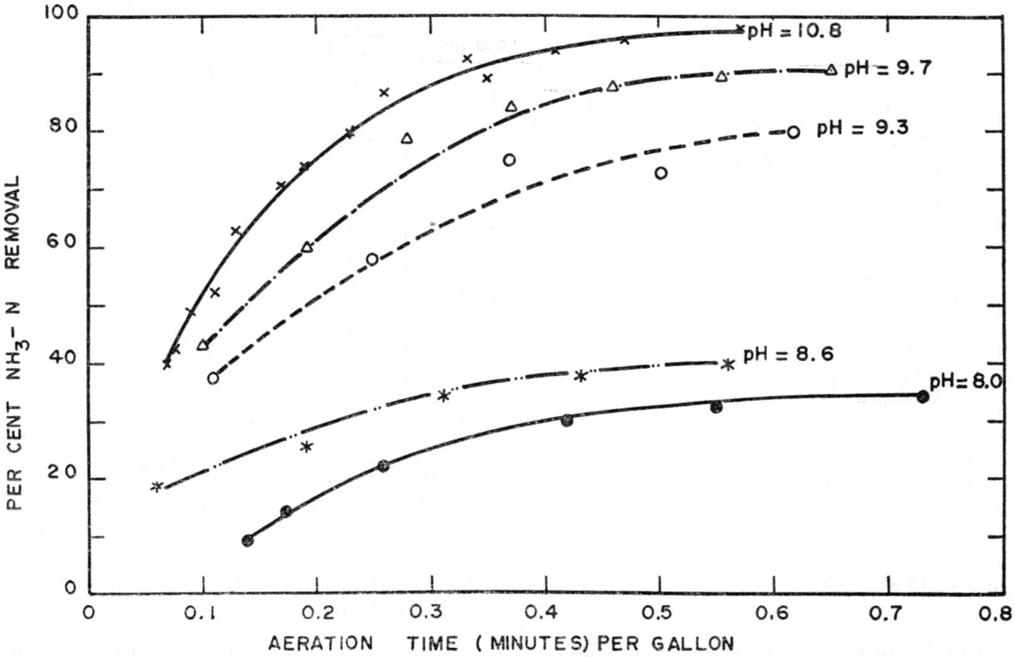

Figure 7 Ammonia removal by air stripping, tower packed with redwood slates having a depth of 2 ft. and of 5 ft.[2] The air flow through the tower is 1520 cfm.

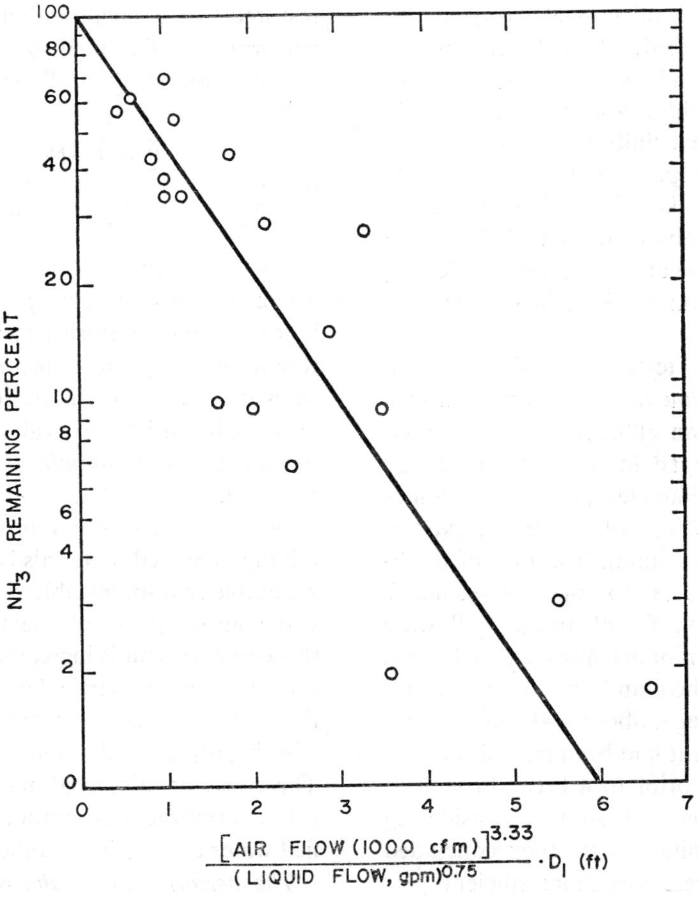

Figure 8 Ammonia removal by air stripping. pH 11.5; tower packed with 1 1/2 inch × 3/8 inch redwood slats mounted on 2 inch centers horizontally and 1 1/2 inch centers vertically.[28]

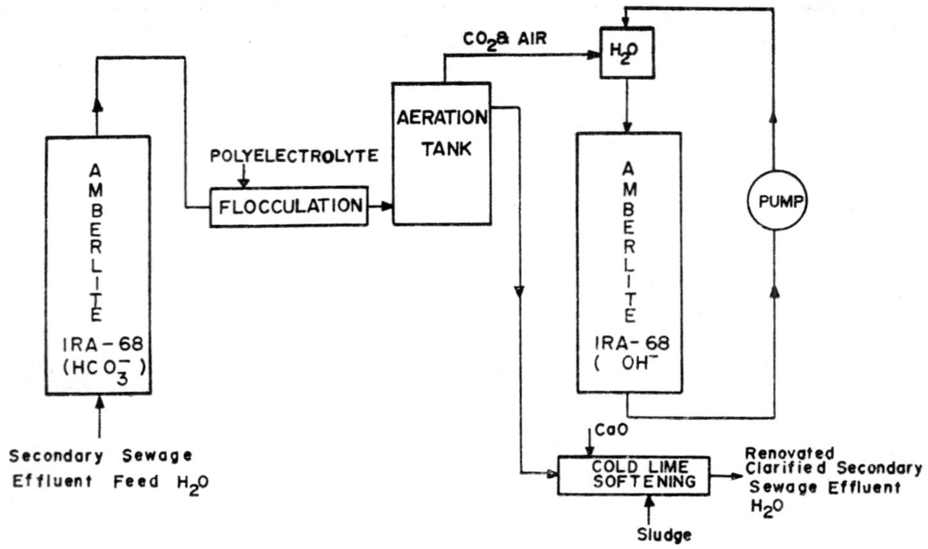

Figure 9 Flow diagram of the ion-exchange process (modified Desal process) for the renovation of secondary sewage effluent water (with CO_2 recovery).

small quantity of bentonite and cationic flocculent, Prima floc C–7, followed by aeration to drive out carbon dioxide, and lime softening in proportion to its hardness concentration. Dosage of 30 mg/l of bentonite, 3 to 5 mg/l of poly-electrolyte, and normal lime levels are used. The effluent which is partially desalinated and is essentially free of nitrates, phosphates, chlorides, ABS, and COD can be produced. If the salinity is too high, it may be reduced further by passing a portion of the effluent through a weak acid cation, Amberlite IRC–84. It has been observed that IRA–68 can remove much of the organic contents and COD, thereby eliminating or markedly reducing the need for carbon treatment.

Slechta and Culp[8] tested a cationic resin, Duolite C–25, for the removal of ammonia nitrogen from the carbon column effluent which was containing ammonia nitrogen in the range of 18–28 mg/l as N. A 4 in. diameter plexiglass cylinder filled to a depth of 27.5 in. with the resin served as the pilot ion-exchange column. The rate of application of influent waste to the ion-exchange column was 3 gpm/cu. ft. of resin. Following breakthrough of the ammonia nitrogen to 1 mg/l, the bed was backwashed and the resin was regenerated. On the average, about 400 bed volumes of carbon column effluent had been passed through the ion-exchange resin prior to a breakthrough to 1 mg/l ammonia nitrogen. However, considering the operating and capital costs, they concluded that the stripping process was more efficient.

Nitrate nitrogen, present in the effluent from the activated sludge process, has been removed by anion exchange regenerated with brine by Eliassen and Bennett.[49] This ion-exchange process also removes phosphate and some other ions, however, pretreatment by filtration is essential. The resin is restored by treatment with acid and methanol. The performance of 11 mgd size plant operating on this system showed the following average characteristics.

	P mg/l	NO_3 mg/l	COD mg/l	SS mg/l
Influent	8	18	40	>15
Effluent	0.9	1.3	20	< 2

E. Reverse osmosis

There are several reverse-osmosis units currently in use to produce fresh water from sea water. With recent improvements in membrances, this process is showing a promise in purification of wastewater also. Substantial removal in BOD, COD, TDS, phosphate and ammonia by this process has been reported.[50]

In a reverse-osmosis process, wastewater containing dissolved materials is placed in contact with a suitable semi-permeable membrance in one of the two compartments of the tank. The pressure on this compartment is increased to exceed the osmotic pressure for that particular waste in order to cause the water to penetrate the membrance, carrying with it only a small amount of dissolved materials. Therefore, the dissolved material in the wastewater gets concentrated continuously, while highly purified water collects in the other compartment.

The performance of the reverse osmosis process depends mainly on (a) the membrane semi-permeability or its efficiency to separate dissolved material

TABLE V
Results of Processing Secondary Sewage Effluent With Cellulose-Acetate Membranes at 200 psi

Test	Feed Concentration	Concentration in product form: Type A light	Type B intermediate	Type C grit permeable
Alkalinity, ppm Ca CO_3	213	14	15	100.0
Total hardness, mg/1,Ca CO_3	213	1.4	5.2	40.6
TDS, mg/1	531	20.0	90.0	250.0
COD, mg/1	38.8	0.9	2.7	4.8
Potassium, mg/1	13.8	1.1	3.8	9.1
Sodium, mg/1	88.2	6.6	21.8	62.2
Chloride, mg/1	98.0	4.0	26.0	73.0
Magnesium, mg/1 as Ca CO_3	71.5	0.5	2.8	9.9
Calcium, mg/1, Ca CO_3	141.5	0.9	2.4	30.7
Sulfate, mg/1	70.6	0.0	0.0	11.9
Total phosphate, mg/1	28.0	0.0	0.0	1.8

from the wastewater, and (b) the membrane permeability or the total amount of water than can be produced with appropriate efficiency for the removal of dissolved materials. It has been reported that the conventional cellulose–acetate membranes give adequate separation efficiency, but the flow rate of water is too small to be of practical interest. However, the recently modified cellulose–acetate membranes allow much higher flow rate of product water, at the same separation efficiency, which makes it applicable in wastewater treatment practices.[51]

The operating pressure, as well as the rejection performance of the membrane are dependent on the membrane porosity. Rejection performance of three graded membranes with secondary sewage effluent were investigated by Bray *et al.*[52] Some of their results are shown in Table V. Membrane designated type A is the one normally used in sea water desalination.

Merten, *et al.*[53] evaluated the performance of a 5,000 gallons per day pilot reverse-osmosis unit in removing small amounts of organic material found in the effluent of carbon columns treating secondary effluent. With a feed pressure of 400 psi and water recovery of 80–85%, 84 percent removal of COD present in carbon column effluent (averaging 10.8 mg/l) was achieved. Problems of clogging have occurred when operating with waters containing high concentrations of bicarbonate, and as such, adjustment of pH to prevent calcium carbonate precipitation is normally required.

F. Electrodialysis

Electrodialysis involves the removal of inorganic ions from water by creating an electrical potential across two metal strips dipped in water. One of the two strips serves as a cathode and the other as an anode. *The treatment which can be achieved by electrodialysis include*:

i) Removal of Inorganic Ions Under the effect of applied potential, cations and anions migrate to the cathode and anode respectively. By alternately placing anionic and cationic permeable membranes, a series of concentrating and diluting compartments can be created. For a long run and better efficiency, it is essential that turbidity, SS, colloids, and trace organics are removed from the wastewater before it enters the electrodialysis unit.

ii) Effective Bacterial Reduction in Wastewater Most of the municipal wastewaters contain high concentration of chloride ions. Oxidation of chloride at the anode produces chlorine, hypochlorite, or chloramines depending on the nature of the wastewater. Chlorine in these forms is a good disinfectant and also provides an effective means of reducing soluble BOD.

In order to reduce the operating cost of the electrodialysis process, the eroding anodes made of aluminum or iron are now being replaced by nonconsumable noble anodes which appear to have more potential in wastewater treatment.[54] The cost of disinfection by electrodialysis is reported to be $2/per million gallons of wastewater as compared to $3.6 per million gallon for conventional chlorination.[55] However, some other sources[54] have reported that the cost of electrolytic treatment of wastewater was too high for the removal of a large percentage of secondary effluent COD.

G. Activated carbon adsorption

Application of adsorption on granular active carbon, in columns of counter flow fluidized beds, for the removal of traces of organic pollutants, detergents, pesticides and other substances in wastewater that are resistant to biological degradation has become firmly established as a practical, reliable, and economical treatment.[8,56-59]

Adsorption can be accomplished with powdered carbon,[60,61] which is mixed in wastewater, flocculated, and ultimately settled. However, there are certain problems associated with the use of powdered carbon. These are: (1) large quantities of activated carbon are needed in wastewater treatment because it is used only on once through basis. Handling of such large quantities of carbon also creates a dust problem, and (2) problems in disposal of precipitated carbon unless incinerated along with the sewage sludge.

Theory Less polar molecules, including the soluble organic pollutants are removed by adsorption on large surface area provided by the activated carbon. Smaller carbon particles enhance the rate of pollutant removal by providing more total surface area for adsorption, for partial deposition of colloidal pollutants, and for filtration of larger particles. However, it is almost necessary to remove finely divided suspended matter from wastewater by pretreatment prior to its application on carbon bed.

Depending on the direction of flow, the granular carbon beds are either of the downflow-bed type or upflow-bed type. *Downflow carbon beds* provide the removal of suspended and flocculated materials by filtration beside the adsorption of organic pollutants. As the wastewater passes through the bed the carbon nearest the feed point eventually becomes saturated and must be replaced with fresh or reactivated carbon. A countercurrent flow using multiple columns in series is considered more efficient. The first column is replaced when exhausted and the flow of water is changed to make that column the last in the series. Full countercurrent operation can best be obtained in upflow beds.[54]

Upflow carbon columns for full countercurrent operation may be either of packed-bed type or expanded-bed type. Packed-beds are well suited to treatment of wastes that contain little or no suspended solids, i.e. turbidity less than 2.5 JTU.[54] However, the suspended solids invariably present in municipal and industrial wastewaters lead to progressive clogging of the carbon beds. Therefore, expanded-bed upflow columns have certain potential advantages in operation over packed-bed adsorbers for treating wastes which contain suspended solids. In expanded-bed type adsorbers, water must be passed with a velocity sufficient to expand the bed by about 10% so that the bed will be self-cleaned.

Experiments conducted by Weber *et al.*[5] have shown that expanded-bed and packed-bed adsorption systems have nearly the same efficiency with regard to the removal of soluble organic materials from trickling filter effluent, under otherwise similar conditions. The packed-bed system was found to be more effective for removal of suspend solids, but the clogging that resulted from these solids required higher pumping pressure and more frequent cleaning of the carbon bed. Because of the time elapsed in cleaning, the expanded bed production was about 9% more than the packed-bed production.

Lake Tahoe Water Reclamation Facilities, described by Slechta and Culp,[8] include pretreatment of secondary effluent by chemical clarification and filtration thereby providing a highly clarified feed and permitting an extended operation of carbon beds. Carbon beds are of the upflow full-countercurrent columns and are usually operated as packed types since the turbidity of the applied water is always less than 0.3 JTU. The columns have also been operated at times as expanded beds by drawing 10% of the carbon.

The efficiency of carbon bed treatment depends on:

a) Contact time between the carbon and the wastewater,

b) The pH of the wastewater. Below pH of 9.0, rate of adsorption of organics in wastewater increases with decreasing pH,

c) Temperature of the wastewater, and

d) Quality of the influent.

Carbon Bed Design The following are the important design parameters used in the design of activated-carbon beds.

i) Properties of filtering material: The two most common sizes of granular carbon normally used for wastewater treatment are 8 x 30 mesh and 12 x 14 mesh. 8 x 30 mesh carbon is preferable, although its surface area is less, because it reduces losses during regeneration, head loss is less, and the operation of the filter becomes easier. Culp and Culp[54] have reported the desirable physical properties for granular activated carbon for use in wastewater treatment, and these are tabulated in Table VI.

ii) Depth of carbon bed, 10–30 ft.

iii) Flow rates, 2–10 gpm/ft^2 of column cross-sectional area. For optimum performance of the bed, the actual depth and rate of flow should be

TABLE VI
Desirable Physical Properties of Activated Carbon[a]

Total surface area (m^2/g)	950–1500
Bulk density (lb/ft^3)	26
Particle density, wetted in water (g/cc)	1.3–1.4
Effective size (mm)	0.8–0.9
Uniformity coefficient	1.9 or less
U.S. standard series, sieve size	
Larger than No. 8	max 8%
Smaller than No. 30	max 5%
Mean particle diameter (mm)	1.5–1.7
Iodine number	min 900
Abrasion number	min 70
Ash	max 8%
Moisture	max 2%

[a]Source—Reference 54.

determined by a dynamic pilot plant test in the laboratory.

iv) Activated carbon contact time: 15–35 min depending on the objective of treatment and the impurities to be removed from the wastewater.

H. Foam separation

Surface active contaminants, if present in wastewater, will produce foam upon aeration. This foam rises to the surface of the wastewater and can be separated and concentrated. Moreover, as the foam generates and rises, certain suspended impurities also get removed by entrainment. Thus, the foam separation process can be developed to provide a selective removal of soluble and colloidal pollutants in various concentrations from water or wastewater. The process may either utilize the surface active impurities present in the wastewater or may require the addition of a specific surface active agent to act as a collector. Sometimes, prior to aeration, soluble or colloidal impurities of interest may be precipitated to improve their removal.

Factors affecting the efficiency of the process of foam separation are:

i) Air flow rate/surface active agent or air flow rate to waste flow rate ratio: the removal efficiency increases with increasing the rate of air flow, but yields a wetter foam.

ii) Air bubble size: fine bubbles aeration improves the efficiency of foam separation, whereas coarse bubbles or deck aeration are not efficient.

iii) Nature and concentration of surface active agents.

iv) Foam stability.

v) pH of the wastewater.

vi) Detention period: short aeration time (5 minutes or so) is considered sufficient.

vii) Surface to volume ratio: large surface area to volume ratios are conducive to higher efficiency.

The process of foam separation has been used successfully in a number of waste-treatment applications. These include (a) removal of surface active materials such as alkyl benzene sulfonate (ABS) from secondary effluent sewage,[62–65] (b) the removal of radioactive ions from dilute aqueous solutions by the addition of anionic surface agents,[66–68] (c) removal of specific surfactants from refining and petrochemical wastewaters,[69] (d) foam fractionation of phenol (phenolate) from aqueous solution using a cationic surfactant, ethyl hexadecyldi-methylammonium bromide, as the foaming agent,[70] (e) the treatment of cyanide and acid chromate wastes. Cyanide is precipitated with ferrous iron, and the ferrocyanide precipitates are floated with a cationic surfactant in a pH range of 5 to 7. Acid chromate is reduced and precipitated as $Cr(OH)_3$ and these precipitates are floated with an anionic surfactant,[71] (f) the treatment of liquid wastes from the scrubbing of phosphate and fluoride from air pollution emissions of the phosphoric acid manufacturing industry. These include precipitation by Lanthanum (III), followed by flotation with an anionic surfactant,[71] (g) clarification of turbid raw water supplies by microflotation-activated carbon process,[71] and (h) physical separation of suspended solids and coagulated dissolved organic impurities from sewage and wastewater. ABS serves as activator for bubble attachment in flotation treatment of sewage.[62] Other application includes the treatment of mine drainage wastes combined with secondary sewage effluents and removal of H_2S from sour wastes.

REFERENCES

1. Rudolfs, W. and E. H. Trubnick, "Activated Carbon in Sewage Treatment", *Sewage Works Journal*, **7**, 5, 852, 1935.
2. Stander, G. J. and L. R. J. Van Vuuren, "The Reclamation of Potable Water From Wastewater", *Journal Water Pollution Control Federation*, **41**, 3, 355, 1969.
3. Rizzo, J. L. and R. E. Schade, "Secondary Treatment With Granular Activated Carbon", *Water and Sewage Works*, **116**, 8, 307, 1969.
4. Zuckerman, M. M. and A. H. Molof, "High Quality Reuse Water By Chemical-Physical Wastewater Treatment," *Journal Water Pollution Control Federation*, **42**, 3, 437, 1970.
5. Weber, W. J., C. B. Hopkins and R. Bloom, "Physicochemical Treatment of Wastewater", *Journal Water Pollution Control Federation*, **42**, 1, 83, 1970.
6. Villiers, R. V., E. L. Berg, C. A. Brunner and A. N. Masse, "Municipal Wastewater Treatment By Physical and Chemical Methods". *Water and Sewage Works*, **118**, 8, R62, 1971.

7. Shuckrow, A., Battelle's Northwest Laboratories. *American Society of Civil Engineers Newsletter*, p. 4, August 1971.
8. Slechta, A. F. and G. L. Culp, "Water Reclamation Studies at the South Tahoe Public Utility District," *Journal Water Pollution Control Federation*, **39**, 5, 787, 1967.
9. Ecodyne Physical-Chemical Sewage Treatment Plant for the Villiage of Rosemount, Environmental Currents News, *Environmental Science and Technology*, **6**, 4, 306, 1972.
10. A New Process for Treating Wastewater-Phosphorus Removal, Technology Transfer, Environmental Protection Agency, Washington, D.C., 20460.
11. Rich, L. G., *Unit Processes of Sanitary Engineering*, John Wiley and Sons, Inc., N.Y., 1963, p. 140.
12. Eckenfelder, W. W., *Industrial Water Pollution Control*, McGraw-Hill Book Company, New York, 1966, p. 91.
13. Rohlich, G. A., *Advances in Water Pollution Research, Vol. 2*, Pergamon Press, New York, p. 207, 1964.
14. Yuan, W. L. and P. H. Hsu, "Effect of Foreign Components on the Precipitation of Phosphate by Aluminum," Presented at the 5th International Water Pollution Conference, July–August, 1970.
15. Harringer, R. D. and F. L. Hoffman, *Phosphate Removal Tests—Springfield, Ohio, for Black and Veatch Consulting Engineers*, Technical Service Department, Allied Chemical Corporation, Industrial Chemicals Divison, Syracuse, New York, 1971.
16. Harringer, R. D. and F. L. Hoffman, *Phosphorus Removal Tests–Two Rivers, Wisconsin for Black and Veatch Consulting Engineers*, Technical Service Department, Allied Chemical Corporation, Industrial Chemical Divison, Syracuse, New York, 1970.
17. Steel, E. W., *Water Supply and Sewage*, McGraw-Hill, Book Company, New York, 1960, pp. 249, 250.
18. Babbit, H. E., J. J. Donald and J. L. Cleasby, *Water Supply Engineering*, Mc Graw-Hill Book Company, Inc., New York, 1962, p. 442.
19. Wuhrmann, K., "Objectives Technology, and Results of Nitrogen and Phosphorus Removal Processes," *Advances in Water Quality Improvement*, University of Texas Press, Austin, I, 1968, p. 21.
20. Wukasch, R. F., "The Dow Process for Phosphate Removal." Presented at FWPCA Seminar on Phosphate Removal, Chicago, Illinois, June 26, 1968.
21. Wukasch, R. F., "New Phosphate Removal Process," *Water and Wastes Engineering*, **5**, 9, 58, 1968.
22. Schmid, L. A. and R. E. McKinney, "Phosphate Removal By a Lime-Biological Treatment Scheme," *Journal Water Pollution Control Federation*, **41**, 7, 1259, 1969.
23. Buzzell, J. C. and C. N. Sawyer, "Removal of Algal Nutrients from Raw Wastewater With Lime," *Journal Water Pollution Control Federation*, **39**, 10, R 16, 1967.
24. Bishop, D. F., T. P. O'Farrell and J. B. Stanberg, "Physical-Chemical Treatment of Municipal Wastewater," *Journal Water Pollution Control Federation*, **44**, 3, 361, 1972.
25. Albertson, O. E. and R. J. Sherwood, "Phosphate Extraction Process," Paper presented at the Water Pollution Control Federation meeting in Yakima, Washington, October, 1967.
26. Recht, H. L., M. Ghassemi and E. V. Kleber, "Precipitation of Phosphates From Water and Wastewater Using Lanthanum Salts," Presented at the 5th International Water Pollution Research Conference, July-August, 1970.
27. Riddick, T. M., "Zeta Potential and Its Application to Difficult Waters." *Journal American Water Works Association*, **53**, 8, 1007, 1961.
28. Eckenfelder, W. W., *Water Quality Engineering For Practicing Engineers*, Barnes and Noble, Inc., New York, 1970, p. 232.
29. Black and Veatch Consulting Engineers, *Process Design Manual For Phosphate Removal*. Prepared for U.S. Environmental Protection Agency, Kansas City, Missouri 64114, October 1971. pp. 4.1–4.9.
30. Convery, J. J., "Phosphorus Removal by Tertiary Treatment with Lime and Alum." FWPCA Symposium on Nutrient Removal and Advanced Waste Treatment, Tampa, Florida, Nov. 15, 1968.
31. Rose, J. L., "Removal of Phosphorous by Alum," Presented at the Phosphorous Removal Conference Sponsored by the FWPCA, Chigago, Illinois, 1968.
32. Kalinske, A. A. and G. L. Shell, "Phosphate Removal From Waste Effluent and Raw Wastes Using Chemical Treatment." Presented at the Phosphorus Removal Conference Sponsored by the FWPCA, Chicago, Illinois, 1968.
33. Tchobanoglous, G. and R. Eliassen, "Filtration of Treated Sewage Effluent," *Journal Sanitary Engineering Divison, A.S.C.E.* **96**, 4 (SA2), 243, 1970.
34. Lynam, B., G. Ettelt and T. McAloon, "Tertiary Treatment at Metro Chicago by Means of Rapid Sand Filtration and Microstrainers." *Journal Water Pollution Control Federation*, **41**, 2, 247, 1969.
35. Culp, G. L. and S. P. Hansen, "How to Reclaim Wastewater For Reuse," *American City*, June, 1967, p. 96.
36. Culp, G. L. and S. P. Hansen, "Extended Aeration Effluent Polishing by Mixed Media Filtration," *Water and Sewage Works*, **114**, 2, 46, 1967.
37. Dillingham, J. H., J. L. Cleasby and E. R. Baumann, "Diatomite Filtration Equations for Flat and Cyclindrical Septa," *Journal of the Sanitary Engineering Divison, A.S.C.E.*, **93**, 2 (SA1), 41, 1967.
38. Dillingham, J. H., J. L. Cleasby, and E. R. Baumann, "Optimum Design and Operation of Diatomite Filtration Plants," *Journal of the American Water Works Association*, **58**, 6, 657, 1966.
39. Shatto, J., "Aerobic Digestion and Diatomite Filter," *Public Works*, Dec. 1960, p. 82.
40. Eliassen, R. and G. E. Bennett, "Renovation of Domestic and Industrial Waste Water". Presented at the International Conference on Water for Peace, Washington, D.C., May 1967.
41. Baumann, E. R. and C. S. Oulman, "Sand and Diatomite Filtration Practices." *Water Quality Improvement by Physical and Chemical Processes*, Water Resources Symposium No. 3, University of Texas Press, Austin and London, 1970, p. 104.
42. Truesdale, G. A. and A. E. Birkbeck "Tertiary Treatment Processes for Sewage Works Effluents." Presented to the Scottish Centre of the Institution of Public Health Engineers, March 28, 1966.
43. Anonymous, "Renovation and Reuse of Wastewaters in Britain." Published by Water Pollution Research Laboratory, 1967.
44. Conley, W. R., Jr. and K. Hsiung, "Design and Application of Multimedia Filters," *Journal American Water Works Association*, **57**, 10, 1333, 1965.
45. Johns-Manville Corporation, "Moving Bed Filter System," *Water and Sewage Digest*, May–June 1972, p. 47.
46. Eckenfelder, W. W. and E. L. Barnhart, "Performance of High Rate Trickling Filter Using Selected Media." *Journal Water Pollution Control Federation*, **35**, 12, 1535, 1963.
47. Kuhn, P. A., "Removal of Ammonium Nitrogen from Sewage Effluent." M.S. Thesis, University of Wisconsin, Madison, Wis., 1956.
48. Gaffney, J. G., R. Kunin and D. G. Downing, "Ion

Exchange for Industrial Water," *Water Quality Improvement by Physical and Chemical Processes*, Water Resources Symposium No. 3, University of Texas at Austin, 1970, p. 258.
49. Eliassen, K. and G. Bennett, "Anion Exchange and Filtration Techniques For Wastewater Renovation." *Journal Water Pollution Control Federation*, **39**, 10, R. 81, 1967.
50. Robinson, W. T. and R. J. Maltson, "A New Product Concept for Improvement of Industrial Water," presented at Annual Meeting, Water Pollution Control Federation, New York, 1967.
51. Goff, D. L. and E. F. Gloyna, "Reverse Osmosis Development." *Water Quality Improvement by Physical and Chemical Processes*. Water Resources Symposium No. 3, University of Texas at Austin, 1970, p. 312.
52. Bray, D. T., U. Merten and M. Augustus, *Chemical Engineering*, **76**, 4, 60, 1969.
53. Merten, U., I. Nusbaum and R. Miele, "Organic Removal by Reverse Osmosis." Presented at the American Chemical Society Symposium on Organic Residue Removal from Wastewaters, Atlantic City, New Jersey, Sept. 1968.
54. Culp, R. L. and G. L. Culp, *Advanced Wastewater Treatment*. Van Nostrand Reinhold Company, New York, pp. 136, 241, 246, 1971.
55. Unpublished proposal to Clark County Sanitation District prepared by Pacific Engineering and Production, Co., Henderson, Nevada, 1970.
56. Weber, W. J., Jr., "Fluid-Carbon Columns For Sorption of Persistent Organic Pollutants," *Advances in Water Pollution Control Research*, Proceedings of the Third International Conference on Water Pollution Research, Washington, D.C., Water Pollution Control Federation, 1, 253, 1967.
57. Parkhurst, J. D., F. D. Dryden, G. N. McDermott and J. English, "Pomona Activated Carbon Pilot Plant." *Journal Water Pollution Control Federation*, **39**, 10, R. 70, 1967.
58. Stevens, D. B. and J. Peters, "Long Island Recharge Studies." *Journal Water Pollution Control Federation*, **38**, 12, 2009, 1966.
59. Presecan, N. L., J. C. Touhill and A. J. Shuckrow, "Cleveland Westerly Physical Chemical Wastewater Treatment Plant," presented at the Second Annual Environmental Engineering and Science Conference, University of Louisville, Louisville, Kentucky, April 20–21, 1972.
60. Davies, D. S. and R. A. Kaplan, "Activated Carbon Eliminates Organics," *Chemical Engineering Progress*, **60**, 12, 46, 1964.
61. Beebe, R. L. and J. I. Stevens, "Activated Carbon System for Wastewater Renovation," *Water and Waste Engineering*, **4**, 1, 43, 1967.
62. Klein, S. A. and P. H. McGauhey, "Detergent Removal by Surface Stripping." *Journal Water Pollution Control Federation*, **35**, 1, 100, 1963.
63. Grieves, R. B., C. J. Crandall and R. K. Wood, "Foam Separation of ABS and Other Surfactants." *Air and Water Pollution International Journal*, **8**, 8/9, 501–513, 1964.
64. Brunner, C. A. and R. Lemlich, "Foam Fractionation: Standard Separator and Refluxing Columns, *Industr. Engng. Chem.*, **2**, 297–300, 1963.
65. Fldib, I. A., "Renovation of Wastewater by Foam Fractionation." Presented before the divison of Water and Waste Chemistry, American Chemical Society, 143rd national meeting, Cincinnati, Ohio, 15 January, 1963.
66. Schoen, H. M. and G. Mazella, "Foam Separation." *Industr. Water Wastes*, **6**, 71–74, 1961.
67. Schoen, H. M., E. Rubid and D. Ghosh, "Radium Removal from Uranium Mill Wastewater." *Journal Water Pollution Control Federation*, **34**, 10, 1026, 1962.
68. Schnepf, R. W., E. L. Gaden, E. Y. Mirocznik and E. Schonfeld, "Foam Fractionation: Metals," *Chem. Engng. Progr.*, **55**, 42–46, 1959.
69. Grieves, R. B. and R. K. Wook, "Continuous Accumulation in Foam for the Treatment of Refining and Petrochemical Wastes." *Chem. in Can.*, **15**, 13–15, 1963.
70. Grieves, R. B. and R. C. Aronica, "Foam Separation of Phenol With A Cationic Surfactant." *Air and Water Pollution International Journal*, **10**, 1, 31–40, 1966.
71. Grieves, R. B., "Water and Wastewater Treatment Applications of the Foam Separation Process." Presented at the Second Annual Environmental Engineering and Science Conference, University of Louisville, Louisville, Kentucky, April 20–21, 1972.

H. I. ALI,
J. K. BEWTRA
University of Windsor

WASTEWATER TREATMENT: see BIOLOGICAL TREATMENT OF WASTEWATER; MUNICIPAL WASTEWATER

WASTEWATER: TREATMENT FOR SPECIAL APPLICATIONS

Recent concern regarding water pollution and general world-wide public awareness of the problem associated with pollution has resulted in increased pressures on all waste dischargers to provide effective treatment and disposal of their waste streams. Small subdivisions, motels, resorts, movable homes, watercraft, railroads, etc., have not escaped these pressures, although in many respects their total waste contribution to the environment may be small. However, as a result of the public awareness of pollution and increasing regulatory pressures, there has been a rapid commercial growth in recent years in plants designed and built specifically for such applications. In this article the state of the art of the treatment systems developed for such special applications is presented.

Individual Homes

Of the approximately 200 million people in the U.S., roughly 126 million are connected to central sewage systems, while 74 million use individual disposal systems.[1] Several different types of treatment systems have been used for individual homes. Among the most common systems are the anaerobic and aerobic biological treatment. However, no treatment system as yet has been entirely satisfactory either to homeowners or to health officials.[2]

Anaerobic system

The septic tank is the most commonly used individual waste disposal system. A National Housing Census data of 1960 indicated a total of nearly 14 million septic tanks or cesspools in the country.[2] Approximately 1-1/2 million new homes have been equiped with septic tanks since 1960.

A septic tank consists of a tank in which wastes are accumulated and digested under anaerobic condition. The effluent from septic tanks is malodorous and the bacterial count is often quite high. Subsurface absorption field is necessary to absorb the effluent from the septic tank. Capacity, hydraulic design and soil condition are most important factors influencing the septic tank performance. A detailed discussion on septic tank design, performance, and economics is available in several publications.[2–6]

An important variation in conventional septic tank design is currently being manufactured. The system requires wash waters be separated from sanitary and kitchen wastes. The sanitary and kitchen wastes are thus held in an upper compartment for a longer period of anaerobic digestion, providing more concentrated treatment to the sanitary wastes.[2] The wash waters are treated in a lower compartment for shorter periods where effluent from the upper chamber is mixed. The system is sold as a package unit in a fiberglass housing. A soil absorption system is also included in this package which is designed to make the system independent of the natural soil characteristics.[7]

Aerobic system

Several types of household treatment systems are available which utilize aerobic stabilization of organic wastes. Most systems are designed for continuous flow.

The raw wastewater enters an anaerobic tank where solids are settled and partially digested. The liquid enters an aerobic compartment. Air is supplied either by mechanical aerators or by diffusers. The bacterial action thus produced is similar to that in an activated sludge plant. The solids in the aerated liquid are settled into a separate tank. This tank most commonly has a sloping bottom to return the settled sludge into the aeration tank by gravity. System components of such units are schematically shown in Figure 1.

Some of the manufacturers variation in the aerobic system include (1) absence of anaerobic digestion tank, (2) different methods of aeration and (3) use of tube settlers for increasing the sedimentation rate.[8] Bailey reported that there are about 15 individual home aerobic treatment manufacturers in the U.S., and about 50,000 of the individual aerobic-type treatment devices are in operation in this country.[2]

The effluent from an aerobic system is generally

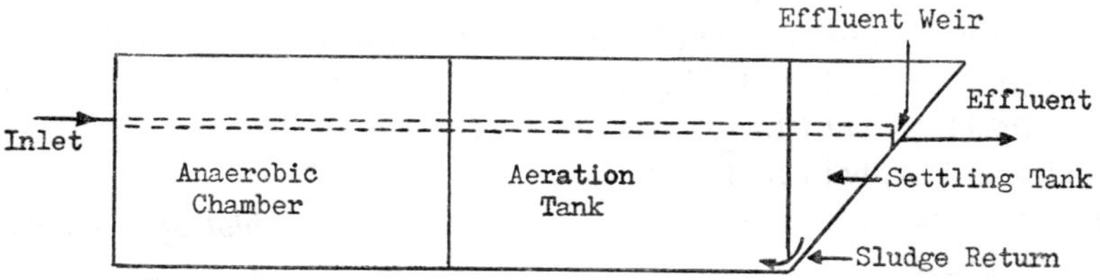

Figure 1 System components of an aerobic treatment unit.

better than that from a septic tank. Manufacturers claim BOD and suspended solids removal of about 90 percent. The effluent from aerobic systems has lower clogging effect on soil absorbtion system. If the system operates properly, the effluent is suitable for surface drainage. The disadvantages of the aerobic system are higher operating costs, susceptability to shock loadings, and variation in effluent quality. The design criteria, operational characteristics and cost data on aerobic systems are extensively available in the literature.[2,9,10]

Small Establishments

Small establishments as defined in this article include motels, restaurants, stores, theatres, clubs, camps, rest areas, institutions, apartment houses, small factories, subdivisions, small communities, etc. Disposal of wastewaters from these establishments in suburban areas certainly proposes serious problems. Construction of public sewer systems may not be economically feasible to convey the wastewaters to an existing treatment plant. Since the flows are relatively large, often septic tanks and subsurface absorption fields may not provide safe disposal, causing a very serious public health hazard or pollution of ground or surface waters.

Package treatment plants were first introduced about fifteen years ago to treat wastes from small establishments. During this time, there has been a rapid commercial growth in package plant industry. A recent survey uncovered a total of about 35 manufacturers of package plants in this country.[11] New product lines and manufacturers continue to appear quite frequently.

The package plants are prefabricated in the factory and, in most cases, completely assembled prior to delivery to the plant site. Most of the plants are made of steel but many concrete plants are also available. During earlier years of package plant usage, the plant size was usually limited to the maximum size that could be shipped by truck. This was about 50,000 to 60,000 gallons per day (gpd) maximum plant size. Currently, the manufacturers fabricate the plants in sections or cut and round the construction materials in the factory and assemble the plants in the field. Thus package plants with capacities over one million gallons a day (mgd) can be obtained.

The earlier package plants were designed as extended aeration plants. Currently available package plants utilize many treatment processes. Some of these processes are listed below.

Biological
Extended aeration
Contact stabilization
Completely mixed
Step aeration
Trickling filter
Rotating biological contactor
Ultrafiltration
Chemical
Chemical precipitation
Electrochemical flotation

A detailed discussion on package plants including manufacturers, process alternatives, size, weight, design criteria, and cost is extensively available in the literature.[11-15] These plants have been successfully applied in the treatment of wastewaters in the suburban areas. The range of these plants has expanded from small establishments to large municipal and industrial applications. Manufacturers broadly group the models or design series into flow capacity, BOD loading, dimensions, air supply, motor horse power, etc., which has simplified the job of unit-size selection.

Polar Regions

Waste handling in polar regions is a complex problem. Conventional waste water collection and treatment systems have severe limitations due to cold weather. Sewers constructed through snow, ice or permafrost* must be insulated to transport the wastes without freezing. Waste treatment by chemical or biological methods may not be possible due to retarded reaction rates.

The predominant sanitary facility used in small Alaskan villages is manual collection of human

† In northern Alaska, the greatest depth of permafrost exceeds 1000 feet.

fecal waste and their disposal to ground, snow or ice. In many cases, pit privies, vaults, bored holes, straddle trenches, box and can, and crude chemical toilets are also used. Problems with these systems are: inconvenient to use especially in cold climates, unaesthetic features such as odor and unsightly conditions, and health hazards.

Perhaps the first comprehensive analysis of waste problems in Arctic areas was conducted by the Federal Housing Administration about 20 years ago.[16] Subsequently, a number of research programs were conducted by the U.S. Public Health Service, National Research Council, U.S. Navy, U.S. Air Force, and U.S. Army in developing suitable systems for use in Greenland, Alaska and most recently in the Antarctic.[17] Prime requirements for a system suitable for installation in these areas were: (1) minimum water use as year-round water supply in these areas may be lacking, (2) non-electric operation, (3) freeze-free, (4) minimum final disposal problems, (5) odor-free, and (6) minimum of maintenance. Systems investigated in these research programs included: (1) incinerating toilets, (2) chemical toilets, and (3) chemical and biological toilets with recirculation.

Incinerating toilets

Incinerating toilets have been designed to destroy human body wastes. The thermal energy required may be obtained from electricity, fuel oil, or liquified petroleum gas (LPG). Several designs of incinerating toilets are now commercially available. Although these toilets provide complete prevention of pollution from human wastes, they are relatively inefficient in terms of fuel consumption and often fail to provide complete burning which may result in a noxious odor or excessive smoke.[17]

Chemical toilets

Chemical toilets require addition of chemicals into the waste storage tank. These chemicals liquify the fecal wastes, produce bactericidal effect and supress fecal odors. Most commonly used chemicals are (1) halogens and their compounds, (2) coal–tar distillate (phenols and cresols), (3) heavy metals and their salts (zinc, copper and silver salts), (4) quarternary ammonium compounds, and (5) alkaline substances such as sodium and potassium hydroxide and lime. Various chemicals are sold in the market under different trade names.

One mechanical-flush chemical toilet was developed by Naval Civil Engineering Laboratory, Port Huneme, California (U.S. Patent No. 3,460,165) for use at remote Antarctic stations. This toilet was extensively tested by the military personnel and found satisfactory for polar applications.

Chemical and biological toilets with recirculation

A special application of waste treatment unit for polar use is a unit where treated effluent could be recirculated as a flush fluid. Such concepts with both chemical and biological treatment systems were investigated. Walters developed a recirculating chlorinator toilet which used standard toilet fittings.[18] The heavily chlorinated effluent from the storage tank was reused for flushing the toilet bowl. The system was tested in Alaskan single homes and results were found esthetically acceptable.

Another study evaluated three extended aeration plants in which the effluent was recirculated for toilet flushing.[19] The findings of this investigation showed that the flushing fluid turned brown during the first week and remained that color for the entire test period of several months. However, no odors were detected.

Both the chemical and biological treatment system with effluent recirculation have great promise in developing toilets for use in polar regions. These toilets would have unique features such as: no water requirement, non-electrical (with hand pump), non-freezing, no odor, conventional toilet design, and a minimum of maintenance.

Watercraft

Use of the waterways for pleasure boating has increased enormously in this country. Because of a substantial increase in the number of recreational vessels, the public has become aware of the potential seriousness of the waterborne pollution resulting from this source. The magnitude of this problem may be judged by the fact that approximately 110,000 commercial vessels, 1,500 federal vessels and over 8 million recreational watercraft use the nation's navigable waters.[20] About 90 percent of the recreational watercraft and most of the commercial and government vessels discharge untreated human fecal wastes into the water. Recreational watercraft are highly mobile, and may reach beaches, commercial fisheries, shell fish growing areas and may seriously contaminate the waters, thereby rendering them dangerous for public water supplies and water contact sports. Contamination may also seriously affect the commercial fisheries and the shellfish industry.

Although a number of individual states within the United States have had rigid restrictions on overboard discharge of wastes from watercraft for several years, the United States as a nation has recently established legislation with the passage of the Water Pollution Control Act of 1970 (Section 13). Legislation already exists for the St. Lawrence Seaway and the Port of London, and it is now being formulated in Canada and other nations.

Sewage equipment for use aboard watercraft is already available in the form of (1) maceration–disinfection devices, (2) holding tanks and recirculating toilets, (3) incinerator devices, and (4) chemical and biological treatment facilities. A brief discussion of these systems is given below. For details on manufacturers, cost and unit variations, etc., readers are referred to several sources in the literature.[21–25,38]

Maceration–disinfection devices

Maceration–disinfection devices utilize a mechanical macerator to grind the human fecal wastes, mixes a disinfecting chemical (usually hypochlorite) and retains the disinfected sewage mixture for a brief period before discharging it into the water. A number of companies manufacture such units for installation aboard virtually every type of watercraft. Such units are small, light weight, and relatively easy to install, however, their performance in terms of BOD and suspended solids reduction, and degree of disinfection achieved may be questionable.

Holding tanks and recirculating toilet

A holding tank is a closed container for retaining sewage onboard a watercraft until it can be properly emptied, usually into an onshore sewage receiving facility. Holding tanks include chemical toilets, recirculating flush toilets, classic holding tanks, and any variation which simply retains the sewage for future disposal at appropriate site.

One potentially useful variation of the holding tank is the recirculating flush toilet. This device requires a small amount of precharge of chemically treated water in the retention tank integrated into the toilet design. Waste deposited in this toilet accumulates in the retention tank. For subsequent flushing, an internal separation mechanism recovers a fraction of this precharge/waste mixture for continued reuse as flushing fluid. The tank retains sewage from 80 to 100 toilet usages before it must be emptied. It uses minimum space and requires no water for flushing.

Although holding tanks completely prevent the discharge of sewage from watercraft, they require extensive shore support facilities for emptying and cleaning.

Incinerator devices

As described earlier, several types of incinerating toilets have been developed to reduce human waste to a small amount of ash. The most common problems encountered with incinerator devices in watercraft include the difficulty of supplying electrical power, as most small craft do not have the generating equipment required. If gas or oil burner type incinerators are used, space is also required. Such burners also provide fire hazards if improperly designed. Regardless of the type of fuel used, however, burning of human wastes may result in emission of odor from the venting stack.

Chemical and biological treatment plants

Waste water treatment plants similar to those frequently used for land-base sewage treatment have been adopted for vessel use. The most successful of the biological treatment systems are the extended aeration activated sludge process.[26] Attempts have been made also to adapt thermally heated aeration systems for increased biological activity. Trickling filter-type biological treatment systems with forced air aeration have also been adopted to shipboard application.[11] These systems, although providing treatment to all waste streams generated aboard the watercraft, are relatively large and heavy, and easily upset due to change in salinity of flush water.

Among the chemical systems, an electrochemical flotation plant for shipboard waste treatment was designed and built by Colt Industries' Fairbanks-Morse Research Center under the grant from the Naval Ships Systems Command.[27] This system utilizes chlorine gas for disinfection, and partial oxidation and flotation of organic matter. Another chemical process-oriented system is currently being developed by Koehler-Dayton, Inc., under the grant from the Naval Ships Systems Command. This system is a comprehensive approach to the management of sewage waste on-board ship and is concerned not only with an improved treatment but also with an innovative and improved collection system. The system employs two main elements: (1) a recirculating chemical toilet, and (2) an evaporative system for solid/liquid separation.[18,29] Condensed liquid is discharged overboard after chlorination. Concentrated sludge is stored for subsequent disposal to shore facility or into unrestricted waters.

Commercial Aircraft

Until about 1940, waste management problems aboard aircraft were considered minor; human wastes were simply discharged overboard. In January of 1943, the U.S. Public Health Service published the "Sanitation Manual for Land and Air Conveyance Operating in Interstate Traffic," which formulated policy regarding "Discharge of Wastes From Conveyance En Route."[30] Following this publication, the International Sanitary Convention for Aerial Navigation issued a publication in February, 1945, forbidding aircraft to throw or let fall matter capable of producing an outbreak of infectious disease.[31] Federal laws and regulations now prohibit airplanes (42 C.F.R. 72.155) indiscriminately discharging untreated human wastes.[32]

Early waste management practices for aircraft included carry-out pail methods of waste collection within aircraft and hand-carrying them to the ground servicing facilities. Subsequently, this system was replaced by built-in retention tanks. These retention tanks utilized wash and galley water for toilet flushing purposes and posessed external servicing facilities. The system posed several operational problems, including the fact that the flushing water taxed the capacity of the retention tanks on longer flights, and was later replaced by recirculating chemical toilets.

Recirculating chemical toilets currently being used aboard commercial aircraft have highly improved features to fulfill the requirements of the modern planes. Reinforced fiberglass retention tanks for lightness, teflon-coated toilet bowls for cleanliness, timer assemblies to control the flush cycle, improved reversible-motor-operated pumps, and a number of filter and filter-cleaning devices have all been developed to provide trouble-free operation and an aesthetic facility.

The recirculating chemical toilets provide efficient operation but, depending upon the capacity of the water tank, the system requires frequent ground servicing. Furthermore, the amount of space and weight available for waste storage in aircraft is quite limited. Therefore, a system to concentrate the wastes during the flight is considered highly desirable. To achieve this, several waste-volume-reduction techniques have been investigated for use aboard commercial aircraft. These include:

1) Evaporation of the liquid to yield dry or highly concentrated solids to reduce the waste-storage space in the aircraft and eliminate the frequent ground servicing need.

2) Incineration devices which utilize electrical and fuel energy for waste incineration. Several improved incineration systems for aircraft application have been built and evaluated.[33-35]

3) Evapo-combustion system to burn the macerated waste into a combustion chamber of the jet engine.

Railroad Trains

Historically, waste from railroad trains have been discharged to the environment without benefit of any treatment. This primitive practice poses a threat to the public health. Although passenger traffic on trains in the U.S. has declined in recent years, large numbers of persons, including railroad employees still use toilet facilities on trains. According to Food and Drug Administration (FDA), about 23 million pounds of human excretement or 16 million gallons of wastewater are discharged annually from locomotives and cabooses, and about 9.5 million gallons of "untreated human wastes" were discharged in 1968 from intercity and commuter passenger train cars.[32]

Federal laws and regulations now prohibit buses (42 C.F.R. 72.156) from discharging untreated human wastes.[32] As a result, the passenger buses are equiped with suitable types of chemical or recirculating toilets. Only railroads continue to have this primitive practice.

Early in 1970, the FDA stated that it was revising its regulations to impose restrictions on all railroads concerning the discharge of human wastes similar to those imposed on buses and airplane companies. However, at the subcommittee meeting on July 28, 1970, the Commissioner of FDA testified that he intends to prohibit such discharges only from railroad cars built after December 1971.[32]

Currently, several types of waste treatment and disposal systems are being marketed which are designed and built for railroad trains. These include incincerating toilets, retention tanks, and recirculating toilets.

Incincerating toilets built for railroad cars operate on natural gas, propane, diesel fuel, or electricity. These toilets operate without the use of water or chemicals and require no holding tanks or plumbing fixtures.

Recirculating toilets of various types are also available for railroad use. One system built for locomotives, cabooses and crew cars uses a vacuum system. In this system air, rather than water, is used to carry waste from the toilets to a centrally located tank.[32,36] This system enables locating the holding tank elsewhere in the railroad car and two or more toilets can be connected to this tank.

Pickup Campers, Travel-Trailers, Tent Camping

Various types of portable recirculating toilets are currently manufactured. These units have suitcase-style handles molded into their cases for easy carrying; can be used in tent or in campers.[37] A small family can get a few days' use before they must be emptied and recharged.

A unique system for reducing the volume of wastes from recirculating toilets has been developed. In this system, the fecal wastes are liquified by adding chemicals. The liquid mixture is pumped to a sanitizer which is a short, stainless steel tank connected to the exhaust pipe of the vehicle. The sanitizer operates at about 500°F. At this operating temperature, the waste is concentrated and the microorganisms are destroyed.[37] The operating temperature of the sanitizer is reached at a vehicle speed of about 35 mph.

REFERENCES

1. "Problems of Combined Sewer Facilities and Overflows 1967," WP–20–11, FWPCA, U.S. Dept. of the Int., Washington, D.C. (1968).
2. Bailey, James and Harold Wallman, A Survey of Household Waste Treatment Systems," *Journal Water Pollution Control Federation*, **43**, No. 12, pp. 2349–2360 (Dec. 1971).
3. Babbit, H. E. and E. R. Baumann, *Sewerage and Sewage Treatment*, John Wiley and Sons, Inc., N.Y. (1952).
4. Manual of Septic-Tank Practice," USPHS, Publication No. 526, U.S. Department of the Interior, Washington, D.C. (1967).
5. Coulter, J. B., The Septic Tank System in Suburbia," Pub. Health Rept. 73, 488 (1958).
6. Winneberger, J. H., *et al.*, 'Biological Aspects of Failure of Septic Tank Percolation Systems, Final Report," Sanitary Engineering Research Laboratory, University of California, Berkeley (August 1969).
7. Ziemke, H. R. and G. S. Allen, "Functional Testing Reports, The Armon System," Sanitary Engineering Research Co., Minneapolis, Minn. (1966).
8. Reid, Leroy C., Jr., "Design of Wastewater Disposal Systems for Individual Dwellings," *Journal Water Pollution Federation*, **43**, No. 10, pp. 2004–2010, (October 1971).
9. "Report on Individual Household Aerobatic Sewage Treatment Systems," National Research Council—National Academy of Science, Publivation No. 586, (February 1958).
10. Thomas, H. A., Jr., *et. al.*, "Technology and Economics of Household Sewage Disposal Systems," *Journal Water Pollution Control Federation*, **32**, No. 2, p. 113 (February 1960).
11. Qasem, S. R., N. L. Drobny and B. W. Valentine, "Process Alternatives Available in Packaged Wastewater Treatment Plants," *Water and Sewage Works*, **117**, Reference Number, pp. R–99 (November 1970).
12. Mahoney, J. A., "Summary of Commercial Waste Water Treatment Plants," Report No. AD 860 067, Air Force Systems Command, Kirtland Air Force Base, New Mexico, September 1969.
13. Seymour, G. G., "Operation and Performance of Package Treatment Plants," *Journal Water Pollution Control Federation*, **44**, No. 2, pp. 274 (February 1972)·
14. Dafne, R. R., G. E. Elbert and M. D. Rockwell, "Contact Stabilization in Small Package Plants," *Journal Water Pollution Control Federation*, **44**, No. 2, pp. 255 (February 1972).
15. Sancier, J. W., "The Application of Package Wastewater Treatment Plants to Suburban Areas," *Water and Wastes Engineering*, pp. 33, (December 1969).
16. Alter, A. J., "Arctic Sanitary Engineering," Federal Housing Administration, Washington, D.C. (1950).
17. Clark and Groff Engineers, "Sanitary Waste Disposal for Navy Camps in Polar Regions," Final Report to Naval Civil Engineering Laboratory on Contract NBy–32205 (1962).
18. Walters, Charles F., "Promise Disposal System," *Water and Sewage Works*, (August 1962).
19. Walters, Charles F. and J. A. Anderegg, "Water Conservation Through Reuse of Flushing Liquid in an Aerobic Sewage Treatment Process," paper presented at 11th Alaska Science Conference (August 20, 1960).
20. Federal Water Pollution Control Administration, "Wastes from Watercraft," U.S. Senate, 90th Congress 1st Session, Document No. 48, U.S. Government Printing Office, Washington, D.C. (August 7, 1967).
21. Hertzberg, R. H., "Waste Disposal from Watercraft," *Journal Water Pollution Control Federation*, **40**, No. 12, pp. 2055, (December 1968).
22. Oertle, Lee, "Plan A Head, Monomatic Self-Contained Recirculating Head," *Popular Mechanics*, pp. 140, (December 1968).
23. Manning, A. P., "Head Space and Horse Sense on Chlorinitor," *Motor Boating*, pp. 42-47, (March 1968).
24. Dugan, P. R. and R. M. Pfisfer, "Evaluation of Marine Toilet Chlorinator Units," New York State Department of Health, Project No. GL–WP–1 (July 1962).
25. Yacht Safety Bureau, Inc., "Requirements for Marine Sewage Incinerating Devices," (February 1968).
26. Stewart, M. J. and H. F. Ludwig, "Shipboard Extended-Aeration Waste-Water Treatment Plant Design," *Naval Engineering Journal*, pp. 985, (December 1963).
27. Singerman, H. H. and E. T. Kinney, "The Navy's Technological Progress in Water Pollution Abatement," *Naval Engineers Journal*, pp. 795 (October 1968).
28. Qasim, S. R. and N. L. Drobny, "Development of a Waste Treatment System for Naval Vessels Phase I—Laboratory Studies," Research Report, Battelle Memorial Institute, Columbus Laboratories, (October 1970).
29. Drobny, N. L., S. R. Qasim and A. Cornish, "Waste Management Systems for Naval Vessels," Proceedings of the 17th Annual Meeting and Equipment Exposition, Institute of Environmental Sciences, Los Angeles, California, (April, 1971).
30. "Sanitation Manual for Land and Air Conveyance Operation in Interstate Traffic," Public Health Service Report, Vol. 58, No. 5, pp. 157–193 (January 29, 1943).
31. "Handbook on Sanitation of Airlines," U.S. Department of Health, Education and Welfare, Public Health Service Publication No. 308, Vol. **31**, Washington, D.C. (1953).
32. "Environmental Pollution: Discharge of Raw Human Wastes From Railroad Trains," 32nd Report by the Committee on Government Operations, Washington, D.C., (October 8, 1970).

33. Fredric, E. W. and B. Mangus "Waterless Toilet," U.S. Patent 3,110,037 (Cl 4–131) (November 1963).
34. Kruckeberg, C. W. and R. J. Jauch, Assignors to Tokheium Corporation, Indiana, "Incinerating Toilet," U.S. Patent 2,995,097 (Cl 110–9) (August 1961).
35. Duncan, Leon L., Assignor to William J. King, Palos Park, Ill., "Total Disposal Unit and Method," U.S. Patent 3,319,588 (Cl 110–9) (May 1967).
36. Watkins, A. M., "Sanivac—Revolutionary Vacuum Toilet," *Popular Science*, pp. 99 (August 1970).
37. "For the Travelling Family: Take Along Comfort Station," *Popular Science*, pp. 86, (July 1970).
38. "Safety Standards for Small Craft. American Boat and Yacht Council, Inc., New York, 1972.

SYED R. QASIM
University of Texas at Arlington

WATER CHEMISTRY

Aquatic Chemical Equilibria

In this section a few examples will be given that demonstrate how elementary principles of physical chemistry can aid in the recognition of interrelated variables that establish the composition of natural waters. Natural water systems usually consist of numerous mineral assemblages and often of a gas phase in addition to the aqueous phase; they nearly always include a portion of the biosphere. Hence, natural aquatic habitats are characterized by a complexity seldom encountered in the laboratory In order to distil the pertinent variables out of a bewildering number of possible ones, it is advantageous to compare the real systems with their idealized counterparts.

Thermodynamic equilibrium concepts represent the most expedient means of identifying the variables relevant in determining the mineral relationships and in establishing chemical boundaries of aquatic environments. Since minimum free energy describes the thermodynamically stable state of a system, a comparison with the actual free energy can characterize the direction and extent of processes that are approaching equilibrium. Discrepancies between equilibrium calculations and the available data of real systems give valuable insight into those cases where chemical reactions are not understood sufficiently, where non-equilibrium conditions prevail, or where the analytical data are not sufficiently accurate or specific.

Alkalinity and acidity for aqueous carbonate systems

Alkalinity and acidity are defined, respectively, as the equivalent sum of the bases that are titratable with strong acid and the equivalent sum of the acids that are titratable with strong base; they are therefore capacity factors which represent, respectively, the acid and base neutralizing capacities of an aqueous system. Operationally, alkalinity and acidity are determined by acidimetric and alkalimetric titrations to appropriate pH end points. These end points (equivalence points) occur at the inflection points of titration curves as shown in Figure 1 for the carbonate system.

As described in Section II, the atmosphere contains CO_2 at a partial pressure of 3×10^{-4} atmosphere, while CO_2, H_2CO_3, HCO_3^- and CO_3^{2-} are important solutes in the hydrosphere. Indeed, the carbonate system is responsible for much of the pH regulation in natural waters.

The following equations define for aqueous carbonate systems the three relevant capacity factors: Alkalinity (Alk), Acidity (Acy) and total dissolved carbonate species (C_T):

$$[\text{Alk}] = [HCO_3^-] + 2[CO_3^{2-}] + [OH^-] - [H^+] \quad \text{(i)}$$

$$[\text{Acy}] = 2[H_2CO_3{}^*] + [HCO_3^-] + [H^+] - [OH^-] \quad \text{(ii)}$$

$$C^b = [H_2CO_3{}^*] + [HCO_3^-] + [CO_3^{2-}], \quad \text{(iii)}$$

where $[H_2CO_3{}^*] = [CO_2(aq)] + [H_2CO_3]$.

These equations are of analytical value because they represent rigorous conceptual definitions of the acid neutralizing and the base neutralizing capacities of carbonate systems. The definitions of alkalinity and acidity algebraically express the net proton deficiency and net proton excess of the systems with respect to specific proton reference levels (equivalence points). The definitions can be

† Brackets of the form [ ] refer to concentration, e.g., in moles per liter.

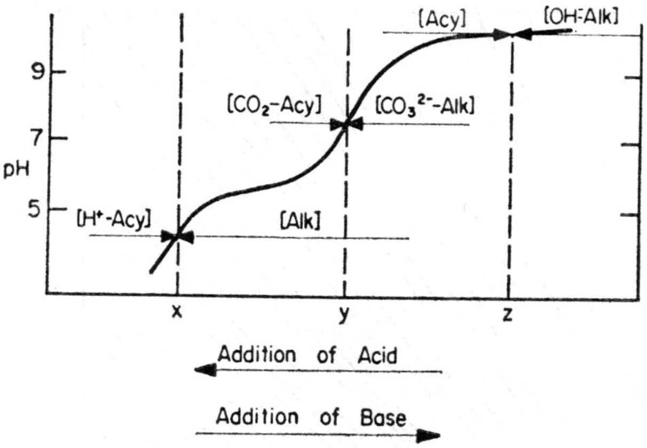

Term	Equivalence point	Definition	
		I Acid Neutralizing Capacity (ANC)	
Caustic alkalinity	z	$[OH^- \text{-Alk}] = [OH^-] - [HCO_3^-] - 2[H_2CO_3^*] - [H^+]$	(1)
Carbonate alkalinity	y	$[CO_3^{2-}\text{-Alk}] = [OH^-] + [CO_3^{2-}] - [H_2CO_3^*] - [H^+]$	(2)
Alkalinity	x	$[Alk] = [HCO_3^-] + 2[CO_3^{2-}] + [OH^-] - [H^+]$	(3)
		II Base Neutralizing Capacity (BNC)	
Mineral acidity	x	$[H^+\text{-Acy}] = [H^+] - [HCO_3^-] - 2[CO_3^{2-}] - [OH^-]$	(4)
CO_2-acidity	y	$[CO_2\text{-Acy}] = [H_2CO_3^*] + [H^+] - [CO_3^{2-}] - [OH^-]$	(5)
Acidity	z	$[Acy] = 2[H_2CO_3^*] + [HCO_3^-] + [H^+] - [OH^-]$	(6)

III Combinations

$[H_2CO_3^*] + [HCO_3^-] + [CO_3^{2-}] = C_T$	(7)	$[Alk] + [CO_2\text{-Acy}] = C_T$	(11)
$[Alk] + [H^+\text{-Acy}] = 0$	(8)	$[Alk] + [Acy] = C_T$	(12)
$[Acy] + [OH^-\text{-Alk}] = 0$	(9)	$[Alk] - [CO_3^{2-}\text{-Alk}] = C_T$	(13)
$[CO_3^{2-}\text{-Alk}] + [CO_2\text{-Acy}] = 0$	(10)	$[CO_2\text{-Acy}] - [H^+\text{-Acy}] = C_T$	(14)

Figure 1 Alkalinity and acidity titration curve for the aqueous carbonate system. The conservative quantities alkalinity and acidity refer to the acid neutralizing and base neutralizing capacities of a given aqueous system. These parameters can be determined by titration to appropriate equivalence points with strong acid and strong base. The equations given below define the various capacity factors rigorously.
Figure from Stumm, W. and J. Morgan, *Aquatic Chemistry*, Wiley-Interscience, New York, 1970, p. 130.

readily amplified to account for the presence of buffering components other than carbonates. For example, in the presence of borate and ammonia the definition for alkalinity becomes

$$[Alk] = [HCO_3^-] + 2[CO_3^{2-}] + [B(OH)_4^-] + [NH_3] + [OH^-] - [H^+]. \quad \text{(iv)}$$

Although individual concentrations or activities, such as $[H_2CO_3{*}]$ and pH, are dependent on pressure and temperature, [Alk], [Acy] and C_T are conservative properties that are pressure and temperature independent. (Alkalinity, acidity and C_T must be expressed in terms of concentration, e.g., as molarity, molality, equivalents per liter or parts per million as $CaCO_3$. Note that

$$1 \text{ meq/l} = 50 \text{ ppm as } CaCO_3.)$$

The use of these conservative parameters facilitates the calculation of the effects of the addition or removal of acids, bases, carbon dioxide, bicarbonates and carbonates to aqueous systems. As shown in Figure 2, each of these conservative quantities remains constant for particular changes in the chemical composition. The case of the addition or removal of dissolved carbon dioxide is of special interest. Respiratory activities of aquatic biota contribute carbon dioxide to the water whereas photosynthetic activities decrease the concentration of this weak acid. An increase in carbon dioxide increases both the acidity of the system and C_T, the total concentration of dissolved carbonic species, and it decreases the pH, but it does not affect the alkalinity. Alternately, acidity remains unaffected by the addition or removal of $CaCO_4$(s) or Na_2CO_3(s). C_T, on the other hand, remains unchanged in a closed system upon addition of strong acid or strong base. For practical purposes, systems may be considered closed if they are

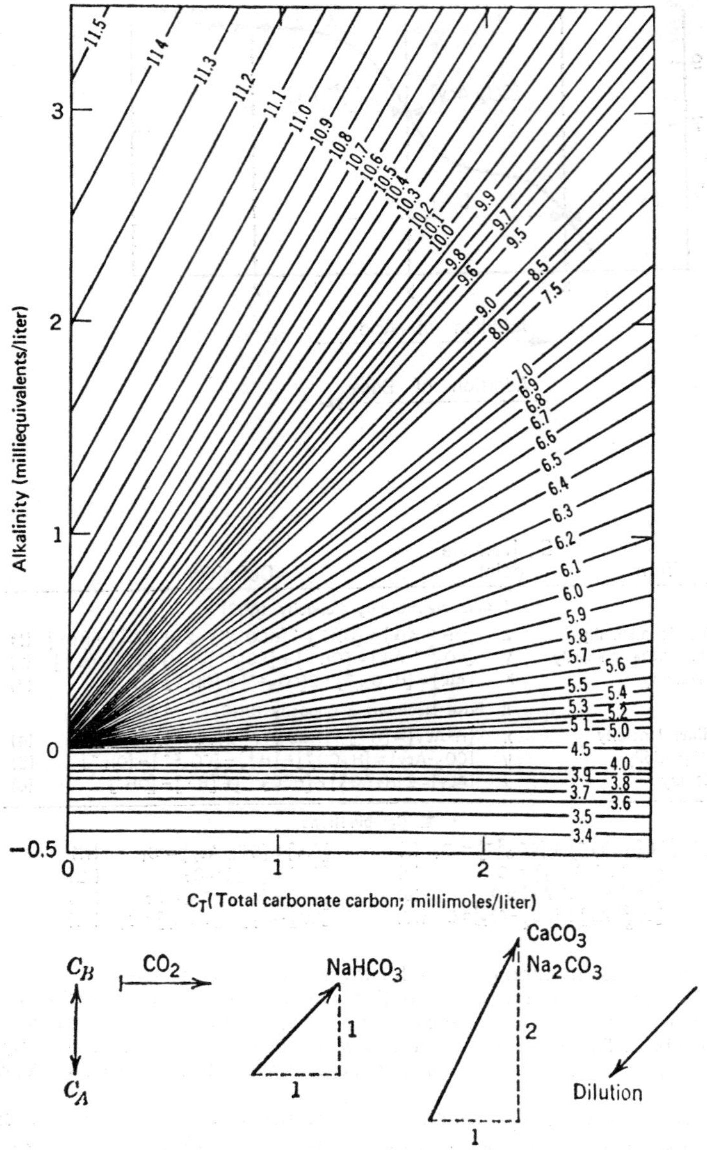

Figure 2 Closed system capacity diagram: pH contours for alkalinity versus C_T (total carbonate carbon). The point defining the solution composition moves as a vector in the diagram as a result of the addition (or removal) of CO_2, $NaHCO_3$ and $CaCO_3$ (Na_2CO_3) or C_B (strong base) and C (strong acid). (After K. S. Deffeyes, Limnol., *Oceanog.*, **10**, 412, 1965.)
Figure from Stumm, W. and J. Morgan, *Aquatic Chemistry*, Wiley-Interscience, New York, 1970, p. 133.

shielded from the atmosphere and lithosphere or exposed to them only for short enough periods to preclude significant dissolution of CO_2 or solid carbonates.

Dissolution of carbon dioxide

Though much of the CO_2 which dissolves in solution may ionize to form HCO_3^- and CO_3^{2-} depending upon the pH, only a small fraction. (0.3% at 25°C) is hydrated as H_2CO_3. Hence, the concentration of the unhydrated dissolved carbon dioxide, $CO_2(aq)$, is nearly identical to the analytically determinable concentration of $H_2CO_3^*$ (= $[CO_2(aq)] + [H_2CO_3]$).

The equilibrium of a constituent between a gas phase and a solution phase can be characterized by a mass law relationship. Table I gives the various expressions and their interrelations for the characterization of the CO_2 dissolution equilibrium. A water that is in equilibrium with the atmosphere ($p_{CO_2} = 10^{-3.5}$ atm.) contains at 25°C approximately 0.44 milligram per liter (10^{-5}M) of CO_2; K_H (Henry's Law constant) at 25°C is $10^{-1.5}$ mole per liter-atm.

TABLE I
Solubility of Gases

Example[a]: $CO_2(g) \rightleftharpoons CO_2(aq)$
Assumptions: Gas behaves ideally; $[CO_2(aq)] = [H_2CO_3{}^*]$

I. Expressions for Solubility Equilibrium[b]

(1) Distribution (mass law) constant, K_D:

$$K_D = [CO_2(aq)] \,/\, [CO_2(g)] \text{ (dimensionless)} \quad (1)$$

(2) Henry's law constant, K_H:
In (1), $[CO_2(g)]$ can be expressed by Dalton's law of partial pressure:

$$[CO_2(g)] = p_{CO_2}/RT \quad (2)$$

Combination of (1) and (2) gives

$$[CO_2(aq)] = (K_D/RT)p_{CO_2} = K_H p_{CO_2}, \quad (3)$$

where $K_H = K_D/RT$ (mole liter^{-1} atm^{-1})

(3) Bunsen absorption coefficient, a_B:

$$[CO_2(aq)] = (a_B/22.414)p_{CO_2} \quad (4)$$

where $22.414 = RT/p$ (liter mole^{-1}) and

$$a_B = K_H \times 22.414 \text{ (atm}^{-1}) \quad (5)$$

Partial Pressure and Gas Composition

$$p_{CO_2} = x_{CO_2}(P_T - w) \quad (6)$$

where x_{CO_2} = mole fraction or volume fraction in dry gas, P_T = total pressure and w = water vapor pressure

Values of Henrys Law Constants at 25°C

Gas		K_H(mole liter^{-1}atm^{-1})
Carbon Dioxide	CO_2	33.8×10^{-3}
Methane	CH_4	1.34×10^{-3}
Nitrogen	N_2	0.642×10^{-3}
Oxygen	O_2	1.27×10^{-3}

[a] Same types of expressions apply to other gases.
[b] The equilibrium constants defined by (1)–(4) are actually constants only if the equilibrium expressions are formulated in terms of activities and fugacities.
Table from Stumm, W. and J. Morgan, *Aquatic Chemistry*, Wiley-Interscience, New York, 1970, p. 125.

Dissolved carbonate equilibria

Two systems may be considered: (1) a system closed to the atmosphere and (2) one that is in equilibrium with the atmosphere.

Closed Systems In this case $H_2CO_3{}^*$ is considered a non-volatile acid. The species $H_2CO_3{}^*$, $HCO_3{}^-$ and CO_3^{2-} are interrelated by the equilibria:†

$$[H^+]\,[HCO_3{}^-]/[H_2CO_3{}^*] = K_1 \quad \text{(v)}$$

$$[H^+]\,[CO_3^{2-}]/[HCO_3{}^-] = K_2 \quad \text{(vi)}$$

where K_1 and K_2 represent the equilibrium constants (acidity constants).

The ionization fractions, whose sum equals unity (see Equation (iii)), can be defined as follows:

$$\alpha_0 = [H_2CO_4{}^*]/C_T \quad \text{(vii)}$$

$$\alpha_1 = [HCO_4{}^-]/C_T \quad \text{(viii)}$$

$$\alpha_2 = [CO_4{}^{2-}]/C_T. \quad \text{(ix)}$$

From Equations (iii) to (ix) the ionization fractions can be expressed in terms of $[H^+]$ and the equilibrium constants:

$$\alpha_0 = (1 + K_1/[H^+] + K_1K_2/[H^+]^2)^{-1} \quad \text{(x)}$$

$$\alpha_1 = ([H^+]/K_1 + 1 + K_2/[H^+])^{-1} \quad \text{(xi)}$$

$$\alpha_2 = ([H^+]^2/K_1Q_2 + [H^+]/Q_2 + 1]^{-1}. \quad \text{(xii)}$$

Values for K_1 and K_2 are given in Tables IIa and IIB. Because $HCO_3{}^-$ and $CO_3{}^{2-}$ may form complexes with other ions in the system (e.g., in sea water, $MgCO_3$, $NaCO_3{}^-$, $CaCO_3$,$MgHCO_3{}^+$, it is operationally convenient to define a total concentration of the species to include an unknown number of these complexes. For example,

$$[CO_{4T}{}^{2-}] = [CO_4{}^{2-}] + [MgCO_4] + [CaCO_4] + [NaCO_4{}^-] + \ldots \quad \text{(xiii)}$$

The distribution of carbonate species in sea water as a function of pH is given in Figure 3.

Systems Open to the Atmosphere A very elementary model showing some of the characteristics of the carbonate system in natural waters is provided by equilibrating pure water with a gas phase (e.g., the atmosphere) containing CO_2 at a constant partial pressure. Such a solution will remain in equilibrium with p_{CO_2} despite any variation of pH by the addition of strong base or strong acid. This simple model has its counterpart in nature when CO_2 reacts with bases of rocks, e.g., with clays and silicates.

Figure 4 shows the distribution of the solute species of such a model. A partial pressure of CO_2 equivalent to that in the atmosphere and equilibrium constants valid at 25°C have been assumed. The equilibrium concentrations of the individual carbonate species can be expressed as a function of P_{CO_2} and $[H^+]$.$_2$ From Henry's Law,

$$[H_2CO_3{}^*] = K_H p_{CO_2}, \quad \text{(xiv)}$$

and Equations (v) to (ix), one obtains

$$C_T = \frac{1}{\alpha_0} K_H p_{CO_2} \quad \text{(xv)}$$

$$[HCO_3{}^-] = \frac{\alpha_1}{\alpha_0} K_H p_{CO_2} = \frac{K_1}{[H^+]} K_H p_{CO_2} \quad \text{(xvi)}$$

and

$$[CO_3{}^{2-}] = \frac{\alpha_2}{\alpha_0} K_H p_{CO_2} = \frac{K_1K_2}{[H^+]^2} K_H p_{CO_2}. \quad \text{(xvii)}$$

† To facilitate calculations the equilibria are written here in terms of concentration quotients. The activity corrections can be considered incorporated in the equilibrium "constants" which therefore vary with the particular solution. Such constants for given media of constant ionic strength, as well as the true thermodynamic constants, are listed in Tables IIA and IIB.

TABLE IIA

Equilibrium Constant for CO_2 Solubility

Equilibrium: $CO_2(g) + aq = H_2CO_3$

Henry's law constant: $K = [H_2CO_3]/p_{CO_2}$ (M atm^{-1})

Temp., °C	→0	Medium, 1 M $NaClO_4$	Seawater, 19% Cl^-
	$-\log K$	$-\log {}^cK$	$-\log {}^cK$
0	1.11[a]		1.19[a]
5	1.19[a]		1.27[a]
10	1.27[a]		1.34[a]
15	1.32[a]		1.41[a]
20	1.41[a]		1.47[a]
25	1.47[ab]	1.51[c]	1.53[a]
30	1.53[a]		1.58[a]
35	—	1.59[c]	
40	1.64[b]		
50	1.72[b]		

[a] Values based on data taken from Bohr and evaluated by K. Buch, Meeresforschung, 1951.
[b] A. J. Ellis, *Amer. J. Sci.*, **257,** 217 (1959).
[c] G. Nilsson, T. Rengemo and L' G. Sillen, *Acta Chem. Scand.*, **12,** 878 (1958).

Ref: Stumm, W. and J. Morgan, *Aquatic Chemistry*, Wiley-Interscience, New York, 1970, p. 148.

TABLE IIB

First Acidity Constant: $H_2CO_3 = HCO_3^- + H^+$

$$K_1 = \frac{\{H^+\}\{HCO_3^-\}}{\{H_2CO_3^*\}} \qquad K_1 = \frac{\{H^+\}[HCO_{3T}^{\ -}]}{[H_2CO_3^*]} \qquad {}^cK_1 = \frac{[H^+][HCO_{3T}^{\ -}]}{[H_2CO_3^*]}$$

		Medium		
Temp., °C	→0	Seawater, 19% Cl^-	Seawater	1 M $NaClO_4$
	$-\log K_1$	$-\log K_1$	$-\log {}^cK_1$	
0	6.579[a]	6.15[b]		
5	6.517[a]	6.11[b]	6.01[e]	
10	6.464[a]	6.08[b]		
14	—	—	6.02[f]	
15	6.419[a]	6.05[b]		
20	6.381[a]	6.02[b]		
22	—	6.00[c]	5.89[c]	
25	6.352[a]	6.00,[b] 6.09[d]		6.04[g]
30	6.327[a]	5.98[b]		
35	6.309[a]	5.97[b]		
40	6.298[a]			
50	6.285[a]			

[a] H. S. Harned and R. Davies, Jr., *J. Amer. Chem. Soc.*, **65,** 2030 (1943).
[b] After Lyman (1956), quoted in G. Skirrow, *Chemical Oceanography*, Vol. I, J. P. Riley and G. Skirrow, Eds., Academic Press, New York, 1965, p. 651.
[c] A. Distèche and S. Distèche, *J. Electrochem. Soc.*, **114,** 330 (1967).
[d] Calculated as log ($K_1/f_{HCO_3^-}$) from $f_{HCO_3^-}$ as determination by A. Berner, *Geochim. Cosmochim. Acta*, **29,** 947 (1965).
[e] D. Dryssen and L. G. Sillen, *Tellus*, **19,** 810 (1967).
[f] D. Dryssen, *Acta Chem. Scand.*, **19,** 1265 (1965).
[g] M. Frydman, G. N. Nilsson, T. Rengemo and L. G. Sillén, *Acta Chem. Scand.*, **12,** 878 (1958).

Ref: Stumm, W. and J. Morgan, *Aquatic Chemistry*, Wiley-Interscience, New York, 1970, p.148.

Second Acidity Constant: $HCO_3^- = H^+ + CO_3^{2-}$

$$K_2 = \frac{\{H^+\}\{CO_3^{2-}\}}{\{HCO_3^-\}} \qquad K_2' = \frac{\{H^+\}[CO_{3T}^{2-}]}{[HCO_{3T}^-]} \qquad {}^cK_2 = \frac{[H^+][CO_{3T}^{2-}]}{[HCO_3^-]}$$

	Medium			
Temp., °C	→0	Seawater	0.75 *M* NaCl	1 *M* KClO₄
	$-\log K_2$	$-\log K_2'$	$-\log K_2'$	$-\log {}^cK_2$
0	10.625[a]	9.40[b]		
5	10.557[a]	9.34[b]		
10	10.490[a]	9.28[b]		
15	10.430[a]	9.23[b]		
20	10.377[a]	9.17[b]		
22	—	9.12[c]	9.49[c]	
25	10.329[a]	9.10[b]		9.57[d]
30	10.290[a]	9.02[b]		
35	10.250[a]	8.95[b]		
40	10.220[a]	—		
50	10.172	—		

[a] H. S. Harned and S. R. Scholes, *J. Amer. Chem. Soc.*, **63**, 1706 (1941).
[b] After Lyman, quoted in G. Skirrow, *Chemical Oceanography*, Vol. I, J. P. Riley and G. Skirrow, Eds., Academic Press, New York, p. 651.
[c] A. Disteche and S. Disteche, *J. Electrochem. Soc.*, **114**, 330 (1967).
[d] M. Frydman, G. N. Nilsson; T. Rengemo and L. G. Sillen, *Acta Chem. Scand.*, **12**, 878 (1958).

Ref: Stumm, W. and J. Morgan, *Aquatic Chemistry*, Wiley-Interscience, New York, 1970, pp. 149 and 150.

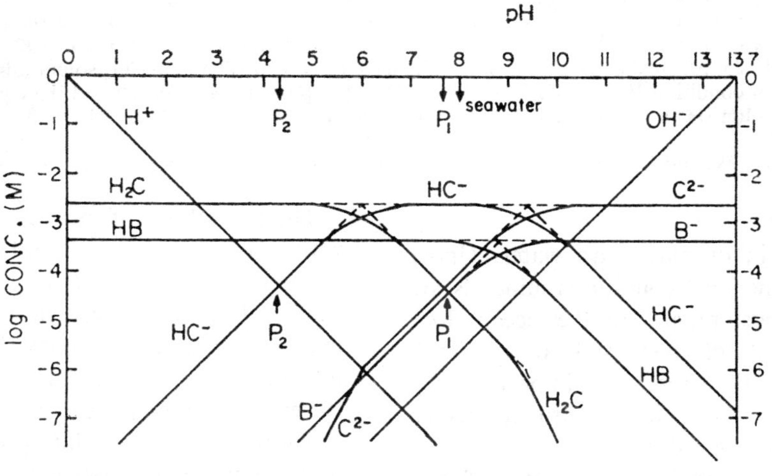

Figure 3 Logarithmic concentration—pH equilibrium diagram for seawater as a closed system. For seawater $\log B_T = -3.37$, $\log C_T = -2.62$ and the following pK values: 6.0 for H_2CO_3*, 9.4 for HCO_3^- and pK = 13.7. B_T = total borate boron and C_T = total carbonate carbon. Arrows gives $[H^+]$ for seawater (pH = 8.0) and for two equivalence points(points of minimum buffer intensity): P_1, corresponding to a proton reference level of HB + HC^- + H_2O, and P_2, corresponding to a proton reference level of HB + H_2C + H_2O. (From Dryssen, D., and L. G. Sillen, *Tellus*, **19**, 110, 1967.)

It follows from these equations that in a logarithmic concentration–pH diagram (Figure 4) the lines of H_2CO_3*, HCO_3^- and CO_3^{2-} have slopes of 0, +1 and +2, respectively.

If we equilibrate pure water with CO_2, the system is defined by two independent variables, for example, temperature and p_{CO_2}. In other words, the equilibrium concentrations of all solute components can be calculated by means of Henry's Law, the acidity constants and the proton condition or charge balance if, in addition to temperature, one variable, such as p_{CO_2}, $[H_2CO_3^*]$ or $[H^+]$, is known or measured. Use of the proton condition instead of the charge balance generally facilitates calculations because species irrelevant to the calculation need not be considered. The proton condition merely expresses the equality between the proton excess and the proton deficiency of the various species with respect to a convenient proton reference level. Figure 4 furnishes a graphic illustration of its use.

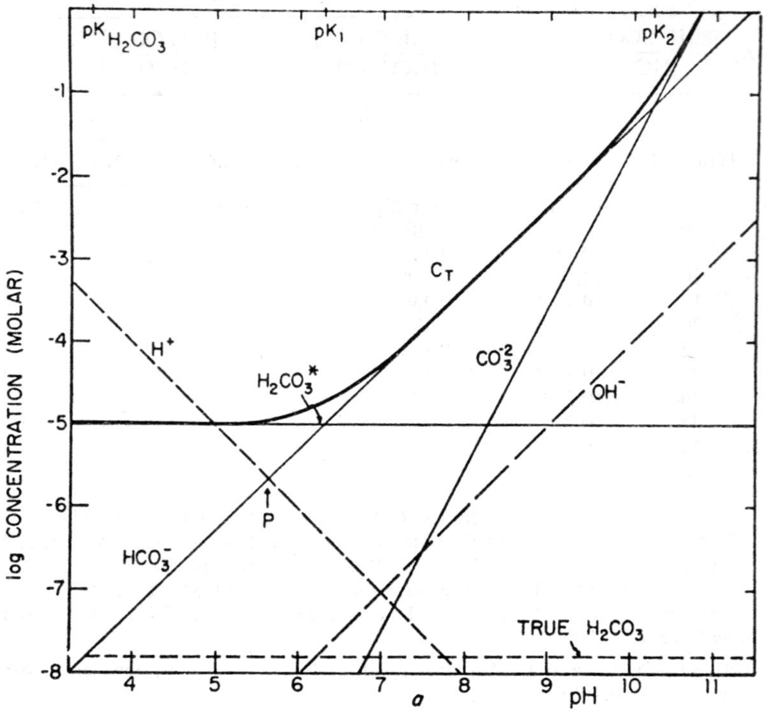

Figure 4 Logarithmic concentration—pH equilibrium diagram for the aqueous carbonate system open to the atmosphere. Water is equilibrated with the atmosphere ($p_{CO_2} = 10^{-3.5}$ atm) and the pH is adjusted with strong base or strong acid. Equations (xiv, xv, xvi, xvii) with the constants (25°C) $pK_H = 1.5$, $pK_1 = 6.3$, $pK_2 = 10.25$, pK (hydration of CO_2) $= -2.8$ have been used. The pure CO_2 solution is characterized by the proton condition $[H^+] = [HCO_3^-] + 2[CO_3^{2-}] + [OH^-]$ (see point *P*) and the equilibrium concentrations $-\log [H^+] = -\log [HCO_3^-] = 5.65$; $-\log[CO_2aq] = -\log[H_2CO_3] = 5.0$; $-\log [H_2CO_3] \approx 7.8$; $-\log[CO_3^{2-}] = 8.5$

Ref: Stumm, W. and J. Morgan, *Aquatic Chemistry*, Wiley-Interscience, New York, 1970, p. 127.

Solubility equilibria

Minerals dissolve in or react with water. Under different physico-chemical conditions minerals are precipitated and accumulate on the ocean floor and in the sediments of rivers and lakes. Dissolution and precipitation reactions impart to the water and remove from it constituents which modify its chemical properties.

It is difficult to generalize about rates of precipitation and dissolution other than to recognize that they are usually slower than reactions between dissolved species. Data concerning most geochemically important solid–solution reactions are lacking, so that kinetic factors cannot be assessed easily. Frequently the solid phase initially formed is metastable with respect to a thermodynamically more stable solid phase. Relevant examples of such metastability are the formation of aragonite under certain conditions instead of calcite, the more stable form of calcium carbonate, and the oversaturation of quartz in most natural waters. This oversaturation persists due to the extremely slow establishment of equilibrium between silicic acid and quartz.

The solubilities of most inorganic salts increase with increasing temperature. However, a number of compounds of interest in natural waters (e.g., $CaCO_3$, $CaSO_4$) decrease in solubility with increasing temperature. The dependence of solubility on pressure is very slight but must be considered for the extreme pressures encountered at ocean depths. For example, the solubility product of $CaCO_3$ will increase by approximately 0.2 logarithmic units for a pressure of 200 atmospheres (ca. 2000 meters).

Solubility of oxides and hydroxides

If a pure solid oxide or hydroxide is in equilibrium with free ions in solution, for example,

$$Me(OH)_2(s) = Me^{2+} + 2OH^- \qquad \text{(xviii)}$$

$$MeO(s) + H_2O = Me^{2+} + 2OH^- \qquad \text{(xix)}$$

the conventional (concentration) solubility product is given by

$$c_{K_{s0}} = [Me^{2+}][OH^-]^2 (\text{mole}^3\ \text{liter}^{-3}), \qquad \text{(xx)}$$

where the subscript "0" refers to solution of the simple, uncomplexed forms of the metal ion.

Sometimes it is more appropriate to express the

TABLE III

Equilibrium Constants for Oxides, Hydroxides, Carbonates, Hydroxide Carbonates, Sulfates, Sulfides, Silicates and Acids

Reaction	Symbol for equilibrium constants[a]	log K (25°C)	I
I. *Oxides and Hydroxides*			
$H_2O(1) = H^+ + OH^-$	K_W	−14.00	0
		−13.77	1M $NaClO_4$
$(am)Fe(OH)_3(s) = Fe^{3+} + 3OH^-$	K_{s0}	−38.7	3M $NaClO_4$
$(am)Fe(OH)_3(s) = FeOH^{2+} + 2OH^-$	K_{s1}	−27.5	3M $NaClO_4$
$(am)Fe(OH)_3(s) = Fe(OH)_2^+ + OH^-$	K_{s2}	−16.6	3M $NaClO_4$
$(am)Fe(OH)_3(s) + OH^- = Fe(OH)_4^-$	K_{s4}	− 4.5	3M $NaClO_4$
$2(am)Fe(OH)_3(s) = Fe_2(OH)_2^{4+} + 4OH^-$	K_{s22}	−51.9	3M $NaClO_4$
$(am)FeOOH(s) + 3H^+ = Fe^{3+} + 2H_2O$	$^*K_{s0}$	3.55	3M $NaClO_4$
$\alpha-FeOOH(s) + 3H^+ = Fe^{3+} + 2H_2O$	$^*K_{s0}$	1.6	3M $NaClO_4$
$\alpha-Al(OH)_3$(gibbsite) $+ 3H^+ = Al^{3+} + 3H_2O$	$^*K_{s0}$	8.2	0
$\gamma-Al(OH)_3$(bayerite) $+ 3H^+ = Al^{3+} + 3H_2O$	$^*K_{s0}$	9.0	0
$(am)Al(OH)_3(s) + 3H^+ = Al^{3+} + 3H_2O$	$^*K_{s0}$	10.8	0
$Al^{3+} + 4OH^- = Al(OH)_4^-$	K_4	32.5	0
$CuO(s) + 2H^+ = Cu^{2+} + H_2O$	$^*K_{s0}$	7.65	0
$Cu^{2+} + OH^- = CuOH^+$	K_1	6.0 (18°C)	0
$2Cu^{2+} + 2OH^- = Cu_2(OH)_2^{2+}$	K_{22}	17.0 (18°C)	0
$Cu^{2+} + 3OH^- = Cu(OH)_3^-$	K_3	15.2	0
$Cu^{2+} + 4OH^- = Cu(OH)_4^{2-}$	K_4	16.1	0
$ZnO(s) + 2H^+ = Zn^{2+} + H_2O$	$^*K_{s0}$	11.18	0
$Zn^{2+} + OH^- = ZnOH^+$	K_1	5.04	0
$Zn^{2+} + 3OH^- = Zn(OH)_3^-$	K_3	13.9	0
$Zn^{2+} + 4OH^- = Zn(OH)_4^{2-}$	K_4	15.1	0
$Cd(OH)_2(s) + 2H^+ = Cd^{2+} + 2H_2O$	$^*K_{s0}$	13.61	0
$Cd^{2+} + OH^- = CdOH^+$	K_1	3.8	1M $LiClO_4$
$Mn(OH)_2(s) = Mn^{2+} + 2OH^-$	K_{s0}	−12.8	0
$Mn(OH)_2(s) + OH^- = Mn(OH)_3^-$	K_{s3}	− 5.0	0
$Fe(OH)_2$(active) $= Fe^{2+} + 2OH^-$	K_{s0}	−14.0	0
$Fe(OH)_2$(inactive) $= Fe^{2+} + 2OH^-$	K_{s0}	−14.5 (−15.1)	0
$Fe(OH)_2$(inactive) $+ OH^- = Fe(OH)_3^-$	K_{s3}	− 5.5	0
$Mg(OH)_2$(active) $= Mg^{2+} + 2OH^-$	K_{s0}	− 9.2	0
$Mg(OH)_2$(brucite) $= Mg^{2+} + 2OH^-$	K_{s0}	−11.6	0
$Mg^{2+} + OH^- = MgOH^+$	K_1	2.6	0
$Ca(OH)_2(s) = Ca^{2+} + 2OH^-$	K_{s0}	− 5.43	0
$Ca(OH)_2(s) = CaOH^+ + OH^-$	K_{s1}	− 4.03	0
$Sr(OH)_2(s) = Sr^{2+} + 2OH$	K_{s0}	− 3.51	0
$Sr(OH)_2(s) = SrOH^+ + OH^-$	K_{s1}	0.82	0
$AgOH(s) = Ag^+ + OH^-$	K_{s0}	− 7.5	0
II. *Carbonates and Hydroxide Carbonates*			
$CO_2(g) + H_2O = H^+ + HCO_3^-$	K_{p1}	− 7.82	0
		− 7.5	Seawater
		− 7.3	5°C, 200 atm, seawater
$HCO_3^- = H^+ + CO_3^{2-}$	(K_2)	−10.33	0
		− 9.0	Seawater
		− 9.0	5°C, 200 atm, seawater
$CaCO_3$(calcite) $= Ca^{2+} + CO_3^{2-}$	K_{s0}	− 8.35	0
		− 6.2	Seawater
$CaCO_3$(aragonite) $= Ca^{2+} + CO_3^{2-}$	K_{s0}	− 8.22	0
$SrCO_3(s) = Sr^{2+} + CO_2^{2-}$	K_{s0}	− 9.03	0
		− 6.8	Seawater
$ZnCO_3(s) + 2H^+ = Zn^{2+} + H_2O + CO_2(g)$	$^*K_{ps0}$	7.95	0
$Zn(OH)_{1.2}(CO_3)_{0.4}(s) + 2H^+ = Zn^{2+} + H_2O + CO_2(g)$	$^*K_{ps0}$	9.8	0
$Cu(OH)(CO_3)_{0.5}(s) + 2H^+ = Cu^{2+} + 3/2H_2O + 1/2CO_2(g)$	$^*K_{ps0}$	7.08	0
$Cu(OH)_{0.67}(CO_3)_{0.67}(s) + 2H^+ = Cu^{2+} + 4/3H_2O + 2/3CO_2(g)$	$^*K_{ps0}$	7.08	0
$MgCO_3$(magnesite) $= Mg^{2+} + CO_3^{2-}$	K_{s0}	− 4.9	0
$MgCO_3$(nesquehonite) $= Mg^{2+} + CO_3^{2-}$	K_{s0}	− 5.4	0
$Mg_4(CO_3)_3(OH)_2.3H_2O$(hydromagnesite) $= 4Mg^{2+} + 3CO_3^{2-} + 2OH^-$	K_{s0}	29.5	0
$CaMg(CO_3)_2$(dolomite) $= Ca^{3+} + Mg^{2+} + 2CO_3^{2-}$	K_{s0}	−16.7	0
$FeCO_3$(siderite) $= Fe^{2+} + CO_3^{2-}$	K_{s0}	−10.4 (−10.24)	0

TABLE III (*continued*)

Reaction	Symbol for Equilibrum	log K (25°C)	
$CdCO_3(s) + 2H^+ = Cd^{2+} + H_2O + CO_2(g)$	K_{ps0}	6.44	1M $NaClO_4$
$MnCO_3(s) = Mn^{2+} + CO_3{}^{2-}$	K_{s0}	−10.41	0
III. *Sulfates, Sulfides and Silicates*			
$CaSO_4(s) = Ca^{2+} + SO_4{}^{2-}$	K_{s0}	− 4.6	0
$H_2S = H + HS^-$	K_1	− 7.0	0
$HS^- = H^+ + S^{2-}$	K_2	−12.96	0
Mns(green) $= Mn^{2+} + S^{2-}$	K_{s0}	−12.6	0
MnS(pink) $= Mn^{2+} + S^{2-}$	K_{s0}	− 9.6	0
$FeS(s) = Fe^{2+} + S^{2-}$	K_{s0}	−17.3	0
SiO_2(quartz) $+ 2H_2O = H_4SiO_4$	K_{s0}	− 3.7	0
(am)$SiO_2(s) + 2H_2O = H_4SiO_4$	K_{s0}	− 2.7	0
$H_4SiO_4 = H^+ + H_3SiO_4{}^-$	K_{s0}	− 9.46	0
IV. *Acids*			
$NH_4{}^+ = H^+ + NH_3(aq)$	K_a	− 9.3	0
$HOCl = H^+ + OCl^-$	K_a	− 7.53	0

The constants given here are taken from quotations or selections in (a) L. G. Sillén and A. E. Martell, *Stability Constants of Metal-Ion Complexes*, Special Publ., No. 17, The Chemical Society, London, 1964; (b) W. Feitknecht and P. Schindler, *Solubility Constants of Metal Oxides, Metal Hydroxides and Metal Hydroxide Salts in Aqueous Solutions*, Butterworths, London, 1963; (c) P. Schindler, "Heterogeneous Equilibria Involving Oxides, Hydroxides, Carbonates and Hydroxide Carbonates", in *Equilibrium Concepts in Natural Water Systems, Advances in Chemistry Series*, No. 67, American Chemical Society, Washington, D.C., 1967, p. 196; and (d) J. N Butler, *Ionic Equilibrium, A Mathematical Approach*, Addison-Wesley Publishing, Reading Mass., 1964. Unless otherwise specified a pressure of 1 atm is assumed.

[a] Most of the symbols used for the equilibrium constants are those given in *Stability Constants of Metal-Ion Complexes*.

Table from Stumm, W. and J. Morgan, *Aquatic Chemistry*, Wiley-Interscience, New York, 1970, pp. 168 and 169.

solubility in terms of reaction with protons, for example,

$$Me(OH)_2(s) + 2H^+ = Me^{2+} + 2H_2O \quad \text{(xxi)}$$

$$MeO(s) + 2H^+ = Me^{2+} + H_2O. \quad \text{(xxii)}$$

In the general case for a cation of charge z, the solubility equilibrium for Equations (xxi) and (xxii) is characterized by

$$c^*{}_{K_{s0}} = \frac{[Me^{z+}]}{[H^+]}[\text{mole}^{(1-z)}\,\text{liter}^{(z-1)} = \frac{c_{K_{s0}'}}{K_w^z} \quad \text{(xxiii)}$$

where K_w is the ion product of water. This constant and also a number of solubility equilibrium constants relevant to natural waters are given in Table III.

Equation (xxiii) can be written in logarithmic form to express the equilibrium concentration of a cation Me^{z+} as a function of pH:

$$\log[Me^{z+}] = \log{}^c{}^*K_{s0} - \text{pH}. \quad \text{(xxiv)}$$

Equation (xxiv) is plotted for a few oxides and hydroxides in Figure 5.

The relations given in Figure 5 do not fully describe the solubility of the corresponding oxides and hydroxides, since in addition to free metal ions, the solution may contain hydrolyzed species (hydroxo complexes) of the form $[Me(OH)_n^{z-n}]$. The solubility of the metal oxide or hydroxide is therefore expressed more rigorously as

$$Me_T = [Me^{z+}] + \sum_1^n [Me(OH)_n^{z-n}]. \quad \text{(xxv)}$$

Plots of this equation as a function of pH are given in Figure 6 for ferric hydroxide, zinc oxide and cupric oxide.

Solubility of carbonates

The maximum soluble metal ion concentration is a function of pH and concentration of total dissolved carbonate species. Calculation of the equilibrium solubility of the metal ion for a given carbonate for a water of a specific analytic composition discloses whether the water is oversaturated or undersaturated with respect to the solid metal carbonate. In the case of calcite

$$[Ca^{2+}] = \frac{K_{s0}}{[CO_3^{2-}]} = \frac{K_{k0}}{C_T\alpha_2}{}_0 \quad \text{(xxvi)}$$

Since α_2 is known as a function of pH, Equation (xxvi) gives the equilibrium saturation value of Ca^{2+} as a function of C_T and pH. An analogous equation can be written for any metallic cation in

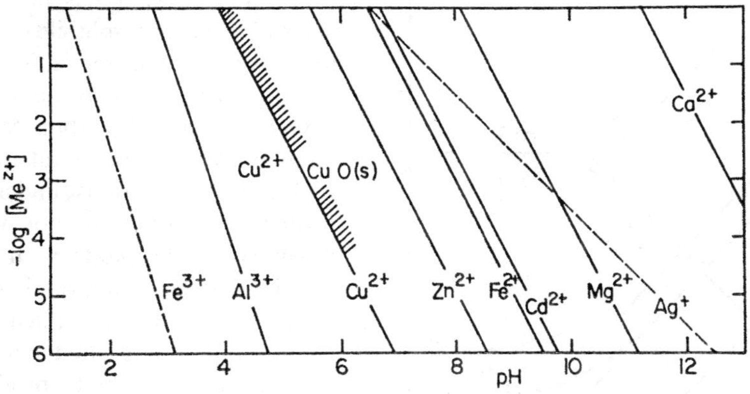

Figure 5 Solubility of oxides and hydroxides: free metal ion concentration in equilibrium with solid oxides or hydroxides. As shown explicitly by the equilibrium curve for copper, free metal ions are constrained to concentrations to the left of (below) the respective curves. Precipitation of the solid hydroxides and oxides commences at the saturation concentrations represented by the curves. The formation of hydroxo metal complexes must be considered for the evaluation of complete solubility of the oxides or hydroxides.

Ref: Stumm, W. and J. Morgan, *Aquatic Chemistry*, Wiley-Interscience, New York, 1970, p. 171.

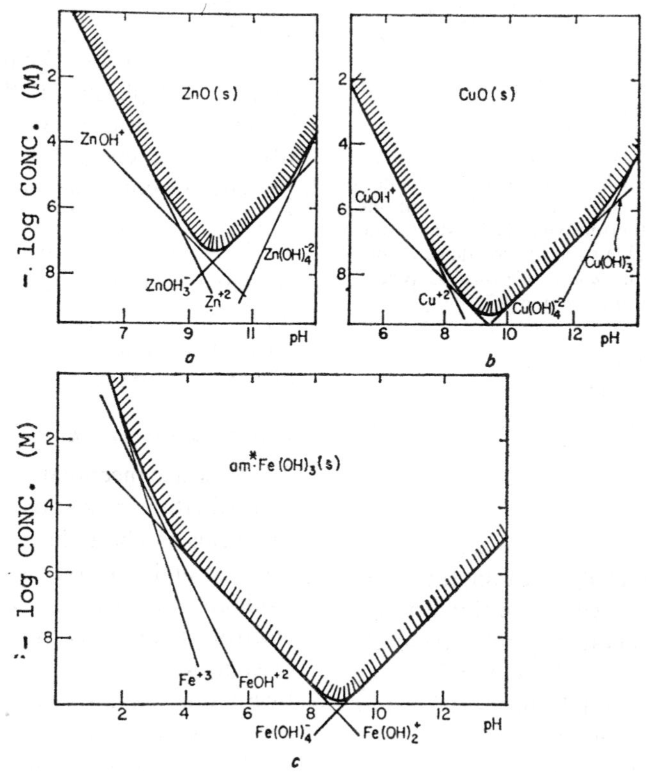

Figure 6 Solubility of amorphous $Fe(OH)_3$, ZnO and CuO. The equilibrium solubility curves for the hydroxo metal complexes and for the free metal ion have been combined to yield the composite curve bordered by the cross hatching. The constituent curves were constructed from the data in Table III. The possible occurrence of polynuclear complexes, for example $Fe_2(OH)_2^{2+}$, $Cu_2(OH)_2^{2+}$, has been ignored. Such complexes do not change the solubility characteristics markedly for the solids considered here. Also ignored is complexing with other ligands such as NH_3.

Ref: Stumm, W. and J. Morgan, *Aquatic Chemistry*, Wiley-Interscience, New York, 1970, p. 173.

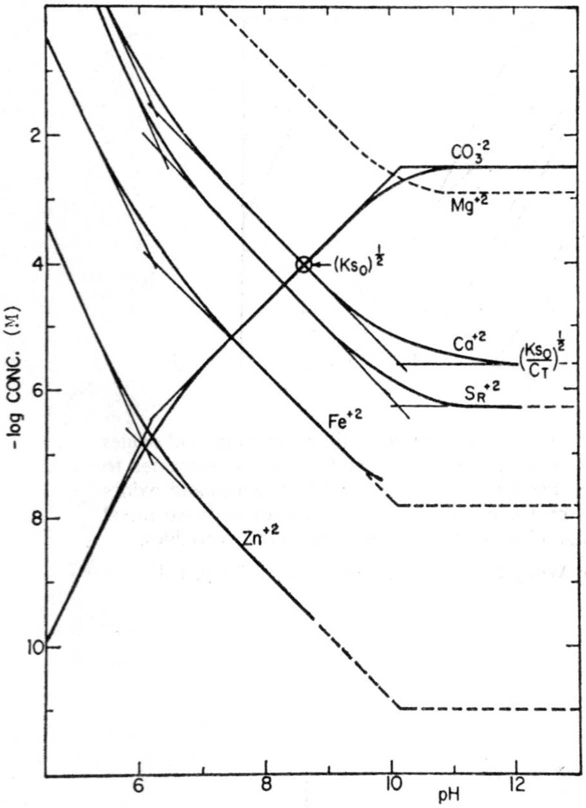

Figure 7 Solubility of carbonates in solutions of constant total dissolved carbonate carbon. The maximum soluble metal ion concentration ($[Me^{2+}] = Ks_0/[CO_3^{2-}] = Ks_0/\alpha_2 C_T$) is shown as a function of pH for $C_T = 10^{-2.5}$ M. The acidity constants for H_2CO_3* are indicated on the horizontal axis. Dashed portions of the curves indicated conditions under which $MeCO_3(s)$ is not thermodynamically stable due to the formation of the more stable solid hydroxide or oxide. Ref: Stumm, W. and J. Morgan, *Aquatic Chemistry*, Wiley-Interscience, New York, 1970, p. 179.

equilibrium with its solid metallic carbonate. These equations are amenable to simple graphical representation in a log concentration versus pH diagram as illustrated in Figure 7.

Control of solubility

Solubility calculations, such as those exemplified above, give thermodynamically meaningful conclusions, under the specified conditions (e.g., concentrations, pH, temperature and pressure), only if the solutes are in equilibrium with that solid phase for which the equilibrium relationship has been formulated. For a given set of conditions the solubility is controlled by the solid giving the smallest concentration of solute. For example, within the pH range of carbonate bearing natural waters, the stable solid phases regulating the solubility of Fe(II), Cu(II) and Zn(II) are, respectively, $FeCO_3$ (siderite), Cu0 (tenorite, and Zn (OH) (CO_3) (hydrozincite).

Unfortunately, it has not yet been possible to determine precise solubility data for some solids important in the regulation of natural waters. Among these are many clays and dolomite (CaMg $(CO_3)_2$), a mixed carbonate which constitutes a large fraction of the total quantity of carbonate rocks. The conditions under which dolomite is formed in nature are not well understood and attempts to precipitate it in the laboratory from solutions under atmospheric conditions have been unsuccessful. These difficulties in ascertaining equilibrium have resulted in a diversity of published figures for its solubility product, ($\{Ca^{2+}\}\{Mg^{2+}\}\{CO_3^{2-}\}^2$),† ranging from $10^{-16.5}$ to $10^{-19.5}$ (25°C).

The activity of the solid phase

In a solid–solution equilibrium, the pure solid phase is defined as a reference state and its activity is, because of its constancy, set equal to unity. This means that the activity of the solid phase is implicitly contained in the solubility equilibrium constant. Therefore, experimental differences from precisely known equilibrium constants can be used to deduce information about the constitution of the solid phase.

There are various factors that affect the activity of the solid phase: (a) the lattice energy, (b) the degree of hydration, (c) solid solution formation, (d) the free energy of the surface and (e) the presence of constituents affecting the purity of the solid.

The solids occurring in nature are seldom pure substances. For example, isomorphous replacement by a foreign constituent in the crystalline lattice is an important factor by which the activity of the solid phase may be decreased.

Redox equilibria and electron activity

There is a conceptual analogy between acid–base and oxidation–reduction reactions. In a similar way that acids and bases have been interpreted as proton donors and proton acceptors, reductants and oxidants are defined as electron donors and electron acceptors. Since free electrons do not exist in solution, every oxidation is accompanied by a reduction and *vice versa*. An oxidant is thus a substance which causes oxidation to occur, while itself becoming reduced.

The oxidation states of the reactants and products change as a result of the electron transfer which mechanistically may occur as a transfer of a group that carries one or more electrons. Since

† Note that this solubility product is expressed for activities, as represented by { }.

electrons are transferred in every redox reaction they can be treated conceptually like any other discrete reacting species, namely, as free electrons. The following redox reaction is illustrative:

$$O_2 + 4H^+ + 4e = 2H_2O \quad \text{reduction}$$
$$4Fe^{2+} = 4Fe^{3+} + 4e \quad \text{oxidation}$$
$$O_2 + 4Fe^{2+} + 4H^+ = 4Fe^{3+} + 2H_2O \quad \text{redox reaction} \qquad \text{(xxvii)}$$

This treatment of electrons is no different from that of many other species such as hydrogen ions and silver ions, which do not actually exist in aqueous solution as free and unhydrated species but which are expressed as H^+ and Ag^+ in reactions. For example, the H^+ really takes the form of hydrated protons ($H_9O_4^+$) or hydrogen complexes (acids such as HCl).

Redox intensity

By introducing the definition $pH = -\log[H^+]$, which under idealized conditions is formulated as

$$pH = -\log\{H^+\}, \qquad \text{(xxviii)}$$

Sørenson (1909) established a convenient intensity parameter that measures the relative tendency of a solution to donate or transfer protons. In an acid solution this tendency is high and in an alkaline solution it is low.

Similarly, Jørgensen (1945) has established an equally convenient redox intensity parameter,

$$p\varepsilon = -\log\{e\}, \qquad \text{(xxix)}$$

that measures the relative tendency of a solution to donate or transfer electrons. In a highly reducing solution the tendency to donate electrons, i.e., the hypothetical "electron pressure" or electron activity, is relatively large. Just as the activity of hypothetical hydrogen ions is very low at high pH, the activity of hypothetical electrons is very low at high pε. Thus a high $p\varepsilon$ indicates a relatively high tendency for oxidation. In equilibrium equations H^+ and e are treated in an analogus way. Thus oxidation or reduction equilibrium constants can be defined and treated similarly to acidity constants as shown by the following equations:

For protolysis:

$$HA = H^+ + A^- \qquad \text{(xxx)}$$

$\{H^+\}\{A^-\}/\{HA\} = K_{HA}$, or

$$pH = -\log K_{HA} + \log(\{A^-\}/\{HA\}) \qquad \text{(xxxi)}$$

For the oxidation of Fe^{2+} to Fe^{3+}:

$$Fe^{2+} = Fe^{3+} + e \qquad \text{(xxxii)}$$

$\{e\}\{Fe^{3+}\}/\{Fe^{2+}\} = K_{ox}$, or

$$p\varepsilon = -\log K_{ox} + \log(\{Fe^{3+}\}/\{Fe^{2+}\}. \qquad \text{(xxxiii)}$$

As seen from Equation (xxxiii) $p\varepsilon$ increases with the ratio of the activities (or concentrations) of oxidized to reduced species.†

From the following general reduction reaction:

$$aA + bB + ne = cC + dD$$

the generalized expression for any redox couple is given by

$$p\varepsilon = p\varepsilon^0 - \frac{a}{n^{pA}} - \frac{b}{n^{pB}} + \frac{c}{n^{pC}} + \frac{d}{n^{pD}} = \frac{1}{n}\frac{\Delta G}{2.3RT}, \qquad \text{(xxxiv)}$$

where $pX = -\log[X]$

and $$p\varepsilon; = -\frac{1}{n}\log K_{ox} = \frac{1}{n}\log K_{red} = \frac{1}{n}\frac{\Delta G;}{2.3RT}$$

K_{ox} and K_{red} are the equilibrium constants for the oxidation and reduction reactions; n is the number of electrons transferred in the reaction. ΔG represents the free energy change for the reduction. Thus it is seen that $p\varepsilon$ is a measure of the electron free energy level per mole of electrons.

Equation (xxxiv) permits the expression of the redox intensity by $p\varepsilon$ for any redox couple for which the equilibrium constant is known. Numerical illustrations of the calculation of $p\varepsilon$ values (25°C) are given for the following equilibrium systems in which the ionic strength, I,‡ is assumed to approach O:

a) An acid solution 10^{-5} M in Fe^{3+} and 10^{-3} M in Fe^{2+}.

b) A natural water at pH = 7.5 in equilibrium with the atmosphere ($Po_2 = 0.21$ atm.).

c) A natural water at pH = 8 containing 10^{-5} M Mn^{2+} in equilibrium with $\gamma - MnO_2(s)$.

"Stability Constants of Metal–Ion Complexes" gives the following equilibrium constants (K_{red}):

a) $Fe^{3+} + e = Fe^{2+}$;

$$K = \frac{\{Fe^{2+}\}}{\{Fe^{3+}\}\{e\}}; \log K = 12.53$$

b) $1/2\, O_2(g) + 2H^+ + 2e$;
$= H_2O(1)$

$$K = \frac{1}{Po_2^{1/2}\{H^+\}^2\{e\}^2}; \log K = 41.55$$

† The sign convention adopted here is that recommended by IUPAC (International Union of Pure and Applied Chemistry).

‡ Ionic strength, I, is a measure of the interionic effect resulting primarily from electrical attraction and repulsions between the various ions; it is defined by the equation $I = \frac{1}{2}\sum_i C_i Z_i^2$. The summation is carried out for all types of ions, cations and anions, in the solution.

c) $\gamma - MnO_2(s) + 4H^+ + 2e$
$= Mn^{2+} + 2H_2O(1);$

$$K = \frac{\{Mn^{2+}\}}{\{H^+\}^4\{e\}^2}\ ; \log K = 40.84.$$

For the conditions stipulated the following $p\varepsilon$ values are obtained:

a) $p\varepsilon = 12.53 + \log \frac{\{Fe^{3+}\}}{\{Fe^{2+}\}} = 10.53$

b) $p\varepsilon = 20.78 + 1/2 \log (Po_2^{1/2}\ \{H^+\}^2) = 13.11$

c) $p\varepsilon = 20.42 + 1/2 \log \frac{\{H^+\}^4}{\{Mn^{2+}\}} = 6.92.$

Equilibrium distribution in the sulphur system

Figure 8 shows the $p\varepsilon$ dependence of a 10^{-4} M $SO_4^{2-} - HS^-$ system at pH = 10 and 25°C. The reaction is

$$SO_4^{2-} + 9H^+ + 8e = HS^- + 4H_2O(1) \quad \text{(xxxv)}$$

and the redox equilibrium equation is

$$p\varepsilon = 1/8 \log K + 1/8 \log \frac{[SO_4^{2-}][H^+]}{[HS^-]}, \quad \text{(xxxvi)}$$

where log K (for the reduction reaction) is 10^{34}. Hence,

$$p\varepsilon = 4.25 - 1.125\text{pH} + 1/8 \log [SO_4^{2-}] - 1/8 \log [HS^-]$$

or, for pH = 10,

$$p\varepsilon = -7 + 1/8 \log [SO_4^{2-}] - 1/8 \log [HS^-].$$

HS^- is the predominant S($-$II) species at pH = 10. Figure 8 shows that the lines for $[SO_4^{2-}]$ and $[HS^-]$ intersect at $p\varepsilon = -7$. The asymptotes for $[SO_4^{2-}]$ have slopes of +8 and 0, whereas those for $[HS^-]$ have slopes of 0 and -8.

Lines for the equilibrium partial pressure of O_2 and H_2 are also given in the diagram. As the diagram shows, rather high relative electron activities are necessary to reduce SO_4^{2-}. At the pH value selected, the reduction takes place at $p\varepsilon$ values slightly less negative than for the reduction of water. Thus in the presence of oxygen and at pH = 10, only sulfate can exist; its reduction is possible only at $p\varepsilon$ values less than -6.

Equilibrium constants for redox reactions

Equilibrium constants for some redox processes pertinent in aquatic conditions are listed in Table IV. A quite comprehensive reference source for such constants is *Stability Constants for Metal–Ion Complexes*, L. G. Sillén and A. E. Martell, The Chemical Society, London (1964) and its Supplement (1971). Significantly, the first section of this reference deals with the electron as a ligand, similarly to its treatment above. Another compilation, somewhat outdated though still very useful, is *Oxidation Potentials*, 2nd ed., W. M. Latimer, Prentice-Hall, (1952). This treatise lists redox potentials rather than equilibrium constants, but, as shown in the next section, the latter are readily obtained from the former.

The determination of pε and redox potential

As with pH, $p\varepsilon$ can be measured with a potentiometer using an indicator electrode (e.g., a platinum

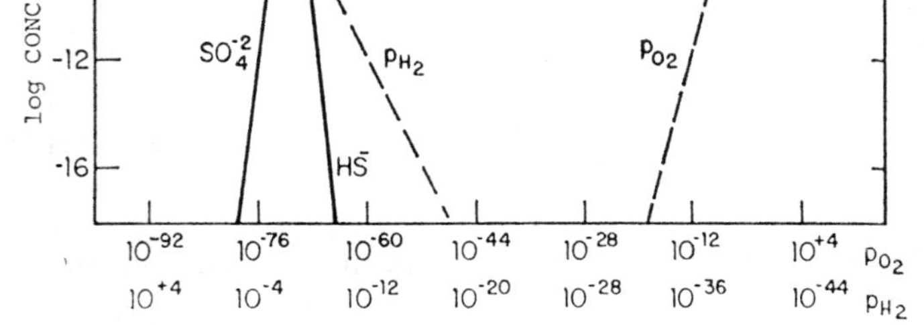

Figure 8 Equilibrium distribution of sulfur compounds as a function of $p\varepsilon$ at pH = 10 and 25°C. Total concentration is 10^{-4} M. The dotted curve shows that solid sulfur cannot exist thermodynamically at pH = 10, since its activity never becomes unity.
Figure from stumm, W. and J. Morgan, *Aquatic Chemistry*, Wiley-Interscience, New York, 1970, p. 311.

TABLE IV

Equilibrium Constants of Redox Processes Pertinent in Aquatic Conditions (25°C)

Reaction	$p\varepsilon°$ (= − log K)	$p\varepsilon°$ (W)[a]
(1) $1/4\ O_2(g) + H^+(W) + e = 1/2\ H_2O$	+20.75	+13.75
(2) $1/5\ NO_3^- + 6/5\ H^+(W) + e = 1/10\ N_2(g) + 3/5\ H_2O$	+21.05	+12.65
(3) $1/2\ MnO_2(s) + 1/2\ HCO_3^- + 3/2\ H^+(W) + e$	+20.46	+ 9.96
$= 1/2\ MnCO_3(s) + 3/8\ H_2O$		+ 8.46
(3a) $1/2\ MnO_2(s) + 2H^+(W) + e = 1/2\ Mn^{2+} + H_2O$	+20.42	+ 6.42
(4) $1/2\ NO_3^- + H^+(W) + e = 1/2\ NO_2^- + 1/2\ H_2O$	+14.15	+ 7.15
(5) $1/8\ NO_3^- + 5/4\ H^+(W) + e = 1/8\ NH_4^+ + 3/8\ H_2O$	+14.90	+ 6.15
(6) $1/6\ NO_2^- + 4/3\ H^+(W) + e = 1/6\ NH_4^+ + 1/3\ H_2O$	+15.14	+ 5.82
(7) $1/2\ CH_3OH + H^+(W) + e = 1/2\ CH_4(g) + 1/2\ H_2O$	+ 9.88	+ 2.88
(8) $1/4\ CH_2O + H^+(W) + e = 1/4\ CH_4\ (g) + 1/4\ H_2O$	+ 6.94	− 0.06
(9) $FeOOH(s) + HCO_3^- + 2H^+(W) + e = FeCO_3(s) + 2H_2O$	+15.33	+ 1.33
		− 1.67[b]
(9a) $Fe^{3+} + e = Fe^{2+}$	+12.53	+12.53
(10) $1/2\ CH_2O + H^+(W) + 3 = 1/2\ CH_3OH$	+ 3.99	− 3.01
(11) $1/6\ SO_4^{2-} + 4/3\ H^+(W) + e = 1/6\ S(s) + 2/3\ H_2O$	+ 6.03	− 3.30
(12) $1/8\ SO_4^{2-} + 5/4\ H^+(W) + 3 = 1/8\ H_2S(g) + 1/2\ H_2O$	+ 5.75	− 3.50
(13) $1/8\ SO_4^{2-} + 9/8\ H^+(W) + e = 1/8\ HS^- + 1/2\ H_2O$	+ 4.13	− 3.75
(14) $1/2\ S(s) + H^+(W) + e = 1/2\ H_2S(g)$	+ 2.89	− 4.11
(15) $1/8\ CO_2(g) + H^+(W) + e = 1/8\ CH_4(g) + 1/4\ H_2O$	+ 2.87	− 4.13
(16) $1/6\ N_2(g) + 4/3\ H^+(W) + e = 1/3\ NH_4^+$	+ 4.68	− 4.68
(17) $1/2\ (NADP^+) + 1/2\ H^+(W) + e = 1/2\ (NADPH)$	− 2.0	− 5.5[c]
(18) $H^+(W) + e = 1/2\ H_2(g)$	0.0	− 7.00
(19) Oxidized ferredoxin + e = reduced ferredoxin	− 7.1	− 7.1[d]
(20) $1/4\ CO_2(g) + H^+(W) + e = 1/24$ (glucose) $+ 1/4\ H_2O$	− 0.20	− 7.20[e]
(21) $1/2\ HCOO^- + 3/2\ H^+(W) + e = 1/2\ CH_2O + 1/2\ H_2O$	+ 2.82	− 7.68
(22) $1/4\ CO_2(g) + H^+(W) + e = 1/4\ CH_2O + 1/4\ H_2O$	− 1.20	− 8.20
(22a) $1/4\ HCO_3^- + 5/4\ H^+(W) + e = 1/4\ CH_2O + 1/2\ H_2O$	+ 0.76	− 7.99
		− 8.74[b]
(23) $1/2\ CO_2(g) + 1/2\ H^+(W) + e = 1/2\ HCOO^-$	− 4.83	− 8.73
(24) $1/2\ Cl_2(aq) + e = Cl^-$	+23.6	+23.6
(25) $HOCl + H^+(W) + e = 1/2\ Cl_2(aq) + H_2O$	+26.9	+19.9

[a] (W) signifies that the pH = 7.

[b] These data correspond to (HCO_3^-) = 10^{-3}M rather than unity and so are not exactly $p\varepsilon°(W)$; they represent typical aquatic conditions more nearly than $p\varepsilon°(W)$ values do.

[c] M. Calvin and J. A. Bassham, *The Photosynthesis of Carbon Compounds*, Benjamin, New York, 1962.

[d] D. I. Arnon, *Science*, **149**, 1460 (1965).

[e] A. L. Lehninger, *Bioenergetics*, Benjamin, New York, 1965.

Table from Stumm, W. and J. Morgan, *Aquatic Chemistry*, Wiley-Interscience, New York, 1970, p. 318.

or gold electrode) and a reference electrode. The result is read as a potential difference in volts. When a reversible hydrogen electrode, at which the electrode reaction is $H_2 = 2H^+ + 2e$, is used as the reference, the resulting potential difference is termed the redox potential, E_H, where the suffix H refers to the hydrogen electrode as the reference. Usually another reference electrode is used, e.g., a calomel electrode, but the addition of a constant factor (i.e., the potential difference between the calomel electrode and the hydrogen electrode) to the observed voltage gives E_H. $p\varepsilon$ is then readily computed by dividing E_H by a constant factor according to Equation (xxxvii):

$$p\varepsilon = \frac{E_H}{(2.3\ RT/F)}, \qquad \text{(xxxvii)}$$

where F = the Faraday constant (96,500 coulombs per equivalent),

R = the gas constant (8.314 volt-coulombs per degree—equivalent),

and T = the absolute temperature in degrees Kelvin.

At 25°C, $(2.3\omega T/F) = 0.059$ volt.

Both conceptually and computationally, it is more convenient to use the dimensionless $p\varepsilon$ rather than the more directly measured E_H as a measure of the redox intensity. Every tenfold change in the activity ratio of Equation (xxxiv) causes a change in $p\varepsilon$ of one unit divided by the number of electrons transferred in the redox reaction. The fact that one electron can reduce one proton is another reason for expressing the intensity parameter for oxidation in a form equivalent to that used for acidity.

Incidentially, pH is also not measured directly. It is determined by measuring the potential (in volts) of an indicator electrode (e.g., a glass electrode) with respect to a reference electrode. If the hydrogen electrode is used or referred to as the reference electrode, the resulting potential difference is called the acidity potential. The pH is calculated by dividing the acidity potential by 2.3 RT/F.

The Peters–Nernst equation

Since much literature still describes the electron activity in volts rather than on a scale† similar to that for other reagents, the Peters–Nernst equation is still of utility. It is easily expressed by substituting Equation (xxxvii) into Equation (xxxiv):

$$E_H = E_H^0 + \frac{2.3RT}{nF}\log\frac{\{\text{oxidized}\}}{\{\text{reduced}\}} = \frac{-\Delta G}{nF}, \quad \text{(xxxviii)}$$

where

$$E_H^0 = (2.3RT/F)p\varepsilon; = \frac{-\Delta G^0}{nF}. \quad \text{(xxxix)}$$

Measurement of E_H

It is essential to distinguish between the concept of a potential and the measurement of a potential. Redox or electrode potentials (as listed in "Stability Constants of Metal–Ion Complexes" and other references) have been derived from equilibrium data, thermodynamic data, the chemical behavior of a redox couple with respect to known oxidizing and reducing agents, and from direct measurements of electrochemical cells.

Direct measurement of E_H for natural water environments involves complex theoretical and practical problems in spite of the apparent simplicity of the electrochemical technique. For example, the E_H of aerobic (dissolved oxygen containing) waters, measured with a platinum or gold electrode, does not agree with that predicted by Equation (xxxviii). Even when reproducible results are obtained, they often do not represent reversible Nernst potentials. Among the considerations hindering the direct measurement of E_H are the rates of electron exchange at certain electrodes and the occurrence of mixed potentials. A mixed potential results when the rate of oxidation of one redox couple is compensated by the rate of reduction of a different couple during the measurement. Although aqueous systems containing oxygen or similar oxidizing agents will usually give positive E_H values and anaerobic systems will usually give negative ones, detailed quantitative interpretation with respect to concentrations of redox species is generally unwarranted.

Since natural waters are normally in a dynamic rather than an equilibrium condition, even the concept of a single oxidation–reduction potential characteristic of the aqueous system as a whole cannot be justified. At best, measurement can give rise to an E_H value applicable to a particular redox reaction or to redox species in partial chemical equilibrium and even then only if these redox agents are electrochemically reversible at the electrode surface at a rate that is rapid compared with the electron drain or supply by the measuring electrode system.

pε–pH diagrams

A $p\varepsilon$–pH stability field diagram shows in a panoramic way which species predominate at equilibrium under any condition of $p\varepsilon$(or E_H) and pH. The primary value of a $p\varepsilon$–pH diagram is its simultaneous representation of the consequences of the equilibrium constants of many reactions for any combination of $p\varepsilon$ and pH. Figure 9 shows stability fields for the various species pertinent to the chlorine system. These diagrams are readily constructed from thermodynamic data such as those listed in Table IV.

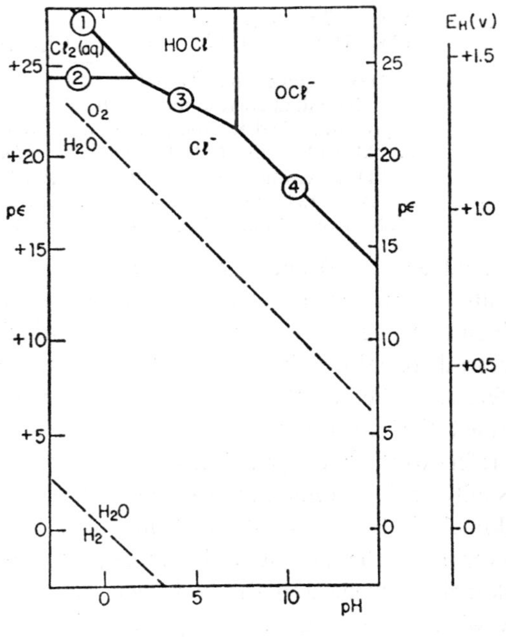

Figure 9 Stability field diagram for the chlorine system: $p\varepsilon$ versus pH. The curves labelled 1, 2, 3 and 4 represent equilibria derived from equations (25) and (26) of Table IV and pK_a for HOCl. This latter value is 7.53 at 25°C and is represented by the vertical line between HOCl and OCl^- stability fields. In dilute solutions Cl_2(aq) exists only at low pH. Cl_2, OCl^- and HCOl are all unstable or metastable in water since they are all slowly reduced by water as shown by the position of their stability fields, with respect to the H_2O–O_2 equilibrium curve.

Figure from Stumm, W. and J. Morgan, *Aquatic Chemistry*, Wiley-Interscience, New York, 1970, p. 320.

† With dilute solutions it is convenient to express concentrations on a minus log concentration scale, e.g., $pNa^+ = -\log [Na^+]$.

Log concentration–pε diagrams

The predominant redox species are depicted as a function of *pε* or redox potential in *pε*–log concentration diagrams. Upper or lower bounds of *pε* values for the occurrence of specific redox reactions are immediately evident from these double logarithmic diagrams. Such diagrams, constructed from the data in Table IV with pH = 7, are shown in Figure 10 for a few elements important in the biochemical cycle.

The boundary conditions for the stability of water (Figure 10–d) are given at high *pε* values by the oxidation of water to oxygen:

$$1/2\ H_2O = 1/4\ O_2 + H^+ + e \qquad \text{(xxxx)}$$

and at low *pε* values by the reduction of water to hydrogen:

$$H_2O + e = 1/2\ H_2 + OH^-. \qquad \text{(xxxxi)}$$

Water in equilibrium with the atmosphere ($Po_2 =$ 0.21 atm.) at pH = 7.0 (25°C) has a $p\varepsilon = 13.6$ ($E_H = 0.8$ volt).

Figure 10–a gives the relationships among several oxidation states of nitrogen as a function of *pε*. For most of the aqueous range of *pε*, N_2 gas is the most stable species. However, at large negative *pε* values ammonia becomes predominant and for *pε* greater than +12 nitrate dominates at pH = 7. The fact that the nitrogen gas of the atmosphere has not been converted largely into nitrate under the prevailing aerobic conditions at the land and water surfaces indicates a lack of efficient biological mediation.

Because of these perculiarities in equilibria with N_2, Figure 10–b has been constructed for the metastable equilibria between NO_3^-, and NO_2^- NH_4^+ by assuming the transition between bound nitrogen and N_2 to be hindered. This diagram shows that the shifts in relative predominance of the three species, NH_4^+, NO_2^- and NO_3^-, occur within a rather narrow *pε* range. That each of these species has a dominant zone within this range would seem to be a contributing factor to the highly mobile characteristics of the fixed species of the nitrogen cycle. Note that the relevant species of N(−III) at pH = 7 is NH_4^+ rather than NH_3 since the ammonia system $pK_a = 9.3$.

The reduction of SO_4^{2-} to H_2S or HS^- provides a good example of the application of equilibrium concepts to aquatic relationships. Figure 10–d shows that significant reduction of SO_4^{2-} to H_2S at pH = 7 requires $p\varepsilon < -3$. The biological enzymes that mediate this reduction must therefore operate at or below this *pε*. Because the system is dynamic rather than static only an upper bound can be set in this way, for the excess driving force in terms of *pε* at the mediation site cannot be determined by equilibrium computations. Since,

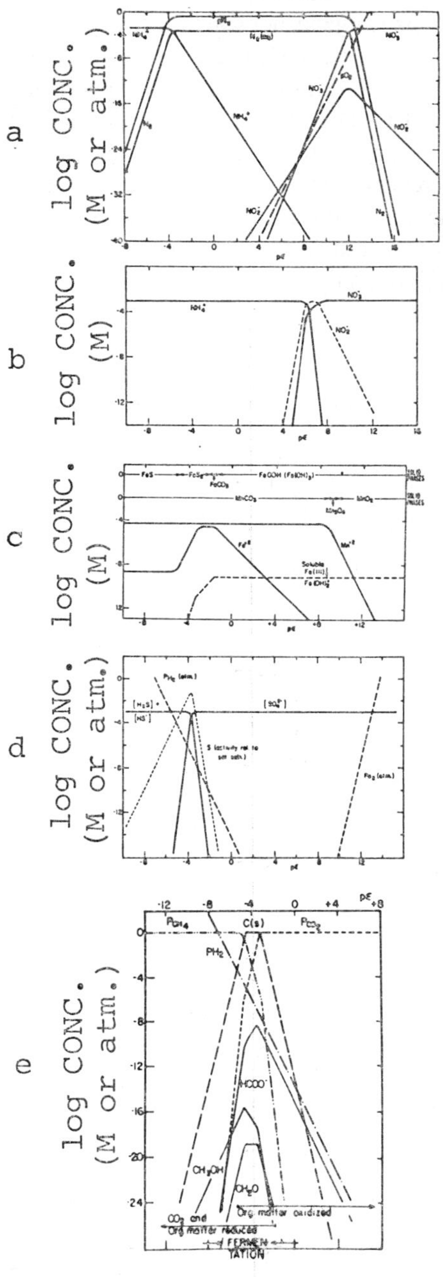

Figure 10 Equilibrium concentrations of biochemically important redox components as a function of *pε* at a pH of 7.0. These equilibrium diagrams have been constructed from equilibrium constants listed in Tables III and IV for the following concentrations representative of natural water systems: pH = 7.0; C_T (total carbonate carbon) = 10^{-3} M; $[H_2S(aq)] + [HS^-] + [SO_4^{2-}] = 10^{-3}$ M; $[NO_3^-] + [NO_2^-] + [NH_4^+] = 10^{-3}$ M; $p_{N2} = 0.78$ atm. and thus $[N_2(aq)] = 0.5 \times 10^{-3}$ M.

Figure from Stumm, W. and J. Morgan, *Aquatic Chemistry*, Wiley-Interscience, New York, 1970, p. 331.

however, many biologically mediated reactions seem to operate with relatively high efficiency in utilizing free energy, it appears likely that the operating *pε* value does not differ greatly from the equilibrium value. The diagram also indicates the possibility of formation of elemental sulfur within a narrow *pε* range at neutral and low pH.

The major feature of the carbon system, shown in Figure 10–e, is simply the interconvertibility of C(IV) to C(−IV): i.e., the reduction of carbon dioxide, bicarbonates and carbonates to methane and the reverse oxidation reactions. Formation of solid carbon is thermodynamically possible close to $p\varepsilon = -4$ but its inclusion does not change other relationships. Other carbon compounds exist under equilibrium conditions only at very small concentrations ($<10^{-9}$ M). The existence of myriad synthetic and biochemical organic compounds at ambient *pε* levels is due to their exceedingly slow rates of equilibration to CO_2 or CH_3 or, in the case of the complicated organic structures in living systems, to the constant input of energy.

Microbial mediation and free energy of redox reactions

To survive and hence reproduce, microorganisms must not only capture a significant fraction of the thermodynamically available energy but must also acquire this energy at a rate compatible with the maintenance of life. Thus the salient capability

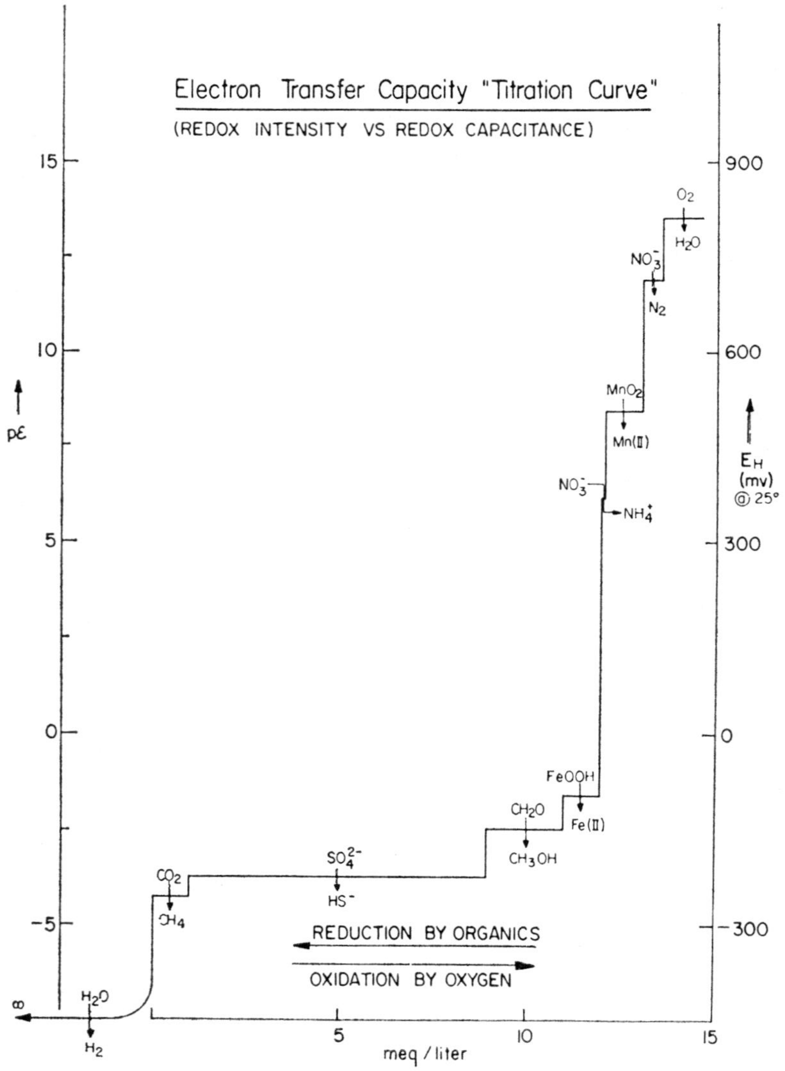

Figure 11 Electron transfer capacity "Titration Curve." In a system with excess organic material, the redox intensity falls as the electron acceptors are successively reduced. This diagram was constructed from the redox intensities and initial concentrations (expressed as electron equivalents) listed in Table III. The reactions indicated on the curve proceed sequentially during the stagnation period in the deeper waters of a polluted lake, vertically downward or temporally in sediments, sequentially after starting an anaerobic digester and chronologically in ground water contaminated with organic nutrients.

is that of power production per unit biomass and therefore kinetics (or the rate of movement toward equilibrium) should be considered as well as thermodynamics. To provide for such energy production microorganisms have developed highly efficient and specific biological compounds (enzymes) which catalyze energy yielding reactions and cell constituent producing processes.

Organisms do not oxidize organic substrates or reduce O_2 or SO_4^{2-}; they only mediate those reactions which are thermodynamically possible, or more specifically, the electron transfer occurring in these reactions. The $p\varepsilon$ range in which certain oxidation or reduction reactions are possible be estimated by calculating the equilibrium concentrations of the relevant species as a function of $p\varepsilon$. Since, for example, SO_4^{2-} can be reduced only below a given $p\varepsilon$ or redox potential, an equilibrium model can characterize the $p\varepsilon$ ranges in which reduction of sulfate is possible and is not possible. Such models are graphically presented in Figure 10, where all the reactions are amenable to microbial mediation. These diagrams manifest the use of $p\varepsilon$ as a parameter that characterizes the ecological milieu in a restrictive fashion.

The data in Table IV permit the calculation of combinations of the listed half reactions to give complete redox reactions. Those that are thermodynamically possible are always accompanied by a decrease in free energy. The free energy change the complete redox reaction, $\sum \Delta G$, is easily calculated from the $p\varepsilon$ values through rearrangement of Equation (xxxiv):

$$\sum \Delta G = -2.3RT[(np\varepsilon)_{\text{for reduction}} \sum (np\varepsilon)_{\text{for oxidation}}]. \qquad \text{(xxxxi)}$$

If $-\Delta G$ is negative, the reaction can occur. Combinations that lead to energetically possible reactions are given in Table III. All of these reactions are mediated by microorganisms.

REFERENCES

American Chemical Society: "Equilibrium Concepts in Natural Water Systems". *Advances in Chem. Series*, **67**, Washington (1967).

Butler, J. N., *Ionic Equilibrium, a Mathematical Approach*, Addison-Wesley, Reading, Mass. (1964).

Conway, B. E., *Annual Review of Physical Chemistry*, **17**, Annual Reviews Inc., Palo Alto Calif., (1966).

Dorsey, N. E. *Properties of Ordinary Water-Substance*, A.C.S. monograph No. 81, Reinhold Publishing Corp., New York (1940).

Eisenberg, D. and W. Kauzmann, *The Structure and Properties of Water*, Oxford University Press, England (1969).

Fletcher, N. H., *The Chemical Physics of Ice*, Cambridge University Press, England (1970).

Frank, H. S., *Science*, **169**, 635 (1970).

Garrels, R. M. and C. L. Christ, *Solutions, Minerals and Equilibria*, Harper and Row, New York (1965).

Horne, R. A., *Marine Chemistry, The Structure of Water and the Chemistry of the Hydrosphere*, Wiley-Interscience, New York (1969).

Horne, R. A., *Water and Aqueous Solutions, Structure, Thermodynamics, and Transport Processes*, Wiley-Interscience, New York (1972).

Horne, R. A., *Surv. Progr. Chem.*, **4** (1968) 2.

Hush, N. S., *Reactions at Electrodes*, Wiley-Interscience, New York (1971).

Kamb, "Structure of the Ices" in Horne, R. A., *Water and Aqueous Solutions*, Wiley-Interscience, New York (1972).

Kavanau, J. L., *Water and Solute–Water Interactions*, Holden-Day, San Francisco, (1964).

Keyes, F. G., *J. Chem. Phys.* **17**, 923 (1949).

King, T., *Water: Miracle of Nature*, The Macmillan Company, New York (1953).

Krindel, P. and I. Eliezer, *Coord. Chem. Rev.*, **6**, 217 (1971).

Narten, A. H. and H. A. Levy, *Science*, **165**, 447 (1969).

Pimentel, G. C. and A. L. McClellan, *The Hydrogen Bond*, W. H. Freeman and Co., San Francisco (1960).

Riley, J. P. and G. Shirrow (eds.), *Chemical Oceanography*, 2 Volumes, Academic Press, London (1965).

Riley, J. P. and R. Chester, *Introduction to Marine Chemistry*, Academic Press, London (1971).

Skinner, B. J., *Earth Resources*, Prentice-Hall, Inc., Englewood Cliffs, New Jersey (1969).

Stumm W. and J. J. Morgan, *Aquatic Chemistry: An Introduction Emphasizing Chemical Equilibria to the Chemistry of Natural Waters*, Wiley-Interscience, New York (1970).

"Water II" Topic of *Journal Colloid Interface Science*, **36**, No. 4, (1971).

STEVEN GHERINI

MARTIN FORSBERG

Harvard University

WERNER STUMM

Swiss Federal Republic Institute of Technology.

WATER: DESALTING: see DESALINATION

WATER FLOW

1. Properties of Fluids

The fluid properties most commonly encountered in water flow problems are presented in the following paragraphs. The foot-pound-second system of units is used throughout the discussion unless otherwise stated to the contrary.

The unit of *mass*, m, is the slug. A mass of one slug will be accelerated by a force of one pound at the rate of 1 ft. per sec^2.

The *density*, ρ, of a fluid is its mass per unit volume and is expressed in slugs per ft^3.

The *specific weight*, γ, is the weight per unit volume and denotes the gravitational force on a unit volume of fluid and is expressed in pounds per cubic foot.

Fluid density and specific weight are related by the expression:

$$\rho = \frac{\gamma}{g} \tag{1}$$

in which g is the acceleration due to gravity.

The *specific gravity* of a fluid is found by dividing its density by the density of pure water at 39.2°F (4°C).

The relative shearing force required to deform a fluid gives a measure of the *viscosity* of the fluid. An increase in temperature causes a decrease in viscosity of a liquid and *vice versa*. Consider the space between two parallel plates (Fig. 1) which is filled with fluid; the bottom plate remains at rest while the upper plate moves with velocity V under an applied force. The velocity of the fluid particles will range from V at the top boundary to zero at the bottom as they will assume the same velocity as the boundary in which they are in contact. Experiments have demonstrated that the shear stress, τ, is directly proportional to the rate of deformation, du/dy. Mathematically, this can be written as:

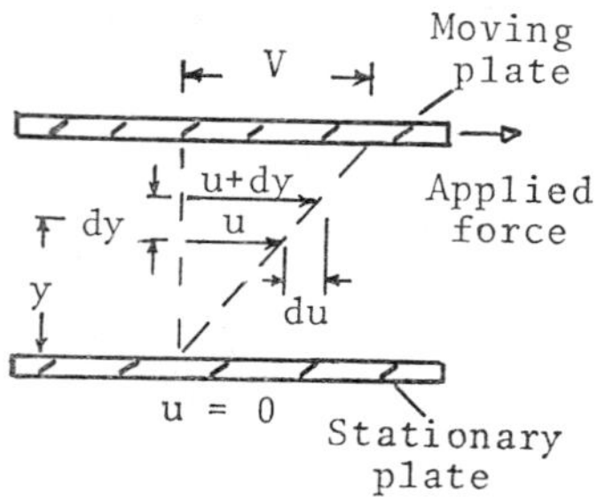

Figure 1 Fluid shear.

$$\tau = \frac{du}{dy}. \tag{2}$$

Equation (2) is known as Newton's equation of viscosity. The constant of proportionality, μ, in lb-sec per ft^2, is termed the coefficient of viscosity, the dynamic viscosity or the absolute viscosity.

The *kinematic viscosity*, γ, is defined as the ratio of the coefficient of viscosity to the density and is expressed in square feet per second:

$$\nu = \frac{\eta}{\rho}. \tag{3}$$

A more proper term for *surface tension*, σ, would be surface energy. Surface tension is a liquid surface phenomenon and is caused by the relative forces of cohesion, the attraction of liquid molecules for each other, and adhesion, the attraction of liquid molecules for the molecules of another liquid or solid. Surface tension has the units of pounds per foot. When a liquid surface is in contact with a solid, a contact angle, θ, greater than 90° results with depression of the liquid surface if the liquid does not "wet" the tube such as mercury and glass. If the solid boundary has a greater attraction for a liquid molecule than the surrounding liquid molecules, then the contact angle is less than 90° and the liquid is said to "wet" the wall leading to a capillary rise as in the case of water and glass.

Table 1 gives the values of the fluid properties discussed in the preceding paragraphs for a few common fluids.

2. Pressure Flow

Friction formulae

Darcy–Weishbach's equation The Darcy–Weishbach formula was first proposed empirically but later found by dimensional reasoning to have a rational basis:

$$h_f = \frac{fLV^2}{2gD} \tag{4}$$

TABLE 1
Fluid Properties

Fluid	Temperature °F	Density	Specific weight lb./ft³	Viscosity lb–sec/ft²	Kinematic viscosity ft²/sec	Surface tension lb./ft
Water	39.2	1.000	62.43	3.27×10^{-5}	1.69×10^{-5}	0.0051
	60.0	0.999	62.37	2.36×10^{-5}	1.22×10^{-5}	0.0050
	70.0	0.998	62.30	2.05×10^{-5}	1.06×10^{-5}	0.0049
Mercury	32.0	13.60	848.7	3.55×10^{-5}		
Sea water			64			

in which f = friction factor, L = pipe length, V = mean velocity, D = diameter, h = head loss, g = acceleration due to gravity.

Equation (4) was derived for circular sections flowing full and the equation itself is dimensionally homogeneous. It can be extended to other cross-sections provided these shapes are not too different from circular; in this case, the equation has to be transformed by using the hydraulic radius, R, instead of the diameter, D:

$$h_f = \frac{fLV^2}{8gR}, \tag{5}$$

where $R = D/4$ for flow at full bore. The use of Darcy's equation in the form given by Equation (5) is sometimes extended to open channel flow.

The determination of the friction factor, f, depends on the flow regime, that is, whether the flow is laminar, critical, transitional, smooth turbulent or rough fully turbulent.

Laminar Flow Consider the mean pipe velocity, V, as given by Hagen-Poiseuille's equation for laminar flow:

$$V = \frac{\gamma SD}{32\mu} \tag{6}$$

in which S = energy slope.

Combining Equation (4) with Equation (6) and noting that $S = h_f/L$, $\gamma = \rho g$, and $v = \mu/\rho$, the friction factor is given by:

$$f = \frac{64}{R_e}, \tag{7}$$

where $R_e = vD/\gamma$ is the Reynolds number. Equation (7) can be used for all pipe roughness as the friction factor in laminar flow is independent of the wall protuberances and is inversely proportional to the Reynolds number. The energy loss varies directly as the mean pipe velocity in laminar flow which persists up to a Reynolds number of about 2000.

The velocity profile, which has a parabolic distribution, can be obtained from Hagen-Poiseuille's equation. The velocity, u, at any radius, r, of the pipe of diameter, D, is given by:

$$u = \frac{\gamma S}{4\mu}\left(\frac{D^2}{4} - r^2\right). \tag{8}$$

At the centre line, the velocity is a maximum:

$$u_{\text{max}} = \frac{\gamma SD^2}{16\mu}. \tag{9}$$

The mean velocity is:

$$u_{\text{mean}} = (u_{\text{max}})/2 = \frac{\gamma SD^2}{32\mu}. \tag{10}$$

Critical Flow From a Reynolds number of about 2000 and extending to 4000 lies a critical zone where the flow may be either laminar or turbulent. The flow regime is unstable and no equation adequately describes it.

Smooth Turbulent For pipes fabricated from hydraulically smooth materials such as copper, plexiglass and glass, the flow is smooth turbulent for a Reynolds number exceeding 4000. The von Karman-Nikuradse smooth pipe equation is:

$$\frac{1}{\sqrt{f}} = 2\log_{10}(R_e\sqrt{f}) - 0.80. \tag{11}$$

Equation (11) indicates that the friction factor depends on the fluid properties and decreases with increasing Reynolds number.

Rough Fully Turbulent Nikuradse experimented with pipes artificially roughened with uniform sand grains. The results were fitted to the theory of Prandtl–Karman to give the well known rough-pipe equation:

$$\frac{1}{\sqrt{f}} = 2\log_{10}(D/\varepsilon) + 1.14. \tag{12}$$

Equation (12) states that beyond a certain Reynolds number, when the flow is fully turbulent, the friction factor is influenced only by the relative roughness, ε/D and independent of the Reynolds number.

Transitional Flow Most commercial pipe flows do not follow either the smooth pipe or rough pipe equations. Colebrook and White proposed a transitional flow equation which would be asymptotic to both:

$$\frac{1}{\sqrt{f}} = -2\log_{10}\left(\frac{\varepsilon/D}{3.7} + \frac{2.51}{R_e\sqrt{f}}\right). \tag{13}$$

Equation (13) approaches the smooth pipe equation for low and the rough pipe equation for high values of the Reynolds number respectively. Unlike Nikuradse's ε, which represents the actual height of the sand grains, the ε of Colebrook–White's equation is not an actual roughness dimension but a representative height describing the roughness projections. It is referred to as the equivalent sand-grain diamenter since the friction loss it represents is the same as the equivalent sand-grain diameter; Table 2 gives experimentally observed values:

TABLE 2
Equivalent Sand-Grain Diameter

Pipe material	ε (ft)
Riveted steel	0.030
Rough concrete	0.010
Smooth concrete	0.001
Steel	0.00015

Moody Diagram (Moody, 1944) The Moody Diagram (Fig. 2) summarises and solves graphically the four friction factor equations (Equation 7, 11, 12, 13) as well as delineating the zones of the various flow regimes. The line separating transitional and fully turbulent flow is given by Rouse's equation:

$$\frac{1}{\sqrt{f}} = \frac{R_e}{200}\frac{\varepsilon}{D}. \tag{14}$$

Manning's Equation The Manning equation, although originally developed for open channel flow has often been extended for use in pressure conduits. The equation is usually favored for rough textured material (rough concrete, unlined rock tunnels) and cross-sections that are not circular (rectangular, horseshoe). It is most commonly given in the form:

$$v = \frac{1.486}{N} R^{2/3} S^{1/2}, \tag{15}$$

in which N = roughness coefficient. Equation (15) can also be transformed to:

$$h_f = 29.1\, N^2 \frac{L}{R^{4/3}} \frac{V^2}{2g} \tag{16}$$

$$S = \frac{Q^2 N^2}{2.21\, A^2 R^{4/3}}. \tag{17}$$

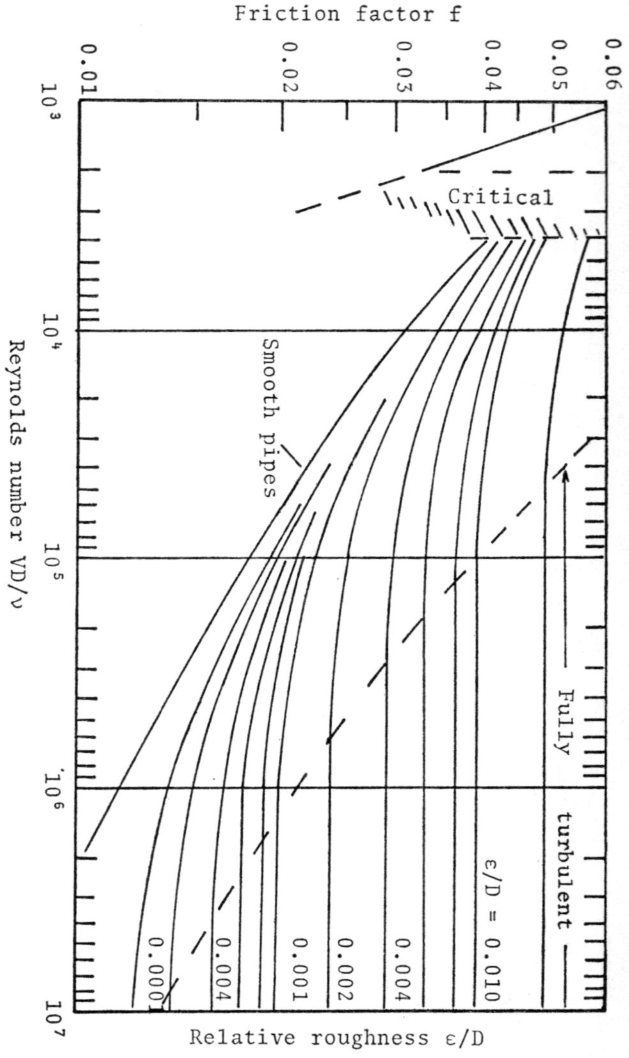

Figure 2 Pipe friction factors.

The dimension of the roughness coefficient, N, is frequently taken as $L^{1/6}$ as the equation by itself is not dimensionally homogeneous. Table 3 provides values of Manning's N for the more widely used pipe materials.

TABLE 3
Normal Values of Manning's N

Material	N
Brass	0.010
Corrugated metal	0.024
Glass	0.010
Concrest, unfinished	0.014
Vitrified clay	0.014
Steel	0.012
Cement	0'012
Brick	0.013

Hazen–William's Equation This equation is used mainly in sanitary engineering.

$$V = 1.318\, C R^{0.63} S^{0.54}, \tag{18}$$

where C = roughness coefficient. Typical values of the Hazen–William's C is given in Table 4.

TABLE 4
Hazen-William's C

Material (new)	C
Cast iron	130
Welded Steel	119
Riveted Steel	110
Concrete	130
Wood-stave	120
Vitrified clay	110

Energy losses due to cross-sectional changes, bends, and valves

Cross-Sectional Changes

Expansion Energy loss in an expansion is principally a form loss:

$$h_{\text{exp}} = \left[1 - \left(\frac{D_1}{D_2}\right)^2\right]^2 \frac{V_1^2}{2g}, \tag{19}$$

in which D = diameter of the conduit, and subscripts 1 and 2 denote upstream and downstream values. From Equation (19), if D_2 is very large compared to D_1, such as the discharge into a reservoir, the entire velocity head is lost.

Contraction The contraction loss equation can be expressed in terms of the downstream velocity, V_2, as:

$$h_{\text{con}} = \left(\frac{1}{C_c} - 1\right)^2 \frac{V^2}{2g}. \tag{20}$$

Typical values of the coefficient of contraction, C_c, are given in Table 5.

TABLE 5
Coefficient of Contraction

A_2/A_1	C_c
0.25	0.64
0.50	0.68
0.75	0.78
1.00	1.00

Entrance Loss The head loss at the entrance of a conduit can be compared to that of a short tube:

$$h_{\text{ent}} = \left(\frac{1}{C^2} - 1\right) \frac{V^2}{2g} \tag{21}$$

or

$$h_{\text{ent}} = K_{\text{ent}} \frac{V^2}{2g}, \tag{22}$$

in which C = coefficient of discharge, K = entrance loss coefficient. Typical values of C and K are given in Table 6.

TABLE 6
Values of C and K_{ent}

Type of entrance	C	K_{ent}
Circular bellmouth	0.98	0.05
Square bellmouth	0.93	0.16
Fully rounded	0.95	0.10
Moderately rounded	0.89	0.25
Sharp cornered	0.82	0.50

Transition In gradual contractions and expansions, the head losses are calculated in terms of the difference of velocity heads in the upstream and downstream pipes:

$$\text{Gradual contraction: } h_{tc} = K_{tc}\left(\frac{V_2^2}{2g} - \frac{V_1^2}{2g}\right) \tag{23}$$

$$\text{Gradual expansion: } h_{te} = K_{te}\left(\frac{V^2}{2g} - \frac{V^2}{2g}\right). \tag{24}$$

K_{tc} values vary from 0.1 to 0.5 for gradual to sudden contractions. Values of K_{te} range from 0.03 to 0.80 for flare angles of 2° to 60°.

Bends The effect of the presence of bends is to induce secondary flow currents which are responsible for the additional energy dissipation:

$$h_b = K_b \frac{V^2}{2g}. \tag{25}$$

The bend loss coefficient, K_b, depends on the ratio of the bend radius, r, to the pipe diameter, d, as well as the bend angle. For a 90° bend and r/d ratio varying from 1 to 12, values of K_b range from 0.20 to 0.07.

Gates and Gate Valves The gate and gate valve loss can be expressed as:

$$h_g = K_g \frac{V^2}{2g}. \tag{26}$$

The value of the loss coefficient, K_g, for gates depends on a variety of factors. The value of K_g for the case having the bottom and sides of the jet suppressed, ranges from 0.5 to 1.0. Typical values of K_g for gate valves are:

TABLE 7
K_g for Gate Values

Valve opening	K_g
Fully open	0.2
3/4 open	1.3
1/2 open	5.5
1/4 open	24.0

Exit Loss In general the entire velocity head is lost at exit and the exit loss coefficient, K_e is unity in the equation:

$$h_e = K_e \frac{V^2}{2g}. \tag{27}$$

Energy-discharge relation

In pressure conduit flow, the water is transmitted through a closed boundary conveying structure without a free surface. Fig. 3 illustrates graphically the various forms of energy losses which could take place within the conduit. The following energy relation can be written:

$$h_l = h_{ent} + h_{tc} + h_f \tag{28}$$

in which h_{ent} = entrance loss, h_{tc} = transition loss.

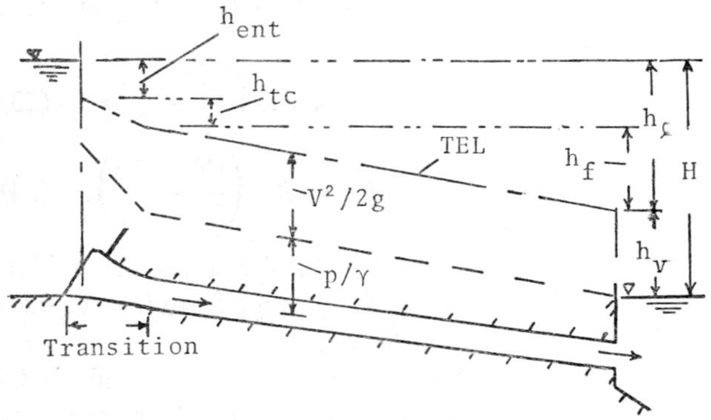

Figure 3 Energy relations.

h_f = skin friction loss. If H denotes the total head required to produce the discharge and h_v represents the exit velocity head,

$$H = h_l + h_v. \tag{29}$$

Writing Equation (29) in terms of the velocity heads and their respective loss coefficients,

$$H = C_l \frac{V_2^2}{2g} = \left[K_{ent}\frac{V_1^2}{2g} + K_{tc}\left(\frac{V_2^2}{2g} - \frac{V_1^2}{2g}\right) + f\frac{LV_2^2}{2gD_2} + K_v\frac{V_2^2}{2g}\right], \tag{30}$$

where K_v = combined velocity head and exit loss coefficient. By the continuity equation:

$$A_1V_1 = A_2V_2 \tag{31}$$

and

$$\frac{V_1^2}{2g} = \frac{A_2^2}{A_1^2}\frac{V_2^2}{2g}.$$

Equation (30) could be expressed as,

$$H = C_l\frac{V_2^2}{2g} = \frac{V_2^2}{2g}\left[K_{ent}\left(\frac{A_2}{A_1}\right)^2 + K_{tc}\left(1 - \frac{A_2^2}{A_1^2}\right) + \frac{fL}{2gD_2} + K_v\right] \tag{32}$$

in which

$$C_l = \left[K_{ent}\left(\frac{A_2}{A_1}\right)^2 + K_{tc}\left(1 - \frac{A_2^2}{A_1^2}\right) + \frac{fL}{2gD_2} + K_v\right] \tag{33}$$

$$V_2 = \frac{1}{C_l^{1/2}}\sqrt{2gH} \tag{34}$$

$$Q = A_2V_2 = \frac{A_2}{C_l^{1/2}}\sqrt{2gH} = CA_2\sqrt{2gH}, \tag{35}$$

in which $C = 1/C_l^{1/2}$ is the discharge coefficient. Equation (35) can be readily extended to multiple conduits in parallel.

Pipe networks

Introduction The Hardy Cross method is most suitably adapted to the solution of pipe networks. The statement of the problem resolves itself into:

a) the method of balancing heads is directly applicable if the discharges at inlets and outlets are known,

b) the method of balancing flows is very suitable if the heads at inlets and outlets are known.

It is assumed that:

i) sizes, lengths and roughness of pipes in the system are given,

ii) law governing friction loss and flow for each pipe is known,

iii) equations for losses in junctions, bends, and other minor losses are known. These relations are most conveniently expressed in terms of equivalent lengths of pipes.

The objectives of the analysis are:

i) to determine the flow distribution in the individual pipes of the network,

ii) to compute the pressure elevation heads at the junctions.

In applying the Hardy Cross method, two sets of conditions have to be satisfied:

i) the total change in pressure head along any closed circuit is zero:

$$\sum H = 0, \tag{36}$$

ii) the total discharge arriving at any nodal point equals the total flow leaving it:

$$\sum Q = 0. \tag{37}$$

For the pressure head change in any closed path, the clockwise positive sign convention is used.

For the discharge continuity requirement at a nodal point, the inward flow positive sign convention is adopted.

The friction head loss equation is used in the form:

$$H = rQ^2. \tag{38}$$

Using Darcy's formula:

$$H = \frac{fLV^2}{2gD} = \left(\frac{8fL}{g\pi^2 D^5}\right) Q^2$$

and
$$r = \frac{8fL}{g\pi^2 D^5}.$$

Method of Balancing Heads Based on the condition required by Equation (36), the following equations for any closed pipe loop results (Fig. 4):

$$\Sigma H = \Sigma r(Q_0 + \Delta Q)^2 = 0, \quad (39)$$

where Q_0 = assumed flow in the circuit for any one pipe, ΔQ = required flow correction. Expanding Equation (39) and approximating by retaining only

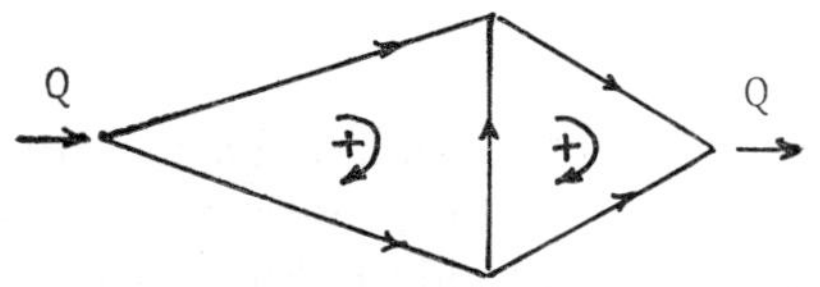

Figure 4 Pipe network.

the first two terms, the flow correction, ΔQ, can be expressed as:

$$\Delta Q = \frac{-\Sigma r Q_0^2}{\Sigma 2 r Q_0}. \quad (40)$$

Method of Balancing Flows Utilising the continuity requirement at a pipe junction as given by Equation (37), the head correction, ΔH, at a nodal point is given by the relation:

$$\Delta H = \frac{\Sigma \left(\frac{H}{r}\right)^{1/2}}{\Sigma \frac{1}{2H}\left(\frac{H}{r}\right)^{1/2}}. \quad (41)$$

In both Equation (40) and (41), the proper sign conventions must be used in the numerators.

Open Channel Flow

Introduction

Open channel flow refers to that class of water discharge in which the water flows with a free surface. The stream flow is said to be *steady* if the discharge does not vary with time. If the discharge is time dependent, the water flow is termed *unsteady*. *Uniform* flow refers to the case in which the mean velocities at any cross-section of the stream are identical; if these mean velocities vary from one cross-section to another, the flow is considered *non-uniform*. Steady uniform flow requires the conveyance section of the stream channel to be prismatic. Where the water surface profile is controlled principally by channel friction, this phenomen is known as *grdually varied flow*. For the type of flow in which the water surface changes substantially within a very short channel length due to a sudden variation in bed slope or cross-section, this category is referred to as *rapidly varied flow*.

Open channels fabricated from concrete are often rectangular or trapezoidal in shape. Canals excavated in erodible material have trapezoidal cross-sections. Although sewer pipes are closed sections, they are still considered as open channels so long as they are not flowing full; these cross-sections are usually circular.

Channel friction equation

The most widely used open channel friction formula is the Manning equation as mentioned earlier in pressure flow:

$$Q = \frac{1.486}{N} AR^{2/3} S^{1/2} \quad (42)$$

$$S = \frac{Q^2 N^2}{2.21 A^2 R^{4/3}}. \quad (17)$$

Manning's equation in hydraulic engineering is used for fully turbulent flow and, as such, the values of Manning's N apply to this flow regime.

In a natural tortuous stream channel, the mean value of Manning's N can be obtained from the following considerations:

a) estimate an equivalent basic N_s for a straight channel of that material,

b) select modifying values of N_m for non-uniform roughness, irregularity, variation in shape of cross-section, vegetation, and meandering,

c) sum the basic N_s together with the modifying values to obtain the total mean N.

Normal values of Manning's N for straight channels and various modifying values are given in Table 8.

TABLE 8
Values of Mannings' N

Basic N_s for straight channels	
Type of channel	N_s
Earth	0.010
Sand	0.012
Fine gravel	0.014
Rock	0.015
Coarse gravel	0.028
Cobbles and boulders	0.040
Modifying values of N_m	N_s
Irregularity	0.005 to 0.020
Changes in shape	0.005 to 0.020
Vegetation	0.005 to 0.100
Meander	0.10 N_s to 0.40 N_s

The total mean N value for the channel is obtained from the relation:

$$N = N_s + \sum N_m. \tag{43}$$

Energy principles

In deriving the energy relationships for open channel flow, the following assumptions are normally used:

a) a uniform velocity distribution over the cross-section is assumed, that is, the velocity coefficient, α, in the velocity head term, $\alpha V^2/2g$, is taken as unity. In practice, the value of α depends on the shape of the stream channel and has an average value of about 1.02 which makes this assumption sufficiently valid,

b) streamlines are essentially parallel,

c) channel slopes are small.

Consider the water particle of mass, m, and of weight, W (Fig. 5). The elevation and pressure energies of the particle are Wh_1 ft-lb and Wh_2 ft-lb respectively. Thus, the potential energy of the

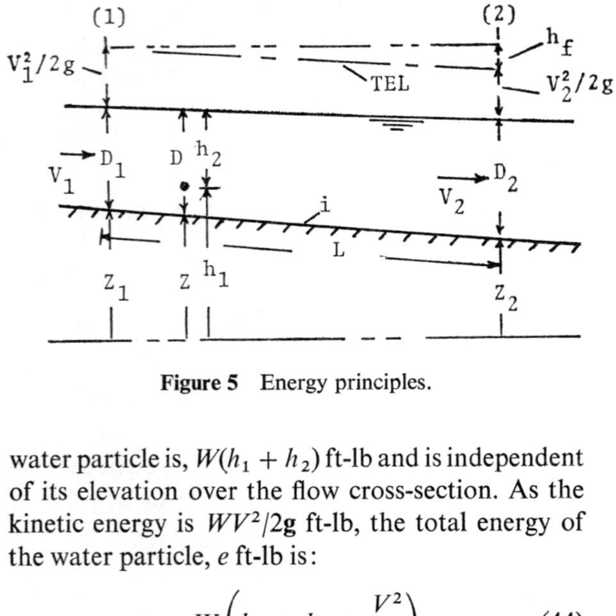

Figure 5 Energy principles.

water particle is, $W(h_1 + h_2)$ ft-lb and is independent of its elevation over the flow cross-section. As the kinetic energy is $WV^2/2g$ ft-lb, the total energy of the water particle, e ft-lb is:

$$e = W\left(h_1 + h_2 + \frac{V^2}{2g}\right). \tag{44}$$

Using the geometric relation:

$$Z + D = h_1 + h_2 \tag{45}$$

and noting that the total flow passing the cross-section is γQ lb/sec, the total energy of the water passing the cross-section per second, E_t ft-lb per second is given by:

$$E_t = \gamma Q\left(Z + D + \frac{V^2}{2g}\right). \tag{46}$$

Thus, the energy per pound of water passing the cross-section per second, H ft is:

$$H = Z + D + \frac{V^2}{2g}. \tag{47}$$

The term, $Z + D + V^2/2g$, is known as the total head or total energy level (TEL); the latter name is used here. The slope of the total energy level line is the energy gradient or friction slope and gives the rate of energy dissipation in the flow.

The energies at sections (1) and (2) are related by the expression:

$$Z_1 + D_1 + \frac{V^2{}_1}{2g} = Z_2 + D_2 + \frac{V^2{}_2}{2g} + \frac{Q^2N^2L}{2.21A^2R^{4/3}} \tag{48}$$

in which the Manning equation is used to calculate the friction slope and the mean values for the flow area, A, and the hydraulic radius, R, are to be used.

Flow regimes

Critical Flow The specific energy, E, is defined as the total head referred to the channel bottom (Fig. 6):

$$E = D + \frac{Q^2}{2gA^2}. \tag{49}$$

Differentiating Equation (47) with respect to D and equating the derivative to zero to obtain its minimum value,

$$\frac{dE}{dD} = 1 - \frac{Q^2}{gA^3}\frac{dA}{dD} = 0. \tag{50}$$

Noting that $dA = T\,dD$, Equation (50) becomes:

$$\frac{Q^2}{g} = \frac{A^3}{T}. \tag{51}$$

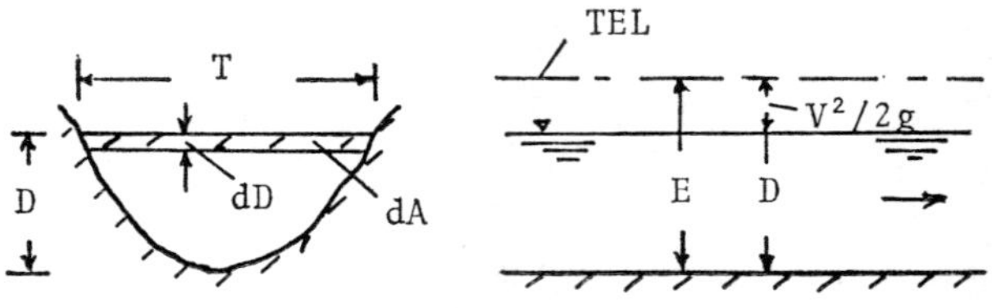

Figure 6 Derivation of critical flow.

Equation (51) is the fundamental equation for critical flow and is applicable to all shapes of cross-sections.

If the mean depth of the flow section is defined as $D_m = A/T$, substitution of this relation into

Equation (49) would give the significant expressions:

$$\frac{V_c^2}{2g} = \frac{D_m}{2} \tag{52}$$

and

$$\frac{V_c}{\sqrt{gD_m}} = 1. \tag{53}$$

At critical flow, Equation (52) demonstrates that the velocity head equals one-half the mean depth and Equation (53) indicates that the Froude number equals unity.

Specific Energy Diagram for Rectangular Channel For a rectangular channel, $Q = qB$ in which $q =$ discharge per unit width, $B =$ channel width, and Equation (49) becomes,

$$E = D + \frac{q^2}{2gD^2}. \tag{54}$$

A plot of Equation (54) for any given constant unit discharge gives Fig. 7, which is known as the *specific energy diagram.* The following flow regimes could be defined with reference to the specific energy diagram.

Subcritical flow denotes tranquil flow in which the Froude number and mean velocity are less than unity and the celerity of a gravity wave respectively.

Critical flow represents the discharge phenomenon where: (a) for a constant specific energy, the discharge is a maximum; (b) the specific energy is a minimum for a constant discharge; (c) the critical velocity equals the celerity of a small gravity wave; (d) the Froude number equals unity; (e) the critical depth is also the depth of minimum pressure–momentum force.

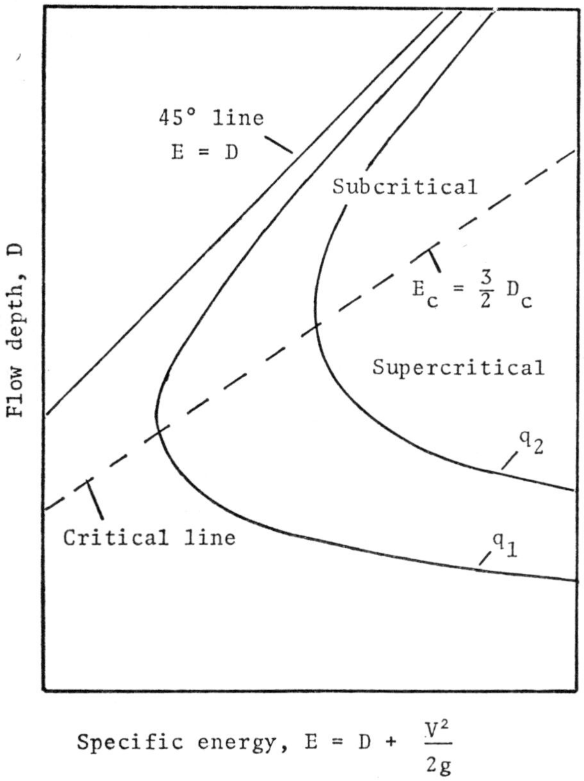

Figure 7 Specific energy diagram.

Supercritical flow which is also known as shooting or rapid flow, is that state of water flow where the Froude number and mean velocity exceed unity and the speed of transmission of a surface wave respectively.

Based on the equations developed earlier for critical flow, particular formulae can be derived for a rectangular section:

$$D_c = \left(\frac{q_c}{g}\right)^{1/3} \tag{55}$$

$$D_c = \frac{2}{3}(E_c) \tag{56}$$

$$D_c = \frac{V_c^2}{g} \tag{57}$$

$$\frac{V_c}{\sqrt{gD_c}} = 1. \tag{58}$$

Flow Transition The concept of the *normal depth* is an important parameter in the study of flow transition. For a given channel and any fixed discharge, uniform flow will occur at one unique depth. It is the depth attained in a long channel when the component of gravity force is just balanced by the frictional resistance of the channel.

When the normal and critical depth are equal, the flow is critical and the bed and energy slopes are the same. The channel bed then has a *critical slope.* The bed slope is termed *mild* when the normal depth exceeds the critical depth; the bed slope is then less than the critical energy slope and the flow regime is subcritical. When the normal depth lies below the critical depth and, hence, the bed slope is greater than the critical energy slope, the channel slope is considered to be *steep* and the supercritical flow regime prevails.

When water makes a transition from a channel with a mild slope to another with a steep slope, or vice versa, the flow passes through the critical depth close to the junction of the two channels. The section in which the water depth is critical defines a channel control. The weir acts as a control when water flows over it as critical depth is attained there.

Hydraulic Jump A hydraulic jump occurs when supercritical flow makes a transition to subcritical flow. A common occurrence of a hydraulic jump takes place at the base of a chute spillway. Fig. 8

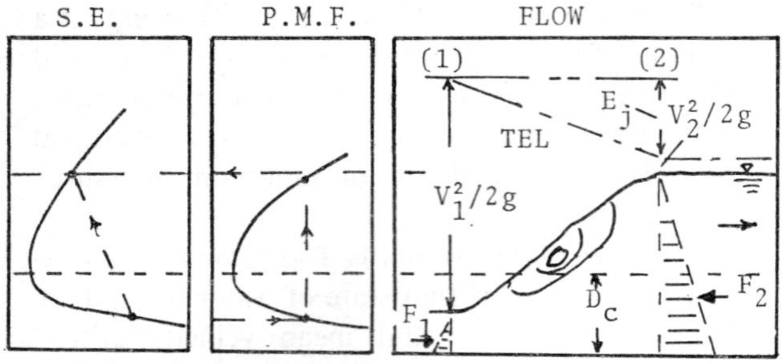

Figure 8 Hydraulic jump relations.

shows the energy momentum and depth relations for a hydraulic jump and also defines the symbols to be used.

In developing the equations for the hydraulic jump, the following assumptions are used:

a) the bed slope is considered small and neglected,

b) frictional resistance along the bed and sides of the channel are omitted.

Consider the control volume between sections 1 and 2. Applying the impulse–momentum principle:

$$F_1 - F_2 = \frac{\gamma}{g} Q(V_2 - V_1) \tag{59}$$

or

$$F_1 + \frac{\gamma}{g} QV_1 = F_2 + \frac{\gamma}{g} QV_2 \tag{60}$$

in which F_1 and F_2 denote the hydrostatic forces at sections 1 and 2 respectively. The term $\left(F + \frac{\gamma}{g} QV\right)$ is given the name pressure–momentum force. Let A = flow area, $\bar{y}$ = distance of centroid of flow area from surface; then the hydrostatic force = $\gamma A\bar{y}$ and Equation (60) can be written as:

$$A_1\bar{y}_1 + \frac{Q^2}{gA_1} = A_2\bar{y}_2 + \frac{Q^2}{gA_2}. \tag{61}$$

Equation (60) states the condition for the formation of a hydraulic jump and suggests a graphical solution. A plot of Equation (60) for any fixed discharge is shown in Fig. 8. For any given upstream supercritical water depth, which is usually known such as at the toe of a spillway, the subcritical hydraulic jump depth or *sequent* depth can be obtained from the graph.

For a rectangular cross-section channel and utilising the continuity relation:

$$Q = V_1A_1 = V_2A_2. \tag{62}$$

Equation (61) can be written as:

$$\frac{D_2}{D_1} = \frac{1}{2}(\sqrt{1 + 8F_1^2} - 1), \tag{63}$$

where $F_1 = V_1/\sqrt{(gD_1)}$ is the upstream Froude number.

The energy loss E_j across the hydraulic jump on a horizontal floor can be obtained by combining Equations (61), (62) and the energy equation:

$$D_1 + \frac{V_1^2}{2g} = D_2 + \frac{V_2^2}{2g} + E_j \tag{64}$$

to give:

$$E_j = \frac{(D_2 - D_1)^3}{4D_1D_2}. \tag{65}$$

The head loss E_j is graphically shown in the specific energy and flow diagrams (Fig. 8).

Surface water profiles

Non-Uniform Differential Equation Using the notation given in Fig. 9, the energy relations can be expressed as:

$$i\,dL + D + \frac{V^2}{2g} = S\,dL + (D + dD) + \left(\frac{V^2}{2g} + d\frac{V^2}{2g}\right) \tag{66}$$

$$dL = \frac{d(D + V^2/2g)}{(i - S)} \tag{67}$$

$$\frac{dE}{dL} = (i - S). \tag{68}$$

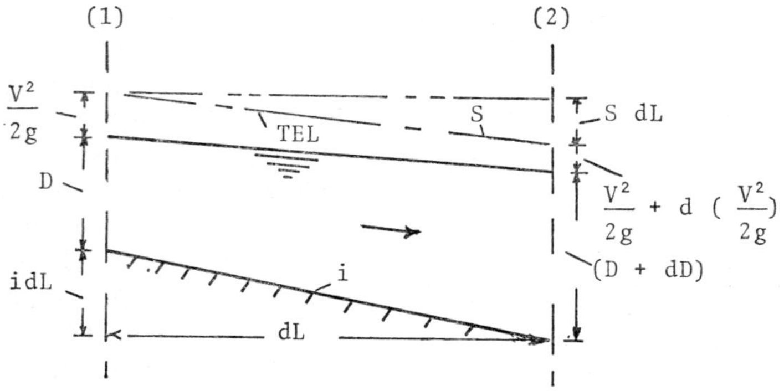

Figure 9 Non-uniform flow derivation.

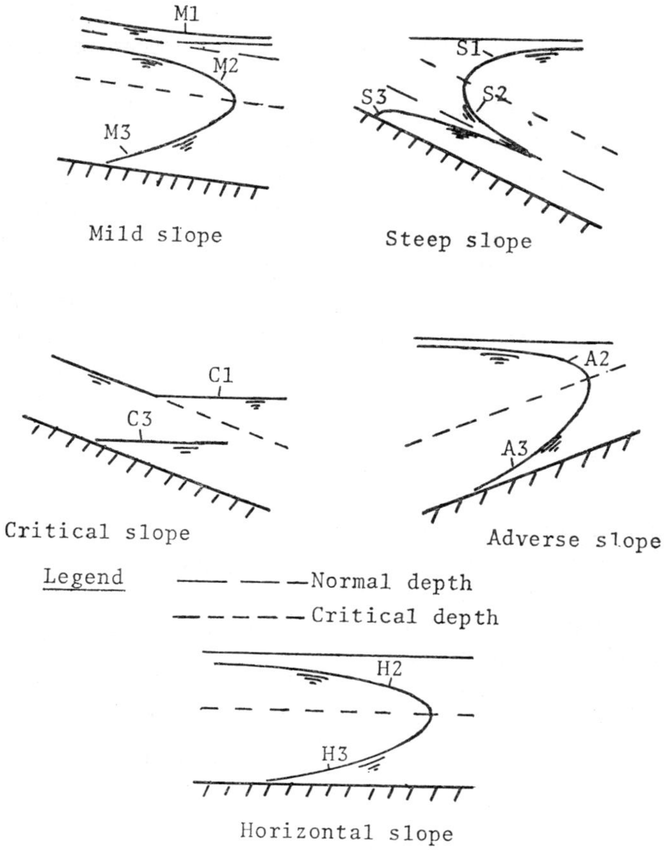

Figure 10 Surface water profiles.

For a finite length, ΔL, Equation (67) becomes:

$$\Delta L = (L_2 - L_1) = \left[\frac{(D_1 + V_1^2/2g) - (D_2 + V_2^2/2g)}{i - Q^2N^2/2.21A^2R^{4/3}}\right], \quad (69)$$

where the Manning equation is used to calculate the energy slope. Flow computation must start at a control section where all the flow parameters are known. The calculation proceeds upstream for subcritical and downstream for supercritical flow. In Equation (69), the solution of the reach length, ΔL, is direct if the immediate upstream depth, D_2, is given a value. If ΔL is given a value, D_2 has to be solved by trial. This method of computing surface water profiles is suitable for regular channels.

Classification of Flow Profiles Twelve distinct types of non-uniform profiles have been systematically classified (Fig. 10).

a) Firstly, the curves are identified according to bed slopes as mild (M), steep (S), horizontal (H), critical (C) and adverse (A).

b) Secondly, numbers are assigned to flow regions. The numeral 1 refers to actual flow depths exceeding both critical (D_c) and normal (D) depths. For flow depths less than both critical and normal, the number 3 is affixed to it. The numeral 2 is for depths intermediate between critical and normal.

Water Profiles in Irregular Channels The river channel has to be divided into panels (Fig. 11) with the side panels conveying overbank flow. Let Q = total flow, Q_c = central channel discharge, Q_l = left overbank flow, Q_r = right overbank flow. The continuity condition requires that:

$$Q = Q_c + Q_l + Q_r. \quad (70)$$

By Manning's Equation:

$$Q = \frac{1.486}{N_c} A_c R_c^{2/3} S^{1/2} + \frac{1.486}{N_l} A_l R^{2/3} S^{1/2} + \frac{1.486}{N_r} A_r R_r^{2/3} S^{1/2}. \quad (71)$$

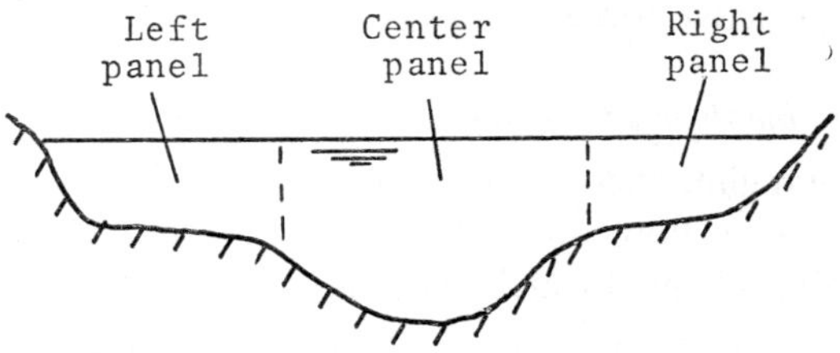

Figure 11 River channel division.

The energy slope, S, has been taken as the same for Q_c, Q_l, Q_r; this assumption seemed to be justified in practice. Due to different channel roughness, vegetative and other obstructions, Manning's N for the three flow panels would not have the same values. As the energy gradient, S, is common to the panels in Equation (71), water level versus energy slope curves can be plotted for any selected discharge for water level computations. The energy equation for the step method of surface profile calculation can conveniently be written in the form:

$$WL_2 + \frac{1}{2g}\frac{Q^2}{A_2^2} = WL_1 + \frac{1}{2g}\frac{Q^2}{A_1^2} + \bar{S}L_{1,2}. \quad (72)$$

If, in practice, the change in kinetic head, $(Q^2/2g A_2^2 - Q^2/2gA_1^2)$, is small and could be removed from Equation (72), this would greatly simplify the work. In determining the wetted perimeter for the calculation of the hydraulic radius, only the water–channel contact lines are relevant and the water–water contact lines between panels are excluded.

Flow in Erodible Channels

Introduction

Flow in erodible channels can be divided into two types, namely, canal and river flows. Blench describes canal flow as possessing three degrees of freedom due to its ability to adjust itself with respect to its flow depth, bed slope, and side widths which are taken to be the dependent variables. River flow, in addition to having the three degrees of freedom of canals, has a fourth degree by virtue of its ability to meander. It is assumed that constant maintenance of canals suppresses the canals tendency to meander. The water–sediment flow is usually regarded as the independent parameter.

In the concept of flow in mobile channels where the transport of sediment is an integral part of the system, two philosophies have emerged. Based on the work of Lindley (1919), Lacey (1952), Inglis (1949), and Blench (1953, 1966) in India and Pakistan, the regime theory has evolved. On the other hand, the United States Bureau of Reclamation under the direction of Lane (1952, 1953) developed the tractive force method.

Regime theory for canals

The regime theory postulates that for given water–sediment flow and bed material, there exists a regime channel which determines uniquely the flow area, cross-sectional shape and bed slope. The regime channel is considered a stable channel which on the average will neither silt nor scour. The flow occupying the regime channel is the dominant discharge and it is also variously referred to as the formative, regime, or bank-full discharge.

Lacey's Equations Based on extensive flow observations of the canals in India, Lacey (1952) proposed a set of formulae for alluvial channels with sandy mobile beds with the discharge ranging from 25 cfs to 2500 cfs, the bed material size varying from 0.2 mm to 0.6 mm and with the quantity of solids conveyed being less than 50 ppm:

Wetted perimeter: $$P = 2.67\, Q^{1/2} \quad (73)$$

Flow area: $$A = \frac{1.25\, Q^{5/6}}{f^{1/3}} \quad (74)$$

Bed Slope: $$S = \frac{0.000547\, f^{5/3}}{Q^{1/6}} \quad (75)$$

Silt factor: $$f = 8d_{\text{inch}}^{1/2}. \quad (76)$$

From the above equations, the following two equations can be derived:

Mean velocity: $$V = 0.895\, f^{1/3}\, Q^{1/6}$$

Flow depth: $$D = \frac{0.473\, Q^{1/3}}{f^{1/3}}. \quad (77)$$

Blench's Equations Blench (1953, 1966) using the concept that canals possessing three degrees of freedom must, therefore, have three basic equations to describe their motion, presented the stream equations for small bed load as:

$$\frac{V^2}{D} = F_b \quad (78)$$

$$\frac{V^3}{B} = F_s \quad (79)$$

$$\frac{V^2}{gDS} = 3.63\,(VB/\nu)^{1/4}. \quad (80)$$

In Equation (78), F_b is the bed factor and the equation itself expresses the statement that channels with similar water–sediment flows tend towards the same Froude number in relation to a suitable depth. Equation (79) describes the scouring action on the hydraulically smooth sides and defines the side factor, F_s. The dissipation of energy per unit mass of water per unit time in the channel is given by Equation (80) in which S is the energy gradient.

For appreciable bed load, Equation (80) becomes:

$$\frac{V^2}{gDS} = 3.63\left(1 + \frac{C}{233}\right)\left(\frac{VB}{\nu}\right)^{1/4}, \quad (81)$$

where C is the bed load charge in parts per hundred thousand by weight of fluid discharge.

The bed factor, F_b, for sand for subcritical flow is given by the empirical equations:

$$F_b = F_{b0}(1 + 0.12\,C) \qquad (82)$$

$$F_{b0} = 1.9\sqrt{d_{mm}} \qquad (83)$$

in which F_{b0} = zero bed factor and is the value of F_b when C tends to zero, d_{mm} = median bed material size by weight in millimeter. As a guide to the value of the side factor, F_s, the following table has been suggested by Blench (1966):

TABLE 9
Values of the Bed Factor

Material	$(F_s)_{max}$	Remarks
Very sandy loam banks	0.1	Erosion if > $(F_s)_{max}$
Silty clay loam	0.2	Erosion if > $(F_s)_{max}$
Very cohesive banks	0.3	Erosion if > $(F_s)_{max}$

Tractive force method for Canals

Unit Tractive Force The stability of an erodible channel depends on (a) the resistance of the material lining the bottom and sides against the erosive force of the stream and (b) the ability of the stream to transport the sediment load without giving rise to significant deposition.

The shear or drag force exerted by the water on the bed and sides of the channel is termed the tractive force. The average unit tractive force, τ, in uniform flow is the component of the gravity force acting on the water parallel to the channel bottom per unit area, thus:

$$\tau = \gamma RS. \qquad (84)$$

For wide channels, the flow depth can replace the hydraulic radius:

$$\tau = \gamma DS. \qquad (85)$$

The distribution of tractive force has been investigated by the United States Bureau of Reclamation (Lane, 1953, 1952; Olsen and Florey, 1951, 1952). The maximum values of the unit tractive force for the bottom and sides of rectangular and trapezoidal cross-sections are given in Fig. 12.

Tractive Force Ratio A soil particle of effective area, A_e, resting on the side of a channel is acted on by the tractive force, $A_e\tau_s$, in the direction of the flow and the gravity force component, $W_s \sin\phi$ which attempts to cause the particle to roll down the side slope, where τ_s = unit tractive force on the side of the channel, W_s = submerged weight of the particle, ϕ = angle of the channel side. The resultant of these two forces, F, is:

$$F = (W_s^2 \sin^2\phi + A_e^2\,\tau_s^2)^{1/2}. \qquad (86)$$

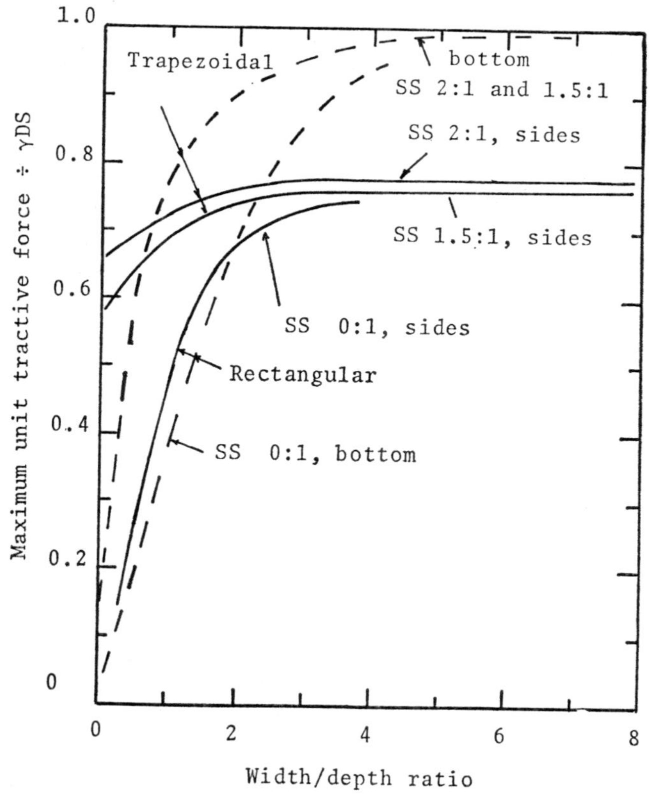

Figure 12 Maximum tractive force.

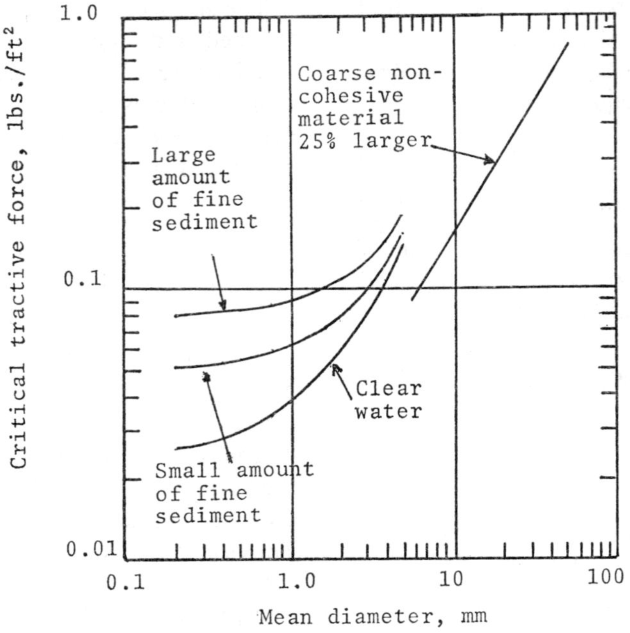

Figure 13 Critical tractive force for canals.

The motion of the particle is resisted by its frictional force (R):

$$R = W_s \cos\phi \tan\theta, \tag{87}$$

where $\tan\theta$ is the coefficient of friction and θ is the angle of repose of the material.

Equating Equation (86) and (87) for the condition of impending motion and solving for τ_s:

$$\tau_s = \frac{W_r}{A_e}\cos\phi \tan\theta \left(1 - \frac{\tan^2\phi}{\tan^2\theta}\right). \tag{88}$$

A similar equation can be written for the case of a particle on a level bed when motion is impending, thus:

$$\tau_l = \frac{W_r}{A_e}\tan q, \tag{89}$$

where τ_l denotes the unit tractive force on the level bed.

The tractive force ratio, K, is defined as, τ_s/τ_l, is obtained by dividing Equation (87) by Equation (88) and simplifying:

$$K = (1 - \sin^2\phi/\sin^2\theta)^{1/2}. \tag{90}$$

From Equation (89) it can be seen that the tractive force ratio, K, is a function of the side slope and angle of repose of the material only.

Critical Tractive Force The permissible tractive force is the maximum unit tractive force that will not cause significant scour of the material lining the channel bed on a level surface. It is often found from laboratory observations and is known as the critical tractive force. It is influenced by the amount of organic matter and fine suspended sediment in the water. The effect of the fine sediment is to increase the allowable critical tractive force. Fig. 13 shows curves of permissible tractive forces as recommended by the United States Bureau of Reclamation.

River engineering

In river flows, a greater number and range of factors have to be considered in addition to those parameters used in the analysis of canals. These variables include bigger size bed materials, large suspended and bed sediment loads, unsteady and a wide variation of flood flows, meandering and braiding, large changes in stream channel cross-sections, obstructions to flow, and other factors involved. An analysis of river engineering is, therefore, beyond the scope of this chapter. Readers are recommended to consult the works of Blench (1966), Shen (1971, 1972), Inglis (1949), and Leopold, Wolman and Miller (1964). More specialised treatment of sediment transport, bedforms and stream geometry can be found in the publications of Einstein (1972), Leopold and Maddock (1953), Richardson and Simons (1967), Yalin (1971), Kennedy (1963), Christensen (1972), and Ackers (1964). Standard texts which covers the subject more formally include those of Graf (1971), Henderson (1966), Raudkivi (1967) and Leliasky (1955).

BIBLIOGRAPHY

Ackers, P., Experiments on small streams in alluvium, Proceedings, *American Society of Civil Engineers Journal*, Hydraulics Division, **90**, no. HY4, pp. 1–37, July 1964.

Albertson, M. L., J. R. Barton and D. B. Simons, *Fluid Mechanics for Engineers*, Prentice-Hall, Inc., Englewood Cliffs, N. J., 1961

Allen, J. and S. P. Chee, The resistance to the flow of water round a smooth circular bend in an open channel, Proceedings, Institution of Civil Engineers, London, Vol. 23, pp. 423–434, November 1962.

Blench, T, Regime theory equations applied to a tidal river estuary, Proceedings, Minnesota International Hydraulics Convention I.A.H.R. and A.S.C.E. Joint Meeting, pp. 77–83, September 1953.

Blench, T., "Mobile-Bed Fluviology," University of Alberta, 1966.

Chow, Ven Te, *Open-Channel Hydraulics*, McGraw-Hill Book Company, Inc., New York, 1959.

Christensen, B. A., Incipient motion on cohesionless banks, Chapter 4 in Shen, Hsieh Wen, *Sedimentation*, Colorado, 1972.

Einstein, H. A., The bed load function for sediment transportation in open channel flows, Technical Bulletin No. 1026, U.S. Department of Agriculture, Soil Conservation Service, September 1950. Also reprinted in Appendix B in Shen, Hsieh Wen, *Sedimentation*, Colorado, 1972.

Graf, W. H., *Hydraulics of Sediment Transport*, McGraw-Hill Book Company, New York, 1971.

Henderson, F. M., *Open Channel Flow*, The Macmillan Company, New York, 1966.

Inglis, C. C., The behavior and control of river and canals, Research Publication No. 13, Central Waterpower Irrigation and Navigation Research Station, Poona, 1949.

Kennedy, J. F., The mechanics of dunes and antidunes in erodible bed channels, *J. Fluid Mechanics*, **16**, part 4, 1963.

King, H. W., *Handbook of Hydraulics*, McGraw-Hill Book Company Inc., New York, 1954.

Lacey, G., Flow in alluvial channels with sandy mobile beds, Proceedings, Institution of Civil Engineers, London, Vol. 9, pp. 145–164, 1952.

Lane, E. W., Progress report on studies on the design of channels by the Bureau of Reclamation, Proceedings, American Society of Civil Engineers, Irrigation and Drainage Division, Vol. 79. pp. 280–1–280–31, September 1953.

Lane, E. W., Progress report on results on design of stable channels, U.S. Bureau of Reclamation, Hydraulic Laboratory Report No. Hyd–352, June 1952.

Leliavsky, Serge, *An Introduction to Fluvial Hydraulics*, Constable and Co. Ltd., London, 1955.

Loepold, L. B. and T. Maddock, Jr., The hydraulic geometry of stream channels and some physiographic implications, U.S. Geological Survey, Professional Paper 252, 1953.

Leopold, L. B., M. G. Wolman and J. P. Miller, *Fluvial Process in Geomorphology*, W. H. Freeman and San Francisco, 1964.

Lindley, E. S., Regime channels, Minutes of Proceedings, Punjab Engineering Congress, Lahore, India, Vol. 7, pp. 63–74, 1919.

Moody, L. F., Friction factors for pipe flow, *Trans. ASME.*, **66**, No. 8, 1944.

Morris, H. M., *Applied Hydraulics in Engineering*, The Ronald Press Company, New York, 1963.

Olsen, O. J. and Q. L. Florey (compilers), Stable Channel Profiles, Hydraulic Laboratory Report No. Hyd–325, U. S. Bureau of Reclamation, 1951.

Olsen, O. J. and Q. L. Florey (compilers), Sedimentation Studies in open channels: boundary shear and velocity distribution by membrane analogy, analytical and finite difference methods, U. S. Bureau of Reclamation, Laboratory Report No. Sp–34, 1952.

Raudkivi, A. J., *Loose Boundary Hydraulics*, Pergamon Press, Oxford, 1967.

Richardson, E. V. and D. B. Simons, Resistance to flow in sand channels, Twelfth Congress, I.A.H.R., Vol. 1, pp. 141–150, 1967.

Rouse, H., Editor, *Engineering Hydraulics*, John Wiley and Sons, Inc., New York, 1950.

Shen, Hsieh Wen, Editor, *River Mechanics*, Vols. I and II, Colorado, 1971.

Shen, Hsieh Wen, Editor, *Sedimentation: Symposium to honour Professor H. A. Einstein*, Colorado, 1972.

Streeter, S. L., *Fluid Mechanics*, McGraw-Hill Book Company, New York, 1966.

United States Bureau of Reclamation, "Design of Small Dams," U.S. Printing Office, 1961.

Yalin, M. S., On the formation of dunes and meanders, Paper C–13, Proceedings Fourteenth Congress, I.A.H.R., Vol. 3, 1971.

S. P. Chee

University of Windsor

WATER: PROPERTIES, STRUCTURE AND OCCURRENCE IN NATURE

1. The Cycle of Water—Structure and Properties

The origin of the hydrosphere

The assumption that the elemental composition originally present in all regions of the solar system was similar to that currently present in the sun furnishes a paradox in the marked deficiency of the unreactive noble gases, such as neon and argon, on the planet earth. Thus it is assumed that these gases, as well as those of comparable molecular weight such as water, nitrogen, oxygen and carbon dioxide, escaped from the earth's surface before the planet cooled down. Thus the accumulation of the water necessary to form the hydrosphere by condensation of any primordial envelope of steam is inconsistent with the conditions of the primitive earth.

Rather, degassing, after the formation of the earth, is considered to be the mechanism through which the "excess volatiles" of water, nitrogen, chlorine, etc. accumulated on the earth's surface. According to Rubey, if only 1% of the water emerging from hot springs and related phenomena is truly juvenile water, then this process would have been sufficient to produce the oceans and hence the hydrosphere.

The hydrologic cycle and solar energy

The dynamic equilibrium or steady state existing between evaporation, precipitation, percolation, and runoff comprises the hydrologic cycle.

Except for the small amount of radioactive energy and heat transfer from within the earth, the sun provides the energy to run this complex cycle by evaporating surface water and heating the humid air, which then results in stirring of the weather systems. Four-fifths of the solar energy radiating toward the earth actually reaches the earth's surface. This incoming energy totals 1.6×10^{18} watts, about one-third of which recharges the hydrologic cycle by vaporization. Under normal conditions it requires about 540 calories per gram to evaporate water.

Evaporation

Of the 3.61×10^{20} grams per year evaporated from the sea, approximately 90% is returned directly to the ocean in the various forms of precipitation. The remaining 10% is transported in the atmosphere and eventually released on the land masses, as illustrated in Figure 1.

Evaporation from the land, 6.21×10^{19} gms per year, is dependent on the soil and climatic conditions. It is strongly influenced by the relative humidity. For a given atmospheric water content, the relative humidity increases and the evaporation decreases as the temperature falls. Wind enhances evaporation by continually removing the vaporized water and thus locally lowering the relative humidity. With all other factors equal, sea water containing 3.5% salts will evaporate 3.5% more slowly than fresh water. Barometric pressure has little direct effect on the rates of evaporation.

Transpiration

Water loss from land is enhanced by the transpiration process by which plants and other photosynthetic organisms draw solutions containing essential growth nutrients from the soil to provide for maintenance and growth. The excess fluid is exuded to the atmosphere through the mesophyll cells. From 97 to 99% of the water which enters plants from soil is lost by evaporation from the leaves. The amount of dry matter produced in grams per 1000 grams of water transpired is called the transpiration efficiency. Odum has estimated typical efficiencies to be 2 or less, with drought-resistant crops such as sorghum and millet having only slightly higher values. An acre of red maple trees in a soil with ample moisture may lose water sufficient to cover the acre with 0.7 meter of water during a single growing season. Transpiration is

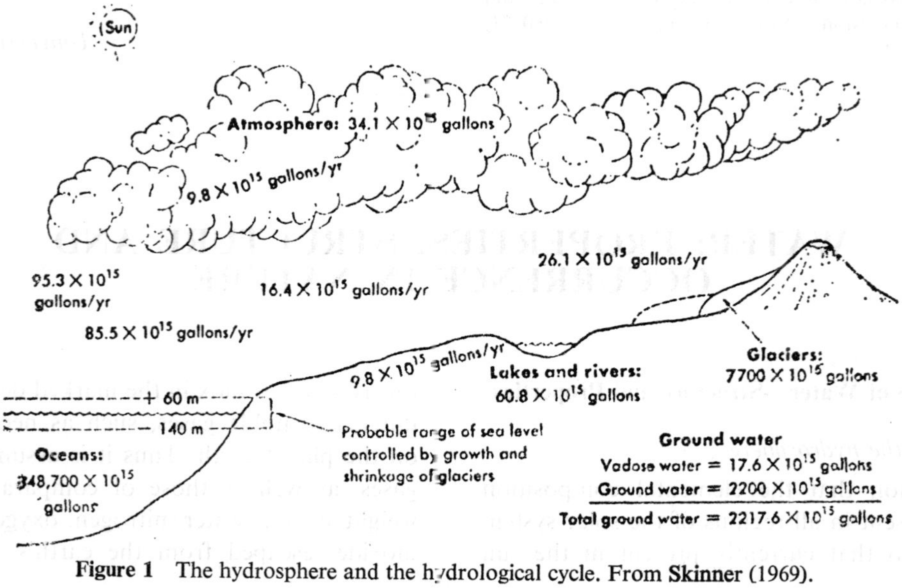

Figure 1 The hydrosphere and the hydrological cycle. From **Skinner** (1969).

also affected by the factors governing evaporation, as well as light and soil conditions.

Atmospheric water

The water in the atmosphere amounts to 1.29×10^{19} grams or approximately one-tenth of that in all fresh water lakes and is responsible for the pressure differences which create weather. It has been estimated that without this atmospheric water blanket, radiational cooling would reduce the earth's average surface temperature from 15°C to about 0°C. Low humidity desert environments often experience temperatures of 65°C during the day and below freezing at night. Under ordinary conditions the water vapor in the air allows only 20% of the earth's surface heat to radiate back through the atmosphere directly. As previously mentioned it is through the atmosphere that fresh water evaporated from the sea is transported over the global land masses.

Precipitation

Precipitation of atmospheric moisture occurs only when the temperature of an air mass is lowered to or below the point of saturation, the dew point. Air temperature is lowered by combinations of the following phenomena:

1) heat loss by infrared radiation,

2) adiabatic cooling as large air masses expand under reduced pressure after they have risen or been lifted to higher altitudes and

3) temperature decrease due to mixing with cooler air masses.

During the condensation of water the heat of vaporization, 540 cals. per gram is released. Various mechanisms of coalescence account for the different forms of precipitation such as rain, snow, hail and sleet. Condensation at ground level is responsible for the formation of dew, frost, and rime or hoarfrost.

The unequal worldwide distribution of precipitation, which varies from 0 to 10 meters per-year, is determined to a large extent by the movement of large air masses or weather systems as directed by the profiles of mountain ranges.

The total precipitation, its annual distribution and the balance between precipitation and evapotranspiration are the chief limiting factors that determine the resulting climax biotic communities for terrestrial ecosystems. The following average annual precipitations are general biotic determinants: 0 to 10 inches, deserts; 10 to 30 inches, grass lands, savanna or open woodland; 30 to 50 inches, dry forest; and greater than 50 inches, wet forest. Thus the supply of water not only severely limits man's own agricultural, domestic, and industrial activities, but also dictates the products of nature. As ecologists have pointed out, the availability of water, more than any other factor, determines the ultimate population of a geographic province.

The influence on the earth is affected not only by the quantity of water which reaches the land masses from the sea but also by the natural processes which follow. Some precipitation is intercepted directly by the flora and soon evaporates. Some rainfall may never reach the ground. For example, in hot deserts rain on its downward flight through warm dry air often completely re-evaporates.

Runoff and ground water

Precipitation reaching the surface at rates greater than those of infiltration, evaporation, and surface retention, will flow overland in drainage systems which may eventually reach the sea. This overflow is termed runoff. Although the 8.33×10^{21} grams of ground water which exists is a massive quantity, it moves too slowly to act as a significant transport process in the overall hydrologic cycle. In fact, rapid withdrawal from the ground at a given site can cause serious local depletion.

Water from the hydrocycle which infiltrates into the ground water systems extracts soluble mineral matter from soil, sand and rock. According to King, "Water partakes of and is conditioned by the character of the land on which it falls, and through which it flows."

Hydrologic weathering

These surface and subsurface waters weather natural geologic formations through physical, chemical and biological means. Physical weathering of formations is the initial mechanical weathering action which, through cycles of freezing and thawing, mechanical stress reversals, and swelling and contracting, exposes rock and mineral surfaces to chemical weathering processes.

Chemical weathering results from changes in the chemical environments surrounding the minerals: i.e., from environments conducive to their formation to those in which they are no longer thermodynamically stable. Specifically, these are chemical conditions which subject the minerals to hydrolysis, oxidation and reaction with aqueous carbon dioxide. The minerals also react with weak organic acids, which can be considered biological weathering, since these acids result from the microbially mediated decay of biomass. Whereas surface runoff streams erode, transport and eventually deposit much of their suspended weathering products in river beds on the ocean, the dissolved species generally remain in solution.

Global ice

Most of the earth's fresh water exists as ice in glaciers and in ice sheets, which together comprise about 2% of the earth's total water and which cover about 10% of the earth's land masses with thicknesses of up to several thousand feet. These solid forms may well be the most potent of the agencies that have changed and shaped the surface of the earth, according to King. Their mass causes the land to sink and their physical force performs erosion, transport and deposition of mineral matter.

Ocean currents

Water eventually returns to the sea with the wastes of nature such as dissolved minerals and suspended matter and, ever more significantly, also the wastes of man. To the sea belongs 97% of the planet's water. The sea is not a stagnant reservoir; instead it contains large "rivers" such as the Gulf Stream which convey hugh masses of water and perhaps more important great quantities of heat. For example, if the temperature difference between the warm current of the Gulf Stream and the cold receiving waters is 20°F then each cubic mile of water can transfer about 2×10^{14} BTU.

Determinants of physico-chemical properties

The properties of water and its interactions with other substances are in a class by themselves. The chief contributant to the anomalous physical characteristics of water and to many of its chemical properties is its powerful intermolecular forces, with which it attracts not only its own molecules, but also those of many other substances. The major intermolecular attractive force of water is hydrogen bonding, which in turn results from the nature of the chemical bonds holding the atoms of the individual water molecule together.

There are two well-founded approaches toward an explanation of physico-chemical properties. The first, a deductive procedure, considers in detail the balance between intramolecular and intermolecular attractive and repulsive energies. The other, a more statistical approach, makes use of thermodynamic principles that have been developed by inductive methods.

Electrostatic Interactions in chemical bonding

The strength of a chemical bond is a function of the electron affinity of the atoms. If a bond forms between two atoms the total energy of the constituent atoms must be lower when the atoms are near each other. The bond is established one or more electrons come under the electrostatic attraction of two or more positive nuclei simultaneously. This phenomenon is quantized by the Coulomb law, which is the fundamental priciple of chemical bonding. The Coulomb force varies with the product of the charges and inversely with the square of the distance between them; the energy, being the integral of force with distance, is inversely proportional to the distance.

The repulsion of the electrons for each other and that of the nuclei also enter into the total energy balance and prevent very close approach of the two atoms. The mobility of the electrons allows them to assume positions closer to both nuclei than to each other, thereby reducing their mutual repulsion. The resulting repulsive force between the electronic fields of two atoms is inversely proportional approximately to the 10th power of the distance between the atoms.

Electron orbitals

Since the electrons surrounding the nucleus do not all have the same energy level, they are divided into quantum shells, with those shells closest to the nucleus having the lowest energies. The electrons of each quantum shell are associated with subshells, in which the spatial description of the electron motion is called an orbital. The energy of each electron is constantly changing back and forth so that only its probable radial position can be indicated. This probable position is affected if the electron comes under the influence of other nuclei. It is the electrons of the outer quantum shell which enter into chemical bonding. For an atom with no more than eight electrons in its outer shell, the *s* orbital of this shell will contain two electrons, whose distribution probability is spherical with respect to the nucleus. If there are more than two electrons in the outer shell, the remaining electrons will be found in the *p* orbitals, where the distribution probability lies along the orthogonal axes.

Directional bonds and molecular architecture

The shape of a molecule depends on the directional characteristics of the bonding orbitals involved in the bonds. For example, no bonding yields a monatomic molecule, an *s* bonding orbital gives a linear diatomic molecule and *sp* bonding orbitals result in a linear triatomic molecule. When two or three *p* orbitals are involved in the bonding of two or three other atoms to a given atom the angle between the bonds is expected to be about 90° except as modified by steric considerations. Thus, the angles of H_2O with p^2 bonding and for NH_3 with p^3 bonding are 104.5 and 107, respectively.

Covalent bonds

Chemical bonds are categorized into covalent bonds, ionic bonds and metallic bonds. Covalent bonding results from the sharing of pairs of outer electrons, as occurs in the bonds of oxygen to the hydrogen atoms in the water molecule. In a purely covalent bond the two nuclei have equivalent electron affinities such that the stable electronic distribution is symmetrical. The interatomic bond distance between two atoms tends to be smaller as the number of electrons constituting the covalent bond increases. For example, the bond distances for F—F, O=O and N≡N are 1.46, 1.30 and 1.10 Angstroms, respectively. Typical covalent bond energies do not vary by more than a factor of two from 100 kilocalories per gram-mole, which corresponds to an energy of 4.34 electron-volts. For example, the bond energies for C—C, C=C, C≡C and O—H are 83, 146, 185, 111 kilocalories per gram-mole, respectively.

Ionic bonds

An ionic bond results from the predominant displacement of both electrons toward one atom; the model of the ionic bond considers that one or more electrons of one atom, the cation, are given up to the other atom, the anion. The strength of an ionic bond is determined in large part by the ionization energies of the two atoms. The ionization energy or ionization potential is defined as that energy required to separate an electron from the gaseous atom. Ionization energies increase in traversing the periodic table from left to right. Thus the ionization energies for lithium and fluorine are 124.3 and 401.5 kilocalories per gram-mole, respectively. Ionization energies decrease in progressing down a given column of the periodic table since, as the size of the atom increases, the distance between the outer electron and the nuclear charge increases. Ionic bonds are stronger between atoms of different ionization energies. The ionization energies for removal of successive electrons from an atom increases and the resultant cations become progressively smaller since the positive nucleus become proportionately stronger than the electron cloud. For example, the effective sizes of Fe, Fe^{2+} and Fe^{3+} are 1.24, 0.83 and 0.67 Angstron, respectively. Conversely, as an atom gains electrons, its anions become larger since the additional electrons are not attached as strongly as the original electrons. Ionic bond energies vary from low values up to about 100 kilocalories per gram-mole.

Bonds of mixed character

The foregoing discussion shows that the covalency or ionicity of a chemical bond is the result of the electronic distributions around the two atoms and that the character of the bond could be intermediate between the two categories. Thus, a covalent bond is to be expected when the ionization energies of the two atoms are similar but where the bonding electrons are not shared equally, e.g., in a molecule of two atoms with different ionization energies, the bond becomes partially ionic. Ionic bonds which are slightly covalent are also possible. In chemical seactions, which are based upon the interaction of outer shell electrons, ionic bonds are generally favored over covalent bonds since lower energy systems are more stable.

Metallic bonds

Metallic bonds form in metallic solids and liquids due to the free electrons which are simultaneously near two or more positive nuclei. The fact that metals have low ionization energies gives rise to these free electrons which form an electron cloud throughout the condensed phase, thereby holding the positively charged metal atoms together. In a sense, the metallic bond can be considered to be a non-directional covalent bond. The mobility of these electrons endows metals with high electrical and thermal conductivity compared with ionic and covalent substances. Also, since the energies of the visible spectrum correspond to the ionization potentials of metals, light is easily absorbed by metallic electrons. For example, 100 kilocalories per gram-mole corresponds to electromagnetic energy with a wavelength of 2860 Angstroms.

Oxidation potentials

Oxidation potentials result from the gaseous ionization potentials as modified by the particular surroundings. For example, the difference in ionization potentials of lithium and fluorine is about 12 electron-volts, whereas the difference in their oxidation potentials in a 1 molar aqueous solution is only 5.9 volts. The reason for this is that electrons are more easily removed in some environments than in others. Thus, iron rust results when oxygen reacts with the electrons of iron only after water molecules have shifted these electrons away from the iron nucleus and effectively lowered the energy needed to remove them. Oxidation potentials, sometimes expressed as electrode potentials, depend therefore on both the nature of the species and the nature of the solution. Electrode potentials are usually tabulated for species in contact with 1 molar aqueous solutions of their corresponding ions.

Coordination numbers

Non-metallic condensed phases can result from ionic bonds, where the exchange of electrons holds ionic solids together in crystals structures, and from covalent bonds in such substances as diamond The number of nearest neighbors of an atom in a condensed phase is called the coordination number. For covalent solids the coordination number depends on the number of orbital bonds that can be formed around the atom, whereas for ionic solids it is governed by the packing efficiency. Various atomic radii ratios of pairs of atoms favor different coordination numbers for the solid lattice. As the ratio increases from 0.155 to 1.0, the coordination number increases from 3 to 4 to 6 to 8 to 12. An increasing number of adjacent atoms decreases the attraction to any specific atom and thereby increases interatomic distances. Generally a crystalline solid has a more efficient packing factor than the liquid so that shrinkage occurs as the liquid freezes. Exceptions can occur in substances which develop strong directional bonds within the crystal.

Complex ions

Dissolved species can also become coordinated in solution due to ionic or covalent bonding to form complex ions. The species bonded to the central ion are known as ligands. The effect that a group of substances in solution has on the colligative properties and on solution conductance can help to determine whether given ions exist as complex ions or as separate ionized species. Attachment of uncharged ligands will decrease the mobility and lower the conductance of the larger complex ion relative to the unencumbered free ion. Ligands possessing a charge will have a more complicated effect.

The coordination number, which is indicative of the geometry of the complex ion depends upon the atomic sizes and, in the case of covalent bonds, upon which orbital electrons are available for bonding. Thus, an octahedral complex ion with a coordination number of 6 has six ligands at the ends of three orthogonal axes and a coordination number of 4 is indicative of either a tetrahedral complex ion with the coordinated ligands at the vertices of a tetrahedron or a square planar configuration. Transition elements, which have several electrons in the outermost orbitals with low ionization energies, are especially subject to the formation of a great variety of complex ions with various types and numbers of ligands.

Dipoles

The existence of the liquid and solid forms of many substances, including a large proportion of the covalently bound molecules, the coordinated forms of many species in solution such as solvated or hydrated ions and certain weak organo-metallic complexes depends upon intermolecular attractions weaker than the three types of chemical bonding. These so-called physical bonds, the Van der Waals bonds and the hydrogen bond, depend upon the electrical dipoles set up throughout the entire molecule.

Molecular polarization

The molecular dipole results from the sum of the dipoles of all the bonds. A permanent dipole or molecular polarization exists in any asymmetric molecule due to the permanent asymmetric electron distribution. The dipole moment, μ, or dipole strength, is due to the separation of the centers of positive and negative charges at equilibrium and is thus influenced by the ionic character of the bonds and the shape of the molecule.

Molecules possessing permanent dipole moments are termed polar molecules.

Electronic polarization

A momentary dipole or electronic polarization results from the random movement of the electrons. These rapidly varying dipole moments, which oscillate at the frequency of electronic movements (10^{15} to 10^{16} per second), give rise to the electronic dispersion energy. The dispersion effect is dependent upon the polarizability, α, of the atoms and is greater for large atoms where the outer electron shell is more displaceable due to the smaller influence of the nuclear charge. The polarizability is thus related to the ionization potential of the atoms.

These polarizations are made evident in the response of materials to electrical fields in the measurement of such bulk properties as dielectric constant and index of refraction, both of which vary with the frequency of the field. At high frequencies, polar groups of molecules cannot respond and the dielectric constant decreases to that resulting from the electronic polarization alone.

Van der Waals forces

Electrical dipoles have a strong effect on the forces between molecules. These dipole forces manifest themselves in the Van der Waals attractions, which are the major intermolecular forces within substances whose condensed phases are not structured with atoms possessing definite coordination numbers.

The Van der Waals bond can be considered the attraction of one molecule's nucleus for another molecule's electrons. Several types of Van der Waals forces are distinguished depending upon the nature of the electrical dipoles.

Keesom forces result from the orientation energy arising between particles both possessing permanent dipole moments. Its relation with the dipole moment and particle separation is proportional to μ^4/r^6. The Debye attraction results from the induction energy set up between a permanent molecular dipole and a dipole induced in another molecule by the field of the permanent dipole. Its magnitude varies with the polarizability of the atoms of the molecule in which the dipole is induced. The Debye attraction is thus proportional to $\mu^2 \alpha/r^6$. The London exchange forces have their origin in the dispersion energy which results from the instantaneous dipole moments as the electrons spin around the nucleus. The rapidly varying dipole in one molecule furnishes an electric field which polarizes other atoms and thus induces other dipoles. The attractive force so produced depends upon the polarizability of both particles and is proportional to α^2/r^6. It is the existence of London dispersion forces which explains the cohesion of molecules which have no dipole moment, such as the liquifaction of helium.

The Keesom and Debye effects are a consequence of classical physical concepts whereas the London attraction is a quantum mechanical effect. The London force is stronger than the Keesom attraction except for very polar molecules like water and ammonia. The Debye effect is always very small. For small molecules the order of magnitude of the Van der Waals energies is 1 kilocalorie per mole. For normal hydrocarbons the Van der Waals energy is about 1 kilocalorie per carbon atom and accounts for the increase in melting point and boiling point with molecular weight. It is thus impossible for hydrocarbons of more than 80 carbon atoms to exist as vapor since an energy of 80 kilocalories necessary to separate the molecules corresponds to that required to break a carbon–carbon bond. Since the strength of the Van der Waals bonds falls off so rapidly with distance ($1/r^6$), their effect is restricted to nearest neighbors.

The permanent dipoles, which give rise to the Keesom and Debye attractions, are weakened by increased temperature. The mean thermal energy at 300°K, 0.025 electron-volt, is sufficient to counteract some of the weak Van der Waals bonds. However, the London dispersion forces are not affected by temperature since the frequencies of infrared vibrations, about 10^{23} cycles per second at room temperature, are much smaller than the frequencies of the orbiting electrons responsible for the instantaneous dipoles.

Hydrogen bonds

Hydrogen bonding is a special case of dipole–dipole interaction resulting from the molecular polarization when the hydrogen atom is covalently bonded to a highly electronegative atom. Such a condition produces a large dipole moment by displacing the electrons of the shared bond, which includes the sole electron of the hydrogen atom, toward the negative atom and gives a strong partial ionogencity to the bond and a strong positive character to the hydrogen atom. This leaves an intense unshielded electric field on the other side of the hydrogen nucleus which can attract the unshared electrons of the negative atoms of other molecules. Within the hydrogen bond, the polarly bound hydrogen is termed a proton donor and the negative atom of the other molecule is described as the acceptor.

The small size of the hydrogen nucleus or proton allows a relatively close approach of other atoms, especially of those which are also small. Thus, the strongest hydrogen bonds, sometimes called hydrogen bridges, occur with the electronegative atoms of the first row of the periodic table. The strength decreases in the order of fluorine, oxygen and nitrogen. Thus, OH is a stronger proton donor than NH so that hydrogen bonding gives rise to $HOH \ldots NH_3$ in preference to $H_2O \ldots HNH_2$. This implies that NH_3(aq) exists in preference to NH_4OH. The hydrogen bonding in hydrogen fluoride is so strong that this compound remains associated even in the vapor state. Much weaker attractions occur with elements in the second row as is manifested by the lower boiling points of HCl, H_2S and PH_3 when compared, respectively with HF, H_2O and NH_3. When hydrogen bonding becomes non-existent in this analog, SiH_4 is found to have a higher boiling point than CH_4, consistent with their relative molecular weights when no special interactions are present.

Typical energies of hydrogen bonds vary between 3 and 6 kilocalories per mole. Since formation of the bond is exothermal due to the strong volume contraction, its strength decreases with increasing temperature. This effect is especially noticeable at ordinary temperatures since $3/2\,RT$, the average translational energy, at 300°K is about 1 kilocalorie per mole, thereby approaching the value of hydrogen bond energies. The covalent bond of the proton involved in the hydrogen bond is somewhat weakened due to the electrostatic attraction of the acceptor atom involved in the hydrogen bond, through the proton still remains closer to the atom with which it shares an electron pair than to that with which it has the hydrogen bridge. This bond stretching is manifested by frequency shifts in the absorption spectra of nuclear magnetic resonance, infrared and Raman spectroscopy.

Hydrogen bonding has an effect on almost every physical property. Thus intermolecular hydrogen bonding results in higher boiling and freezing points, deviation from ideal gas and solution laws and in modified dielectric properties and electrical conductivities. In addition, hydrogen bonding alters liquid and vapor densities, viscosity, surface tension, sonic velocity, and electromagnetic energy transport phenomena.

Association polymers

The possession of two or more sites available for hydrogen bonding in a molecular structure is conducive to polymer formation. Thus carboxylic acids frequently form dimers, especially since no bond deformation is required within the constituent molecules:

HOOCR

RCOOH

The effect is pronounced in non-polar solvents where competition for the proton donor and shielding of the proton by solvation are absent. The dimers of formic acid, acetic acid and other aliphatic acids have lowered dipole moments and dielectric constants due to their structure and therefore an increased solubility in non-polar solvents such as ether and benzene.

Non-stoichiometric polymerization or three-dimensional spatial ordering as occurs in water and alcohols can result in very large dielectric constants. This has the effect of augmenting the heat of evaporation and also the entropy of evaporation due to the high degree of ordering in the liquid phase. Similarly, the boiling point, viscosity and surface tension are all higher. The number of molecules in an association polymer is determined by the point at which the attractive forces are balanced by the disruptive forces due to thermal agitation. An example of this type of polymer is phenol, which forms a linear complex of over ten units and exists as a solid at room temperature. In a strongly polar solvent the dimers and other polymers exist chiefly as the monomeric species due to hydrogen bonding with the solvent; however, the amount that dissolves in these polar solvents is often much smaller than that in non-polar solvents as is the case with the fatty acids.

Intramolecular hydrogen bonding

Intramolecular hydrogen bonding results in molecules which possess two electronegative groups and which have opportune spatial orientations. When this self-chelation occurs in a dibasic acid, it lowers the dissociation constant and decreases the values of other physical properties dependent on intermolecular attraction. An interesting comparison of dibasic acids is presented by maleic acid (cis-HOOC—CH=CH—COOH), whose steric orientation allows the formation of intramolecular hydrogen bonds and thus has a lower melting point than its trans isomer, fumaric acid, which can only form intermolecular hydrogen bonds.

In aromatic compounds, intramolecular hydrogen bonds are possible only with substituents which are ortho to each other. Again, since the internal bonding diminishes the external interactions, the decreased dielectric constant of ortho compounds versus the meta and para analogs will be reflected by decreased solubility in polar solvents and increased solubility in non-polar solvents. Furthermore, the melting and boiling points will be depressed. Thus, the intramolecular hydrogen bonding in *o*-nitrophenol prevent the three-dimensional polymerization whose presence in the meta and para isomers due to intermolecular hydrogen bonding results in their disparate melting points of 45°C, 96°C, and 114°C, respectively.

Intramolecular hydrogen bonds are found in many substances present in living systems. They are especially ubiquitous in proteins, which often coil up under their action. In the double helix, the individual coils are themselves held together with hydrogen bridges. The fact that the temperatures at which living organisms exist provide thermal energies comparable to those manifested by hydrogen bonds results in a rapidly reversible equilibrium of bond formation. The action of many biochemical processes appears designed to take advantage of this sensitive equilibrium.

Dielectric constant of solvents

The dielectric constant of a substance includes the contributions of the permanent dipole of the molecule and the polarizability manifested by the momentary electronic dipoles. The inertia of the molecular dipole results in a frequency dependence for the dielectric constant.

According to Coulomb's Law, the higher the dielectric constant of the medium, the more it insulates the electrostatic interaction between charged particles and the more it enables ionic compounds to ionize and dissolve. In less polar solvents, i.e., in those of low dielectric constant, oppositely-charged ions are less free to move around since they attract each other more strongly and may form ion-pairs. The constituent ions of ion-pairs are considered to be completely ionized but incompletely dissociated and are effectively unavailable as current carriers, behaving like non-ionized molecules. An example of the effect of dielectric constant is provided by the solubility of silver iodide in water, where the dielectric constant is 80, and acetone, where the dielectric constant is 21; the respective solubility products are 10^{-16} and 10^{-22} moles^2 per liter^2. Furthermore, the solubility of the salt decreases as the fraction of acetone increases in a mixture of the two solvents.

Solvation of the solute generally tends to decrease the polarizability of the medium due to the strong orienting forces thereby applied to the solvent molecules. This can result in decrease of the dielectric constant for a medium which has a small permanent dipole moment. A solvent with a high dielectric constant and with a high capacity for solvation is a very powerful solvent for ionic compounds, since it acts both to reduce the forces between the solute ions and to increase the forces between the solute and solvent by furnishing the ions with a shell of solvent molecules, thereby making them less distinguishable from the solvent itself. Solution occurs much more readily when the solvent and solute are structurally similar.

Cohesive density

The stability of condensed phases in dependent upon intermolecular attraction, which can be quantized by means of the cohesive energy. This is defined as the heat of evaporation at constant volume; a hypothetical cohesive energy can be calculated for substances which would experience thermal decomposition before vaporization. The specific cohesion, or cohesive density, is the quotient of the cohesive energy divided by the volume. This index, which has the units of pressure, is sometimes called the internal pressure; it varies between 1000 and 10,000 atmospheres for most substances. Properties such as volatility, solubility, miscibility, viscosity, plasticity and surface tension all result from intermolecular attraction and can thus be correlated by means of the cohesive density.

Lattice energy

Where the condensed phase forms a regular structure, as in ionic compounds, the total attractive energy is known as the lattice energy, which includes all Van der Waals and electrostatic contributions. The lattice energy is defined as the energy released in forming the crystal lattice from free gaseous positive and negative ions. It is therefore proportional to the product of the charges of the ions.

The type of bond holding a solid together and thus bond strength is manifested by the melting point. Thus, ionic crystals typically have high melting points whereas those condensed phases depending on Van der Waals forces generally have low melting points.

Repulsive energies

Increase in temperature causes greater thermal vibrations of all atoms, which are manifested by the thermal expansion of the bulk material. The resultant increase in bond distances serves to counteract the intramolecular and intermolecular bonds. Thus, temperature, possessing a disaggregating effect on molecules, acts as a repulsion.

There is also an inherent repulsion due to the contact of non-bonded atoms or ions originating in the general mutual repulsion of the electrons when the electron clouds begin to penetrate each other. This effect, the Born repulsion, increases very rapidly with decreasing distance, in conformity with the model of atoms as hard spheres. Calculations of its magnitude versus distance from compressibility data show a proportionality of $1/r^9$. The total energy interaction between non-polar particles is sometimes expressed by the Lennard-Jones potential, $V = \frac{A}{r^{12}} - \frac{B}{r^6}$ where the exponent for the repulsive energy of the first term is chosen for computational simplicity. Repulsion is defined as a positive potential energy and attraction as negative.

Electronic structure of water

A model of the single isolated water molecule with its electronic cloud is shown in Figure 2. The three nuclei are surrounded by ten electrons, with

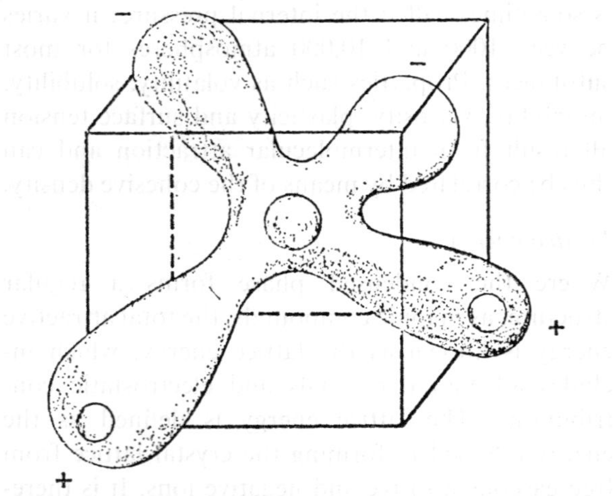

Figure 2 Single isolated water molecule with associated electronic cloud. Note the two regions of negative electrification which project above and below the H—O—H plane. From Horne (1970).

the two ls electrons of the oxygen atom confined to the vicinity of its nucleus. The other eight electrons make up the four orbitals which point to the vertices of a somewhat distorted tetrahedron. Two of the four orbitals are directed along the OH bonds and the so-called lone pair electrons constitute the remaining two orbitals, which project above and below the H—O—H molecular plane. These lone pair electrons provide regions of negative electrification, which can attract the positively charged nuclei of hydrogen atoms in other water molecules thereby giving rise to hydrogen bonds. The charge distribution within the molecule results in the relatively large dipole moment of 1.84×10^{-18} esu.

Molecular structure of water

The planar H—O—H angle in the water molecule is 104°31, and the OH bond length is 0.9572 Angstrom. The symmetry group is C_{2v}: it has twofold axis of rotational symmetry, C_2, (the line bisecting the H—O—H angle) and a plane of reflection, v passing through this axis and normal to the plane of the molecule.

Precise calculations indicate that the average electron distributions forming the covalent OH bonds do not lie directly along the lines from the oxygen nucleus to the hydrogen nuclei, but are bent inward. Furthermore, the normal mode analysis of vibrational spectrum of the two OH bonds shows that the equilibrium length of one bond is dependent on the length of the other bond. The interdependence ot the two OH bonds is also observed in their different dissociation energies. At O°K, the dissociation energy of H—OH is 117.8 kilocalories per mole or 5.11 eV whereas these respective values for H—O are 101.5 and 4.40. Thus the energy of formation of a water molecule from the individual atoms is −219.3 kilocalories per gram-mole.

Pressure–volume–temperature relationships of water

The thermodynamic pressure–volume–temperature surface for water is illustrated by Figure 3. At high pressures and low temperatures the equilibrium forms of water are liquid and solid. The triple point for water, i.e., the sole point where all three phases of solid, liquid and vapor exist simultaneouly at equilibrium, occurs at 0.01°C and 4.58 m. of mercury. At this point the specific volumes of ice, liquid water and water vapor are 1.00, 1.09 and 206,100 cm^3 per gram, respectively. The critical point, i.e., the pressure and temperature above which the distinction between the liquid and vapor properties vanishes, is 374.15°C and 218.39 atm.

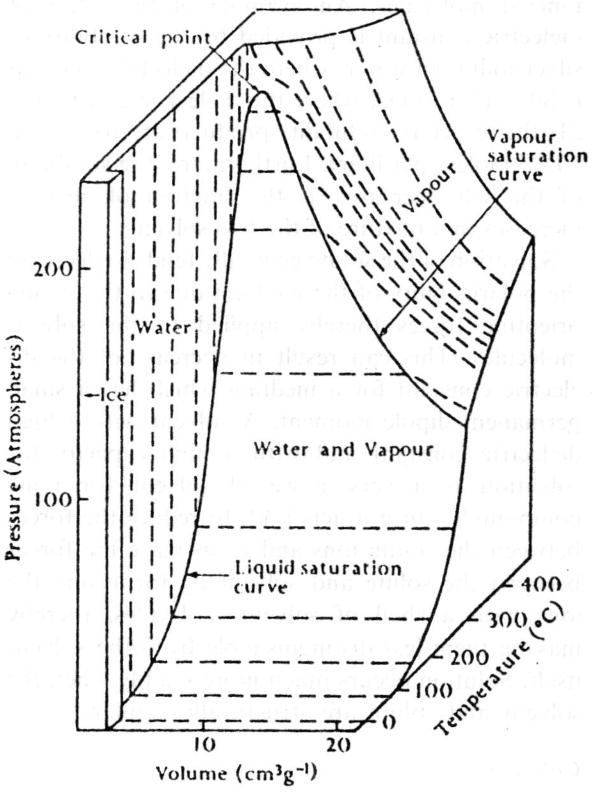

Figure 3 Thermodynamic pressure–volume–temperature surface for water. From Eisenberg (1969).

The resulting critical volume at this point is 59.1 cm^3 per gram-mole.

Eisenberg calls attention to the marked differences in the volume ratios of the fluid phases between the triple point and the critical point. The density of the liquid decreases by a factor of 3, due chiefly to the temperature rise from 0 to 374°C. The density of the vapor, on the other hand, increases by a factor of 62,000, due mainly to the pressure increase in progressing from the triple point to the critical point.

The vapor phase of water

In the vapor phase, water is mostly monomeric with the occurrence of an occasional dimer and, perhaps, a very rare trimer. At low pressure and low temperature the molecules do not interact to any appreciable extent.

An equation of state for water vapor relating pressure, temperature and specific volume has been developed by Keyes based on data extending up to 460°C and 360 atm. This equation, which is a satisfactory model outside of the critical region, is expressed as follows:

$$\log_{10}\frac{RT}{pv} = \log_{10}\frac{w}{v} + \psi w/v^2$$

where R = Gas law constant; 4.5546

T = Temperature, °K,

T_c = critical temperature for water $T_c = 374.15$°K

$\tau = 1/T$

p = pressure in atmospheres

$w = v - \delta$

$\delta = 2.0624x \exp(-0.87498/v)$

$\psi = \psi_0 1 + (\psi_1 v) + (\psi_2/v^2)$

$\psi_0 = 1260.17\tau \times \exp(17.09 \times 10^4\tau^2)$

for $T<T_c$ $\psi_1 = 305.6\psi_0\tau \times \exp(34.19 \times 10^4\tau^2)$

$\psi_2 = 0$

$T>T_c$ $\psi_1 = (479.76 + 141.5 \times 10^3\tau)\psi_0\tau$

$\psi_2 = (75.364 - 27.505\psi_0\}/\psi_0{}^3$

The solid phases of water

The structure of the solid phases of water is relatively well known compared to that of the liquid phase. Kamb recognizes 13 distinct ice phases by including among the distinctions certain "temperature dependent order–disorder" phenomena. The transition points and the densities of these phases are listed in Table 1.

Ordinary ice

Ordinary ice, ice I, also known as I_h ($I_{hexagonal}$), is the only solid phase stable at normal low pressures. The presence in each water molecule of the two lone pairs of electrons on the oxygen atom and the two protons in approximately tetrahedral geometry creates the opportunity for four intermolecular hydrogen bonds resulting in a coordination number of four for the ice structure. The arrangement of the oxygen atoms is isomorphous with tridymite, one of the crystalline forms of silica, and with wurtzite,

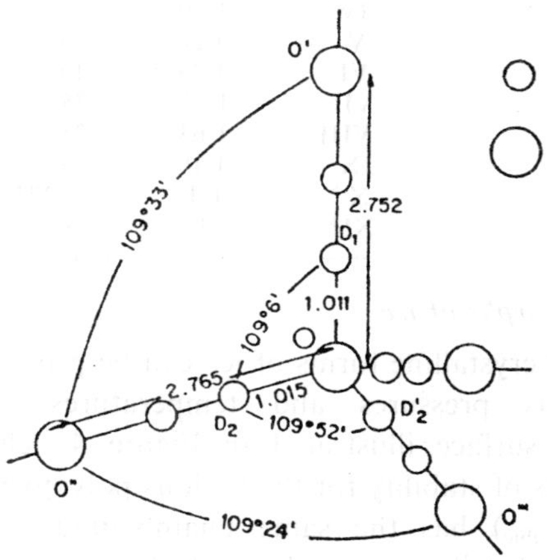

Figure 4 Structural relationships in one tetrahedron of the ice structure. The distances and angles are those at −50°C. From Krindel (1971).

a crystalline form of zinc sulfide. As shown by *X*-ray diffraction ice I is a hexagonal lattice with each oxygen atom surrounded tetrahedrally by four other oxygen atoms at a distance of 2.76A. The oxygen atoms form what many authors call "puckered" hexagonal rings. Each ring layer is a mirror image of its neighbors. The hexagonal arrangement of ice I gives rise to an open structure thereby explaining the low density of ordinary ice, 0.9168 g/cm^3 at 0°C, relative to its melt, 0.99987 g/cm^3 at 0°C.

The OH bond length has been determined to be 0.99 Å by studies of stretching vibrations. As Figure 4 illustrates, a hydrogen atom occupies one of two possible positions on each O—O line, amounting therefore to four hydrogen atoms around each oxygen consistent with the tetrahedral spacing of the oxygen atoms. These allowable positions are 1.05 Å from each molecule along the O—O axis. Early theoretical work by Pauling based on the residual entropy in ice at 0;Q predicted that over a sufficiently long time interval, the hydrogen atom between the two oxygen atoms occupies each of these positions half of the time. This was later confirmed by neutron diffraction experiments.

TABLE I
The Ice Phases

Phase	Density g cm^{-3}	Pressure kb	Limits of Temperature range Lower °C	Upper °C	Transition at upper limit
I	0.92	0	−273°	0°	melts
Ic.	0.92	0	−150° (?)	−90°	inv. to I
vit.	0.94	0	−273° (?)	−120°	inv. to Ic
II	1.21	3	−273°	−30°	trans. to III
III	1.15	3	90°	−20°	melts
IV	1.29	5	−40° (?)	−25°	melts
V	1.28	5	−150° (?)	−10°	melts
VI	1.38	14	−150° (?)	+50°	melts
VII	1.57	25	+2°	+110°	melts
VIII	1.63	25	−273°	+2°	trans. to VII
IX	1.19	3	−273°	−105°	trans. to III
X*	~1.4	−273°	−273°	−150° (?)	trans. to VI
XI*	~1.3	5	−273°	−150° (?)	trans. to V

The polymorphs of ice

The other crystalline forms of ice can be produced at various pressures and temperatures. The P—V—T surface illustrated in Figure 4 defines the regions of stability for the various polymorphs. Ice I_c (I_{cubic}) has the same unambiguous half-hydrogen distribution as I_h, and thus the same configurational entropy. At about −90°C its cubic crystalline structure readily converts to the hexagonal form, ice I_h, at a rate dependent on its previous history.

Vitreous ice is so named since it is considered to be a glass. This amorphous structure is formed by the condensation of vapor below −150°C. Warming above this temperature transforms it irreversibly to I_c, and then to I_h upon further heating.

Ices II through VII are formed at high pressure but can subsequently exist at atmospheric pressure. Ice II is produced by a transition from ice III at about −100°C. The oxygen atoms of ice II, whose rhombohedral unit cell contains 12 water molecules, are apparently in the same tetrahedral positions as those in ice III and the volume change of transition is very small but the resulting spatial ordering yields a much lower dielectric constant. Ices II, III, V and VI, all of which contain distorted hydrogen bonds, have internal energies only several tenths of a kilocalorie per gram-mole greater than ice I. In comparison, the internal energy of liquid water at 0°C is 1.88 kilocalorie per gram-mole greater than that of ice I.

The crystal lattice of ice V is a monoclinic unit cell with 28 water molecules. Ices VI, VII and VIII have extremely high densities of 1.38, 1.57 and 1.63 grams/cm^3, respectively. These high densities result from interpenetrating but not interconnecting structures. According to Fletcher "dense packing is achieved by placing water molecules upon two separate, completely hydrogen bonded four-coordinated lattices which are allowed to interpenetrate so that the molecules of one lattice occupy the cavities of the other." Thermodynamic criteria indicate that ice VI is probably metastable. Ice VII forms at 22 to 200 kilobars; only one additional allotrope, ice VIII, has been identified in this high pressure range.

Tables 2 and 3 from Kamb (1972) and Eisenberg (1969) summarize the properties of the ice polymorphs.

The structure of liquid water

The structure of liquid water still remains a greater enigma than highly complex molecules such as DNA and hemoglobin. Nevertheless, newly acquired data of various properties have increased the constraints operative in the hypothesis of models for the liquid structure.

An acceptable model must explain anomalous properties of liquid water such as the following listed by Krindel and Eliezer:

1) The density maximum at 4°C above the melting point.

2) A liquid specific heat approximately twice that of the solid.

3) The extraordinarily large heat of fusion.

4) The increase in the coefficient of thermal expansion with increasing pressure (or, equivalently, the decrease in compressibility with temperature rise) between 0°C and 45°C compared with a decrease in this coefficient under the same conditions for normal liquids.

5) The singular decrease in viscosity with increasing pressure (in the temperature range

TABLE II
Structural Characteristics of Ice Polymorphs[a]

Ice	I	Ic	II	III	V	VI	VII	VIII
Number of nearest neighbors	4	4	4	4	4	4	8[b]	8[b]
Distances of nearest neighbors (Å)	2.74	2.75[c]	2.75–2.84	2.76–2.80	2.76–2.87	2.81	2.86[d]	2.86[d]
Distance of closest non-H-bonded neighbor (Å)	4.49	4.50[c]	3.24	3.47	3.28, 3.46	3.51	2.86[d]	2.86[d]
O—O—O angles (deg)	109.5° ± 0.2°	109.5°	80°–128°	87°–141°	84°–135°	76°–128°	109.5°	109.5°
Hydrogen positions	Disordered	Disordered	Ordered	Disordered above −40°C	Disordered	Disordered	Disordered	Ordered

[a] Entries, except where noted, refer to −175°C and 1 atm pressure. Data for ices I and Ic are from Lonsdale (1958); data for the high-pressure polymorphs are from Kamb and Datta (1960), Kamb (1964), Kamb (1965 *a*, *b*), Kamb (1967), and Kamb *et al.* (1967).
[b] 4 are hydrogen-bonded to central molecule.
[c] At −130°C.
[d] At 25 kbar. In quenched ice VII at atmospheric pressure the nearest-neighbour distance is 2.95 Å (Bertie *et al.* 1964).

20°C) to a minimum near 1000 kg/cm^2, above which the normal increase is exhibited.

6) The exceptional dependence on pressure of the dielectric constant, the self-diffusion coefficient and other thermodynamic and transport properties.

The model must also be consistent with the interpretations from infrared, nuclear magnetic resonance, Raman and X-ray spectra of liquid water.

Eisenberg has outlined the sequence by which most of the current theories have been developed. Experimental evidence and some intuition the postulation of a model after which it is translated into mathematical terms, often by expressing it as a simple partition function containing several variable parameters. The number of adjustable parameters has typically ranged from 9 to 18. The thermodynamic expressions derived from the partition function are fitted to the empirical measurements by varying the parameters. That the model furnishes a good correlation is not nessarily proof of its validity, due to the inductive nature of the method.

The different water models may be roughly divided into two classes: the continuum models (also called homogeneous or uniform models) and the mixture models (also called solution models). Models in both classes achieve partial success in explaining the properties of water.

TABLE III
Crystallographic Properties of Ice Polymorphs[a]

Ice	I	Ic	II	III	V	VI	VII	VIII
Crystal system	Hexagonal	Cubic	Rhombohedral	Tetragonal	Monoclinic	Tetragonal	Cubic	Cubic
Space group[b]	P6/mmc	F$\bar{4}$3m	R$\bar{3}$	P4$_1$2$_1$2	A2/a	P4$_2$/nmc	Im3m	Im3m
Unit cell dimensions (A)[c]	*a* 4.48 *c* 7.31	*a* 6.35	*a* 7.78 α 113.1°	*a* 6.73 *c* 6.83	*a* 9.22, *b* 7.54 *c* 10.35, *β*109.2°	*a* 6.27 *c* 5.79		*a* 3.41
No. molecules/unit cell	4	8	12	12	28	10	2	2
Density at −175°C, 1 atm (g cm^{-3})	0.94	—	1.17	1.14	1.23	1.31	—	1.50
Density at (*T*°C, *P* kbar) in region of stability (g cm^{-3})	0.92 (0°, 1)	0.93 (−130°, 1)	1.18 (−35°, 2.1)	1.15 (−22°, 2.0)	1.26 (−5°, 5.3)	1.34 (15°, 8)	~ 1.65 (25°, 25)	~ 1.66 (−50°, 25)

[a] Data for ices I and Ic are from Lonsdale (1958); data for the high-pressure polymorphs are from Kamb (1965 *a*, *b*), Kamb
[b] The space groups for ice VI, VII, and VIII are not entirely certain.
[c] For 1 atm and −175°C, except for ice Ic which refers to −130°C.

The models of Pople and Frank–Wen, representative of the continuum and the mixture classes, respectively, are summarized here. Eisenberg and Kauzmann give a comprehensive review of the various models.

The Pople distorted bond model

The continuum theories ascribe essentially complete hydrogen bonding to water, at least at low temperature. Associated with the hydrogen bonds is a distribution of angles, distance and energies. The average bond energy varies with temperature due to the changes in the distributions of bond lengths and bond angle distortions.

Pople's model (1951) postulates that when ice melts the hydrogen bonds become more flexible and disorder is introduced into the structure by the bending and stretching of the bonds rather than by breaking them. Thus the water molecules in the liquid phase, like those in the ice, retain a coordination number of four. All the molecules have essentially the same environments, thereby giving rise to the continuum. The model allows for a continuous spectrum of induced hydrogen bond disorders. This model is strongly supported by Raman and infrared spectral studies of liquid water. As Fletcher points out, "the uniform model of Pople stands or falls on the energy required to bend the hydrogen bond joining two molecules which are already participating in hydrogen bonds to other molecules." Pople and Lennard-Jones propounded that a significant percentage of broken hydrogen bonds in liquid water is thermodynamically impossible since the hydrogen bond energy between two water molecules is 4.5 kcal./mole whereas the latent heat of fusion is 1.4 kcal./mole and the average thermal energy, *RT*, at 0°C is 0.5 kcal./mole.

The Frank–Wen flickering cluster model

The flickering cluster model described water as a mixture of hydrogen bonded clusters surrounded by monomeric water. Frank and Wen (1957) treat the formation of hydrogen bonds in water as a cooperative phenomenon, with a sizeable covalent contribution to the energy of the bond The existence of a hydrogen bond on one of the hydrogen atoms of water promotes the tendency of the other hydrogen to form a similar bond to another neighboring molecule. According to Krindel and Eliezer, "Frank and Wen considered that hydrogen bonded molecules are mutually polarized, the resulting charge separation being such that the free ends of the associated molecules have a higher affinity for further hydrogen bonding than the ends of non-hydrogen bonded molecules." This susceptibility to further hydrogen bonding gives the process an element of positive feedback until the disaggregating thermal energies from the additional molecules supply negative compensation. Thus the formation of one hydrogen bond tends to a cluster while the breaking of one hydrogen bond leads to the dissociation of a cluster, thereby resulting in clusters flickering into and out of existence with half-lives estimated at 10^{-10} to 10^{-11} second.

Though the model does not define the details of the organization of the water molecules, the clusters are thought to be compact and highly hydrogen bonded. The existence of a single dielectric relaxation time and a structural relaxation time approximating the neutron residence time appear to rule out the presence of Frank-Wen clusters in pure water according to Davis and Jarzynski.

Polywater

Fedyakin produced a new form of liquid water, water II, in 1962 by condensing ordinary water vapor on the surface of silica or fused quartz under certain conditions. The properties of water II, also known as polywater, are quite different from those of ordinary water. The density of polywater is greater than 1.2 grams/cm^3. It has a lower vapor pressure and a viscosity up to 15 times greater than ordinary water. It exhibits different thermal expansion behavior. Solidification of polywater occurs at −40°C or lower temperatures. It is stable to temperatures of the order of 500°C and it is also stable to cooling and aging.

Nevertheless, the data available at the present time are not sufficiently conclusive to allow total acceptance of polywater as another phase of liquid water.

II, Chemical Processes in Natural Water

Natural waters acquire their chemical characteristics by dissolution of and by chemical reactions with solids, liquids and gases with which they have come into contact during the various parts of the hydrologic cycle. Waters vary in their chemical composition, but these variations are at least partially understandable if the environmental history of the water and the chemical reactions of the rock–water–atmosphere systems are considered. Dissolved mineral matter is provided by the crustal materials of the earth; water disintegrates and dissolves mineral rocks by weathering. Gases and

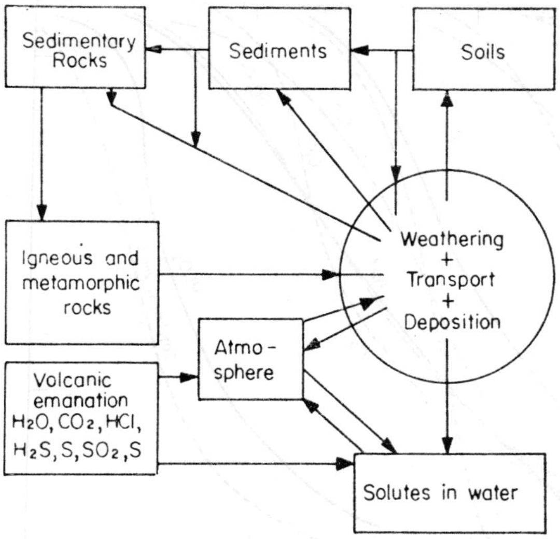

Figure A Interaction between the cycles of waters and rocks.

volatile substances participate in these processes. As a first approximation, seawater may be interpreted as the result of a gigantic acid–base titration: acids of volcanoes (sulfur dioxide, hydrochloric acid, hydrogen sulfide) reacting with bases of rocks (oxides, carbonates, silicates). The composition of fresh water similarly may be represented as resulting from the interaction of the carbon dioxide of the atmosphere with mineral rocks. The earth may be regarded as a heat engine which extracts energy from solar radiation in order to drive winds, ocean currents, hydrogeochemical cycles (cycles of water and rocks) and life cycles. Water, acting as a transport medium as well as a chemical reagent, gradually converts primary rocks into soil, sediments, and sedimentary rocks (Figure A).

Weathering processes

Dissolution reactions due to weathering take place because many constituents of the earth's crust are thermodynamically unstable in the presence of water and the atmosphere. Most important among the weathering reactions is the incongruent (partial) dissolution of aluminum silicates which may be represented schematically as follows:

$$\text{Me-Al-silicate (s)} + H_2CO_3^* + H_2O =$$
$$n\,HCO_3^- + H_4SiO_4 + Me^{n+} + \text{Al-silicate (s)}, \text{(a)}\dagger$$

where Me is a cation such as Na^+ or Ca^{2+}. Table α shows specific examples of this type as well as) weathering reactions of limestone (calcite).

In essence, primary minerals are converted into secondary minerals. The secondary minerals are frequently structurally ill-defined or X-ray amorphous. The structural breakdown of aluminum silicates is accompanied by a release of cations and usually of silicic acid. As a result of such reactions solution increases during the weathering process, the solid residue has a higher acidity than the original aluminum silicate.

Because $H_2CO_3{}^*$ is usually the acid in the attack of water on the primary silicates, $HCO_3{}^-$ is the predominant anion in most fresh waters. Because of respiration by organisms, the CO_2 composition in soils can be a few hundred times larger than that in the atmosphere. Correspondingly ground waters tend to contain higher concentrations of $HCO_3{}^-$ and other solutes. Minerals of the kaolinite group are the main alteration products of the weathering of feldspar. In addition to kaolinites, montmorillonites and micas are also found as intermediates or end products. Mica (illite) has been identified as an intermediate in the decomposition of potassium feldspar–orthoclase.

The dissolution kinetics of feldspars may cause them to reach their final products through temporally stable intermediates. Virtually all bonds must be broken in the tetrahedric aluminum framework before the structure can be rearranged

† $H_2CO_3{}^*$ represents the sum of dissolved CO_2 and H_2CO_3.

TABLE IV
Weathering Reactions

$CaCO_3(s)$	$+ H_2O$		$= Ca^{2+} + HCO^- + OH^-$
Calcite			
$VaCO_3(s)$	$+ H_2CO_3{}^{*a}$		$= Ca^{2+} + 2\,HCO_3{}^-$
$NaAlSi_3O_8(s)$	$+ 5\,1/2\,H_2O$		$= Na^+ + OH^- + 2\,H_4SiO_4 + 1/2\,Al_2Si_2O_5(OH)_4(s)$
Albite (Na-Feldspar			Kaolinite
$NaAlSi_3O_8(s)$	$+ H_2CO_3{}^*$	$+ 4\,1/2\,H_2O$	$= Na^+ + HCO^- + 2\,H_4SiO_4 + 1/2\,Al_2Si_2O_5(OH)_4(s)$
$CaAl_2Si_2O_8(s)$	$+ 3\,H_2O$		$= Ca^{2+} + 2\,OH^- + Al_2Si_2O_5(OH)_4(s)$
Anorthite (Ca-Feldspar)			Kaolinite
$CaAl_2Si_2O_8(s) + 2\,H_2CO_3{}^* + H_2O$			$= Ca^{2+} + 2\,HCO^- + Al_2Si_2O_5(OH)_4(s)$
$3\,Ca_{0.33}Al_{4.67}Si_{7.33}O^2{}_0(OH)_4(s) + 2\,H_2CO_3{}^* + 23\,H_2O$			$= Ca^{2+} + 2\,HCO^- + 8\,H_4SiO_4 + 7\,Al_2Si_2O_5(OH)_4(s)$
Montmorillonite			Kaolinite

[a] $[H_2CO_3{}^*] = [CO_2(aq)] + [H_2CO_3]$.
Table from Stumm, W. and E. Stumm-Zollinger, Chemische Prozesse in naturlichen Gewassern, *Chimia*, **22**, 8, 326 (1968).

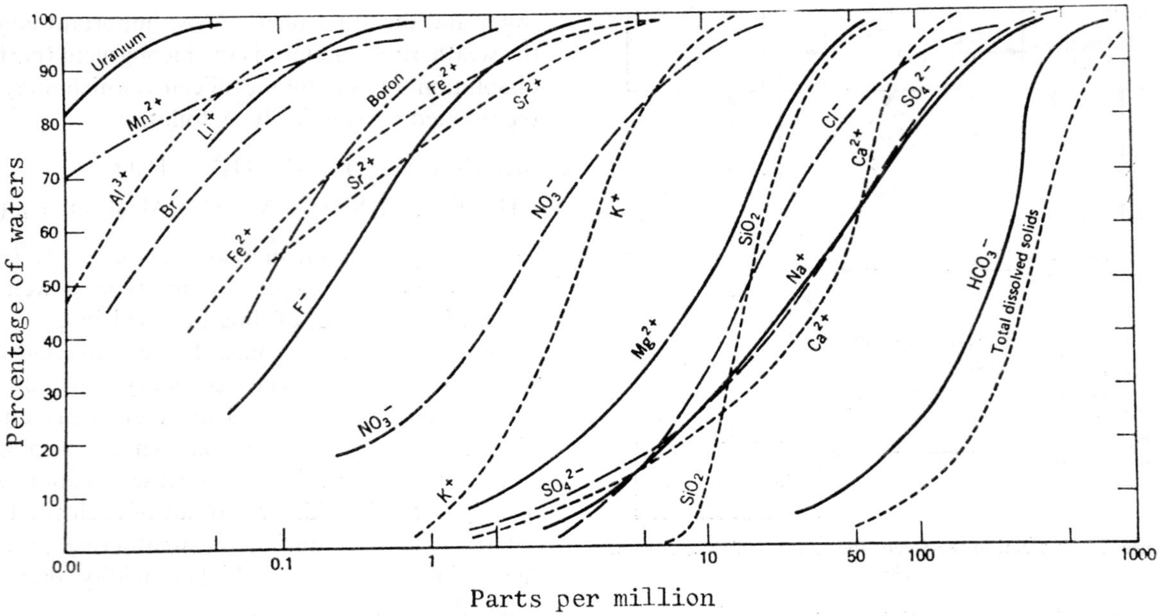

Figure B Cumulative distribution of inorganic species terrestrial waters. The curves represent the percentage of waters with concentrations below that indicated on the horizontal axis. Data are mostly from the United States from various sources. S. N. Davies and R. C. M. DeWiest, *Hydrogeology*, Wiley, New York, 1966.

Figure from Stumm, W. and J. Morgan, *Aquatic Chemistry*, Wiley-Interscience, New York, 1970, p. 384.

to a lattice having six coordination bonds around the aluminum as in kaolinite. Understandably, the rate of reaction is very slow. Physical weathering processes, that is, processes which by physical or mechanical means alter the size and hence the specific surface area of the minerals, enhance reaction rates since the weathering processes take place only at the rock–water interface.

The composition of water is obviously influenced by these weathering reactions. While Ca^{2+}, $HCO_3{}^-$, H^+ and perhaps Mg^{2+} may be controlled by dissolution of carbonate rocks, the source of Na^+, K^+ and H_4SiO_4, and possibly also of Ca^{2+} and Mg^{2+}, is the silicate minerals that make up 70% or more of the rocks in contact with underground waters and streams.

Table A presents the major solutes contained in seawater and in typical river water. A recent survey of the frequency distribution of various constituents of terrestrial waters by Davies and DeWiest (Figure B) shows that many of the aquatic constituents exhibit little natural variation in heir concentrations. For example, according to Figure B, 80 % of the water analyses for dissolved silica show

TABLE A

Composition of Sea[a] *and Average River Water*[b]

Ion	Present ocean	Average river
Na^+, M	0.47	2.7×10^{-4}
K^+, M	1.0×10^{-2}	5.9×10^{-5}
Ca^{2+}, M	1.0×10^{-2}	3.8×10^{-4}
$Mg_2{}^+$, M	$5.4 \times 10^{-}{}_2$	1.7×10^{-4}
F^-, M	7×10^{-5}	5.3×10^{-6}
Cl^-, M	0.55	2.2×10^{-4}
$SO_4{}^{2-}$, M	3.8×10^{-2}	1.2×10^{-4}
pH	7.89	—
Alkalinity, eq liter^{-f}	2.3×10^{-3}	9.6×10^{-4}
P_{CO_2}' atm	4×10^{-4}	4×10^{-4}
Total phosphorus, M	1.5×10^{-6}	—
Ionic strength, M	0.65	—

[a] From H. U. Sverdrup, M. W. $_5$ohnson and R. H. Fleming, *The Oceans, Their Physics, Chemistry and General Biology*, Prentice-Hall, New York, 1942.

[b] From D. A. Livingstone, "Chemical Composition of Rivers and Lakes", U.S. Geol. Survey Paper 440 G, 1963.

Ref: Stumm, W. and J. Morgan, *Aquatic Chemistry*, Wiley-Interscience, New York, 1970, p. 385.

concentrations between $10^{-3.8}$ and $10^{-3.2}$ M. The range of H^+ concentration in naturally occurring bodies of water is generally $10^{-6.5}$ to $10^{-8.5}$ M.

Because the relationship between geological environment and water composition depends upon so many interdependent variables, and because there is substantial variation in each genetic type of water, no reliable generalizations are possible with such a small number of examples. A few qualitative characteristics are apparent from Table B. As expected, ground waters have higher ionic strengths than surface waters. This results from the difference in CO_2 partial pressure to which these two type of waters are exposed. In comparing waters Nos. 5, 6 and 7, the influence of calcium plagioclase, which is less stable than the silicic rocks, becomes apparent. Sandstone beds are important aquifers and as sedimentary rocks may often contain carbonates besides grains of quartz. Thus the pH of sandstone waters tends to be higher than that of waters from igneous rocks. Shales are laminated sediments whose constituent particles have sizes similar to those of clay. Most of these fine-grained sediments were deposited in saline environments. The relatively high HCO_3^- concentrations of slate ground waters may be due to high CO_2 concentrations resulting from oxidation of organic carbon. Waters from limestone and dolomite contain substantial quantities of Ca^{2+}, Mg^{2+} and HCO_3^-, the concentrations of which are usually controlled by carbonate equilibria.

The composition of the ocean–atmosphere system

Goldschmidt (1933) suggested that for each liter of presently existing sea water, 600 grams of igneous rocks had reacted with about 1 kilogram of volatile substances (H_2O, HCl, CO_2, etc.). Concomitantly formed during this process were about 600 grams of sediment and three liters of air.

As seen in Table A, the solute proportion introduced by rivers differs from that in seawater; in other words, simple concentration of freshwater does not produce ocean water. An important group of constituents of the ocean-atmosphere system (Cl^-, N_2, rare gases) is controlled largely by degassing of the earth. The concentration of O_2 is controlled by the biological reactions of photosynthesis and respiration. Mineral reactions control the concentrations of major cations. Illustrative of these is the following proposed reaction:

$$\text{Amorphous Al-silicate(s)} + HCO_3^- + H_4SiO_4 + \text{cations} = \text{cation-Al-silicate(s)} + CO_2 + H_2O. \qquad \text{(b)}$$

Such reactions are essentially "reverse weathering" reactions. The direct inorganic precipitation of insoluble salts is relatively rare in the ocean, but carbonates, e.g. $CaCO_3$ and apatite (carbonato fluoro apatite) can be formed either biogenically or by precipitation. Under anoxic conditions insoluble metal sulfides can form.

Many constituents (e.g., CO_2, O_2, NO_3^-, HPO_4^- and H_4SiO_4) are involved in biological cycles in the

TABLE B

Examples of Natural Waters

	1	2	3	4	5	6	7	8	9	10	11
Type[a]	Stream	Stream	Stream	Lake Erie	Ground Water	Ground Water	Ground Water	Ground Water	Ground Water	Ground Water	Closed Basin Lake
Type of Rocks Being Drained	Granite	Quartzite	Sandstone[b]		Granite	Gabbro plagioclase	Sandstone	Shale	Limestone	Dolomite	Soda Lake
*p*H	7.0	6.6	8.0	7.7	7.0	6.8	8.0	7.3	7.0	7.9	9.6
*p*Na	4.0	4.6	4.3	3.4	3.4	3.0	3.3	2.6	3.0	3.5	0.0
*p*K	4.7	5.1	4.8	4.3	4.0	4.5	4.0	4.2	3.7	—	1.7
*p*Ca	4.0	4.3	3.1	3.0	3.5	3.1	3.0	2.5	2.7	2.8	4.5
*p*Mg	4.6	5.1	4.0	3.4	3.8	3.2	3.5	2.5	3.4	2.8	4.6
pH_4SiO_4	3.8	4.2	4.1	4.7	3.2	3.0	3.9	3.5	3.7	3.4	2.8
$pHCO_3$	3.6	4.0	2.9	2.7	2.9	2.5	2.6	2.1	2.3	2.2	0.4
*p*Cl	5.3	5.8	5.3	3.6	4.0	3.5	3.7	4.0	3.2	3.3	0.3
pSO_4	4.5	4.7	3.7	3.6	4.2	4.0	3.2	2.2	3.4	4.7	2.0
−log (ionic strength)	3.5	3.8	2.7	2.5	2.8	2.4	2.4	1.7	2.2	2.2	0.0

Note: $pX = -\log[X]$.

[a] 1–3: "Small Streams in New Mexico," *U.S. Geol. Surv. Bull.*, **1535F** (1961). 4: J. Kramer, *Geochim. Cosmochim. Acta*, **29**, 921 (1965). Types 5–10 are from *U.S. Geol. Surv. Bull.*, **440F** (1963). 5: Granite McCormick Co. (Table 1). 6: Harrisburg (Table 2). 7: Home Wood (Table 3). 8: Cuyahoga (Table 5). 9: Edwards limestone (Table 6). 10: Precambrian dolomite (Table 7). 11: "Albert Summer Lake Basin, Oregon," *North. Ohio Geol.*, J. L. Rau, Ed., 1966, p. 181.

[b] With slate and limestone beds.

Ref: Stumm, W. and J. Morgan, *Aquatic Chemistry*, Wiley-Interscience, New York, 1970, p. 408.

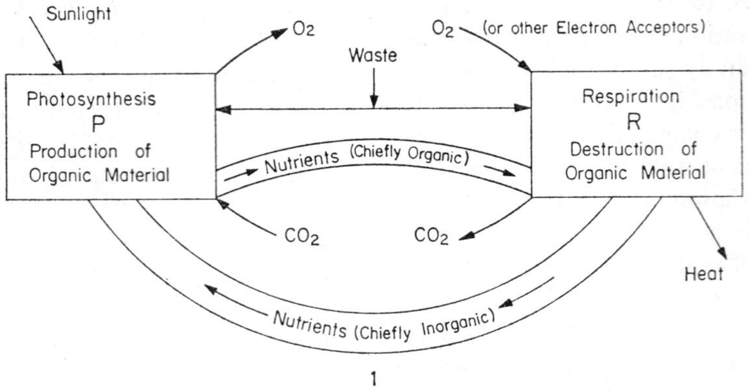

Figure C-1 Photosynthesis and the nutrient cycle. Solar energy and inorganic nutrients including inorganic runoff are converted by photosynthesis into chemical energy stored within the organic material of algae and plants. Heterotrophic consumers and bacteria mobilize this energy by degrading the organic nutrients including organic waste during respiration and other oxidative processes. A steady state of continuous circulation of biochemical materials is indicative of unpolluted water.

sea; their distribution and redistribution depend upon the physical circulation of the water and the settling and mineralization of plankton.

The cycles of life: photosynthesis and respiration

A few hundred million years ago the earth became covered with a thin layer of vegetation. In photosynthesis a small fraction of the light energy reaching the earth's surface is absorbed by algae (autotrophic producers) to convert CO_2, H_2O and other nutrients (e.g., NO_3^-, NH_4^+ and HPO_4^-) into organic material. In respiration some of the organic matter in turn becomes oxidized liberating energy in order to support the life processes of heterotrophic decomposer and consumer organisms (bacteria and animals) (Figure C-1). Organisms and their abiotic environment are interrelated and interact with each other.

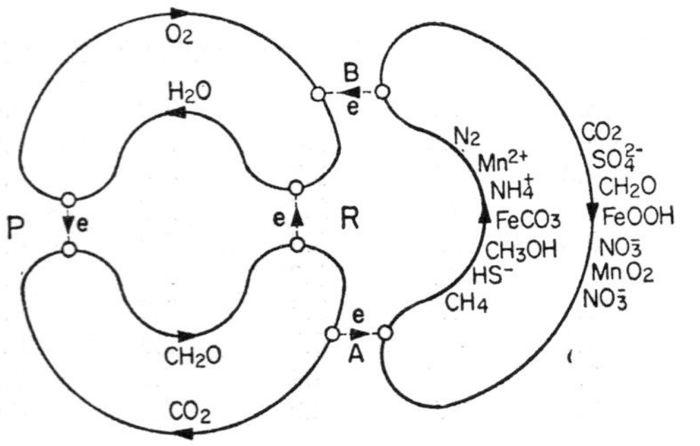

Figure C-2 Biochemical oxidation and electron cycles. Excessive organic input into an aqueous system may exhaust the dissolved oxygen (point R) and lead to a series of anaerobic reactions with other electron acceptors (point A), thereby lowering the redox potential ($p\epsilon$). Subsequent photosynthetic oxygen production (point P) promotes reoxidation of the reduced species (point B). Each of the electron transfer reactions is subject to biological mediation.

Photosynthesis

Conceptually, photosynthesis may be epitomized as a process leading to products of high oxidation intensity (e.g., oxygen) and products of high reduction intensity (e.g., carbohydrates and other organic molecules.) As a reaction this is often characterized by a simplified equation:

$$CO_2 + H_2O + \text{Energy} \underset{\text{Respiration}}{\overset{\text{Photo-synthesis}}{\rightleftharpoons}} CH_2O + O_2. \quad \text{(c)}$$

However, other nutrients participate in the reaction and a more involved (but still simplified) equation has been used to characterize photosynthetic, *P*, and respirative, *R*, reactions in the aquatic environment:

$$106\ CO_2 + 16\ NO_3^- + HPO_4^{-2} + 122\ H_2O + 18\ H^+ + \text{Energy (+ Trace elements)}$$
$$P \downarrow \uparrow R$$
$$\underset{\text{Algal Protoplasm}}{\{C_{106}H_{263}O_{110}N_{16}P_1\}} + 138\ O_2 \quad \text{(d)}$$

The assemblage of plants, animals and microbes interacting reciprocally with the chemical and physical environment comprises an *ecological system* (*ecosystem*) whose food chain or trophic structure reflects the flow of energy. The ecosystem may be regarded as an "entropy pump" which extracts solar energy to order its biological structure, to produce statistically improbable aggregations of matter and energy as living beings, and to drive the nutrient cycles and the cycle of electrons (Figures C-1 and C-2).

Respiration

The steady input of photosynthetic energy tends to displace a natural water system from equilibrium conditions. Consumer and decomposer organisms, however, tend to restore equilibrium by catalytically decomposing, through energy yielding redox reactions, the unstable end products of photosynthesis. As long as sufficient oxygen is available, the reverse of reactions (c) and (d) takes place. After the depletion of oxygen, other oxidants (electron acceptors), such as NO_3^-, SO_4^{2-} and CO_2, react with organic matter and are reducted to N_2 or NH_4^+, H_2S and CH_4. The typical chronological sequence of these reactions is given in Table C and illustrated in Figures C-1 and C-2.

It is important to remember that organisms act only as mediators or catalysts for reaction or electron transfer between the oxidizing and reducing substances. Thus, in their non-photosynthetic activities, organisms can induce only those reactions that are thermodynamically possible in closed systems, i.e., those leading to a decrease in free energy.

The balance between photosynthesis and respiration is primarily responsible for regulating the concentration of O_2 in the atmosphere. Thus biological processes regulate the partial pressure of oxygen and in turn the redox intensity of the interface between atmosphere and hydrosphere. In natural waters no total redox equilibrium is

TABLE C

Progressive Reduction of Redox Potential in Closed Aqueous Systems by Excess Organic Material: Sequence of Microbially Mediated Reactions

	Combination of Equations from Table H	$p\varepsilon$[a] of oxidant	ΔG[a] (kcal per electron equivalent)	Electrons transferred[a] (milli-equivalents)
(1) *Respiration*[b]				
$\frac{1}{4}CH_2O + \frac{1}{4}O_2(g) = \frac{1}{4}CO_2(g) + \frac{1}{4}H_2O$	(1) – (22)	13.58	−29.73	1.0
$\frac{1}{4}CH_2O + \frac{1}{4}O_2(g) = \frac{1}{4}HCO_3^- + \frac{1}{4}H^+$	(1) – (22a)			
(2) *Denitrification*				
$\frac{1}{4}CH_2O + \frac{1}{5}NO_3^- + \frac{1}{5}H^+ = \frac{1}{4}CO_2(g) + \frac{1}{10}N_2(g) + \frac{7}{20}H_2O$	(2) – (22)	11.86	−27.39	0.45[c]
(3) *Manganese oxide reduction*				
$\frac{1}{4}CH_2O + \frac{1}{2}MnO_2(s) + H^+ = \frac{1}{4}CO_2(g) + \frac{1}{2}Mn^{2+} + \frac{3}{4}H_2O$	(3a) – (22)	8.42	−22.70	0.1
$\frac{1}{4}CH_2O + \frac{1}{2}MnO_2(s) + \frac{1}{4}H^+ + \frac{1}{4}HCO_3^- = \frac{1}{2}MnCO_3(3) + \frac{1}{2}H_2O$	(3) – (22a)	8.46	−22.76	0.9[d]
(4) *Nitrate reduction*				
$\frac{1}{4}CH_2O + \frac{1}{8}NO_3^- + \frac{1}{4}H^+ = \frac{1}{4}CO_2(g) + \frac{1}{8}NH_4^+ + \frac{1}{8}H_2O$	(5) – (22)	6.15	−19.61	0.08[c]
(5) *Ferric oxide reduction*				
$\frac{1}{4}CH_2O + FeOOH(s) + 2H^+ = \frac{1}{4}CO_2(g) + Fe^{2+} + \frac{7}{4}H_2O$	(9a) – (22)	−1.74	−8.86	0.1
$\frac{1}{4}CH_2O + FeOOH(s) + \frac{3}{4}H^+ + \frac{3}{4}HCO^{3-} = \frac{3}{4}HCO_3^- = FeCO_3(s) + \frac{3}{2}H_2O$	(9) (22a)	−1.67	−8.95	0.9[d]
(6) *Fermentation*				
$\frac{3}{4}CH_2O + \frac{1}{4}H_2O = \frac{1}{4}CO_2 + \frac{1}{2}CH_3OH$	(10) – (22)	−2.51	−7.81	2.0
(7) *Sulfate reduction*				
$\frac{1}{4}CH_2O + \frac{1}{8}SO_4^- + \frac{1}{8}H^+ = \frac{1}{4}CO_2(g) + \frac{1}{8}HS^- + \frac{1}{4}H_2O$	(13) – (22)	−3.75	−6.12	8.0
(8) *Methane fermentation*				
$\frac{1}{4}CH_2O = \frac{1}{8}CO_2(g) + \frac{1}{8}CH_4(g)$	(15) – (22)	−4.28	−5.39	1.0
			(Total)	14.53

[a] The tabulated values have been computed from equilibrium constants in Tables E, G and H, Equations (xxxiv), (xxxvi) and (xxxxi) and the following concentrations and partial pressures (for which the activity coefficients have been assumed equal to unity): pH = 7; $[HCO_3^-] = 10^{-3}$ M; $[NO_3^-] = 10^{-4}$ M; $p_{O_2} = 0.21$ atm. and thus $[O_2(aq)] = 0.25 \times 10^{-3}$ M; $p_{N_2} = 0.78$ atm. and thus $[N_2(aq)] = 0.5 \times 10^{-3}$ M; $[SO_4^{2-}] = 10^{-3}$ M; $[CH_2O] = 10^{-2}$ M; $[NH_4^+] = 10^{-4}$ M; $[Mn^{2+}] = 10^{-4}$ M; $[Fe^{2+}] = 10^{-4}$ M; $[CH_3OH] = 10^{-3}$ M; $[HS^-] = 10^{-3}$ M; $p_{CH_4} = 0.1$ atm. and thus $[CH_4(aq)] = 0.125 \times 10^{-3}$ M. Temperature = 25°C.

[b] Any form of the carbonate species may be used in the reactions, as illustrated for respiration, as long as mutually consistent concentrations are used in the calculations. Thus for pH = 7 and $[HCO_3^-] = 10^{-3}$ M, p_{CO_2} is constrained to be $10^{-2.18}$ atm.

[c] 90% of the incipient NO_3^- is assumed to undergo dentitrification and 10% nitrate reduction.

[d] Sufficient colloidal manganese and ferric oxides are assumed initially present to exceed the solubility products of the reduced carbonates by a factor of 10. After the sulfate reduction, the ferrous carbonate will be transformed to ferrous sulfides.

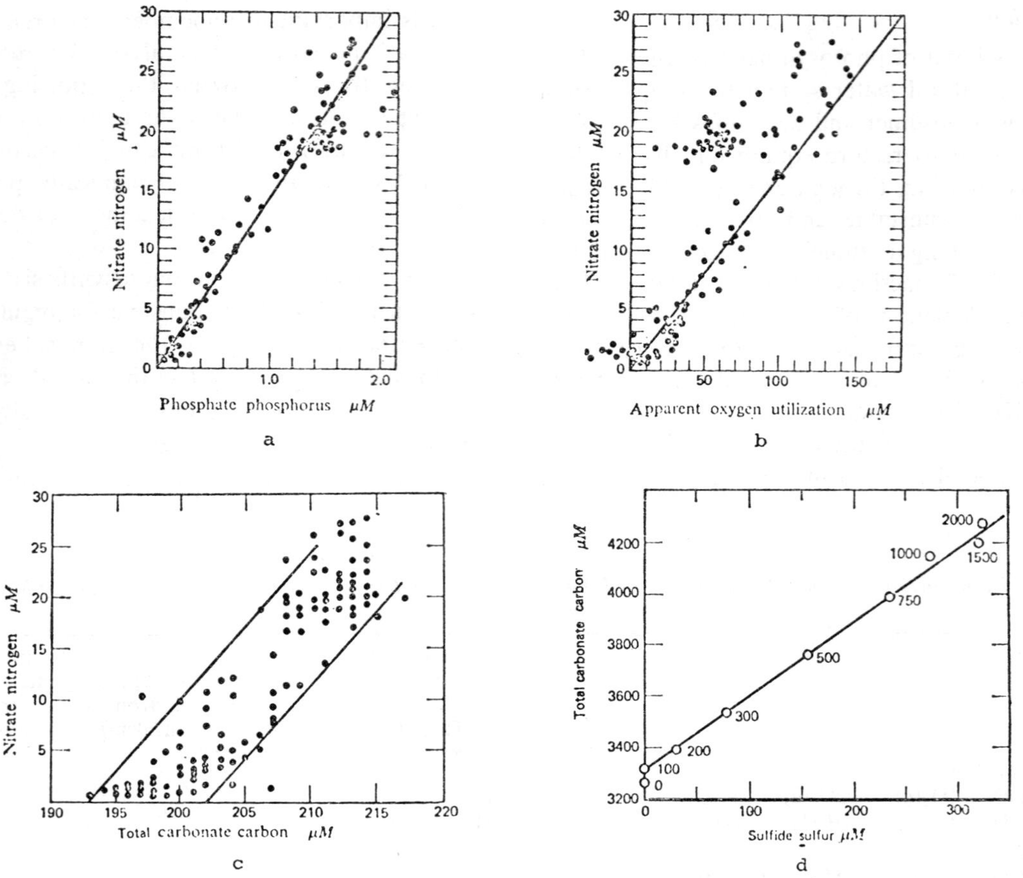

Figure D Stoichiometric correlations between nitrate, phosphate, oxygen, sulfide and carbonate in the oceans. The correlations can be explained by the stoichiometry of reactions such as that of Equation (d).
a. Correlation between nitrate nitrogen and phosphate phosphorus in waters of the western Atlantic. Phosphorus is corrected for salt error.
b. Correlation between nitrate nitrogen and apparent oxygen utilization in the same samples.
c. Correlation between nitrate nitrogen and carbonate carbon in waters of the western Atlantic.
d. Relation of sulfide sulfur and carbonate carbon in waters of the Black Sea. Numbers indicate depth of samples. Slope of line corresponds to $\Delta S^{2-}/\Delta C = 0.36$.

a, b and c from A. C. Redfield, James Johnstone Memorial Volume, 1934, p. 177, Liverpool. a and b reproduced with permission from Interscience Publishers. d from data of Skopintsev *et al.*, 1958, as quoted in A. C. Redfield, B. H. Ketchum and F. A. Richards, in *The Sea*, Volume 2, M. N. Hill, Ed., Wiley-Interscience, New York, 1963.

Figures from Stumm, W. and J. Morgan, *Aquatic Chemistry*, Wiley-Interscience, New York, 1970, pp. 430–431.

achieved; however, in the surface films of oxygen-containing waters, most elements should exist virtually completely in their highest oxidation states: C as CO_2, HCO_3^- or CO_3^{2-}; N as NO_3^-; S as SO_4^{2-}; Fe as FeOOH(s) or Fe_2O_3(s); and Mn as MnO_2(s).

In the sea or in a lake at all depths below the trophogenic (photosynthetic) layer, there is a net consumption of oxygen as a consequence of the oxidation of biogenic debris that has settled.

Figure D shows Redfield's correlation between dissolved nitrate and dissolved phosphate for the waters of the western Atlantic. The molar ratio $\Delta N/\Delta P$ equals 16. The fact that in other seas the same constant correlation also occurs is a further example of how organisms influence the composition of natural waters. The slope of the correlation curve in Figure D is readily understood by considering the stoichiometry of reaction (d). In the photosynthetic zone, phosphate and nitrate are eliminated from the water in a 1 : 16 ratio and incorporated into algal cell material. Settled algae are mineralized by decomposer bacteria in the deeper water layers and, as a result, phosphate and nitrate are released into solution again with a ratio of 1 : 16. Because O_2 participates in the photosynthesis and respiration reactions, corresponding correlations between phosphate and O_2 ($\Delta O_2/\Delta P \simeq 138$) and between nitrate and O_2 ($\Delta O_2{}^4/\Delta N \simeq 9$) obtain. Figure D also shows the correlation between carbonate–carbon and nitrate–nitrogen ($\Delta C/\Delta N = 106:15$). These correlations are in accord with the stoichiometric composition of plankton.

As shown in Table C, the dissolved oxygen becomes exhausted first; then the oxidation of organic matter continues with nitrate serving as the oxidant; subsequently organic fermentation reactions and redox reactions occur with SO_4^{2-} and CO_2 as electron acceptors. The reduced and oxidized products of the decomposition of organic matter accumulate in the water. The formal equations given in Table C can be modified to develop stoichiometric models that predict how the components of the anoxic water will change as a result of the mineralization of settled plankton. Such stoichiometric models have been developed by Richards (1965), who corroborated the validity of these models for a large number of anoxic basins and fjords. For example, under conditions of sufficiently low redox intensity, planktonic material becomes oxidized by SO_4^{2-}, which is reduced to S(−II).† For the oxidation of one $\{C_{106}H_{263}O_{110}N_{16}P_1\}$ the transfer of approximately 424 electrons is necessary. (Note that the carbon in the plankton formula has a formal oxidation state of approximately zero.) In the reduction of SO_4^{2-} to S(−II), 53 SO_4^{2-} ions can accept the requisite 424 electrons; hence, one would expect a ratio $\Delta S(-II)/\Delta C = 0.5$. As Figure D shows, the ratio is somewhat smaller for the waters of the relatively anoxic Black Sea.

The cycle of organic carbon

The cycle of carbon in natural waters is especially important because it is interrelated with the cycles of all other elements. Furthermore, the organic material produced in the oceans constitutes one of man's most significant marine resources. Despite its importance, the chemistry of aqueous organic matter is one of the least elucidated subjects in the chemistry of natural waters.

Organic matter in natural waters includes a great variety of organic compounds, which are usually present in minute concentrations that elude direct isolation and identification. Collective parameters, such as chemcal oxygen demand (COD), biochemical oxygen demand (BOD) and total organic carbon by combustion (C_{org}), have therefore often been used to estimate the total quantity of organic matter present. COD is obtained by measuring the equivalent quantity of an oxidizing agent, usually permanganate or dichromate in acid solution, necessary for the oxidation of the organic constituents; the amount of oxidant consumed is customarily expressed in equivalents of oxygen. The BOD test measures the oxygen uptake directly in the microbiologically mediated oxidation of organic matter. In both tests not all the organic matter reacts with the oxidant. Determinations of total organic carbon measure the CO_2 produced in the oxidation or combustion of the dry residue of a water sample (from which carbonate has been removed). Bio-assay methods are frequently of great sensitivity and permit direct determination of very low concentrations of organic nutrients in water.

Most of the carbon in the earth's crust has cycled through organisms and plants; as a result it has been incorporated into unstable but long-lived biochemical structures. Information on the catabolic pathway of organic life substances permits prediction of the type of organic substances to be found in natural waters. Table D gives a greatly condensed and simplified survey of the decomposition products of life substances and includes an abbreviated list of specific organic compounds reportedly found in natural waters.

In fresh water bodies one typically encounters concentrations of a few milligrams carbon per liter, but occasionally (e.g., in bog or swamp waters) concentrations may be as high as 50 mg C per liter. In the oceans the concentrations of organic carbon range from 0.5 to 1.2 mg C per liter, with the higher values occurring in the surface waters. Particulate organic carbon, including planktonic organisms, generally accounts for about 10% of the total organic carbon. In much of the ocean there is a "soluble" organic carbon concentration of around 500 micrograms C per liter, and a total particulate organic carbon concentration of some 50 μg C per liter, all ultimately derived from a surface phytoplankton population equivalent to a concentration of about 5 μg C per liter. Below a depth of 400 to 600 meters the concentration variations in organic carbon become very slight. This suggests that materials present in deep waters are resistant to further metabolic decomposition.

The cycles of nitrogen and phosphorus

Nitrogen and phosphorus play a dominant role in the life cycles because both are essential and frequently "growth-limiting" nutrients.

† Roman numerals are commonly used to refer to the oxidation state of an element, especially when conditions are not sufficiently known to define the predominant species in which the element occurs. Thus S(−II) refers to the existence of sulfur in an oxidation state of −2, e.g., as H_2S, HS^-, S^{2-}, FeS, CuS, etc., depending on the concentrations of H^+ and other ions in the medium.

TABLE D
Naturally Occurring Organic Substances

Life Substances	Decomposition Intermediates		Intermediates and Products Typically Found in Nonpolluted Natural Waters
Proteins	Polypeptides → $RCH(NH_2)COOH$ → amino acids	$RCOOH$, $RCH_2OHCOOH$, RCH_2OH, RCH_3, RCH_2NH_2	NH_4^+, CO_2, HS^-, CH_4, HPO_4^{2-}, peptides, amino acids, urea, phenols, indole, fatty acids, mercaptans
Polynucleotides	Nucleotides → purine and pyrimidine bases		
Lipids			
Fats, Waxes, Oils	$RCH_2CH_2COOH + CH_2OHCHOHCH_2OH$ → fatty acids, glycerol	RCH_2OH, $RCOOH$, shorter chain acids, RCH_3, RH	CO_2, CH_4, aliphatic acids, acetic, lactic, citric, glycolic, malic, palmitic, stearic, oleic acids, carbohydrates, hydrocarbons
Carbohydrates			
Cellulose, Starch, Hemicellulose	$C_x(H_2O)_y$ → monosaccharides, oligosaccharides, chitin	→ hexoses, pentoses, glucosamine	HPO_4^{2-}, CO_2, CH_4, glucose, fructose, galactose, arabinose, ribose, xylose
Lignin	$(C_2H_2O)_x$ → unsaturated aromatic alcohols →	polyhydroxy carboxylic acids	
Porphyrines and Plant Pigments			
Chlorophyll, Hemin, Carotenes and Xantophylls	Chlorin → pheophytin → hydrocarbons		Pristane, carotenoids
Complex Substances Formed from Breakdown Intermediates, e.g.,			
	Phenols + quinones + amino compounds	→	Melanins, melanoidin, gelbstoffe
	Amino compounds + breakdown products of carbohydrates	→	Humic acids, fulvic acids, "tanic" substances

Ref: Stumm, W. and J. Morgan, *Aquatic Chemistry*, Wiley-Interscience, New York, 1970, p. 344.

Nitrogen is abundantly present in the atmosphere (79% by volume) but because of the inertness of N_2 it cannot be used as such by most organisms. Nitrogen plays a complicated role because it occurs in various oxidation states. In plants and animals most nitrogen exists in the reduced forms of ammonium ion or amino groups. In the presence of oxygen the most stable form of fixed nitrogen in aqueous environments is nitrate. A few organisms have the ability to fix nitrogen, i.e., to convert N_2 to ammonia. Man has also learned to fix N_2 for the production of fertilizer. In 1970 about 30 million tons of nitrogen were fixed industrially. This quantity now probably exceeds the amount that is biologically fixed. The mining of phosphate and its application in agriculture, industry and the household have increased nearly exponentially over the last few decades.

The flow of nutrients from land to water has been enhanced by various technological measures, land clearing, deforestation, establishment of monocultures, municipal waste disposal and urban drainage. This has resulted in progressively increased concentrations of phosphorus and nitrogen compounds in rivers and lakes and in turn in serious ecological unbalance in the receiving waters.

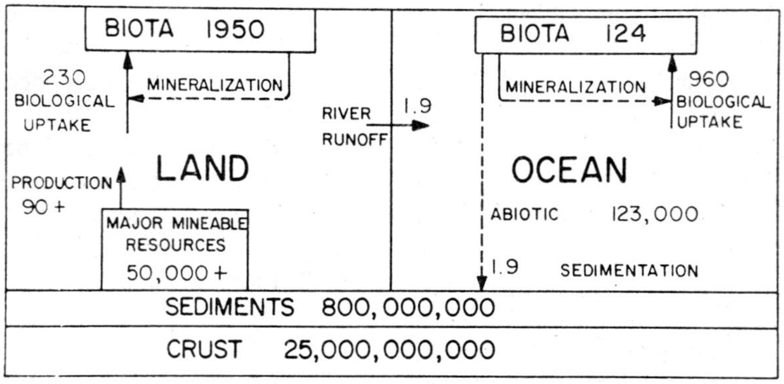

Figure E Distribution and circulation of phosphorus. Abundance and transfer of phosphorus in millions of metric tons P and millions of metric tons P per year.

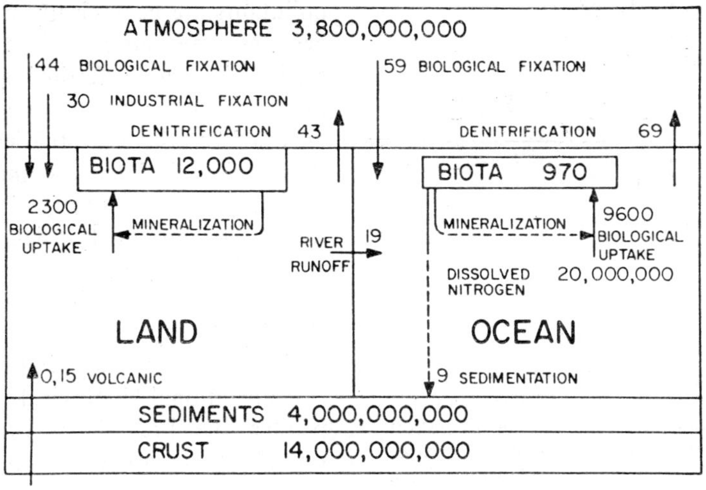

Figure F Distribution and circulation of nitrogen. Abundance and transfer rates in millions of metric tons N and millions of metric tons N per year. Modified from C. C. Delwiche, "The Nitrogen Cycle", *Sci. Am.*, **223**, No. 3 (Sept. 1970), p. 136.

Figures E and F give simplified schemes for the distribution and circulation of phosphorus and nitrogen. It is quite apparent that the annual use of nutrients by the phytoplankton in the sea far exceeds the annual contribution to the ocean; hence most of these nutrients must be continuously regenerated from organic debris. At steady state, the rate of accumulation of phosphorus in sediments equals its rate of supply to the ocean. Phosphorus exemplifies a sedimentary cycle. A similar pathway of circulation is followed by other non-volatile elements such as iron, manganese, silicon, and boron.

Nitrogen, on the other hand, forms volatile compounds (N_2, N_2O, NH_3) which circulate between the hydrosphere, atmosphere and the land, thereby following the hydrological cycle and the cycles of other elements that form volatile compounds (e.g., CO_2, H_2S, SO_2).

III· Water Quality Criteria and Water Pollution Control

In a broad sense, pollution has been defined as an alteration of man's surroundings in such a way that they become unfavorable to him. This implies that pollution is not solely caused by contaminants or pollutants added to the environment but can also result from other direct or indirect consequences of man's action. Anything that produces a maladjustment of the ecological balance constitutes pollution.

Every ecosystem has a rather delicate balance of inputs and outputs. Ecological unbalance results, for example, when the rate of extraction of an element (e.g., by mining) by man exceeds the natural rates of cycling or when the output of a product (e.g., crops or forests) is maximized.

Disturbance of the balance between photosynthesis and respiration

Pollution of surface waters frequently results from a disturbance in the balance between photosynthesis (P) and respiration (R). (Reactions (c) and (d)). As Figure G illustrates, this balance is upset by adding either an excess of organic wastes or an excess of inorganic algal nutrients (e.g., phosphorus and nitrogen compounds). In the first case ($P \ll R$), heterotrophic processes tend to dominate and dissolved oxygen may become exhausted due to the biochemical oxygen demand and ultimately NO_3^-, SO_4^{2-} and CO_2 may become reduced to $N_2(g)$, NH_4^+, HS^- and $CH_4(g)$. In the second case, the incipient result is progressive accumulation of autotrophic biomass (e.g., algae and aquatic plants). Eventually this biomass decomposes enhancing the rate of respiration, which again may reduce dissolved oxygen levels. In either case the initial perturbation is followed by a readjustment, such as a shift in biological species, that finally leads to a new balance.

The P–R balance may also be disturbed by a localized, physical separation of the P and R functions. For example, in a stratified lake an excessive production of algae and oxygen in the upper layers may be paralleled by anaerobic conditions (i.e., lack of dissolved oxygen) at the bottom because much of the photosynthetic oxygen escapes to the atmosphere and does not

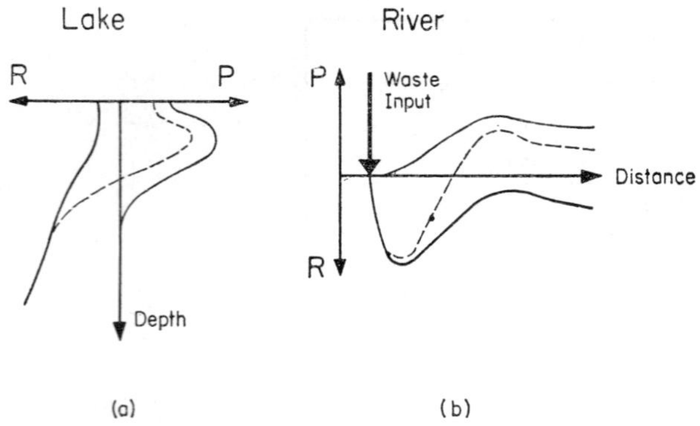

Figure 6 Separation of photosynthesis and respiration in polluted lakes and rivers. The separation of photosynthesis and respiration causes pollution by impeding the circulation of chemical constituents with consequent localized increases in photosynthetic or heterotrophic microbial populations. The dashed curves represent the net disturbance of the *P–R* balance and are indicative of the net rate of oxygen production or consumption.

a. Vertical separation of the *P–R* functions in lakes can be induced by inorganic nutrients, chiefly nitrogen and phosphorus, which fertilize surface algal growth. Upon settling, the algae stimulate bacterially mediated oxygen utilization and other redox reactions of lower $p\varepsilon$. The resultant anaerobiosis stifles higher trophic levels.

b. Longitudinal separation of the *P–R* functions in rivers can be caused by localized injection of organic waste, which stimulates increased bacterial activity and concomitant oxygen consumption. The resultant mineralized nutrients enhance algal growth downstream which upon decay exerts an oxygen demand still further along the river.

become available to heterotrophs in the deeper water layers.

When $P \simeq R$, the organic material is decomposed as fast as it is produced photosynthetically. Such a balance,

$$\text{Import}_{\text{org. materia}}{}^{1} + P \simeq \text{Export}_{\text{org. materia}} + R,$$

is necessary to maintain a water in an aesthetically pleasing condition.

The pollutants

Much of our concern in the future should be with the fact that most of the energy dissipation by our industrial society for agriculture, landscaping, urban construction and other interventions of civilization ultimately causes a simplification of the ecosystem: specifically, a reduction of the food web and a shortening of the food chains. Generally the less complex a natural ecosystem, i.e., the smaller the number of species (less diversity), the more liable it is to perturbations and to catastrophe.

Most of the conscious and reasonably successful efforts of environmental and sanitary engineers have been and may well continue to be directed toward the removal of organic carbon of *biological* wastes. For many natural waters, however, other pollutants are ecologically more harmful and may become even more so in the future. As shown earlier, inorganic fertilizing elements are often more serious pollutants than biological wastes for most of our lakes, estuaries and littoral waters. While biological wastes and inorganic fertilizers cannot yet cause substantial alterations (besides local and temporal transients) in the composition and biology of the oceans, the invasion of the seas by man-made chemicals (e.g., persistent petrochemicals) may cause substantial modification of ecological interrelations in the marine environment.

Conventional biological waste treatment expedites the breakdown of those organic compounds that would eventually be degraded in receiving waters whose self-purification capacities are not overloaded. Such treatment is relatively inefficient with regard to many synthetic organic chemicals. Thus, for many inland waters more emphasis upon the elimination of refractory carbon compounds is necessary.

The inability of some rivers and lakes to readjust rapidly to their initial conditions after even minor shock loadings (e.g., of pesticides or excess quantities of organic wastes) is frequently indicative of a loss of diversity (heterogeneity) in the aquatic biological communities. While many refractory chemicals, at the low concentrations encountered, do not impair the dissolved oxygen balance and do not interfere with the apparent health and survival of fish, they may prevent some fish from returning to their streams of birth for breeding. Often an environmental stress and a decrease in community diversity is signalled by the disappearance of a species, e.g., a salmon in a particular stream.

Because of the continuous increase in industrial energy generation, heat will become one of the most significant water pollutants of the future. Woodwell (1969), has shown that many types of environmental disturbances (chronic irradiations, exposure to SO_2, pollution by pesticides, hydrocarbons, heavy metals, excess nutrients) cause similar and roughly predictable gross changes in ecosystems. In each case there is a shift away from complex arrangements of specialized species toward monotype, away from tight nutrient cycles toward loose ones with terrestrial systems becoming overloaded, away from stability toward instability.

Global water pollution

A comparison of the fluxes of materials resulting from geological processes and weathering with those of substances introduced by civilization (e.g., agricultural and industrial wastes) shows the relative importance of the role of man as a geological agent and manipulator.

The energy fixed by all plants on the surface of the earth is approximately 8 × 10^{17} kilocalories per year. Man's metabolism (3 × 10^{15} kilocalories per year) plays a minor role in the physiology of the biosphere. Man in his capacity to manipulate nature dissipates from 10 to 20 times (in developed countries, 50 to 100 times) as much energy as he requires for his metabolism. Much of the energy utilized by our industrialized society causes localized simplification of the ecosystem and tends to accelerate the cycling of individual elements.

Table E illustrates that some of the fluxes caused by man's manipulation are of similar magnitude to those which do not involve man. The combustion of fossil fuels may introduce some elements into the atmosphere and subsequenty into the hydrosphere at rates comparable to those of natural processes.

Chemical management of water and waste water quality

Assigning a level of quality to water is relative and depends on the user of the water. For example, different quality criteria apply to drinking waters, to waste water effluents and to receiving waters. Table F summarizes some of the objectives of chemical unit processes typically used in water and waste treatment. Water treatment schemes often include several of these processes since generally no single one can achieve the desired water quality objectives. Pertinent chemical reactions in the management of water and waste water are listed in Table G.

Precipitation reactions are used to remove objectionable ionic species from solution. Hard water containing calcium and magnesium ions, which form insoluble films with soap, is softened by precipitating the ions as calcium carbonate and magnesium hydroxide. Iron and manganese which cause undesired turbidity and stain surfaces are removed by oxidation and precipitation. Phosphate, a critical aquatic nutrient, can be precipitated as aluminum, iron or calcium solids.

Ion exchange involves the interchange of ions between a solid polymer resin and solution and is used in water treatment for softening and demineralization.

Coagulation is a physico-chemical process involving the agglomeration of colloidal particles for subsequent removal by sedimentation and filtration. The addition of chemical coagulants

TABLE E
Some Fluxes in the Major Sedimentary Cycle

Material	Geosphere receiving region	Flux in million tons per year
Suspended river solids	Ocean	18,000
Dissolved river solids	Ocean	3,900
Continental rock and soil particles	Atmosphere	100–500
Sea Salt	Atmosphere	300
Volcanic debris	Stratosphere	4
Wastes of mankind (excluding fossil fuels)	Hydrosphere Atmosphere Lithosphere	3,000
Carbon and fly ash from fossil fuel combustion	Atmosphere	25
Industrial particulates	Atmosphere	56
Ocean dumping of solid wastes including dredge spoils	Ocean	50
Oil (petroleum)	Ocean	3–10
Vaporization of petroleum products	Atmosphere	90
Carbon dioxide production from fossil fuel combustion	Atmosphere	13,400
Sulfur dioxide discharge from fossil fuel combustion	Atmosphere	100
Sulfate pollution by rivers	Ocean	100
DDT	Geosphere	0.1
DDT by rivers	Ocean	0.003
Lead atmosphere rainout	Ocean	0.3
Copper atmosphere rainout	Ocean	0.2
Synthetic organics	Geosphere	1
Carbon dioxide from heterotrophic metabolism	Atmosphere	100,000
Sulfur dioxide from heterotrophic metabolism	Atmosphere	2,000

Adapted in part from E. D. Goldberg, *Geophysics*, **1**, 117 (1971).

TABLE F

Chemical Unit Processes in Water and Waste Water Treatment

Substance to be removed	Precipitation	Filtration (chemical aided)	Coagulation Flocculation	Disinfection by Chlorination	Ion exchange	Activated carbon adsorption	Aeration
Algae	−	+++	+++	+	−	−	−
Bacteria	−	++	++	+++	−	−	−
Colloids turbidity	−	+++	+++	−	−	−	−
Natural color	−	++	++	−	+	++	−
Odor, taste	−	+	+	+	−	+++	+
Organic macromolecules	−	++	++	−	−	+	−
Organic solutes	−	−	−	−	+	++	−
Ca^{2+}, Mg^{2+}	+++	−	−	−	+++	−	−
Phosphate	+++	−	−	−	+	−	−
Inorganic nitrogen compounds	−	−	−	+	+	−	+
Heavy metal ions	+++	−	−	−	++	−	−
Dissolved Fe, Mn	++	+	−	+	+	−	+++

Effectiveness: +++ very effective, ++ effective, + marginally effective, − ineffective.

TABLE 6

Reactions Pertinent to the Chemical Management of Water and Waste Water Quality
(Reagents used are underlined)

Precipitation

Softening

a) Carbonate hardness (temporary or non-incrustant hardness)

$Ca^{2+} + 2HCO_3^- + \underline{Ca(OH)_2} = 2CaCO_3(s) + 2H_2O$

$Mg^{2+} + 2HCO_3^- + \underline{2Ca(OH)_2} = Mg(OH)_2(s) + 2CaCO_3(s) + 2H_2O$

b) Non-carbonate hardness (permanent or incrustant hardness)

$Ca^{2+} + SO_4^{2-} + \underline{Na_2CO_3} = CaCO_3(s) + 2Na^+ + SO_4^{2-}$

$Mg^{2+} + SO_4^{2-} + \underline{Ca(OH)_2} + \underline{Na_2CO_3} = Mg(OH)_2(s) + CaCO_3(s) + 2Na^+ + SO_4^{2-}$

Iron and Manganese Removal

$2Fe^{2+} + \underline{1/2\ O_2(g)} + 5H_2O = 2Fe(OH)_3(s) + 4H^+$

$Mn^{2+} + \underline{1/2\ O_2(g)} + H_2O = MnO_2(s) + 2H^+$

$Fe^{2+} + HCO_3^- + \underline{OH^-} = FeCO_3(s) + H_2O$

Phosphate Removal

$\underline{Al^{3+}} + H_nPO_4^{n-3} = AlPO_4(s) + nH^+$

$\underline{Fe^{3+}} + H_nPO_4^{n-3} = FePO_4(s) + nH^+$

$\underline{10\ Ca^{2+}} + 6H_nPO_4^{n-3} + \underline{(n+2)OH^-} = Ca_{10}(PO_4)_6(OH)_2(s) + nH_2O$

Ion Exchange

(Brackets, { }, are used to designate a positively or negatively charged polymer network of cation or anion exchange resin with many exchange sites)

$\{HR\} + Na^+ = \{NaR\} + H^+$

$2\{NaR\} + Ca^{2+} = \{CaR\} + 2Na^+$

$\{RCl\} + OH^- = \{ROH\} + Cl^-$

$2\{ROH\} + SO_4^{2-} = \{R_2SO_4\} + 2OH^-$

Formation of Coagulants and Flocculants

$\underline{nFe^{3+}} + mH_2O = Fe_n(OH)_m^{3n-m} + mH^+$

$\underline{nAl^{3+}} + mH_2O = Al_n(OH)_m^{3n-m} + mH^+$

$\underline{mNa_2SiO_3} + (n-2m)H + mH_2O = H_n(SiO_4)_m^{n-4m} + 2mNa^+$

Polyelectrolytes; Flocculation Aids

$\underline{CH_3(CH_2CHCOO^-)_nCH_3}$ (polyacrylate, anionic)

$\underline{CH_3(CH_2CHC_5H_5NCH_3^+)_nCH_3}$ (polyvinylpyridinium, cationic)

Chlorination

$\underline{Cl_2(g)} + H_2O = HOCl + H^+ + Cl^-$

$NH_3 + HOCl = NH_2Cl + H_2O$

$NH_2Cl + HOCl = NHCl_2 + H_2O$

enhances the mutual attachment of colloidal particles by reducing the repulsive forces acting between these particles (destabilization). In water and waste water treatment practice the hydrolyzed metal ions of Al and Fe(III) salts are commonly used as coagulants. Initial particle contact due to thermal motion (perikinetic coagulation) is normally augmented by the introduction of velocity gradients in solution by slow mixing (orthokinetic coagulation).

The coagulation process may be aided by the addition of macromolecular polymers (polyelectrolytes) which bridge dispersed colloidal particles. Such destabilization is frequently called flocculation.

Gaseous chlorine is one of the economically most useful disinfectants for municipal and industrial waters. During the chlorination process diatomic chlorine gas hydrolyzes in solution to form hypochlorous acid and hydrochloric acid. Hypochlorous acid is a stronger disinfectant in its undissociated form (HCOl). Aqueous chlorine, a powerful oxidizing agent ($p\varepsilon = 23.6$), will react with reduced compounds as shown in Table G by the formation of chloramines by reaction with aqueous ammonia. (Also see Figure 15, Water Chemistry Article.)

Water pollution control and improvement of water quality cannot solely depend on water purification and waste treatment. Various physical and biological means of stream management must be directed towards restoring an ecological balance. Because unlimited growth in energy dissipation is incompatible with maintenance of ecological stability and high quality of life, the ecological constraints demand the alteration of social and economic activity toward a situation where resources and materials are recycled.

REFERENCES

American Chemical Society: "Equilibrium Concepts in Natural Water Systems". *Advances in Chem. Series*, **67**, Washington (1967).

Butler, J. N., *Ionic Equilibrium, a Mathematical Approach*, Addison-Wesley, Reading, Mass. (1964).

Conway, B. E., *Annual Review of Physical Chemistry*, **17**, Annual Reviews Inc., Palo Alto Calif. (1966).

Dorsey, N. E. *Properties of Ordinary Water-Substances*, A.C.S. monograph No. 81, Reinhold Publishing Corp., New York (1940).

Eisenberg, D. and W. Kauzmann, *The Structure and Properties of Water*, Oxford University Press, England (1969).

Fletcher, N. H., *The Chemical Physics of Ice*, Cambridge University Press, England (1970).

Frank, H. S., *Science*, **169**, 635 (1970).

Garrels, R. M. and C. L. Christ, *Solutions, Minerals and Equilibria*, Harper and Row, New York (1965).

Goldschmidt, *Fortschr. Mineral Krist. Petr.* **17**, 112 (1933).

Horne, R. A., *Marine Chemistry, The Structure of Water and the Chemistry of the Hydrosphere*, Wiley-Interscience, New York (1969).

Horne, R. A., *Water and Aqueous Solutions, Structure, Thermodynamics, and Transport Processes*, Wiley-Interscience, New York (1972).

Horne, R.A., *Surv. Progr. Chem.*, **4**, 2 (1968).

Hush, N. S., *Reactions at Electrodes*, Wiley-Interscience, New York (1971).

Kamb, "Structure of the Ices" in Horne, R. A., *Water and Aqueous Solutions*, Wiley-Interscience (1972).

Kavanau, J. L., *Water and Solute–Water Interactions*, Holden-Day, San Francisco (1964).

Keyes, F. G., *J. Chem. Phys.* **17**, 923 (1949).

King, T., *Water: Miracle of Nature*, The Macmillan Company, New York (1953).

Krindel, P. and I. Eliezer, *Coord. Chem. Rev.*, **6** 217 (1971).

Narten, A. H., and H. A. Levy, *Science*, **165**, 447 (1969).

Pimental, G. C. and A. L. McClellan, *The Hydrogen Bond*, W. H. Freeman and Co., San Francisco (1960).

Richards, F. A. in *Chemical Oceanography*, J. P. Riley and G. Skirrow, Eds., Academic Press, New York, Chap. 13 (1965).

Riley, J. P. and G. Shirrow (eds.), *Chemical Oceanography*, 2 Volumes, Academic Press, London (1965).

Riley, J. P. and R. Chester, *Introduction to Marine Chemistry*, Academic Press, London (1971).

Skinner, B. J., *Earth Resources*, Prentice-Hall, Inc., Englewood Cliffs, New Jersey (1969).

Stumm, W. and J. J. Morgan, *Aquatic Chemistry: An Introduction Emphazing Chemical Equilibria to the Chemistry of Natural Waters*, Wiley-Interscience, New York (1970).

"Water II," Topic of *Journal Colloid Interface Science*, **36**, No. 4, (1971).

Woodwell, *Diversity and Stability in Ecological Systems*, Brookhaven, Nat. Lab. Publ. No. 22 (1969).

MARTIN FORSBERG

STEVEN GHERINI

Harvard University

WERNER STUMM

Swiss Federal Republic Institute of Technology

WATER PURIFICATION: see DISINFECTION AND CHEMOSTERILIZATION; WATER TREATMENT

WATER QUALITY: see ESTUARINE WATER QUALITY; WATER TREATMENT

WATER REUSE

Introduction

What is water reuse? On spaceship Earth little new water is formed, and little lost. Of the three forms, solid, liquid, and vapor, our primary concern is with the liquid form. Historically, water has been used, abused, and discarded. Reuse brings the abused water back to the use point. A special case of reuse, called recycle, is the use of the polluted water after suitable quality upgrading for the original use. The following statement was sent to the authors of papers for an International Water Reuse Symposium held by the American Institute of Chemical Engineers in Detroit, Michigan in December, 1966:[1]

In order to avoid misunderstanding of the scope of the paper you are preparing, reuse should be defined. When water is discharged to a stream, the owner has lost control. Another user taking his supply downstream from the point where the first user discharged his wastewater is just taking his supply from a polluted stream. He is not reusing the first user's wastewater. If the second user accepts the wastewater while the first user has control, he is reusing the wastewater. Multiple intraplant uses of water is reuse, because the owner has control of the water.

Every use is a potential reuse. Each use has its quality requirements. The use of fresh water to be abused (polluted) and discarded, or to upgrade the polluted wastewater for use will depend on an evaluation of many factors. Most of these will be tangible to which a dollar value can be assigned. Some are intangible, to which no dollar value can be assigned, but may nevertheless be the deciding factors.

Complete water reuse, with no discharge of treated wastewater or the concentrates from the various treating processes will free the pollution producer from the need to have discharge permits and therefore no regular contact with regulatory agencies. This freeing of management from pollution control concern is an intangible, but very important benefit.

Why is the historical use, abuse, and discard pattern breaking? Examination of case histories of reuse shows there is always an element of compulsion. It may be financial, legal, or social. A careful evaluation of these case histories shows that even in the legal or social compulsions the financial aspect is dominant. Compulsion factors are increasing rapidly. Public awareness of pollution, greater leisure time for recreation, increased water consumption leading to fresh water shortage, stringent water quality for discharge to surface waters, and damage suits by downstream users are the principal compulsion factors.

R and D programs are of no practical value until they are put into use by the producer of polluted water. The tremendous amount of literature in government publications, technical society journals, trade association reports, and commercial journals on water reuse proves the often repeated statement: "We have the technology to stop water pollution, all we need to do is spend the money."

United States Government Involvement

About 1955 the Water Supply and Pollution Control Division of the U.S. Public Health Service began an investigation of the potential for reuse in cleaning up our surface waters and alleviating the growing water shortage. In 1959 McCallum presented the concept of the Advanced Waste Treatment Research Program.[2] This was started in 1960 at the Robert A. Taft Sanitary Engineering Center in Cincinnati, Ohio. The Federal Water Pollution Control Act (Public Law 87–88) directed the Secretary of Health, Education, and Welfare

... to develop and demonstrate practicable means of treating municipal sewage and other water-borne wastes to remove the maximum possible amounts of physical, chemical, and biological pollutants in order to restore and maintain the maximum amount of the nations' water at a quality suitable for repeated reuse.

A total of nineteen AWTR reports were issued covering the period from July, 1960 through July, 1967.

A Federal Executive Reorganization moved the Water Supply and Pollution Control Division from HEW to the Interior Department where it became the Federal Water Pollution Control Administration (FWPCA). Research and Development work continued at the Robert A. Taft Water Research Center. A number of reports presenting the results of intramural and contract research carried out under the guidance of the technical staff of the Center were issued as TWRC reports.

Another Executive Reorganization moved this group, as well as certain others from other departments into the new Environmental Protection Agency. As part of a greatly expanded R and D contract program, special attention was given to reuse of industrial effluents, resulting in a number of publications.

The Congress of the United States, after years of hearings, floor debates, committee action (and mounting public sentiment) passed the Water Quality Act of 1965 by overwhelming majorities. It was signed into law by President Johnson on October 2, 1965. This law expanded previous laws and marks the important beginning of the Federal Government's move into all phases of water pollution control in the United States. Accelerated R and D programs, substantial subsidies for construction of treatment plants, establishment of water quality standards, and in cooperation with the States, a vigorous enforcement campaign grew from this law. Subsequent water quality acts have strengthened the programs. There is now before Congress an act that may require no point discharge of wastewater, which is just another way of saying complete water reuse. This applies to municipal as well as industrial wastewater. Even if it is subsequently modified before it becomes law, it will give an enormous impetus to water reuse.

Applied Water Reuse

Water reuse is not a science. It is not even a technology. It is a management technique. Methods of treating water for use were developed for fresh water. Methods of treating wastewater have been worked out to meet disposal quality criteria. When wastewater is to be reused the treating technique or techniques from both areas are selected as needed to upgrade the quality for the desired use. It is an axiom in water reuse that quality should not be upgraded more than necessary for the desired use. The converse of this is that as water quality is degraded by one use it may be reused without quality upgrading for other less critical uses. In a complex industrial system it might be possible to select sequential uses of descending quality requirements until the increasingly polluted water is completely consumed by such uses as quenching of hot gases or hot solids such as coke or slag. In most industrial systems there is not complete consumption, so the polluted water must be quality upgraded to reenter the use system at some point.

In dealing with reuse of municipal wastewater the volume is so large there is seldom a single use that will take all of it. The complexity of the pollutants is so great that there is a series of unit operations, each producing a certain quality effluent, until the final effluent is suitable to reuse in the water mains. Water can be reused at any point in the system if it is of satisfactory quality. Thus, as the quality and the cost increase the volume decreases. The final volume not accepted for other reuses can be upgraded to drinking water quality at a high per unit cost. When the costs for all of the operations is integrated it will be usually a reasonable unit cost on the original volume.

A variation of this handling of municipal wastewater is the "in transit" use. Many times there is a large water consuming industry, or a golf course or large park inside a city. The sewage from the trunk line can be treated for local use, with the concentrates returned to the trunk line to be handled downstream at the main wastewater treatment plant.

Urban sprawl has produced two situations favoring water reuse. Metropolitan Sanitary Districts find a high local population concentration with such a long distance to the next density area they cannot afford the transportation cost across the sparsely populated area. It costs less to build and operate a regional treatment plant developing local reuse of the effluent, with only the concentrate piped to the main plant

Large water using industries once located in the country with adequate wastewater pond area now are surrounded by residential subdivisions. There is no additional land for expansion. Management may find the installation of a small area mechanical treatment plant for water reuse, with the pond area now available for factory expansion, a good decision.

Quality Criteria for Discharge to Surface Waters

These criteria are in a state of flux. The Environmental Protection Agency, working through the States, tried to use stream standards for control of individual discharges. This has not been satisfactory, so consideration is being given to the use of effluent standards. The proposed criteria are in part:

Each discharge shall conform with the following general guidelines:

1) The discharge shall not cause or contribute to pollution of any surface or ground water.

2) The discharge shall not cause or contribute to a nuisance by reason of odors or unsightliness.

3) The discharge shall not cause or contribute to visible oil or grease slicks in the receiving waters.

4) The discharge shall not cause or contribute to sludge deposits.

5) The discharge shall not contain floating or suspended materials of recognizable industrial waste origin.

6) The discharge shall not cause or contribute to visible discoloration of the receiving waters.

7) The discharge shall not cause or contribute to nuisance algal densities, slime or bacteriological growths or other nuisance biological populations.

8) The discharge shall not cause or contribute to detectable taste or odor in any water supply nor in aquatic life used for human food.

9) The discharge shall not contain any materials in concentrations which are deleterious to human, plant, animal or aquatic life.

10) The discharge shall not cause or contribute to causing the receiving water temperature to increase to a level that would adversely affect the habitation or propagation of native fish or aquatic life.

Each discharge shall conform with the following additional specific guidelines:

1) The hydrogen ion concentration (pH) of the discharge shall remain between 6.5 and 8.5 units.

2) The settleable solids content of the discharge shall not exceed .2 ml/l per half-hour and shall include no mercury.

3) The discharge shall not contain Methylene Blue active substances (MBAS) in excess of 0.5 mg/l

4) The oil, insoluable liquids and grease content of the discharge shall not exceed 1.0 mg/l.

5) The phenolic content of the discharge shall not exceed 0.001 mg/l.

6) The trace metals content of the discharge shall not exceed the following levels:

a)	Arsenic	0.01 mg/l
b)	Barium	0.01 mg/l
c)	Cadmium	None
d)	Chromium Total	None
e)	Cyanide	0.01 mg/l
f)	Copper	0.01 mg/l
g)	Iron	0.05 mg/l
h)	Lead	None
i)	Manganese	0.10 mg/l
j)	Mercury	None
k)	Selenium	0.01 mg/l
l)	Silver	0.001 mg/l
m)	Zinc	0.04 mg/l

7) The total biocide content of the discharge shall not exceed 1 ug/l. Individual biocides shall be further restricted to the following levels:

a) Aldrin	0.05 ug/l
b) Chlordane	0.02 ug/l
c) DDT	0.006 ug/l
d) Dieldrin	0.003 ug/l
e) Endrin	0.002 ug/l
f) Heptachlor	0.002 ug/l
g) Heptachlor Epoxide	0.0002 ug/l
h) Lindane	0.002 ug/l
i) Methoxychlor	0.004 ug/l
j) Organic phosphates plus Carbamates	0.0003 ug/l
k) Toxaphene	0.03 ug/l
l) Herbicides	2.0 ug/l

8) The radioactivity of the discharge shall not exceed the following levels:

a) Gross beta	500.0 pc/l
b) Radium-226	1.0 pc/l
c) Strontium-90	10.0 pc/l
d) Tritium	3,000.0 pc/l

9) The discharge shall not cause or contribute to causing the salinity content of the receiving water to increase more than 1% over natural ambient salinities.

10) The discharge shall not contain materials having a biochemical oxygen demand that will lower the dissolved oxygen content below the following levels:

a) Cold water fishery	7.0 mg/l
b) Warm water fishery	6.0 mg/l

11) The discharge of industrial wastes shall not have a turbidity exceeding 10 Jackson units.

Each discharge to waters which may be used for irrigation shall conform with the following additional specific guidelines:

1) The concentration of boron in the discharge shall not exceed 0.5 mg/l.

2) The amount of sodium in the discharge shall not exceed 60% of the total cations being discharged, expressed in milliequivalents per liter (me/l).

3) The discharge shall not contain more than 5.0 milliequivalents per liter of chloride.

In addition there are severe limitations, varying from State to State, on the concentration of ammonia and chloramines, both toxic to fish.

Although these may be modified before issuance as standards, they will be rigorous. These, combined with the determined drive of the environmentalists for a zero discharge law, makes a complete water reuse decision by management look attractive.

The first comprehensive book on this subject was published by the California State Water Quality Control Board in 1952.[3] A larger second edition was issued in 1963.[4] The extensive studies in aqueous pollution by the Federal Government resulted in publication of the Report of the Committee on Water Quality Criteria by FWPCA in 1968.[5] These three books covered all phases of pollution and its effect on the environment.

The flood of data on water quality criteria in the literature was so great the State of California, rather than update its book, requested FWPCA to assume this responsibility. A new series titled "Water Quality Criteria Data Book" was started in 1970 and is continued by FWPCA's successor, the Environmental Protection Agency (EPA). Four volumes have been issued, with more to come These cover "Organic Pollution of Fresh Water,"[6] "Inorganic Chemical Pollution,"[7] "Effects of Industrial Chemicals on Aquatic Life,"[8] and "Recreational Water Quality Criteria."[9].

Literature Search

The first step in deciding on water reuse is to learn what has been done. There are many sources of literature information, of which the most promising are:

—The Annual Literature Review of the Journal of the Water Pollution Control Federation. Always the June issue.

—Chemical Abstracts—American Chemical Society,
Section 60—Sewage, Wastes, Section 61—Water.

There are three broad overviews of water reuse that are worth reading, and will give leads to other good information sources:

—Journal of the American Water Works Association, October 1971 covering the Symposium on Water Reuse at annual AWWA meeting in Denver, 1971. This includes ten articles covering both municipal and industrial water reuse.

—Water Reuse. 1967 Chemical Engineering Progress Symposium Series of the American Institute of Chemical Engineers. These thirty-nine articles include nine on conservation of water by reuse in various countries.

—Water in the Chemical and Allied Industries. Society of Chemical Industry, London Monograph 34. 1970. This covers sources of supply, quality criteria for use, and factors influencing decisions whether to treat for disposal or reuse. A very good outline of European practices.

Individual organizations may have unique problems. Someplace in the above list will be found references that will bear directly on their problems. Particular attention should be paid to the literature references at the end of each article.

EPA has issued a book on Water Quality Management[10] that puts water reuse in perspective. It is important to know about not only what has been published, but also what is being developed and when it will result in publication. EPA lists ongoing projects of the National Water Quality Research Program[11] and one dealing in part with reuse in the Water Utilities Industry.[12]

EPA considers promotion of industrial water reuse one of its most important objectives. Its book on how industrial waste projects are selected for funding[13] and its three books detailing active projects [14–16] should be studied carefully by any Pollution Control Technology for the following industrial areas:

Metal and Metal Products
Chemicals and Allied Products
Power Production—Non-Thermal
Paper and Allied Products
Petroleum and Coal Products
Food and Kindred Products
Machinery and Transportation
Stone, Clay, and Glass Products
Textile Mill Products
Lumber and Wood Products
Rubber and Plastics Products
Miscellaneous Industrial Sources
Joint Industrial/Municipal Wastes.

Basin management for water reuse

An extensive study was made by the Alamo Area Council of Governments for complete water reuse in the San Antonio River Basin.[17] The cost of this completely closed cycle was compared to importation of surface water to make up the expected deficit of well water by the year 2000, with conventional treatment for disposal. The comparable costs were so close (within the expected error of the estimates) that a decision would be made on some basis other than cost. The report was computerized, and the formulae so developed that any other basin could plug in its data and get a reliable answer.

Studies are starting to compare wide area gathering systems having a single treating plant with localized treatment plants for effluent reuse at the point of origin. The former has the advantage of a single set of operators, but the disadvantage of an expensive gathering system. Also the production of such a large volume of treated water at one point may exceed the reuse capacity at that point, necessitating an expensive distribution system. The latter has the advantage of low cost gathering systems, but the dual disadvantages of the cost of multiple treating plants, and a set of operators at each.

Disposal of treated wastewater underground (either by surface flooding or subsurface injection) comes under the classification of disposal into a public supply. Water is continually moving into and out of the basin, as with a surface stream. An exception would be in the case of a closed basin with no water outflow. Such a study was made at Hemet, California[18,19] on re-utilization of wastewater recycled through groundwater. The major portion of the study was to demonstrate it is a closed basin.

Agricultural irrigation

The practice of using sewage for agricultural irrigation has been carried on as long as there has been sewage. Blaney[20] says that the future and the economic welfare of agriculture in the state of Israel is more dependent on supply and quality of irrigation water than any other single resource. The total water resources are estimated at two billion cubic meters of which 1.5 billion cubic meters will be used for agriculture. The return flow from sewage and irrigation will be 165 million cubic meters. Dye[21] reviews practices of the use of treated sewage in irrigation in the western United States and stresses the value of the fertilizer content of the effluent. He gives detailed data on the fertilizing value of the Tucson, Arizona effluent. Eldridge[22] in a statistical study of irrigation in the United States finds that, on an average, two-thirds of the applied sewage is lost by evaporation on land and water surfaces and by transpiration by plants. One-third passes into the ground water table and is returned for reuse as irrigation water. He gives a detailed study of the degradation of water quality in passage through the soil.

Guyman[23] says that plans to use sewage effluent at Coronado, California for golf course irrigation had to be abandoned because of the high chloride content of 350 to 1200 parts per million. Interestingly enough, Sloan[24] reports that the 0.5 million gallon per day activated sludge effluent at the Virginia Keys plant near Miami, Florida is used for golf course irrigation after rapid sand filtration and blending with city water to reduce the chloride content from 1300 parts per million to 900 parts per million. The difference may lie in the leaching effect of much higher rainfall in Florida.

Hyde[25] gives a very interesting report on the use of activated sludge effluent in Golden Gate Park at San Francisco. The treatment plant was constructed in 1932 with a capacity of one million gallons per day. He describes the source and quality of the raw sewage, the quality and various uses of the effluent and describes plans for the future expansion. Merz[26] discusses the desirability of nutrients in sewage as fertilizers and describes in detail the use of treated sewage effluent on twelve golf courses. He reports that in a few cases there have been some odor problems but there has never been a health problem. Prochel,[27] reporting on the reuse of sewage for agricultural purposes in eastern Europe, gives the content of nitrogen, phosphorus, and potassium of the treated sewage and says it contains a small amount of toxic sulfides and a large amount of toxic lipids. In spite of this, it is estimated that irrigation with this sewage will increase the meadow crops five times, the field crops two times, and the yield of fish from ponds by four times.

Some entirely new chapters are being written in the history of irrigation reuse of wastewater. Thermal pollution control restrictions aimed at power generating plants and industries automatically catch some municipal wastewater plants. If effluent discharge to surface water systems is to be restricted, application to land is the most likely alternate. Treatment costs are much lower than for industrial or municipal reuse. Land application of sewage sludges for their fertilizer value, such as the "Prairie Plan" of the Metropolitan Sanitary District of Greater Chicago, can be extended to include the effluent also. There are intriguing possibilities for use of the effluent as it is being transported to its land destination. It can be used as an elongated cooling pond for electric generating plants. It might be used for some of its distance for freight barges. It would be a dependable supply for water using industries that want a rural site. If properly treated it could be used for recharge of underground water strata enroute.

The imminent prohibition of disposal of sewage sludge at Los Angeles to the ocean or by incineration makes transport eastward to the desert the next best alternate. As in the Chicago case, the system could be expanded to include at least some of the effluent.

This turning inland of municipal wastewater will bring many interesting chemical, health, and engineering problems. It may also help solve some social problems by aiding the dispersal of many urban industries. Perhaps it will also aid the return to the family farm of many who left the farm for the city welfare check.

Irrigation has its own wastewater problem[28,29]. Irrigation return flows, with dissolved mineral salts and nitrogen nutrients leached from the soil, are a serious surface water pollution problem that must be solved. The Firebaugh, California Study[30] originally started to remove nitrogen nutrients for disposal to surface water has been expanded to upgrade the return flow for irrigation reuse. The membrane processes developed by the Office of Saline Water may make this a practical system.

The 300,000 acre feet per year irrigation return flow from the Wellton-Mohawk project in Southwestern Arizona introduces so much mineral salts into the already salty Colorado River that the water is unsatisfactory for irrigation in Mexico. The present scheme of diverting the irrigation return flow through a canal to the Gulf of California may be superceded by reuse of the water for subsurface injection into the geothermal formations in the Imperial Valley of California to prevent land subsidence as superheated water is withdrawn for power production and desalting for fresh water.

Recreation

For a long time the health hazard prevented the direct use of treated effluent for recreational purposes. Irrigation of golf courses and parks, which perhaps belongs under irrigation, has been practiced for years with no known adverse health results. The classic Santee Project [31] produced such a wealth of information, especially on the microbiological and virological aspects, that other similar projects are developing.

A second problem with treated sewage effluent in recreational lakes is algal growth. Not only do such growths make the water unsightly, but they limit fish production. Algae generate oxygen during daylight hours, but not during dark time. They do continue to use oxygen during dark time, and may so deplete the dissolved oxygen content that fish cannot survive.

Dryden and Stern[32] report in meticulous detail the work at Lancaster, California leading to the use of sewage effluent from oxidation ponds in an aquatic park with three lakes totaling nineteen acres area. The concentration effect of evaporation is overcome by withdrawal of lake water for park irrigation.

The Lake Tahoe, California Project is perhaps even better known than the one at Santee[33,34]. The sewage from the Sanitary District in the area is treated in an elaborate tertiary treatment plant to a very high quality. The effluent is transported over a divide to another watershed. In a one billion gallon lake on Indian Creek is a recreational lake used for water sports and fishing. During the summer lake water is used for agricultural irrigation. A significant feature is that the dissolved oxygen content has never been below saturation.

These three California projects are reported in such detail they can be the basis for development of any recreational project involving the use of treated municipal wastewater. Once the effluent is upgraded to recreational quality it can be used for many other purposes.

Potable

There will be times and places it is necessary to treat waste water for return to the water mains. Limited supply of fresh water restricts the development of a community, even with careful use of water. Other than lawn watering there is little actual consumption of water in a municipality. Assuming a 5% or 10% loss in concentrates from the treating operations, a community can sustain a ten to twentyfold growth in non-irrigation season. Records at San Antonio, Texas show a 35% loss during the summer, but a very low loss during the winter.[17] A highly industrialized community is likely to lose a large quantity of water because of evaporation in cooling operations.

The overriding concern in this service is health. Pathogenic bacterial control is well established, but assurance of viral control is not so certain. Testing for viruses is difficult. It is not possible for the analyst to report the water contains no viruses. All he can report is that no viruses have been found. Nevertheless many careful studies, and the history of potable reuse of wastewater, give assurance the health danger is minimal.

The American Water Works Association policy statement on "The Use of Reclaimed Wastewaters as a Public Water-Supply Source"[35] concludes with the statement:

> The Association believes that the use of reclaimed wastewaters for public water-supply purposes should be deferred until research and development demonstrates that such use will not be detrimental to the health of the public and will not affect adversely the wholesomeness and potability of water for domestic use.

Such a conservative attitude is proper for this organization. It does not prevent communities where the need is great from going ahead with reuse of treated wastewater to augment their water supplies.

South Africa has led the way. Stander[36] reports the intensive study that led to the recommendation for the reuse of sewage effluent at Windhoek. Cillie, *et al.*,[37] report the activation of this recommendation to practice. Stander[38] reports details of six years of operation. Shuval[39] discusses the health application of reclaimed wastewater in Israel, and Obr[40] its use in Arizona.

Jopling, *et al.*,[41] details the unreliability of treatment plants now in use and the need to design plants with fail-safe features. Merrell, *et al.*,[31] do cover in detail such features in the existing recreational use at Santee, and Almgren[42] details the study to upgrade the Santee effluent from recreational to potable use. The City of Denver, Colorado is proceeding along the line of the AWWA policy statement to a successive step study started in 1969 to upgrade its effluent for potable use in 1985.[43,44]

A very significant study reported by Gouveia and Hooton[45] on the reuse of hospital wastewater for potable purposes by the U.S. Army Medical Department demonstrates the desirability of semipermeable membranes, such as for reverse osmosis, for the simultaneous removal of bacteria, ova, cysts, viruses, and most of the dissolved mineral content. The system designed for the Military is small in capacity and is capable of being run by non-technical operators. It produces a minimum of concentrate which is incinerated. It is well designed for use in disaster areas. Its sequential processes which give fail-safe backup can be applied in any larger size.

In spite of the AWWA caution, present technology can produce potable water from wastewater. The treating plant will be different from the present municipal water treating plants, and more costly, both in capital and operating expense. In those locations where the need is urgent the benefits will be great and the costs trivial.

Industrial

The author's experience with industrial water reuse began in 1931. One Oklahoma petroleum refinery and a nearby natural gasoline plant were being sued for stream pollution.[46] This suit was won by going to zero discharge, with the treated effluent used for cooling tower make-up. Another Oklahoma refinery was running out of water, and was kept in operation by recovery of all its wastewater, another case of zero discharge.[47] In 1937 the water shortage was so severe its own wastewater was inadequate, and it used the treated sewage from a nearby city to augment its supply.[48] In 1943 the first refinery supplemented its water supply for a wartime expansion by taking sewage effluent from a nearby city, combining it with its own wastewater in a new treatment plant with a unique control system with separate controls on each wastewater integrated into a single set of chemical feeders.[48] These two case histories are typical of what some other industrial plants were doing.

A zinc smelter in the desert near Chihuahua, Mexico could not get enough fresh water to supply the demand for cooling furnace walls, granulating slag, and supplying domestic demand. Installation of equipment for tertiary treatment of its primary treated sewage effluent produced an effluent that gave no odor when used for slag granulation.[48]

At Odessa, Texas an industrial complex consisting of a Shell Oil Company refinery, several El Paso Products Company petrochemical and fertilizer plants, a General Tire Company rubber plant, and a Rexall Chemical Company plastics plant moved into a water-poor but petroleum feed stock-rich area. Odessa was selected because it had the most and best sewage in the area.[49] The entire 6 mgd secondary effluent is upgraded in the complex for all services, including boiler feed. The wastewater from the industrial complex is treated for subsurface injection for secondary oil recovery in a nearby oil field, a tertiary use of the wastewater and a zero discharge for the complex. The city is not generating additional sewage fast enough to meet the expanding needs of the complex. The oil field needs are decreasing because of an increase in salt water production. At present the complex wastewater not taken by the oil producing company is injected into disposal wells at the complex. El Paso Products Company is considering tertiary treatment, probably reverse osmosis, for recovery of 1.5 mgd water. The General Tire Company is operating a distillation plant for recovery of 0.5 mgd water from its high dissolved solids wastewater.

Kimberly-Clark Corporation's tissue plant at Fullerton, California installed a wastewater reuse system[50] to demonstrate that it could build product plants near its market, even in water short areas. The cost of shipping paper pulp is small compared to the cost of shipping the finished products.

These case histories are typical of what is going on all through industry. The reasons vary, but they all have that compulsion factor, and usually it is money.

Sawyer[51] in a comprehensive article looks at the total picture on wastewater treatment technology. He includes most of the newer techniques. such as reverse osmosis and freezing, now becoming practical. Cecil[52] evolves a management technique of evaluating the wastewater volume that will be produced and available for reuse before establishing how much fresh water will be needed for make-up in designing a new manufacturing plant.

The massive support by EPA, as outlined in Projects of the Industrial Pollution Control Branch 1970,[14] 1971,[15] and 1972[16] brings to a focus the potential for reuse in every branch of industry. The solid design and operating data developed, sometimes by pilot plant studies and other times by full-scale demonstration plants, will permit management to proceed to water reuse instead of disposal with assurance of satisfactory results.

It seems reasonable to assume that with the knowledge to design workable reuse treatment plants, the high cost of treatment for disposal, the management involvement with disposal permits and regular reports, reuse may become accepted practice, and disposal of treated wastewater to the aqueous environment the exception.

REFERENCES

1. Water Reuse, 1967. Lawrence K. Cecil, Editor, *Chem. Eng. Prog. Symp. Series*, **63**, No. 78, 273 p.
2. McCallum, G. E., 1959. Tomorrow's Challenge in Water Pollution Control. Proc. 14th Ind. Waste Conf. Engineering Bulletin, Purdue Univ., Vol. 64, No. 5. pp. 669–677.
3. McKee, Jack E. and Richard H. Gilman. 1952. Water Quality Criteria. State Water Quality Control Board, Sacramento, California.
4. McKee, Jack E. and Harold W. Wolf. 1963. Water Quality Criteria, Second Edition. State Water Quality Control Board, Sacramento, California. Publication No. 3–A. 550 p.
5. Report of the Committee on Water Quality Criteria. 1968. Federal Water Quality Administration, Washington, D.C. 234 p.
6. Water Quality Criteria Data Book. Vol. 1. 1970. Organic Chemical Pollution of Fresh Water. EPA Water Pollution Control Research Series 18010DPV12/70. 380 p.
7. Water Quality Criteria Data Book, Vol. 2. 1971. Inorganic Chemical Pollution of Fresh Water. EPA Water Pollution Control Research Series 18010DPV07/71. 281 p.
8. Water Quality Criteria Data Book, Vol. 3. 1971. Effects of Chemicals on Aquatic Life. EPA Water Pollution Control Series 18050GWV05/71. 628 p.
9. Water Quality Criteria Data Book, Vol. 4. 1971. Recreational Water Quality Criteria. EPA Water Pollution Control Series.
10. Enviro Control, Inc. 1971. Systems Analysis for Water Quality Management-Surveys and Abstracts. EPA Office of Water Programs. SD 1 09/71. 257 p.
11. Projects of the National Water Quality Control Research Program. 1971. EPA Water Pollution Control Research Series 16080(328203) 35 p.
12. AWWA Research Foundation. 1971. Information Resource: Water Pollution Control in the Water Utilities Industry. EPA Water Pollution Control Research Series 12120EUR 11/71. 169 p.
13. Synectics Corp. 1971. A System for Industrial Waste Treatment RD&D Project Priority Assignment. EPA Water Pollution Control Research Series 12000FLX02/71. 92 p.
14. Projects of the Industrial Pollution Control Branch. 1970. EPA Water Pollution Control Research Series 12000 07/70.
15. Projects of the Industrial Pollution Control Branch. 1971. EPA Water Pollution Control Research Series 12000 07/71.
16. Projects of the Industrial Pollution Control Branch. 1972. EPA Water Pollution Control Research Series. In Press.
17. Alamo Area Council of Governments. 1972. Basin Management for Water Reuse. EPA Water Pollution Control Research Series 16110EAX02/72. 292 p.
18. Boen, Doyle F., James H. Bunts, Jr., and Robert J. Currie. 1971. Study of Reutilization of Wastewater Recycled Through Groundwater. Vol. 1. EPA Water Pollution Control Research Series. 16060DDZ07/71. 180 p.
19. Boen, Doyle F., James H. Bunts, Jr. and Robert J. Currie. 1971. Study of Reutilization of Wastewater Recycled Through Groundwater. Vol. 2. EPA Water Pollution Control Research Series 16060DDZ07/71.
20. Blaney, H. F. 1962. Utilization of Water and Irrigation in Israel. *J. Irrigation and Drainage Div., Am. Soc. Civil Eng'rs.* **88**:1R2:55.
21. Dye, E. O. 1958. Crop Irrigation with Sewage Plan Effluent. *Sewage Ind. Wastes.* **30**:825–828.
22. Eldridge, Edward F. 1963. Irrigation as a Source of Water Pollution. *J. Water Pollution Control Federation.* **35**:614–625.
23. Guyman, B. C. 1957. Coronado to Use Effluent for Golf Course Irrigation. *Wastes Engr.* **28**:80.
24. Sloan, G. 1960. Waste Water Reclamation for Golf Course Irrigation. *J. Sanit. Eng. Div., Am. Soc. Civil Eng'rs.* **86**:SA3:167.
25. Hyde, Chas. G. 1937. The Beautification and Irrigation of Golden Gate Park with Activated Sludge Effluent. *Sewage Works J.* **9**:929–941.
26. Merz, Robert C. 1959. Wastewater Reclamation. *J. Sanit. Eng. Div., Am. Soc. Civil Eng'rs.* **85**:SA6:79–8.5
27. Prochal, P. 1958. Agricultural Usage of Sewage from the Town of Zory. *Rolnictwo* **51** : 165.
28. Skogerboe, Gaylord V. and James P. Law, Jr. 1971. Research Needs for Irrigation Return Flow Quality Control. EPA Water Pollution Control Research Series 13030 11/71.
29. U.S. Bureau of Reclamation. 1971. Techniques to Nitrogen in Drainage Effluents During Transport. EPA Water Pollution Control Research Series 13030ELY 6/71–10. REC–R2–71–10 DWR NO. 174–17.
30. Law, James F., Jr. 1971. National Irrigation Return Flow Research and Development Program. EPA Water Pollution Control Research Series 13030 GJS 12/71.
31. Merell, John C., Jr., William F. Jopling, Roderick F. Bott, Albert Katko and Herbert E. Pintler. 1967. The Santee Recreation Project, Santee, California. Final Report. Federal Water Pollution Control Administration Research Series WP–20–7.
32. Dryden, Franklin D. and Gerald Stern. 1969. From Phosphate and Algae to Fish and Fun with Waste Water—Lancaster, California. EES Series Report No. 34. College of Engineering, Univ. of Arizona, Tucson, Arizona.
33. Culp, Russell L. 1969. Reclaimed Water as a Resource. EES Series Report No. 34. College of Engineering, Univ. of Arizona, Tucson, Arizona. pp. 41–58.

34. South Tahoe Public Utility District. 1971. Advanced Waste Water Treatment as Practiced at South Tahoe. EPA Water Pollution Control Research Series 170110-ELQ8/71. 437 pp.
35. American Water Works Association. 1971. Policy Statement on the Use of Reclaimed Wastewaters as a Public Water Supply Source. *J. AWWA* **63**, p. 609. October 1971.
36. Stander, G. J. 1965. Final Report on Reclamation of Purified Sewage Effluent for Augmentation of Domestic Water Supply of Windhoek. CSIR Contract Report No. C WAT 4. Pretoria, South Africa. 74 pp.
37. Cillie, G. G., L. R. J. van Vuuren, G. J. Stander and F. F. Kolbe. 1966. The Reclamation of Sewage Effluents for Domestic Use. *Proc. Third International Conference, Int. Assoc. on Water Pollution Research*. S. H. Jenkins and L. Mendia, Editors. Pub. by Water Pollution Control Federation, Washington, D.C. pp. 1–35.
38. Stander, G. J. 1972. Tertiary Treatment—The Cornerstone of Water Quality Protection and Water Resources Optimization. Proc. Applications of New Concepts of Physical–Chemical Wastewater Treatment. Vandergilt Univ., Nashville, Tennessee. Sept. 1972.
39. Shuval, Hillel I. 1972. Health Applications of Reclaimed Water. Proc. Applications of New Concepts of Physical–Chemical Wastewater Treatment. Vanderbilt Univ., Nashville, Tennessee. Sept. 1972.
40. Obr, Joseph E. 1969. Waste Water Reuse and Public Health. EES Series Report No. 24. College of Engineering, Univ. of Arizona, Tucson, Arizona. pp. 111–12.
41. Jopling, William F., David G. Deaner and Henry J. Ongerth. 1971. Fitness Needs for Wastewater-Reclamation Plants. *J. AWWA* **63**, pp. 626–629. October 1971.
42. Almgren, Howard. 1972. Upgrading Recreation Water for Domestic Use at Santee, California. EPA Water Pollution Control Research Series. In Press.
43. Linstedt, K. D., K. J. Miller and E. R. Bennett. 1971. Metropolitan Successive Use of Available Water. *J. AWWA* **63**, pp. 610–615. October 1971.
44. Heaton, Richard. 1972. It's Reuse in the Rockies. *Water Wastes Engr*. **9**, pp. 32–34. June 1972.
45. Gouveia, Americo and K. A. H. Hooton. 1968. Potable Water from Hospital Wastes by Reverse Osmosis. *Water*—**1968**. L. K. Cecil, Editor. Chem. Eng. Prog. Symp. Ser. 90. pp. 280–284.
46. Frost, H. N. (Jack) and L. K. Cecil. 1932. Reclamation of Waste Water from Oil Refineries. Unpublished Paper resented at American Chemical Society Meeting at Denver, Colorado. August 1932.
47. Willson, C. O. 1931. Two Oklahoma Refineries Install Waste Water Recovery Plants. *Oil Gas J*. **30**:18.
48. Cecil, Lawrence K. 1964. Sewage Treatment Plant Effluent for Water Reuse. *Water and Sewage Works*. Vol. III, pp. 421–423. September 1964.
49. Kirkpatrick, F. W., Jr. and E. F. Smythe. 1967. History and Possible Future of Multiple Reuse of Sewage Effluent at the Odessa, Texas Industrial Complex. *Water Reuse*, Lawrence K. Cecil, Editor. Chem. Eng. Prog. Symp. Ser. 78, Vol. 63. pp. 201–209.
50. Billings, R. M. 1962. One Paper Company's Policies and Approach to the Pollution Problem. *J. Water Pollution Control Federation* **34**: pp. 883–890.
51. Sawyer, George A. 1972. New Trends in Wastewater Treatment and Recycle. *Chem. Eng*. **79**, No. 16, pp. 120–128. July 24, 1972.
52. Cecil, Lawrence K. 1969. Water Reuse and Disposal. *Chem. Eng*. **76**, No. 10, pp. 92–104. May 5, 1969.

LAWRENCE K. CECIL
Champaign, Illinois 61820

WATER TRANSPORT: see HYDROLOGY; WATER FLOW

WATER TREATMENT

Introduction

Water of course is used for many purposes associated with human activity. In its natural state it occurs in and on the ground in subsurface and surface reservoirs. The quality and reliability of a source of water will vary considerably, both in time and space. This means that characteristics (chemical, physical and biological) will differ greatly depending upon the location and type of source. It also means that a given source may vary over the seasons of the year.

Thus in the selection of a water source, consideration is usually given to the use to which the water will ultimately be put so as to minimise the cost of treatment. Simultaneously consideration must be given to the reliability of the source to provide an accurate and constant source of supply. It will be seen later in this section that a groundwater supply may enjoy the benefit of requiring little or no treatment, while a surface supply such as a river, pond or lake may require considerable and perhaps seasonally varying treatment. However, a surface supply is visible and therefore more reliable whereas a groundwater supply may just disappear with no warning or notice.

In certain areas, freshwater is so scarce that the source must be accepted and choices are not available. The history of water treatment dates back to the early Egyptian civilizations where the murky waters of the Nile River were held in large open basins to allow the mud to settle out. The earliest archeological records of a piped water supply and wastewater disposal system date back some five thousand years to Nippur of Samaria.[1] In the Nippur ruins there exists an arched drain with an extensive system of drainage from palaces and residences to convey wastes to the outskirts of the City. Water was drawn through a similar system from wells and cisterns.

The earliest records of water treatment appear in the Sanskrit medical lore and Egyptian wall inscriptions.[2] Writings from about 2000 BC describe how to purify "foul water" by boiling in copper vessels, exposing to sunlight, filtering through charcoal and cooling in an earthenware vessel. There is little concerning water treatment in the Old Testament, but Elisha under instruction from the Lord "healed" certain waters so that "there shall not be from thence any more death or barren land." This "healing" was accomplished when Elisha "went forth unto the spring of the waters and cast salt in there . . ." It is not clear if this "salt" was a fertilizer to help grow crops or if it was some chemical to render the water safe.

Settling was first introduced as a modification of decanting apparatus used for water or wine. This apparatus was pictured on the walls of the tombs of Amentootep II and Rameses II in the 15th and 13th centuries BC. An engineering report on water supply was written by the then water commissioner for Rome in 98 AD. He described an aqueduct with a settling basin.

In 1627 the experiments of Sir Francis Bacon were published just after his death, and were the first to describe coagulation as well as sedimentation and filtration as a means of treating drinking water. The first filtered supply of water for an entire town was built in Paisley, Scotland in 1804. Starting with a carted supply, a piped distribution system was added in 1807.[2]

However it was not until 1854, in London, that it was demonstrated that certain diseases could be transmitted by water. Dr. John Snow suggested that a cholera outbreak in a certain area in London resulted directly from the use of the Broad Street pump, and was in fact the source of infection in the parish of St. James. Dr. Snow recommended that the use of the pump should be discontinued and the vestrymen of the parish agreeing, the disease subsequently abated in that area.

This discovery was all the more incredible as the germ theory of disease, defined by Pasteur and subsequently postulated by Koch, had not at that time been clarified. Subsequently disinfection of water by the addition of chlorine was introduced on a municipal scale. This step, together with an adequate and sanitary distribution system, probably did more to reduce the deaths due to typhoid and cholera than any other single item.

In 1854, cholera claimed a mortality of 10,675 people in London, England. In 1910, the death rate from typhoid fever in the City of Toronto, Canada, was 40.8 per 100,000. By 1931 it had fallen to 0.5 per 100,000. These improvements all related to the extensive water purification and sterilization techniques which are being introduced to municipal water treatment systems during that period.[3]

In general, the treatment processes of water can be subdivided into three groups: physical, chemical and biological processes. The biological processes are generally reserved for waters grossly contaminated with organic (putrescible) carbon such as sewage or industrial waste waters. These waters are not normally considered as suitable for drinking supplies, but undoubtedly as demand for water increases *all* available sources will have to be examined. However, for the present purposes we will consider that the biological stabilization of organically polluted waters will be dealt with under the section wastewater treatment. It should, however, be realized that there is a very fine line between treated wastewater discharged into a water body and the use of that water body as a source for drinking water and the treatment of the wastewater before discharge. Clearly in those areas where wastes are still not treated prior to release, a water treatment plant is essentially dealing with the treatment of diluted wastewater.

We must therefore determine the significance of water quality before we examine the types of treatment which is necessary to achieve this quality. Water quality very much depends upon the use for which the water was intended. For example, industrial boiler feed water requires a very low hardness because the hardness tends to deposit on the pipes in the boiler system and reduces the efficiency of the heat transfer. However, if the hardness of the boiler feed water is zero, the water tends to be very corrosive and this of course is also very undesirable for a boiler system.

If the water is to be used for a brewery or a distillery, a number of other chemcal parameters are important. If the water is to be used for cooling then clearly the temperature is one of the most impoıtant parameters.

In the past the methods for setting standards for water supplies was very much a hit and miss affair and relied pretty well upon the philosophy of "If no one complains, all is well." Clearly, that is not a very satisfactory criterion. There are a number of drinking water standards or objectives published by various nations of the world, such as the World Health Organization International and European drinking water standards (1963 and 1961), the U.S. Public Health Service Drinking Water Standards (1962) and the Canadian Drinking Water Standards and Objectives (1968). These standards are established on the principle that water in a public water supply system must be treated to the degree which is suitable for the highest and best use. The highest and best use for water of course is human consumption. This can frequently be argued as a rather unnecessary quality when one considers that much water which is processed in a municipal plant is used for watering lawns, washing cars and windows. However, the difficulty in ensuring that a second-class, perhaps unsafe water supply is not used as a potable supply is extremely difficult. It will be found that very few cities have a dual water supply representing a drinking water system and a non-potable system.

A few large cities, particularly when they are adjacent to large standing bodies of water, occasionally have a fire water supply system where the water is taken untreated from the lake or river and pumped under high pressure through a system connected only to fire hydrants and sprinklers.

Thus, assuming that natural water requires some kind of treatment in order to achieve certain predetermined standards, and the processes of treating these waters can be subdivided into physical and chemical processes, the remainder of this section will deal with the physical and chemical methods of treating water for municipal or industrial use.

Water Sources

The magnitude of the problem of supplying water to the major cities of the world is in fact a huge engineering problem. According to a U.S. Department of Commerce estimate, the cities of the United States in 1955 with a total population of 110 million produced and distributed 17 billion gallons of water daily to their domestic, commercial and industrial consumers. Of this, 12.88 billion gallons were from surface water sources which usually, it will be seen, require more elaborate treatment, whereas the remaining 4.12 billion gallons came from groundwater sources—only a small proportion of which would require treatment.[4] The most voluminous source of water is the oceans. It is estimated that they contain about 1,060 trillion acre-feet.[5] Clearly this water is of little value as a potable source, but it certainly remains the main reservoir in the hydrologic cycle.

It can be seen from Figure 1 that evaporation is the first step in the purification of ocean water, and this requires the full energy of the sun in order to accomplish. Precipitation, percolation and runoff are all parts of the cycle of water which is without a beginning or an ending. Of the water which falls upon the earth, part of it directly runs off to the nearest stream or lake, and part of it infiltrates down to the groundwater table and percolates through the groundwater, also into a stream or lake. Transpiration takes place through the leaves of green plants, and evaporation takes place from the groundwater, where it surfaces through swamps, lakes or rivers, and of course from the ocean. Of the water that soaks into the ground, part of it is retained in the capillary voids near the surface. Thus it can be said that the potential sources of water for society consist of wells, which are drilled or dug down to the groundwater table and withdraw water from that level; springs, which are natural outcroppings of groundwater table through rocks or ground; rivers, where the groundwater table has naturally broken through the ground and flown in a certain direction sufficiently to gouge out a channel for the water to flow in; lakes, where large bodies of water gather usually somewhere along a river system; and finally the ocean, if no other sources are available and the ocean is close by. The benefit derived from the costly treatment required to desalinate the ocean under these circumstances is outweighed by the necessity of having a fresh water source at any cost.

There are new water sources which exist deep in the earth's crust. These sources are rarely considered, due to the high salt and sulphur content which is frequently found in them.

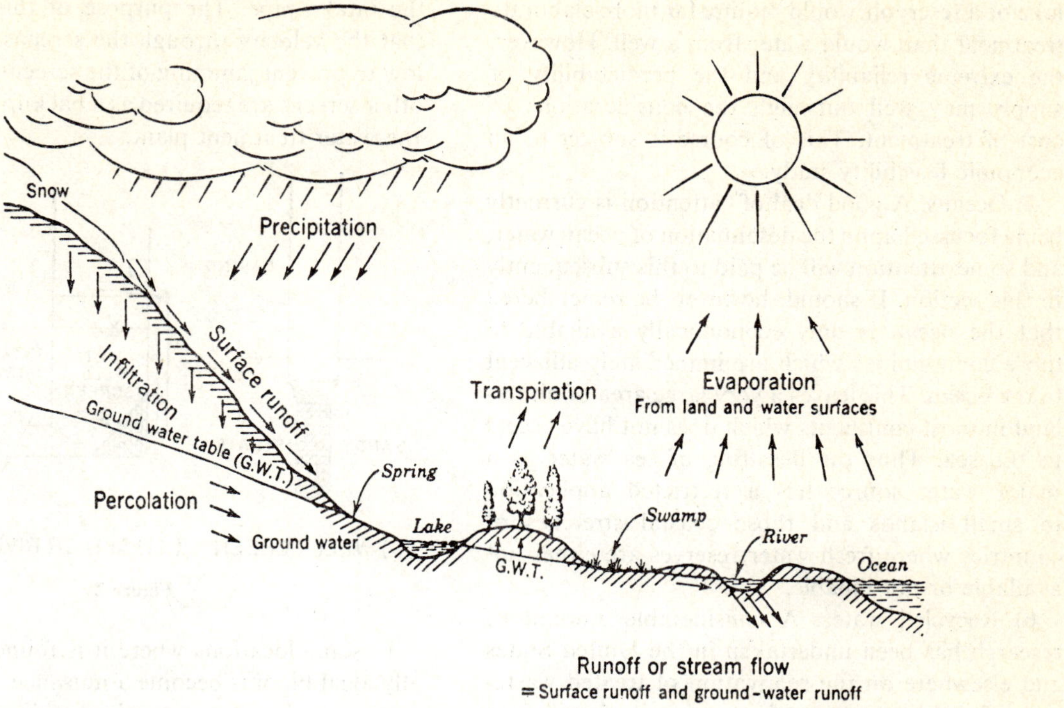

Figure 1 Hydrologic Cycle (Fair and Geyer, Water Supply and Wastewater Disposal)

The recycling of used water of course is a further source which may be tapped directly. It can be seen from the hydrologic cycle that all water is being continually reused, but the direct recycling of municipal treated sewage into the potable water treatment plant is being considered in some water-scarce areas.

Some of the advantages and disadvantages which might be listed for the various sources of water are as follows:

1) Wells provide usually an extremely pure source of potable water. Rarely is any treatment required of this water, certainly before it is safe to drink, although certain industrial uses may require the removal of some of the soluble salts such as hardness. One of the major disadvantages of wells is that they cannot be observed and therefore must be considered as somewhat unreliable. Frequently it has been experienced in the country, if a drought has persisted for a few days or a few weeks (depending on the environment) and the well has been pumped unusually hard, that the well will run dry. There is never very much warning of this kind of occurrence and therefore for a municipal supply it has the distinct disadvantage of being considered somewhat unreliable.

2) Springs are similarly unreliable, and have a further disadvantage in that they require a rather elaborate engineering system to capture them and concentrate them into one manageable system. Also, springs require rather a large protected area to ensure that man does not pollute this environment, thereby rendering the springwater unsafe.

3) Rivers tend also to be a little unreliable, although they do have the advantage that they can be observed and to some extent controlled through dams and other waterflow structures. Thus it can be seen, if the water level is falling, that a municipality may wish to impose water use restrictions to conserve water until such time as further augmentation of the supply is received through the hydrologic cycle. One of the major problems with a river source is that there is a considerable variation in the quality of the water. During the high flow flood period, there is frequently a considerable amount of silt and organic material which is washed off the ground, whereas at other times of year the water may be relatively clean and require remarkably little treatment prior to distribution. This of course means that water treatment facilities must be installed to deal with the worst possible condition, and at other times of the year it may not in fact be necessary and therefore the equipment may lie idle.

4) Lakes and manmade reservoirs, due to the nature of flow through them, have a certain stability both from the point of view of quantity and quality. Undoubtedly, water coming from a

lake or a reservoir would require far more elaborate treatment than would water from a well. However, the extreme reliability and the predictability of supply may well outweigh the considerations of cost of treatment. This of course is subject to an economic feasibility study.

5) Oceans. A good deal of attention is currently being focussed upon the desalination of ocean water, and some attention will be paid to this subsequently in this section. It should, however, be remembered that the ocean is only economically available to those communities which are immediately adjacent to the ocean. This leaves a very large area of hinterland in most continents which does not have access to the sea. Thus the desalting of sea water as a major water source has a restricted application to small islands and those coastal stretches of countries where fresh water reserves are either not available or not reliable.

6) Recycled water. A considerable amount of research has been undertaken in the United States and elsewhere on the renovation of treated wastewater for the purposes of returning it directly into the potable supply. Some rather complex chemical and physical processes are required to make this a satisfactory process, and the details of many of these processes will be described subsequently in the next section of this chapter.

Physical Treatment

The items of treatment described under this section will be only those which alter the physical properties of the water or represent a unit process which is physical in nature. All of the processes described may be used individually, collectively or in any combination, in order to accomplish a pre-determined water quality.

1. *Screens*

Whatever the source of water, it is necessary to insert some kind of a screen in the system in order to prevent the passage of solids into the subsequent steps of water treatment. If the source of water is simply a well, the screens tend to be simply designed to prevent the admission of sand from the water-bearing strata into the pumping system. Where water supply is drawn from rivers or lakes, the intakes usually have to be screened and built of corrosion-resistant materials in order to prevent the admission of fish or logs or any other undesirable solids into the system. Intake screens are usually provided with openings approximately equal to one and one-half to two times the area of the intake pipe. The purpose of this is to ensure that the velocity through the screens is sufficiently low to prevent jamming of the screens. On occasion other screens are required as a backup system within the water treatment plant.

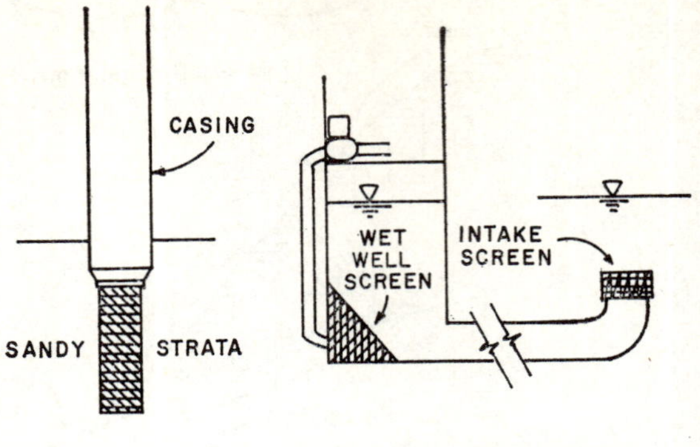

(I) WELL SCREEN (II) LAKE OR RIVER SCREEN

Figure 2

In some locations where it is found that seasonally algal blooms become a nuisance, a new type of screening known as microstraining has been introduced. Microstrainers are a very fine weave of stainless steel wire with apertures sufficiently small to prevent the passage of the microscopic algae which is normally found in an algal bloom. Such a screening system is normally only required on a seasonal basis and in certain locations where these problems are prevalent. Microstraining is conducted at such a very small diameter orifice that it is sometimes considered to be a part of a filtration process.

2. *Coagulation*

Although the basis of coagulation is in fact chemical treatment and will be discusses in the next section, the coagulation process itself (sometimes referred to as flocculation) is accomplished by a physical process involving the gentle agitation of the fluid which allows the small suspended particles to collide and agglomerate into heavier particles or flocs and settle out. Flocculation or coagulation is the principle used in the removal of turbidity from water. It will be shown subsequently that colloidal or very finely divided material will not settle very rapidly, whereas those same particles when coagulated into larger floc will settle quite rapidly. Various processes have been employed to accomplish flocculation. Some of these are: diffused air, baffles, transverse or parallel shaft mixers, vertical turbine mixers, to mention but a few.

The most common type of flocculator used today is the paddle type, the other methods having shown some disadvantage such as being too severe

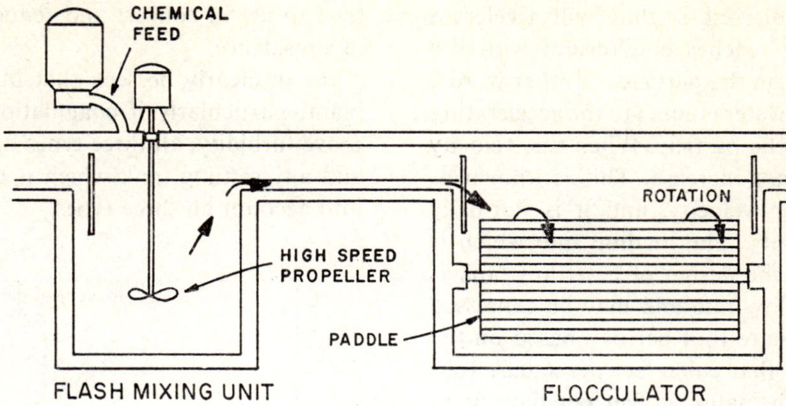

Figure 3

for the fragile floc, or being too inflexible, or being too costly to operate. Horizontally mounted paddles, either located transverse or parallel to the floor, consist of a shaft with a number of protruding arms on which are mounted various blades. The shaft rotates at a very slow rate of 60 to 100 rpm, causing a very gentle agitation which results in the flocculation of the particles. The time required for the flocculation process is very carefully controlled and strongly related to the dosage of chemical which is used. The chemicals used and the chemistry of this process will be described later.

Prior to the flocculation step which has just been described, occurs a flash mixing step when the chemicals are added and mixed very rapidly at high speed to get uniform distribution of the chemical in the stream. A variety of devices are used for this rapid mixing operation; frequently one of the most common includes the low lift pumps which are usually located adjacent to the intake where the water is lifted up into the treatment plant. Here of course the chemicals must be pumped into the pump casing at a higher pressure than the pump is producing, and the mixing takes place in the casing of the pump.

Other devices frequently used are venturi flumes, air jets, paddles, turbines, propellers, the latter being one of the most favoured and most widely used of the rapid mixing devices. It usually is composed of a vertical shaft driven by a motor on which one or more propeller blades are mounted. Baffles are frequently used to reduce the vortexing about the propeller shaft. Vortexing hinders the mixing operation. Detention periods are usually of the order of one to five minutes, usually at the lower end of this range. Considerable study has been done on the baffling arrangement in a flash mixing unit, and a variety of arrangements have been shown to be successful.

3. *Sedimentation*

Sedimentation or settling may be accomplished by a variety of means and mechanisms, depending on the material which is to be settled from the liquid.

a. Discrete Settling. This type of sedimentation is primarily concerned with the settling out of non-flocculent discrete particles in a fairly dilute system. The primary feature of this type of settling is that the particles do not flocculate and therefore their settling velocity and particle size remain the same throughout the period of settling. It will be seen later that this is quite different from other forms of settling.

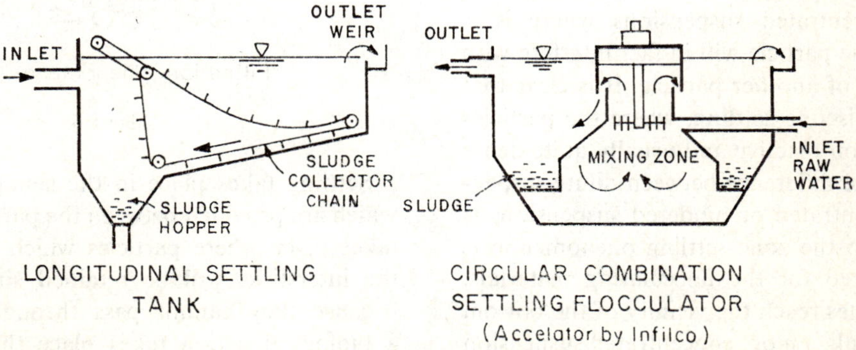

Figure 4

The particles in discrete settling will accelerate until the fluid/drag reaches equilibrium with the driving force acting on the particle. In other words, the resistance of the water is equal to the accelerating force of gravity on the particle. When this velocity is reached, it will not increase. This is known as the terminal settling velocity, and it is normally achieved quite rapidly. The loading rate which is used frequently for the design of a settling tank is known as the overflow rate and may be expressed in cubic feet per square foot per day based on the area. It can be seen that cubic feet per square foot per day is in fact the same as feet per day, or in fact a simple velocity. This velocity is defined as the settling velocity of the particles which are removed in this ideal basin if they enter at the surface.

Overflow rates or surface loadings of 150 gallons per day per square foot of tank surface are not unusual where the settling of sand, silt or clay are being accomplished by plain sedimentation.

b. Flocculent Settling The primary difference between this type of settling and the previous one is that in a flocculent system the larger particles subsiding at a slightly higher rate will overtake and coalesce with smaller particles to form even larger particles, which in turn increases the overall settling rate. Clearly, the greater the liquid depth, the greater will be the opportunity for this type of contact. There is no mathematical relationship which can be used to determine the general effect of flocculation on sedimentation, and empirical data is still required by studying individual laboratory cases. As a result, in flocculent settling the removal of suspended matter depends not only on the clarification rate but also on the depth.

This is one of the significant differences between non-flocculent and flocculent settling.

c. Zone Settling The previous two types of settling described have one property in common, and that is that they both deal with dilute suspensions. Zone settling, on the other hand, deals with very concentrated suspensions where it is assumed that one particle will in fact interfere with the settling rate of another particle. It is clear that in the type of discrete settling, where the particles are somewhat non-reactive and usually quite dense such as sand, the difference between dilute suspensions and concentrated or hindered suspensions is less apparent, so the zone settling phenomenon is usually considered for the flocculating materials. When the particles reach the vicinity of the bottom of the settling tank, a more concentrated suspension zone will be formed and the settling particles will tend to act in concert and reduce the overall rate of subsidence.

It can clearly be seen that in a water treatment plant, particularly if coagulation is applied to remove turbidity, all three types of settling will occur and any settling tank which is designed must take into account all three types.

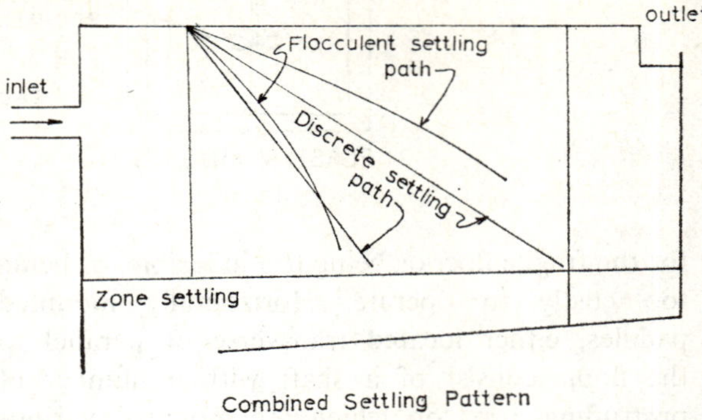

Figure 5

4. *Filtration*

As described earlier, it has been found in even the early Egyptian days that passing water through sand resulted in a reduction in suspended and colloidal matter, and resulted in a further clarification of the water. Water which is on occasion extremely turbid should, of course, first of all be treated by some coagulation or settling or combination of both. However, water which is normally not too turbid may be directly applied to filters or water which has previously been treated by sedimentation and/or coagulation may also be applied to filters to provide the final polishing and the production of clear, aesthetically acceptable water.

The filtration process actually consists of three phenomena occuring simultaneously.

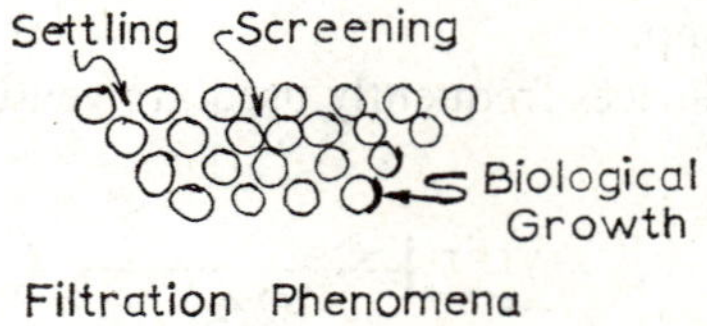

Figure 6

Settling takes place in the small settling basins which are provided between the particles. Screening takes place where particles which are larger than the interstices will be retained simply physically because they cannot pass through. And finally, a biological action takes place through bacterial growth which may occur on the particles of the

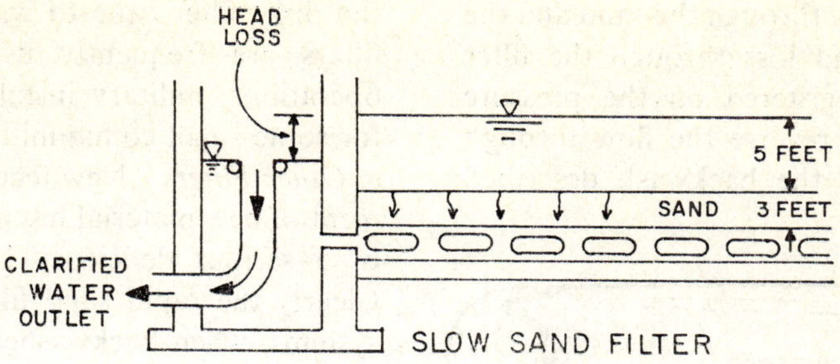

Figure 7

filter which grow at the expense of the soluble organic carbon passing through in the water. This latter phenomenon is not a very satisfactory way of removing organic carbon, because it does tend to plug up the filter fairly rapidly and reduce its effectiveness.

Filters have been developed through the ages through a series of steps which are mainly related to their operating characteristics or the material which is used as a filtering medium.

a. Slow sand filter The slow sand filter is, as it suggests, a process whereby water is allowed to pass very slowly through the system at rates of 2.5 to 7.5 million gallons per acre per day.

Although this type of filter has been used traditionally and has been very effective in the past, it has certain operating disadvantages in that it cannot readily be cleaned. While some of these filters are still in use in some parts of the Orient, in Europe and North America where labour tends to be more costly, other types of filters have been developed. When the difference in water level between the outlet and the water over the filter becomes too great, the filter is taken out of service and the top inch or two of sand is removed from the bed and may or may not be replaced with fresh sand before the filter is put back into operation.

b. Rapid Sand Filter A far more popular and common process for the filtration or water is the rapid sand filter. Instead of sitting on a sand bed of approximately three feet, as is the case in the slow sand filter, the bed is twelve to thirty inches thick and supported on a layer of gravel or other coarse grain, heavy material six to eighteen inches thick. Filtration rates on the rapid sand filter are of the order of three to four gallons per square foot per minute. Occasionally a plant is designed to operate at two gallons per square foot per minute, but provided for an overload when necessary.

The cleaning of the rapid sand filter instead of throwing the filter out of service, is accomplished by simply backwashing. This is accomplished by passing clean water backwards through the filter at a high velocity. This velocity should not be greater than the terminal settling velocity of the smallest particle of sand which is in the filter which is not to be washed over the side. Through this mechanism the sand bed is expanded and the sand is lifted and floated while the particles rub mechanically against one another and wash off the foreign material. The dirty water washed away in drains. After this has been conducted for a few moments, the filter is allowed to go back into service and the head loss is now smaller so the rate of flow through the filter is increased once more.

c. Pressure Filters Whereas the rapid sand filter is indeed a gravity filter, a pressure filter is somewhat the same type of system only pressure is applied to the water to pass it through the filter. The most common household unit nowadays would be the swimming pool filter, where the

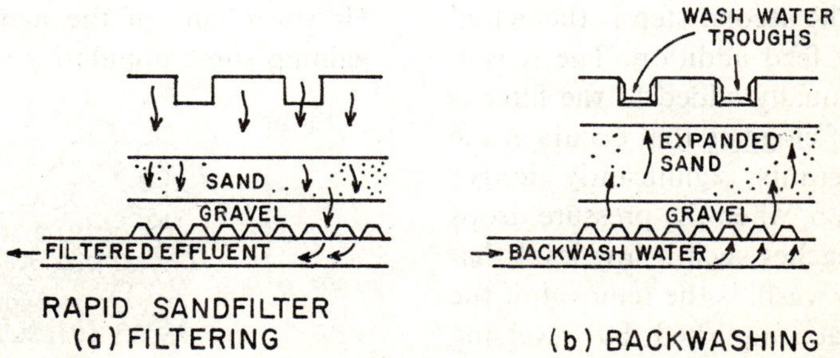

Figure 8

water is pumped vertically through the sand and the filter, and when the head loss through the filter becomes excessive as registered on the pressure gauge, the operator will reverse the flow through the filter, accomplishing the backwash described above.

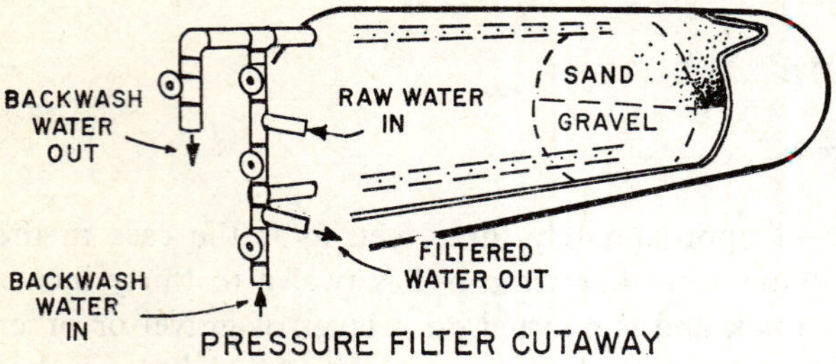

Figure 9

d. Diatomaceous Earth Filter Diatomaceous earth is the silicious residue of the bodies of diatoms which were deposited in past geological ages and now form extensive beds where they are mined. The earth is processed and ground, and the silica particles are extremely irregularly shaped and thus provide a very good porous coating. The diatomaceous earth filter was developed by the army for field use to remove certain chlorine-resistant organisms responsible for dysentery.

the dirty filter cake to wash. Diatomaceous earth filters are frequently used for swimming pool operations, military installations in the field, and for some small communities.

e. Other Filters New technology and the development of new material has allowed for the correction of a serious deficiency in the filtration process. Clearly the rapid sand filtration and the pressure systems, when backwashed, will result in the sand settling back into position with the small particles on the top and the larger particles, with the higher settling velocities, on the bottom. The result of this, of course, is that the top few millimeters or centimeters of sand will get plugged up and the remainder of the filter is not really effective. The development of new materials with different densities has permitted the development of multi-media filtration systems where the large low-density particles may occur on the top, smaller medium-density particles in the middle, and finer high-density particles on the bottom. This results in "in-depth" filtration and upon backwashing and disturbing the bed, the arrangement of large particles on the top through to small particles on the bottom is maintained.

5. Ultra-Violet Disinfection. As previously mentioned, the transmission of disease is one of

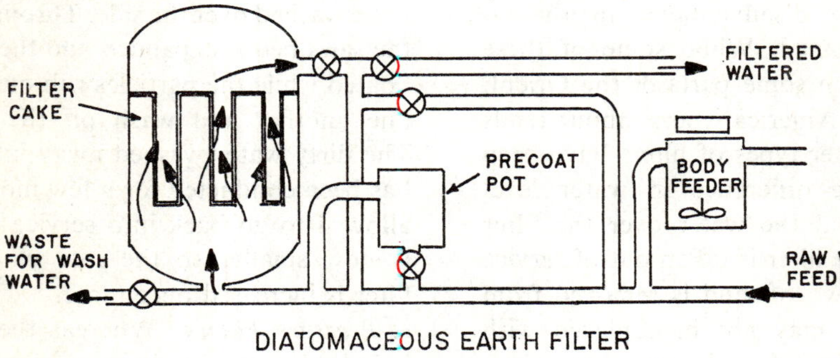

Figure 10

The filter medium is supported on a fine metal screen or a porous material. There are three steps in the filtration cycle. First of all, the deposit of a pre-coat, which is a thin layer of diatomite deposited on the filter element. The second step is the actual filtration and the body feed addition. The reason why body feed is continually added to the filter is to reduce the amount of clogging that occurs at the surface. This also permits significantly longer filter runs. The third step, when the pressure drops or the filtration rate reaches such a low level that it becomes necessary to wash, is the removal of the filter cake which is accomplished by reversing the flow through the filter element and discharging

the most serious hazards associated with drinking water. For this reason, many types of disinfecting processes have been examined; most of them being chemical will be considered in the next chapter. However, one of the methods which is currently gaining some popularity is ultra-violet irradiation.

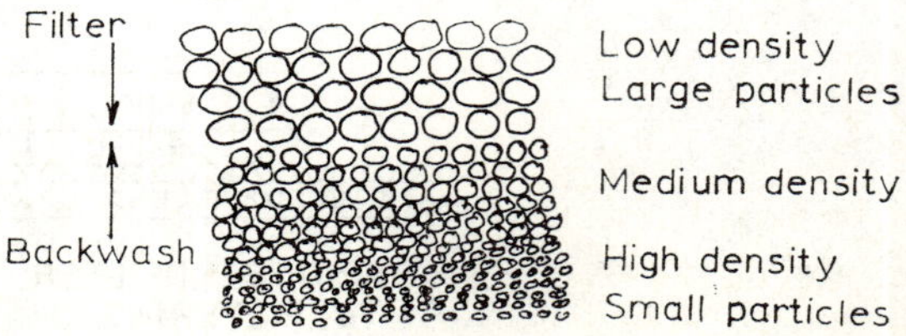

Figure 11

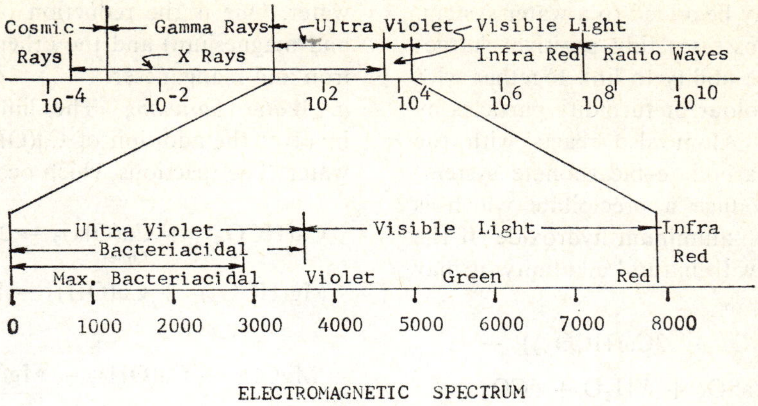

Figure 12

It of course was indicated in the historical discussion of water treatment earlier in this chapter, that exposure to sunlight for a period of time is a natural means of disinfection. This is of course due to the irradiation by the ultra-violet light component of the electromagnetic spectrum. Unfortunately, water is a very strong absorber of ultra-violet irradiation. and in order to use this technique to accomplish complete disinfection, it is necessary that the waier be passed in a very thin film over or under the source of irradiation. Commercial equipment is currently being developed for the individual water supply of the small household or institution, and is gaining some acceptance in some quarters. The irradiation of water by ultra-violet light of suitable wave-lengths for a proper period of time will kill bacteria, spores, moulds and viruses and in fact all microorganisms. The bactericidal wave-lengths extend from about 2,000 to 2950Å (angstrom units) with a maximum effect around 2,540 Å.

Chemical treatment

The unit operations of chemical coagulation, precipitation, ion exchange and stabilization all produce change in the chemical quality of the water. Some of these are aimed at the removal of the suspended and colloidal substances, others are aimed at the removal of dissolved substances. Finally, some chemicals are simply added for their own sake, but these will not be discussed in this section.

To understand some of the basic chemistry of the treatment processes, it is first of all essential to understand a phenomenon known as chemical equilibrium and reaction velocities. An analogy might be considered as the physical equilibrium between ice and water.

$$\text{Ice} \underset{\text{Add Heat}}{\overset{\text{Remove Heat}}{\rightleftharpoons}} \text{Water}$$

If the ice–water system is maintained at 0°C, then molecules of water are transferred from the solid to the liquid state and back again at the same rate. The addition of heat or the removal of heat from the system will result in the equilibrium moving in one direction or the other. The same principles might be applied to what is known as ionic equilibrium, which like molecular equilibria, are subject to a shift under given stresses.

As an example, we might consider pure water

$$H_2O \rightleftharpoons H^+ + OH^-.$$

Certain stresses will give rise to an increase in hydrogen ion concentration (H^+). The expression of this shift is a reduction in pH, whereas an increase in the OH^- concentration brings about an increase of pH. One of the most important equilibria which exists in natural waters is the relationship between carbon dioxide and carbonate ion, which is shown in the following four equilibrium expressions.

$$CO_2(gas) \rightleftharpoons CO_2(solution) \quad 1$$

$$CO_2(solution + H_2O \rightleftharpoons H_2CO_3 \quad 2$$

$$H_2CO_3 \rightleftharpoons H^+ + HCO_3^- \quad 3$$

$$HCO_3^- \rightleftharpoons H^+ + COz_3^-. \quad 4$$

The equilibrium of the first of these equations is purely physical, since the solubility of gas and water is determined by the pressure of that gas and the temperature and a number of other physical parameters.

1. *Coagulation*

The principle function of chemical coagulation is known as destabilization, aggregation and binding together of colloids. Alum, or aluminum sulphate, ($Al_2(SO_4)_3$. $18H_2O$) is one of the most common coagulants which may be added to a water system. Such a coagulant possesses tiny positive charges and therefore has the ability to link together with negatively charged colour or turbidity particles by mutual coagulation. Alum also reacts with the natural alkalinity (carbonate–bicarbonate system) of the water to produce a precipitate which is usually thought to be aluminum hydroxide. If the reaction takes place with natural alkalinity, it may be expressed as follows:

$$Al_2(SO_4)_3.XH_2O \ + \ 3Ca(HCO_{32}) \ \rightarrow$$
$$2Al(OH)_3 + 3CaSO_4 + XH_2O + 6CO_2.$$

In the event that there is insufficient natural alkalinity for this to occur, then calcium oxide (lime) may be added to create the same effect. Because this system is very poorly understood, the optimum dosage required in practice has to be done by trial and error through a series of tests known as jar tests.

In these jar tests, the flash mixing and flocculation steps described previously are stimulated at various concentrations of alum and the clarification which takes place and the reduction of turbidity and the rate at which the floc settles are all observed in order to determine the optimum dosage of coagulant. If too much coagulant is added, then the collodial system which is primarily negatively charged will become supersaturated by the aluminum system which is primarily positively charged and the suspension will become re-stabilized and this can be observed by conducting jar tests over a wide range of concentrations of coagulant.

The reason why alum is so generally used is that it is highly effective over a wide pH range in waters of vastly different chemical make-up. Other materials such as ferrous sulphate are occasionally used to increase the settling rate of plankton and thus increase the time of the filter run, making the filtering process more efficient.

2. *Precipitation*

There are two important processes which are associated with precipitation in the treatment of water. One is the reduction of hardness (calcium and magnesium) and the other is the reduction of iron and manganese.

a. Water Softening The lime–soda-ash process involves the addition of $Ca(OH)_2$ and Na_2CO_3 to water. The reactions which occur are as follows.

$$Ca(HCO_3)_2 + \underset{\text{Lime}}{Ca(OH)_2} \rightarrow \underline{2CaCO_3^{\dagger}} + 2H_2O \quad 1$$

$$Mg(HCO_3)_2 + Ca(OH)_2 \rightarrow MgCO_3 + \underline{CaCO_3} + 2H_2O \quad 2$$

$$MgCO_3 + Ca(OH)_2 \rightarrow \underline{Mg(OH)_2} + \underline{CaCO_3} \quad 3$$

$$CaSO_4 + \underset{\text{Soda Ash}}{Na_2CO_3} \rightarrow \underline{CaCO_3} + Na_2SO_4. \quad 4$$

In this reaction it can be seen that the lime is added to precipitate the carbonate hardness, while the soda ash provides the carbonate ion to precipitate the non-carbonate hardness.

b. Precipitation of Iron and Manganese Normally, iron and manganese are only highly soluble if they are in their ferrous (Fe^{2+}) and manganous (Mn^{2+}) forms. Normally, these two metals will only occur in ths form if there is an absence of dissolved oxygen. However, on occasions when the water is particularly acid, such as might occur in mine drainage areas, the metals may remain in solution even though a very high dissolved oxygen is present. Under these circumstances, aeration is frequently sufficient to drive off the surplus carbon dioxide, increase the pH and bring about a natural precipitation of these materials in their ferric and manganic form. In order to catalyze or accelerate this reaction, the water is frequently caused to trickle over coke or crushed stone, or to flow upward through some contact material. This allows deposits of iron and manganese to accumulate on the surfaces and catalyze the further precipitation of ferric and manganic oxides.

If the pH of the system is forced to values higher than 7.1, the positively charged ferric hydroxide

† Underlined chemicals are poorly soluble and result in a precipitate.

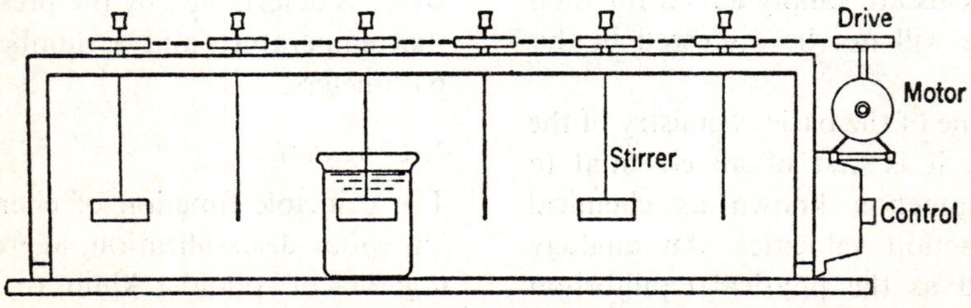

Figure 13 Jar Test Equipment—Coagulant dosage varied in each jar to determine optimum concentration.

particles may be adsorbed on the negatively charged calcium carbonate particles and a stable colloidal suspension may result. Iron and manganese are objectionable constituents of water supplies because they impart a brown colour to laundry goods and frequently will stain household plumbing fittings.

Precipitation of iron and manganese can also be satisfactorily accomplished by using the lime-soda-ash process as described above for softening.

3. *Ion Exchange*

Ion exchange units are most frequently used for softening waters, but are also used by certain industries for the production of de-ionized water. This is quite common in the brewery industry, where an attempt is made to strip the water down to its most pure constituents so that water in one part of the world is similar to water in other parts of the world. Following de-ionization breweries and often distilleries will reconstitute the water so that the water used for the production of a certain type of beer will be the same all over the continent and not have the variations which were characteristic of beers when native waters were used for their production.

The chemistry of the ion exchange process is shown below, where a cation resin is a resin which will exchange the sodium (Na^+) for the calcium and magnesium (Ca^{2+}, Mg^{2+}). When the resin is saturated with calcium and magnesium, a regeneration is required such as is used in household water softening units, when a very strong brine solution is forced back through the resin and in turn displaces the calcium and magnesium into the backwash line and restores the sodium on the resin for further softening.

$$\text{Softening}\quad Na_2R + \begin{matrix} Ca \\ Mg \end{matrix} \begin{bmatrix} (HCO_3)_2 \\ SO_4 \\ Cl_2 \end{bmatrix} \rightarrow \begin{bmatrix} Ca \\ Mg \end{bmatrix} R + \begin{bmatrix} 2NaHSO_4 \\ Na_2SO_4 \\ 2NaCl \end{bmatrix} \qquad (1)$$

$$\text{Regeneration}\quad \left.\begin{matrix} Ca \\ Mg \end{matrix}\right] R + 2NaCl \rightarrow Na_2R + \left.\begin{matrix} Ca \\ Mg \end{matrix}\right] Cl_2 \qquad (2)$$

4. *Desalination*

Although the principles of desalination were fully known in Julius Caesar's time, the energy requirements of this process are presently so high that these will be usually considered as a last resort after all other water sources have been explored. Water quality is frequently referred to as fresh, brackish, sea water or brine. Fresh water normally contains less than 1,000 mg/liter of dissolved salts, while brackish water ranges from 1,000–35,000 mg/liter of dissolved salts. Sea water contains 35,000 mg/liter of disolved salts, whereas brine contains very much more dissolved salts, as may be found in the Great Salt Lake or the Dead Sea.

While there are many potential and theoretical processes for the production of fresh water from

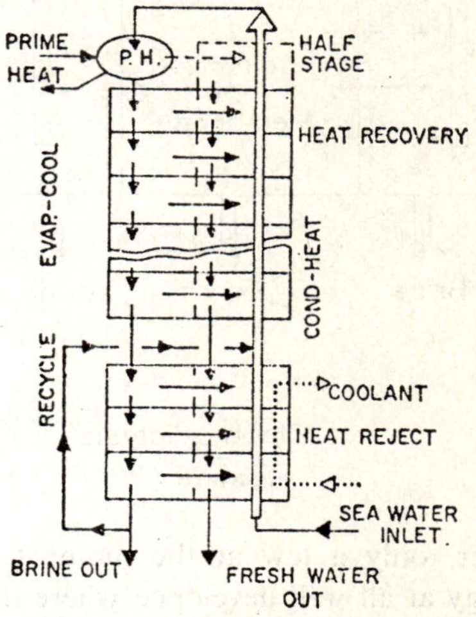

Figure 14 Conventional multistage flash evaporation—MSF evaporating and cooling of hot feed brine (vertical arrows down) on left side at sucessively lower pressures after heating to highest temperature in prime heater (P.H.) at top; vapors (horizontal arrows) from MSF, passing to preheat the sea water by condensation-heating on right side; fresh water condensate passing stagewise from top to discharge at bottom; additional sea water coolant (dotted line) rejecting heat in lower stages, withdrawing of vapors from prime heater to be condensed in half-stage (dashed lines) increasing the production of fresh water.

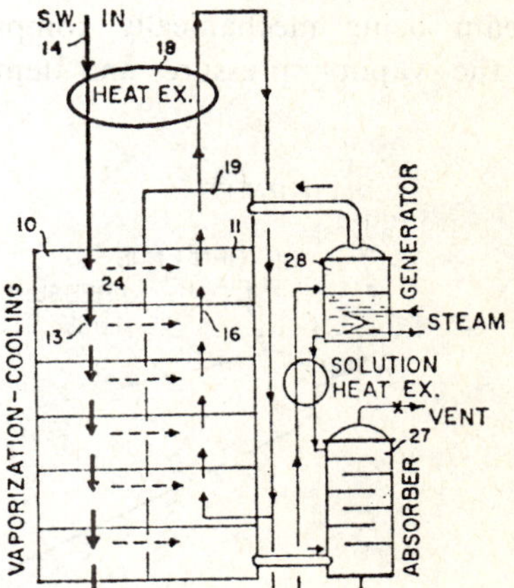

Figure 15 Vapor reheat with vapur recompression by absorbtion (from U.S. Patent 3,288,686). Vapor reheat MSF, vapors formed in low pressure stage pass to Absorber, 27, and are absorbed in the hydrophilic liquid from solution heat exchanger which cycles through heat exchanger to evaporator or generator, 28, for concentration at higher pressure. Vapors leave at higher pressure to half-stage, 19, to supply prime heat to evaporator.

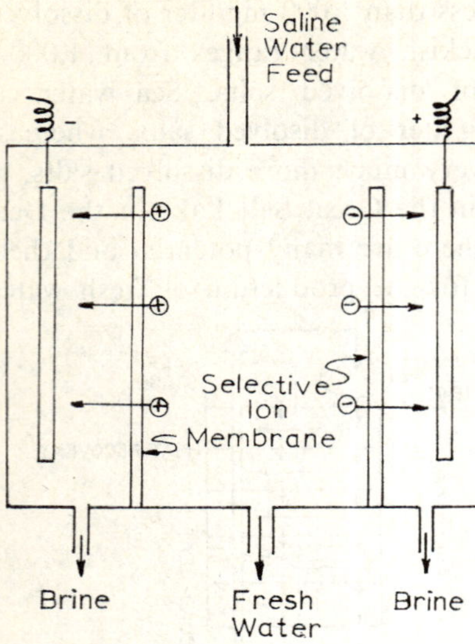

Electrodialysis

Figure 16

salt water, only a few at the moment have the technology at all well developed where they might be commercially used. In this section we will consider a few of these.

a. Multi-stage Flash Distillation This allows for higher operating temperatures, and flash evaporation due to reduced pressures in a series of units. The multi-stage flash distillation unit presently offers the most reliable and extensively used process.

b. Vapour Compression Distillation This process is often used on board ship and it involves boiling brine steam being mechanically compressed to increase the vapour pressure and temperature. This then condenses to form water and evaporate more brine. It has a low energy consumption but is frequently expensive, and has proved to be disappointing in large installations.

c. Electrodialysis Electrodialysis has proven only to be economical when the salinity has been low, because water production is proportional to the power input. It is not proven particularly effective at separating fresh water from water with a salinity of more than 6000 mg/liter of solids. Principally a direct current is applied to the water and the negative electrode attracts the cations in the saline water which passes through the selective ion membrane and a similar action occurs with the anions towards the positive electrode. The resulting fresh water then passes out of the container. Unfortunately due to the very low conductivity of pure water, this process will not reach lower concentrations than about 400 mg/liter before the electric current fails to bring about the migration of the anions and cations.

d. Reverse Osmosis Theoretically one of the most attractive processes for producing fresh water from brackish. It is based upon the principle that if fresh water is separated from salt water by a semi-permeable membrane, the fresh water will tend to flow into the salt water to equalize the concentration of salts on both sides of the membrane. Bearing in mind that the membrane will not allow the salts to pass back, it is clear that a certain pressure which is known as the osmotic pressure is forcing the fresh water through to the brine side of the membrane. If a force greater than this osmotic pressure is applied on the sea water side,

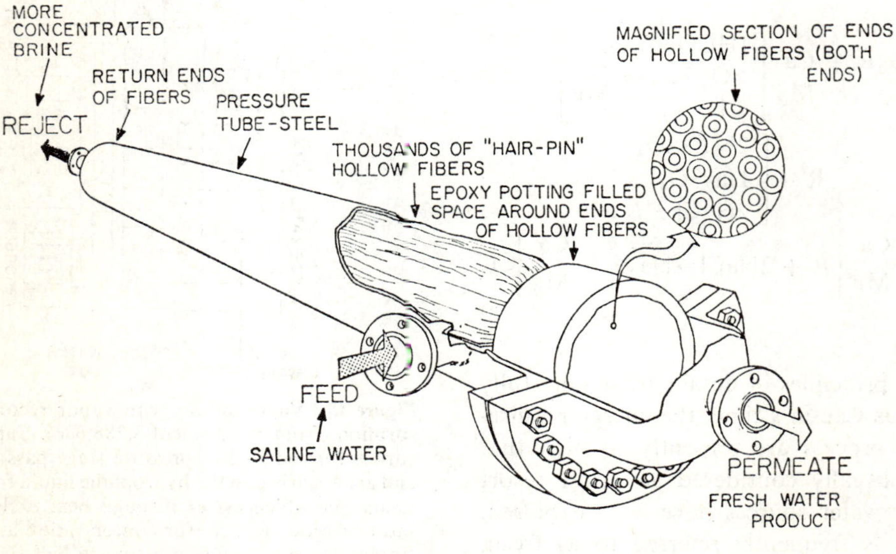

Figure 17

then fresh water will flow backwards through the semi-permeable membrane at a rate proportional to the incremental pressure over the osmotic pressure. In practice, quite high pressures are required in order to get a useful volume of water to pass through the membrane—such pressures as 40–100 kg per square centimeter. This has been shown to work for waters of fairly high dissolved solids, but the structural properties of the membranes must be fairly well developed and of course the membranes must be very well supported. Membranes used for this type of process are frequently cellulose acetate or some derivatives thereof. The power requirement for this process is considerably less than electrodialysis, but it is a process which offers considerable promise for the desalination of brackish waters.

e. The Vacuum Freezing Process Cooled saline water passes into a low pressure chamber where flash evaporation brings about further cooling. Close to freezing ice crystals will form with a brine coating, and washing of these crystals will yield fresh water from the washed ice. Small plant application appears to be feasible at the moment Considerable development work on this was done by the Technion Institute in Israel.

f. A Secondary Refrigerant Process This involves the use of a liquid hydrocarbon refrigerant, such as butane, that will not mix with water. A great deal of care must be exercised here to ensure that the product is stripped of butane; otherwise serious explosion hazards exist. It has a low energy input and has minimized corrosion and scale-forming properties. However, so far this process has not been examined on a very large-scale basis.

g. Other Processes There are a number of other processes which are being considered for desalination, such as solar distillation, but so far this has been restricted to use on a very small scale such as survival kits. Ion exchange, such as was described previously, has some potential here but it is very much limited down to approximately 3000 mg/liter solids. A hydrate process has been considered where propane is added to form a hydrate and react with the water, leaving the salt behind. Then the propane hydrate is decomposed to recover the propane and the water; this one is rather difficult to handle.

5. *Disinfection*

As mentioned earlier, water has long since been identified as a means of distributing pathogenic organisms among society. The purpose therefore of disinfecting water supplies is to prevent the spread of water-borne disease by destroying

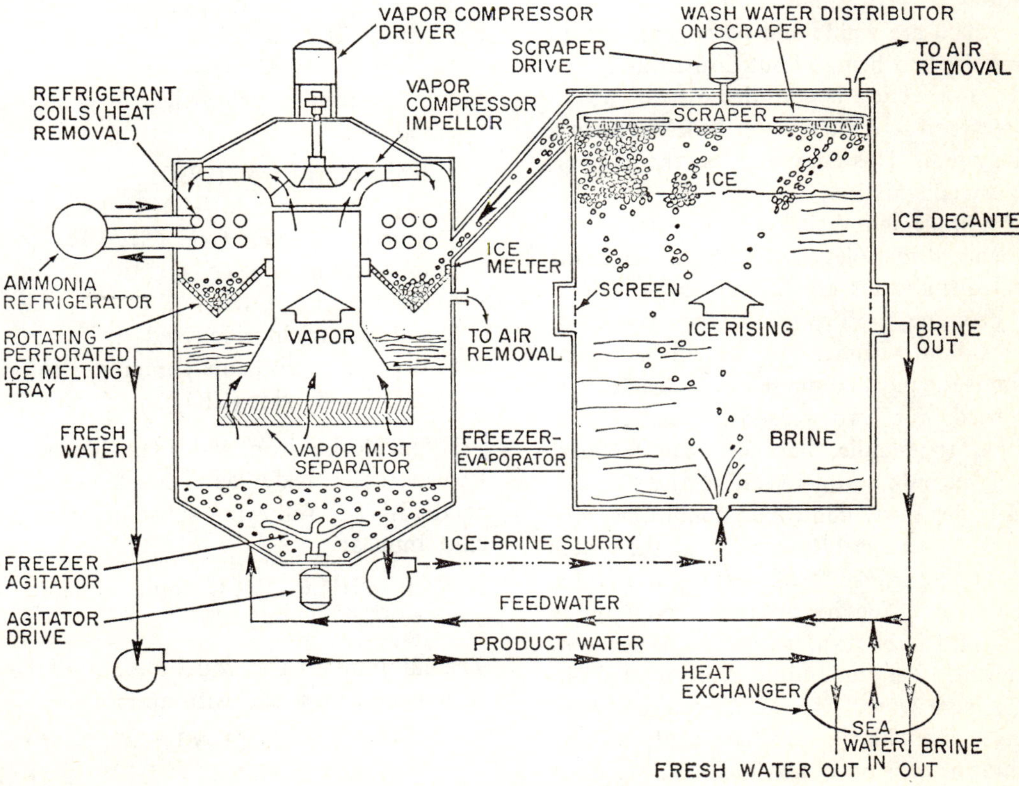

Figure 18 Vacuum freezing process

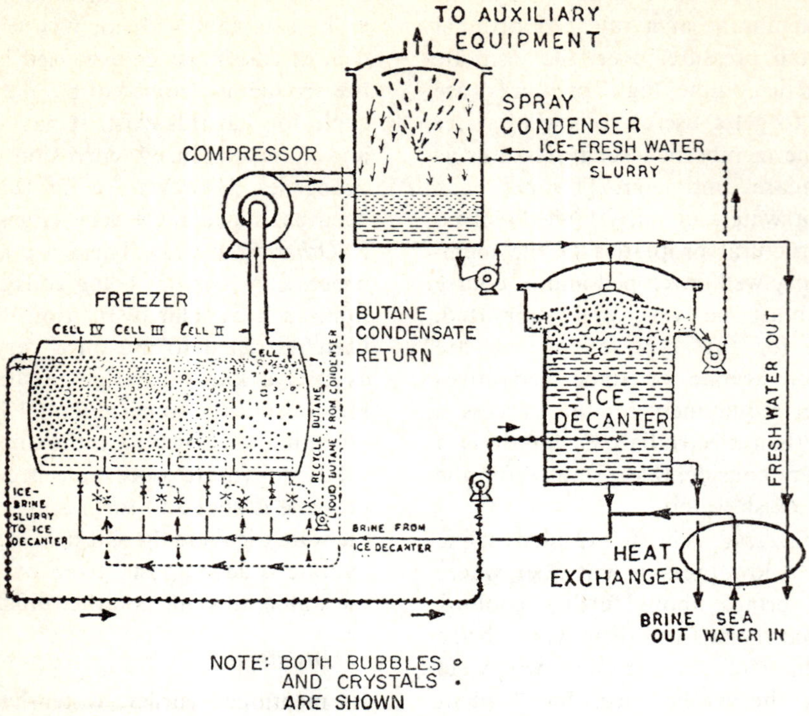

Figure 19 Secondary refrigerant freezing process.

pathogenic organisms. Most of the physical and chemical treatment processes described previously will remove most of the micro-organisms to some extent. However, very small numbers of micro-organisms which are viable and pathogenic are all that are required to bring about disastrous epidemics. Thus, disinfection is considered to be necessary final step before treated water is delivered to a municipal system. This may not be the case in certain industrial supplies.

A physical process for disinfection was previously described using ultra-violet irradiation. Other forms of chemical disinfectant are the halogens such as chlorine, bromine, iodine and the powerful, unstable oxidant, ozone. In North America chlorination is the most common of the disinfectant processes used, for two reasons. Firstly, it is fairly simple to handle, can be manufactured inexpensively in bulk and delivered to the site, can be applied under fairly controlled conditions, and can maintain a measurable residual in the water supply to indicate safety at all points on a water distribution system. The first attempt at continuous chlorination of a public water supply was made in England during 1904, and subsequently in 1908 in Jersey City, New Jersey, U.S.A. There are certain disadvantages of chlorination, in that a high residual chlorine will bring about a taste which is unacceptable to many people; and chlorine furthermore will react with certain micro-constituents of water, such as phenols, to bring about substantial odours (chlorophenols) quite out of proportion to the concentration of the causative chemicals. The addition of chlorine to water releases a group of substances, all of which have some disinfecting properties. The substances so released are:

1) hypochlorite iron (OCl);
2) hypochlorous acid (HOCl);
3) monochloramine (NH_2Cl);
3) monochloramine (NH_2Cl);
4) dichloramine ($NHCl_2$);
5) nitrogen trichloride (NCl_3);
6) organic compounds containing chloride; and
7) chlorine dioxide (ClO_2).

Hypochlorite iron and hypochlorous acid are known collectively as free available chlorine residuals. The following substances are known as chloramines:

NH_2Cl, $NHCl_2$ NCl_3 and organic chlorine compounds.

The chloramines are brought about by the reaction of hypochlorous acid with ammonia

$$NH_3 + HOCl \rightarrow NH_2Cl + H_2O$$
$$NH_2Cl + HOCl \rightarrow NHCl_2 + H_2O$$
$$NHCl_2 + HOCl \rightarrow NCl_3 + H_2O.$$

The process which brings about the various chloramines are shown above. Chlorination is applied in a series of different forms as follows:

a. Superchlorination This process represents the addition of very high concentrations of chlorine which are intended to oxidise not only the pathogenic and potential pathogenic micro-organisms in the system, but also to oxidise those organic compounds which might bring about taste and odour. Following superchlorination, a step involving dechlorination which involves the addition of sulphur dioxide, sodium bisulphite or sodium sulphite or some similar reducing agent. The bisulphite is frequently used in practice because it is cheaper and more stable.

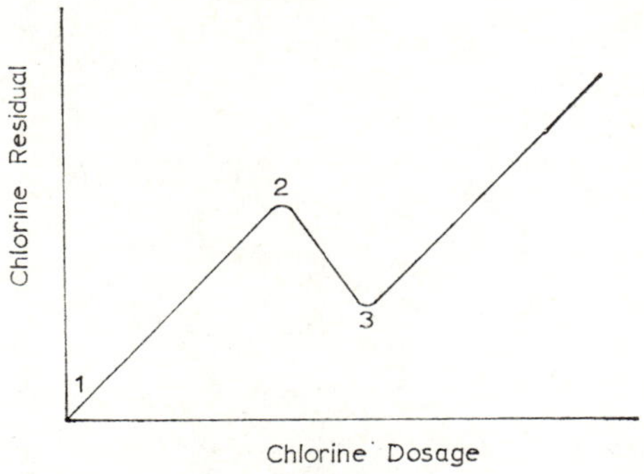

Figure 20

If there is any amount of ammonia naturally present in the water, a strange phenomenon will occur such as shown above in the graph. On the initial part of the graph, labelled 1 to 2, the ratio (molar) of chlorine to ammonia is less than one and the residual chlorine is essentially all monochloramine. In the next section, between 2 and 3, the oxidation of ammonia and reduction of chlorine continue until the complete oxidation reduction occurs at point 3. At this point once again, all the residual chlorine is in the form of monochloramine. Beyond point 3, all chlorine added remains in solution. This phenomenon is known as break-point chlorination, and in order to ensure satisfactory disinfecting properties, chlorination must go beyond the break-point 3 on the curve.

In certain instances, such as when phenols are present in the water, small concentrations of free available chlorine will combine with the phenols, forming chlorphenols which produce a distinctive taste and odour at very, very small concentrations. When this occurs, chlorine dioxide is frequently used as a disinfecting agent as this does not react with the phenols but in facts destroys them.

Other substances which are used for disinfecting purposes are the other halogens such as bromine and iodine, although these are not commonly used in water supplies. Occasionally they have been used in swimming pools for similar purposes.

Ozone is a particularly effective disinfectant, but it has certain disadvantages in that it must be manufactured on the site, using fairly sizeable and expensive capital equipment. No residual can be maintained due to the instability of the substance, and the methods of detection are rather imperfect. However to compensate for this, the disinfecting properties of ozone are considerably greater than chlorine.

REFERENCES

1. Durant, Will. 1954. *Our Oriental Heritage* (New York: Simon and Shuster, Inc.) p. 132.
2. Baker, M. N. 1949. "The Quest for Pure Water" (New York: American Water Works Association) pp. 1–3, 6, 11.
3. Brown, J. R. and D. M. McLean, 1967. "Water-Borne Diseases: An Historical Review" *Medical Services Journal Canada*, **23**, no. 8, pp. 1011–1026.
4. "Estimates of the Water and Sewerage Industries and Utilities Division." Jan. 1956. Business Service Bulletin —136, Business and Defence Services Administration, U.S. Department of Commerce.
5. Ackerman, E. A. and G. O. Lof, 1959. *Technology in American Water Development* (Baltimore: Johns Hopkins Press).

BIBLIOGRAPHY

Clark, J. W. and Warren Viessman, 1965. *Water Supply and Pollution Control.* (Scranton: International Textbook Company).

Fair, G. M. and J. C. Geyer, 1954. *Water Supply and Waste-Water Disposal* (New York: John Wiley and Sons, Inc.).

Steel, E. W. 1960. *Water Supply and Sewerage* (New York: McGraw-Hill Book Company Inc.,) 4th Ed.

PHILIP H. JONES
University of Toronto

APPENDIX

Selected Properties

TABLE 1
Conversion Factors

To Convert from	To	Multiply by
Angstrom units	Centimeters	1×10^{-8}
Angstrom units	Microns	1×10^{-4}
Atmospheres	Centimeters of mercury at 0°C	76
Atmospheres	Dynes per square centimeter	1.01325×10^{6}
Atmospheres	Feet of water at 39.1°F	33.899
Atmospheres	Grams per square centimeter	1,033.3
Atmospheres	Inches of mercury at 32°F	29.921
Atmospheres	Millimeters of mercury	760
Atmospheres	Pounds per square inch	14.696
Atmospheres	Bars	1.0133
Barrels, oil	Gallons (U.S.)	42
Boiler horsepower	Btu per hour	33,479
Btu	Calories (gram)	252
Btu	Foot-pounds	777.98
Btu	Joules (absolute)	1,054.8
Btu per minute	Foot-pounds per second	12.96
Calories, gram	Btu	3.968×10^{-3}
Calories, gram	Foot-pounds	3.087
Calories, gram	Joules	4.185
Candles (International)	Lumens (International) per steradian	1.0000
Candlepower (spherical)	Lumens	12.566
Candles per square inch	Lamberts	0.48695
Centimeters	Angstrom units	1×10^{8}
Centimeters	Feet (British or U.S.)	0.032808
Centimeters	Inches (U.S.)	0.393700
Centimeter of mercury at 0°C	Atmospheres	0.013158
Centimeters of mercury at 0°C	Dynes per square centimeter	1.33322×10^{4}
Centimeters of mercury at 0°C	Kilograms per square meter	135.95
Centimeters of mercury at 0°C	Pounds per square foot	27.845
Centimeters per second	Feet per minute	1.9685
Centimeters per second	Miles per hour	0.02237
Centipoises	Pound mass per foot-second	0.672×10^{-3}
Centipoises	Kilogram mass per meter-second	1×10^{-3}
Cubic feet (U.S.)	Gallons (U.S.)	7.481
Cubic feet (U.S.)	Liters	28.316
Dynes per square centimeter	Millimeters of mercury	7.5006×10^{-4}
Dynes per square centimeter	Pounds per square foot	0.0020886
Dynes per square centimeter	Pounds per square inch	1.4504×10^{-5}
Ergs	Btu (mean)	9.4805×10^{-11}
Ergs	Calories, gram (mean)	2.3889×10^{-8}
Ergs	Joules	1×10^{-7}
Ergs per square centimeter	Dynes per centimeter	1
Feet (U.S.)	Centimeters	30.48006096
Feet per minute	Centimeters per second	0.508001
Feet per minute	Meters per second	0.00508001
Feet per minute	Miles per hour	0.011364
Foot-candles	Lumens incident per square foot	1
Foot-candles	Lumens per square meter	10.764
Gallons (U.S.)	Barrels (U.S., liquid)	0.031746
Gallons (U.S.)	Liters	3.78533
Gallons (U.S.)	Cubic feet	0.13368
Grains	Grams	0.064798918
Grains	Milligrams	64.798918
Grains	Pounds (avoirdupois)	1/7,000
Grains per cubic foot	Milligrams per cubic meter	2.796×10^{-3}
Grains per gallon (U.S.)	Parts per million	17.118
Grams	Grains	15.4324
Gravity	Centimeters per square second	980.665
Gravity	Feet per square second	32.174
Kilometers	Centimerers	1×10^{5}
Kilometers	Feet	3280.83
Kilometers	Miles (U.S.)	0.6213699495
Liters	Cubic feet	0.035316

Table 1—*continued*

To Convert from	To	Multiply by
Liters	Gallons (U.S.)	0.26417762
Liters	Ounces (U.S., fluid)	33.8143
Liters	Quarts (U.S., liquid)	1.056681869
Lumens per square foot	Foot-candles	1
Meters	Feet (U.S.)	3.280833333
Meters	Inches (U.S.)	39.3700
Micrograms per cubic meter	Grains per cubic foot	0.35757
Microns	Inches	3.937×10^{-5}
Microns	Centimeters	1×10^{-4}
Miles (U.S., statute)	Feet	5,280
Miles (U.S., statute)	Yards	1,760
Miles per hour	Centimeters per second	44.7041
Miles per hour	Feet per minute	88
Miles per hour	Feet per second	1.4667
Miles per hour	Meters per minute	26.82
Millibars	Atmospheres	98.692
Millibars	Millimeters of mercury	1.329×10^{-5}
Millibars	Dynes per square centimeter	1.000×10^{9}
Milligrams	Grains	0.01543236
Milligrams	Ounces (avoirdupois)	3.52739×10^{-5}
Milligrams per cubic meter	Grains per cubic foot	357.57
Milliliters	Cubic centimeters	1.000027
Milliliters	Cubic inches	0.061025
Millimeters	Inches (U.S.)	0.0393700
Millimeters of mercury at 0°C	Atmospheres	0.00131579
Millimeters of mercury at 0°C	Dynes per square centimeter	1,333.22
Millimeters of mercury at 0°C	Grams per square centimeter	1.3595
Millimicrons or Micromillimeters	Angstrom units	10
Millimicrons	Meters	1×10^{-9}
Ounces (avoirdupois)	Grams	28.349527
Ounces (avoirdupois)	Grains	437.5
Ounces (U.S., fluid)	Milliliters	29.5729
Parts per million	Per cent	1×10^{4}
Per cent	Parts per million	1×10^{-4}
Pints (U.S., dry)	Liters	0.550599
Pints (U.S., liquid)	Cubic inches	28.875
Pints (U.S., liquid)	Liters	0.473168
Pounds (avoirdupois)	Grains	7,000
Pounds (avoirdupois)	Grams	453.5924277
Pounds (avoirdupois)	Tons (long)	4.464286×10^{-4}
Pounds (avoirdupois)	Tons (metric)	4.5359243×10^{-4}
Pounds (avoirdupois)	Tons (short)	5×10^{-4}
Pounds per hour	Grams per second	0.12599
Pounds per hour	Tons per stack day	1.2×10^{-2}
Quarts (U.S., dry)	Cubic centimeters	1,101.23
Quarts (U.S., dry)	Cubic inches	67.2006
Quarts (U.S., dry)	Cubic feet	0.038889
Quarts (U.S., dry)	Liters	1.10120
Quarts (U.S., liquid)	Milliliters	946.358
Quarts (U.S., liquid)	Cubic inches	57.749
Quarts (U.S., liquid)	Liters	0.946333
Square centimeters	Square feet	0.0010764
Square centimeter	Square inch	0.15500
Square feet (U.S.)	Square meters	0.09290341
Square feet (U.S.)	Acres	2.29568×10^{-5}
Square inches (U.S.)	Square yards	1/1,296
Square kilometers	Square miles (U S.)	0.3861006
Square meters	Square yards (U.S.)	1.195985
Square miles	Acres	640
Square miles	Square feet	2.78784×10^{7}
Square miles	Square yards	3.0976×10^{6}
Square miles	Square meters	2,589,998
Square yards (U.S.)	Square meters	0.83613
Tons per stack day	Pounds per hour	83.3
Yards (U.S.)	Meters	0.91440183
Yards (U.S.)	Miles	5.68182×10^{-4}

TABLE 2

Viscosity and Density of Water

Calculated from International Critical Tables, 1928 and 1929.

Temperature, C	Density ρ, γ (grams/cm^3), also s	Absolute viscosity μ, centipoises[a]	Kinematic viscosity γ, centistokes[b]
0	0.99987	1.7921	1.7923
1	0.99993	1.7320	1.7321
2	0.99997	1.6740	1.6741
3	0.99999	1.6193	1.6193
4	1.00000	1.5676	1.5676
5	0.99999	1.5188	1.5188
6	0.99997	1.4726	1.4726
7	0.99993	1.4288	1.4288
8	0.99988	1.3872	1.3874
9	0.99981	1.3476	1.3479
10	0.99973	1.3097	1.3101
11	0.99963	1.2735	1.2740
12	0.99952	1.2390	1.2396
13	0.99940	1.2061	1.2068
14	0.99927	1.1748	1.1756
15	0.99913	1.1447	1.1457
16	0.99897	1.1156	1.1168
17	0.99880	1.0876	1.0888
18	0.99862	1.0603	1.0618
19	0.99843	1.0340	1.0356
20	0.99823	1.0087	1.0105
21	0.99802	0.9843	0.9863
22	0.99780	0.9608	0.9629
23	0.99757	0.9380	0.9403
24	0.99733	0.9161	0.9186
25	0.99707	0.8949	0.8975
26	0.99681	0.8746	0.8774
27	0.99654	0.8551	0.8581
28	0.99626	0.8363	0.8394
29	0.99597	0.8181	0.8214
30	0.99568	0.8004	0.8039
31	0.99537	0.7834	0.7870
32	0.99505	0.7670	0.7708
33	0.99473	0.7511	0.7551
34	0.99440	0.7357	0.7398
35	0.99406	0.7208	0.7251
36	0.99371	0.7064	0.7109
37	0.99336	0.6925	0.6971
38	0.99299	0.6791	0.6839
39	0.99262	0.6661	0.6711

[a] 1 centipoise $= 10^{-2}$ (gram mass)/(cm)(sec).
[b] 1 centistoke $= 10^{-2}$ cm^2/sec.

TABLE 3a

Composition of Some Typical Natural Waters

(After Baldwin, 1948)

	Na	K	Ca	Mg	Cl	SO_4	CO_3	Total (g/liter)
Soft fresh water	0.016	—	0.010	—	0.019	0.007	0.012	0.065
Hard fresh water	0.021	0.016	0.065	0.014	0.041	0.025	0.119	0.30
Sea water	10.7	0.39	0.42	1.31	19.3	2.69	0.073	34.9

TABLE 3b

Relative Abundance of Ions (by Weight) in Natural Waters

	Na	K	Ca	Mg	Cl	SO_4	CO_3
Soft fresh water	100	—	62.5	3.3	119.0	43.8	75.0
Hard fresh water	100	76.0	310.0	66.8	195.0	119.0	567.0
Sea water	100	3.6	3.9	12.1	181.0	20.9	0.7

TABLE 4

Saturation Values of Dissolved Oxygen in Fresh and Sea Water Exposed to an Atmosphere Containing 20.9% Oxygen under a Pressure of 760 mm of Mercury[a]

Calculated by G. C. Whipple and M. C. Whipple from measurements of C. J. J. Fox

Temperature, C	Dissolved oxygen (mg/l) for stated concentrations of chloride, mg/l					Difference per 100 mg/l chloride
	0	5,000	10,000	15,000	20,000	
0	14.62	13.79	12.97	12.14	11.32	0.0165
1	14.23	13.41	12.61	11.82	11.03	.0160
2	13.84	13.05	12.28	11.52	10.76	.0154
3	13.48	12.72	11.98	11.24	10.50	.0149
4	13.13	12.41	11.69	10.97	10.25	.0144
5	12.80	12.09	11.39	10.70	10.01	.0140
6	12.48	11.79	11.12	10.45	9.78	.0135
7	12.17	11.51	10.85	10.21	9.57	.0130
8	11.87	11.24	10.61	9.98	9.36	.0125
9	11.59	10.97	10.36	9.76	9.17	.0121
10	11.33	10.73	10.13	9.55	8.98	.0118
11	11.08	10.49	9.92	9.35	8.80	0.114
12	10.83	10.28	9.72	9.17	8.62	0.110
13	10.60	10.05	9.52	8.98	8.46	.0107
14	10.37	9.85	9.32	8.80	8.30	.0104
15	10.15	9.65	9.14	8.63	8.14	.0100
16	9.95	9.46	8.96	8.47	7.99	.0098
17	9.74	9.26	8.78	8.30	7.84	.0095
18	9.54	9.07	8.62	8.15	7.70	.0092
19	9.35	8.89	8.45	8.00	7.56	.0089
20	9.17	8.73	8.30	7.86	7.42	.0088
21	8.99	8.57	8.14	7.71	7.28	.0086
22	8.83	8.42	7.99	7.57	7.14	.0084
23	8.68	8.27	7.85	7.43	7.00	.0083
24	8.53	8.12	7.71	7.30	6.87	.0083
25	8.38	7.96	7.56	7.15	6.74	.0082
26	8.22	7.81	7.42	7.02	6.61	.0080
27	8.07	7.67	7.28	6.88	6.49	.0079
28	7.92	7.53	7.14	6.75	6.37	.0078
29	7.77	7.39	7.00	6.62	6.25	.0076
30	7.63	7.25	6.86	6.49	6.13	.0075

[a] For other barometric pressures the solubilities vary approximately in proportion to the ratios of these pressures to the standard pressures.

TABLE 5

Standard Atmosphere

Altitude (m)	Temperature (°C)	Pressure (mb)	Density (kg/m^3)
0	15.0	1,013.2	1.2250
500	11.8	954.6	1.1673
1,000	8.5	898.8	1.1117
1,500	5.2	845.6	1.0581
2,000	2.0	795.0	1.0066
2,500	− 1.2	746.9	0.9569
3,000	− 4.5	701.2	0.9092
3,500	− 7.7	657.8	0.8634
4,000	−11.0	616.6	0.8194
4,500	−14.2	577.5	0.7770
5,000	−17.5	540.5	0.7364
5,500	−20.7	505.4	0.6975
6,000	−24.0	472.2	0.6601
6,500	−27.2	440.8	0.6243
7,000	−30.4	411.0	0.5900
7,500	−33.7	383.0	0.5572
8,000	−36.9	356.5	0.5258
8,500	−40.2	331.5	0.4958
9,000	−43.4	308.0	0.4671
9,500	−46.7	285.8	0.4397
10,000	−49.9	265.0	0.4140
10,500	−53.1	245.4	0.3886
11,000	−56.4	227.0	0.3648
11,100	−56.5	223.5	0.3593
11,500	−56.5	209.8	0.3374
12,000	−56.5	194.0	0.3119
13,000	−56.5	165.8	0.2666
14,000	−56.5	141.7	0.2279
15,000	−56.5	121.1	0.1948
16,000	−56.5	103.5	0.1665
17,000	−56.5	88.5	0.1423
18,000	−56.5	75.6	0.1216
19,000	−56.5	64.7	0.1040
20,000	−56.5	55.3	0.0889
25,000	−51.6	25.5	0.0401
30,000	−46.6	12.0	0.0184
35,00	−36.6	5.7	0.0085
40,000	−22.8	2.9	0.0040
45,000	− 9.0	1.5	0.0020
50,000	− 2.5	0.8	0.0010
60,000	−17.4	0.225	0.000306
70,000	−53.4	0.055	0.000088
80,000	−92.5	0.010	0.000020
90,000	−92.5	0.002	0.000003

TABLE 6

Dynamic Viscosity of Gases in Absolute C.G.S. Units

(Data from "*Technical Data on Fuels*", Ed. Spiers)

Temperature °C	Poise × 10^6									
	Air	N_2	O_2	CO_2	CO	H_2	CH_4	C_2H_4	C_2H_6	Water vapour
−160	78.1	77.1	87.9		74.4	46.0	44.9			
−140	92.0	90.0	103		87.4	51.5	52.8			
−120	105	103	117		99.9	56.8	60.5			
−100	117	114	131		112	61.8	68.1	62		
− 80	129	126	144		124	66.5	75.1	68		
− 60	140	136	157	108	135	71.1	82.5	74		
− 40	151	147	169	118	145	75.6	89.3	81		
− 20	162	157	181	127	156	79.9	95.9	88		
0	172	166	192	137	166	84.1	102	94	86	
20	181	175	203	146	175	88.2	109	101	92	95.6
40	191	184	213	156	185	92.2	115	108	98	103
60	200	193	223	165	194	96.1	121	115	104	110
80	209	201	233	173	202	100.0	127	122	109	117
100	217	209	243	182	211	104	133	128	115	125
150	238	229	266	203	231	113	147	142	129	143
200	257	247	288	222	251	122	160	156	142	161
250	275	265	309	241	269	130	173	169	155	179
300	293	282	329	259	287	139	184	181	166	197
350	309	298	348	276	304	147	196	192	176	215
400	325	313	367	293	320	154	207	202	184	233
450	340	328	385	309	336	162	217	212	195	251
500	355	342	402	324	352	169	227	222	204	269
550	369	355	419	339	367	177	237			287
600	383	369	436	354	382	184	246		230[a]	306
650	396	381	452	368	396	191	256			327
700	409	393	468	382	410	198	265		249[a]	348
800	433	417	500	408	437	211	283		269[a]	387
900	457	440	530	434	464	223	300		283[a]	424
1000	479	461	559	459	490	235	316		299[a]	456
Sutherland[a] Equation factors										
$K = 10^{-7}\times$	150	143	176	158	135	66	—	—	—	—
C	124	110	131	240	102	72	—	—	—	—

TABLE 7

Kinematic Viscosity of Gases in Stokes

(Data from "*Technical Data on Fuels*", Ed. Spiers)

Temperature °C	μ/ϱ = Kinematic Viscosity—Stokes									
	Air	N_2	O_2	CO_2	CO	H_2	CH_4	C_2H_4	C_2H_6	Water vapour
−160	0.0249	0.0252	0.0251			0.212				
−140	0.0346	0.0348	0.0348			0.279				
−120	0.0455	0.0458	0.0457			0.354	0.0466			
−100	0.0575	0.0577	0.0579			0.436	0.0599			
− 80	0.0707	0.0709	0.0712			0.523	0.0738	0.0374		
− 60	0.0849	0.0849	0.0855		0.0839	0.618	0.0894	0.0456		
− 40	0.100	0.100	0.101	0.0506	0.0991	0.718	0.106	0.0545		
− 20	0.116	0.116	0.117	0.0596	0.115	0.824	0.124	0.0644		
0	0.133	0.133	0.134	0.0693	0.133	0.936	0.143	0.0749	0.0635	
20	0.151	0.151	0.152	0.0796	0.151	1.05	0.163	0.0860	0.0730	5.53*
40	0.170	0.169	0.171	0.0905	0.169	1.18	0.184	0.0981	0.0833	2.01*
60	0.190	0.188	0.191	0.102	0.189	1.30	0.206	0.111	0.0941	0.845*
80	0.210	0.208	0.211	0.114	0.209	1.44	0.230	0.125	0.105	0.400*
100	0.231	0.229	0.233	0.126	0.231	1.58	0.254	0.140	0.117	0.208
150	0.287	0.283	0.289	0.160	0.287	1.95	0.318	0.177	0.148	0.272
200	0.340	0.343	0.349	0.196	0.348	2.35	0.388	0.216	0.184	0.344
250	0.410	0.406	0.414	0.235	0.413	2.78	0.462	0.258	0.221	0.424
300	0.478	0.474	0.483	0.277	0.482	3.23	0.540	0.302	0.260	0.512
350	0.549	0.545	0.557	0.321	0.555	3.72	0.622	0.350	0.299	0.608
400	0.623	0.618	0.633	0.367	0.632	4.23	0.711	0.399	0.342	0.713
450	0.701	0.695	0.714	0.416	0.713	4.77	0.801	0.449	0.385	0.825
500	0.782	0.774	0.798	0.467	0.797	5.33	0.898	0.502	0.430	0.946
550	0.865	0.856	0.886	0.521	0.885	5.92	0.999			1.07
600	0.951	0.942	0.977	0.576	0.976	6.53	1.10			1.22

TABLE 8

Densities of Gases at Standard Conditions (0°C., 1 *atm*)

Gas	Formula	Mol. wt.	Density	
			G./l.	Lb./cu. ft.
Acetylene	C_2H_2	26.02	1.1708	0.0732
Air	—	—	1.2928	0.0808
Ammonia	NH_3	17.03	0.7708	0.0482
Argon	A	39.91	1.7828	0.1114
Bromine	Br_2	159.83	7.1388	0.4460
Butane	C_4H_{10}	58.08	2.5985	0.1623
Carbon dioxide	CO_2	44.0	1.9768	0.1235
Carbon monoxide	CO	28.00	1.2501	0.0781
Carbon oxychloride	$COCl_2$	98.91	4.5313	0.2830
Carbon oxysulfide	COS	60.06	2.7201	0.1700
Chlorine	Cl_2	70.91	3.2204	0.2011
Chlorine monoxide	Cl_2O	86.91	3.8874	0.2428
Cyanogen	C_2N_2	52.02	2.3348	0.1459
Ethane	C_2H_6	30.05	1.3567	0.0848
Ethyl chloride	C_2H_5Cl	64.50	2.8700	0.1793
Ethylene	C_2H_4	28.03	1.2644	0.0783
Fluorine	F_2	38.00	1.6354	0.1022
Helium	He	4.00	0.1769	0.0111
Hydrogen	H_2	2.016	0.0898	0.0056
Hydrogen chloride	HCl	36.47	1.6394	0.1024
Hydrogen fluoride	HF	20.01	0.9218	0.0576
Hydrogen iodide	HI	127.94	5.7245	0.3576
Hydrogen selenide	H_2Se	81.22	3.6134	0.2258
Hydrogen sulfide	H_2S	34.08	1.5392	0.0961
Hydrogen telluride	H_2Te	129.52	5.8034	0.3625
Krypton	Kr	82.90	3.6431	0.2275
Methane	CH_4	16.03	0.7167	0.0448
Methyl chloride	CH_3Cl	50.48	2.3044	0.1440
Neon	Ne	20.40	0.8713	0.0544
Nitric oxide	NO	30.01	1.3401	0.0837
Nitrogen	N_2	28.02	1.2507	0.0782
Nitrous oxide	N_2O	44.02	1.9781	0.1235
Nitrosyl chloride	NOCl	65.47	2.9864	0.1865
Oxygen	O_2	32.00	1.4289	0.0892
Phosphine	PH_4	34.05	1.5293	0.0955
Silicon fluoride	SiF_2	104.06	4.6541	0.2907
Sulfur dioxide	SO_2	64.06	2.9268	0.1828
Xenon	X	130.20	5.7168	0.3570

TABLE 9

C_p/C_v: Ratios of Specific Heats of Gases at 1 Atm. Pressure[a]

Compound	Formula	Temperature, °C.	Ratio of specific heats, (γ) = C_p/C_v
Acetaldehyde	C_2H_4O	30	1.14
Acetic acid	$C_2H_4O_2$	136	1.15
Acetylene	C_2H_2	15	1.26
		−71	1.31
Air	—	925	1.36
		17	1.403
		−78	1.408
		−118	1.415
Ammonia	NH_3	15	1.310
Argon	A	15	1.668
		−180	1.76 (?)
		0–100	1.67
Brenzene	C_6H_6	90	1.10
Bromine	Br_2	20–350	1.32
Carbon dioxide	CO_2	15	1.304
		−75	1.37
disulfide	CS_2	100	1.21
monoxide	CO	15	1.404
		−180	1.41
Chlorine	Cl_2	15	1.355
Chloroform	$CHCl_3$	100	1.15
Cyanogen	$(CN)_2$	15	1.256
Cyclohezane	C_6H_{12}	80	1.08
Dichlorodifluormethane	CCl_2F_2	25	1.139
Ethane	C_2H_6	100	1.19
		15	1.22
		−82	1.28
Ethyl alcohol	C_2H_6O	90	1.13
ether	$C_4H_{10}O$	35	1.08
		80	1.086
Ethylene	C_2H_4	100	1.18
		15	1.255
		−91	1.35
Helium	He	−180	1.660
Hexane (n-)	C_6H_{14}	80	1.08
Hydrogen	H_2	15	1.410
		−76	1.453
		−181	1.597
bromide	HBr	20	1.42
chloride	HCl	15	1.41
		100	1.40
Hydrogen (*contd.*)			
cyanide	HCN	65	1.31
		140	1.28
		210	1.24
iodide	HI	20–100	1.40
sulfide	H_2S	15	1.32
		−45	1.30
		−57	1.29
Iodine	I_2	185	1.30
Isobutane	C_4H_{10}	15	1.11
Krypton	Kr	19	1.68
Mercury	Hg	360	1.67
Methane	CH_4	600	1.113
		300	1.16
		15	1.31
		−80	1.34
		−115	1.41
Methyl acetate	$C_4H_6O_2$	15	1.14
alcohol	CH_4O	77	1.203
ether	C_2H_6O	6–30	1.11
Methylal	$C_3H_8O_2$	13	1.06
		40	1.09
Neon	Ne	19	1.64
Nitric oxide	NO	15	1.400
		−45	1.39
		−80	1.38
Nitrogen	N_2	15	1.404
		−181	1.47
Nitrous oxide	N_2O	100	1.28
		15	1.303
		−30	1.31
		−70	1.34
Oxygen	O_2	15	1.401
		−76	1.415
		−181	1.45
Pentane (n-)	C_5H_{12}	86	1.086
Phosphorus	P	300	1.17
Potassium	K	850	1.77
Sodium	Na	750–920	1.68
Sulfur dioxide	SO_2	15	1.29
Xenon	Xe	19	1.66

[a] From "International Critical Tables," Vol. 5, pp. 80–82.

TABLE 10

Fuel-oil Grades[a]

Grade of fuel oil[b]	Flash point, F°	Pour point, °F	Water and sediment, % by vol.	Carbon residue on 10% bottoms	Ash, % by wt	Distillation temperatures, °F: 10% point	Distillation temperatures, °F: 90% point	Distillation temperatures, °F: End point	Saybolt viscosity, sec: Universal at 100°F		Saybolt viscosity, sec: Furol at 122°F		Kinematic viscosity, centistokes: At 100°F		Kinematic viscosity, centistokes: At 122°F		Gravity, °API	Corrosion at 122°F (50°C)[d]
	Min	Max	Max	Max	Max	Max	Max	Max	Max	Min	Max	Min	Max	Min	Max	Min	Min	
No. 1: A distillate oil intended for vaporizing pot-type burners and other burners requiring this grade of fuel	100 or legal	0	Trace	0.15	—	420	—	625	—	—	—	—	2.2	1.4	—	—	35	Pass
No. 2: A distillate oil for general-purpose domestic heating for use in burners not requiring No. 1 fuel oil	100 or legal	20[c]	0.10	0.35	—	[e]	675	—	40	—	—	—	(4.3)	—	—	—	26	
No. 4: An oil for burner installations not equipped with preheating facilities	130 or legal	20	0.50	—	0.10	—	—	—	125	45	—	—	(26.4)	(5.8)				
No. 5: A residual-type oil for burner installations equipped with preheating facilities	130 or legal	—	1.00	—	0.10	—	—	—	—	150	40	—	—	(32.1)	(81)			
No. 6: An oil for use in burners equipped with preheaters permitting a high-viscosity fuel	150	—	2.00[f]	—	—	—	—	—	—	—	300	45	—	—	(638)	(92)		

[a] Recognizing the necessity for low-sulfur fuel oils used in connection with heat-treatment, nonferrous metal, glass and ceramic furnaces, and other special uses, a sulfur requirement may be specified as follows:

Grade of Fuel Oil	*Sulfur, Max %*
No. 1	0.5
No. 2	1.0
No. 4	No limit
No. 5	No limit
No. 6	No limit

Other sulfur limits may be specified only by mutual agreement between the purchaser and the seller.

[b] It is the intent of these classifications that failure to meet any requirement of a given grade does not automatically place an oil in the next lower grade unless in fact it meets all requirements of the lower grade.

[c] Lower or higher pour points may be specified whenever required by conditions of storage or use. However, these specifications shall not require a pour point lower than 0°F under any conditions.

[d] Report as passing when the copper test strip shows no gray or black deposit.

[e] The 10 per cent point may be specified at 440°F maximum for use in other than atomizing burners.

[f] The amount of water by distillation plus the sediment by extraction shall not exceed 2.0 per cent. The amount of sediment by extraction shall not exceed 0.50 per cent. A deduction in quantity shall be made for all water and sediment in excess of 1.0 per cent.

After ASTM Standards on Petroleum Products and Lubricants, p. 184, November, 1953.

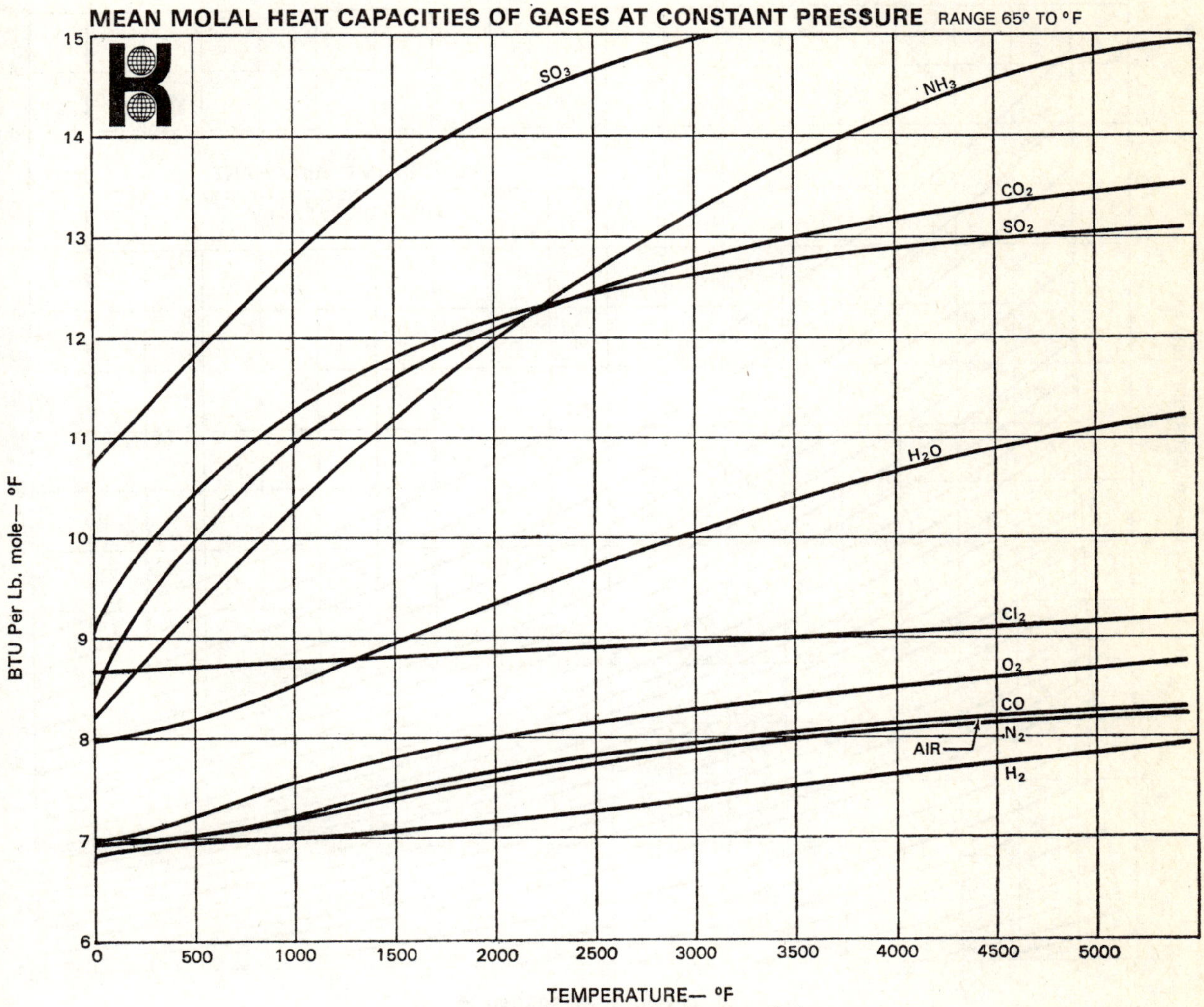

Figure 1 (Courtesy of Koch Engineering)

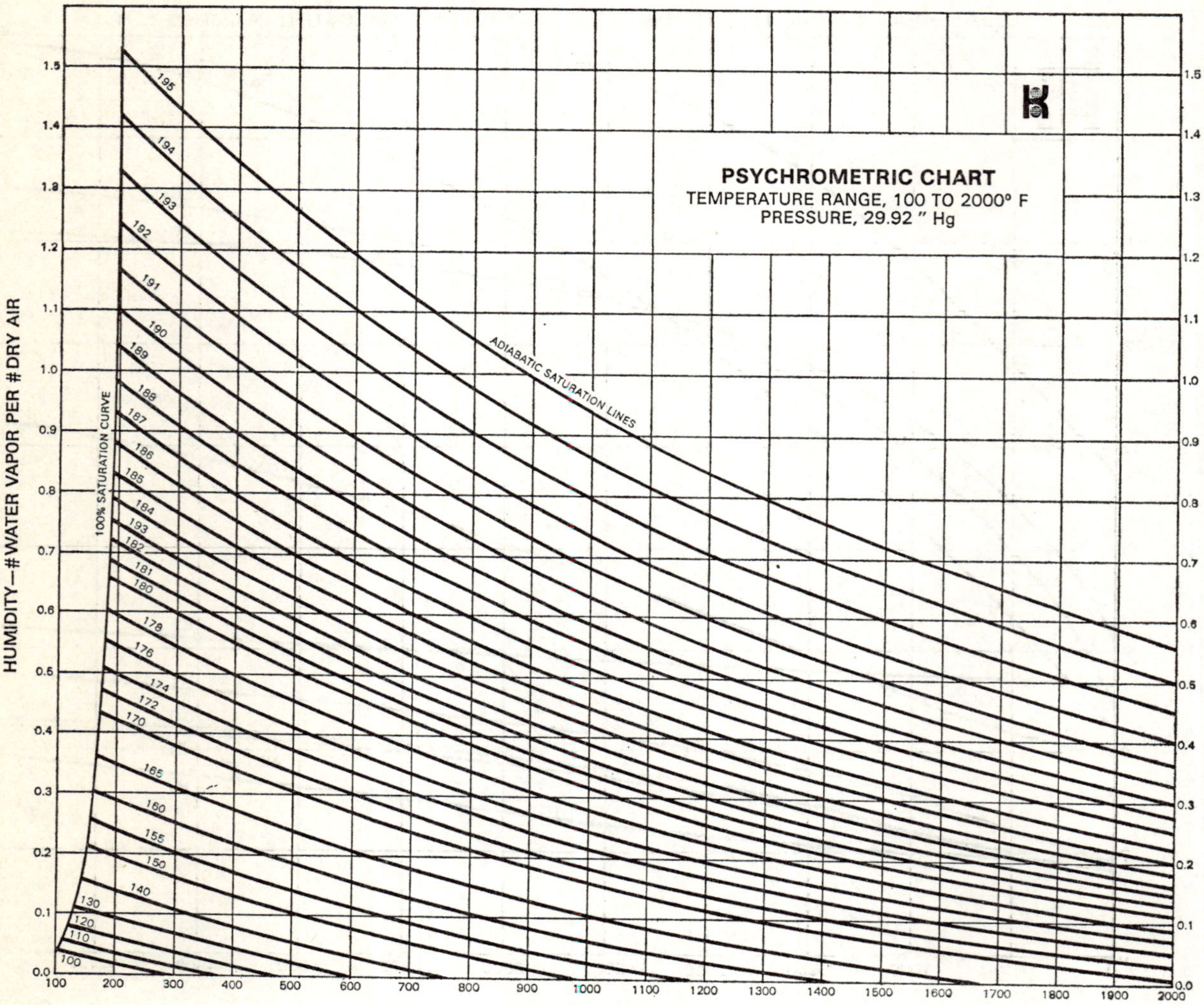

Figure 2 (Courtesy of Koch Engineering)

Table of Environmental Speeds† (a useful selection)

I. Flow of, and through, gases (or vacuum)

Very low	*Meters/second*
Evaporation from oceans	5×10^{-8}
Diffusional transport of molecules through another gas	3×10^{-6}
0.1 *m/s*	
Low process air	1×10^{-1}
Low flame propagation (laminar combustion)	3×10^{-1}
Migration velocities for particles smaller than 6μm (max.)	3×10^{-1}
1 *m/s*	
Flue gas (moderate)	1×10^{0}
Transitional flame propagation	3×10^{0}
Gas inside rotating kiln	5×10^{0}
Wind (35% of time @ 10 m elevation)	$5\text{–}8 \times 10^{0}$
Man running (fastest for 1000 m)	7.5×10^{0}
10 *m/s*	
Man running (fastest short distance)	1×10^{1}
Man skating (fastest for 500 m)	1.2×10^{1}
Escaping from asteroid Eros gravity	1.6×10^{1}
Home burner	2×10^{1}
Flue gas (high)	2×10^{1}
Horse running (fastest for 400 m)	2×10^{1}
Sun moving towards constellation Hercules	2×10^{1}
Indianapolis 500	7×10^{1}
100 *m/s*	
Moderate instrument air	1×10^{2}
Hydrogen molecules at room temperature (random motion in atmosphere)	1.7×10^{2}
Limit on propellor aircraft	2×10^{2}
Jet stream	2.2×10^{2}
High speed passenger plane	2.8×10^{2}
High instrument air through tube	3.3×10^{2}
Sound in air—room temperature	3.3×10^{2}
Sound in water vapor	4×10^{2}
Oxygen in air—random motion at room temperature	4.3×10^{2}
Steam rate in turbine	5×10^{2}
Battleship muzzle (max.)	7.1×10^{2}
Airplane (fastest)	9.2×10^{2}
1000 *m/s*	
Sound in hydrogen	1.3×10^{3}
Gas at Sun's surface rotating about axis (max.)	1.8×10^{3}
Escape from moon's surface gravity	2.8×10^{3}
Escape from Mercury's surface gravity	4.2×10^{3}
Arcaturus approaches solar system	5×10^{3}
Escape from Mars' surface gravity	5.2×10^{3}
Hydrogen molecules in sun—random motion	7.5×10^{3}
Escape from Earth's surface gravity	7.8×10^{3}
Gases at Saturn's surface rotating about axis (max.)	1.0×10^{4}
Escape from Venus' surface gravity	1.1×10^{4}
Sun moving relative to ensemble of nearer stars	2×10^{4}
Sirius moving away from solar system	4.1×10^{4}
Sun and nearby stars traveling relative to galactic center	2.1×10^{5}
Very high velocity	
Stars relative to each other within Seyfert Galaxy	1.4×10^{6}
Cloud of rapidly expanding gas leaving nucleus of a spiral nebulae—Seyfert Galaxy	4.3×10^{6}
Atoms in stellar interiors	1.6×10^{7}
Proton traveling in 24 BEV Strong Focusing Synchrotron (Geneva)	1×10^{8}
Velocity of distant objects in universe—as of 1960	3×10^{8}
Light in air (vacuum)	3×10^{8}

II. Flow of, and through, liquids

Low velocity	*Meters/second*
Blood through capillary	1×10^{-3}
Blood through venule	2×10^{-3}
Blood through arteriole	5×10^{-3}
Spitsbergen Drift, 81°N @ T = 1.9°C	7×10^{-2}
0.1 *m/s*	
Blood through vein	1×10^{-1}
Gulf Stream (Atlantic Drift), 61°N @ T = 6.5°C	2.5×10^{-1}
Blood through vena cava	3.8×10^{-1}
Blood through arteries	4.5×10^{-1}
Blood through aorta	4.8×10^{-1}
Kuro Shio Current, Shionomisake, Japan	5×10^{-1}
1 *m/s*	
Man swimming—moderate distances	1.5×10^{0}
Household water flow (fast)	1.6×10^{0}
Man swimming—fastest	2×10^{0}
Soil-laden ocean water which forms canyons	2.7×10^{0}
Canoe—fastest	4×10^{0}
Men rowing—Team (fastest)	6×10^{0}
100 *m/s*	
Steam ship—fastest	2×10^{1}
Motorboat—long distance (fastest)	3×10^{1}
Sound in water	1.5×10^{3}
Light in water	2.2×10^{8}

III. Objects in rotation about axis

Low velocity	*Meters/second*
Tape recorder surface (low speed)	4.8×10^{-2}
Tape recorder surface (moderate speed)	9.5×10^{-2}
Tape recorder surface (high quality)	1.9×10^{-1}
Surface of Venus (highest)	1.8×10^{0}
Surface of Mercury (highest)	2.0×10^{0}
100 *m/s*	
Surface of Mars (highest)	2.4×10^{2}

(cont.)

† Speeds are typical, averaged over a fixed cross sectional area and relative to the local speed of the earth unless otherwise noted.

Table of Environmental Speeds (cont.)

Surface of Earth (highest)	4.7×10^2
Moon about Earth	9.7×10^2
Surface of Sun (highest)	1.8×10^3
Surface of Neptune (highest)	2.5×10^3
Surface of Uranus (highest)	3.8×10^3
Pluto about Sun	4.8×10^3
Neptune about Sun	6.2×10^3
Uranus about Sun	6.8×10^3
Satellite about Earth	7.1×10^3
Man leaving Spacecraft (Leonov from Voskhod II—1965)	8×10^3
Saturn about Sun	9.7×10^3
10^4 *m/s*	
Surface of Jupiter (highest)	1×10^4
Surface of Saturn (highest)	1×10^4
Jupiter about Sun	1.2×10^4
Mars about Sun	2.4×10^4
Earth about Sun	3.0×10^4
Venus about Sun	3.5×10^4
Mercury about Sun	4.9×10^4

IV. Layers and growth

	Meters/second
Sediment laid down by action of water	1×10^{-11}
Destruction of Greenland glacier raises level of world oceans (1973)	$3–5 \times 10^{-11}$
Growth rate in child 2–12 years	2.05×10^{-9}
Sea level reduction by isolating Mediterranean via "Gibraltar Dam" and evaporation loss	3×10^{-8}
Wet forest precipitation (maximum accumulation)	3.8×10^{-8}
Himalayan glacier receded at	2.7×10^{-7}
Glacier recession (high rate)	8×10^{-7}
Northern fauna and flora advance at	3×10^{-5}

V. Wave propagation

	Meters/second
Nerve impulses (max.)	1×10^2
Sound in air	3.3×10^2
Sound in cork	5×10^2
Sound in water	1.5×10^3
Secondary wave of earthquake	5×10^3
Sound in iron	5×10^3
Primary wave of earthquake near surface	7×10^3
Primary wave of earthquake (1600 km below surface)	1.1×10^4
Light in glass	2×10^8
Light in water	2.2×10^8
Light in air	3×10^8

Conversion factors:

1 meter/sec = 100 cm/sec = 60 meters/min = 3.6 km/hr
= 3.281 ft/sec = 196.85 ft/min =
1.09×10^8 ft/yr
= 2.237 miles/hr = 1.943 knots =
6.21×10^{-4} miles/sec

INDEX TO VOLUMES 1 AND 2

Pp. 1–600: Vol. 1; pp. 601–1082: Vol. 2.

Pp. 1–600: Vol. 1; pp. 601–1082: Vol. 2.

Pp. 1–600: Vol. 1; pp. 601–1082: Vol. 2.

Pp. 1–600: Vol. 1; pp. 601–1082: Vol. 2.

Pp. 1–600: Vol. 1; pp. 601–1082: Vol. 2.

Pp. 1–600: Vol. 1; pp. 601–1082: Vol. 2.

Pp. 1–600: Vol. 1; pp. 601–1082: Vol. 2.

Pp. 1–600: Vol. 1; pp. 601–1082: Vol. 2.

Pp. 1–600: Vol. 1; pp. 601–1082: Vol. 2.